DIRECTORY

OF

AMERICAN PHILOSOPHERS

1974—75

SEVENTH EDITION

INTERNATIONAL DIRECTORY OF PHILOSOPHY

AND PHILOSOPHERS

A Companion Volume to the **DIRECTORY OF AMERICAN PHILOSOPHERS.**

Contains information on philosophical activities in Europe, Central and South America, Asia, Australia, and Africa.

DIRECTORY

OF

AMERICAN PHILOSOPHERS

1974-75

SEVENTH EDITION

Edited by

ARCHIE J. BAHM

in cooperation with

Richard H. Lineback

Published By

**PHILOSOPHY DOCUMENTATION CENTER
BOWLING GREEN UNIVERSITY
BOWLING GREEN, OHIO 43403
U.S.A.**

Library of Congress Card Number: 62-4947

ISBN   0-912632-29-1

TABLE OF CONTENTS

PREFACE

The Directory of American Philosophers is a biennial publication. This Seventh Edition provides up-to-date information on philosophical activities in the United States and Canada. Is is the companion volume of the International Directory of Philosophy and Philosophers, which supplements this volume by providing information on philosophical activities in Europe, Central and South America, Asia, Africa and Australia.

Most of the information contained in this edition was obtained from questionnaires returned by philosophers during the second half of 1973. Parts I and II consist of a directory of colleges and universities in the United States and Canada, alphabetized first by states and provinces and then by institutional titles within each state and province.

For each institution in the UNITED STATES (Part I), we have included its mailing address and zip code number. In addition, we have sought to include data regarding accreditation, type of control, type of student body, type of academic calendar, its levels and kinds of offerings, and enrollment. This information was obtained from the Education Directory, 1972-73, Higher Education, and is included in parentheses. Following this information we list the highest level of instruction in philosophy, the college division under which philosophy is taught and the telephone number of that division.

For each institution in CANADA (Part II), we have given its address and, in parentheses, its undergraduate and graduate enrollments. Canadian colleges and universities are of four kinds: independent, constituent, affiliated and federated. An independent institution is not only self controlled, but is also a degree granting institution. A constituent college is an integral part of a university, governed by the university administration and sharing the university's budget. An affiliated college is governed in academic affairs and degree-granting powers by the university with which it is affiliated but is administered and financed independently. A federated university or college holds its degree-granting powers in abeyance during its term of federation with another university, thus functioning similarly to an affiliated college. The information about affiliation was obtained from Universities and Colleges of Canada, 1972, published by the Association of Universities and Colleges of Canada. Information on enrollment was taken from the Survey of Higher Education, 1971-72, published by the Dominion Bureau of Statistics.

Following the information on each university or college is an alphabetical listing of the faculty members who teach philosophy. In addition to each faculty member's name, information is given on his highest degree earned, his rank and his areas of specialty.

Information on assistantships and fellowships at institutions which offer graduate work in philosophy immediately follows the directory of colleges and universities. Universities with doctoral programs are listed first, followed by those with masters programs. For each university, the number and types of assistantships and fellowships are listed, along with the amount of financial support.

Data on societies, journals and publishers is also given in Parts I and II. Information on societies occurs in the following order: name, date of founding, number of members, address, purpose, activities, meetings, principal officers, publications, membership requirements and dues. Information on centers and institutes is listed in the following manner: name, date of founding, number of members, address, purpose, activities, meetings, principal officers, publications, membership requirements, and dues. Informations on journals is given in the following sequence: name, date of founding, name and address of editor(s), purpose, sponsor, frequency of publication, circulation, number of philosophical articles per year, book review section, publisher's name and address and subscription price. Information on publishers is presented in the following order: name, date of founding, address, journals published and series published.

LATE REPORTS (Part III) contains information received after 20 November 1973. All late reports from the United States and Canada appear in one alphabetical list.

STATISTICS ON PHILOSOPHY DEPARTMENTS AND PHILOSOPHERS (Part IV) provides information by state and province on the size of philosophy departments, the highest level of specialization offered in philosophy by each department and the number of philosophers in each state and province. National totals are given at the end of each table.

INDICES (Part V) include an index of universities and colleges, an index of societies, an index of centers, councils and institutes, an index of journals, an index of publishers and a list of names and addresses of philosophers.

I wish to thank the staff of the Philosophy Documentation Center for the collection of the data and the preparation of this manuscript.

A.J.B.

ABBREVIATIONS

A	Assistantships
A Bapt	American Baptist
A Evan Luth	American Evangelical Lutheran Church
AB	Bachelor of Arts
ACPA	American Catholic Philosophical Association
Act	Acting
Ad Christ	Advent Christian Church
Adj	Adjunct, Adjoint
Admin	Administration
ADNUR	National League for Nursing; Associate degree program in Nursing
Advanc	Advanced
Aero	Aeronautics
Aes	Aesthetics
Afr	African
Agr	Agrégé, Agricultural
AK	Alaska
AL	Alabama
Ala	Alabama
ALB	Alberta
AMA	American Missionary Association
AME	American Methodist Episcopal Zion Church
Amer	American
Anal	Analysis, Analytic
Anc	Ancient
Anglo-Amer	Anglo-American
Ann	Annually
Anthrop	Anthropology
Apol	Apologetics
Appl	Applied
AR	Arkansas
Arch	Archaeology
Argument	Argumentation
Ariz	Arizona
Ark	Arkansas
Assem of God	Assemblies of God Church
Assoc	Associate, Association
Asst	Assistant
Aux	Auxiliaire
AZ	Arizona
B C	British Columbia
B Litt	Bachelor of Literature
BA	Bachelor of Arts
Bapt	Baptist Church
Bch	Beach
BD	Bachelor of Divinity
Behav, behavior	Behavioral
BI	Accredited by Association of Bible College
Bi-ann	Bi-annually
Bib	Bible
Bibl	Biblical
Bk Rev	Book Reviews
Blfs	Bluffs
Br	Branch
Breth	Brethren Church

BPhil	Bachelor of Philosophy
BS	Bachelor of Science
Bus Mgr	Business Manager
Cal	California
Can	Canada
Cand	Candidate
Car	Carolina
CC	Community College
Cen	Central
Cent	Century
Ch de C	Chargé de Cours
Ch d'Enseign	Chargé d'Enseignement
Ch of Breth	Church of Brethren
Ch of Christ	Church of Christ
Ch of God	Church of God
Chm	Chairman
Chris and Miss	Christian and Missionary Alliance
Chris Ref	Christian Reformed Church
Christ	Christian
Circ	Circulation
Civ	Civil, Civilization
Class	Classical
CME	Christian Methodist Episcopal Church
Co	County, Colorado
Coadj	Coadjunct
Col	College
Colo	Colorado
Com	Community
Comm	Communism, Committee
Communic	Communications
Comp	Comparative
Concept	Conceptual
Con	Conservative
Conn	Connecticut
Contemp	Contemporary
Continen	Continental
Cord	Coordinate, Coordinator
Cosmol	Cosmology
Cpe	Cape
Cult	Cultural
CUNY	City University of New York
Ctr	Center
Cy	City
D Litt	Doctor of Literature
D Min	Doctor of Ministry
DC	District of Columbia
DD	Doctor of Divinity
DE	Delaware
DEd	Doctor of Education
Del	Delaware
Dept	Department
Descrip	Descriptive
Devel	Development
DH	Dental Hygiene
DHL	Doctor of Hebrew Literature
Dialect	Dialectical
Dir	Director
Disc of Christ	Disciples of Christ Church
Dist	Distinguished

Div	Division, Divinity
Dl	Dale
Doct	Doctoral
Domin	Dominican
DPh	Docteur en Philosophie
DPhil	Doctor of Philosophy
Dr	Doctorate
DSc	Doctor of Science
DTh	Docteur en Theologie
E	Accredited by New England Association of Colleges and Secondary Schools, East
East	Eastern
Econ	Economics
EdD	Doctor of Education
Ed(s)	Editor(s)
EdS	Specialist in Education
Educ	Education
Emer	Emeritus
Empir	Empiricist, Empiricism
Eng	English, Engineering
Environ	Environmental
Epis	Episcopal
Epistem	Epistemology
Esth	Esthétique
Euro	European
Evan Cong	Evangelical Congregational Church
Evan Cov	Evangelical Covenant Church of America
Evan F	Evangelical Free Church of America
Evan Luth	Evangelical Lutheran Church
Evan U B	Evangelical United Brethern Church
Exist	Existentialism
Ext	Extension
F	Fellowship
F Bapt	Free Baptist Church
F Meth	Free Methodist Church
F Will Bapt	Free Will Baptist
F X	François Xavier
Fac	Faculty
Fed	Federal
Fel	Fellow, Fellowship
Fig	Figurative
FL, Fla	Florida
Fls	Falls
Found	Foundation
Fr	Friends
Fran	Francisco
Ft	Fort
Fund	Fundamental
g	Graduate enrollment
G Orth	Greek Orthodox Church
GA	Georgia
Gen	General
Ger	German
Gov	Government
Grad	Graduate
Grnd	Grand
Grt	Greater
GU	Guam

ABBREVIATIONS

HA	Accredited by Commission of Graduate Programs in Hospital Administration
Hbr	Harbor
HED	Doctorate in Church History
Hermen	Hermeneutics
Hist	History, Historical
Hl	Hill
Hls	Hills
Honor	Honorary
Hum, Human	Humanities
Hts	Heights
IA	Iowa
ID	Idaho
Ideal	Idealist
IL	Illinois
Immac	Immaculate
Inc	Incorporated
Induc	Inductive, Induction
Indust	Industrial
Inf	Information
Inst	Institute
Instr	Instructor
Intell	Intelligence, Intellectual
Interdenom	Interdenominational
Internat, Intnl	International
Irr	Irregular
Is	Island, Islands, Isle
JD	Doctor of Jurisprudence
JE	Accredited by New England Association of Colleges and Secondary Schools as a junior college
Jewish	Jewish Congregation
JM	Accredited by Middle States Association of Colleges and Secondary Schools as a junior college
JN	Accredited by North Central Association of Colleges and Secondary Schools as a junior college
JNW	Accredited by Northwest Association of Colleges and Secondary Schools as a junior college
Jour	Journalism, Journal
JR	Junior
JRCB	Junior College of Business
JS	Accredited by Southern Association of Colleges and Secondary Schools as a junior college
Jurisp	Jurisprudence
JW	Accredited by Western Association of Schools and Colleges as a junior college
Kan	Kansas
Knowl	Knowledge
KS	Kansas
KY	Kentucky
LA	Louisiana
Lang	Language
LDS	Latter Day Saints
Lect	Lecturer
Libr	Liberal
Lic	Licentiate, Licence
Lic Theol	Licencié en Theologie
Ling	Linguistics
Lit	Literature

Litt B	Bachelor of Literature
Litt D	Doctor of Literature
Lk	Lake
Lndg	Landing
LST, LTh	Licentiate in Sacred Theology
Luth	Lutheran
Luth CA	Lutheran Church in America
M	Accredited by Middle States Association of Colleges and Secondary Schools as a junior college
M Div	Master of Divinity
MA	Massachusetts, Master of Arts
Mag	Magister
Man	Manitoba
Mass	Massachusetts
Mater	Materialism
Math	Mathematics
MD	Maryland
Mech	Mechanical
MEd	Master of Education
Med	Medieval, Medical Association
Menn	Mennonite Church
Metaph	Metaphysics
Metaphil	Metaphilosophy
Meth	Methodist
Method	Methodology
Metro	Metropolitan
MI, Mich	Michigan
Mil	Military
Minn	Minnesota
Miss	Mississippi
MN	Minnesota
MO	Missouri
Mod	Modern
Mont	Montana
Morav	Moravian Church
MPh, MPhil	Master of Philosophy
MS	Master of Science, Mississippi
MT	Montana, Mount, Mountain
Mus	Music Accreditation
Myst	Mysticism
N	Accredited by North Central Association of Colleges and Secondary Schools as a junior college, North, Northern
N B	New Brunswick
N F	Newfoundland
N S	Nova Scotia
N T	New Testament
Natur	Naturalism, natural
Naz	Nazarene Church
NC	North Carolina
ND	North Dakota
NDEA	National Defense Education Act
NE	Nebraska, Northeast, Northeastern
Nebr	Nebraska
Nev	Nevada
NH	New Hampshire
NJ	New Jersey
NM	New Mexico
NP	No Philosophy
NR	No response to questionnaire

NSF	National Science Foundation
Nur	Accredited in Nursing
NW	Accredited by Northwest Association of Colleges and Secondary Schools as a junior college, North, Northern
Nw	New
NY	New York
O T	Old Testament
OA	Other Assistance
OH	Ohio
OK, Okla	Oklahoma
Ont	Ontario
OR	Oregon
Ord	Ordinaire
Ore	Oregon
Orient	Oriental
Osteo	Osteopathy
p	Controlled by a private corporation, independent of a church
PA	Pennsylvania
PE	Protestant Episcopal Church
PEI	Prince Edward Island
Penn	Pennsylvania
Pent Hol	Pentacostal Holiness Church
Person	Personality
Phar	Pharmacy
Phenomen	Phenomenology
Phil	Philosophy
Phy	Physics
Phys	Physical
Pk	Park
Pnsla	Penninsula
Pod	Podiatry
Polit	Political
Polytech	Polytechnic, Polytechnical
PR	Puerto Rico
Prag	Pragmatism
Preb	Presbyterian
Pres	President
Prof	Professor
Prot	Protestant
Prov	Provost
Psych	Psychology
Pt	Point
Publ	Published, Publisher
Q	Quarterly
qr	Quarter
Que	Québec
R Orth	Russian Orthodox
Ration	Rationalism
RC	Roman Catholic Church
Ref	Reformed Church
Ref E	Reformed Episcopal Church
Ref Preb	Reformed Presbyterian Church
Relig	Religion
Reorg LDS	Reorganized Latter Day Saints
Rep	Representative
Res	Research
Rhet	Rhetoric

RI	Rhode Island
S	Accredited by Southern Association of Colleges and Secondary Schools, South, Southern
S Bapt	Southern Baptist
Sas	Saskatchewan
SC	South Carolina
Sch	School
Schol	Scholar, Scholasticism
Sci	Science
SD	Seventh Day Baptist Church, South Dakota
SDA	Seventh Day Adventist Church
SE	Southeast, Southeastern
Sec	Secretaire, Secretary
Sem	Semester, Seminary
Seman	Semantics
Semi-ann	Semi-annually
Sess	Sessional
Sn	San
Soc	Society, Social
Soc Sci	Social Science
Sociol	Sociology
Spec	Special
Spg	Spring
Spgs	Springs
Sr	Senior
SRCB	Senior College of Busines
St	Saint, State
st	State controlled
sta	Station
STD	Doctor of Sacred Theology
STL	Licentiate of Sacred Theology
STM	Master of Sacred Theology
Stud	Studies
Subject	Subjectivity
SUNY	State University of New York
SW	Southwest, Southwestern
Sym	Symbolic
Syst	Systematic
TA	Teaching Assistantships
Teach	Teaching, Teachers
Tech	Technic, Technical
Technol	Technology
Temp	Temporary
Tenn	Tennessee
Ter	Terrace
Tex	Texas
TF	Teaching Fellowship
ThD	Doctor of Theology
Theol	Theology, Theological
Theor	Theoretical
ThM	Master of Theology
Tht	Thought
Tit	Titulaire
TN	Tennessee
Transcendent	Transcendentalism
Tri	Trimester
TW	Tuition Waver
TX	Texas

ABBREVIATIONS

U	University
u	Undergraduate enrollment
U Breth	United Brethren Church
U Ch Christ	United Church of Christ
U Luth	United Lutheran Church
U Meth	United Methodist
U Miss	United Missionary Church
U Preb	United Presbyterian Church
Unit	Unitarian Church
Univ	University
Univer	Universalist
UT	Utah
V Pres	Vice President
VA	Virginia
VI	Virgin Islands
Visit	Visiting
Vl	Ville
Vly	Valley
VT	Vermont
W	Accredited by Western Association of Schools and Colleges, West, Western
W Va	West Virginia
WA, Wash	Washington
Wes	Wesleyan Church
Wes Meth	Wesleyan Methodist Church
West	Western
WI, Wis	Wisconsin
Wo	Women
WV	West Virginia
WW	Woodrow Wilson
WY, Wyo	Wyoming
XRDS	Crossroads
--	When it refers to accreditation it means either not accredited or information not available. Elsewhere it means information not available.
*	An asterisk indicates that no information was received from this philosophical activity
I	Two, but less that 4 years of work beyond the twelfth grade
II	Bachelor's degree
III	Master's and/or first professional degree
IV	Doctor's degree
V	Other

PART I

UNITED STATES

UNIVERSITIES

ALABAMA

ALABAMA AGRICULTURAL AND MECHANICAL UNIVERSITY
Normal, Alabama 35762 (S; st; coed; sem; III; 3009) Courses with no degree
specialization, Dept of Hist and Polit Sci, 205-859-7228

Taylor, Gene F, PhD, Assoc Prof, Act Chm, Phil of Culture
Marbury, Carl H, PhD, Prof, Phil of Relig
Rao, D V, MA, Asst Prof, Eastern Phil

ALABAMA CHRISTIAN COLLEGE
Montgomery, Alabama 36109 (S; Ch of Christ; coed; qr; I; 325) NP

ALABAMA LUTHERAN JUNIOR COLLEGE
Selma, Alabama 36701 (--; Luth; coed; sem; I; 22) NP

ALABAMA STATE UNIVERSITY
Montgomery, Alabama 36101 (S; st; coed; qr; III; 2704) BA minor, Dept of Sociol,
Hist, and Polit Sci, 205-262-3581 Ext 292

Hardy, J Garrick, PhD, Prof
James, Felix E, DD, Instr

ALBERT P BREWER STATE JUNIOR COLLEGE
Fayette, Alabama 35555 (--; st; coed; qr; I; 207) NP

ALEXANDER CITY STATE JUNIOR COLLEGE
Alexander City, Alabama 35010 (S; st; coed; qr; I; --) Courses with no degree
specialization, 205-234-6346

Pullium, Ray Carl, MA

ATHENS COLLEGE
Athens, Alabama 35611 (S; U Meth; coed; 4-1-4; II; 916) BA major, Dept of Relig
and Phil, 205-232-1802

Jones, Daniel, ThD, Prof, Ethics, Metaph
West, Charles, BD, Assoc Prof, Ethics

AUBURN UNIVERSITY
Auburn, Alabama 36830 (S; st; coed; qr; IV; 14,503) MA minor, Dept of Phil,
205-826-4344

McKown, D B, PhD, Assoc Prof, Chm, Phil of Relig, Marxology, Soc Ethics
Andelson, R V, PhD, Prof, Ethics, Soc Phil, Phil of Law
Bole, T J, PhD, Asst Prof, Hegel, German Phil, Phenomen
Brown, C D, PhD, Asst Prof, Logic, Epistem, Phil of Sci
Davis, W H, PhD, Assoc Prof, Phil of Relig, Metaph, Prag
Paucheri, L U, PhD, Asst Prof, Hist of Phil, Class Phil, 17th Cent Phil
Walters, K W, PhD, Asst Prof, Aes, Exist, Hist of Phil

AUBURN UNIVERSITY AT MONTGOMERY
   Montgomery, Alabama 36109 (S; st; coed; qr; II; 1539) NP

BIRMINGHAM SOUTHERN COLLEGE
   Birmingham, Alabama 35204 (S; Meth; coed; --; II; 1031) BA major, Dept of Phil,
   205-328-5250 Ext 265

   Franke, J Paul, PhD, Assoc Prof
   Weaver, Oliver C, PhD, Prof

BISHOP STATE JUNIOR COLLEGE
   Mobile, Alabama 36603 (S; st; coed; qr; I; 1051) NP

CULLMAN COLLEGE
   Cullman, Alabama 35055 (S; RC; coed; sem; I; 201) Courses with no degree
   specialization, Dept of Human, 205-734-4622

   Mullin, Richard, MA, Lect, Phenomen

DANIEL PAYNE COLLEGE
   Birmingham, Alabama 35212 (--; Afr Meth Epis; coed; sem; II; 312) NR

ENTERPRISE STATE JUNIOR COLLEGE
   Enterprise, Alabama 36330 (S; st; coed; qr; I; 1619) Courses with no degree
   specialization, Div of Hist and Soc Sci, 205-347-2623

FAULKNER STATE JUNIOR COLLEGE
   Bay Minette, Alabama 36507 (S; st; coed; qr; I; 1011) NP

FLORENCE STATE UNIVERSITY
   Florence, Alabama 35630 (S; st; coed; sem; III; 3425) Courses with no degree
   specialization, --, 205-766-4100

GADSDEN STATE JUNIOR COLLEGE
   Gadsden, Alabama 35903 (S; st; coed; qr; I; 3189) NP

GEORGE WALLACE STATE TECHNICAL JUNIOR COLLEGE
   Dothan, Alabama 36301 (S; st; coed; qr; I; 1367) NP

HUNTINGDON COLLEGE
   Montgomery, Alabama 36106 (S; U Meth; coed; sem; II; 673) NR

JACKSONVILLE STATE UNIVERSITY
   Jacksonville, Alabama 36265 (S; st; coed; --; III; 5749) Courses with no degree
   specialization, Dept of Psych and Phil, 205-435-9820 Ext 302

   Wilson, Jerry B, PhD, Assoc Prof, Ethics

JEFFERSON DAVIS STATE JUNIOR COLLEGE
   Brewton, Alabama 36426 (S; st; coed; qr; I; 717) NP

JOHN C CALHOUN STATE TECHNICAL JUNIOR COLLEGE
Decatur, Alabama 35601 (S; st; coed; qr; I; 2215) NP

JUDSON COLLEGE
Marion, Alabama 36756 (S; S Bapt; wo; sem; II; 390) BA major, Dept of Relig and
Phil, 205-683-2011 Ext 25

Stringfield, Leroy P, ThD, Assoc Prof, Chm, Christ Soc Ethics
Lindsey, Jonathan A, ThD, Assoc Prof

LIVINGSTON UNIVERSITY
Livingston, Alabama 35470 (S; st; coed; qr; III; 1638) NP

LURLEEN B WALLACE STATE JUNIOR COLLEGE
Andalusia, Alabama 36420 (--; st; coed; qr; I; 701) NP

MARION INSTITUTE
Marion, Alabama 36756 (S; P; men; sem; I; 246) NR

MILES COLLEGE
Birmingham, Alabama 35208 (S; Christ Meth Epis; coed; sem; II; 1270) Courses with
no degree specialization, Dept of Human, 205-786-5281 Ext 49

Felkenes, Sandra W, MA, Instr

MOBILE COLLEGE
Mobile, Alabama 36613 (S; S Bapt; coed; sem; II; 606) NP

NORTHEAST ALABAMA STATE JUNIOR COLLEGE
Rainsville, Alabama 35968 (S; st; coed; qr; I; 783) NP

PATRICK HENRY STATE JUNIOR COLLEGE
Monroeville, Alabama 36460 (S; st; coed; qr; I; 485) Courses with no degree
specialization, Dept of Soc Sci, 205-743-3157 Ext 24

Blow, William O, EdD, Phil of Educ

SAINT BERNARD COLLEGE
St Bernard, Alabama 35138 (S; RC; coed; sem; II; 632) BA major, Dept of Human,
205-734-4110

Eramian, Robert, MA, Instr, Logic, Amer Phil
Mullin, Richard P, MA, Asst Prof, Phenomen, Hist of Phil

SAMFORD UNIVERSITY
Birmingham, Alabama 35209 (S; S Bapt; coed; 4-1-4; III; 2973) BA minor, Div of Relig
and Phil, 205-871-0351

Davison, Vernon G, PhD, Prof, Asian Tht
Gallman, R Lee, ThD, Prof, Exist
Joines, Karen R, ThD, Assoc Prof, Phil of Relig
Lunceford, W Mabry, ThD, Prof, Hist of Phil, Logic, Ethics

SELMA UNIVERSITY
  Selma, Alabama 36701 (--; Bapt; coed; sem; II; 430) Courses with no degree
  specialization, Dept of Phil and Theol, 205-872-2533

SNEAD STATE JUNIOR COLLEGE
  Boaz, Alabama 35957 (S; st; coed; qr; I; 1510) NP

SOUTHEASTERN BIBLE COLLEGE
  Birmingham, Alabama 35205 (BI; p; coed; sem; II; 241) Courses with no degree
  specialization, Dept of Gen Educ, 205-251-2311

  Gillaspie, Leon, MA, Prof
  Sproule, John, ThM, Prof

SOUTHERN UNION STATE JUNIOR COLLEGE
  Wadley, Alabama 36276 (S; st; coed; qr; I; 794) NP

SPRING HILL COLLEGE
  Mobile, Alabama 36608 (S; RC; coed; sem; II; 930) BA major, Dept of Phil,
  205-460-2377

  Brandon, Melvin J, PhD, Asst Prof, Act Chm
  Elliot, Clyde J, PhD, Assoc Prof
  Kobelja, Carl D, PhD, Asst Prof
  Linehan, Elizabeth, MA, Asst Prof
  McFarland, John, MA, Assoc Prof
  Stacer, John, PhD, Asst Prof
  Walsh, Joseph M, PhD, Assoc Prof
  Watson, S Youree, PhD, Prof

STILLMAN COLLEGE
  Tuscaloosa, Alabama 35401 (S; Preb; coed; sem; I; 660) BA joint or combined minor,
  Div of Human, 205-752-2548

TALLADEGA COLLEGE
  Talladega, Alabama 35160 (S; p; coed; sem; II; 520) Courses with no degree
  specialization, Div of Human, 205-362-2752

  Wright, Richard, PhD, Asst Prof, Phil of Lang

THEODORE A LAWSON STATE JUNIOR COLLEGE
  Birmingham, Alabama 35228 (S; st; coed; qr; I; 1127) NR

TROY STATE UNIVERSITY
  Troy, Alabama 36081 (S; st; coed; qr; III; 3264) BA minor, Dept of Phil and Relig,
  205-566-3000 Ext 394

  Kennedy, Bart F, MA, Asst Prof

TROY STATE UNIVERSITY, FORT RUCKER
  Fort Rucker, Alabama 36360 (S; st; coed; qr; III; 1399) NR

TROY STATE UNIVERSITY, MONTGOMERY
  Maxwell AFB, Alabama 36112 (S; st; coed; qr; III; 1527) NR

TUSKEGEE INSTITUTE
  Tuskegee Institute, Alabama 36088 (S; p; coed; sem; III; 3073) BA major, Dept of
  Phil, 205-727-8284

  Hamilton, J Brooke, PhD, Asst Prof, Chm, Contemp Ethics, Hist of Phil
  Halbrook Stephen P, PhD, Asst Prof, Soc and Polit Phil, Phil of Hist
  Price, Connie C, PhD, Asst Prof, Soc and Polit Phil, Aes
  Price, J Thomas, PhD, Assoc Prof, Phil of Lang, Contemp Euro Phil
  Wiesmann, Robert J, MA, Asst Prof, Anal Phil, Phil of Mind

  Oke, Jenudo U, Dubois Fel   Thomas, Larry L, Dubois Fel
  Murungi, John J, Dubois Fel

UNIVERSITY OF ALABAMA
  University, Alabama 35486 (S; st; coed; sem; IV; 13,564) PhD minor, Dept of Phil,
  205-348-5942

  Jenkins, Iredell, PhD, Prof, Chm, Aes, Ethics, Phil of Law
  Clark, James W, PhD, Prof, Logic, Epistem
  Hocutt, Max O, PhD, Prof, Logic, Ontology
  McMinn, J B, ThD, Assoc Prof, Greek Phil, Hist of Phil
  Richards, Norvin W, PhD, Asst Prof, Anal Phil, Ethics, Phil of Mind
  Wu, Kathleen G J, PhD, Asst Prof, Math Logic

  Brooke, Margaret G, Grad Asst   Sosnin, Carl H, Grad Asst
  Hood, Jo Rogers, Grad Asst

UNIVERSITY OF ALABAMA AT BIRMINGHAM
  Birmingham, Alabama 35233 (S; st; coed; qr; IV; 7168) BA major, Div of Human,
  205-934-2290

  Thompson, Charles W, AB, Asst Prof, Phil of Mind
  Vause, Stephen F, MA, Asst Prof, Ethics, Polit Phil

UNIVERSITY OF ALABAMA AT HUNTSVILLE
  Huntsville, Alabama 35807 (S; st; coed; qr; IV; 2883) BA minor, 205-895-6250

  Braden, A W, PhD, Prof, Phil of Relig, Amer Phil
  Burns, Robert W, MA, Instr, Hist of Phil

UNIVERSITY OF MONTEVALLO
  Montevallo, Alabama 35115 (S; st; coed; sem; III; 2564) BA minor, Dept of Soc Sci,
  205-665-2521 Ext 253

  Van Tuyll, Hendrik, ThD, Prof, Ethics

UNIVERSITY OF SOUTH ALABAMA
  Mobile, Alabama 36688 (S; st; coed; qr; III; 5440) BA major, Dept of Phil, 205-460-6248

  Perkins, Robert L, PhD, Prof, Chm, 19th Cent Phil
  Buckley, John J, PhD, Asst Prof, Amer Phil
  Baldwin, Harold W, PhD, Asst Prof, Epistem, Logic
  Donaldson George, PhD, Asst Prof, Mod Phil

Greenwood, Robert L, PhD, Assoc Prof, Phil of Mind
Sun, G C H, PhD, Asst Prof, Aes, Orient Phil
Youngblood, Susan P, MA, Instr, Epistem

WALKER COLLEGE
   Jasper, Alabama 35501 (S; p; coed; sem; I; 723) Courses with no degree specialization,
   Dept of Relig and Phil, 205-387-0511

ALASKA

ALASKA METHODIST UNIVERSITY
   Anchorage, Alaska 99504 (NW; U Meth; coed; --; III; 814) BA joint or combined major,
   Div of Human, 907-272-4401 Ext 213

   Gay, Richard R, MEd, Prof, Phil of Relig
   Lethcoe, James, PhD, Asst Prof
   Sinclair, Jon, BD, Asst Prof

ANCHORAGE COMMUNITY COLLEGE, UNIVERSITY OF ALASKA
   Anchorage, Alaska 99503 (NW; st; coed; tri; II; 4546) Courses with no degree
   specialization, Dept of Phil, 907-279-6622 Ext 256

   Kuhner, Robert, MA, Asst Prof

JUNEAU-DOUGLAS COMMUNITY COLLEGE, UNIVERSITY OF ALASKA
   Juneau, Alaska 99801 (NW; st; coed; sem; I; 246) NP

KETCHIKAN COMMUNITY COLLEGE, UNIVERSITY OF ALASKA
   Ketchikan, Alaska 99901 (NW; st; coed; sem; I; 205) NP

SHELDON JACKSON COLLEGE
   Sitka, Alaska 99835 (NW; U Preb; coed; 4-1-4; I; 247) Courses with no degree
   specialization, Dept of Relig and Phil, 907-747-5238

   Zeiger, William, M Div

SITKA COMMUNITY COLLEGE, UNIVERSITY OF ALASKA
   Sitka, Alaska 99835 (--; st; coed; sem; I; 85) Courses with no degree specialization, --
   907-747-8393

UNIVERSITY OF ALASKA, FAIRBANKS CAMPUS
   Fairbanks, Alaska 99701 (NW; st; coed; sem; IV; 3984) Courses with no degree
   specialization, Dept of Phil, 907-479-7211

   Kuhner, R, MA, Instr
   Lethcoe, N, PhD, Lect, Buddhism

ARIZONA

ARIZONA STATE UNIVERSITY
Tempe, Arizona 85281 (N; st; coed; sem; IV; 26,564) MA major, Dept of Phil, 602-965-3394

Carney, James D, PhD, Prof, Chm, Logic
Arner, Douglas G, PhD, Prof, Ethics
Gieschen, Donald W, PhD, Assoc Prof, Theory of Knowl
Guleserian, Theodore, PhD, Assoc Prof, Phil of Mind
Howells, Edmund G, MA, Asst Prof, Hist of Phil
Humphrey, Theodore, PhD, Asst Prof, Hist of Phil
Rein'l, Robert, PhD, Prof, Phil of Relig
Von Bretzel, Philip, MA, Asst Prof, Metaph
Votichenko, T Alex, MA, Asst Prof, Soc and Polit Phil
White, Peter J, PhD, Asst Prof, Hist of Phil

Long, Mary Katherine, Grad Asst
Melser, Terry, Grad Asst
Mockbee, Jim Michael, Grad Asst
Royer, Torrence L, Grad Asst
Schlesinger, Steven Alan, Grad Asst
Timmons, Mark C, Grad Asst
Vishner, Andrew B, Grad Asst

ARIZONA WESTERN COLLEGE
Yuma, Arizona 85364 (N; st; coed; sem; I; 3014) AA major, Div of Soc Sci, 602-726-1000 Ext 254

Ahearn, John, MA, Chm

CENTRAL ARIZONA COLLEGE
Coolidge, Arizona 85228 (--; local, coed; sem; I; 7571) Courses with no degree specialization, Dept of Soc and Behavior Sci, 602-723-4141 Ext 238

Buys, Ekdal, MA
Marks, Joe, MA

COCHISE COLLEGE
Douglas, Arizona 85607 (N; local; coed; sem; I; 2158) Courses with no degree specialization, Dept of Human, 602-432-5737 Ext 284

Gilliland, Joe, MA, Prof, Chm, Eastern Phil
Meyer, Allan, MA, Prof, Ethics
O'Connell, Desmond, MA, Instr, Ethics

COLLEGE OF GANADO
Ganado, Arizona 86508 (--; p; coed; sem; I; 98) NR

EASTERN ARIZONA COLLEGE
Thatcher, Arizona 85301 (N; st; coed; sem; I; 1792) AA major, Dept of Soc Sci, 602-428-1133

Highby, Patricia, MA

GLENDALE COMMUNITY COLLEGE
Glendale, Arizona 85301 (N; local; coed; sem; I; 6589) Courses with no degree specialization, Dept of Phil, 602-934-2211

Hubbard, Robert R, MA
Nelson, Bonnie A, MA
Smelser, Philip S, MA
Walcott, Lyle O, MA

GRAND CANYON COLLEGE
Phoenix, Arizona 85017 (N; S Bapt; coed; sem; II; 796) BA major, Dept of Relig,
602-939-9421 Ext 19

Puckett, J Niles, ThD, Prof, Chm
Martin, D C, ThD, Prof

MARICOPA TECHNICAL COLLEGE
Phoenix, Arizona 85004 (N; local; coed; sem; I; 5686) Courses with no degree
specialization, Div of Gen Stud, 602-258-7251 Ext 321

MESA COMMUNITY COLLEGE
Mesa, Arizona 85201 (N; local; coed; sem; I; 6723) Courses offered with no degree
specialization, Dept of Phil, 602-833-1261 Ext 238

Smith, R W, MA, Chm, Plato
Jensen, R M, MA
Nesby, Robert, MA, Logic
Phearson, George, MA
Price, Joan, MA, Orient Phil
Walsh, Thomas, MA

NAVAJO COMMUNITY COLLEGE
Chinle, Arizona 86503 (--; p; coed; sem; I; 380) NP

NORTHERN ARIZONA UNIVERSITY
Flagstaff, Arizona 86001 (N; st; coed; sem; IV; 9869) BA major, Dept of Phil,
602-523-2648

Nietmann, William F, PhD, Assoc Prof, Cord, Phil of Relig, Contemp Continen Phil
Jensen, A Dewey, PhD, Asst Prof, Phil of Relig, Wittgenstein, Kierkegaard
Mahan, Wayne W, PhD, Assoc Prof, Ethics, Exist
Malone, Michael E, PhD, Asst Prof, Phil of Sci, Phil of Mind
Walder, John, MA, Instr, Ethics, Anc Phil
Wood, Richard A, PhD, Asst Prof, Wittgenstein, Exist

PHOENIX COLLEGE
Phoenix, Arizona 85013 (N; local; coed; sem; I; 10,133) Courses with no degree
specialization, Dept of Soc Sci, 602-264-2492

Fielden, John, MA
Gangadean, Surrendra, MA, East Phil
Greenwell, James, MA
Hill, Myles, MA
Sullivan, Robert, PhD, Schol

PIMA COLLEGE
    Tucson, Arizona (--; local; coed; sem; I; 5586) Courses with no degree specialization,
    Dept of Fine and Applied Arts, 602-884-6827

    McHolland, Larry, MA, Cord
    Barnes, John, MA

PRESCOTT COLLEGE
    Prescott, Arizona 86301 (N; p; coed; qr; II; 367) BA major, Center for the Person,
    602-445-3254 Ext 235

    Keen, Sam, PhD, Prof
    Keen, Heather, BA, Asst Prof
    Keyes, Ralph, BA, Instr
    Longfellow, Layne, PhD, Assoc Prof, Phil of the Person
    Johnson, Don, PhD, Asst Prof

SCOTTSDALE COMMUNITY COLLEGE
    Scottsdale, Arizona 85252 (N; local; coed; sem; I; 2099) AA major, --, 602-947-
    5401 Ext 257

    Greenwell, James R, MA, Prof, Ethics

THUNDERBIRD GRADUATE SCHOOL
    Phoenix, Arizona 85001 (N; p; coed; 4-1-4; III; 667) NP

UNIVERSITY OF ARIZONA
    Tucson, Arizona 85721 (N; st; coed; sem; IV; 26,558) PhD major, Dept of Phil,
    602-884-3120

    Murphy, Jeffrie G, PhD, Prof, Chm, Phil of Law, Soc and Polit Phil, Ethics, Kant
    Bretall, Robert W, PhD, Prof, Phil of Relig, Exist, Phil in Lit, Kierkegaard
    Byerly, Henry C, PhD, Assoc Prof, Phil of Natural Sci, Logic, Metaph
    Caldwell, Robert L, PhD, Prof, Epistem, Phil of Mind, Contemp Anglo-Amer Phil
    Cowan, Joseph L, PhD, Prof, Phil Psych, Contemp Phil, Ethics
    Harnish, Robert M, PhD, Asst Prof, Logic, Phil of Lang, Phil of Ling, Seman
    Hertzberg, Lars H, PhD, Asst Prof, Phil of Behavior Sci, Phil of Lang, Wittgenstein
    Jensen, Henning, PhD, Assoc Prof, Ethics, Aes
    Kreyche, Robert J, PhD, Prof, Med Phil, Amer Phil, 19th Cent Phil
    Laska, Peter J, PhD, Asst Prof, Soc and Polit Phil, Phil of Hist, Kant, Hegel, Marx
    Milo, Ronald D, PhD, Assoc Prof, Ethics, Greek Phil
    Raab, Francis V, PhD, Prof, Metaph, Phil of Mind
    Salmon, Merrilee H, PhD, Asst Prof, Phil of Math, Aes
    Salmon, Wesley C, PhD, Prof, Phil of Sci, Logic

    Walraff, Charles F, PhD, Prof Emer, Hist of Phil, Mod Continen Phil

    Ambrose, James, MS, Grad Asst   Irons, Theodore, BA, Grad Asst
    Carr, Charles, BA, Grad Asst   Levenbook, Barbara, MA, Grad Asst
    Dawson, George, BS, Grad Asst   Panichas, George, BA, Grad Asst
    Herod, John, BA, Grad Asst   Richard, Joseph, BA, Grad Asst
    Hillman, Brent, BA, Grad Asst   Sack, Susan, BA, Grad Asst
    Hodson, John, BA, Grad Asst   Wilson, James, BA, Grad Asst
    Hubin, Donald, BA, Grad Asst

YAVAPAI COLLEGE
    Prescott, Arizona 86301 (--; local; coed; sem; I; 1383) NP

ARKANSAS

ARKANSAS BAPTIST COLLEGE
  Little Rock, Arkansas 72200 (N; Preb; coed; sem; II; 430) NR

ARKANSAS COLLEGE
  Batesville, Arkansas 72501 (N; Preb; coed; sem; II; 396) Courses with no degree
  specialization, Dept of Relig and Phil, 501-793-9352

  Mosley, Elis G, MA, Assoc Prof, Hist of Relig
  Rhodes, Ann Adams, MA, Asst Prof
  Spragins, C Fitzhugh, PhD, Prof

ARKANSAS POLYTECHNIC COLLEGE
  Russellville, Arkansas 72801 (N; st; coed; sem; II; 2525) BA major, Dept of Phil,
  501-968-0265

  Harrison, Christian L, BA, Instr
  Safran, Theodore R, MA, Instr
  Wilson, Tom B, PhD, Prof

ARKANSAS STATE UNIVERSITY
  State University, Arkansas 72467 (N; st; coed; sem; III; 6605) MA major, Div of Eng,
  Phil and Lang, 501-972-3043

  Claiborne, John H, PhD, Instr, Logic
  Stroud, Bill, PhD, Instr, Phil of Relig

ARKANSAS STATE UNIVERSITY, BEEBE BRANCH
  Beebe, Arkansas 72012 (N; st; coed; sem; I; 780) NP

THE COLLEGE OF THE OZARKS
  Clarksville, Arkansas 72830 (N, U Preb; coed; 4-1-4; II; 528) BA minor, Div of Human,
  501-754-8253

  Angell, Charles E, EdD, Prof

CROWLEY'S RIDGE COLLEGE
  Paragould, Arkansas 72450 (--; Ch of Christ; coed; sem; I; 123) NP

HARDING COLLEGE
  Searcy, Arkansas 72143 (N; Ch of Christ; coed; sem; III; 2060) Courses with no degree
  specialization, 501-268-6161

HARDING GRADUATE SCHOOL OF RELIGION
  Memphis, Tennessee 38117 (--; Ch of Christ; coed; sem; III; 159) MA major, Div of
  Phil of Relig and Apologetics, 901-767-4831

  Warren, Thomas B, PhD, Prof, Chm

HENDERSON STATE COLLEGE
Arkadelphia, Arkansas 71923 (N; st; coed; sem; III; 3300) BA minor, Dept of Phil and Human, 501-246-5511 Ext 317

Gentry, Jr, William C, PhD, Assoc Prof, Ethics

HENDRIX COLLEGE
Conway, Arkansas 72032 (N; U Meth; coed; qr; III; 997) BA major, Dept of Phil, 501-329-6811 Ext 358

Shoemaker, Robert G, PhD, Assoc Prof, Chm, Epistem, Ethics, Phil of Mind
Christie, Francis, PhD, Prof Part-time, Phil of Relig

Ellis, Matt L, PhD, Prof Emer

JOHN BROWN UNIVERSITY
Siloam Springs, Arkansas 72761 (N; p; coed; sem; II; 756) Courses with no degree specialization, Dept of Christ Educ and Phil, 501-524-3131 Ext 235

Weaver, Gilbert B, ThD, Assoc Prof, Chm
Bowling, Andrew C, PhD, Assoc Prof, Near East Stud

OUACHITA BAPTIST UNIVERSITY
Arkadelphia, Arkansas 71923 (N; S Bapt; coed; sem; III; 1375) BA major, Dept of Phil, 501-246-4531 Ext 278

Berryman, James, ThD, Prof, Chm, Phil of Relig, Contemp Phil
Coppenger, Raymond, PhD, Prof, Anc Phil, Med Phil
McCommas, Betty Jo, MA, Assoc Prof

PHILANDER SMITH COLLEGE
Little Rock, Arkansas 72203 (N; U Meth; coed; sem; II; 670) BA joint or combined major, Dept of Relig and Phil, 501-375-9845 Ext 46

Slinkard, R Thomas, MA, Assoc Prof, Chm, Hist of Phil
Corbitt, John H, BD, Adj Instr, Ethics

PHILLIPS COUNTY COMMUNITY COLLEGE
Helena, Arkansas 72342 (N; local; coed; sem; I; 522) NP

SHORTER COLLEGE
North Little Rock, Arkansas 72114 (--; AME; coed; sem; I; 229) NP

SOUTHERN BAPTIST COLLEGE
Walnut Ridge, Arkansas 72476 (N; S Bapt; coed; sem; I; 1420) --, Dept of Relig and Phil, 501-886-6741

Behannon, Woodrow, ThD, Prof, Phil of Relig

SOUTHERN STATE COLLEGE
Magnolia, Arkansas 71753 (N; st; coed; sem; II; 2052) BA minor, Dept of Phil, 501-234-5120 Ext 260

Chaffin, Bill M, PhD, Asst Prof, Phil of Mind

STATE COLLEGE OF ARKANSAS
  Conway, Arkansas 72032 (N; st; coed; sem; III; 4481) BA major, Dept of Phil, 501-
  329-2931 Ext 269

  Murray, Noland Patrick, PhD, Prof, Chm, Phil of Relig
  Shelton, Jimmy Dale, MPhil, Asst Prof, Epistem

UNIVERSITY OF ARKANSAS
  Fayetteville, Arkansas 72701 (N; st; coed; sem; IV; 12,974) PhD major, Dept of Phil,
  501-575-3551

  Kraemer, William S, PhD, Prof, Chm, Epistem, Ethical Theory
  Bashor, Philip S, PhD, Prof, Phil of Relig, 19th Cent Exist
  Edwards, Sandra S, PhD, Asst Prof, Med Phil
  Hantz, Harold D, PhD, Prof, Hist of Phil
  Nissen, Lowell A, PhD, Assoc Prof, Logic, Phil of Sci
  Scott, James H, PhD, Asst Prof, Ethics, Phil of Culture
  Vernon, Thomas S, PhD, Assoc Prof, Ration, Ethics

  Archie, Lee, BA, Grad Asst   Jones, Charles, AB, Grad Asst
  Hurdle, Burton, MA, Grad Asst

UNIVERSITY OF ARKANSAS AT LITTLE ROCK
  Little Rock, Arkansas 72204 (N; st; coed; sem; II; 4536) BA major, Dept of Phil and
  Relig, 501-565-7531, Ext 341

  Frothingham, Richard, PhD, Prof, Head, Phil of Relig
  Griffiths, Leslie, PhD, Asst Prof, Anal Phil, Logic, Epistem
  Kiger, Barry W, M Div, Lect
  Smith, Thomas M, BA, Lect
  Woolard, Harold I, ThD, Prof, Dean, Anc Phil, Med Phil

UNIVERSITY OF ARKANSAS AT MONTICELLO
  Monticello, Arkansas 71655 (N; st; coed; sem; II; 1958) Courses with no degree
  specialization, Dept of Lang and Lit, 501-367-6811 Ext 38

  Carpenter, Tom, MA, Instr

UNIVERSITY OF ARKANSAS AT PINE BLUFF
  Pine Bluff, Arizona 71601 (N; st; coed; sem; II; 2936) NR

UNIVERSITY OF ARKANSAS, MEDICAL CENTER
  Little Rock, Arkansas 72201 (ADNUR; st; coed; sem; IV; 821) NP

WESTARK COMMUNITY COLLEGE
  Fort Smith, Arkansas 72901 (ADNUR; local; coed; sem; I; 1790) Courses with no degree
  specialization, Dept of Soc and Behavior Sci, 501-783-6101 Ext 68

  Rappeport, Dorothy K, MEd

CALIFORNIA

ALLAN HANCOCK COLLEGE
Santa Maria, California 93454 (W; local; coed; sem; I; 6568) AA major, Dept of Soc Sci, 805-922-7711

Bostwick, James, MA, Instr, Exist, Ethics, Metaph

AMERICAN BAPTIST SEMINARY OF THE WEST
Covina, California 91724 (Theol; Bapt; coed; qr; IV; 108) DMin major, Dept of Phil of Relig and Syst Theol, 213-332-4034

Doss, R, PhD, Assoc Prof, Personalism
Ramm, B, PhD, Prof, Phil of Sci, Hist of Phil, Exist
Rutenber, C, PhD, Prof, Greek Phil

AMERICAN BAPTIST SEMINARY, WEST-BERKELEY
Berkeley, California 94704 (Theol; Amer Bapt; coed; qr; IV; 77) NR

AMERICAN RIVER COLLEGE
Sacramento, California 95841 (W; st; coed; sem; I; 14,710) Courses with no degree specialization, 916-484-8011

Dumont, Guilbert, MA
Field, Edwin, MA
Frank, Robert, MA
Sertic, John, MA
Waters, Gardner

ANTELOPE VALLEY COLLEGE
Lancaster, California 93534 (W; local; coed; sem; I; 3973) Courses with no degree specialization, Div of Soc Sci, 805-943-324 Ext 216

Loffbourrow, Richard C, MA, Instr

ARMSTRONG COLLEGE
Berkeley, California 94704 (W; p; coed; qr; III; 430) NP

ART CENTER COLLEGE OF DESIGN
Los Angeles, California 90020 (W; p; coed; tri; III; 1022) Courses with no degree specialization, Dept of Phil, 213-938-5166

Vick, George, PhD, Aes, Metaph

AZUSA PACIFIC COLLEGE
Azusa, California 91702 (W; p; coed; III; 939) AA major, Dept of Soc Sci, 213-335-0521 Ext 272

Shirey, Keith, MA, Polit Phil
White, Joan, MA

CALIFORNIA

BAKERSFIELD COLLEGE
  Bakersfield, California 93305 (W; local; coed; sem; I; 11,277) AA major, Dept of
  Phil, 805-871-7120 Ext 259

  Thiroux, Jacques P, MA, Prof, Chm, Ethics, Gen Phil, Phil of Relig, Aes
  Barry, Vincent, MA, Assoc Prof, Logic, Gen Phil
  Hernandez, John P, EdD, Assoc Prof, Ethics, Gen Phil
  Nielsen, William, MA, Prof, Sym Logic
  Rhea, David, MA, Assoc Prof, Logic, Gen Phil

BARSTOW COLLEGE
  Barstow, California 92311 (W; local; coed; sem; I; 1202) Courses with no degree
  specialization, Dept of Phil, 714-252-2411

BETHANY BIBLE COLLEGE
  Santa Cruz, California 95060 (S; Assem of God; coed; sem; II; 491) BA minor, Div
  of Bibl Lit and Phil, 408-438-3803 Ext 405

  Smith, Kevin, MA, Instr Part-time

BIOLA COLLEGE
  La Mirada, California 90638 (W; p; coed; sem; III; 1851) BA Minor, Dept of Phil,
  213-723-6121 Ext 373

  Bass, William, PhD, Prof
  Hanson, Delbert, MA, Asst Prof

BROOKS INSTITUTE, SANTA BARBARA
  Santa Barbara, California 93103 (W; p; coed; tri; II; 646) NP

BUTTE COLLEGE
  Durham, California 95938 (W; local; coed; qr; I; 4049) Courses with no degree
  specialization, Div of Soc Sci, 916-345-2481 Ext 75

  Bordoli, James, MA

CABRILLO COLLEGE
  Aptos, California 95003 (W; local; coed; 4-1-4; I; 6118) Courses with no degree
  specialization, 408-475-6000

CALIFORNIA BAPTIST COLLEGE
  Riverside, California 92504 (W; S Bapt; coed; sem; II; 675) BA minor, Dept of Relig,
  714-689-5771

  Ortegon, Samuel M, PhD, Prof, Hist of Phil, Phil of Relig

CALIFORNIA COLLEGE OF ARTS AND CRAFTS
  Oakland, California 94618 (W; p; coed; sem; III; 1509) NR

CALIFORNIA INSTITUTE OF ARTS
  Burbank, California 91504 (W; p; coed; qr; III; 825) NR

CALIFORNIA INSTITUTE OF TECHNOLOGY
Pasadena, California 91101 (W; p; men; qr; IV; 1504) PhD minor, Div of Human and
Soc Sci, 203-795-6841

Bures, Charles E, PhD, Prof, Theor of Human Nature
Hertz, Richard, PhD, Asst Prof
Thompson, Fred, PhD, Prof, Math Ling

Stern, Alfred, Prof Emer, Exist

CALIFORNIA LUTHERAN COLLEGE
Thousand Oaks, California 91360 (W; Luth; coed; 4-1-4; qr; II; 1449) BA major,
Dept of Phil, 805-492-2411

CALIFORNIA MARITIME ACADEMY
Vallejo, California 94590 (--; st; men; tri; II; 237) NP

CALIFORNIA POLYTECHNIC STATE UNIVERSITY AT SAN LUIS OBISPO
San Luis Obispo, California 93407 (W; st; coed; qr; III; 12,107) Courses with no
degree specialization, Dept of Phil, 805-546-2041

Culbertson, James T, PhD, Prof, Head
Bethel, Arthur Charles Walter, MA, Asst Prof
Dundon, Stanislaus J, PhD, Assoc Prof
Lascola, Russel A, PhD, Assoc Prof
O'Toole, Frederick, PhD, Asst Prof
Sweet, Dolores M, PhD, Assoc Prof

Hogan, Wilbur C, MA, Prof Emer

CALIFORNIA SCHOOL OF PROFESSIONAL PSYCHOLOGY, LOS ANGELES CAMPUS
Los Angeles, California 90004 (--; p; coed; tri; IV; 149) NR

CALIFORNIA SCHOOL OF PROFESSIONAL PSYCHOLOGY, SAN FRANCISCO CAMPUS
San Francisco, California 94110 (--; p; coed; tri; IV; 106) NR

CALIFORNIA STATE COLLEGE AT BAKERSFIELD
Bakersfield, California 93309 (W; st; coed; qr; III; 1775) BA major, Dept of Phil
and Relig Stud, 805-833-3051

Kegley, Charles W, PhD, Prof, Chm, Ethics, Aes, Polit Phil
Angus, Robert J, MA, Lect, Logic, Metaph
Betty, L Stafford, MA, Lect, Eastern Relig and Phil
Kegley, Jaquelyn A K, PhD, Asst Prof, Phil of Sci, Epistem, Phil of Lang
Kessler, Gary E, PhD, Assoc Prof, Phil of Relig
Prigge, Norman K, MA, Lect, Ethics, Logic, Epistem, Hist of Phil

CALIFORNIA STATE COLLEGE AT DOMINGUEZ HILLS
Dominguez Hills, California (W; st; coed; qr; III; 3611) BA major, Dept of
Phil, 213-532-4300 Ext 493

Shimomisse, Eiichi, PhD, Assoc Prof, Chm, Phenomen, Eastern Phil
Balslev, Anindita, PhD, Lect Part-time, Indian Phil, Exist
Fay, Charles, PhD, Prof, Phil of Law, Ethics
Grossman, Ross, PhD, Assoc Prof, Aes, Phil of Art
Hagan, William, PhD, Assoc Prof, Phil of Relig, Metaph
Kaye, Claire, MA, Lect Part-time, Phil of Educ

La Corte, John, PhD, Asst Prof, Phil of Relig, Phil of Mind
Lewis, Donald, PhD, Assoc Prof, Exist, Marxism
Liotta, James, PhD, Asst Prof, Phil of Lang, Phil of Cult, Epistem
McMahon, Arnold, MA, Lect Par-time, Soc and Polit Phil
Puett, William, MA, Lect Part-time, Logic
Pyne, Thomas, MA, Asst Prof, Epistem, Anal Phil

CALIFORNIA STATE COLLEGE AT SAN BERNARDINO
San Bernardino, California 92407 (W; st; coed; qr; III; 2556) BA major, Dept of
Phil, 714-887-6311

Van Marter, Leslie, PhD, Prof, Chm, Aes
Crocker, Sylvia, PhD, Lect Part-time, Metaph, Exist
Johnson, Paul, PhD, Assoc Prof, Polit Phil, Ethics
Kroll, Joseph, AM, Lect Part-time
Zoecklein, Walter, PhD, Assoc Prof, Greek Phil, Med Phil

CALIFORNIA STATE COLLEGE AT SONOMA
Rohnert Park, California 94928 (W; st; coed; sem; III; 5206) BA major, Dept of
Phil, 707-795-2163

Alderman, Harold, PhD, Assoc Prof, Phenom
McDaniel, Stanley, MA, Asst Prof, East Tht
Mooney, Edward, PhD, Assoc Prof, Phil of Relig
Paul, Richard, PhD, Assoc Prof, Soc Phil
Proctor, George, PhD, Prof, Phil of Sci
Smaby, John, PhD, Assoc Prof, Soc Phil
Temko, Philip, PhD, Prof, Phil of Lang

CALIFORNIA STATE COLLEGE AT STANISLAUS
Turlock, California 95380 (W; st; coed; qr; III; 2687) BA minor, Dept of Phil,
209-634-9101 Ext 457

Hayes, William H, PhD, Prof, Aes

CALIFORNIA STATE POLYTECHNIC UNIVERSITY AT POMONA
Pomona, California 91768 (W; st; coed; qr; III; 9893) BA minor, Dept of Soc Sci,
714-595-1241 Ext 1856

Ackley, Charles W, PhD, Assoc Prof, Soc Ethics
Breckenridge, James, PhD, Lect
Hatfield, John, PhD, Asst Prof, Hist of Relig
Kinzel, Margaret M, PhD, Asst Prof, Phil of Relig
Richards, Richard C, MA, Assoc Prof, Aes
Ross, Floyd H, PhD, Prof, Hist of Relig

CALIFORNIA STATE UNIVERSITY AT CHICO
Chico, California 95926 (W; st; coed; sem; III; 10,654) BA major, Dept of Phil,
916-345-6183

Bruder, Kenneth J, PhD, Hist of Phil, Contemp Euro Phil, Phil of Psych, Metaph
Carter, David K, Soc Phil, Amer Phil, Theory of Value
Easterling, Marvin L, PhD, Aes, Ethics, Phil of Relig
Ficarra, Frank T, PhD, Hist of Phil, Phil in Lit, Hist and Phil of Jazz
Haecker, Dorothy A, Soc Phil, Phil of Hist, Feminist Tht
Hirschbein, Ron L, PhD, Soc Phil, Phil of Soc Sci, Phil of Rel

Moore, Brooke N, PhD, Anal Phil, Epistem, Metaph
Parker, Richard B, PhD, Anal Phil, Logic, Phil of Law
Svitak, Ivan, PhD, Hist of Phil, Marxism, Phil Anthrop
Tiedeman, Kent, PhD, Epistem, Phil of Sci, Exist, Phenom

CALIFORNIA STATE UNIVERSITY AT FRESNO
Fresno, California 93740 (W; st; coed; sem; III; 14,846) BA major, Dept of Phil
209-487-2621

Kessler, Warren L, PhD, Assoc Prof, Chm, Continen Ration, Mod Phil, Ethics
Colver, A Wayne, PhD, Prof, Hist of Phil, Hume, Descartes
Foster, Hague D, PhD, Assoc Prof, Exist, Marxism, Polit Phil
Gibson, Geoffrey J, MA, Asst Prof, Hist of Phil, Polit Phil, Ethics
Hall, Elton A, MA, Asst Prof, Orient Phil, Plato, Contemp Anglo-Amer Phil
Pitt, Jack A, PhD, Prof, Metaph, Phil of B Russell, Phil of Lang
Slinger, James W, PhD, Asst Prof, Epistem, Phil of Lang, Contemp Anal Phil
Smith, James M, PhD, Prof, Legal and Soc Phil, Ethics, Phil of Relig
Uphold, W B, PhD, Prof, Comp Relig, Phil of Relig, Phil and Lit
Walker, Harold, PhD, Prof, Theol, Phil of Relig

CALIFORNIA STATE UNIVERSITY AT FULLERTON
Fullerton, California 92634 (W; st; coed; sem; III; 15694) BA major, Dept of Phil,
714-870-3611

Russell, J Michael, PhD, Assoc Prof, Chm, Exist, Phil of Mind
Alamshah, William H, PhD, Prof, Anc Phil, Kant
Catanzaro, James L, PhD, Lect Part-time
Cronquist, John, PhD, Assoc Prof, Ethics, Anc Phil, Med Phil
Ihara, Craig K, PhD, Asst Prof, Ethics, Orient Phil, Soc and Polit Phil
Painter, Alfred, PhD, Lect Part-time, Phil of Relig
Ring, Merrill, PhD, Assoc Prof, Metaph, Epistem
Rock, Gloria, MA, Asst Prof, Ethics, Logic, Soc and Polit Phil
Safford, Betty C, BA, Lect Part-time, Logic
Simon, Stephen, CPhil, Asst Prof, Metaph, Epistem
Smith, E Diane, BA, Lect Part-time, Exist, Phil of Action
Smith, Richard L, PhD, Asst Prof, Logic, Phil Sci, Phil Lang, Creativity
Verges, Frank G, PhD, Assoc Prof, Epistem, British Empir
Weinzweig, Marjorie, PhD, Asst Prof, Phenom, Epistem, Mod Phil

CALIFORNIA STATE UNIVERSITY AT HAYWARD
Hayward, California 94542 (W; st; coed; qr; III; 12,520) BA major, Dept of Phil
415-884-3225

Harrell, Jean G, PhD, Chm, Prof, Aes
Bartley, William W, PhD, Prof, Contemp Phil
Bassen, Paul C, PhD, Asst Prof, Anal Phil
Birmingham, John T, PhD, Lect, Phenomen, Exist
Buder, Norman, BA, Asst Prof, Ethics
Goheen, John D, PhD, Prof, Hist of Phil
Hodge, John L, PhD, Asst Prof, Soc Ethics
Kissin, Peter P, PhD, Asst Prof, Epistem, Logic
Langan, William J, PhD, Asst Prof, Exist, Phenomen
MacKinnon, Edward M, PhD, Prof, Phil of Sci
Mayers, Eugene D, PhD, Prof, Phil of Law
Sapontzis, Steve F, PhD, Asst Prof, Phenomen
Sarkar, Anil K, PhD, Prof, Asian Phil
Wogast, Elizabeth, PhD, Assoc Prof, Anal Phil, Epistem
Zuniga, Joaquin A, PhD, Asst Prof, Aes

CALIFORNIA STATE UNIVERSITY AT HUMBOLDT
Arcata, California 95521 (W; st; coed; qr; III; 5917) BA major, Dept of Phil, 707-826-4124

Armstrong, Susan B, AB, Asst Prof, Chm, Metaph, Ethics, Phil of Soc Sci, Process Phil
Bazemore, Wallace D, PhD, Assoc Prof, Indian Phil
Derden, Jr, James K, PhD, Asst Prof, Phil of Sci, Logic
Early, Thomas, PhD, Lect, Chinese Phil, Soc Phil, Greek Phil, Phil of Relig
Engel, Elizabeth, PhD, Asst Prof, Anc Phil
Howe, Clarence S, PhD, Prof, Phil Anthrop, Phil of Cult, Phil of Art, Phil of Hist, Hist of Phil, Plato, Hegel, Dilthey, Dewey, Cassirer, Heidegger, Merleau-Ponty

CALIFORNIA STATE UNIVERSITY AT LONG BEACH
Long Beach, California 90840 (W; st; coed; sem; III; 28,450) MA major, Dept of Phil, 213-498-4332

Ringer, Virginia Hartt, PhD, Prof, Chm, Polit Phil, Phil of Law, Phil of Hist
Andre, Shane, PhD, Assoc Prof, Epistem
Bonis, William D, PhD, Prof, Exist, Phil of Relig
Clark, Cheryl, MA, Asst Prof, Phil of Soc Sci, Logic
Fels, Leonard, EdD, Assoc Prof, Prag
Guerrieri, Daniel, PhD, Asst Prof, Phenomen, Anc Phil
Johnson, William, BA, Asst Prof, Contemp Anglo-Amer Phil
Kim, Hyung I, PhD, Assoc Prof, East Phil
Massey, G Eric, MA, Prof, Aes
Maue, J Brooks, PhD, Prof, Phil of Sci
Noren, Stephen, PhD, Assoc Prof, Phil of Sci
Peccorini, Francisco L, PhD, Prof, Med Phil, Metaph
Quest, Edward, PhD, Assoc Prof, Logic
Spangler, G A, MA, Asst Prof, Anc Phil
Strickler, Gerald B, STD, Prof, Phil of Relig

Davis, James Arlis, MA, Grad Asst   Malin, Glen P, BA, Grad Asst

CALIFORNIA STATE UNIVERSITY AT LOS ANGELES
Los Angeles, California 90032 (W; st; coed; qr; III; 23,252) MA major, 213-224-0111

Annese, Thomas, PhD, Assoc Prof, Chm, Phil of Mind
Albert, Sidney, PhD, Prof, Aes
Anderson, Anthony C, MA, Asst Prof Part-time, Logic
Benson, Arthur, MA, Assoc Prof, Phil of Sci
Burrill, Donald, PhD, Prof, Ethics, Soc and Polit Phil
Cotton, David A H, PhD, Asst Prof, Anc Phil
Engel, Morris, PhD, Prof Part-time
Finkenbinder, Michael, MA, Instr
Garry, Ann, PhD, Asst Prof, Phil of Mind
Glathe, Alfred, PhD, Asst Prof, Hist of Phil
Hill, Sharon, PhD, Assoc Prof, Ethics, Soc and Polit Phil
Hitterdale, Larry, PhD, Asst Prof Part-time
Johnson, Major, PhD, Asst Prof Part-time
Lott, Tommy, BA, Instr Part-time, Perception
Lubow, Neil, MA, Instr Part-time, Phil of Mind
Price, Sheila, MA, Asst Prof Part-time
Simon, Jerome, PhD, Asst Prof, Hist of Phil
Trivus, Sidney, MA, Asst Prof, Logic
Vick, George, PhD, Assoc Prof, Continen Phil
Wilson, James, PhD, Prof

CALIFORNIA STATE UNIVERSITY AT NORTHRIDGE
  Northridge, California 91324 (W; st; coed; sem; III; 24,450) MA major, Dept of
  Phil, 213-885-2757

  Forthman, William, PhD, Assoc Prof, Acting Chm, Phil of Relig
  Baran, Gary, MA, Instr, Ethics
  Champawat, Narayan, PhD, Assoc Prof, Phil of Sci
  Crandon-Graef, David, MA, Asst Prof, Logic
  Crittenden, Charles, PhD, Assoc Prof, Metaph
  Garfinkel, Alan, MA, Asst Prof, Polit Phil
  Henze, Donald, PhD, Prof, Hist of Phil
  Hersh, Thomas, PhD, Asst Prof, Exist
  Kellenberger, James, PhD, Assoc Prof, Phil of Relig
  Luckenbach, Sidney, PhD, Assoc Prof, Phil of Sci
  McGuinness, Frank, MA, Asst Prof, Logic
  Richfield, Jerome, PhD, Prof, Hist of Phil
  Salter, Donald, MA, Assoc Prof, Ethics
  Saltzman, Gerald, MA, Asst Prof, Ethics
  Saunders, John Turk, PhD, Prof, Epistem
  Sedey, Daniel, PhD, Assoc Prof, Metaph
  Sicha, Jeffrey, DPhil, Assoc Prof, Phil of Math
  Tomberlin, James, PhD, Assoc Prof, Metaph
  Weinzweig, Marjorie, PhD, Asst Prof, Phenomen

CALIFORNIA STATE UNIVERSITY AT SACRAMENTO
  Sacramento, California 95819 (W; st; coed; sem; III; 17,477) BA major, 916-454-6424

  Weddle, Perry, PhD, Assoc Prof, Chm
  Anderson, Clifford, MA, Asst Prof
  Faurot, Jean H, PhD, Prof
  Foreman, Robert A, MA, Asst Prof
  Long, David W, PhD, Assoc Prof
  Lovitt, C W, PhD, Prof
  McGreal, Ian P, PhD, Prof
  Nammour, Jamil, PhD, Asst Prof
  Wedin, Gale J, PhD, Asst Prof
  Wu, Joseph S, PhD, Prof

CALIFORNIA STATE UNIVERSITY AT SAN DIEGO
  San Diego, California 92115 (W; st; coed; sem; IV; 26,227) MA major, Dept of Phil,
  714-286-5263

  Koppelman, Walter, PhD, Assoc Prof, Chm, Phil of Law, Polit Phil
  Carella, Michael J, PhD, Assoc Prof, Soc Ethics, Phil of Soc Sci
  Crawford, Patricia A, PhD, Prof, Mod Phil, Kant, Phil of Relig
  Feenberg, Andrew L, PhD, Asst Prof, Polit Phil, 19th Cent Phil
  Howard, Roy J, PhD, Prof, Med Phil, Phenomen
  Lauer, Rosemary Z, PhD, Assoc Prof, Anc Phil, Mod Phil
  McClurg, Jack, PhD, Prof, Metaph
  Nelson, Sherwood M, PhD, Prof, Phil of Hist, Ethics
  O'Reilly, Peter, PhD, Prof, Med Phil, Theory of Knowl
  Rosenstein, Leon, PhD, Asst Prof, Exist, Phenomen
  Ruja, Harry, PhD, Prof, 20th Cent Phil, Jewish Phil, Phil of Relig
  Shields, Allan E, PhD, Prof, Aes
  Snyder, William S, PhD, Prof, Metaph, East Phil, Polit Phil
  Troxell, Eugene A, PhD, Assoc Prof, Ordinary Lang Anal
  Warren, Edward W, PhD, Prof, Anc Phil
  Weissman, Stanley N, PhD, Prof, Phil of Lang, Phil of Sci, Logic

  Mendenhall, Mary, PhD, Prof Emer

CALIFORNIA STATE UNIVERSITY AT SAN FRANCISCO
San Francisco, California 94132 (W; st; coed; sem; IV; 18,878) MA major, Dept of
Phil, 415-469-1596

Royse, James R, PhD, Assoc Prof, Chm, Logic, Mod Phil
Bach, Kent, PhD, Assoc Prof, Phil of Mind, Exist
Bierman, Arthur K, PhD, Prof, Epistem, Metaph
Epstein, Ronald B, MA, Lect, Orient Phil
Glanville, John J, PhD, Prof, Med Phil, Anc Phil
Haecker, Dorothy, MPhil, Lect, Soc Phil, Polit Phil
Harrison, Craig, PhD, Assoc Prof, Phil of Sci, Logic
Kahl, Russell, PhD, Prof, Phil of Soc Sci
Milne, Gretchen, PhD, Lect, Women's Stud
Needleman, Jacob, PhD, Prof, Phil of Relig
Provence, Donald L, PhD, Assoc Prof, Epistem, Theory of Value, Theory of Meaning
Radcliff, Peter E, PhD, Prof, Ethics, Phil of Law
Roque, Alicia, MA, Lect, Latin American Phil
Silvers, Anita, PhD, Assoc Prof, Ethics, Aes
Syfers, James W, PhD, Assoc Prof, Mod Phil, Soc Phil
Tilden, Nancy L, PhD, Prof, Phil of Relig

McGill, V Jerauld, PhD, Prof Emer

CALIFORNIA STATE UNIVERSITY AT SAN JOSE
San Jose, California 95114 (W; st; coed; sem; III; 25,981) MA major, Dept of Phil,
408-277-2871

Eastman, Jr, Lucius R, PhD, Assoc Prof, Chm
Albright, Gary L, PhD, Assoc Prof
Black, Carolyn C, PhD, Asst Prof
Black, Edward J, PhD, Assoc Prof
Brock, Jarrett E, PhD, Asst Prof
Canty, John T, PhD, Lect
Cody, Arthur B, PhD, Prof
Davis, Philip E, PhD, Prof
Deininger, Whitaker T, PhD, Prof
Dommeyer, Frederick C, PhD, Prof
Dutton, John D, PhD, Prof
Fallico, Arturo B, PhD, Prof
Fox, Marie C, PhD, Assoc Prof
Goldworth, Amnon, PhD, Prof
Jacklin, Phillip D, PhD, Assoc Prof
Keyes, William T, MA, Lect
Klor De Alva, J Jorge, MA, Lect
Koestenbaum, Peter, PhD, Prof
Scott, Frederick J D, PhD, Prof
Schmidt, Michael F, PhD, Assoc Prof
Shapiro, Herman, PhD, Prof
Sharma, Ved P, PhD, Assoc Prof
Stewart, Calvin G, MA, Lect
Terakawa, Shunsho, PhD, Asst Prof
Waterhouse, Joseph B, PhD, Asst Prof

Freeman, Eugene, PhD, Prof Emer

CANADA COLLEGE
Redwood City, California 94061 (W; local; coed; sem; I; 6056) NR

CERRITOS COLLEGE
  Norwalk, California 90650 (W; local; coed; sem; I; 22,694) Courses with no degree
  specialization, Dept of Phil, 213-860-2451

  Hengsteler, V Elizabeth, PhD, Chm
  Armantage, Walter W, ThD, Part-time
  Bloomfield, Edward H, MA
  Casey, John, PhD, Part-time
  Reeder, Paul, PhD, Part-time
  Wessell, Douglas F, MA

CHABOT COLLEGE
  Hayward, California 94545 (W; local coed; qr; I; 8445) Courses with no degree
  specialization, Div of Human, 415-782-3000 Ext 287

  Hoitsma, Kenmont, MA
  Marker, Eugene, MA
  Mastroyannis, Constantine, MA
  Reiff, Allan, MA

CHAFFEY COLLEGE
  Alta Loma, California 91701 (W; local; coed; sem; I; 7865) Courses with no degree
  specialization, 714-987-1737

  Rose, Bea, MA, Prof

CHAPMAN COLLEGE
  Orange, California 92666 (W; p; coed; 4-1-4; III; 4892) BA major, Dept of Phil,
  714-633-8821 Ext 235

  Williams, Bert C, PhD, Prof, Chm
  Auth, Kurt, MA, Instr
  Dodson, Dave, PhD, Asst Prof
  Huntington, Ron, PhD, Prof, Orient Phil

  Delp, Paul, MA, Assoc Prof Emer

CHURCH DIVINITY SCHOOL OF THE PACIFIC
  Berkeley, California 94709 (Theol, PE; coed; qr; III; 79) NP

CITRUS COLLEGE
  Azusa, California 91702 (W; local; coed; sem; I; 7901) Courses with no degree
  specialization, Dept of Soc Sci, 213-335-0521

  Shivey, Keith, MA
  White, Joan, MA

CITY COLLEGE OF SAN FRANCISCO
  San Francisco, California 94112 (W; local; coed; sem; I; 19,979) AA major, Dept of
  Soc Sci, 415-587-7272 Ext 218

  Everall, Patricia, MA
  Green, Dennis C, MA
  Struckman, Robert, MA
  Utter, Robert P, MA

CLAREMONT GRADUATE SCHOOL
Claremont, California 91711 (W; p; coed; sem; IV; 1317) PhD major, Dept of Phil,
714-626-8511 Ext 3925

Louch, Alfred, PhD, Prof, Chm, Phil of Mind, Phil of Law, Polit and Soc Phil
Hutchison, John, PhD, Prof, Phil of Relig
Vickers, John, PhD, Assoc Prof, Logic, Epistem
Winance, Eleutherius, PhD, Lect, Phenomen, Med Phil
Young, Charles, PhD, Asst Prof, Class Phil, Ethics, Logic

Schneider, Herbert W, PhD, Prof Emer, Hist of Phil, Polit Phil

CLAREMONT MEN'S COLLEGE
Claremont, California 91711 (W; p; men; sem; II; 804) BA major, Dept of Phil,
714-626-8511 Ext 2826

Smith, Steven A, PhD, Asst Prof, Chm, Ethics, Hist of Phil
Henry, Jr, Granville C, PhD, Assoc Prof, Phil of Math
Kucheman, Clark A, PhD, Prof, Ethics
Roth, John K, PhD, Assoc Prof, Amer Phil, Phil of Relig

COGSWELL POLYTECHNIC COLLEGE
San Francisco, California 94110 (Tech; p; coed; sem; I; 70) NR

COLEGIO DE LA TIERRA
Fresno, California 93701 (--; p; coed; --; I; 48) NP

COLLEGE OF ALAMEDA
Alameda, California 94501 (--; local; coed; qr; I; 5249) AA major, Div of Soc Sci,
415-522-7221

Chichester, Jr, Helon L, MA

COLLEGE OF MARIN
Kentfield, California 94904 (W; local; coed; sem; I; 6092) AA major, Dept of Human,
415-454-3962 Ext 367

Dhillon, S S, MA, Instr Part-time, Asian Phil
Groven, Blair, MA, Instr Part-time
Palmer, Donald, MA, Assoc Prof
Weber, Cornelius G, EdD, Prof

COLLEGE OF NOTRE DAME
Belmont, California 94002 (W; RC; coed; sem; II; 1181) BA major, Dept of Phil,
415-593-7674

Sullivan, Mark, PhD, Prof, Chm
Fee, Diana, Asst Prof
Moderbacher, Johannes, PhD, Lect
Weierich, Andre, PhD, Lect

Zimmerman, Gabriel, PhD, Lect

COLLEGE OF SAN MATEO
   San Mateo, California 94402 (W; local; coed; sem; I: 13,190)

   Cooper, Baron, PhD, Chm
   Fellows, Ward, MA
   Porter, Donald, MA
   Sides, Henry, PhD

COLLEGE OF THE CANYONS
   Valencia, California (--; local; coed; qr; I; 1586) Courses with no degree
   specialization, 805-259-7800

COLLEGE OF THE DESERT
   Palm Desert, California 92260 (W; local; coed; sem; I; 3737) BA minor, Dept of Phil
   and Rel, 714-346-8041 Ext 243

   Flatt, Charles, MA, Prof
   Goodwin, George D, PhD, Prof

COLLEGE OF THE HOLY NAMES
   Oakland, California 94619 (W; p; wo; sem; III; 813) BA major, Dept of Phil, 415-
   436-1074

   Gibson, Sheila, PhD, Asst Prof, Ethics
   Mondini, Raymond, MA, Instr, Orient Phil
   Thurn, Richard, MA, Instr, Contemp Phil
   Woodward, Irene, PhD, Asst Prof, Syst Phil
   Yee, Richard, PhD, Assoc Prof, Med Phil, 19th Cent Phil

COLLEGE OF THE REDWOODS
   Eureka, California 95501 (W; local; coed; qr; I; 4564) Courses with no degree
   specialization, Div of Human, 707-443-8411

   Dawson, Lawrence, MA, Instr
   McDaniel, Stanley, MA, Instr
   Nash, Lewis, MA, Instr

COLLEGE OF THE SEQUOIAS
   Visalia, California 93277 (W; local; coed; sem; I; 5898) Courses with no degree
   specialization, --, 209-732-4711

   Murray, Thomas, PhD, Chm

COLLEGE OF THE SISKIYOUS
   Weed, California 96094 (W; local; coed; sem; I; 823) --, Dept of Phil, 916-938-4463

   Greer, Yates Calvert, ML

COLUMBIA JUNIOR COLLEGE
   Columbia, California 95310 (W; st and local; coed; qr; I; 1669) Courses with no
   degree specialization, Area of Soc Sci, 209-532-3141 Ext 237

   Hamilton, Robert H, MA, Chm, Ethics, Phil of Relig

CALIFORNIA

Crowley, James, MA, Epistem, Metaph
Kamber, Matild, MA, Logic, Hist of Phil

COMPTON COLLEGE
Compton, California 90221 (W; local; coed; sem; I; 6715) AA major, Dept of Eng
and Phil, 213-635-8081 Ext 289

Migaud, Ronald, MA, Asst Prof, Act Chm
Grange, Kathleen, PhD, Assoc Prof
Ponnech, Ben, MA, Asst Prof

CONTRA COSTA COLLEGE
San Pablo, California 94806 (W; local; coed; sem; I; 6380) NR

COSUMNES RIVER COLLEGE
Sacramento, California 95823 (W; local; coed; sem; I; 2707) Courses with no degree

Bernoff, Maxon A, MA, Instr

CRAFTON HILLS COLLEGE
Yucaipa, California 92399 (--; local; coed; sem; I; 1276) Phil and Relig Stud,
714-794-2161 Ext 264

Gatchel, Richard H, PhD, Instr
Harry, Shirley A, MA, Instr Part-time

CUESTA COLLEGE
San Luis Obispo, California 93401 (W; local; coed; sem; I; 4255) Courses with no
degree specialization, --, 805-544-2943

CYPRESS COLLEGE
Cypress, California 90630 (W; local; coed; sem; I; 7791) Courses with no degree
specialization, Dept of Phil, 714-826-2220 Ext 267

Cooney, Neill L, MA
Gruver, Eric W, MA
Hickey, Denis, PhD
Ricci, Paul O, MA

DQ UNIVERSITY
Davis, California 95616 (--; p; coed; tri; IV; 72) Courses with no degree
specialization, Grad Native Amer Stud, 916-758-0902

Racine, Albert J, MA, Prof, Native Amer Phil

DE ANZA COLLEGE
Cupertino, California 95014 (W; st and local; coed; qr; I; 6050) AA major, Dept of
Phil, 408-257-5500

Foster, Marguerite, PhD, Head, Logic, Theory of Knowl, Exist
Vician, Thomas, PhD, Phil of Relig, Hist of Phil, Phil of the Person

DEEP SPRINGS COLLEGE
Deep Springs, California, Via Dyer, Nevada 89010 (W; p; men; --; I; 22) NR

DIABLO VALLEY COLLEGE
Pleasant Hill, California 94523 (W; local; coed; sem; I; 14,057) Courses with no degree specialization, --, 415-685-1230

Murphy, Jack, MS, Instr
Neudstadt, Robert, MA, Instr
Reed, Ted, MA, Instr
Wood, Clara, ThD, Instr

DOMINICAN COLLEGE OF SAN RAFAEL
San Rafael, California 94901 (W; p; coed; sem; III; 953) BA minor, Dept of Phil, 415-453-1047

Adnou, Etel, Assoc Prof
Numaghi, MA, Instr

DON BOSCO TECHNICAL INSTITUTE
Rosemead, California 91770 (W; p; men; sem; I; 180) Dept of Phil, 213-283-6561

Ralph, Simeone, MA

EAST LOS ANGELES COLLEGE
Los Angeles, California 90022 (W; local; coed; sem; I; 14,042) Courses with no degree specialization, Dept of Psych, 213-263-7261 Ext 297

Bergel, Alice Rose, PhD, Prof
Konrich, Eva, PhD, Assoc Prof, Orient Phil
Mairesse, Jean V, MA, Prof
Morales, Goldieb, MA, Asst Prof

EL CAMINO COLLEGE
Torrence, California 90506 (W; local; coed; sem; I; 22,068) AA major, Dept of Phil, 213-532-3670

Anagnostis, Mary W, MA, Prof
Barger, Bill D, PhD
Shepard, Paul B, MA, Prof
Shuler, Robert, PhD
Thureson, Joan I, MA

FEATHER RIVER COLLEGE
Quincy, California 95971 (W; local; coed; qr; I; 790) NP

FOOTHILL COLLEGE
Los Altos Hills, California 94022 (W; local; coed; qr; I; 5716) AA major, Div of Soc Sci, 415-948-8590 Ext 322

Engle, Gale, PhD, Prof, Ethics, Logic
Stietzel, Eric, MA, Asst Prof, Logic, Phil of Relig
Tinsley, William, MA, Prof, Soc and Polit Phil, Ethics

FRESNO CITY COLLEGE
Fresno, California 93704 (W; local; coed; sem, II, 13,040) Courses with no degree specialization, --, 209-264-4721

FULLER THEOLOGICAL SEMINARY
Pasadena, California 91101 (W; p; coed; qr; IV; 460) Courses with no degree specialization, Dept of Relig, 213-449-1745

FULLERTON JUNIOR COLLEGE
Fullerton, California 92634 (W; local; coed; sem; I; 14,580) Courses with no degree specialization, --, 714-871-8000

GAVILAN COLLEGE
Gilroy, California (W; local; coed; qr; I; 1645) AA major, Dept of Phil, 408-842-8221

Gissler, Antoinette, MA
Hughes, Patrich, PhD, Prof, Phil of Law

GLENDALE COMMUNITY COLLEGE
Glendale, California 91208 (W; local; coed; sem; I; 6163) Courses with no degree specialization, Div of Soc Sci, 213-240-1000

Hardison, Richard C, EdD, Prof
Horton, Jr, Ernest, PhD, Prof
Parker, William L, MA, Assoc Prof, Hist of Phil, Logic
Williams, Richard L, MA, Instr, Polit Tht

GOLDEN GATE BAPTIST THEOLOGICAL SEMINARY
Mill Valley, California 94941 (W; S Bapt; coed; qr; IV; 268) Courses with no degree specialization, 415-388-8080

Cunningham, Richard Bryan, ThD, Assoc Prof, Phil of Relig

GOLDEN GATE UNIVERSITY
San Francisco, California 94105 (W; p; coed; tri; III; 4499) Courses with no degree specialization, 415-391-7800

GOLDEN WEST COLLEGE
Huntington Beach, California 92647 (W; local; coed; sem; I; 13,014) Courses with no degree specialization, Div of Soc Sci, 714-892-7711 Ext 518

Grimes, Pierre, PhD, Instr, Hist of Phil
Melville, Michael J, MA, Instr, Hist of Phil, Logic, Ethics

GRADUATE THEOLOGICAL UNION
Berkeley, California 94709 (W; p; coed; qr; IV; 254) PhD major, Dept of Syst and Phil Theol and Phil of Religion, 415-841-9811

Baur, Francis, PhD, Visit Asst Prof
Berry, Cornelius, PhD, Assoc Prof
Bonifazi, Conrad, DD, Assoc Prof, Phil Theol, Phil of Relig
Bridston, Keith, PhD, Prof
Bucher, Raymond, PhD, Asst Prof
Buckley, Michael, PhD, Asst Prof
Come, Arnold, ThD, Prof
De Man, Peter, STL, Asst Prof

Foster, A Durwood, ThD, Prof
Gelinas, Elmar, PhD, Visit Prof
Hobbs, Edward, PhD, Prof
Kimball, Robert, PhD, Prof, Theol Ethics
Loomer, Barnard, PhD, Prof, Phil Theol
Mara, James, STD, Asst Prof
Martinez, Ernest R, STD. Asst Prof
McClendon, James, ThD, Prof
Moreno-Elosequi, Antonio, PhD, Assoc Prof
Nishi, Shunji, PhD, Prof, Phil Theol
O'Hanlon, Daniel, STD, Prof
Osborne, Kenan, DTh, Prof
Pfisterer, Robert, STD, Prof
Powers, Joseph, Asst Prof
Raftery, Paul, JCD, Assoc Prof
Reist, Benjamin, ThD, Prof
Rutenber, Culbert, PhD, Prof, Phil of Relig
Singh, Surjit, PhD, Prof, Christ Phil
Sullivan, John, PhD, Visit Prof
Wall, Joseph, STD, Prof
Wall, Kevin, PhD, Prof
Wright, John, STD, Prof

GROSSMONT COLLEGE
El Cajon, California 92020 (W; local; coed; sem; I; 12,356) Courses with no degree specialization, Dept of Human and Phil, 714-465-1700

Saetti, John A, MA, Instr, Chm
Campbell, R Alan, MA, Instr
Gray, William D, MA, Instr Part-time
Kain, Phillip J, MA, Instr Part-time
Kuttnauer, Michael V, MA, Instr Part-time
La Moure, Spencer, MA, Instr
Mijuskivoc, Ben L, MA, Instr Part-time
Mullin, James T, MA, Instr Part-time
Press, Gerald, A, MA, Instr Part-time
Sager, Gene C, MA, Instr Part-time
Simpson Jr, Hoke S, MA, Instr
Wheatcroft, N Paul, MA, Instr
Wood, Bradley, MA, Instr

HARTNELL COLLEGE
Salinas, California 93901 (W; local; coed; sem; I; 2759) Courses with no degree specialization, --, 408-422-9606

Bedford, Mitchell, EdD, Exist
Cacace, Maxine, MA

HARVEY MUDD COLLEGE
Claremont, California 91711 (W; p; coed; sem; III; 404) Courses with no degree specialization, Dept of Human and Soc Sci, 714-626-8511 Ext 2891

Beckman, Tad A, PhD, Assoc Prof, Phil of Sci, Epistem
Waldman, Theodore, PhD, Prof, Polit Phil

HEALD ENGINEERING COLLEGE
San Francisco, California 94109 (--; p; coed; qr; II; 1122) NR

29

HUMPHREYS COLLEGE
   Stockton, California 95207 (W; p; coed; qr; I; 288) NP

IMMACULATE HEART COLLEGE
   Los Angeles, California 90027 (W; RC; coed; sem; III; 559) BA minor, --, 213-462-1301

   Beerman, Leonard, MHL, Lect
   Burrill, Donald, PhD, Lect, Soc and Polit Phil
   Dunn, Dorothy, PhD, Asst Prof, Amer Phil
   Erickson, Stephen, PhD, Lect
   Reif, Patricia, Hist of Phil

IMPERIAL VALLEY COLLEGE
   Imperial, California 92251 (W; local; coed; sem; I; 2951) Courses with no degree specialization, Area of Human, 714-352-8320

   Hann, Richard K, MA

JESUIT SCHOOL OF THEOLOGY AT BERKELEY
   Berkeley, California 94709 (W; RC; men; qr; II; 98) Courses with no degree specialization, Dept of Syst Theol, 415-841-8804

   Gelpi, Donald, PhD, Assoc Prof, Amer Phil
   Stagaman, David, MA, Visit Prof, Lang Anal

JOHN F KENNEDY UNIVERSITY
   Martinez, California 94553 (--; p; coed; qr; III; 271) BA minor, Dept of Phil, 415-228-6770

   Lu, Mathias, PhD, Assoc Prof, Chinese Phil
   Shulak, Allen, MA, Asst Prof
   Wellmuth, John, PhD, Prof, Math Logic, Med Phil

LANEY COLLEGE
   Oakland, California 94606 (W; local; coed; sem; I; 11,772) Courses with no degree specialization, Dept of Human, 916-257-4101

   Shepherd, Robert T, MA, Instr

LA VERNE COLLEGE
   La Verne, California 91750 (W; Breth; coed; --; IV; 1682) BA major, Dept of Phil and Relig, 714-593-3511 Ext 269

   Eller, Vernard, ThD, Prof, Exist
   Gingrich, John, PhD, Asst Prof, Phil of Relig, Ethics
   Willoughby, William G, PhD, Prof, Hist of Phil, Logic, Aes

LINCOLN UNIVERSITY
   San Francisco, California 94118 (--; p; 4-1-4; III; 492) NR

LOMA LINDA UNIVERSITY
   Riverside, California 92505 (W; SDA; coed; qr; IV; 3620) BA joint or combined major, Depts of Hist, Music, Relig, Phys, and Interdisciplinary Stud, 714-796-7311

Guy, Fritz, PhD, Assoc Prof, Phil of Relig
Hannum, Harold B, MMus, Prof, Aes
Hodgen, Maurice D, EdD, Prof, Axiology, Phil of Educ
Ross, Gary M, PhD, Assoc Prof, Epistem, Hist of Phil
Smith, Albert E, PhD, Prof, Metaph, Phil of Sci

LONE MOUNTAIN COLLEGE
San Francisco, California 94118 (W; RC; coed; 4-1-4; III; 774) MA major, Dept of
Phil, 415-752-7000 Ext 240

Hudson, Frederic, PhD, Prof, Hist of Phil
Tobey, Herbert, MC, Asst Prof, British Phil, Amer Phil

LONG BEACH CITY COLLEGE
Long Beach, California 90808 (W; local; coed; sem; I; 26,825) AA major, Dept of
Soc Sci, 213-420-4342

Mize, John, PhD
Pendleton, Billy, MA
Speegle, Lyle, MPhil
Spurney, Richard, MA

LOS ANGELES BAPTIST COLLEGE-THEOLOGICAL SEMINARY
Newhall, California 91321 (--; Bapt; coed; sem; III; 280) Courses with no degree
specialization, Dept of Phil, 805-259-3540

Price, Thomas, M Div, Asst Prof

LOS ANGELES CITY COLLEGE
Los Angeles, California 90029 (W; local; coed; sem; I; 17,802) Courses with no
degree specialization, Dept of Phil, 213-663-9141 Ext 327

McKnight, Eugene C, MA, Prof, Chm, Ethics
Bornstein, Alfred, MA, Instr
Critelli, Michael, PhD, Instr, Greek Phil
Lerner, Arthur, PhD, Prof, Phil of Lit
Reichenbach, Maria M, PhD, Prof, Logic
Thich, Thien-An, PhD, Instr, Orient Phil
Workman, Allen J, PhD, Prof, Aes

Myers, Orvil Floyd, Prof Emer
Reeder, Paul A, Prof Emer

LOS ANGELES COLLEGE OF OPTOMETRY
Los Angeles, California 90007 (W; p; coed; qr; II; 249) NR

LOS ANGELES HARBOR COLLEGE
Wilmington, California 90744 (W; local; sem; T; 9130) AA major, Dept of Phil,
213-835-0161

Mundstock, Lorenz, MA, Instr, Chm, Metaph
Farren, Cornelius, MA, Instr, Phil of Relig
Grassian, Victor, PhD, Instr, Phil of Law

LOS ANGELES PIERCE COLLEGE
Woodlands Hills, California 91364 (W; local; coed; sem; I; 16,317) Courses with no
degree specialization, Dept of Phil, 213-347-0551

LOS ANGELES SOUTHWEST COLLEGE
  Los Angeles, California 90047 (W; local; coed; sem; I; 3858) AA major, Dept of
  Phil, 213-757-9251

  Wallace, Donald, MA, Assoc Prof, Phil of Relig
  Zucker, Alfred, PhD, Prof, Hist of Phil

LOS ANGELES TRADE-TECHNICAL COLLEGE
  Los Angeles, California 90015 (W; local; coed; sem; I; 15,645) AA major, Dept of
  Art, Phil and Soc Sci, 213-746-0800 Ext 381

  Heanue, Helen, MA, Asst Prof

LOS ANGELES VALLEY COLLEGE
  Van Nuys, California 91401 (W; local; coed; sem; I; 19,066) NR

LOYOLA UNIVERSITY OF LOS ANGELES
  Los Angeles, California 90045 (W; RC; men; qr; III; 3822) BA major, --, 213-776-
  0400

  Blystone, Jasper, PhD, Assoc Prof, German Phil
  Chervin, Ronda, PhD, Asst Prof, Relig Phil
  DeGennaro, Angelo, PhD, Prof, Italian Phil
  Delaney, Howard, PhD, Prof
  Eckhart, Dennis, MA, Instr, Amer Phil
  Guilhamet, James, MA, Instr, Greek Phil
  Kearley, Carroll, PhD, Assoc Prof, Ethics
  Kristovich, Michael, STL, Assoc Prof, Logic
  Morris, Richard, BA, Asst Prof, Ling Phil
  Taylor, Robert, PhD, Assoc Prof, Ethics

MARYMOUNT COLLEGE, LOS ANGELES CAMPUS
  Los Angeles, California 90045 (W; RC; coed; tri; II; 1161) BA major, Dept of Phil,
  213-670-6551

  Kearley, Carroll C, PhD, Chm
  Blystone, Jasper, PhD
  Casassa, Charles S, PhD
  Chervin, Ronda, PhD
  DeGennaro, Angelo, PhD
  Delaney, Howard R, PhD
  Eckhart, Dennis, MA
  Guilhamet, James N, MA
  Kristovich, Michael J, JCL
  Morris, Richard J, BA
  Taylor, Robert H, STL

MARYMOUNT COLLEGE, PALOS VERDES CAMPUS
  Palos Verdes Peninsula, California 90274 (W; RC; coed; sem; I; 194) NR

MENLO COLLEGE
  Menlo Park, California 94025 (W; p; coed; 4-1-4; II; 565) Courses with no degree
  specialization, Dept of Human, 415-323-6141 Ext 321

  Bales, Royal Eugene, PhD, Prof, Ethical Theory

MENNONITE BRETHREN BIBLICAL SEMINARY
  Fresno, California 93727 (W; Menn Breth; coed; qr; III; 52) NP

MERCED COLLEGE
  Merced, California 95340 (W; local; coed; sem; I; 5450) Courses with no degree
  specialization, Dept of Phil, 209-723-4321

  Bean, Edward H F, MA, Head, Polit Phil
  Mello, Michael, MA
  Moldrup, William, MA, Epistem
  Petersen, E J, MA, Metaph

MERRITT COLLEGE
  Oakland, California 94619 (W; local; coed; qr; I; 7178) Courses with no degree
  specialization, 415-655-6110

  Green, Lucile W, PhD, Aes
  MacMahon, Charles E, MA, Logic, Metaph, Ethics
  Wolfe, Maurice R, MA, Hist of Phil

MILLS COLLEGE
  Oakland, California 94613 (W; p; wo; 4-1-4; III; 1040) BA major, Dept of Phil,
  415-632-2700

  Clegg, Jerry Stephen, PhD, Assoc Prof
  Provence, Merrill Bristow, BA, Asst Prof

  Diller, Elliot Van Nostrand, Prof Emer, Mental and Moral Phil

MIRA COSTA COLLEGE
  Oceanside, California 92054 (W; st; coed; sem; I; 2948) NR

MODESTO JUNIOR COLLEGE
  Modesto, California 95350 (W; local; coed; sem; I; 9196) Courses with no degree
  specialization, Dept of Behavior and Soc Sci, 209-524-1451 Ext 409

  Markgraf, G Karl, MA
  Starr, Benjamin S, MA

MONTEREY INSTITUTE OF FOREIGN STUDIES
  Monterey, California 93940 (W; p; coed; sem; III; 364) NP

MONTEREY PENINSULA COLLEGE
  Monterey, California 93940 (W; st and local; coed; sem; I; 3664) AA major, Dept of
  Phil, 408-375-9821

  Menmuir, Ronald J, PhD, Chm, Phil of Relig
  O'Brien, Robert J, PhD, Instr, Exist

MOORPARK COLLEGE
  Moorpark, California 93021 (W; local; coed; sem; I; 6153) AA major, Dept of Soc
  Sci, 805-529-2321

  Fink, Paul F, MA

MOUNT SAINT MARY'S COLLEGE
    Los Angeles, California 90049 (W; RC; coed; --; III; 1201) BA major, Dept of Phil,
    213-272-8791

    Larkin, Miriam Therese, PhD, Assoc Prof, Chm, Ethics, Exist, Amer Phil
    Dumont, Michele Therese, MA, Instr, Phil of Mind, Phil of Knowl
    Sharkey, Paul W, PhD, Asst Prof, Hist of Phil, Ethics, Polit Phil
    Tripodes, Peter, PhD, Asst Prof, Phil of Lang, Phil of Sci
    Walendy, Thomas, MA, Asst Prof, East Phil, Phil of Relig, Exist

MOUNT SAN ANTONIO COLLEGE
    Walnut, California 91789 (W; local; coed; sem; I; 15,371) Courses with no degree
    specialization, Dept of Psych, Soc and Phil, 714-595-2211 Ext 286

    Honer, Stanley M, PhD
    Jacinto, José S, MA
    Johnson, Roger K, MA
    Loy, Harold A, BD
    Thomas, James D, MA

MOUNT SAN JACINTO COLLEGE
    Gilman Hot Springs, California 92340 (W; local; coed; sem; I; 1622) Courses with no
    degree specialization, Dept of Phil, 714-654-7321

NAIROBI COLLEGE
    East Palo Alto, California 94303 (--; p; coed; qr; I; 258) Courses with no degree
    specialization. Dept of Communic and Human, 415-323-8501

    Hoover, Mary R, MA

NAPA COLLEGE
    Napa, California 94558 (W; local; coed; qr; I; 3408) AA major, Dept of Soc Sci,
    707-255-2100 Ext 55

    O'Shea, Michael, MA, Prof
    Trepp, Leo, PhD, Prof, Phil of Relig

NEW COLLEGE OF CALIFORNIA
    Sausalito, California 94965 (--; p; coed; sem; II; 65) BA major, Humane Stud,
    415-332-6900

    Cudmore, Anne Kreilkamp, PhD, Wittgenstein, Exist
    Dayron, Norman, PhD, Phil Anal, Ethics
    Leary, John, PhD, Soc Phil, Logic

NORTHROP INSTITUTE OF TECHNOLOGY
    Inglewood, California 90306 (W; p; coed; qr; III; 1667) BA minor, Dept of Human
    and Soc Sci, 213-776-3410

    Woods, Martin, PhD, Assoc Prof, Hist of Phil

OCCIDENTAL COLLEGE
    Los Angeles, California 90041 (W; p; coed; qr; III; 1876) BA major, Dept of Phil,
    213-255-5151

    Lauter, Herman A, PhD, Assoc Prof, Chm, Phil of Sci, Logic, Aes
    Glidden, David K, PhD, Asst Prof, Hist of Phil, Epistem

Neblett, William R, PhD, Assoc Prof, Ethics
Ross, Floyd H, PhD, Visit Prof, Orient Phil
Smith, Robin, PhD, Asst Prof, Hist of Phil, Epistem

Gloyn, Cyril K, PhD, Prof Emer, Phil of Relig

OHLONE COMMUNITY COLLEGE
Fremont, California 94537 (W; local; coed; qr; I; 3956) Courses with no degree specialization, 415-657-2100

Steinke, Joseph T, MA, Asst Prof

ORANGE COAST COLLEGE
Costa Mesa, California 92626 (W; local; coed; sem; I; 21,396) Courses with no degree specialization, Dept of Soc Sci, 714-834-5753

Johnston, David W, MA, Asst Prof, Phys Phil
Katz, Eleanor F, MA, Instr
Painter, Alfred W, PhD, Prof
Wall, Theodore E, STM, Asst Prof

OTIS ART INSTITUTE, LOS ANGELES COUNTY
Los Angeles, California 90057 (W; local; coed; sem; II; 383) NP

PACIFIC CHRISTIAN COLLEGE
Long Beach, California 90804 (W; Ch of Christ, coed; qr; II; 243) Courses with no degree specialization, Div of Educ, and Div of Gen Educ, 213-434-9991

Rowe, John P, STM, Assoc Prof

PACIFIC COLLEGE
Fresno, California 93702 (W; Menn; coed; qr; II; 447) BA minor, Div of Human, 209-251-7194

Weins, Delbert, PhD, Asst Prof

PACIFIC LUTHERAN THEOLOGICAL SEMINARY
Berkeley, California 94708 (Theol; Luth CA; coed; qr; III; 154) NP

PACIFIC OAKS COLLEGE
Pasadena, California 91105 (W; p; coed; sem; III; 255) Courses with no degree specialization, 213-795-9161

PACIFIC SCHOOL OF RELIGION
Berkeley, California 94709 (Theol; p; coed; qr; IV; 139) NP

PACIFIC STATES UNIVERSITY
Los Angeles, California 90006 (--; p; coed; tri; III; 544) NR

PACIFIC UNION COLLEGE
Angwin, California 94508 (W; SDA; coed; qr; III; 1977) NP

PALOMAR COLLEGE
San Marcos, California 92069 (W; local; coed; sem; I; 6229) AA major, Dept of
Behavior Sci, 714-744-1150

Lollar, James, MA, Instr, Ethics
Sager, Gene, MA, Instr, Ethics
Schettler, John, PhD, Instr, Logic
Vessey, Clifford, MA, Instr

PALO VERDE COLLEGE
Blythe, California 92225 (W; local; coed; sem; I; 578) NR

PASADENA COLLEGE
Pasadena, California 91104 (W; Naz; coed; qr; III; 1330) BA major, Div of Phil and
Relig, 213-798-0541 Ext 18

Haney, M Estes, A, Assoc Prof
Lown, John, MA, Asst Prof
Prince, Herbert, M Div, Asst Prof

PASADENA CITY COLLEGE
Pasadena, Califronia 91106 (W; local; coed; sem; I; 15,206) AA major, Dept of Soc
Sci, 213-795-6961

Hallman, Ralph J, PhD, Prof, Chm
Christopher, John F, MA, Prof
Cottle, Ronald E, PhD, Instr
Levis, Robert C, MA, Asst Prof
Reeves, Sandra, MA, Instr
Reynolds, Ann C, MA, Instr

PEPPERDINE UNIVERSITY, LOS ANGELES CAMPUS
Los Angeles, California 90044 (W; p; coed; tri; III; 5504) Courses with no degree
specialization, Dept of Hist, Phil and Polit Sci, 213-753-1411 Ext 272

Gibson, David E, PhD, Asst Prof, Contemp German Phil

PEPPERDINE UNIVERSITY, MALIBU CAMPUS
Malibu, California 90265 (W; p; coed; tri; III; --) BA joint or combined major
Dept of Human, 213-456-4225

PITZER COLLEGE
Claremont, California 91750 (W; p; coed; sem; II; 792) BA major, Dept of Phil,
714-626-8511

Bogen, James, Assoc Prof, Perception, Phil Psych, Wittgenstein
Rubin, Ronald G, PhD, Asst Prof, Phil of Sci, Mod Phil, Locke

POMONA COLLEGE
Claremont, California 91711 (W; p; coed; sem; II; 1383) BA major, Dept of Phil,
714-626-8511 Ext 2921

Erickson, Stephen A, PhD, Prof, Chm, Phenomen, Heidegger, Kant, Freud, Marx, Neitzsche
Atlas, Jay, BA, Instr, Advanc Logic, Phil of Lang
Beckner, Morton, PhD, Prof, Phil of Sci, Phil of Mind
King, Charles, PhD, Assoc Prof, Polit Phil, Ethics, Mod Phil

McKirahan, Richard, BA, Asst Prof, Class Phil, Metaph
Sontag, Frederick, PhD, Prof, Metaph, Exist, Phil Psych

PORTERVILLE COLLEGE
Porterville, California 93257 (W; st and local; coed; sem; 1689) NR

RAND GRADUATE INSTITUTE OF POLITICAL STUDIES
Santa Monica, California 90406 (--; p; coed; qr; IV; 18) NR

RAYMOND COLLEGE, UNIVERSITY OF THE PACIFIC
Stockton, California 95204 (W; p; coed; 4-1-4; --; 250) Courses with no degree
specialization, 209-946-2101

Orpinela, Robert R, ThD, Asst Prof, Contemp Phil
Zimmerman, Walter, PhD, Assoc Prof, Phil of Sci

REEDLEY COLLEGE
Reedley, California 93654 (W; local; coed; sem; I; 2352) Courses with no degree
specialization, Dept of Phil, 209-638-3641 Ext 257

Hutchings, Assoc Prof, Chm
Eastman, Roger, MA, Instr
Wood, Bruce Kenneth, PhD

RIO HONDO JUNIOR COLLEGE
Whittier, California 90608 (W; local; coed; sem; I; 10,570) NR

RIVERSIDE CITY COLLEGE
Riverside, California 92506 (W; local; coed; sem; I; 10,128) --, Dept of Soc Sci,
714-684-3240 Ext 273

Ardis, Jule, MA, Asst Prof
Gladden, Garnet Lee, MA, Assoc Prof
Long, Cynthia, MA, Instr
Schneider, Richard, MEd, Assoc Prof

ROSEMEAD GRADUATE SCHOOL OF PSYCHOLOGY
Rosemead, California 91770 (--; p; coed; sem; IV; 24) NP

RUSSELL COLLEGE
Burlingame, California 94010 (W; RC; wo; sem; II; 42) See Late Reports

SACRAMENTO CITY COLLEGE
Sacramento, California 95822 (W; local; coed; sem; I; 11,387) AA major, Dept of
Phil, 916-449-7559

Read, Leslie C, MA, Chm, Ethics, Logic
Merritt, Robert K, MA, Phil of Relig
Simmons, Joseph, MA, World Relig

SADDLEBACK COLLEGE
Mission Viejo, California 92675 (--; local; coed; qr; I; 3941) --, Dept of Soc Sci,
714-837-9700 Ext 64

Clancy, John P, MA, Instr, Phil, World Relig
Hoffman, Robert, MA, Instr, Logic

SAINT ALBERT'S COLLEGE
Oakland, California 94618 (W; RC; men; qr; III; 71) MA major, --, 415-654-5725

Gelinas, Elmer T, PhD, Visit Prof, Metaph
Martin, Hilary J, B Litt, Prof, Hist of Phil
Moreno-Elosequi, Antonio, PhD, Prof, Phil of Nature
Sullivan, John Edward, PhD, Prof, Metaph
Wall, Kevin, PhD, Prof, Metaph
Zagar, Janko, PhD, Prof, Moral and Soc Phil

SAINT JOHN'S COLLEGE
Camarillo, California 93010 (W; RC; men; 4-1-4; III; 296) BA major, --, 805-482-2755

Anslow, Thomas C, MA, Epistem, Hist of Phil
Galvin, James M, EdD, Logic
Van Dorst, Cornelius A, PhD, Syst Phil
Winance, Eleuthere, PhD, Contemp Tht

SAINT MARY'S COLLEGE OF CALIFORNIA
Moraga, California 94575 (W; RC; coed; 4-1-4; III; 1266) --; --; 415-376-4411

Carroll, Owen, PhD, Asst Prof, Chm
Beatie, William, MA, Asst Prof
Dolan, S Edmund, PhD, Assoc Prof
Dragstedt, John Albert, Assoc Prof
Ellis, Frank, PhD, Assoc Prof
Gelinas, Elmer T, PhD, Assoc Prof
Lanigan, Joseph F, PhD, Prof
McArthur, Ronald P, PhD, Prof
Rosenberg, Richard, MA, Instr
Smith, S Robert, PhD, Prof

SAINT PATRICK'S COLLEGE
Mountain View, California 94040 (W; RC; men; qr; II; 112) BA major, Dept of Phil,
415-967-9501

Crowley, Cale, PhD, Assoc Prof, Chm, Metaph
Sorenson, Martin, PhD, Assoc Prof, Ethics

SAINT PATRICK'S SEMINARY
Menlo Park, California 94025 (W; RC; men; qr; III; 86) NR

SAN BERNARDINO VALLEY COLLEGE
San Bernardino, California 92403 (W; st and local; coed; sem; I; 13,808) AA major,
Dept of Phil and Relig Stud, 714-885-0231 Ext 384

Schmidt, Roger, MA, Assoc Prof, Chm
Biffle, James, MA, Asst Prof Part-time
Douglas, Walter D, MA, Assoc Prof
McKie, William, MA, Asst Prof Part-time

SAN DIEGO COMMUNITY CITY COLLEGE
San Diego, California 92101 (W; st and local; coed; sem; I; 4880) --, Dept of Soc
Sci, 714-234-8451 Ext 243

Ford, Robert, MA, Part-time
Young, Dwight J, PhD, Phil of Law

SAN DIEGO COMMUNITY EVENING COLLEGE
San Diego, California 92101 (W; st and local; coed; sem; I; 12,453) NR

SAN DIEGO MESA COLLEGE
San Diego, California 92111 (W; st and local; coed; sem; I; 6907) Courses with no
degree specialization, Dept of Soc Sci, 714-279-2300 Ext 240

Cyran, William T, PhL
Kuttnauer, Michael V, MA
Pidgeon, Patrick F, MA

SAN FRANCISCO ART INSTITUTE COLLEGE
San Francisco, California 94133 (W; p; coed; sem; III; 1033) NP

SAN FRANCISCO CONSERVATORY OF MUSIC
San Francisco, California 94122 (W; p; coed; 4-1-4; III; 173) NP

SAN FRANCISCO THEOLOGICAL SEMINARY
San Anselmo, California 94960 (Theol; U Preb; coed; qr; IV; 503) PhD major, Dept
of Christ Phil, 415-453-2280 Ext 26

Surjit, Singh, PhD, Prof, Gen and Comp Phil

SAN JOAQUIN DELTA COLLEGE
Stockton, California 95204 (W; local; coed; sem; II; 11,903) --, Dept of Phil, 209-
466-2631

Laughlin, Lloyd, MA, Instr

SAN JOSE BIBLE COLLEGE
San Jose, California 95108 (BI; Ch of Christ; coed; qr; II; 329) Courses with no
degree specialization, Dept of Gen Educ, 408-293-9058

Alder, George, MA, Prof, Logic
North, James, PhD, Prof, Hist of Phil
Sargent, Robert, MS, Dean
Ratzlaff, Ruben, M Div, Prof

SAN JOSE CITY COLLEGE
San Jose, California 95114 (W; local; coed; sem; I; 14,814) --, Dept of Hist, Phil
and Soc Sci, 408-298-2181 Ext 203

Green, William, MA, Instr
West, William, MA, Instr

SANTA ANA COLLEGE
Santa Ana, California 92706 (W; local; coed; sem; I; 8969) Courses with no degree
specialization, Dept of Phil, 714-547-9561 Ext 263

CALIFORNIA

SANTA BARBARA ART INSTITUTE
Santa Barbara, California 93103 (--; p; coed; sem; II; 193) NP

SANTA BARBARA CITY COLLEGE
Santa Barbara, California 93105 (W; local; coed; sem; I; 6246) AA major, Dept of
Phil, 805-965-0581 Ext 332

Angeles, Peter, PhD, Prof
Culmback, Barrett, MA, Instr
Fetler, Timothy, PhD, Prof

SANTA MONICA COLLEGE
Santa Monica, California 90405 (W; local; coed; sem; I; 12,254) --, Dept of Soc Stud,
213-392-4911

Buchanan, Mary L, MA, Prof, Ethics, Logic
Hawkins, James P, MA, Prof, Hist of Phil
Shamey, Katherine, MA, Instr
Warner, Seth R, MA, Prof, Hist of Phil

SANTA ROSA JUNIOR COLLEGE
Santa Rosa, California 95401 (W; local; coed; sem; I; 10,681) Courses with no degree
specialization, Dept of Human and Phil, 707-542-0315

Traverso, Everett, CPhil, Instr, Chm
D'Abbracci, Anthony, MA, Instr
Hall, Jay, Instr
Livergood, Norman, PhD, Instr

SCRIPPS COLLEGE
Claremont, California 91711 (W; p; wo; sem; II; 526) BA major, Dept of Phil, 714-
626-8511 Ext 3077

Neumann, Harry, PhD, Prof, Polit Phil, Phil of Educ
Ross, Ralph, PhD, Prof, Polit Phil, Aes

SHASTA COLLEGE
Redding, California 96001 (W; local; coed; sem; I; 7866) --, Dept of Soc Sci, 916-
241-3523

Black, Milton, MA
Fetters, Ross

SIERRA COLLEGE
Rocklin, California 95677 (W; local; coed; sem; I; 4446) AA major, Dept of Phil,
916-624-3333

Sessions, George S, MA, Chm, Phil of Sci

SIMPSON COLLEGE
San Francisco, California 94134 (W; Chris and Miss; coed; sem; II; 306) BA major,
Dept of Phil, Hist and Soc, 415-334-7400

Humphries, Hugh, PhD, Prof, Chm, Phil of Relig, Exist
Dorman, Laurence, PhD, Instr, Epistem, Logic

SKYLINE COLLEGE
San Bruno, California 94066 (W; local; coed; sem; I; 4742) AA major, Dept of Phil,
415-355-7000 Ext 245

Petropoulos, Gus J, MA, Chm
Gump, M Arthur, MA
Marcus, Debbe, MA

SOLANO COLLEGE
Suisun City, California 94585 (W; local; coed; sem; I; 6139) --, Div of Soc Sci,
707-422-4750

Biggs, Theodore, BA
Low, Clyde M, MIA
McCarney, Everett F, MA
Shulak, Allen, MA

SOUTHERN CALIFORNIA COLLEGE
Costa Mesa, California 92626 (W; Assem of God; coed; 4-1-4; II; 562) BA joint or
combined major, Div of Relig and Phil, 714-545-1178

Dempster, Murray W, MA, Instr, Soc Ethics

SOUTHERN CALIFORNIA SCHOOL OF THEOLOGY
Claremont, California 91711 (W; Prot; coed; sem; IV; 275) --, --, 714-626-3521

Castuera, Ignacio, Lect, Ethics and Soc
Horton, Frank L, Lect, Ethics and Soc
Hough, Jr, Joseph C, BD, Prof, Christ Ethics
Hutchison, John A, PhD, Prof, Phil of Relig
Kucheman, Clark A, PhD, Assoc Prof, Christ Ethics
Rhoades, Dan D, PhD, Prof, Christ Ethics
Rhoades, Donald D, Prof, Phil of Relig
Seifert, Harvey J, PhD, Prof, Christ Ethics
Sontag, Frederick, PhD, Prof

SOUTHWESTERN COLLEGE
Chula Vista, California 92010 (W; local; coed; sem; I; 8008) --, Dept of Phil,
714-420-1080

Ford, Edward, MA, Instr Part-time
Wolfe, Robert A, MA, Instr

SOUTHWESTERN UNIVERSITY SCHOOL OF LAW
Los Angeles, California 90015 (Law; p; coed; sem; II; 1001) NP

STANFORD UNIVERSITY
Stanford, California 94305 (W; p; coed; qr; IV; 12,479) PhD major, Dept of Phil,
415-321-2300 Ext 2547

Moravcsik, J M, PhD, Prof, Chm, Anc Phil, Phil of Lang
Cartwright, Nancy, PhD, Asst Prof, Phil of Sci
Feferman, Solomon, PhD, Prof, Found of Math,
Follesdal, Dagfinn, PhD, Prof, Phenomen, Phil of Lang
Gabbay, Dov, PhD, Assoc Prof, Logic, Intensional Logic
Hintikka, Jaakko, PhD, Prof, Phil of Lang, Hist of Phil
Howell, Robert, PhD, Asst Prof, Hist of Mod Phil, Aes

Kreisel, Georg, PhD, Prof, Found of Math
Mothershead, John, PhD, Prof, Hist of Phil, Ethics
Nivison, David, PhD, Prof, Chinese Phil
Serene, Eileen, PhD, Asst Prof, Med Phil
Suppes, Patrick, PhD, Prof, Phil of Sci, Phil of Lang
Tooley, Michael, PhD, Asst Prof, Epistem, Phil of Relig
Wasow, Thomas, PhD, Asst Prof, Ling Theory

Goheen, John, Prof Emer
Rhinelander, Philip, Prof Emer

STARR KING SCHOOL FOR MINISTRY
Berkeley, California 94709 (--; Unit Univer; coed; qr; III; 35) NP

TAFT COLLEGE
Taft, California 93268 (W; local; coed; sem; I; 653) Courses with no degree
specialization, Dept of Soc Sci, 805-765-4191 Ext 416

Tufft, John R, PhD, Assoc Prof, Chm

UNITED STATES INTERNATIONAL UNIVERSITY, CALIFORNIA WESTERN CAMPUS
San Diego, California 92131 (W; p; coed; qr; IV; 4480) BA major, Dept of Phil
and Relig Stud, 714-224-3211 Ext 223

Coss, Thurman, PhD, Prof, Chm, Relig Stud
Box, Robert, ThD, Assoc Prof, Phil of Relig
Martin, Dean, PhD, Asst Prof, Mod Relig Tht, Ordinary Lang Phil
Schmiege, Oscar, PhD, Asst Prof, Phil of Man

UNITED STATES NAVAL POSTGRADUATE SCHOOL
Monterey, California 93940 (W; nat; coed; qr; IV; 1766) NR

UNIVERSITY OF CALIFORNIA AT BERKELEY
Berkeley, California 94720 (W; st; coed; qr; IV; 27,712) PhD major, Dept of Phil,
415-642-2723

Searle, John R, DPhil, Prof, Chm, Phil of Lang
Adams, Ernest W, PhD, Prof, Phil of Logic
Aschenbrenner, Karl, PhD, Prof, Hist of Phil
Chihara, Charles S, PhD, Assoc Prof, Phil of Logic
Clarke, Thompson M, PhD, Assoc Prof, Phil of Knowl
Craig, William, PhD, Prof, Phil of Logic
Dreyfus, Hubert L, PhD, Prof, Applied Phil
Feyerabend, Paul K, PhD, Prof, Phil of Sci
Frede, Michael J, PhD, Assoc Prof, Anc Phil
Grice, H Paul, MA, Prof, Phil of Lang, Logic
Mates, Benson, PhD, Prof, Phil of Logic
Matson, Wallace I, PhD, Prof, Hist of Phil
Myro, George, PhD, Assoc Prof, Phil of Mind, Logic, Phil of Knowl
Schiffer, Stephen R, DPhil, Asst Prof, Phil of Lang
Scriven, Michael, DPhil, Prof, Phil of Natur and Soc Sci
Sluga, Hans, BPhil, Assoc Prof, Logic, Hist of Phil
Staal, Johan F, PhD, Prof, Indian Phil
Stroud, Barry G, PhD, Assoc Prof, Phil of Knowl
Tussman, Joseph, PhD, Prof, Phil of Law
Vermazen, Bruce, PhD, Asst Prof, Phil of Lang

Dennes, William R, DPhil, Prof Emer
Hungerland, Isabel, PhD, Prof Emer
Rynin, David, PhD, Prof Emer
Strong, Edward W, PhD, Prof Emer

UNIVERSITY OF CALIFORNIA AT DAVIS
Davis, California 95616 (W; st; coed; qr; IV; 13,983) PhD major, Dept of Phil,
916-752-0607

Bossart, William H, PhD, Prof, Chm, Metaph, Epistem, Continen Phil, Aes
Arbini, Ronald A, PhD, Assoc Prof, Logic, Phil of Lang, Phil of Mind
Beal, Melvin W, PhD, Asst Prof, Hist of Mod Phil, Epistem
Berger, Fred R, PhD, Asst Prof, Ethics, Soc and Polit Phil
Child, Arthur, PhD, Prof, Metaph, Epistem, Aes, Phil of Relig, Phil of Hist
Friedman, Joel, PhD, Asst Prof, Logic, Phil of Math, Phil of Sci
Gilbert, Neal W, PhD, Prof, Hist of Phil, Med and Renaissance Tht
Grene, Marjorie, PhD, Prof, Epistem, Phil of Biology, Continen Phil
Malcolm, John F, PhD, Assoc Prof, Greek Phil, Metaph
Wedin, Jr, Vernon E, PhD, Asst Prof, Metaph, Greek Phil, Phil of Lang

UNIVERSITY OF CALIFORNIA AT IRVINE
Irvine, California 92664 (W; st; coed; qr; IV; 6881) PhD major, Dept of Phil,
714-833-6526

Santas, Gerasimos, PhD, Prof, Chm, Greek Phil
Buroker, Barbara Jill, MA, Asst Prof, Phil of Sci
Holzman, Richard, MA, Asst Prof, Soc and Polit Phil
Lambert, Joseph, PhD, Prof, Logic
Melden, A I, PhD, Prof, Ethics
Pike, Nelson, PhD, Prof, Phil of Relig
Sircello, Guy, PhD, Assoc Prof, Aes
Smith, David, PhD, Asst Prof, Phenomen
Ulrich, William, BA, Asst Prof, Phil of Lang
Woodruff, Peter, PhD, Asst Prof, Logic

Arieux, Marianne, Teach Asst
Battin, Peggy, Teach Asst
Bernal, Juan, Teach Asst
Blue, Craig, Teach Asst
Boothe, Stephen, Teach Asst
Bourgeois, Warren, Teach Asst
Dimas, Thomas, Teach Asst
Ferejohn, Michael, Teach Asst
Ford, Thomas, NDEA Fel
Gillis, Edward, Teach Asst
Hunter, Daniel, Teach Asst
Karlin, Larry, Teach Asst
Martin, Michael, Teach Asst
Sauvageot, William, Teach Asst

UNIVERSITY OF CALIFORNIA AT LOS ANGELES
Los Angeles, California 90024 (W; st; coed; qr; IV; 27,904) PhD major, Dept of
Phil, 213-825-4641

Furth, Montgomery, PhD, Prof, Chm
Adams, Marilyn M, PhD, Assoc Prof
Adams, Robert M, PhD, Assoc Prof

43

CALIFORNIA

Boxill, Bernard R, PhD, Asst Prof
Burge, C Tyler, PhD, Asst Prof
Church, Alonzo, PhD, Prof
Donnellan, Deith S, PhD, Prof
Foot, Philippa, MA, Prof
Hill, Jr, Thomas E, PhD, Assoc Prof
Kalish, Donald, PhD, Prof
Kaplan, David, PhD, Prof
Kavka, Gregory, MA, Asst Prof
Morris, Herbert, PhD, Prof
Perry, John R, PhD, Assoc Prof
Quinn, Warren S, PhD, Asst Prof
Wasserstrom, Richard, PhD, Prof
Yost, Robert M, PhD, Prof

Miller, Hugh, PhD, Prof Emer
Moody, Ernest A, PhD, Prof Emer
Robson, Wesley, PhD, Prof Emer

Alberts, Kelly, BA, Teach Asst
Alfaro, Bonita, BA, Teach Asst
Alvy, Ralph, BA, Teach Asst
Boxill, Jeanette, MA, Teach Asst
Chapman, Marilyn, MA, Will Rogers
  Memorial Fel
Collier, John, BS, Teach Asst
Deigh, John, BA, Teach Asst
Denney, Robert, BA, Teach Asst
Fefferman, Mark, BA, Teach Asst
Flemming, Arthur, MA, Teach Asst
Giuliano, John, BA, Teach Asst
Houts, Ronald, BA, Teach Asst
Hysong, Thomas, BA, Teach Asst
Kaufman, Marjorie, BA, Chancellor's
  Grad Intern Fel
La Rusch, Michele, BA, Chancellor's
  Grad Inter Fel
Levey, Steve, MA, Teach Asst

Lott, Tommy, MA, Teach Asst
Malitz, Richard, BA, Chancellor's Grad Intern Fel
McAllen, Peter, BA, Teach Asst
Morrow, Richard, BA, Teach Asst
Rathbun, Timothy, BA, Teach Asst
Rodewald, Richard, BA, Teach Asst
Sendry, Jeanette, MA, Teach Asst
Shamey, Kathy, BA, Teach Asst
Shartin, Daniel, BA, Teach Asst
Silvey, Frank, BA, Regent's Grad Intern Fel
Ucuzoglu, Nathan, Regent's Grad Intern Fel
Walker, Penelope, BA, Teach Asst
Weirich, Paul, MA, Teach Asst
Weisman, Jeffrey, BA, Teach Asst
Wetzel, Thomas, BA, Teach Asst
Whitney, Richard, MA, Teach Asst
Wikler, Daniel, BA, Chancellor's Grad Intern
  Fel
Woo, Christina, MA, Teach Asst

UNIVERSITY OF CALIFORNIA AT RIVERSIDE
Riverside, California 92502 (W; st; coed; qr; IV; 6168) PhD major, Dept of Phil
714-787-5208

Magnus, Bernd, PhD, Assoc Prof, Chm
Cranor, Carl F, PhD, Asst Prof
Harrah, David, PhD, Prof
Johnson, Oliver A, PhD, Prof
Keller, Marcia L, PhD, Asst Prof
Marcolongo, Francis J, PhD, Asst Prof
McDade, Jesse N, PhD, Asst Prof
Winslade, William J, PhD, Asst Prof
Wright, C E Larry, PhD, Asst Prof

Evans, William G, BA, Teach Asst
Hill, Ronald R, BA, Teach Asst
Lohman, Philip M, MA, Teach Asst

Sterling, Marvin C, MA, Teach Asst
Traficanto, Denise C, BA, Teach Asst

UNIVERSITY OF CALIFORNIA AT SAN DIEGO
  La Jolla, California 92037 (W; st; coed; qr; IV; 6442) PhD major, Dept of Phil,
  714-453-2000 Ext 1221

  Olafson, Frederick, PhD, Prof, Chm, Exist, Phenomen, Soc and Polit Phil
  Allison, Henry, PhD, Prof, Hist of Phil
  Anagnostopoulos, Georgios, PhD, Asst Prof, Class Phil
  Arneson, Richard, PhD, Act Asst Prof, Soc and Polit Phil
  Lee, Edward, PhD, Assoc Prof, Class Phil, Phil of Lang
  Longino, Helen, PhD, Asst Prof, Hist of Phil, Phil of Sci
  Marcuse, Herbert, PhD, Honor Prof, Soc and Polit Phil
  Mark, Thomas, PhD, Asst Prof, Hist of Phil, Spinoza
  Moore, Stanley, PhD, Prof, Ethics, Soc Theory, 19th Cent Phil
  Scales, Ronald, PhD, Asst Prof, Logic, Metaph, Phil of Lang
  Stroll, Avrum, PhD, Prof, Contemp Anglo-Amer Phil, Phil of Lang

UNIVERSITY OF CALIFORNIA AT SAN FRANCISCO, MEDICAL CENTER
  San Francisco, California 94122 (DH; st; coed; qr; IV; 2675) NR

UNIVERSITY OF CALIFORNIA AT SANTA BARBARA
  Santa Barbara, California 93106 (W; st; coed; qr; IV; 12,916) PhD major, Dept of
  Phil, 805-961-3121

  Dauer, Francis W, PhD, Asst Prof, Logic
  Fingarette, Herbert, PhD, Prof, Phil Psych
  Fleming, Noel, DPhil, Prof, Epistem
  Forgie, J William, PhD, Asst Prof, Phil of Mind
  Girvetz, Harry, PhD, Prof, Polit and Soc Phil
  Ketchum, Richard, PhD, Asst Prof, Class Phil, Logic
  Reinhardt, Lloyd, BA, Asst Prof, Phil of Mind
  Schwyzer, Hubert, PhD, Assoc Prof, Metaph
  Sesonske, Alex, PhD, Prof, Aes
  Stough, Charlotte, PhD, Assoc Prof, Class Phil
  Tannenbaum, Jerry, MA, Asst Prof, Phil of Law
  Wienpahl, Paul, PhD, Prof, Hist of Phil
  Wilkins, Burleigh, PhD, Prof, Phil of Hist

  Averill, Edward, Teach Asst
  Below, William A, R W Church Fel
  Bleser, Robert, Teach Asst
  Boekelheide, Carol J, R W Church
      Fel
  Cheney, David, Teach Asst
  Consentino, Dante, Teach Asst
  Dozoretz, Jerry, Teach Asst
  Greene, Philip B, Teach Assoc

  Heintz, Lawrence, Teach Asst
  Hunt, Lester, Teach Asst
  Johnson, Patricia, Teach Asst
  Johnson, Robert, Teach Asst
  Kummel, Marc S, Teach Assoc
  Lee, Jig Chuen, Teach Asst
  Mack, Darryl, Teach Asst
  Schufreider, Gregory J, R W Church Fel
  Webb, Steven, Teach Asst

UNIVERSITY OF CALIFORNIA AT SANTA CRUZ
  Santa Cruz, California 95060 (W; st; coed; qr; IV; 4396) PhD major, Board of Stud
  in Phil, 408-429-2070

  Brief, Jean-Claude, BA, Lect
  Goff, Robert A, PhD, Asst Prof
  Hofstadter, Albert, PhD, Prof
  Kashap, S Paul, B Litt, Lect
  Lee, Paul A, PhD, Asst Prof
  Macann, Christopher, PhD, Asst Prof

Natanson, Maurice A, PhD, Prof
Noble, Richard S, BA, Act Asst Prof
Noreña, Richard S, BA, Act Asst Prof
Wolin, Sheldon S, PhD, Prof

UNIVERSITY OF CALIFORNIA, HASTINGS COLLEGE OF LAW
San Francisco, California 94102 (Law; st; coed; sem; II; 1523) NP

UNIVERSITY OF JUDAISM
Los Angeles, California 90028 (W; Jewish; coed; sem; IV; 355) BA major, Dept of
Hist and Phil of Relig, 213-463-1161

Dorff, Elliot, PhD, Asst Prof, Chm, Ethics, Phil of Relig
Elstein, Yoav, MA, Instr, Phil of Relig
Lieber, David, DHL, Prof, Ethics, Phil of Relig
Schulweis, Harold, PhD, Assoc Prof, Phil of Relig

UNIVERSITY OF REDLANDS
Redlands, California 92373 (W; p; coed; 4-1-4; III; 2005) BA major, Dept of Phil,
714-793-2121 Ext 386

Hunt, Robert W, MA, Asst Prof, Chm, Anal Phil
Arras, John, PhD, Asst Prof, Exist
Davis, Thomas, MA, Visit Asst Prof, Exist
Pruitt, Sylvia, PhD, Asst Prof, Aes

UNIVERSITY OF SAN DIEGO
San Diego, California 92110 (W; RC; coed; sem; II; 1501) BA major, Col of Arts and
Sci, 714-291-6480

Swanke, John W, PhD, Prof, Act Chm, Contemp Phil
Carlin, Thomas J, PhL, Asst Prof
George, Richard J, PhD, Assoc Prof, Aristotelian Thomism
Ghougassian, Joseph P, PhD, Assoc Prof, Arabian Phil
Glowienka, Emerine, PhD, Asst Prof
Hurley, Patrick, PhD, Asst Prof, Process Phil
Shipley, William L, PhD, Prof

UNIVERSITY OF SAN FRANCISCO
San Francisco, California 94117 (W; RC; coed; sem; III; 6351) BA major, Dept of
Phil, 415-666-6598

FitzGerald, Desmond J, PhD, Prof, Chm
Aldridge, Wilson A, PhD, Assoc Prof
Bridges, Geoffrey G, PhD, Assoc Prof
Brusher, Edward W, AB, Asst Prof
Corcoran, Albert C, PhD, Prof
Crem, Theresa, PhD, Assoc Prof
Cunningham, Robert L, PhD, Prof
Everall, David G, PhD, Lect
Gordon, Jack, MA, Instr
Jonsen, Albert R, PhD, Assoc Prof
Koller, Kerry J, MA, Asst Prof
MacKinnon, Barbara A, PhD, Asst Prof
Moran, Vincent J, PhD, Assoc Prof
Nugent, Francis R, PhD, Assoc Prof
O'Sullivan, Daniel A, MA, Asst Prof
Sargent, Benjamin F, STB, Asst Prof
Smith, Albert J, STL, Assoc Prof
Woznicki, Andrew N, PhD, Asst Prof

NIVERSITY OF SANTA CLARA
   Santa Clara, California 95053 (W; RC; coed; qr; IV; 6085) BA major, Dept of Phil,
   408-984-4093

   Fallon, Timothy P, PhD, Asst Prof, Chm, Med Phil
   Burgess, Joseph C, Lect, Logic and Lang, Kant
   Fagothey, Austin, PhD, Prof, Hist of Phil, Ethics
   Felt, James W, PhD, Assoc Prof, Phil of Sci, Whitehead
   Friedman, James W, PhD, Asst Prof, Anal Phil
   Gonsalves, Milton, PhD, Asst Prof, Phenomen
   Hodgkins, Gail, PhD, Part-time, Orient Phil
   Lyons, Leonard S, PhD, Part-time, Anal Phil
   Milburn, Myra M, PhD, Asst Prof, Early Mod Phil, Hegel
   Parent, William, PhD, Asst Prof, Ethics

UNIVERSITY OF SOUTHERN CALIFORNIA
   Los Angeles, California 90007 (W; p; coed; sem; IV; 18,984) PhD major, School of
   Phil, 213-746-2378

   Hospers, John, Prof, Dir, Aes, Ethics, Soc Phil
   Casebier, Allan, PhD, Asst Prof, Aes, Phil of Hist
   Dreher, John, PhD, Asst Prof, Epistem, Hist of Mod Phil, Logic
   Engel, S Morris, PhD, Assoc Prof, Hist of Mod Phil
   Gerber, David, PhD, Asst Prof, Phil of Law
   Johnson, Major PhD, Asst Prof, Phil of Relig, Amer Phil
   Lean, Martin, PhD, Prof, Epistem, Phil of Sci
   MacGregor, Geddes, PhD, Dist Prof, Phil of Relig
   Robb, Kevin, PhD, Assoc Prof, Anc Phil
   Weston, Thomas, MA, Instr, Logic, Phil of Sci
   Willard, Dallas, PhD, Assoc Prof, Metaph, Phenomen
   Zeigler, Gregory, PhD, Visit Asst Prof, Anc Phil, Ethics, Soc Phil

   Long, Wilbur, PhD, Prof Emer
   Robinson, Daniel, PhD, Prof Emer
   Searles, Herbert L, PhD, Prof Emer

UNIVERSITY OF THE PACIFIC
   Stockton, California 95204 (W; p; coed; 4-1-4; IV; 5689) BA major, Dept of Phil,
   209-946-2011

   Reinelt, Herbert R, PhD, Prof, Chm
   Browne, Gwenneth L, PhD, Prof
   Heffermnan, James D, MA, Asst Prof
   Nietmann, William D, PhD, Prof

VENTURA COLLEGE
   Ventura, California 93003 (W; local; coed; sem; I; 8680) --, Dept of Soc Sci,
   805-642-3211

   Clodius, Albert, PhD

VICTOR VALLEY COLLEGE
   Victorville, California 92392 (W; local; coed; sem; I; 2087) NR

WEST COAST BIBLE COLLEGE
  Fresno, California 93710 (--; Ch of God; coed; 4-1-4; II; 109) Courses with no
  degree specialization, 209-299-7205

  Younker, Stephen, MA

WEST COAST UNIVERSITY
  Los Angeles, California 90020 (W; p; coed; tri; III; 845) Courses with no degree
  specialization, 213-487-4433

WEST COAST UNIVERSITY, ORANGE COUNTY CENTER
  Orange, California 92668 (W; p; coed; tri; III; 347) Courses with no degree
  specialization, 714-547-5711

WEST HILLS COLLEGE
  Coalinga, California 93210 (W; local; coed; sem; I; 745) NR

WEST LOS ANGELES COLLEGE
  Culver City, California 90230 (W; local; coed; sem; I; 4832) --, Div of Human
  and Fine Arts, 213-836-7110 Ext 209

  Prince, Gray, MA, Asst Prof

WEST VALLEY COLLEGE
  Campbell, California 95008 (W; local; coed; sem; I; 12,293) Courses with no degree
  specialization, --, 408-379-1733

WESTERN STATES COLLEGE OF ENGINEERING
  Inglewood, California 90301 (--; p; coed; tri; II; 157) NP

WESTMONT COLLEGE
  Santa Barbara, California 93108 (W; p; coed; 4-1-4; II; 845) BA major, Dept of
  Relig Stud and Phil, 805-969-5051 Ext 382

  Obitts, Stanley, PhD, Prof, Hist of Phil, Phil of Relig
  Springer, Randall, PhD, Asst Prof, Metaph
  Wennberg, Robert, PhD, Asst Prof, Ethics

WHITTIER COLLEGE
  Whittier, California 90608 (W; p; coed; 4-1-4; III; 2363) BA major, Dept of Phil
  and Relig, 213-693-0771

  Connick, C Milo, PhD, Prof, Chm
  Kim, Ha Tai, PhD, Prof, Orient Phil, Phil of Relig
  Praetorius, Michael, PhD, Assoc Prof, Continen Phil

WOODBURY COLLEGE
  Los Angeles, California 90017 (W; p; coed; qr; III; 2296) Courses with no degree
  specialization, --, 213-482-8491

Jones, Roland B, DD
Kepler, James H, MTh
Robertson, Donald R, PhD

THE WRIGHT INSTITUTE, GRADUATE DIVISION
Berkeley, California 94704 (--; p; coed; qr; IV; 48) NP

YUBA COLLEGE
Marysville, California 95901 (W; local; coed; sem; I; 5392) --, Dept of Fine Arts,
916-742-7351

Hall, Carl H, MA, Epistem, Logic
Moorman, Lawrence A, Ethics, Polit Phil, Comp Phil
Moore, Curtis, MA, Logic

Bloom, Walter S, PhD, Prof Emer

CANAL ZONE

CANAL ZONE COLLEGE
Balboa, Canal Zone (M; Fed; coed; sem; II; 1310) --, Dept of Soc Sci and Educ,
Balboa 2380

Vosburgh, Clarence R, MA, Instr

COLORADO

ADAMS STATE COLLEGE
  Alamosa, Colorado 81101 (N; st; coed; qr; III; 3070) --, Div of Hist, Gov and
  Phil, 303-589-7771

  Blanco, Enrique, PhD, Asst Prof Part-time
  Oba, William I, ThD, Prof Part-time

AIMS COLLEGE
  Greeley, Colorado 80631 (--; local; coed; qr; I; 3715) Courses with no degree
  specialization, --, 303-353-8008

  Ogden, Mildred C, EdD

ARAPAHOE COMMUNITY COLLEGE
  Littleton, Colorado 80120 (N; st; coed; qr; I; 2366) Courses with no degree
  specialization, Dept of Phil, 303-794-1550

  Smith, G Ross, MA, Ethics

THE COLORADO COLLEGE
  Colorado Springs, Colorado 80903 (N; p; coed; sem; III; 1820) BA major, Dept of
  Phil, 303-473-2233

  Cauvel, Jane, PhD, Assoc Prof, Chm, Aes, Orient Phil
  Gray, J Glenn, PhD, Prof, Euro Phil, Heidegger, Greek Phil
  Krimm, Hans, PhD, Assoc Prof, Logic, Phil of Sci
  Rabbin, Harvey, PhD, Asst Prof, Phil Anthrop, Anal Phil
  Riker, John, PhD, Asst Prof, Amer Phil, Ethics
  Steck, Robert, MA, Instr, Polit Phil

COLORADO ELECTRONIC TECHNICAL COLLEGE
  Manitou Springs, Colorado 80829 (--; p; coed; qr; I; 130) NR

COLORADO MOUNTAIN COLLEGE, EAST CAMPUS
  Leadville, Colorado 80461 (--; local; coed; qr; I; 317) Courses with no degree
  specialization, Dept of Soc Sci, 303-486-2015 Ext 26

  Kindzia, John F, MFA, Asst Prof

COLORADO MOUNTAIN COLLEGE, WEST CAMPUS
  Glenwood Springs, Colorado 81601 (--; local; coed; qr; I; 453) Courses with no
  degree specialization, Dept of Communic and Human, 303-945-7481 Ext 72

  Minor, Gene, MA, Assoc Prof

COLORADO SCHOOL OF MINES
  Golden, Colorado 80401 (N; st; coed; sem; IV; 1699) --, Dept of Human and Soc Sci,
  303-279-3381 Ext 343

  Kalal, Leonard A, MS, Asst Prof, Phil of Sci

COLORADO STATE UNIVERSITY
  Fort Collins, Colorado 80521 (N; st; coed; qr; IV; 17,608) MA major, Dept of Phil,
  303-491-6315

  Eddy, Willard O, MA, Centennial Prof, Chm, Ethics, Soc Phil
  Benson, P Jann, PhD, Asst Prof, Logic, Ethics
  Boersch, Alfred H, PhD, Assoc Prof, Aes
  Boyd, James W, PhD, Assoc Prof, Phil of Relig
  Crocker, David A, PhD, Asst Prof, Hist of Phil
  Crosby, Donald A, PhD, Prof, Metaph
  Freeman, Kenneth P, MA, Asst Prof, Amer Phil
  Johnson, Frederick A, PhD, Asst Prof, Logic, Phil of Math
  Jordan, Robert W, BS, Instr, Phenomen
  Keane, Kevin P, MA, Instr
  King, Winston L, PhD, Prof, Orient Phil
  Kitchener, Richard F, PhD, Asst Prof, Phil of Psych
  Lee, Suk Koo, ThM, Asst Prof, Orient Phil
  Lyons, Daniel D, PhD, Assoc Prof, Ethics, Soc Phil
  McCulloch, Michael L, BA, Instr, Phil of Lang
  McKee, Patrick L, PhD, Assoc Prof, Epistem, Ethics
  Proctor, Robert J, MA, Instr, Ethics
  Rollin, Bernard E, PhD, Asst Prof, Hist of Phil
  Rolston III, Holmes, PhD, Assoc Prof, Phil of Relig
  Williams, Ronald G, MS, Asst Prof, Anal Phil, Phil of Sci

  Hartsock, Donald G, Grad Teach Asst   Turetzky, Philip M, Grad Teach Asst
  Slauson, William L, Grad Teach Asst

COLORADO WOMEN'S COLLEGE
  Denver, Colorado 80220 (N; p; wo; sem; II; 895) BA major, Dept of Phil and Relig,
  303-394-6012

  Spring, Charles, ThD, Assoc Prof, Cord, Relig and Ethics
  Stavrides, Ria, PhD, Prof, Greek Phil, Phenomen
  Yu, David, PhD, Dir, Asian Stud

COMMUNITY COLLEGE OF DENVER, AURARIA CAMPUS
  Denver, Colorado 80204 (--; st; coed; qr; I; 1212) Courses with no degree
  specialization, Dept of Soc Sci, 303-893-8868 Ext 244

  Blasius, Ronald, MA, Part-time Instr

COMMUNITY COLLEGE OF DENVER, NORTH CAMPUS
  Denver, Colorado 80216 (--; st; coed; qr; I; 3542) AA major, Div of Soc Sci, 303-
  287-3311

  Carpenter, Garrett R, MA
  Davis, William Albert, MA

COMMUNITY COLLEGE OF DENVER, RED ROCKS CAMPUS
  Lakewood, Colorado 80215 (--; st; coed; qr; I; 2530) Courses with no degree
  specialization, Div of Soc Sci, 303-238-7531

CONSERVATIVE BAPTIST THEOLOGICAL SEMINARY
  Denver, Colorado 80210 (N; Bapt; coed; sem; III; 194) Courses with no degree
  specialization, Dept of Apologetics and Phil of Relig, 303-761-2482

  Lewis, Gordon, PhD, Prof, Chm

Grounds, Vernon, PhD, Prof, Ethics
Keiper, Ralph, BD, Assoc Prof, Thomistic Tht
Shelley, Bruce, PhD, Prof

EL PASO COMMUNITY COLLEGE
Colorado Springs, Colorado 80903 (--; st; coed; qr; I; 3185) NP

FORT LEWIS COLLEGE
Durango, Colorado 81301 (N; st; coed; tri; II; 2315) BA major, Dept of Phil and
Polit Sci, 303-247-7136

Bass, David, PhD, Assoc Prof, Chm
Coe, William, PhD, Assoc Prof
Pixler, Paul W, PhD, Prof

ILIFF SCHOOL OF THEOLOGY
Denver, Colorado 80210 (Theol; U Meth; coed; qr; IV; 183) PhD major, Dept of Phil
of Relig, 303-744-1287

Milligan, Charles S, PhD, Prof, Chm, Value Theory
Kirk, James A, ThD, Adj Fac, Orient Phil
Potthoff, Harvey H, ThD, Prof, Metaph
Prevallet, Elaine Marie, PhD, Adj Fac, Contemp Theol
Templin, J Alton, PhD, Assoc Prof, Hist of Theol
Wilbanks, Dana W, PhD, Assoc Prof, Ethics

Bernhardt, William H, PhD, Prof Emer, Metaph

Sidorak, Steve, AB, Grad Asst   Whearty, Laura, AB, Grad Asst

LAMAR COMMUNITY COLLEGE
Lamar, Colorado 81052 (--; st; coed; qr; I; 935) Courses with no degree specialization,
--, 303-336-2248

LORETTO HEIGHTS COLLEGE
Denver, Colorado 80236 (N; p; coed; sem; II; 846) Courses with no degree specialization,
Dept of Phil, 303-922-4352

Doyle, Sr, Antoinette M, PhD, Assoc Prof, Ethics, Metaph
Gibson, Robert L, Asst Prof, Logic, Phil of Sci

MESA COLLEGE
Grand Junction, Colorado 81501 (N; local; coed; qr; I; 2504) Courses with no degree
specialization, Div of Human, 303-248-1284

Boschi, Lorraine, M.A., Instr

METROPOLITAN STATE COLLEGE
Denver, Colorado 80204 (N; st; coed; qr; II; 7867) BA major, Dept of Phil, 303-
292-5190 Ext 218

Ahuja, Yoga D, PhD, Assoc Prof, East Tht
Barnes, R T, PhL, Asst Prof, Metaph, Hist of Phil

Michael, Gary, PhD, Asst Prof, Ethics
Phillips, C, BS, Asst Prof, Epistem Logic, Phil of Sci
Rhodes, William E, PhD, Prof, Phil of Relig, Phil of Educ, Aes

MORGAN COMMUNITY COLLEGE
    Fort Morgan, Colorado 80701 (--; st and local; coed; qr; I; 700) NR

NORTHEASTERN JUNIOR COLLEGE
    Sterling, Colorado 80751 (N; local; coed; qr; I; 1233) AA major, Div of Human,
303-522-6600

    Spoon, Jerry W, MA

OTERO JUNIOR COLLEGE
    La Junta, Colorado 81050 (N; st; coed; qr; I; 911) NP

RANGELY COLLEGE
    Rangely, Colorado 81648 (DH; st and local; coed; sem; I; 495) NP

REGIS COLLEGE
    Denver, Colorado 80221 (N; RC; coed; sem; II; 1414) BA major, Dept of Phil, 303-
433-8471 Ext 359

    Blasius, Ron, MA, Lect
    Bonnet, Christian, PhD, Prof
    Mackintosh, William, PhD, Asst Prof
    Malecek, Francis J, PhD, Prof
    Moriarty, Francis J, MA, Assoc Prof
    Squier, Robert, MA, Asst Prof

ROCKMONT COLLEGE
    Denver, Colorado 80226 (--; p; coed; qr; II; 119) Courses with no degree specialization,
303-238-5388

    Nesbitt, LaVerne Fred, MA
    Strauch, Alex, MRE

SAINT THOMAS SEMINARY
    Denver, Colorado 80210 (N; RC; men; qr; III; 175) NR

SOUTHERN COLORADO STATE COLLEGE
    Pueblo, Colorado 81001 (N; st; coed; qr; II; 6344) BA major, Dept of Phil, 303-
549-2209

    Driscoll, Donald J, PhD, Assoc Prof, Chm, Greek Phil, Exist
    Aichele, Ronald G, PhD, Asst Prof, Logic
    Nicholl, Larimore L, MA, Asst Prof, Ethics, Soc and Polit Phil

TRINIDAD STATE JUNIOR COLLEGE
    Trinidad, Colorado 81082 (N; st; coed; qr; I; 1398) Courses with no degree
specialization, Dept of Human, 303-846-5531

    Dossogne, Victor J, PhD

UNITED STATES AIR FORCE ACADEMY
  Colorado Springs, Colorado 80840 (N; Fed; men; sem; I; 4201) Courses with no
  degree specialization, Dept of Polit Sci and Phil, 303-472-2270

  Wakin, Malham M, PhD, Prof, Head, Logic, Ethics, Mil Phil
  Daugherty, Jerry W, MA, Instr
  Martin, Jr, William M, MA, Instr
  Meeko IV, Joseph G, MA, Instr
  Myers, Charles R, MA, Instr, 20th Cent Euro Phil
  Newell, Thomas G, MA, Asst Prof, Ethics, Epistem
  Stayton, William H, MA, Asst Prof, Phil of Relig
  Wenker, Kenneth H, MA, Asst Prof
  Wheeler, Michael O, PhD, Asst Prof, Ethics, Polit and Legal Phil, 20th Cent British
    Phil

UNIVERSITY OF COLORADO
  Boulder, Colorado 80302 (N; st; coed; sem; IV; 21,171) PhD major, Dept of Phil,
  303-443-2211 Ext 6132

  Kimble, James P, PhD, Assoc Prof, Chm
  Anton, Anatole, PhD, Asst Prof
  Barnes, Hazel, PhD, Prof
  Boonin, Leonard, PhD, Assoc Prof
  Carnes, John, PhD, Prof
  Crowe, Lawson, PhD, Prof
  Fisher, John, PhD, Asst Prof
  Frank, James P, PhD, Prof
  Hawkins, David, PhD, Prof
  Holien, Gerald, BA, Asst Prof
  Kenevan, Phillis, PhD, Assoc Prof
  Lang, Berel, PhD, Prof
  Lester, Robert, PhD, Prof
  Machle, Edward, PhD, Prof
  Martin, Jerry, PhD, Asst Prof
  Miller, Eddie L, PhD, Assoc Prof
  Miller, Paul J W, PhD, Prof
  Morris, Bertram, PhD, Prof
  Morriston, Wesley, PhD, Asst Prof
  Nelson, John, PhD, Prof
  Perry, David, PhD, Assoc Prof
  Pinto, Willa, BA, Asst Prof
  Rogers, Robert, PhD, Prof
  Sacksteder, William, PhD, Prof
  Smokler, Howard, PhD, Prof
  Stahl, Gary, PhD, Prof
  Steinman, Diane, BA, Asst Prof
  Visvader, John, PhD, Asst Prof
  Weir, Walter, PhD, Prof
  Williams, Forrest, PhD, Prof

UNIVERSITY OF COLORADO AT COLORADO SPRINGS
  Colorado Springs, Colorado 80907 (N; st; coed; sem; III; 2251) BA major, Dept of
  Phil, 303-598-3737 Ext 306

  Francis, Richard P, PhD, Assoc Prof, Value Theory

UNIVERSITY OF COLORADO AT DENVER
  Denver, Colorado 80202 (N; st; coed; sem; III; 7141) MA minor, Dept of Phil, 303-
  892-1117 Ext 352

  Webster, Glenn A, PhD, Assoc Prof, Discipline Rep, Metaph, Phil of Sci

Kenevan, Charles A, MA, Assoc Prof, Hist of Mod Phil
Leonard, Linda, PhD, Assoc Prof, Heidegger & Jung

Hildreth, Charles, MA, Honorarium, Soc Phil
Weitzel, Ray, MA, Teach Assoc

UNIVERSITY OF COLORADO, MEDICAL CENTER
  Denver, Colorado 80220 (Med; st; coed; qr; IV; 1149) NR

UNIVERSITY OF DENVER
  Denver, Colorado 80210 (N; U Meth; coed; qr; IV; 9119) MA major, Dept of Phil,
  303-753-2063 Ext 2064

  Frazer, Catherine S, PhD, Prof, Chm, Hume
  Brush, Francis W, PhD, Prof
  Cohen, Cynthia B, PhD, Asst Prof
  Hill, Roscoe E, PhD, Asst Prof, Phil of Law
  Hsieh, Shan-yuan, PhD, Asst Prof, Chinese Phil
  Klocker, Harry, PhD, Visit Prof, Kant
  Larson, Lawrence, PhD, Asst Prof, Logic
  Lipschutz, Susan S, PhD, Asst Prof, Soc and Polit Phil
  McGregor, Robert, PhD, Asst Prof, Aes
  Schultz, Robert C, PhD, Asst Prof, Phil of Educ
  Seeburger, Francis, PhD, Asst Prof, Phenomen
  Smith, Edward T, PhD, Asst Prof, Med Phil

UNIVERSITY OF NORTHERN COLORADO
  Greeley, Colorado 80631 (N; st; coed; qr; IV; 13,190) BA minor, Dept of Phil, 303-
  351-2685

  Morelli, Frank H, MA, Asst Prof, Chm, Metaph, Epistem
  Hobapp, P F, PhD, Asst Prof, Ethics, Polit Phil

WESTERN STATE COLLEGE OF COLORADO
  Gunnison, Colorado 81230 (N; st; coed; qr; III; 3629) BA minor, Div of Soc Stud,
  303-943-2091

  Gery, Paul H, MA, Asst Prof
  Fay, Abbott, MA, Asst Prof

YESH TORAS CHAIM TALMUD SEMINARY
  Denver, Colorado 80204 (--; p; men; tri; II; 35) NR

CONNECTICUT

ALBERTUS MAGNUS COLLEGE
New Haven, Connecticut 06511 (E; RC; wo; sem; II; 502) BA minor, Dept of Phil,
203-777-6631

Nicholas, Joan, PhD, Asst Prof, Chm

ANNHURST COLLEGE
Woodstock, Connecticut 06281 (E; RC; wo; sem; II; 425) NR

BRIDGEPORT ENGINEERING INSTITUTE
Bridgeport, Connecticut 06604 (--; p; coed; tri; II; 397) NP

CENTRAL CONNECTICUT STATE COLLEGE
New Britain, Connecticut 06050 (E; st; coed; sem; III; 12,729) BA major, Dept of
Phil, 203-225-7481

Creer, Leland M, PhD, Assoc Prof, Chm
Allen, Douglas M, PhD, Asst Prof
Augur, Sherwood, PhD, Assoc Prof
Garrett, W Eugene, PhD, Assoc Prof
Gaskins, Richard H, PhD, Lect
Greenia, David, MA, Lect
Kahane, Judith, BA, Asst Prof
Kiley, W Paul, MA, Asst Prof
McKenzie, Marian, MA, Asst Prof

CONNECTICUT COLLEGE
New London, Connecticut 06320 (E; p; coed; sem; III; 1962) MA major, Dept of Phil,
203-442-5391 Ext 359

Jordan, Robert W, PhD, Prof, Chm, Plato, Phil of Art
Reiss, Lester J, PhD, Assoc Prof, Metaph, Phil of Relig
Ringelheim, Joan, PhD, Asst Prof
TeHennepe, Eugene, PhD, Asst Prof, Epistem, Anal Phil
Woody, J Melvin, PhD, Assoc Prof, Hegel, 19th Cent Tht, Exist
Woody, Susan M, PhD, Assoc Prof, Kant, Ethics, Phil of Law

Langer, Susanne K, PhD, Prof Emer, Phil of Mind

EASTERN CONNECTICUT STATE COLLEGE
Willimantic, Connecticut 06226 (E; st; coed; sem; III; 2801) BA minor, Dept of Hist
and Related Areas, 203-423-4581

Browne, Robert, PhD, Prof, Phil of Relig, Orient Phil
Connelly, Frank, MA, Asst Prof, Phil of Sci

FAIRFIELD UNIVERSITY
Fairfield, Connecticut 06430 (E; RC; coed; sem; III; 3762) BA major, Dept of Phil,
203-255-5411 Ext 308

Grassi, Joseph G, PhD, Prof, Chm, Hist of Phil, Polit Phil
Cardoni, Albert, PhD, Asst Prof, Med Phil, Metaph
Carr, William, MA, Asst Prof, Med Phil, Ethics
Coleman, Donald A, PhD, Asst Prof, Logic, Anal Phil

Dykeman, King J, PhD, Assoc Prof, Hist of Phil, Phil of Sci
Grossman, Morris, PhD, Prof, Amer Phil
Johnston, Julia, PhD, Assoc Prof, Greek Phil
Long, R James, PhD, Assoc Prof, Med Phil
Myers, Joseph, PhD, Assoc Prof, Hist of Phil
Newton, Lisa, PhD, Assoc Prof, Soc and Polit Phil
Tong, Lik Kuen, PhD, Asst Prof, Orient Phil
Trinkle, Joseph, PhD, Asst Prof, 19th Cent Phil

Maher, John M, PhD, Prof Emer, Ethics, Metaph

GREATER HARTFORD COMMUNITY COLLEGE
   Hartford, Connecticut 06106 (--; st; coed; sem; I; 1518) --, Dept of Psych, Phil
   and Educ, 203-549-4200 Ext 258

   Mantautas, Vaidievutis A, PhD, Assoc Prof, Med Phil, Eckhart
   Sokolowski, William R, BA, Instr Part-time, Phil of Relig

HARTFORD COLLEGE FOR WOMEN
   Hartford, Connecticut 06105 (E; p; wo; sem; I; 216) AA degree, --, 203-236-1215

   Phillips, R M, PhD, Prof, Metaph

HARTFORD SEMINARY FOUNDATION
   Hartford, Connecticut 06105 (Theol; p; coed; sem; IV; 209) Courses with no degree
   specialization, Depts of Bibl Stud, Human Nature and Relig, and Hist of Relig

   Underwood, Richard A, PhD, Phil of Relig

HARTFORD STATE TECHNICAL COLLEGE
   Hartford, Connecticut 06106 (E; st; coed; qr; I; 1575) NR

HOLY APOSTLES COLLEGE
   Cromwell, Connecticut 06416 (--; RC; coed; sem; II; 92) --, Dept of Phil, 203-
   346-8657

   Wisneski, Edward J, MA, Instr, Chm, Hist of Phil
   Halpin, John T, PhD, Med Phil
   Mietzelfeld, Richard A, PhL, Exist, Aes
   Seleman, Stephen, MA, Logic
   Shaw, Brian A, MA, Epistem, Logic
   Traxl, William L, MA, Hist of Phil, Phil of Relig

HOUSATONIC COMMUNITY COLLEGE
   Bridgeport Connecticut 06497 (--; st; coed; sem; I; 2541) --, Dept of Human, 203-
   366-8201

MANCHESTER COMMUNITY COLLEGE
   Manchester, Connecticut 06040 (E; st; coed; sem; I; 3371) Courses with no degree
   specialization, Dept of Phil and Psych, 203-646-4900

   Stager, Jay R, MRE, Assoc Prof, Chm
   Jacobs, John, ThD, Asst Prof, Ethics

MATTATUCK COMMUNITY COLLEGE
   Waterbury, Connecticut 06708 (--; st; coed; sem; I; 2070) Courses with no degree

specialization, Dept of Phil, 203-757-9661

Nolan, Richard T, PhD, Asst Prof, Phil of Relig

MIDDLESEX COMMUNITY COLLEGE
Middletown, Connecticut 06457 (--; st; coed; sem; I; 1579) Courses with no degree
specialization, Div of Soc Sci, 203-347-7411

MITCHELL COLLEGE
New London, Connecticut 06320 (E; p; coed; sem; I; 1153) AA major, Dept of Hist
and Gov, 203-443-2811

Mugge, George A, MA, Head, Hist of Phil

MOHEGAN COMMUNITY COLLEGE
Norwich, Connecticut 06360 (--; st; coed; sem; I; 732) Courses with no degree
specialization, Dept of Human, 203-889-3391

Dunion, Paul, MA

MORSE OF HARTFORD
Hartford, Connecticut 06103 (--; p; coed; qr; I; 130) NR

MOUNT SACRED HEART COLLEGE
Hamden, Connecticut 06514 (--; RC; wo; tri; I; 23) NR

NEW ENGLAND INSTITUTE
Ridgefield, Connecticut 06877 (--; p; coed; --; IV; 4) NP

NORTHWESTERN CONNECTICUT COMMUNITY COLLEGE
Winsted, Connecticut 06098 (E; st; coed; sem; I; 1492) NP

NORWALK COMMUNITY COLLEGE
Norwalk, Connecticut 06854 (--; st; coed; sem; I; 2865) --, Dept of Human, 203-
853-2040

Brown, Margaret

NORWALK STATE TECHNICAL COLLEGE
Norwalk, Connecticut 06854 (E; st; coed; qr; I; 1497) NP

POST JUNIOR COLLEGE
Waterbury, Connecticut 06708 (JRCB; p; coed; 4-1-4; I; 618) NP

QUINEBAUG VALLEY COMMUNITY COLLEGE
Danielson, Connecticut 06239 (--; st; coed; sem; I; 200) Courses with no degree
specialization, Dept of Gen Stud, 203-774-1130

Garrelts, George, MA, Phil of Relig

QUINNIPIAC COLLEGE
    Hamden, Connecticut 06518 (E; p; coed; sem; II; 2975) BA minor, Dept of Phil,
    203-288-5251 Ext 383

    Adams, Richard C, STM, Asst Prof, Phil of Relig, Compar Phil
    Buonocore, Gloria, PhD, Asst Prof Part-time, Hist of Phil
    Doherty, Cornelius, BA, Instr, Phil of Relig
    Morgan, John, MA, Instr Part-time, Phil Theol
    Okrent, Kathy, MA, Instr Part-time, Phil of Relig
    Rethis, Michael, PhD, Assoc Prof Part-time, Hist of Phil
    Smith, Marilyn, MA, Asst Prof Part-time, Phil of Relig
    Stiernotte, Alfred, PhD, Sr Member, Process Phil, Metaph

RENSSELAER POLYTECHNIC INSTITUTE OF CONNECTICUT, INC
    Hartford, Connecticut 06120 (E; p; coed; sem; III; 507) NP

SACRED HEART UNIVERSITY
    Bridgeport, Connecticut 06604 (E; p; coed; sem; II; 2042) BA major, Dept of Phil,
    203-374-9441

    Bordeau, Edward, PhD, Assoc Prof, Chm, Amer Phil
    Bennett, Stephan, MA, Prof
    Lademan, William, PhD, Prof
    O'Shea, Robert, PhD, Assoc Prof

SAINT ALPHONSUS COLLEGE
    Suffield, Connecticut 06078 (E; RC; men; tri; II; 62) BA major, Dept of Phil,
    203-668-7393

    Duffy, John A, PhD, Prof, Hist of Phil
    Krastel, Joseph F, MS, Lect
    Oppitz, Joseph W, PhD, Prof, Metaph
    Pauli, James M, MA, Prof, Contemp Phil

SAINT BASIL'S COLLEGE
    Stamford, Connecticut 06902 (--; RC; men; sem; II; 24) NR

SAINT JOSEPH COLLEGE
    West Hartford, Connecticut 06117 (E; RC; wo; sem; III; 932) MA joint or combined
    major, Dept of Phil, 203-523-4283 Ext 58

    Walton, William M, PhD, Prof, Chm, Thomism
    Crowley, Margaret, PhD, Asst Prof, Phenomen
    Lescoe, Francis J, PhD, Prof, Exist

SAINT THOMAS SEMINARY JUNIOR COLLEGE
    Bloomfield, Connecticut 06002 (E; RC; men; sem; I; 43) AA major, --, 203-242-5573

    Macaluso, Christie A, STM

SOUTH CENTRAL COMMUNITY COLLEGE
    New Haven, Connecticut 06511 (--; st; coed; sem; I; 1550) NP

SOUTHERN CONNECTICUT STATE COLLEGE
New Haven, Connecticut 06515 (E; st; coed; sem; III; 12,727) BA major, Dept of Phil,
203-397-2101

Shalvey, Thomas, PhD, Assoc Prof, Chm, Ethics, Phenomen, Amer Phil
Cullen, John, MA, Asst Prof, Ethics
di Piazza, Joseph, MA, Asst Prof, Phil of Sci
Gatzke, Ken, MA, Asst Prof, Aes
Greco, Joseph, PhD, Assoc Prof, Logic
Lindbeck, Violette, MA, Asst Prof
Lowe, Florence, PhD, Prof, Polit Phil, Phil of Educ
Mohan, P Krishna, MA, Assoc Prof, Orient Phil, Orient Relig
Peterson, Forrest, PhD, Prof, Hegel, Phil of Educ
Rethis, Michael, PhD, Prof, Greek Phil
Voelkel, Theodore, PhD, Asst Prof, Mod Euro Phil

THAMES VALLEY STATE TECHNICAL COLLEGE
Norwich, Connecticut 06360 (E; st; coed; qr; I; 1070) NP

TRINITY COLLEGE
Hartford, Connecticut 06106 (E; p; coed; sem; III; 1994) MA major, Dept of Phil,
203-527-3151 Ext 355

Lee, Richard, PhD, Prof, Chm, Phil of Lang, Ethics, Metaph, Whitehead
Brown, W Miller, PhD, Assoc Prof, Phil of Sci, Anal Phil, Phil of Art
DeLong, Howard, PhD, Prof, Logic, Phil of Math
Hyland, Drew, PhD, Assoc Prof, Anc Phil, 19th Cent Phil, German Phil, Heidegger
Lerner, Michael, PhD, Asst Prof, Polit Phil, Marx, Phil of Mind
Stafford, Sue, PhD, Instr, Phil of Lang, Phil of Psych

Means, Blanchard, PhD, Prof Emer, Ethics, Polit Phil

TUNXIS COMMUNITY COLLEGE
Farmington, Connecticut 06032 (--; st; coed; sem; I; 1218) Courses with no degree
specialization, --, 203-677-7701

Wratchford, Eugene P, MA, Lect

UNITED STATES COAST GUARD ACADEMY
New London, Connecticut 06302 (E; Fed; men; sem; II; 986) NR

UNIVERSITY OF BRIDGEPORT
Bridgeport, Connecticut 06602 (E; p; coed; sem; III; 8318) BA major, Dept of Phil
203-384-0711 Ext 514

Parsons, Howard L, PhD, Prof, Chm, Marxism
D'Angelo, Edward, PhD, Asst Prof, Critical Thinking
DeGrood, David, PhD, Asst Prof, Hist of Phil
Kali, Bhaskararao, M Div, Lect
Miller, Douglas, MA, Lect
Ringelheim, Joan, PhD, Asst Prof, Phil of Soc Sci

UNIVERSITY OF CONNECTICUT
Storrs, Connecticut 06268 (E; st; coed; sem; IV; 17,444) PhD major, Dept of Phil,
203-486-4416

Rollins, C D, D Phil, Prof, Head, Anal Phil, Phil of Mind, Epistem
Brodsky, G M, PhD, Assoc Prof, Amer Phil, Hist of Phil, Phil of Mind

Cobb, W H, Instr, 19th Cent Mod Continen Phil
Ellington, J W, PhD, Assoc Prof, Hist of Phil, Hist of Sci, Aes
Fritz, A D, PhD, Lect, Logic, Hist of Phil, Amer Phil
Fritz Jr, C A, PhD, Prof, Logic, Theory of Knowl, Hist of Phil
Halbasch, K E, PhD, Asst Prof, Lang Theory, Logic
Hancock, R N, PhD, Assoc Prof, Ethics, Soc Phil, Polit Phil
Kirmani, S, Instr, Phil of Relig, Hist of Logic
Krimerman, L I, PhD, Assoc Prof, Soc Phil, Polit Phil, Phil of Educ
Kupperman, J J, PhD, Assoc Prof, Ethics, Phil of Relig, Hist of Phil
Lehmann, S K, PhD, Asst Prof, Math Logic
Lindley, T F, PhD, Prof, Ethics, Lang Theory
Luyster, R W, PhD, Asst Prof, Phil of Relig
McGrade, A S, PhD, Assoc Prof, Med Phil, Greek Phil
Roupas, T G, Instr, Logic, Aes, Epistem
Shaffer, J A, PhD, Prof, Phil of Mind, Metaph, Epistem, Hist of Phil
Simon, M A, PhD, Assoc Prof, Phil of Sci
Troyer, J D, PhD, Asst Prof, Ethics, Anal Phil, Hist of Phil
Wheeler III, S C, PhD, Asst Prof, Ethics, Epistem, Metaph, Lang Theory

UNIVERSITY OF CONNECTICUT, HARTFORD BRANCH
   Hartford, Connecticut 06105 (E; st; coed; sem; I; 1189) NR

UNIVERSITY OF CONNECTICUT, HEALTH CENTER
   Farmington, Connecticut 06032 (E; st; coed; --; II; 186) See Late Reports

UNIVERSITY OF CONNECTICUT, SOUTHEASTERN BRANCH
   Groton, Connecticut 06340 (E; st; coed; sem; I; 525) BA major, Dept of Phil, 203-
   446-1020 Ext 242

   Sommese, Rebecca R, PhD, Asst Prof, 20th Cent British Amer Phil

UNIVERSITY OF CONNECTICUT, STAMFORD BRANCH
   Stamford, Connecticut 06903 (E; st; coed; sem; I; 657) BA major, Dept of Phil,
   203-322-3466 Ext 24

   Colburn, Susan, CPhil, Instr, Metaph, Phil of Lang, 19th Cent Phil

UNIVERSITY OF CONNECTICUT, TORRINGTON BRANCH
   Torrington, Connecticut 06790 (E; st; coed; sem; I; 657) BA major, Dept of Phil,
   203-482-7635

   Grover, Robinson A, PhD, Asst Prof, Ethics

UNIVERSITY OF CONNECTICUT, WATERBURY BRANCH
   Waterbury, Connecticut 06710 (E; st; coed; sem; I; 892) BA major, Dept of Phil,
   203-757-1231 Ext 35

   Buonocore, Gloria, PhD, Part-time, Metaph, Ethics
   Friedman, Howard R, PhD, Asst Prof, Phil Logic

UNIVERSITY OF HARTFORD
   West Hartford, Connecticut 06117 (E; p; coed; sem; IV; 9024) BA major, Dept of
   Phil, 203-523-4811 Ext 745

   Barnes, Mahlon W, PhD, Assoc Prof, Act Chm, Phil of Cult, Process Phil
   Bartlett, Steven, PhD, Asst Prof, Phenomen

DenOuden, Bernard, PhD, Instr, 19th Cent Phil, Phil of Lang
Neville, Marie-Suzanne, MA, Instr, Phil of Sci
Pinton, Giorgio, PhD, Asst Prof, Hist of Phil
Shippee, Arthur, M Div, Asst Prof, Phil of Relig

Hamel, Albert F, PhD, Prof Emer, Metaph

UNIVERSITY OF NEW HAVEN
West Haven, Connecticut 06516 (E; p; coed; sem; III; 5120) BA major, Dept of Phil,
203-934-6321 Ext 204

Collinson, John, PhD, Prof, Epistem, Aes
Sholl, William, BD, Assoc Prof, Phil of Relig, Ethics

WATERBURY STATE TECHNICAL COLLEGE
Waterbury, Connecticut 06708 (E; st; coed; qr; I; 1331) NP

WESLEYAN UNIVERSITY
Middletown, Connecticut 06457 (E; p; coed; sem; IV; 1881) BA major, Dept of Phil,
203-347-9411 Ext 268

Mink, Louis O, PhD, Prof, Chm, Phil of Hist, Phil of Soc Sci, Aes
Bendall, L Kent, PhD, Assoc Prof, Logic, Ling
Fay, Brian, DPhil, Asst Prof, Phil of Soc Sci, Polit Phil
Gourevitch, Victor, PhD, Prof, Hist of Phil, Polit Phil
Hallie, Philip P, PhD, Prof, Moral Phil, Contemp Phil
Harvey, Peter J, PhD, Asst Prof, Phil of Sci, Hist of Phil
Lacock, Darrell D, PhD, Asst Prof, Phil of Educ
Phillips, Robert L, MA, Asst Prof, Anal Phil, Ethics

Krusé, Cornelius, PhD, Prof Emer
Reynolds, Paul A, PhD, Prof Emer

WESTERN CONNECTICUT STATE COLLEGE
Danbury, Connecticut 06810 (E; st; coed; sem; III; 4351) BA minor, Dept of Phil,
203-792-1400

Greenwald, H Jonathan, Chm
Apetz, E
Bruzelius, C
Clark, M
Dow, J
Driscoll, D
Hornick, M
Johnson, R
Kahn, A
Lemmen, C
Moore, G
Quinnell, W
Schutts, E
Troutman, W
Yocum, D

YALE UNIVERSITY
New Haven, Connecticut 06520 (E; p; coed; sem; IV; 8912) PhD major, Dept of Phil,
203-436-8859

Harries, Karsten, PhD, Chm, Prof
Ahern, Dennis, PhD, Asst Prof

Brumbaugh, Robert, PhD, Prof
Carr, David, PhD, Assoc Prof
Casey, Edward, PhD, Assoc Prof
Fitch, Frederic, PhD, Prof
Fogelin, Robert, PhD, Prof
Genova, Judith, PhD, Asst Prof
Jaeger, Robert, PhD, Asst Prof
Jager, Ronald, PhD, Assoc Prof
Körner, Stephan, PhD, Prof
Kronman, Anthony, PhD, Lect
Langer, Monika, MA, Lect
MacLean, Douglas, MA, Lect
Marcus, Ruth, PhD, Prof
Mills, Kenneth, PhD, Asst Prof
Morawetz, Thomas, PhD, Asst Prof
Ogilvy, James, PhD, Asst Prof
Oscanyan, Frederick, PhD, Asst Prof
Rockmore, Tom, PhD, Asst Prof
Schrader, George, PhD, Prof
Smith, John E, PhD, Prof
Veto, Miklos, PhD, Lect
Ward, Benjamin, PhD, Asst Prof
Wells, Rulon, PhD, Prof
Westphal, Merold, PhD, Assoc Prof
Williams, Michael, BA, Lect

Branshard, Brand, PhD, Prof Emer
Findlay, John, PhD, Prof Emer
Hendel, Charles, PhD, Prof Emer
Margenau, Henry, PhD, Prof Emer
Northrop, Filmer, PhD, Prof Emer
Sheldon, Wilmon, PhD, Prof Emer
Weiss, Paul, PhD, Prof Emer

DELAWARE

BRANDYWINE COLLEGE
Wilmington, Delaware 19803 (M; p; coed; sem; I; 1458) Courses with no degree
specialization, Dept of Libr Arts, 302-478-3000

DELAWARE STATE COLLEGE
Dover, Delaware 19901 (M; st; coed; sem; II; 1921) BA minor, Dept of Phil, 302-
678-4901

Price, Bruce W, MA, Instr, Act Chm, Epistem, Metaph, Kant
Miller, Karen, MA, Asst Prof, Polit Phil, Ethics, Amer Phil

DELAWARE TECHNICAL AND COMMUNITY COLLEGE, NORTHERN BRANCH
Wilmington, Delaware 19802 (M; st; coed; qr; I; 1310) NP

DELAWARE TECHNICAL AND COMMUNITY COLLEGE, SOUTHERN BRANCH
Georgetown, Delaware 19947 (M; st; coed; qr; I; 3464) NP

GOLDEY BEACOM COLLEGE
Wilmington, Delaware 19899 (JRCB; p; coed; sem; I; 938) NR

UNIVERSITY OF DELAWARE
Newark, Delaware 19711 (M; st; coed; sem; IV; 12,824) MA major, Dept of Phil, 302-738-2359

Harward, Donald W, PhD, Assoc Prof, Chm, Anal Phil, Logic, Epistem
Boorse, Christopher L, PhD, Asst Prof, Logic, Phil of Lang
Brown, Robert F, PhD, Asst Prof, Phil of Relig, 19th Cent Phil
Dilley, Frank B, PhD, Asst Prof, Phil of Relig, Phil of Mind
Hall, Harrison B, PhD, Asst Prof, Phenomen, Epistem, Exist
Haslett, David W, PhD, Asst Prof, Ethics, Soc Phil, Phil of Law
Hsu, Sung-Peng, PhD, Asst Prof, Orient Phil, Non-Western Relig
Durbin, Paul T, PhD, Assoc Prof, Phil of Sci, Ethics, Anc Phil
Norton, David L, PhD, Assoc Prof, Exist, Amer Phil, Metaph
Palmer, Lucia M, PhD, Assoc Prof, Kant, Mod Phil, Anc Phil
Tovo, Jerome C, PhD, Asst Prof, Aes, Epistem, Phil and Lit

Armstrong, Benjamin F, Teach Asst
Blandford, James C, Teach Asst
Hirsch, Bruce A, Teach Asst
Jacobson, Stephen R, Teach Asst
Lambert, Frank B, Fel
Largent, Christopher L, Teach Asst

O'Donnell, Patrick J, Teach Asst
Ross, David L, Teach Asst
Scully, John, Fel
Wood, Alfred J, Teach Asst
Wright, John, Fel

WESLEY COLLEGE
Dover, Delaware 19901 (M; U Meth; coed; sem; I; 990) Courses with no degree specialization, Dept of Phil, 302-674-4000

Starnes, Ronald Ware, STB, Assoc Prof, Relig and Phil

WILMINGTON COLLEGE
New Castle, Delaware 19720 (--; p; coed; sem; II; 701) Courses with no degree specialization, Gen Stud Core, 302-328-9401

DISTRICT OF COLUMBIA

THE AMERICAN UNIVERSITY
Washington 20016 (M; U Meth; coed; sem; IV; 14,508) PhD major, Dept of Phil and Relig, 202-686-2425

Durfee, Harold A, PhD, Prof, Chm, Metaph
Blose, Barry L, PhD, Asst Prof, Epistem
Flynn, Thomas R, PhD, Exchange Prof, Soc Phil
Greenberg, Gershon, PhD, Assoc Prof, Jewish Phil
Hardwich, Charley D, PhD, Assoc Prof, Phil of Relig

Harper, Mary-Angela, PhD, Prof Lect, Ethics
Hofmeister, Heimo E, PhD, Assoc Prof, Ethics
Krausz, Michael, PhD, Visit Asst Prof, Phil of Hist
Rodier, David F, PhD, Assoc Prof, Anc Phil
Scribner, Phillip H, PhD, Asst Prof, Phil of Sci
Simonds, Roger T, PhD, Prof, Phil of Law
White, Charles S J, PhD, Assoc Prof, East Phil

Boggs, Charles W, AB, Dissertation Fel
Channell, Craig, AB, Teach Fel
Hilmy, Sameer, AB, Dept Fel
Martin, Edward, AB, Teach Fel

McGrath, James, AB, Teach Fel
Papadis, Demetrios, AB, Dept Fel
Reynolds, Bernard, AB, Teach Fel
Romano, Christopher, AB, Dept Fel

THE CATHOLIC UNIVERSITY OF AMERICA
Washington 20017 (M; RC; coed; sem; IV; 6486) PhD major, School of Phil, 202-635-5259

Dougherty, Jude P, PhD, Assoc Prof, Dean, Ethics, Amer Phil
Bode, Roy R, PhD, Asst Prof, Ethics, Hist of Phil
Bonansea, Bernardino M, PhD, Prof, Phil of God, Renaissance Phil
Boudreaux, Jack, PhD, Instr, Logic
Cosgrove, Matthew R, PhD, Asst Prof, Greek Phil
Cua, Antonio S, PhD, Prof, Ethics, Contemp British Phil, Austin
De Nys, Martin J, PhD, Asst Prof, Hist of Mod Phil, Hegel
Flynn, Thomas R, PhD, Asst Prof, Soc Phil, Polit Phil
Foley, Leo A, PhD, Asst Prof, Phil of Nature, Whitehead
McLean, George F, PhD, Prof, Epistem
Mohan, Robert P, PhD, Prof, Phil of Hist, Soc Phil, Polit Phil
Nolan, Paul, PhD, Assoc Prof, Phil Anthrop, Kierkegaard
Prufer, Thomas, PhD, Assoc Prof, Phil Anthrop, Mod German Phil, Hobbes, Hume, Heidegger
Schneider, Marius G, PhD, Prof, Phil of Mind, Contemp German Phil
Siewert, Donald J, PhD, Asst Prof, Epistem, Kant
Sokolowski, Robert, PhD, Assoc Prof, Anc Phil, Husserl
Wallace, William A, PhD, Prof, Phil of Sci
Weiss, Paul, PhD, Prof, Phil of Law, Whitehead, Pierce
Wippel, John F, PhD, Prof, Metaph, Hist of Med Phil, Aquinas
Wolter, Allan B, PhD, Prof, Logic, Hist of Med, Scotus

Ryan, John K, PhD, Prof Emer

Enright, Michael F, MA, Grad Asst
Frank, William A, BA, Grad Asst

Hines, Mary E, MA, Grad Asst
Sterling, Joseph W, MA, Grad Asst

COLLEGE OF THE POTOMAC
Washington 20036 (--; p; coed; qr; I; 39) NR

DISTRICT OF COLUMBIA TEACHERS COLLEGE
Washington 20009 (M; local; coed; sem; II; 2878) NP

DUNBARTON COLLEGE OF HOLY CROSS
Washington 20008 (M; RC; wo; sem; II; 345) NR

FEDERAL CITY COLLEGE
Washington 20001 (--; st and local; coed; qr; III; 7184) BA major, Dept of Hist and Phil, 202-727-2534

Baltazar, Eulalio R, PhD, Prof, Dir, Process Phil

Carew, George, MA, Instr, Ling Anal, Logic
Mosley, Albert, MA, Asst Prof, Soc and Polit Phil
Okadigbo, Chuba, PhD, Asst Prof, Hegel, Marx

GALLAUDET COLLEGE
Washington 20002 (M; p; coed; sem; III; 1100) NR

GEORGETOWN UNIVERSITY
Washington 20007 (M; RC; coed; sem; IV; 8855) PhD major, Dept of Phil, 202-625-4241

Veatch, Henry B, PhD, Prof, Chm
Beauchamp, Tom L, PhD, Asst Prof, British Empir
Bradley, Denis J M, PhD, Asst Prof, Stoicism
Brough, John B, PhD, Asst Prof, Phenomen, Husserl
Callahan, John F, PhD, Prof, Greek Phil
del Carril, Mario F, MA, Instr, Phil of Mind
Desan, Wilfrid, PhD, Prof, Continen Phil, Exist
Farre, George L, PhD, Assoc Prof, Wittgenstein, Phil of Sci
Mann, Jesse A, PhD, Prof, Amer Phil
McTighe, Thomas P, PhD, Prof, Renaissance Phil, Med Phil
Porreco, Rocco E, PhD, Assoc Prof, Ethics
Reuscher, John A, PhD, Asst Prof, Kant
Rolston, Howard L, PhD, Asst Prof, Soc Phil, Polit Phil
Schweder, William H, PhD, Prof, Hist of Phil
Ver Eecke, Wilfried, PhD, Assoc Prof, Hegel, Freud, Continen Phil

Davis, Lewis A, Univ Fel
Drummond, John J, NDEA Fel
Mazaitis, John C, Teach Asst
Neale, Sr, Ann, NDEA Fel
Novotney, Andrew J, Univ Fel
Osheroff, Steven S, Teach Asst
Ostrander, Thomas P, Univ Fel

Pitt, William B, Univ Fel
Rabin, Catherine P, Univ Fel
Rainone, Francine, Univ Fel
Roca, Octavio, Univ Fel
Witkowski, Kenneth S, Univ Fel
Zembaty, Jane S, Univ Fel

GEORGE WASHINGTON UNIVERSITY
Washington 20006 (M; p; coed; sem; IV; 21,469) MA major, Dept of Phil, 202-676-6266

Lavine, T Z, PhD, Prof, Chm, Phil of Hist, Phil of Soc Sci
Griffith, William B, PhD, Assoc Prof, Logic, Ethics
Pfuntner, Carl H, PhD, Assoc Prof, Hist of Phil, Amer Phil
Schlagel, Richard H, PhD, Prof, Phil of Phys Sci, Epistem
Schrenk, Laura, PhD, Assoc Professorial Lect Part-time, Phenomen, Ethics
Soffer, Walter, PhD, Asst Prof, Mod Phil, Phil of Psych

HOWARD UNIVERSITY
Washington 20001 (M; p; coed; sem; IV; 10,152) MA major, Dept of Phil, 202-636-6718

McAllister, Winston K, PhD, Assoc Prof, Chm, Utilitarianism, Epistem, Anal Phil
Banner, William A, PhD, Prof, Ethics
Blank, Leonard B, MA, Instr, Buddhism
Carew, George M, MA, Instr, Epistem, Polit Phil, Soc Phil
Cook, Joyce Mitchell, PhD, Asst Prof, Ethics, Exist
Krikorian, Yervant H, PhD, Vist Prof, Metaph
McGuire, Marcie M, MA, Instr, Wittgenstein
Regis, Jr, Edward, PhD, Asst Prof, Anc Phil, Informal Logic
Rosenbaum, Dorothy H, MA, Instr, Phil of Law
Verharen, Charles C, MA, Instr, Orient Phil, Anal Phil

Arthur, Alcott S, Grad Asst   Jenkins, Anise, Grad Asst

IMMACULATA COLLEGE OF WASHINGTON
  Washington 20016 (M; RC; wo; sem; I; 141) AA major, Dept of Phil, 202-966-0040

  Hof, Robert M, MA, Asst Prof, Chm, Personal Identity
  Carney, Edward J, PhD, Prof, Ethics

MAJORIE WEBSTER JUNIOR COLLEGE
  Washington 20012 (--; p; wo; sem; I; 120) NP

MOUNT VERNON COLLEGE
  Washington 20017 (M; p; wo; 4-1-4; I; 262) Courses with no degree specialization,
  --, 202-331-3400

  Bratton, Morris H, MA, Relig and Phil

OBLATE COLLEGE
  Washington 20017 (M; RC; men; sem; III; 65) NR

SAINT PAUL'S COLLEGE
  Washington 20017 (M; RC; men; sem; III; 66) NP

SOUTHEASTERN UNIVERSITY
  Washington 20024 (SRCB; p; coed; tri; II; 453) --, Div of Human, 202-488-8162

  Barker, Warren J, STL, Adj Prof, Logic, Hist of Phil, Epistem
  Keys, James M, PhD, Adj Prof, Logic, Hist of Phil, Epistem

  Link, S Gordden, PhD, Adj Prof Emer, Logic, Hist of Phil, Epistem

STRAYER COLLEGE
  Washington 20005 (JRCB; p; coed; qr; II; 1765) NR

TRINITY COLLEGE
  Washington 20017 (M; RC; wo; sem; III; 756) BA major, Dept of Phil, 202-269-2285

  John, Sr, Helen James, PhD, Prof, Chm, Exist Phenomen, Hist of Phil
  Guzikowski, Max, PhD, Prof, Logic, Ethics
  Kinnirey, Sr, Ann Julia, PhD, Prof, Aes, Anc and Med Phil

WASHINGTON TECHNICAL INSTITUTE
  Washington 20008 (M; local; coed; qr; I; 3798) NP

WESLEY THEOLOGICAL SEMINARY
  Washington 20016 (Theol; U Meth; coed; sem; IV; 311) --, Dept of Syst Theol and
  Phil of Relig, 202-363-2171

  Morrison II, Roy D, PhD, Assoc Prof, Phil Theol, Phil of Relig

FLORIDA

BARRY COLLEGE
  Miami Shores, Florida (S; RC; coed; sem; III; 1248) BA minor, Dept of Phil, 305-
  758-3392 Ext 271

  Prendergast, Agnes Cecile, PhD, Prof, Chm
  Cassini, Charles J, MEd, Asst Prof
  McKay, John T, PhL, Assoc Prof
  Uritus, Ronald M, MA, Lect

BETHUNE-COOKMAN COLLEGE
  Daytona Beach, Florida 32015 (S; p; coed; sem; II; 1219) BA major, Dept of Relig
  and Phil, 305-255-1401 Ext 251

  Charlesworth, Arthur R, PhD, Head
  Cabotaje, Felisberto, EdD
  Milley, C Ross, PhD

BISCAYNE COLLEGE
  Miami, Florida 33054 (S; RC; men; sem; II; 427) Courses with no degree specialization,
  Div of Human, 305-625-1561

  Burt, Donald, PhD, Prof, Phil of Relig, Ethics, Polit Phil

BREVARD COMMUNITY COLLEGE
  Cocoa, Florida 32922 (S; local; coed; tri; I; 6625) Courses with no degree specialization,
  Div of Soc Sci, 305-632-1111 Ext 344

  Maine, Leonard, MA, Assoc Prof, Logic

BROWARD COMMUNITY COLLEGE
  Fort Lauderdale, Florida 33314 (S; local; coed; sem; I; 7923) AA major, Dept of
  Phil, 305-581-8700 Ext 327

  Linder, M H, MA, Phil of Lang, Anal Phil
  Wells, John D, MA

CENTRAL FLORIDA COMMUNITY COLLEGE
  Ocala, Florida 32670 (S; local; coed; sem; I; 1450) Courses with no degree
  specialization, Dept of Human, 904-237-2111 Ext 84

  Adams, Charles T R, MA, Logic, Kant

CHIPOLA JUNIOR COLLEGE
  Marianna, Florida 32446 (S; local; coed; sem; I; 1267) NP

DAYTONA BEACH COMMUNITY COLLEGE
  Daytona Beach, Florida 32015 (S; local; coed; sem; I; 2708) Courses with no degree
  specialization, Dept of Soc Sci, 904-252-9671 Ext 443

  Moore, Dorothy, MA, Logic
  Rivenbark, W H, MA, Logic, Phil of Relig

ECKERD COLLEGE
St Petersburg, Florida 33733 (S; Preb; coed; 4-1-4; II; 1096) BA major, Collegium of Letters and Collegium of Creative Arts, 813-867-1166 Ext 277

Irwin, Keith W, M Div, Prof, Chm, Phil of Relig, Exist, Aes
Gill, Jerry, PhD, Assoc Prof, Phil of Relig, Anal Phil
Pav, Peter, PhD, Assoc Prof, Hist and Phil of Sci, Logic

EDISON COMMUNITY COLLEGE
Fort Myers, Florida 33091 (S; local; coed; sem; I; 1779) --, Dept of Human, 813-481-2121

Tobin, John P, MA, Soc Phil, Anc Phil

EDWARD WATERS COLLEGE
Jacksonville, Florida 32209 (--; Afr Meth Epis; coed; sem; II; 803) Courses with no degree specialization, Div of Human, 904-355-5411

EMBRY-RIDDLE AERONAUTICAL UNIVERSITY
Daytona Beach, Florida 32015 (S; p; coed; tri; III; 2103) --, Dept of Human and Soc Sci, 904-252-5561 Ext 52

Sain, Daniel D, PhD, Prof

FLAGLER COLLEGE
St Augustine, Florida 32084 (--; p; coed; sem; II; 227) BA minor, Dept of Phil, 904-829-6481

Humphreys, Burton V, EdD, Instr, Logic
Redding, David A, BD, Instr, Phil of Relig
Smith, T David, MA, Instr, Aes

FLORIDA AGRICULTURAL AND MECHANICAL UNIVERSITY
Tallahassee, Florida 32307 (S; st; coed; qr; III; 4944) BA major, Dept of Phil and Relig, 904-222-8030 Ext 597

Chance, Jerry M, ThD, Assoc Prof, Chm, Ethics
Jones, Jr, Elbert W, PhD, Asst Prof, Nietzsche

FLORIDA ATLANTIC UNIVERSITY
Boca Raton, Florida 33432 (S; st; coed; qr; IV; 7142) BA major, Dept of Phil, 305-395-5100 Ext 2683

Schwarz, Robert, PhD, Prof, Chm, Polit Phil
Baxley, Thomas F, PhD, Asst Prof, Logic
Eddy, Janice B, PhD, Interim Instr, Aes
Marietta, Don E, PhD, Assoc Prof, Ethics

FLORIDA COLLEGE
Temple Terrace, Florida 33617 (S; p; coed; sem; I; 457) --, Div of Phil, 813-988-5131

Curry, Jr, Melvin D, MA, Prof
Dowell, Jr, Arthur N, PhD, Prof
Srygley, Jr, Edgar V, MA, Prof

FLORIDA INSTITUTE OF TECHNOLOGY
Melbourne, Florida 32901 (S; p; coed; qr; III; 2119) Courses with no degree
specialization, Dept of Human, 305-723-3701 Ext 248

Jackson, Terry, BD, Adj Lect, Logic Ethics
Maloney, John, PhD, Asst Prof, Ethics

FLORIDA INTERNATIONAL UNIVERSITY
Miami, Florida 33144 (--; st; coed; qr; III; 5500) BA major, Dept of Phil and Relig,
305-223-2300 Ext 2185

Arias, Ricardo, PhD, Assoc Prof, Chm, Med Phil, Soc and Polit Phil
Huchingson, James E, MA, Asst Prof, Phil of Relig
Konkel, Richard H, PhD, Asst Prof, Phil of Educ, Ethics
Kovacs, George, PhD, Assoc Prof, Phenomen, Exist
Kushner, Thomasine, MA, Adj Instr, Aes, East Phil
Monarch, Ira A, MA, Asst Prof, Phil of Sci, Logic

THE FLORIDA JUNIOR COLLEGE AT JACKSONVILLE
Jacksonville, Florida 32205 (S; local; coed; sem; I; 8303) Courses with no degree
specialization, Dept of Human, 904-387-8221

Green, Lawton R, MA, Instr
Vaughan, William H, PhD, Instr, Phil of Educ

FLORIDA KEYS COMMUNITY COLLEGE
Key West, Florida 33040 (S; local; coed; tri; I; 1098) --, --, 305-296-9081

Bingham, William, PhD
Magaz, Theresa, MA
Smith, John Sylvester, PhD

FLORIDA MEMORIAL COLLEGE
Miami, Florida 33054 (S; Bapt; coed; sem; II; 821) NR

FLORIDA SOUTHERN COLLEGE
Lakeland, Florida 33802 (S; U Meth; coed; sem; II; 1728) BA major, Dept of Phil,
813-683-5521

Hartman, Richard O, PhD
Murphy, Walter Y, BD

FLORIDA STATE UNIVERSITY
Tallahassee, Florida 32306 (S; st; coed; qr; IV; 18,367) PhD major, Dept of Phil,
904-599-2690

Gruender, C David, PhD, Prof, Chm, Hist of Sci, Phil of Sci
Abu Shanab, Robert Elias, PhD, Asst Prof, Soc Phil, Med Arab
Beard, Robert W, PhD, Prof, Logic, Dev Anal Phil
Bilbija, Zarko, PhD, Assoc Prof, Econ Phil, Italian Phil
Dalton, Peter C, PhD, Asst Prof, Metaph, Mod Phil
Hodges, Donald C, PhD, Prof, Soc Phil, Contemp Marxism
Kaelin, Eugene F, PhD, Prof, Aes, Phenomen
Lockridge, Thomas F, PhD, Asst Prof, Mod Phil, Phil Soc Sci
Letsinger, Reed, MA, Asst Prof, Epistem, Phil of Lang
Mabe, Alan R, PhD, Asst Prof, Ethics, Legal Phil
Macmillan, C J B, PhD, Assoc Prof, Ord Lang Phil, Phil of Educ
Mercken, H Paul F, PhD, Assoc Prof, Anc Phil, Med Phil, Ethics

Thursby, Vincent V, PhD, Prof, Polit Phil
Werkmeister, William H, PhD, Lect, Value Theory, Kant

Henderson, Edgar H, PhD, Prof Emer
Liddell, Anna Forbes, PhD, Prof Emer
Werkmeister, William H, PhD, Prof Emer

Cadenhead, I Edward, BA, Grad Asst
Christie, Joseph C, BA, NDEA Fel
Croy, Marvin, BA, Grad Asst
Cuneen, Charles, BA, Grad Asst
Durbin, Jack D, MA, Dissertation
   Fel
Gregory, John, BA, Grad Asst
Lindsey, Wanda, BA, Univ Fel
Shang, Paul, BA, Univ Fel
Tattershall, MA, Dissertation Fel
Taylor, Douglas, BA, Univ Fel
Tresca, Ina K, BA, Grad Asst

FLORIDA TECHNOLOGICAL UNIVERSITY
   Orlando, Florida 32816 (S; st; coed; qr; III; 6593) BA major, Dept of Human,
   Phil and Relig, 305-275-2273

   Flick, Robert, PhD, Prof, Chm
   Jones, Donald, MA, Asst Prof, Logic, Phil of Sci, Mod Phil
   Kassim, Husain, PhD, Asst Prof, Metaph, Exist, Anc Phil
   Levensohn, Stephen, PhD, Prof, Ethics, Aes, Phil of Hist
   Riser, John, PhD, Assoc Prof, Phil of Relig, Soc Phil, 19th Cent Phil

FORT LAUDERDALE UNIVERSITY
   Fort Lauderdale, Florida 33301 (SRCB; p; coed; qr; II; 618) BA joint or combined
   major, Dept of Phil, 305-525-4761

   Hennessey, Leo F, PhD, Prof, Ethics, Logic

GULF COAST COMMUNITY COLLEGE
   Panama City, Florida 32401 (S; local; coed; sem; I; 2065) --, Dept of Soc Sci,
   904-769-1551 Ext 255

   Sale, William Frederick, ThM, Asst Prof

HILLSBOROUGH JUNIOR COLLEGE
   Tampa, Florida 33622 (S; local; coed; qr; I; 5559) Courses with no degree
   specialization, Dept of Human, 813-877-0555

   Boyle, Joseph P, MA, Prof
   Williams, Ernie, PhD, Prof

INDIAN RIVER COMMUNITY COLLEGE
   Fort Pierce, Florida 33450 (S; local; coed; sem; I; 1604) Courses with no degree
   specialization, Dept of Soc Sci, 305-464-2000

   Moorman, Joseph, MA, Asst Prof

JACKSONVILLE UNIVERSITY
   Jacksonville, Florida 32211 (S; p; coed; tri; III; 3016) BA major, Div of Human,
   904-744-3950 Ext 251

   Joannides, Peter, PhD, Assoc Prof, Epistem, Contemp Phil
   Pauly, Thomas, PhD, Asst Prof, Logic, Phil of Sci

JONES COLLEGE
  Jacksonville, Florida 32211 (SRCB; p; coed; qr; II; 1731) NP

JONES COLLEGE, ORLANDO CAMPUS
  Orlando, Florida 32801 (JRCB; p; coed; qr; II; 834) Courses with no degree
  specialization, --, 305-241-1407

LAKE CITY COMMUNITY COLLEGE
  Lake City, Florida 32055 (S; local; coed; qr; I; 1462) AA major, --, 904-752-1822

  Bachman, James, MA
  Parnell, Jr, Walter, EdD

LAKE-SUMTER COMMUNITY COLLEGE
  Leesburg, Florida 32748 (S; local; coed; tri; I; 1210) Courses with no degree
  specialization, Depts of Human and Soc Sci, 904-787-3747

  Bishop, Clayton K, PhD
  Ruth, Jr, Lester R, MA

MANATEE JUNIOR COLLEGE
  Bradenton, Florida 33505 (S; local; coed; sem; I; 2958) Courses with no degree
  specialization, Dept of Lang, Lit and Phil, 813-755-1511

  Spears, George J, PhD, Chm
  Frith, Jr, Herbert A, BD
  Gray, Francis C, BD

MARYMOUNT COLLEGE
  Boca Raton, Florida 33432 (S; p; coed; sem; I; 318) Courses with no degree
  specialization, Div of Libr Arts, 305-395-4301 Ext 31

  Belford, Jules, PhD, Assoc Prof, Chm, Epistem
  Wixted, William, PhD, Prof, Hist of Phil

MIAMI-DADE JUNIOR COLLEGE
  Miami, Florida 33156 (S; local; coed; tri; I; 30,853) Courses with no degree
  specialization, Dept of Communic Arts and Phil, 305-274-1203

  Tanenzaph, Stanley, MEd, Assoc Prof, Cord, Polit Phil, Ethics
  Bennett, Howard, MA, Assoc Prof, Logic, Phil of Relig
  Buhr, Marjorie, PhD, Assoc Prof
  Krantzler, Robert, PhD, Asst Prof, Logic

NEW COLLEGE
  Sarasota, Florida (S; p; coed; --; II; 528) BA major, Dept of Phil, 813-355-2988

  Berggren, Douglas C, PhD, Prof, Ethics, Phenomen
  Norton, Bryan, PhD, Asst Prof, Metaph, Phil of Lang
  Riley, Gresham, PhD, Assoc Prof, Phil of Soc Sci, Phil of Mind

NORTH FLORIDA JUNIOR COLLEGE
Madison, Florida 32340 (S; local; coed; sem; I; 1150) --, Dept of Human and Fine Arts, 904-973-2288 Ext 41

Tomlinson, Martha Hart, MA, Asst Prof

NOVA UNIVERSITY
Ford Lauderdale, Florida 33314 (S; p; coed; --; IV; 127) NP

OKALOOSA-WALTON JUNIOR COLLEGE
Niceville, Florida 32578 (S; local; coed; sem; I; 2270) Courses with no degree specialization, Dept of Human, 904-678-5111 Ext 313

Larson, Robert, ABD, Chm
Christmas, Donald, MA

PALM BEACH ATLANTIC COLLEGE
West Palm Beach, Florida 33401 (--; Bapt; coed; 4-1-4; II; 351) Courses with no degree specialization, Dept of Relig and Phil, 305-883-8592

Keathley, Naymond, ThD, Asst Prof
Smothers, Thomas, ThD, Assoc Prof

PALM BEACH JUNIOR COLLEGE
Lake Worth, Florida 33460 (S; local; coed; sem; I; 5985) --, --, 305-965-8000

PENSACOLA JUNIOR COLLEGE
Pensacola, Florida 32504 (S; local; coed; sem; I; 5730) Courses with no degree specialization, Dept of Mus and Human, 904-476-5410 Ext 294

Dicks, Claude, PhD, Prof
Hunt, Ralph, MA, Assoc Prof, Phil of Relig, Ontology
Kleinman, Robert, PhD, Prof, Compar Phil, Metaph
Smith, Jody, MA, Asst Prof

POLK COMMUNITY COLLEGE
Winter Haven, Florida 33880 (S; local; coed; tri; I; 4318) Courses with no degree specialization, Dept of Lang Arts, 813-294-7421 Ext 334

Powell, Arthur J, ThD, Head, Ethics, Gen Phil
Brown, Dion K, MA, Logic
Copps, Henry L, PhD, Logic, Rhet, Gen Phil

ROLLINS COLLEGE
Winter Park, Florida 32789 (S; p; coed; 4-1-4; III; 3547) BA major, Dept of Phil and Relig, 305-646-2000 Ext 2539

Darrah, T S, STB, Prof, Bib Stud
DeNicola, D R, MEd, Instr, Phil of Educ, Phil of Sci
Edge, H L, PhD, Asst Prof, Phil of Mind, Amer Phil
Wavell, B B, PhD, Prof, Logic, Phil of Lang
Wettstein, A A, PhD, Asst Prof, Contemp Relig Tht

SAINT JOHN VIANNEY MINOR SEMINARY
  Miami, Florida 33165 (S; RC; men; sem; I; 30) AA major, Dept of Phil, 305-221-3233

  Dirig, Walter F, MA, Prof, Dir, Syst Schol Phil

SAINT JOHNS RIVER JUNIOR COLLEGE
  Palatka, Florida 32077 (S; local; coed; tri; I; 1299) --, Dept of Human, 904-328-1571

  McKean, William Baggarley, MA, Instr

SAINT LEO COLLEGE
  Saint Leo, Florida 33574 (S; RC; coed; sem; II; 1153) BA major, Div of Phil and Theol, 904-588-2121 Ext 346

  Erpenbeck, James, PhD, Assoc Prof, Chm, Logic, Amer Phil
  Anderson, Tyson, PhD, Asst Prof, Phil of Relig
  Koren, Henry J, STD, Prof, Exist, Phenomen

SAINT PETERSBURG JUNIOR COLLEGE
  Saint Petersburg, Florida 33733 (S; local; coed; sem; I; 9848) AA major, Dept of Soc Sci, 813-546-0011 Ext 375, 639

  Greene, Vincent M, MA, Instr
  Hamilton, Daniel J, MA, Instr
  Marlin, Joseph, MA, Instr
  O'Kelley, Thomas A, PhD, Instr
  Troyer, Thompson L, MA, Instr

SAINT VINCENT DE PAUL SEMINARY
  Boynton Beach, Florida 33435 (S; RC; men; sem; III; 62) BA major, Dept of Phil, 305-732-4424

  Connor, John W, Lic, Prof, Logic, Metaph
  Duncan, Alexander, PhD, Prof, Phil of Man
  Fidalgo, Manuel, PhD, Asst Prof, Mod Phil, Contemp Phil
  Lindon, Luke, PhD, Prof, Hist of Phil, Phil of God

SANTA FE COMMUNITY COLLEGE
  Gainesville, Florida 32601 (S; local; coed; qr; I; 4054) --, --, 904-378-5311

SEMINOLE JUNIOR COLLEGE
  Sanford, Florida 32771 (S; local; coed; tri; I; 2495) --, Div of Human and Communic, 303-323-1450

  Mason, Aimee, MA, Instr
  Stevens, Atlee, MA, Instr Part-time

SOUTH FLORIDA JUNIOR COLLEGE
  Avon Park, Florida 33825 (S; local; coed; tri; I; 489) Courses with no degree specialization, Dept of Human, 813-453-6661

  Askren, Robert, M Div, Prof

SOUTHEASTERN BIBLE COLLEGE
  Lakeland, Florida 33801 (BI; Assem of God; coed; sem; II; 660) Courses with no degree
  specialization, Dept of Phil, 813-688-7671

  Evans, Henry M, MA

STETSON UNIVERSITY
  DeLand, Florida 32720 (S; S Bapt; coed; 4-1-4; III; 3020) BA major, Dept of Phil,
  904-734-4121 Ext 330

  Brady, Robby Ray, Asst Prof, Chm, Phil of Sci
  Myers, Lewis A, Asst Prof, Phil of Relig

TALLAHASSEE COMMUNITY COLLEGE
  Tallahassee, Florida 32304 (S; local; coed; qr; I; 2551) Courses with no degree
  specialization, Dept of Fine Arts, 904-576-5181 Ext 264

  McGinniss, John, PhD, Instr, Amer Phil

UNIVERSITY OF FLORIDA
  Gainesville, Florida 32611 (S; st; coed; qr; IV; 24,830) PhD major, Dept of Phil,
  904-392-2081

  Haring, Ellen S, PhD, Prof, Chm, Greek Phil, Metaph, Process Phil
  Auxter, Thomas P, PhD, Asst Prof, German Idealism
  Elliott, Herschel, PhD, Assoc Prof, Logic, Metaph
  Gallois, Andre, BPhil, Asst Prof, Ethics, Phil of Lang, Phil of Mind
  Fuller, Gary, BLitt, Asst Prof, Phil Psych, Phil of Hist, Ethics, Anal Phil
  Hanna, Thomas L, PhD, Prof, Phenomen, Exist, Somatic Phil
  Haynes, Richard P, PhD, Assoc Prof, Greek Phil, Anal Phil, Phil of Mind, Phil of
     Law
  Jones, William B, PhD, Asst Prof, Phil of Sci, Logical Positivism
  Lewis, Allison L, PhD, Assoc Prof, Anc West Phil, Phil of Relig, Aes
  Megill, Kenneth A, PhD, Asst Prof, Soc and Polit Phil, Marxism, Contemp German Tht
  Mehlberg, Henry, PhD, Prof, Phil of Sci
  Simon, Thomas W, PhD, Asst Prof, Theory of Knowl
  Standley, Gerald B, PhD, Prof, Logic, Phil of Relig
  Zeman, Joseph J, PhD, Assoc Prof, Logic, Prag, Phil of Math
  Zweig, Marilyn, PhD, Asst Prof, Soc and Polit Phil, Phil of Soc Sci, Anal Phil

  Morris, Charles W, PhD, Prof Emer, Prag, Theory of Signs

  Davis, R I   Shitama, G A
  Dinaburg, M P   Sugalski, J R
  Harper, J S   Viscardi, L G
  McNeal, B L   Winn, J
  Self, J M   Yarbrough, M V
  Shelburne, W A

UNIVERSITY OF MIAMI
  Coral Gables, Florida 33124 (S; p; coed; sem; IV; 15,675) PhD major, Dept of Phil,
  305-284-4757

  Lemos, Ramon M, PhD, Prof, Chm, Metaph, Polit Phil
  Carrier, Leonard S, PhD, Assoc Prof, Epistem, Phil of Lang
  Knoblock, John H, PhD, Assoc Prof, Orient Phil
  Pospesel, Howard A, PhD, Assoc Prof, Phil Logic, Epistem
  Rachels, James W, PhD, Assoc Prof, Ethics, Phil of Mind
  Schipper, Gerrit, PhD, Prof, Exist, Phenomen

Schuh, Edward W, PhD, Prof, Logic, Kant
Shea, W Winslow, PhD, Assoc Prof, Aes, Hist of Phil
Watson-Schipper, Edith, PhD, Prof, Clas Phil, Aes
Werner, Charles G, PhD, Assoc Prof, Phil of Relig, Phil of Sci
Westphal, Fred A, PhD, Assoc Prof, Ethics

Bailey, George W, Grad Asst
Bensky, Jerold M, Grad Asst
Garman, Sharon, Grad Asst
Goldberg, Larry, Grad Fel
Herston, Victor D, Grad Asst
Klasing, Sandra, Grad Asst
Knight, Jack C, Grad Asst

Lanning, James B, Grad Asst
Levenshon, Ira, Grad Asst
McClusky, Joseph B, Grad Asst
Rich, Gregory, Grad Asst
Sanabria, Miguel, Grad Asst
Siegmann, William L, Grad Asst
Woollam, Clifford R, Grad Asst

UNIVERSITY OF NORTH FLORIDA
Jacksonville, Florida 32216 (--; st; coed; qr; III; 2000) Courses with no degree specialization, Dept of Phil, 904-646-2545

Loftin, Robert W, PhD, Assoc Prof

UNIVERSITY OF SOUTH FLORIDA
Tampa, Florida 33620 (S; st; coed; qr; IV; 18,496) MA major, Dept of Phil, 813-974-2454

Gould, James A, PhD, Prof, Chm, Legal Phil
Chen, Chung-Hwan, PhD, Prof, Greek Phil
Krimsky, Sheldon, PhD, Asst Prof, Phil of Sci
Taylor, Richard N, MA, Asst Prof, Phil of Relig
Truitt, Willis H, PhD, Assoc Prof, Aes
Weatherford, Roy, PhD, Asst Prof, Epistem

Ebert, Louis, BA, Grad Asst
Mortimer, Robert, BA, Grad Asst

Venn, David, BA, Grad Asst

UNIVERSITY OF TAMPA
Tampa, Florida 33606 (S; p; coed; 4-1-4; II; 2319) BA major, Div of Human, Phil and Relig Area, 813-253-8861 Ext 425, 332

Cave, Jr, George H, STM, Asst Prof, Cord, Phil of Relig
Harder, Robert L, PhD, Prof
Saatkamp, Herman J, PhD, Assoc Prof
Singletary, Rebecca, MA, Asst Prof
Sundheim, Frank, MA, Lect

UNIVERSITY OF WEST FLORIDA
Pensacola, Florida 32504 (S; st; coed; qr; III; 4014) BA major, Faculty of Phil and Relig Stud, 904-476-9500 Ext 481

Armstrong, Robert L, PhD, Prof, Chm, Hist of Phil, Logic, Phil of Educ
Herman, Daniel J, PhD, Asst Prof, Exist, Phenomen, Anc and Med Phil
Knaack, Jay A, PhD, Asst Prof, Ethics, Soc and Polit Phil, Phil of Sci
Mountcastle, Jr, William W, PhD, Assoc Prof, Phil of Relig, Phil of Art, Phil of Hist

VALENCIA COMMUNITY COLLEGE
Orlando, Florida 32811 (S; local; coed; sem; I; 3774) --, Dept of Human, 305-299-5000

WARNER SOUTHERN COLLEGE
Lake Wales, Florida 33853 (--; Ch of God; coed; qr; II; 125) Courses with no degree specialization, Dept of Theol and Phil, 813-638-1212

Jakeway, Wade B, MA, Asst Instr, Ethics, Hist of Phil

WEBBER COLLEGE
Babson Park, Florida 33827 (S; p; coed; sem; I; 110) Courses with no degree specialization, Dept of Human, 813-638-1439

GEORGIA

ABRAHAM BALDWIN AGRICULTURAL COLLEGE
Tifton, Georgia 31794 (S; st; coed; qr; I; 2153) --, --, 912 382-2755

Milam, Thomas R, EdD, Prof, Chm

AGNES SCOTT COLLEGE
Decatur, Georgia 30030 (S; p; wo; qr; II; 665) BA major, Dept of Phil, 404-373-2571 Ext 332

Parry, Richard D, PhD, Assoc Prof, Chm, Theory of Action
Cornett, Linda B, PhD, Part-time Instr, Ethics
Wolters, Richard M, BA, Asst Prof, Phenomen, Ontology

ALBANY JUNIOR COLLEGE
Albany, Georgia 31705 (S; st; coed; qr; I; 1410) Courses with no degree specialization, Div of Soc Sci, 912-435-2011 Ext 72

Hewett, David G, PhD, Prof, Chm, Hist of Phil

ALBANY STATE COLLEGE
Albany, Georgia 31701 (S; st; coed; qr; II; 1926) NP

ANDREW COLLEGE
Cuthbert, Georgia 31740 (S; U Meth; coed; qr; I; 295) --, Dept of Relig and Phil, 912-732-2171

Griffin, Betty S, MA, Instr

ARMSTRONG STATE COLLEGE
Savannah, Georgia 31406 (S; st; coed; qr; III; 2712) BA minor, Dept of Eng and Phil, 912-354-9715

Jones, James L, PhD, Assoc Prof, 19th Cent Phil
Killorin, Joseph, PhD, Prof, Anc Phil, 17th Cent Phil

ATLANTA BAPTIST COLLEGE
    Atlanta, Georgia 30341 (--; S Bapt; coed; qr; II; 270) Courses with no degree
    specialization, Dept of Relig and Phil, 404-451-0331

ATLANTA CHRISTIAN COLLEGE
    East Point, Georgia 30344 (BI; p; coed; sem; II; 295) Courses with no degree
    specialization, Dept of Phil, 404-761-8861

    Root, David, BD

ATLANTA SCHOOL OF ART
    Atlanta, Georgia 30309 (S; p; coed; sem; II; 368) NR

ATLANTA UNIVERSITY
    Atlanta, Georgia 30314 (S; p; coed; sem; IV; 1048) Courses with no degree
    specialization, --, 404-681-0251

AUGUSTA COLLEGE
    Augusta, Georgia 30904 (S; st; coed; qr; III; 2973) BA minor, Dept of Hist, Polit
    Sci and Phil, 404-733-2234

    Peden, Creighton, PhD, Callaway Prof, Soc Phil, Phil of Relig

BERRY COLLEGE
    Mount Berry, Georgia 30149 (S; p; coed; qr; III; 973) BA joint of combined major,
    Dept of Relig and Phil, 404-232-5374 Ext 332, 297

    Hoyt III, William R, PhD, Prof, Phil of Relig
    Sturdivant, Robert V, PhD, Assoc Prof, Hist of Phil, Ethics

BIRDWOOD JUNIOR COLLEGE
    Thomasville, Georgia 31792 (--; Bapt; coed; qr; I; 58) Courses with no degree
    specialization, --, 912-226-1621

BRENAU COLLEGE
    Gainesville, Georgia 30501 (S; p; wo; qr; II; 429) Courses with no degree
    specialization, Div of Soc and Behavior Sci, or Div of Arts and Human, 404-
    532-4341 Ext 72

    Leissner, George R, MS, Asst Prof
    Rigney, Eleanor, MA, Instr

BREWTON-PARKER COLLEGE
    Mount Vernon, Georgia 30445 (S; S Bapt; coed; qr; I; 614) NP

BRUNSWICK JUNIOR COLLEGE
    Brunswick, Georgia 31520 (S; st; coed; qr; I; 1011) NP

CLARK COLLEGE
    Atlanta, Georgia 30314 (S; U Meth; coed; sem; II; 1182) BA joint or combined
    major, Dept of Relig and Phil, 404-681-3080 Ext 280

    Rogers, Herbert F, PhD, Prof, Chm
    Hale, Wimbley, MTh, Lect, Epistem
    Myers, Robert, PhD, Asst Prof

CLAYTON JUNIOR COLLEGE
Morrow, Georgia 30260 (S; st; coed; qr; I; 2250) AA major, Div of Human, 404-363-3800 Ext 221

Doig, James C, PhD, Assoc Prof, Hist of Med Phil, Metaph
McElroy, Elliott W, PhD, Assoc Prof

COLUMBIA THEOLOGICAL SEMINARY
Decatur, Georgia 30031 (Theol; Preb; coed; qr; IV; 179) Courses with no degree specialization, Historical-Doctrinal Dept, 404-378-8821

Guthrie, Jr, S C, ThD, Prof
Kline, C Benton, PhD, Prof

COLUMBUS COLLEGE
Columbus, Georgia 31907 (S; st; coed; qr; II; 3814) BA major, Dept of Human, 404-561-5134

Dunlap, John T, PhD, Assoc Prof, Logic, Phil of Sci
Lieberman, Lewis R, PhD, Assoc Prof, Phil of Psych
Logue, C W, PhD, Assoc Prof

COVENANT COLLEGE
Lookout Mountain, Tennessee 37350 (S; Ref Preb, coed; sem; II; 394) BA major, Dept of Bib, Missions, and Phil, 404-831-6531

McLelland, Reginald F, PhD, Asst Prof, Chm, Metaph, Anal Phil
Sanderson, John W, MA, Prof, Anc and Med Phil, Kant

DALTON JUNIOR COLLEGE
Dalton, Georgia 30720 (S; st; coed; qr; I; 1085) Courses with no degree specialization, Dept of Soc Sci, 404-278-4215

Risher, Charles A, PhD, Asst Prof

DEKALB COMMUNITY COLLEGE
Clarkston, Georgia 30021 (S; local; coed; qr; I; 6645) Courses with no degree specialization, Dept of Soc, 404-292-1520 Ext 234

Yohan, Walter, PhD

EMMANUEL COLLEGE
Franklin Springs, Georgia 30639 (S; Pent Hol; coed; qr; I; 324) NP

EMORY UNIVERSITY
Atlanta, Georgia 30322 (S; U Meth; coed; qr; IV; 5435) PhD major, Dept of Phil, 404-377-2411 Ext 7543, 7544, 7545

Anton, John P, PhD, Fuller E Callaway Prof, Chm, Anc Phil, Plato, Aristotle, Phil of Art
Edwards, William F, PhD, Prof, Med Phil, Renaissance Phil, Spinoza, 17th Cent Phil, Amer nature, Metaph
Fotion, Nicholas, PhD, Assoc Prof, Dir of Undergrad Stud, Ethics and Value Theory Phil of Lang, Anal Phil

Gouinlock, James, PhD, Assoc Prof, Dewey, Ethics and Value Theory, Soc and Polit
    Phil, Soc Phil, Amer Phil
Harrington, Kathleen W, PhD, Asst Prof, Aes, Phil of Art, Greek Phil, Hist of
    Phil, Amer Phil
Kuntz, Paul G, PhD, Prof, Theory of Order, Phil of Relig, Metaph, Aes, Amer Phil
Leclerc, Ivor, PhD, Prof, Metaph, Phil of Nature, 16th and 17th Cent Phil, Leibniz,
    Whitehead, Soc and Polit Phil, Phil Theol
Makkreel, Rudolf, PhD, Asst Prof, Leibniz, Kant, Hegel, Marx, Phenomen, Exist
Nilson, Donald, PhD, Asst Prof, Logic, Phil of Sci

Hocking, Richard O'R, PhD, Prof Emer
Loemker, Leroy, PhD, Prof Emer

Belcher, John C, Grad Asst   Elfstrom, Gerard, Grad Asst
Canevi, Pinar, Grad Asst   Fagan, Kenneth, Grad Asst
Canzoneri, Joseph, Grad Asst   Jaffee, Charlene, Grad Asst
Castellaneta, Nicholas, Grad Asst   Jeffreys, Jeri Lynn, Grad Asst
Danner, Robert P, Grad Asst   Kelmachter, Mark, Grad Asst
Drew, Philip, Grad Asst   Mittler, Bert I, Grad Asst

FLOYD JUNIOR COLLEGE
    Rome, Georgia 30161 (--; st; coed; qr; I; 806) NP

FORT VALLEY STATE COLLEGE
    Fort Valley, Georgia 31030 (S; st; coed; qr; III; 2373) Courses with no degree
    specialization, --, 912-825-8281

    Miles, Robert, PhD, Asst Prof, Phenomen
    Shukair, Ali, PhD, Prof, Ethics, Educ Phil

GAINESVILLE JUNIOR COLLEGE
    Gainesville, Georgia 30501 (S; st; coed; qr; I; 1162) NP

GEORGIA COLLEGE
    Milledgeville, Georgia 31061 (S; st; coed; qr; III; 2363) Courses with no degree
    specialization, Dept of Phil and Relig, 912-452-5541 Ext 366

    Sallstrom, John E, PhD, Prof, Chm
    Curtis, Jr, Oliver Benton, PhD, Instr Part-time
    Littleton, William H, PhD, Assoc Prof Part-time

GEORGIA INSTITUTE OF TECHNOLOGY
    Atlanta, Georgia 30332 (S; st; coed; qr; IV; 8125) Courses with no degree
    specialization, Dept of Soc Sci, 404-894-3195

    Hines, John N, PhD, Instr
    Johnston, Jon J, MA, Asst Prof
    Rossini, F A, PhD, Asst Prof

GEORGIA INSTITUTE OF TECHNOLOGY-SOUTHERN TECHNICAL INSTITUTE
    Marietta, Georgia 30060 (JS; st; coed; qr; II; 1794) NP

GEORGIA MILITARY COLLEGE
    Milledgeville, Georgia 31061 (S; p; coed; qr; I; 148) Courses with no degree
    specialization, --, 912-452-5479

GEORGIA SOUTHERN COLLEGE
  Statesboro, Georgia 30458 (S; st; coed; qr; III; 6156) --, Dept of English,
  Journalism and Phil, 912-764-6611

  Brown, Paul, MA, Asst Prof, Aes
  Parcels, John L, MA, Asst Prof, Epistem, Metaph

GEORGIA SOUTHWESTERN COLLEGE
  Americus, Georgia 31709 (S; st; coed; qr; II; 2383) Courses with no degree
  specialization, Div of Soc Sci, 912-924-6111

GEORGIA STATE UNIVERSITY
  Atlanta, Georgia 30303 (S; st; coed; qr; IV; 16,945) PhD minor, Dept of Phil,
  404-658-2277

  Munster, Ralf F, PhD, Prof, Chm, Phil of Hist, Soc and Phil Phil
  Almeder, Robert F, PhD, Assoc Prof, Amer Phil, Epistem
  Arrington, Robert L, PhD, Assoc Prof, Anal Phil, Ethics
  Bell, Linda A, PhD, Asst Prof, Exist
  Humber, James M, PhD, Asst Prof, British Empir, Continen Ration
  Luckhardt, C Grant, PhD, Asst Prof, Greek Phil
  Medina, Angel de L, PhD, Assoc Prof, Phenomen
  Stephens, Kenneth D, PhD, Asst Prof, Logic, Indian Phil
  Wilson, Kirk D, PhD, Asst Prof, Kant, Phil of Relig
  Woodhouse, Mark B, PhD, Asst Prof, Metaph, Phil of Mind

  Beiswanger, George, PhD, Prof Emer, Aes

GORDON JUNIOR COLLEGE
  Barnesville, Georgia 30204 (S; st; coed; qr; I; 500) NP

INTERDENOMINATIONAL THEOLOGICAL CENTER
  Atlanta, Georgia 30314 (Theol; Interdenom; coed; sem; III; 164) Courses with no
  degree specialization, Dept of Theol and Phil, 404-525-5926

  Diamond, Jr, John C, PhD, Assoc Prof, Metaph
  Young, Henry J, MA, Instr

KENNESAW JUNIOR COLLEGE
  Marietta, Georgia 30060 (S; st; coed; qr; I; 1654) Courses with no degree
  specialization, Div of Human, 404-422-8770

  Greider, John C, PhD, Prof, Chm, Med Phil

LAGRANGE COLLEGE
  LaGrange, Georgia 30240 (S; U Meth; coed; qr; II; 608) Courses with no degree
  specialization, Dept of Relig and Phil, 404-882-2911 Ext 58

  Naglee, David I, PhD, Prof

MACON JUNIOR COLLEGE
  Macon, Georgia 31206 (S; st; coed; qr; I; 1803) NP

MEDICAL COLLEGE OF GEORGIA
  Augusta, Georgia 30902 (Med; st; coed; qr; IV; 1106) NP

MERCER UNIVERSITY
Macon, Georgia 31207 (S; S Bapt; coed; qr; III; 1846) BA major, Dept of Phil,
912-743-1511 Ext 258

Nordenhaug, Theodore D, PhD, Assoc Prof, Chm, Soc Phil, Hist of Phil, Ethics
Brown, Peter C, MA, Instr, Phil of Sci, Aes
Stevens, Rex P, MA, Instr, Phil of Soc Sci, Phil of Lit
Trimble, Thomas M, BD, Asst Prof, Phil of Relig, Exist, Phenomen

MERCER UNIVERSITY SOUTHERN SCHOOL OF PHARMACY
Atlanta, Georgia 30312 (Phar; S Bapt; coed; qr; II; 228) NR

MIDDLE GEORGIA COLLEGE
Cochran, Georgia 31014 (S; st; coed; qr; I; 2075) AA major, Dept of Phil and Relig,
912-934-6221 Ext 222

Freeman, Allen J, ThD, Prof, Chm

MOREHOUSE COLLEGE
Atlanta, Georgia 30314 (S; p; men; 4-1-4; II; 1227) NR

MORRIS BROWN COLLEGE
Atlanta, Georgia 30314 (S; Afr Meth Epis; coed; sem; II; 1524) BA major, Dept of
Phil, 404-525-7831 Ext 66

Moore, Jr, Ernest E, MA, Asst Prof, Act Chm, Phil of Relig

NORTH GEORGIA COLLEGE
Dahlonega, Georgia 30533 (S; st; coed; qr; II; 1366) NR

OGLETHORPE UNIVERSITY
Atlanta, Georgia 30319 (S; p; coed; sem; III; 1116) BA major, Div of Human, 404-
261-1441 Ext 46

Nishimura, Ken, PhD, Prof, Chm, Ethics, Asian Phil
Knott, John B, PhD, Asst Prof, Phil of Relig
Neujuhr, Phillip N, PhD, Asst Prof, Amer Phil, Phil of Sci
Vonk, Paul K, PhD, Prof, Logic, Epistem

OXFORD COLLEGE, EMORY UNIVERSITY
Oxford, Georgia 30267 (S; U Meth; coed; qr; IV; 5435) Courses with no degree
specialization, Dept of Phil, 404-786-7051

Linville, Kent, PhD, Asst Prof

PAINE COLLEGE
Augusta, Georgia 30901 (S; Prot; coed; sem; II; 737) BA joint or combined major,
Div of Human, 404-722-4471 Ext 215

Clayton, Marus, PhD, Prof, Logic, Contemp Phil, Metaph, Anc Phil
Delamotte, Roy, PhD, Prof, Comp Relig

PIEDMONT COLLEGE
    Demorest, Georgia 30535 (S; p; coed; qr; II; 274) BA joint or combined major,
    Dept of Relig and Phil, 404-723-3911

    Morgan, C Shannon, ThD, Prof

REINHARDT COLLEGE
    Waleska, Georgia 30183 (S; U Meth; coed; qr; I; 310) Courses with no degree
    specialization, Dept of Phil, 404-479-2119, 404-479-5094

    Huddlestun, J R, MA, Asst Prof, Chm

SAVANNAH STATE COLLEGE
    Savannah, Georgia 31404 (S; st; coed; qr; III; 2728) NR

SHORTER COLLEGE
    Rome, Georgia 30161 (S; Bapt; coed; sem; I; 591) BA joint or combined major, Dept
    or Relig and Phil, 404-232-2463 Ext 59

    Whitworth, Charles W, PhD, Prof, Dean, Hist of Phil, Phil of Relig

SOUTH GEORGIA COLLEGE
    Douglas, Georgia 31533 (S; st; coed; qr; I; 1270) AA major, Dept of Human, 912-
    384-1100

    Lackey, Ronald D, PhD, Asst Prof

SPELMAN COLLEGE
    Atlanta, Georgia 30314 (S; p; wo; sem; II; 1118) BA major, Dept of Phil and Relig,
    404-681-3643 Ext 225

    Axelsen, Diana E, PhD, Asst Prof, Ethics, Polit Phil, Aes, Phil of Soc Sci

TIFT COLLEGE
    Forsyth, Georgia 31029 (S; Bapt; wo; qr; II; 655) Courses with no degree
    specialization, Dept of Relig, 912-994-2515

TOCCOA FALLS INSTITUTE
    Toccoa Falls, Georgia 30577 (BI; p; coed; sem; II; 306) BA minor, Dept of Phil,
    and Relig, 404-886-6831 Ext 40

    Benson, John, MRE, Prof, Ethics, Phil of Educ
    McClure, Donald, MS, Prof, Metaph, Epistem, Phil of Educ
    McGraw, Gerald E, DD, Prof, Phil of Relig, Metaph
    Sproull, Jerry, MTh, Prof, Metaph, Epistem, Phil Theol
    Vena, Julio, M Div, Phil of Relig

TRUETT MCCONNELL COLLEGE
    Cleveland, Georgia 30528 (S; Bapt; coed; qr; I; 232) NP

UNIVERSITY OF GEORGIA
  Athens, Georgia 30602 (S; st; coed; qr; IV; 21,298) PhD major, Dept of Phil and
  Relig, 404-542-2823

  Clarke, Bowman L, PhD, Prof, Head, Logic, Metaph, Phil of Relig, Amer Phil
  Ayers, Robert H, PhD, Prof, Phil of Relig
  Blackstone, William T, PhD, Prof, Ethics, Polit and Legal Phil
  Burton, Robert G, PhD, Asst Prof, Metaph, Epistem, Phil of Sci
  Dauenhauer, Bernard P, PhD, Asst Prof, Phenomen, Exist, Contemp French Phil
  Granrose, John T, PhD, Assoc Prof, Ethics, Aes, Soc Phil
  Harrison III, Frank R, PhD, Prof, Contemp British Phil, Logic, Phil of Mind
  Heslep, Robert D, PhD, Prof, Phil of Educ
  Kleiner, S A, PhD, Asst Prof, Hist and Phil of the Phys and Soc Sci
  Nemetz, Anthony A, PhD, Prof, Med and Greek Phil, Phil of Law
  Nute, Jr, Donald E, PhD, Asst Prof, Phil of Lang, Logic, Epistem
  O'Briant, Walter H, PhD, Assoc Prof, Hist of Mod Phil
  Richards, John, PhD, Asst Prof, Logic, Phil of Math, Phil of Sci
  Severens, Richard H, PhD, Assoc Prof, Logic, Epistem, Metaph

  Allen, Thomas   Miller, Alvin
  Brewer, Martha   O'Connell, Joseph
  Daniel, Mary   Pape, Tim
  Dowis, Joe   Pfitsch, John
  Frederick, Norris   Ricks, William
  Johnston, Thomas   Schulmeister, Lawrence
  Gregory, Walter   Shafer, Carolyn
  McClatchy, John   Taylor, Jeffrey
  Messer, John   Townsley, Gale

VALDOSTA STATE COLLEGE
  Valdosta, Georgia 31601 (S; st; coed; qr; III; 3851) BA major, Dept of Phil, 912-
  244-6340 Ext 231

  McElroy, Elliott W, PhD, Assoc Prof, Head, Hist of Phil, Metaph, Process Phil,
      Phil of Relig
  Awerkamp, Donald T, MA, Instr, Exist, Ethics, Soc and Polit Phil, Aes, Hist of
      Phil
  Barnette, Ronald L, PhD, Asst Prof, Phil of Mind, Phil of Sci, Phil of Hist, Logic

WESLEYAN COLLEGE
  Macon, Georgia 31201 (S; U Meth; wo; 4-1-4; II; 466) BA joint or combined major
  Dept of Relig and Phil, 912-477-1110 Ext 282

  Gilmer, Harry W, PhD, Chm
  Brown, Walter E, PhD, Prof, Phil of Relig

  Akers, Samuel, PhD, Prof Emer

WEST GEORGIA COLLEGE
  Carrollton, Georgia 30117 (S; st; coed; qr; III; 6114) BA major, Dept of Phil,
  404-834-4411 Ext 435

  Higgins, David J, PhD, Assoc Prof, Head
  Auble, Joel, PhD, Asst Prof
  Cox, James William, PhD, Asst Prof

Dunlavey, Mary, MA, Instr
Wantland, Burdett, MA, Asst Prof

YOUNG HARRIS COLLEGE
   Young Harris, Georgia 30582 (S; U Meth; coed; qr; I; 343) NP

GUAM

UNIVERSITY OF GUAM
   Agana, Guam 96910 (W; st; coed; sem; III; 2349) BA minor, Dept of Phil, 749-2921
   Ext 294

   Owings, Jr, Harry E, PhD, Prof, Chm, Ethics
   Broyles, James E, PhD, Assoc and Visit Prof, Contemp Phil

HAWAII

CHAMINADE COLLEGE OF HONOLULU
Honolulu, Hawaii 96816 (W; RC; coed; sem; II; 1574) BA major, Dept of Phil, 808-732-1471 Ext 114, 139

Lonergan, Martin, PhD, Asst Prof, Chm, Exist, Phil of Man, Ethics
Branick, Vincent, PhD, Asst Prof, Metaph
Unni, Chitharanjan, MA, Asst Prof, Ethics, Logic

THE CHURCH COLLEGE OF HAWAII
Laie, Hawaii 96762 (W; LDS; coed; sem; II; 1299) NP

HAWAII COMMUNITY COLLEGE, UNIVERSITY OF HAWAII
Hilo, Hawaii 96720 (--; st; coed; sem; I; 968) NR

HAWAII LOA COLLEGE
Honolulu, Hawaii 96744 (W; Prot; coed; sem; II; 172) --, --, 808-235-3641

HAWAII PACIFIC COLLEGE
Honolulu, Hawaii 96813 (--; p; coed; qr; II; 210) BA joint or combined major, School of Libr Arts, 808-521-3881

Sh-veev, Charles L, PhD, Asst Prof, Dean, Epistem, Metaph, Phil of Sci, Phil of Logic, Phil of Relig

HONOLULU BUSINESS COLLEGE
Honolulu, Hawaii 96813 (JRCB; p; coed; --; 521) NP

HONOLULU COMMUNITY COLLEGE, UNIVERSITY OF HAWAII
Honolulu, Hawaii (W; st; coed; sem; I; 2167) AA major, Dept of Human, 808-847-2161 Ext 170

Haney, Terrence E, Chm
Andrychowicz, Stanley
Ball, David, MA

KAPIOLANI COMMUNITY COLLEGE, UNIVERSITY OF HAWAII
Honolulu, Hawaii 96814 (W; st; coed; sem; I; 2765) AA major, Dept of Human and Soc Sci, 808-531-4654 Ext 164

Nielke, David, MA, Phil of Relig
Pine, Ron, MA, Logic, Exist
Wall, Brendan, MA, Phil Anthrop, Med Phil
Yamamoto, Louise, MA, East Phil, Japanese Phil, Chinese Phil

KAUAI COMMUNITY COLLEGE, UNIVERSITY OF HAWAII
Lihue, Hawaii 96766 (W; st; coed; sem; I; 839) Courses with no degree specialization, Div of Liberal Arts and Soc Sci, 808-245-6741

Bekeart, Dana, MA, Instr, Buddhist Phil

LEEWARD COMMUNITY COLLEGE, UNIVERSITY OF HAWAII
  Pearl City, Hawaii 96782 (W; st; coed; sem; I; 5177) Courses with no degree
  specialization, Div of Arts and Human, 808-455-0351

  Perz, Joseph, PhD, Chm, Metaph, Logic, Ethics
  Hilbe, Joseph, BA; Hist of Phil
  Stroup, Michael, MA, Logic, Hist of Phil

MAUI COMMUNITY COLLEGE, UNIVERSITY OF HAWAII
  Kahului, Hawaii 96732 (W; st; coed; sem; I; 1094) Courses with no degree
  specialization, Div of Soc Sci and Human, 808-244-9181

  Griffis, Will, MA, Instr, Mod and Contemp Continen Tht

MAUNA OLU COLLEGE
  Paia, Hawaii 96779 (W; p; coed; sem; II; --) AA major, Middle College, 808-579-9565

  Oen, Bing, MA, Instr
  Treadway, Douglas, PhD, Asst Prof

UNIVERSITY OF HAWAII, HILO CAMPUS
  Hilo, Hawaii 96720 (--; st; coed; sem; II; 1671) BA major, Div of Human, 808-935-
  4827 Ext 144

  Aoki, Hideo, PhD, Prof, East Phil
  Wells, Donald A, PhD, Prof, Soc Phil, Polit Phil, Phil of Relig
  Wells, William, PhD, Asst Prof, Logic, Hist of Phil

UNIVERSITY OF HAWAII
  Honolulu, Hawaii 96822 (W; st; coed; sem; IV; 22,009) PhD major, Dept of Phil,
  808-948-8410

  Bender, Frederic L, PhD, Asst Prof, Act Chm, Marxism, Phenomen, Exist Phil
  Assali, Robin N, MA, Asst Prof, Phil of Sci, Phil of Mind, Soc Phil
  Chang, Chung-yuan, PhD, Prof, Taoism, Ch'an Buddhism, Aes
  Cheng, Chung-ying, PhD, Assoc Prof, Phil of Lang, Phil of Math, Confucian Phil
  Copi, Irving M, PhD, Prof, Logic, Metaph, Anal Phil
  Deutsch, Eliot, PhD, Prof on Leave, Indian Phil, Comp Phil, Aes
  Goodman, Lenn E, PhD, Asst Prof, Islamic Phil, Metaph, Ethics
  Harter, Edward D, PhD, Asst Prof, Greek Phil, Hist of Phil, Logic
  Kalupahana, David J, PhD, Assoc Prof, Early Buddhism, Chinese Buddhism
  McCarthy, Harold E, PhD, Prof, Phil of Art, Phil in Lit
  Moore, Ronald M, PhD, Asst Prof, Phil of Law, Ethics, Anal Phil
  Nagley, Winfield E, PhD, Prof, 19th Cent Phil, Phil of Relig, Exist Phil
  Stewart, Donald L, PhD, Asst Prof, Hist of Phil, Exist Phil, Phenomen
  Upadhyaya, K N, PhD, Prof, Indian Phil, Buddhist Phil
  Yamasaki, Beatrice T, PhD, Assoc Prof, Ration, Buddhist Phil, Phil of Relig

  Becker, Carl B, BA, E-WC Grantee   O'Blenes, Gary E, BA, E-WC Grantee
  Chobot, Neal L, MA, E-WC Grantee   Ramashanker, Karuna L J, MA, E-WC Grantee
  Jackson, Thomas E, MA, Grad Asst   Rieper, Byron M, BA, E-WC Grantee
  Kasulis, Thomas P, BA, E-WC Grantee   Ross, Kelley L, BA, HEA Fel
  Kawatsu, Kimiko, BA, Grad Asst   Schwartz, Gerald M, MA, Grad Asst
  Lee, Gun-Won, MA, Grad Asst   Shameam, Arifa, BA, E-WC Grantee

IDAHO

BOISE STATE COLLEGE
Boise, Idaho 83707 (NW; st; coed; sem; III; 8298) Courses with no degree specialization, Dept of Polit Sci and Phil, 208-385-1457

Schoedinger, Andrew B, MA, Instr, Ethics, Phil of Mind, Phil of Relig

THE COLLEGE OF IDAHO
Caldwell, Idaho 83605 (NW; U Preb; coed; --; III; 1131) BA major, Dept of Relig and Phil, 208-459-5203

Tiefel, Hans O, PhD, Assoc Prof, Chm, Ethics
Chalker, William, PhD, Prof, Logic, Phil of Sci
Grob, Ruth, PhD, Prof, Phil of Relig

COLLEGE OF SOUTHERN IDAHO
Twin Falls, Idaho 83301 (NW; local; coed; sem; I; 1789) Courses with no degree specialization, Dept of Eng, 314-733-9554 Ext 314

IDAHO STATE UNIVERSITY
Pocatello, Idaho 83201 (NW; st; coed; sem; IV; 7489) BA major, Dept of Phil, 208-236-3680

King, William L, PhD, Assoc Prof, Chm, Phil Meth, Anal Phil
Allen, Glen O, PhD, Prof, Value Theory
Guerry, Herbert, MA, Instr, Logic, Phil of Sci
Laughlin, Richard, MA, Instr, Hist of Phil

LEWIS AND CLARK STATE COLLEGE
Lewiston, Idaho 83501 (JNW; st; coed; sem; II; 1439) Courses with no degree specialization, Depts of Educ and Psych, 208-746-2341 Ext 213

Mintz, Max, MA, Asst Prof

NORTH IDAHO COLLEGE
Coeur d'Alene, Idaho 83814 (NW; local; coed; sem; I; 1165) AA major, Dept of Communic Arts, 208-667-7422

Connolly, John, MA

NORTHWEST NAZARENE COLLEGE
Nampa, Idaho 83651 (NW; Naz; coed; --; III; 1114) BA major, Dept of Phil, 208-467-8848

Jones, J William, PhD, Head
DuBois, Lauriston, MA

RICKS COLLEGE
Rexburg, Idaho 83440 (NW; LDS; coed; sem; I; 5246) NP

UNIVERSITY OF IDAHO
  Moscow, Idaho 83843 (NW; st; coed; sem; IV; 7935) MA major, Dept of Phil, 208-885-7037

  Seaman, Francis, PhD, Prof, Chm, Phil of Sci
  Gier, Nicholas, PhD, Asst Prof, Phil of Relig
  Holmes, Ronald, MA, Asst Prof, Anal Phil

  Keys, Madeleine, BA

ILLINOIS

AERO-SPACE INSTITUTE
  Chicago, Illinois 60611 (--; p; coed; tri; II; 75) NP

AMERICAN ACADEMY OF ART
  Chicago, Illinois 60604 (--; p; coed; sem; I; 630) NP

AMERICAN CONSERVATORY OF MUSIC
  Chicago, Illinois 60605 (Mus; p; coed; sem; IV; 377) NP

AMUNDSEN-MAYFAIR COLLEGE, CITY COLLEGE OF CHICAGO
  Chicago, Illinois 60630 (N; local; coed; sem; I; 4521) BA minor, Dept of Human, 312-286-1323 Ext 60, 61

  Dehnert, Edmund, PhD, Assoc Prof, Chm, Aes
  Martini, Clare, PhD, Assoc Prof
  Senski, Norman, PhD, Assoc Prof, Ethics
  Upin, Jane, MA, Asst Prof, Polit Phil, Ethics

AUGUSTANA COLLEGE
  Rock Island, Illinois 61201 (N; Luth CA; coed; qr; III; 2255) BA major, Dept of Phil, 309-794-7284

  Arbaugh, George B, PhD, Prof, Chm, Phil of Relig
  Moreland, John M, PhD, Asst Prof, Phil of Sci, Logic
  Sjursen, Harold, MA, Instr, Ethics

  Celms, Theodore, PhD, Prof Emer, Phenomen

AURORA COLLEGE
  Aurora, Illinois 60507 (N; Ad Christ; coed; --; II; 1094) BA major, --, 312-892-6431

  Dunham, Joe Lloyd, MA, Assoc Prof, Chm
  Reiter, James E, MA, Instr Part-time, Aes
  Ward, David, MA, Lect Part-time

BARAT COLLEGE
Lake Forest, Illinois 60045 (N; p; wo; sem; II; 539) BA joint or combined major,
Dept of Phil, 312-234-3000

Hollenhorst, G Donald, PhD, Prof, Chm, Mod Phil, Amer Phil, Epistem
Pellauer, David, MA, Lect, Phil of Relig

BELLEVILLE AREA JUNIOR COLLEGE
Belleville, Illinois 62221 (N; st and local; coed; sem; I; 5163) --, Dept of Eng,
618-235-2707

Jones, Barry, PhD
Saudade, Gil, MA

BETHANY THEOLOGICAL SEMINARY
Oak Brook, Illinois 60521 (N; Ch of Breth; coed; qr; III; 75) --; Dept of Theol and
Ethics, 312-629-2400

BLACK HAWK COLLEGE
Moline, Illinois 61265 (N; local; coed; sem; I; 3815) Courses with no degree
specialization, Dept of Eng, 309-755-1311

McIlvain, Cherry, BA, Part-time
Quayle, Thomas, MA, Asst Prof

BLACK HAWK COLLEGE, EAST CAMPUS
Kewanee, Illinois 61443 (--; local; coed; sem; I; 521) Courses with no degree
specialization, --, 309-853-3381

BLACKBURN COLLEGE
Carlinville, Illinois 62626 (N; U Preb; coed; sem; II; 627) Courses with no degree
specialization, Dept of Phil and Relig, 217-854-3231 Ext 235

Dana, J C, M Div, Hist of West Tht
King, C Wayne, STM, Contemp Phil

BRADLEY UNIVERSITY
Peoria, Illinois 61606 (N; p; coed; sem; III; 5732) BA major, Dept Phil, 309-
676-7611 Ext 406, 428

Scharle, Theodore, PhD, Assoc Prof, Chm, Exist, Ethics, Phil of Relig
Esposito, Joseph L, PhD, Assoc Prof, Aes, 19th and 20th Cent Phil
Liddell, Brendan E A, PhD, Assoc Prof, Ethics, Kant, Hist of Phil
Pascual, Ricardo R, PhD, Prof, Non-Western Phil, Phil of Sci
Witte, William D S, PhD, Prof, Polit Phil, Soc and Legal Phil

Lepley, Ray, PhD, Prof Emer

CARL SANDBURG COLLEGE
Galesburg, Illinois 61401 (XT; st and local; coed; qr; I; 1185) --, --, 309-343-6101

CATHOLIC THEOLOGICAL UNION AT CHICAGO
Chicago, Illinois 60615 (N; RC; coed; qr; III; 145) NP

CENTRAL YMCA COMMUNITY COLLEGE
    Chicago, Illinois 60606 (N; p; coed; sem; II; 4472) AA major, Dept of Phil, 312-222-8208

    Embree, Alan C, MBA, Instr, Chm, Ethics
    Andrews, Stephen T, MA, Instr, Epistem, Metaph
    Chandler, Marthe de R A, MA, Instr, Logic

CHICAGO ACADEMY OF FINE ARTS
    Chicago, Illinois 60601 (--; p; coed; sem; II; 474) Courses with no degree specialization, --, 312-782-1140

CHICAGO COLLEGE OF OSTEOPATHIC MEDICINE
    Chicago, Illinois 60615 (Osteo; p; coed; qr; II; 307) NP

CHICAGO CONSERVATORY COLLEGE
    Chicago, Illinois 60605 (Mus; p; coed; sem; III; 170) Courses with no degree specialization, Dept of Music Hist and Lit, 312-427-0500

CHICAGO STATE UNIVERSITY
    Chicago, Illinois 60628 (N; st; coed; tri; III; 5806) BA minor, Dept of Soc Sci, 312-995-2000

    Parejko, James, PhD, Asst Prof
    Teo, Wesley, PhD, Asst Prof

CHICAGO TECHNICAL COLLEGE
    Chicago, Illinois 60616 (--; p; men; qr; II; 915) NP

CHICAGO THEOLOGICAL SEMINARY
    Chicago, Illinois 60637 (Theol; U Ch of Christ; coed; qr; IV; 144) NR

COLLEGE OF DUPAGE
    Glen Ellyn, Illinois 60137 (N; st and local; coed; qr; I; 8705) BA minor, --, 312-858-2800

    Hombach, Frederich A, MA, Instr
    Joshi, Sunder, PhD, Instr
    Oastler, John, PhD, Instr

COLLEGE OF LAKE COUNTY
    Grayslake, Illinois 60030 (--; local; coed; sem; I; 4554) AA major, Dept of Human, 312-223-8191 Ext 67

    Rosenberg, Milton, MA, Instr
    Simonsen, Kenneth, MA, Instr

COLLEGE OF SAINT FRANCIS
    Joliet, Illinois 60435 (N; RC; coed; 4-1-4; II; 840) BA major, Dept of Phil, 815-726-7311

    Niedzwiecki, Harold, PhD, Prof, Chm, Ethics
    Kerins, Frank, EdD, Prof, Phil of Educ
    Scott, Frances, MA, Asst Prof, Phil of Relig

COLUMBIA COLLEGE
  Chicago, Illinois 60611 (--; p; coed; sem; II; 929) --, Center for Devel Stud,
  and Dept of Human Relations, 312-467-0300

  Butler, William W, PhD, Assoc Prof

COMMUNITY COLLEGE OF DECATUR
  Decatur, Illinois 62523 (--; st; coed; qr; I; 1050) Courses with no degree
  specialization, Div of Communic, 217-422-8387 Ext 21

CONCORDIA TEACHERS COLLEGE
  River Forest, Illinois 60305 (N; Luth; coed; qr; III; 1666) BA major, Dept of Eng
  and Phil, 312-771-8300

  Lehmann, Jr, William, PhD, Prof, Ethics, Metaph, Hist of Phil, Aes

CONCORDIA THEOLOGICAL SEMINARY
  Springfield, Illinois 62702 (Theol; Luth; men; qr; II; 458) Courses with no degree
  specialization, Dept of Syst Theol, 217-544-7401

  Johnson, John F, ThD, Assoc Prof

DANVILLE JUNIOR COLLEGE
  Danville, Illinois 61832 (N; st and local; coed; sem; I; 1874) NR

DELOURDES COLLEGE
  Des Plaines, Illinois 60016 (--; RC; wo; sem; II; 252) Courses with no degree
  specialization, Dept of Phil, 312-298-6760

DEPAUL UNIVERSITY
  Chicago, Illinois 60604 (N; RC; coed; qr; IV; 9394) PhD major, Dept of Phil, 312-
  549-6900 Ext 633

  Kreyche, Gerald F, PhD, Prof, Chm, Exist
  Allemand, L Edward, PhD, Assoc Prof, Amer Phil
  Battle, John, PhD, Assoc Prof, Prag
  Boelen, Bernard J, PhD, Prof, Phenomen, Exist
  Della Penta, J, PhD, Assoc Prof, Thomism
  Dupre, Wilhelm, PhD, Assoc Prof, Phil of Relig
  Emad, Parvis, PhD, Assoc Prof, Hermeneutics, Phenomen
  Eterovich, Francis, PhD, Prof, Soc and Polit Phil
  Feltz, Merlin, PhL, Assoc Prof, Metaph
  Frings, Manfred, PhD, Prof
  Kalin, Martin, PhD, Assoc Prof, Anal, Phil of Mind
  Keating, James W, PhD, Prof, Soc and Polit Phil
  Kimm, Robert, MA, Lect
  Lechner, Robert, PhD, Prof, Contemp French Phil
  Lohr, John, MA, Asst Prof
  Mizicko, Melory, MA, Lect
  Munson, Thomas, PhD, Prof, Phil of Relig, Phil of Hist
  Postma, Hans, MA, Lect
  Switalski, Bruno, PhD, Assoc Prof, Metaph
  Thornbrugh, John, MA, Lect

Abbate, Nancy, BA, Grad Asst
Baysden, Richard, MA, Grad Asst
Biefeld, Rebecca, MA, Grad Asst
Cipollone, Anthony, MA, Grad Asst
Cralle, Harry T, BA, Grad Asst
DeRonne, William, MA, Grad Asst
Fernandez, Madelina, MA, Grad Asst
Koss, Donald, MA, Grad Asst
McPeak, Margaret, MA, Grad Asst

Miritello, Frank, BA, Grad Asst
Nissim-Sabat, Marilyn, MA, Grad Asst
Owens, Wayne, MA, Grad Asst
Pourch, Stephen, MA, Grad Asst
Romanski, Ronald, MA, Grad Asst
Sanders, Victor, BA, Grad Asst
Simpson, Richard, MA, Grad Asst
Stikkers, Kenneth, BA, Grad Asst
Stuart, Albert, MA, Grad Asst

DEVRY INSTITUTE OF TECHNOLOGY
Chicago, Illinois 60641 (Tech; p; coed; qr; II; 2949) NP

EASTERN ILLINOIS UNIVERSITY
Charleston, Illinois 61920 (N; st; coed; qr; III; 8881) BA major, Dept of Phil,
217-581-3012

Kim, Ha Poong, PhD, Assoc Prof, Chm
Barford, Robert, PhD, Asst Prof
Long, Jerome, PhD, Assoc Prof
Penn, Stuart, PhD, Prof
Taylor, Frank, PhD, Assoc Prof

ELGIN COMMUNITY COLLEGE
Elgin, Illinois 60120 (N; local; coed; sem; I; 2921) Courses with no degree
specialization, Dept of Human, Phil and Relig, 312-697-1000

ELMHURST COLLEGE
Elmhurst, Illinois 60126 (N; U Ch of Christ; coed; 4-1-4; II; 2762) BA major, Dept
of Phil, 312-279-4100 Ext 384

Gross, Sidney, PhD, Assoc Prof, Chm, Amer Phil
Halfter, William, PhD, Prof, Phil of Relig

EUREKA COLLEGE
Eureka, Illinois 61530 (N; Christ Ch; coed; --; II; 564) BA major, Dept of Phil,
309-467-3721

Cobb, William Daniel, PhD, Prof
Humbert, E Royal F, DD, Prof

EVANGELICAL THEOLOGICAL SEMINARY
Naperville, Illinois 60540 (N; U Meth; coed; qr; III; 157) MA minor, Dept of Phil
Theol, 312-355-8500

Rademacher, Paul G, ThD, Prof
Will, James E, PhD, Prof

FELICIAN COLLEGE
Chicago, Illinois 60659 (--; RC; wo; 4-1-4; I; 272) Courses with no degree
specialization, Dept of Human, 312-539-1919

Meagher, William, MA, Instr, Chm
Damasia, Mary, MA, Instr

GARRETT THEOLOGICAL SEMINARY
    Evanston, Illinois 60201 (N; U Meth; coed; qr; IV; 288) PhD joint or combined major,
    Dept of Phil of Relig, 312-869-2511

    Cartwright, John H, PhD, Assoc Prof, Ethics
    Polish, David, DHL, Lect, Phil of Relig
    Schaglman, Herman E, MHL, Lect, Jewish Tht
    Thompson, Tyler, PhD, Prof, Phil of Relig

    Kolbe, Henry E, PhD, Prof Emer, Ethics

GEORGE WILLIAMS COLLEGE
    Downers Grove, Illinois 60615 (N; p; coed; qr; III; 932) BA major, --, 312-964-3100

    Netzky, Ralph, PhD

GOVERNORS STATE UNIVERSITY
    Park Forest South, Illinois 60466 (--; st; coed; --; III; 695) NR

GREENVILLE COLLEGE
    Greenville, Illinois 62246 (N; F Meth; coed; 4-1-4; II; 838) BA joint or combined
    major, Dept of Phil and Relig, 618-664-1840 Ext 224

    Mulholland, Royal, EdD, Assoc Prof, Phil of Educ, Exist
    Stuart, William James, MA, Asst Prof, Ethics
    Thompson, Frank, ThM, Assoc Prof, Hist of Phil

HEBREW THEOLOGICAL COLLEGE
    Skokie, Illinois 60076 (--; Jewish; coed; sem; IV; 249) Courses with no degree
    specialization, Dept of Phil and Relig, 312-267-9800

    Berkovits, Eliezer, PhD, Chm, Mod Phil
    Babad, Joseph, PhD, Med Phil
    Shapiro, David, DHL, Relig Phil

HIGHLAND COMMUNITY COLLEGE
    Freeport, Illinois 61032 (--; st; coed; sem; I; 1216) Courses with no degree
    specialization, 815-233-6121

    Zipse, Erwin, MA, Instr

ILLINOIS BENEDICTINE COLLEGE
    Lisle, Illinois 60532 (N; RC; coed; sem; II; 1022) BA major, Dept of Phil, 312-
    968-7270

    Trelo, Virgil, PhD, Prof, Chm, Phil of Relig, Phil Anthrop
    Fauser, Patricia, PhD, Assoc Prof, Amer Phil
    Toussaint, Bernard, PhD, Assoc Prof, Metaph, Phil of Sci

    Tarasevitch, Chrysostom, DD, Prof Emer, Med Phil

ILLINOIS CENTRAL COLLEGE
    East Peoria, Illinois 61611 (N; st and local; coed; sem; I; 8898) Courses with no
    degree specialization, Div of Communic, 309-694-5249

    McDaniel, Brooks, BD, Instr

ILLINOIS COLLEGE
   Jacksonville, Illinois 62650 (N; p; coed; sem; II; 876) BA major, Dept of Phil
   and Relig, 217-245-7126

   Stewart, Malcolm F, PhD, Prof, Chm, Phil of Relig
   Yeager, Iver F, PhD, Prof

ILLINOIS COLLEGE OF OPTOMETRY
   Chicago, Illinois 60616 (N; p; coed; qr; II; 470) NP

ILLINOIS COLLEGE OF PODIATRIC MEDICINE
   Chicago, Illinois 60610 (Pod; p; coed; sem; II; 263) NP

ILLINOIS INSTITUTE OF TECHNOLOGY
   Chicago, Illinois 60616 (N; p; coed; sem; IV; 7067) BA major, Dept of Human, 312-
   225-9600 Ext 1251

   Ladenson, Robert F, PhD, Asst Prof, Chm, Soc and Polit Phil, Moral Phil
   Thrane, Gary A, PhD, Asst Prof, Phil of Sci, Aes
   Stawinski, Arthur W, PhD, Asst Prof, Epistem, Logic
   Weil, Vivian M, PhD, Asst Prof, Action Theory, Phil of Mind

ILLINOIS STATE UNIVERSITY
   Normal, Illinois 61761 (N; st; coed; sem; IV; 18,635) BA major, Dept of Phil,
   309-436-7665

   Kennard, Kenneth C, PhD, Prof, Chm, Phil of Relig
   Andrade, Louis E, PhD, Asst Prof, Epistem, Ethics
   Cadieux, J Andre, BS, Asst Prof, Aes, Metaph, Anal Phil, Phil of Relig
   Godow, Jr, Rew A, MA, Asst Prof, Phil of Soc Sci
   Goodrum, Craig R, AB, Asst Prof, Ethics, Phil of Law
   Gowen, Julie, PhD, Asst Prof, Phil of Relig, Metaph
   Machina, Kenton F, PhD, Asst Prof, Logic, Phil of Lang
   Mann, William E, PhD, Asst Prof, Hist of Phil, Phil of Relig
   Rosenbaum, Stephen E, MA, Asst Prof, Epistem, Hist of Phil
   Stell, Lance K, MA, Asst Prof, Soc and Polit Phil, Chinese Phil

ILLINOIS VALLEY COMMUNITY COLLEGE
   Oglesby, Illinois 61348 (N; local; coed; sem; I; 2808) Courses with no degree
   specialization, Div of Human, 815-224-6309

   Evans, Myrna, PhD, Chm
   Publow, Richard, MA
   Rhoades, Stephen, MA

ILLINOIS WESLEYAN UNIVERSITY
   Bloomington, Illinois 61701 (N; U Meth; coed; 4-1-4; III; 1728) BA major, Dept of
   Phil, 309-556-3179

   Colter, L W, ABD, Asst Prof, Act Chm, Phil of Lang, Logic, Metaph, Epistem
   Casey, John, ABD, Lect, Epistem, Polit Phil
   Koehn, Donald R, PhD, Asst Prof, Ethics, Hist of Phil, Aes
   Meyers, Doris, ABD, Assoc Prof, 19th Cent Phil, Anc Phil

   Browns, Ralph E, PhD, Prof Emer

INSTITUTE OF DRAFTING AND TECHNOLOGY
    Morrison, Illinois 61270 (Tech; p; coed; tri; I; 175) NR

JOHN A LOGAN COLLEGE
    Carterville, Illinois 62918 (N; st and local; coed; qr; I; 1326) Courses with no
    degree specialization, Dept of Communic and Human, 618-985-3741

    Morris, Donald, MA, Instr, Value Theory

JOHN MARSHALL LAW SCHOOL
    Chicago, Illinois 60604 (Law; p; coed; sem; III; 1386) NR

JOLIET JUNIOR COLLEGE
    Joliet, Illinois 60436 (N; local; coed; sem; I; 4769) --, Dept of Eng, 815-729-
    9020

    Asher, Patrick, MS, Instr

JUDSON COLLEGE
    Elgin, Illinois 60120 (--; Bapt; coed; tri; II; 326) BA joint or combined major,
    Div of Phil and Relig, 312-695-2500 Ext 570

    Besancon, Richard, ThD, Prof, Value Phil, Phil of Relig, Ethics

KANKAKEE COMMUNITY COLLEGE
    Kankakee, Illinois 60901 (--; st and local; coed; sem; I; 1492) NP

KASKASIA COLLEGE
    Centralia, Illinois 62801 (N; local; coed; sem; I; 1491) Courses with no degree
    specialization, Dept of Human, 618-532-1981 Ext 54

    Ikamas, Leo, MA, Instr

KENDALL COLLEGE
    Evanston, Illinois 60204 (N; U Meth; coed; 4-1-4; I; 835) Courses with no degree
    specialization, Dept of Phil, 312-869-5240

    Stone, Jerome A, PhD, Chm, Amer Phil, Exist, Polit Phil

KENNEDY-KING COLLEGE, CITY COLLEGE OF CHICAGO
    Chicago, Illinois 60621 (N; local; coed; sem; I; 4803) AA major, Dept of Human,
    312-962-3348

    Roby, Thomas W, PhD, Asst Prof, Chm, Educ Phil, Anc Phil
    Marcell, Noah, PhD, Assoc Prof, Russian Phil
    Marino, John, MA, Instr, Renaissance Phil
    Oklu, Samuel, MA, Instr, Afr Phil
    Schamis, Jeffrey, PhD, Instr, Polit Phil, Mod Phil

KISHWAUKEE COLLEGE
    Malta, Illinois 60150 (XT; st and local; coed; sem; I; 1537) NP

KNOX COLLEGE
   Galesburg, Illinois 61401 (N; p; coed; qr; II; 1403) BA major, Dept of Phil and
   Relig, 343-0112-473

   Factor, R Lance, PhD, Asst Prof, Chm, Logic, Phil of Sci
   Pahel, Kenneth R, PhD, Assoc Prof, Ethics, Amer Phil

LAKE FOREST COLLEGE
   Lake Forest, Illinois 60045 (N; U Preb; coed; --; II; 1223) BA major, Dept of Phil,
   312-234-3100

   Hansen, Forest, PhD, Assoc Prof, Chm, Aes, Hist of Phil
   Gean, William, PhD, Asst Prof, Mod Phil, Phil of Mind, Logic, Phil of Sci
   Lessing, Abba, PhD, Assoc Prof, Exist, Phenomen, Hist of Phil
   Patel, Ramesh, PhD, Asst Prof, Indian Phil, Phil of Relig, Ethics
   Smith, Janet Farrell, PhD, Asst Prof, Anal Phil, Amer Phil, Logic, Phil of Mind

   Williams, Sterling Price, PhD, Prof Emer

LAKE LAND COLLEGE
   Mattoon, Illinois 61938 (DH; st; coed; qr; I; 2857) --, Dept of Soc Sci, 217-235-
   3131

   Kaufman, Harold, MS, Instr, Moral Phil

LEWIS AND CLARK COMMUNITY COLLEGE
   Godfrey, Illinois 62035 (N; st and local; coed; sem; I; 1821) NR

LEWIS COLLEGE
   Lockport, Illinois 60441 (N; p; coed; sem; II; 2536) BA major, Dept of Phil,
   815-838-0500 Ext 415

   Alessia, Raffaele, PhD, Assoc Prof
   Bertling, Martin, PhD, Prof
   Clark, William, PhD, Asst Prof
   Haines, Wayne, PhD, Asst Prof

LINCOLN CHRISTIAN COLLEGE
   Lincoln, Illinois 62656 (BI; Ch of Christ; coed; sem; III; 905) Courses with no
   degree specialization, Dept of Phil and Psych, 217-732-3168

   Ross, Robert, PhD, Part-time Instr
   Strauss, James D, ThM, Assoc Prof

LINCOLN COLLEGE
   Lincoln, Illinois 62656 (N; p; coed; 4-1-4; I; 604) Courses with no degree
   specialization, Div of Human, 217-732-3155 Ext 287

   Pascale, Elmo, MA, Assoc Prof

LINCOLN LAND COMMUNITY COLLEGE
   Springfield, Illinois 62703 (--; local; coed; qr; I; 4000) Courses with no degree
   specialization, Div of Human, 217-529-6661

LINCOLN TRAIL COLLEGE
    Robinson, Illinois 62454 (--; st and local; coed; qr; I; 809) Courses with no
    degree specialization, Dept of Human, 618-544-8657

    Benedict, James, MA, Instr, Communic

LOOP COLLEGE, CITY COLLEGE OF CHICAGO
    Chicago, Illinois 60601 (N; local; coed; sem; I; 9926) --, Dept of Human, 312-269-
    8058

    Conroy, Bernard, MA, Asst Prof
    Stark, Thomas, MA, Assoc Prof

LOYOLA UNIVERSITY
    Chicago, Illinois 60626 (N; RC; coed; sem; IV; 14,480) PhD major, Dept of Phil,
    312-274-3000 Ext 306

    Thompson, Kenneth, PhD, Assoc Prof, Chm, Amer Phil
    Bannan, John F, PhD, Assoc Prof, Metaph
    Barry, Robert M, PhD, Prof, Amer Phil
    Blachowicz, James, PhD, Asst Prof, Logic, Phil of Sci
    Burlage, Carl J, PhD, Assoc Prof, Med Phil
    Catania, Francis J, PhD, Assoc Prof, Med Phil
    Collins, Ardis B, PhD, Assoc Prof, Med Phil
    Connelly, George, PhD, Asst Prof, Amer Phil
    Cunningham, Suzanne, PhD, Asst Prof, Phenomen, Exist
    Dehler, William, MA, Asst Prof, Ethics
    Gini, Alfred, PhD, Asst Prof, Amer Phil
    Grant, G G, MA, Assoc Prof, Ethics
    Hassel, David, PhD, Assoc Prof, Med Phil
    Hecht, F Torrens, PhD, Assoc Prof, Metaph, Epistem
    Llamzon, Benjamin, PhD, Prof, Ethics
    Loftus, Joseph, MA, Asst Prof, Phil of God
    Maxwell, Peter, PhD, Asst Prof, Metaph, Epistem
    Maziarz, Edward A, PhD, Prof, Logic, Phil of Sci
    Merrill, Gary, MA, Instr, Anal Phil
    Nurnberger, Lothar, MA, Assoc Prof, Anc Phil
    O'Grady, Donald, PhD, Assoc Prof, Med Phil
    Ozar, David, MA, Instr, Ethics
    Schaldenbrand, Mary, PhD, Assoc Prof, Phenomen, Exist
    Seigfried, Hans, PhD, Assoc Prof, Anc Phil
    Sheehan, Thomas, PhD, Asst Prof, Phenomen, Exist
    Sweeney, Leo, PhD, Visit Prof, Anc Phil
    VanderNat, Arnold, MA, Instr, Logic
    Vogel, Murel, PhD, Prof, Thomistic Phil
    Walsh, Joseph, MA, Asst Prof
    Westley, Richard, PhD, Assoc Prof, Med Phil
    Woods, Richard, MA, Lect Part-time
    Wren, Thomas, PhD, Assoc Prof, Phenomen, Exist
    Yartz, Francis, PhD, Asst Prof, Anc Phil

    Kelly, James V, PhD, Prof Emer
    LaPlante, Nelson, MA, Asst Prof Emer

LUTHERAN SCHOOL OF THEOLOGY AT CHICAGO
    Chicago, Illinois 60615 (Theol; Luth CA; coed; qr; IV; 239) Courses with no degree
    specialization, Div of Hist and Constructive Theol, 312-667-3500

    Sherman, Franklin Eugene, PhD, Prof, Christ Ethics

    Johnson, Hjalmar Wilhelm, PhD, Prof Emer, Hist and Phil of Relig

MACCORMAC COLLEGE
Chicago, Illinois 60604 (--; p; coed; qr; I; 207) NP

MACMURRAY COLLEGE
Jacksonville, Illinois 62650 (N; U Meth; coed; 4-1-4; II; 980) BA major, Dept of
Phil and Relig, 217-245-6151

Smith, J Weldon, PhD, Assoc Prof, Chm, Aes
Buckey, Donald R, PhD, Asst Prof, Ethics
Palmer, Richard W, PhD, Prof, Metaph
Stanger, Richard L, MA, Asst Prof, Phil of Relig

MALCOLM X COMMUNITY COLLEGE, CITY COLLEGE OF CHICAGO
Chicago, Illinois 60612 (N; local; coed; sem; I; 8017) Courses with no degree
specialization, Dept of Communic Arts and Human Dev, 312-942-3050

Forshey, Gerald, MA, Asst Prof
Jenkins, Ulysses, Instr, Black Phil

MALLINCKRODT COLLEGE
Wonder Lakes, Illinois 60097 (--; RC; wo; 4-1-4; I; 183) Courses with no degree
specialization, Dept of Theol and Phil, 312-256-1094

Wedmore, Delphine, MA, Instr

MCCORMICK THEOLOGICAL SEMINARY
Chicago, Illinois 60614 (Theol; U Preb; coed; qr; IV; 186) Courses with no degree
specialization, Dept of Theol, 312-549-3700

Evans, Robert, ThD, Assoc Prof, Phil of Relig, Lang Phil
Parker, Thomas, PhD, Assoc Prof, 19th Cent German and Amer Prag

MCHENRY COUNTY COLLEGE
Crystal Lake, Illinois 60014 (--; st; coed; sem; I; 1261) AA major, Dept of Human,
815-459-6800

Harm, Frederick R, PhD, Chm, Logic
Frank, Robert F, M Div

MCKENDREE COLLEGE
Lebanon, Illinois 62254 (N; U Meth; coed; 4-1-4; II; 474) BA major, Div of Soc Sci,
618-537-4481

Bryan, Lawrence, PhD, Asst Prof, Phil of Relig
Kennedy, Philip Caddell, MA, Assoc Prof, Orient Phil, Phil of Art

Grandy, Norman, PhD, Prof Emer, Logic

MEADVILLE-LOMBARD THEOLOGICAL SCHOOL
Chicago, Illinois (Theol; Unit Univer; coed; qr; IV; 16) --, --, 312-753-3195

MIDWEST COLLEGE OF ENGINEERING
Lombard, Illinois 60148 (--; p; coed; qr; III; 200) NP

MILLIKIN UNIVERSITY
  Decatur, Illinois 62522 (N; U Preb; coed; 4-1-4; III; 1579) BA major, Dept of Phil,
  217-423-3661

  Adell, Arvid W, PhD, Asst Prof, Chm, Process Phil
  Mosedale, Fred, MA, Instr, Ling
  Thompson, Hugo, PhD, Asst Prof, Ethics

MONMOUTH COLLEGE
  Monmouth, Illinois 61462 (N; U Preb; coed; --; II; 1178) BA major, Dept of Phil,
  309-457-2378 Ext 2379

  Johnson, J Prescott, PhD, Prof, Chm, Theory of Value
  Redmon, Jr, Robert B, PhD, Asst Prof, Anal Phil, Phil of Sci, Logic

  Thompson, Samuel M, PhD, Prof Emer, Phil of Relig, Phil of Law, Aes

MOODY BIBLE INSTITUTE
  Chicago, Illinois 60610 (BI; p; coed; sem; II; 1645) --, --, 312-329-4000

MORAINE VALLEY COMMUNITY COLLEGE
  Palos Hills, Illinois 60465 (--; st and local; coed; sem; I; 3868) Courses with
  no degree specialization, Div of Human, Subdiv A, 312-974-4300

  Gabert, Glen, PhD, Phil of Educ
  Glomb, Julian, MA, East Phil
  Synnestvedt, Justin, ABD, Logic, Phil of Sci

MORTON COLLEGE
  Cicero, Illinois 60650 (N; st and local; sem; I; 2490) --, Dept of Soc Sci, 312-
  656-0404

  Kitzerow, Walter C, MA

MUNDELEIN COLLEGE
  Chicago, Illinois 60626 (N; p; wo; --; III; 1362) BA major, Dept of Phil, 312-262-
  8100

  French, Louise, PhD, Prof, Chm, Metaph, Anc Phil, Exist
  O'Brochta, Thomas, PhD, Asst Prof, Process Phil, Ethics
  Vaillancourt, Daniel, PhD, Asst Prof, Phenomen

NATIONAL COLLEGE OF CHIROPRACTIC
  Lombard, Illinois 60148 (--; p; coed; tri; II; 335) NP

NATIONAL COLLEGE OF EDUCATION, MAIN CAMPUS
  Evanston, Illinois 60201 (N; p; coed; qr; III; 2970) --, Dept of Phil and Relig,
  312-256-5150

  Adler, Hans, MA
  Seren, Marjorie, MA

NATIONAL COLLEGE OF EDUCATION, URBAN CAMPUS
  Chicago, Illinois 60601 (--; p; coed; qr; II; 195) --, Dept of Relig and Phil, 312-
  236-1671

NORTH CENTRAL COLLEGE
  Naperville, Illinois 60540 (N; U Meth; coed; --; II; 932) BA major, Dept of Phil,
  312-355-5500 Ext 46

  Skoglund, Henry L, MA, Assoc Prof, Chm, Ethics
  Rife, William C, PhD, Prof, Phil of Sci
  Rumbaugh, Liela M, PhD, Asst Prof, Aes

NORTH PARK COLLEGE
  Chicago, Illinois 60625 (N; Evan Cov; coed; --; II; 1294) BA major, Dept of Phil
  and Relig, 312-583-2700 Ext 276

  Lindahl, Elder, PhD, Prof, Amer Phil, Hist of Phil, Comp Relig
  Nelson, James, PhD, Assoc Prof Part-time, Phil of Sci
  Sebestyen, Paul, PhD, Lect, 19th Cent Phil, Logic
  Soneson, J Melburn, PhD, Prof, Ethics, Phil of Relig, Hist of Phil

NORTHEASTERN ILLINOIS STATE UNIVERSITY
  Chicago, Illinois 60625 (N; st; coed; tri; III; 7764) BA major, --, 312-583-4050

  Chacon, Roger, PhD, Assoc Prof, Chm, Logic, Anal Phil
  Kerr, Stanley, PhD, Asst Prof
  Moorhead, Hugh, PhD, Assoc Prof
  Rizik, James, PhD, Asst Prof

NORTHERN BAPTIST THEOLOGICAL SEMINARY
  Oak Brook, Illinois 60521 (N; Bapt; coed; qr; II; 84) M Div, Dept of Theol and
  Christ Phil, 312-629-4100 Ext 50

  Young, Warren C, Prof, Chm

NORTHERN ILLINOIS UNIVERSITY
  DeKalb, Illinois 60115 (N; st; coed; sem; IV: 24,669) MA major, Dept of Phil, 815-
  753-1220, 815-753-0410

  Seligman, David B, PhD, Assoc Prof, Chm, Value Theory, Phil Psych, Contemp Anal Phil
  Beanblossom, Ronald E, PhD, Asst Prof, Hist of Mod Phil, Epistem, Metaph
  Brown, Harold I, PhD, Asst Prof, Epistem, Phil of Mod Sci, Metaph
  Cress, Donald A, PhD, Asst Prof, Hist of Phil, Anc Phil, Med and Mod Phil
  Dye, James W, PhD, Assoc Prof, Hist of Phil, Phil of Cult
  Embree, Lester E, PhD, Asst Prof, Epistem, Husserl, Hist of Mod Phil
  Gelven, C Michael, PhD, Assoc Prof, Hist of Phil, Metaph, Phil of Existence
  Gotesky, Rubin, PhD, Prof, Logic, Phil of Sci, Phil of Law
  Hudson, James L, PhD, Asst Prof, Logic, Phil of Math, Metaph
  King, James T, PhD, Assoc Prof, Ethics, Phil of Law, Phil of Relig
  Kisiel, Theodore J, PhD, Assoc Prof, Phil of Sci, Heidegger
  Livingston, Donald W, PhD, Asst Prof, Phil of Hist, Epistem, Hist of Mod Phil
  Metzel, Nancy L, PhD, Asst Prof, Aes, Exist, Phil of Soc Sci
  Myers, C Mason, PhD, Prof, Theory of Knowl, Phil of Lang, Metaphil
  Stanage, Sherman M, PhD, Assoc Prof, Phil of the Soc Sci, Ling Phenomen, Value Theory
  Stormer, Gerald D, PhD, Asst Prof, Hist of Phil, Hegel, Contemp Idealism
  Van Steenburgh, E W, PhD, Assoc Prof, Phil of Lang, Metaph, Epistem

  Fowler, John S, BA, Grad Teach Asst   Nuttal, Steven R, BA, Grad Teach Asst
  Herbster, William H, BA, Grad Teach   Odendahl, Theodore L, BA, Grad Teach Asst
    Asst   Paul, Conrad, BA, Grad Teach Asst
  Lehe, Robert T, BA, Grad Teach Asst   Shaw, Daniel C, BA, Grad Teach Asst

McDonald, Carol, BA, Grad Teach Asst
Mester, John L, BA, Grad Teach Asst
Needham, David L, BA, Grad Teach
    Asst

Solomon, Howard, BA, Grad Teach Asst
Test, Robert, BA, Grad Teach Asst
Vasilopoulos, Ann E, BA, Grad Teach Asst
Wentz, Jan T, BA, Grad Teach Asst

NORTHWESTERN UNIVERSITY
    Evanston, Illinois 60201 (N; p; coed; qr; IV; 15,006) PhD major, Dept of Phil,
    312-492-3656, 312-492-3657, 312-492-3658

    Todes, Samuel J, Assoc Prof, PhD, Chm
    Seeskin, Kenneth R, PhD, Asst Chm
    Browning, Robert W, PhD, Prof
    Earle, William A, PhD, Prof
    Edie, James M, PhD, Prof
    Grier, Philip T, PhD, Visit Asst Prof
    Harris, Errol E, D Litt, Prof
    Levin, David M, PhD, Asst Prof
    Kisiel, Theodore, PhD, Visit Prof
    Kordig, Carl R, PhD, Asst Prof
    Martin, Richard, PhD, Prof
    Moore, John Bruce, PhD, Asst Prof
    Sankowski, Edward, PhD, Asst Prof

    Schilpp, Paul Arthur, PhD, Prof Emer
    Vivas, Eliseo, PhD, Prof Emer

Alwill, John, MA, Teach Intern
Andrews, Thomas, MA, Teach Intern
Barron, William, MA, Teach Asst
Beach, Edward, MA, Teach Asst
Bird, Otto, MA, Teach Asst
Browder, Jimmie, BS, Teach Asst
Brunk, Conrad, MA, Teach Intern--
    Danforth Fel
Coyne, Margaret, MA, Teach Asst
Douglin, Ernest, MA, Teach Asst
Evangelist, William, BA
Fowkes, William, MA, Teach Intern
Fung, Richard, MA, Teach Asst
Galloway, Joseph, MA, Teach Asst
Holliday, Christopher, MA, Teach
    Intern
Israeli, Phineas, BA, Univ Fel
Kenyon, Robert, BA
Krause, Karl, MA, Teach Intern
Lenssen, Mark, BA, Univ Fel

Lobato-Martines, Rafael, BA, Univ Fel
Maletz, William, MA, Teach Intern
Manson, Richard, MA, Teach Intern
Moberg, Dale, MA, Teach Intern
Mulligan, Thomas, MA, Teach Intern
Patrik, Linda, MA, Teach Intern
Pomerleau, Wayne, MA, Teach Asst
Rawlinson, Mary, BA, Danforth Fel
Ray, Alan Chad, MA, Teach Intern
Regan, Brian, BA
Reynolds, Cecil, MA, Teach Intern
Rothermel, Dennis, MA, Teach Asst
Rouse, Joseph, BA, Univ Fel
Stahl, Gerald, MA, Teach Asst
Suber, Peter, BA
Vacek, Edward, BA
Verkennis, Rollance, BA, Univ Fel
Wager, John, MA, Teach Asst
Wears, James, MA, Teach Intern
Yamamoto, Carl, BA

OAKTON COMMUNITY COLLEGE
    Morton Grove, Illinois 60053 (--; st and local; coed; sem; I; 2330) Courses with
    no degree specialization, --, 312-967-5120

    Lockwood, Eugene de V, MA, Asst Prof, Sr Instr, Indian Phil, Thomism
    Hiner, Keith, MA, Asst Prof, Phenomen

OLIVE-HARVEY COMMUNITY COLLEGE, CITY COLLEGE OF CHICAGO
   Chicago, Illinois 60628 (N; local; coed; sem; I; 5172) --, Dept of Human, 312-568-
   3700 Ext 296

   Loseth, Per O, MA, Asst Prof
   Reed, Richard, MA, Instr
   Torres, Daniel, MA, Assoc Prof

OLIVET NAZARENE COLLEGE
   Kankakee, Illinois 60901 (N; Naz; coed; sem; III; 1791) MA minor, Dept of Phil,
   805-939-5264

   Hall, John David, MA, Asst Prof, Chm, Metaph, Logic
   Dai, David, MA, Part-time Instr, Chinese Phil, Soc and Polit Tht
   Lilienthal, Alfred, MA, Assoc Prof, Ethics, Aes, Phil of Relig

OLNEY CENTRAL COLLEGE, ILLINOIS EASTERN JUNIOR COLLEGE
   Olney, Illinois 62450 (--; st and local; coed; qr; I; 2127) NP

PARKLAND COLLEGE
   Campaign, Illinois 61820 (N; local; coed; qr; I; 4007) AA major, Dept of Soc Sci,
   217-351-2200

   Nolen, Donald M, MA, Instr, Ethics

PRAIRIE STATE COLLEGE
   Chicago Heights, Illinois 60411 (N; st; coed; sem; I; 3867) AA major, Dept of Phil
   and Human, 312-755-4371

   McKillip, Thomas, MA, Chm

PRINCIPIA COLLEGE
   Elsah, Illinois 62028 (N; p; coed; qr; II; 841) BA joint or combined major, Dept
   of Relig and Phil, 618-466-2131

   Ballard, Brook B, PhD, Prof, Dean of Fac, Amer Tht
   Becker, James B, PhD, Assoc Prof, Class Phil, Phil of Relig
   Carey, Jr, Archibald, PhD, Asst Prof, Mod Phil, Logic, Ethics

QUINCY COLLEGE
   Quincy, Illinois 62301 (N; RC; coed; sem; II; 2164) BA major, Dept of Phil, 217-
   222-8020

   Hug, Pacific L, PhD, Prof, Chm, Mod Phil
   Freppert, Lucan, PhD, Assoc Prof, Ethics, Soc Phil
   Hoebing, Philibert, MA, Assoc Prof, Logic
   Lakers, John Joseph, PhD, Assoc Prof, Epistem, Anal Phil, Logic
   Mayer, Carol, MA, Asst Prof, Hist of Phil
   Mayer, Edward F, MA, Asst Prof, Logic
   Messerich, Valerius, PhD, Prof, Phenomen

   Fochtman, Vincent, PhD, Prof Emer, Phil of Man

REND LAKE COLLEGE
  Ina, Illinois 62846 (N; local; coed; sem; I; 1101) Courses with no degree
  specialization, Dept of Soc Sci, 618-437-5321

  Doherty, Richard, PhD, Chm

ROBERT MORRIS COLLEGE
  Carthage, Illinois 62321 (--; p; coed; sem; I; 406) NP

ROCKFORD COLLEGE
  Rockford, Illinois 61101 (N; p; coed; 4-1-4; III; 1414) BA major, Dept of Phil and
  Relig, 815-226-4097

  Walhout, Donald, PhD, Prof, Chm
  Keeling, J Keith, Asst Prof

ROCK VALLEY COLLEGE
  Rockford, Illinois 61101 (N; local; coed; sem; I; 3925) BA minor, Dept of Phil,
  815-226-2686

  Kingsbury, Leslie L, PhD, Prof, Head, Phil of Relig, Epistem, Ethics, Realism, Exist

ROOSEVELT UNIVERSITY
  Chicago, Illinois 60605 (N; p; coed; sem; III; 7294) MA major, Dept of Phil, 312-
  341-3734

  Klemke, E D, PhD, Chm
  Carnes, Ralph, PhD, Prof
  Green, Marshall, MA, Instr Part-time
  Jacobson, F A, MA, Assoc Prof
  Mouton, David, PhD, Assoc Prof
  Rohatyn, Dennis A, PhD, Asst Prof
  Temple, Dennis, MA, Asst Prof
  Zabeeh, Farhang, PhD, Prof

  Balduf, Emery W, PhD, Prof Emer
  McMahon, Francis, PhD, Lect Emer
  Ruby, Lionel, PhD, Prof Emer

ROSARY COLLEGE
  River Forest, Illinois 60305 (N; p; coed; sem; III; 1196) MA major, Dept of Phil,
  312-369-6320

  Garey, Jocelyn, PhD, Prof, Aquinas
  McHale, Elwyn, Lect, Contemp Phil
  Papadakis, Basil, MA, Asst Prof, Anc Phil
  Tenzis, Louis, PhD, Asst Prof, Amer Phil

RUSH MEDICAL COLLEGE
  Chicago, Illinois 60612 (Med; p; coed; qr; II; 98) NR

SAINT MARY OF THE LAKE SEMINARY
  Mundelein, Illinois 60060 (--; RC; men; qr; IV; 180) NP

SAINT XAVIER COLLEGE
Chicago, Illinois 60655 (N; RC; coed; sem; III; 1078) BA major, Dept of Phil, 312-779-3300 Ext 248

Ziegler, John, MA, Prof, Chm, Metaph, Phil of Sci, Hist of Phil
Crean, John J, PhD, Assoc Prof, Hist of Phil, Spinoza
Halard, Paul, PhD, Assoc Prof, Ethics, Soc Phil, Polit Phil

SANGAMON STATE UNIVERSITY
Springfield, Illinois 62703 (--; st; coed; qr; III; 1569) BA joint or combined major, Phil Program Sequence, 217-786-6650

Shiner, Larry, PhD, Assoc Prof, Chm, Phenomen
Foust, Conald, PhD, Assoc Prof, Applied Phil
Lesnoff-Caravaglia, Gari, PhD, Asst Prof, Phil of Educ
Schurr, George, PhD, Prof
Walsh, John, PhD, Assoc Prof, Phil of Biology

SAUK VALLEY COLLEGE
Dixon, Illinois 61021 (N; st; coed; sem; I; 1614) --, --, 815-288-5511

SCHOOL OF ART, GOODMAN SCHOOL OF DRAMA
Chicago, Illinois 60603 (N; p; coed; sem; III; 1359) NR

SEABURY-WESTERN THEOLOGICAL SEMINARY
Evanston, Illinois 60201 (Theol; Prot Epis; coed; qr; II; 61) See Late Reports

SHAWNEE COLLEGE
Ullin, Illinois 62992 (--; local; coed; qr; I; 841) Courses with no degree specialization, Dept of Soc Sci, 618-634-2242

Pepper, Henry, PhD

SHERWOOD MUSIC SCHOOL
Chicago, Illinois 60605 (Mus; p; coed; sem; II; 55) NP

SHIMER COLLEGE
Mount Carroll, Illinois 61053 (N; p; coed; sem; II; 348) BA joint or combined major, Human Area, 815-244-2811 Ext 93

Cowan, Denis, PhD
Engel, Elizabeth, PhD, Plato

SOUTHEASTERN ILLINOIS COLLEGE
Harrisburg, Illinois 62946 (--; st and local; coed; sem; I; 809) NR

SOUTHERN ILLINOIS UNIVERSITY
Carbondale, Illinois 62901 (N; st; coed; qr; IV; 22,382) PhD major, Dept of Phil, 618-453-2550

Clarke, David S, PhD, Assoc Prof, Chm, Phil of Lang
Audi, Michael N, PhD, Asst Prof, Phil of Sci

Diefenbeck, James A, PhD, Prof, Phil of Hist
Eames, Elizabeth R, PhD, Prof, Epistem, Bertrand Russell
Eames, S Morris, PhD, Prof, Soc Phil, Dewey
Gillan, Garth J, PhD, Assoc Prof, Phenomen, Critical Semiotics
Hahn, Lewis E, PhD, Res Prof
Hayward, John Frank, PhD, Prof
Frondizi, Risieri, PhD, Visit Prof, Latin Amer Phil
Howie, John, PhD, Assoc Prof, Amer Phil
Kelly, Matthew John, PhD, Assoc Prof, Ethics, Amer Phil
Liu, Shu-Hsien, PhD, Assoc Prof, Orient Phil
McClure, George T, PhD, Prof, Phil of Sci
Mijuskovic, Ben L, PhD, Asst Prof, 19th Cent Phil
Plochmann, George Kimball, PhD, Prof, Class Phil
Schilpp, Paul A, PhD, Visit Prof, Ethics, Polit Phil
Singh, Bhagwan B, PhD, Indian Phil
Tenney, Charles D, PhD, Prof, Aes

Axtelle, George, PhD, Prof Emer
Moore, Willis, PhD, Prof Emer
Wieman, Henry N, PhD, Prof Emer

Abbarno, John, MA, Teach Asst
Albaugh, Steve, BA, Teach Asst
Belcher, John C, BS, Univ Fel
Carruba, Jerry, MA, Teach Asst
Chapman, Samuel C, BA, Teach Asst
Chandler, David, MA, Teach Asst
Chang, Ching-mei, MA, Teach Asst
Connor, John, BA, Teach Asst
Dickerson, Dwayne, BA, Teach Asst
Fay, John, MA, Teach Asst
Ferrara, Frank D, MA, Spec Doct Asst
Franks, Dean K, BA, Teach Asst
Gallagher, Donald K, MA, Teach Asst
Gename, Carolyn, BA, Univ Fel
Gupta, Bina, MA, Teach Asst
Guisti, Bruce, BA, Teach Asst

Kramer, Scott, BA, Teach Asst
Liu, Chang-yuan, MA, Teach Asst
Mannolini, Carol, MA, Teach Asst
Mazzola, John, MA, Univ Fel
McCormick, Janice, MA, Teach Asst
McKelvey, Mike, BA, Teach Asst
Montgomery, Jeffrey, BS, Teach Asst
Rasmussen, Paul C, BA, Teach Asst
Richardson, Charles C, MA, Univ Fel
Roberts, James B, BA, Teach Asst
Schoenly, Steven, BA, Teach Asst
Talbott, Sheridan, BA, Teach Asst
Tobin, John, MA, Teach Asst
Tse, Chung-ming, MA, Spec Doct Asst
Vanterpool, Rudolph, BA, Teach Asst
Walls, Vivien A, BA, Teach Asst

SOUTHERN ILLINOIS UNIVERSITY, EDWARDSVILLE CAMPUS
Edwardsville, Illinois 62025 (N; st; coed; qr; III: 13,286) MA major, Dept of Phil
Stud, 618-692-2250

Keene, Carol A, PhD, Asst Prof, Chm, Class Mod Phil, Contemp Phil, Phil of Self
Barker, John A, PhD, Assoc Prof, Epistem, Logic, Phil of Sci
Broyer, John A, PhD, Assoc Prof, Amer Phil, Phil of Educ, Polit Phil
Collier, Kenneth W, PhD, Asst Prof, Phil Logic
Corr, Charles A, PhD, Assoc Prof, Med Phil, Class Mod Phil, Phil of Relig
Emblom, William J, PhD, Assoc Prof, Metaph, Phil of Sci, Phil of Self
Glossop, Ronald J, PhD, Prof, Hume, Ethics, Phil Psych, Logic
Hamrick, William S, PhD, Asst Prof, Phenomen, Exist
Hudlin, Edward W, PhD, Asst Prof, Aes, Ethics
Kim, Sang-Ki, MA, Instr, German Phenomen, Orient Phil
Lawrence, Edwin G, PhD, Asst Prof, Anc Phil, Ethics
Linden, G William, PhD, Prof, Aes, East Relig
Murungi, Robert W, PhD, Lect, Logic, Phil of Logic
Paxson, Jr, Thomas D, PhD, Asst Prof, Anc Phil, Epistem, Ethics
Pletcher, Galen K, PhD, Asst Prof, Phil of Relig, Ethics
Runkle, Gerald J T, PhD, Prof, Polit Theory

Ruth, Sheila, PhD, Asst Prof, Soc Phil, Polit Phil, Phil of Soc Sci
Wolf, Robert G, PhD, Asst Prof, Phil of Sci, Anc Phil, Phil of Ling

Marti, Fritz, PhD, Prof Emer, Kant, 19th Cent German Phil, Phil of Relig

Adams, Frederick R, BA, Teach Asst   Popovich, Richard E, BA, Teach Asst
Angel, Gary L, BA, Teach Asst   Recker, Doren A, BA, Teach Asst

SOUTHWEST COLLEGE, CITY COLLEGE OF CHICAGO
    Chicago, Illinois 60652 (N; local; coed; sem; I; 5359) AA major, Dept of Art, Human,
    and Foreign Lang, 312-735-3000

    Baker, Ray, MA, Assoc Prof
    Billing, Martin, MA, Assoc Prof
    Walker, Norman, MA, Assoc Prof

SPERTUS COLLEGE JUDAICA
    Chicago, Illinois 60605 (N; p; coed; qr; II; 376) --, --, 312-922-9012

SPOON RIVER COLLEGE
    Canton, Illinois 61520 (--; local; coed; sem; I; 1098) NP

SPRINGFIELD COLLEGE IN ILLINOIS
    Springfield, Illinois 62702 (N; RC; coed; sem; I; 461) Courses with no degree
    specialization, Dept of Relig Stud and Phil, 217-525-1420

    Flood, Damien, LST, Head, Phil Anthrop
    Carpentier, Elizabeth, PhD, Logic
    Swiatek, Stanley, BS, Ethics

STATE COMMUNITY COLLEGE
    East Saint Louis 62201 (--; st; coed; qr; I; 2332) NR

    Stegeman, Beatrice, PhD, Aes
    Nichols, Howard, MA

THORNTON COMMUNITY COLLEGE
    South Holland, Illinois 60473 (N; st and local; coed; 4-1-4; I; 4246) Courses with
    no degree specialization, Div of Arts and Human, 312-596-2000 Ext 286

    Ledbetter, Charles, MA

TRINITY CHRISTIAN COLLEGE
    Palos Heights, Illinois 60463 (--; p; coed; sem; II; 409) BA major, Dept of Phil,
    321-597-3000

    Elliott, Robert, MA, Instr, Anal Phil, Whitehead
    Russell, Richard, MA, Instr, Anal Phil
    Seerveld, Calvin, PhD, Prof, Aes, Hist of Phil

TRINITY COLLEGE
    Deerfield, Illinois 60015 (N; Evan F; coed; sem; II; 796) BA major, Dept of Phil,
    312-945-6700 Ext 226

    Schlafer, David J, PhD, Asst Prof, Act Chm, Ethics, Anc Phil
    Evans, C Stephen, PhD, Asst Prof, Phil of Relig, Contemp Phil

TRITON COLLEGE
   River Grove, Illinois 60171 (N; local; coed; sem; I; 7897) Courses with no degree
   specialization, Dept of Behavior Sci, 312-456-0300 Ext 274

   Jacot, Robert E, PhD, Instr
   Riccardo, Edward, MA, Instr

UNIVERSITY OF CHICAGO
   Chicago, Illinois 60637 (N; p; coed; qr; IV; 9356) PhD major, Dept of Phil, 312-
   753-3847

   Linsky, Leonard, PhD, Prof, Chm
   Cohen, Ted, PhD, Assoc Prof
   Donagan, Alan, PhD, Prof
   Gewirth, Alan, PhD, Prof
   Gibbard, Allan, PhD, Assoc Prof
   Greenspan, Patricia S, PhD, Asst Prof
   Hill, Knox, PhD, Prof
   Kolb, David, PhD, Asst Prof
   McKeon, Richard, PhD, Prof
   Mueller, Ian, PhD, Assoc Prof
   Ricoeur, Paul, PhD, Prof
   Tait, William, PhD, Prof
   Thompson, Manley, PhD, Prof
   Wick, Warner, PhD, Prof
   Wimsatt, William W, PhD, Asst Prof

   Mehlberg, Henryk, PhD, Prof Emer
   O'Meara, William, PhD, Prof Emer
   Perry, Charner, PhD, Prof Emer

UNIVERSITY OF ILLINOIS AT CHICAGO CIRCLE
   Chicago, Illinois 60680 (N; st; coed; qr; IV; 19,370) PhD major, Dept of Phil, 312-
   996-3023

   Brand, Myles, PhD, Assoc Prof, Chm, Metaph
   Bartky, Sandra L, PhD, Assoc Prof, Exist, Phenomen
   Berger, Daniel P, MA, Asst Prof, Metaph
   Blumenfeld, David, PhD, Asst Prof, Ethics, Mod Phil
   Dickie, George T, PhD, Prof, Aes
   Dworkin, Gerald, PhD, Assoc Prof, Soc and Polit Phil, Phil of Law
   Economos, John J, BA, Asst Prof, Hist of Phil, Metaph
   Fine, Arthur I, PhD, Prof, Phil of Sci
   Grossman, Neal K, PhD, Asst Prof, Phil of Sci
   Grover, Dorothy L, PhD, Asst Prof, Logic, Phil of Logic
   Kraut, Richard H, PhD, Asst Prof, Ethics, Anc Phil
   Meerbote, Ralf, PhD, Assoc Prof, Kant, Epistem
   Morris, Daniel J, PhD, Prof, Hist of Phil
   Nahm, Ihru, Asst Prof, Phil of Math, Logic
   Page, Robert R, MA, Asst Prof, Hist of Phil
   Rabinowitz, Joshua, MA, Instr, Soc and Polit Phil, Phil of Law
   Skyrms, Brian F, PhD, Prof, Epistem, Phil of Sci
   Teller, Paul R, PhD, Assoc Prof, Phil of Sci
   Thalberg, Irving, PhD, Prof, Phil of Mind, Soc Phil
   Turner, John S, MA, Asst Prof, Ethics, Soc and Polit Phil
   Wilson, Warren K, PhD, Assoc Prof, Phil of Logic

UNIVERSITY OF ILLINOIS AT URBANA-CHAMPAIGN
Urbana, Illinois 61801 (N; st; coed; sem; IV; 32,296) PhD major, Dept of Phil,
217-333-2889

Wallace, James D, PhD, Prof, Chm
Caton, Charles E, PhD, Prof
Chandler, Hugh S, PhD, Assoc Prof
Diggs, B J, PhD, Prof
Gordon, L D, PhD, Asst Prof
Hugly, P G, PhD, Asst Prof
Melnick, Arthur, PhD, Asst Prof
Monk, Robert, MA, Instr
Neely, F Wright, PhD, Asst Prof
Nickles, T J, PhD, Asst Prof
Robison, Andrew, MA, Instr
Schacht, Richard L, PhD, Assoc Prof
Shapere, Dudley, PhD, Prof
Shapira, Michael S, BA, Lect
Shwayder, David S, PhD, Prof
Tiebout, H M, PhD, Prof
Turquette, A R, PhD, Prof
Wengert, Robert G, PhD, Asst Prof
Werner, Louis, PhD, Asst Prof
Will, Frederick L, PhD, Prof

Fisch, Max H, PhD, Prof Emer
Kubitz, O A, PhD, Assoc Prof Emer

Ariew, Roger, MA, Grad Asst
Arjune, Harry, BA, Grad Asst
Baker, Jeffrey E, BA, Grad Asst
Castleton, Toby, MA, Grad Asst
Caughran, Jackie R, BA, Grad Asst
Checker, Judith A, AB, Grad Asst
Davis, John B, BA, Grad Asst
Dienhart, John, BA, Grad Asst
Drummer, Miro M, MA, Grad Asst
Falvo, Eugenie G, MS, Grad Asst
Gehman, John, BA, Grad Asst
Hancock, Thomas, MA, Grad Asst
Jason, Gary, BA, Grad Asst
Kelly, Steven D, BA, Grad Asst
Lockard, Henry C, MA, Grad Asst
Long, Philip M, BA, Grad Asst
McHarry, John, BS, Grad Asst
Melakopides, Constantine J, MA, Grad Asst
Meyer, Marcia E, BA, Grad Asst
Morrison, Mary Jane, MA, Grad Asst
Rice, K Craig, BA, Grad Asst
Riggs, Donald R, AB, Fel
Robertson, Thomas, MA, Grad Asst
Schubert, Richard E, MA, Grad Asst
Simkins, Ronald, MA, Grad Asst
Spellman, A Lynne, MA, Fel
Spellman, James, MA, Grad Asst
Tanner, Steven, MA, Grad Asst
Taylor, Craig, MA, Grad Asst
Vanderploeg, W Stevens, BA, Grad Asst
Ward, Joel F, BA, Grad Asst
Winston, Morton E, MA, Grad Asst
Zerwekh, Robert, BA, Grad Asst

UNIVERSITY OF ILLINOIS MEDICAL CENTER AT CHICAGO
Chicago, Illinois 60680 (Med; st; coed; qr; IV; 3294) NR

VANDERCOOK CONSERVATORY OF MUSIC
Chicago, Illinois 60616 (N; p; coed; sem; III; 148) NP

WABASH VALLEY COLLEGE, ILLINOIS EASTERN JUNIOR COLLEGE
Mount Carmel, Illinois 62863 (--; st and local; coed; qr; I; 1102) Courses with no
degree specialization, --, 618-262-8641

WAUBONSEE COMMUNITY COLLEGE
Sugar Grove, Illinois 60554 (N; local; coed; sem; I; 3564) Courses with no degree
specialization, --, 312-466-4811

WESTERN ILLINOIS UNIVERSITY
  Macomb, Illinois 61455 (N; st; coed; qr; III; 14,412) BA major, Dept of Phil, 309-295-6155

  Nielsen, Maurice, PhD, Prof, Chm, Phil of Relig
  Hardgrave, Hannah, PhD, Asst Prof, Aes
  Keeling, Bryant, PhD, Assoc Prof, Anal Phil
  Kretzschmar, Blaise, STM, Asst Prof, Exist
  Meyer, Charles, PhD, Asst Prof, Logic, Phil of Sci
  Pfeifer, David, PhD, Asst Prof, Amer Phil
  Morelli, Mario, PhD, Asst Prof, Polit Phil

WHEATON COLLEGE
  Wheaton, Illinois 60187 (N; p; coed; qr; III; 2079) BA major, Dept of Phil, 312-682-5040

  Holmes, Arthur F, PhD, Prof, Chm, Epistem, Soc Ethics
  Hackett, Stuart C, PhD, Prof, Phil of Relig, Ethical Theory
  Tamashiro, David M, MA, Asst Prof, Logic, Phil of Sci, Anal Phil
  Wolfe, David L, PhD, Assoc Prof, Phil of Mind, Contemp Euro Phil

WILLIAM RAINEY HARPER COLLEGE
  Palatine, Illinois 60067 (N; st and local; coed; sem; I; 7359) Courses with no degree specialization, Dept of Phil, 312-397-3000 Ext 260, 404

  Franklin, Stephen T, AM, Asst Prof, Chm, Phil of Relig
  Chapman, Harley, AM, Instr
  Pageler, John, PhD, Asst Prof, Exist, Logic
  Williamson, Willard, AM, Asst Prof, Ethics

WRIGHT CITY COLLEGE, CITY COLLEGE OF CHICAGO
  Chicago, Illinois 60634 (N; local; coed; sem; I; 8165) AA major, Dept of Human, 312-777-7900, Ext 45

  Hudson, Charles L, MA, Asst Prof, Soc Phil, Polit Phil
  Sanborn, Donald H, MA, Asst Prof
  Segal, Jerome L, PhD, Asst Prof
  Telford, Kenneth A, MA, Prof

INDIANA

ANCILLA DOMINI COLLEGE
Donaldson, Indiana 46513 (--; RC; coed; sem; I; 183) Courses with no degree specialization, --, 219-936-9936

Weber, Dorothy M, PhD

ANDERSON COLLEGE
Anderson, Indiana 46011 (N; Ch of God; coed; 4-1-4; II; 1754) BA minor, Dept of Hist, Phil and Gov, 317-644-0951

Brown, Delwin, PhD, Assoc Prof, Phil of Relig
Kleis, Sander, PhD, Assoc Prof, Hist of Phil

ASSOCIATED MENNONITE BIBLICAL SEMINARIES
Elkhart, Indiana 46514 (Theol; Menn; coed; 4-1-4; III; 52) Courses with no degree specialization, Dept of Hist and Theol, 219-523-1385

Yoder, John H, ThD, Prof

BALL STATE UNIVERSITY
Muncie, Indiana 47306 (N; st; coed; qr; IV; 17,933) PhD minor, Dept of Phil, 317-285-1244

Robertson, Robert E, PhD, Prof, Chm, Epistem
Andry, Carl, PhD, Prof, Phil of Relig
Annis, David, PhD, Assoc Prof, Epistem, Logic
Barker, George, MA, Asst Prof, Hist of Phil
Foster, Thomas, MA, Asst Prof, Epistem, Logic
Miracchi, Sylvano, PhD, Asst Prof, Logic, Lang Anal
Mueller, Robert, MA, Asst Prof, Exist, Hist of Phil
Runyan, Mary, PhD, Asst Prof, Aes, Phil of Relig

BETHEL COLLEGE
Mishawaka, Indiana 46544 (N; U Miss; coed; 4-1-4; II; 434) BA minor, Div of Relig and Phil, 219-259-8511

Taylor, Donald M, MA, Assoc Prof, Chm
Burgess, Harold
Culp, John

BUTLER UNIVERSITY
Indianapolis, Indiana 46205 (N; p; coed; sem; III; 4363) MA major, Dept of Phil, 317-283-8000 Ext 219

Beversluis, John, PhD, Assoc Prof, Chm, Hist of Phil, Phil of Lang
Gilpin, R C, PhD, Assoc Prof, Aes, Hist of Phil
Williams, James D, MA, Instr

CHRISTIAN THEOLOGICAL SEMINARY
Indianapolis, Indiana 46208 (Theol; Christ Ch; coed; sem; IV; 268) NP

CONCORDIA SENIOR COLLEGE
Fort Wayne, Indiana 46825 (N; Luth; coed; qr; II; 431) BA joint or combined major,
Div of Human, 219-748-7105 Ext 248

O'Connor, Paul, MA, Instr, Phil of Sci
Peters, Curtis, MA, Instr, 19th Cent German Phil
Soovik, Mihkel, STD, Prof, Hist of Phil, Phil of Relig, Exist

Wente, Walter, PhD, Prof Emer, Anc Phil, Aes

DEPAUW UNIVERSITY
Greencastle, Indiana 46135 (N; Meth; coed; 4-1-4; III; 2274) BA major, Dept of Phil
and Relig, 317-653-9721 Ext 493

Compton, Russell J, PhD, Chm, Ethics
Gustavsson, Roger, PhD, Logic
Simon, Howard L, MA, Phil of Law
Horgan, Terence L, MA, Phil of Sci

Hildebrand, C D W, PhD, Prof Emer

EARLHAM COLLEGE
Richmond, Indiana 47374 (N; Fr; coed; --; III; 1225) BA major, Dept of Phil, 317-
962-6561 Ext 222

Clark, Leonard, PhD, Assoc Prof, Chm, Ethics, Phi of Sci
Horn, Robert, PhD, Prof, Epistem
Wood, Richard, PhD, Assoc Prof, Metaph

FORT WAYNE ART INSTITUTE
Fort Wayne, Indiana 46804 (--; p; coed; sem; II; 244) NP

FORT WAYNE BIBLE COLLEGE
Fort Wayne, Indiana 46807 (BI; p; coed; sem; II; 483) Courses with no degree
specialization, Div of Gen Stud, 219-456-2111

Scharfe, Ronald, ThM, Asst Prof
Beals, Duane, Asst Prof

FRANKLIN COLLEGE OF INDIANA
Franklin, Indiana 46131 (N; Bapt; coed; 4-1-4; II; 739) BA major, Dept of Phil
and Relig, 317-736-8441 Ext 226

Howald, J Thomas, PhD, Asst Prof, Chm, Hist of West Phil, 20th Cent Euro Phil
Murphy, Robert M, MA, Prof, Process Phil
Shelley, John C, M Div, Asst Prof

GOSHEN BIBLICAL SEMINARY
Elkhart, Indiana 46514 (Theol; Menn; coed; 4-1-4; III; 46) Courses with no degree
specialization, Dept of Hist and Theol, 219-523-1385

Bauman, Clarence, ThD, Assoc Prof, Ethics
Yoder, John H, ThD, Prof

GOSHEN COLLEGE
    Goshen, Indiana 46526 (N; Menn; coed; tri; II; 1258) --, --, 219-533-3161

GRACE COLLEGE
    Winona Lake, Indiana 46590 (--; Breth; coed; sem; IV; 947) BA minor, Div of Relig
    and Phil, 219-267-8191 Ext 164

    Dearborn, Stephen C, PhD, Prof, Chm
    Hahnlen, Lee, MA, Instr

HANOVER COLLEGE
    Hanover, Indiana 47243 (N; U Preb; coed; --; II; 1034) BA major, Dept of Phil,
    812-866-2151

    Van Leeuwen, Henry, PhD, Prof, Chm, Hist of Skepticism; Ethics
    Rosenthal, Robert J, PhD, Asst Prof, Phil of Art, Phil of Relig
    Smucker, Jan, PhD, Asst Prof, Logic, Phil of Sci

HOLY CROSS JUNIOR COLLEGE
    Notre Dame, Indiana 46556 (--; RC; coed; sem; I; 286) Courses with no degree
    specialization, --, 219-233-6813

HUNTINGTON COLLEGE
    Huntington, Indiana 46750 (N; U Breth; coed; 4-1-4; III; 545) BA major, Dept of
    Phil, 219-356-6000

    Hasker, William, PhD, Prof, Chm, Phil of Mind
    Yehling, Donald, MA, Asst Prof, Phil of Sci

INDIANA CENTRAL COLLEGE
    Indianapolis, Indiana 46227 (N; U Meth; coed; --; III; 2469) BA major, Dept of
    Phil and Relig, 317-787-6301 Ext 233

    Cassel, Herbert, PhD, Assoc Prof, Chm, Ling Phil, Prag, Phil of Relig

INDIANA INSTITUTE OF TECHNOLOGY
    Fort Wayne, Indiana 46803 (N; p; coed; qr; II; 636) Courses with no degree
    specialization, Dept of Libr Arts, 219-422-5561 Ext 21

    Sprunger, Meredith J, Prof, Chm
    Meussling, Herbert, ThM, Assoc Prof

INDIANA STATE UNIVERSITY
    Terre Haute, Indiana 47809 (N; st; coed; sem; IV; 16,274) MA major, Dept of Phil,
    812-232-6311 Ext 5801

    Riedel, Marcus E, PhD, Chm, Phil of Soc Sci, Moral Phil, Hist of Phil
    Bass, Walter A, PhD, Prof, Logic, Phil of Sci
    Dyche, Eugene I, PhD, Prof, Hist of Phil, Phenomen
    Foulk, Gary J, PhD, Assoc Prof, Ethics
    Shouery, Imad T, PhD, Assoc Prof, Exist
    Wedemeyer, Karl H, PhD, Asst Prof, Metaph

    Davis, Gregory, Grad Asst   Warden, John, Grad Asst

INDIANA STATE UNIVERSITY, EVANSVILLE CAMPUS
Evansville, Indiana 47712 (N; st; coed; sem; II; 2624) BA major, Div of Human,
812-426-1251

Mussard, Richard R, PhD, Asst Prof

INDIANA UNIVERSITY AT BLOOMINGTON (See Late Reports for Dept of Hist & Phil of Sci)
Bloomington, Indiana 47401 (N; st; coed; sem; IV; 30,744) PhD major, Dept of Phil,
812-337-9503

Clark, Romane L, PhD, Prof, Chm, Metaph, Epistem
Castaneda, Hector-Neri, PhD, Prof, Ethics, Metaph, Epistem
Cocchiarella, Nino B, PhD, Assoc Prof, Logic and Formal Seman, Found and Phil of
    Math, Phil of Sci
Deutsch, Harry, BA, Lect, Epistem, Phil of Lang, Aes
Dunn, J Michael, PhD, Assoc Prof, Logic and Found of Math
Eisenberg, Paul D, PhD, Assoc Prof, Ethics, Soc and Polit Phil, 17th Cent Phil, Plato
Fisk, Milton T, PhD, Prof, Metaph of Nature, Contemp Soc and Polit Theory
Grossmann, Reinhardt, PhD, Prof, Metaph, Frege, Brentano, Meinong
Hellman, Geoffrey Paul, PhD, Asst Prof, Phil of Ling, Phil of Sci, Epistem, Aes
    Soc Phil
Martin, Edwin, PhD, Asst Prof, Epistem
Nakhnikian, George, PhD, Prof, Ethics, Epistem, Metaph, Descartes, Plato
Pastin, Mark, PhD, Asst Prof, Epistem, Anc Phil, Metaph, Hist of Mod Phil, Phenomen
Spade, Paul V, PhD, Asst Prof, Med Phil
Thompson, Frank, PhD, Asst Prof, Phil of Lang, Phil of Mind, Polit Phil
Tienson, John L, PhD, Asst Prof, Phil of Lang, Phil of Logic, British Empir

Baker, Irwin, NDEA	Macdonald, James, Assoc Instr
Beach, Jane Adele, Assoc Instr	Martin, Richard, NSF
Burks, Steven Vincent, Assoc Instr	Rapaport, William, Res Asst
Chester, Joseph, Assoc Instr	Reilly, James, Assoc Instr
Fales, Kevin, Assoc Instr	Schoenig, Richard K, Assoc Instr
Farris, S Allen, Assoc Instr	Smith, Gene Ward, Assoc Instr
Fedele, Frank, Assoc Instr	Smith, Michael F, Assoc Instr
Ickes, Keith, Assoc Instr	Teichert, Harry W, Assoc Instr
Joseph, Francine, Assoc Instr	Wilt, Lawrence, Assoc Instr
Kapitan, Tomis, Assoc Instr	Yeh, Shin-yun, Assoc Instr
Lesses, Glenn Warren, Assoc Instr	

INDIANA UNIVERSITY AT FORT WAYNE
Fort Wayne, Indiana 46805 (N; st; coed; sem; III; 4402) NP

INDIANA UNIVERSITY AT INDIANAPOLIS
Indianapolis, Indiana 46204 (N; st; coed; sem; IV; 16,580) --, --, 317-639-8717

INDIANA UNIVERSITY AT KOKOMO
Kokomo, Indiana 46901 (N; st; coed; sem; II; 2118) BA joint or combined major, Div
of Human, 317-453-2000 Ext 263

Ranken, Nani L, PhD, Asst Prof

INDIANA UNIVERSITY AT SOUTH BEND
South Bend, Indiana 46615 (N; st; coed; sem; II; 5445) BA major, Dept of Phil,
219-282-2341

Naylor, Andrew, PhD, Asst Prof, Chm, Epistem, Phil of Mind, Polit Phil
Clark, Ann K, PhD, Exchange Prof, Ethics, Aes

Ledoux, Arthur J, BA, Lect Part-time, Ethics
Ringen, Jon D, PhD, Asst Prof, Hist and Phil of Sci, Phil of Psych
Robbins, J Wesley, PhD, Asst Prof, Phil of Relig, Ethics, Epistem
Rogers, C Thomas, BA, Lect, Logic, Decision Theory
Sartorelli, Linda M, BA, Lect, Inductive Logic, Phil of Sci
Stephenson, Gerald H, MA, Lect Part-time, Logic, Phil of Soc Sci
Washburn, Michael C, PhD, Asst Prof, Hist of Phil, Kant, Marxism

INDIANA UNIVERSITY-PURDUE UNIVERSITY AT INDIANAPOLIS
  Indianapolis, Indiana 46202 (N; st; coed; sem; IV; 16,580) BA major, Dept of Phil,
  317-264-8698

  Nagy, Paul, PhD, Assoc Prof, Chm
  Berg, Richard, MA, Assoc Instr
  Byrne, Edmund F, PhD, Assoc Prof, Phil of Sci and Tech
  Cantin, Eileen, PhD, Assoc Instr, Personalism
  Fisher, Gary, MA, Assoc Instr
  Frye, Robert E, PhD, Assoc Prof, Phil of Culture, Greek Phil
  Lampert, Laurence A, PhD, Asst Prof, Hist of Phil
  Learned, Stephen P, MA, Assoc Instr, Phil of Law
  Moore, Edward C, PhD, Prof, Amer Phil
  Owens, L Gary, MA, Assoc Instr
  Riteris, John M, MA, Instr, Phil of Lang

INDIANA UNIVERSITY, EAST CAMPUS
  Richmond, Indiana 47374 (N; st; coed; sem; I; 716) NR

INDIANA UNIVERSITY, NORTHWEST CAMPUS
  Gary, Indiana, 46408 (N; st; coed; sem; V; 4754) Courses with no degree
  specialization, --, 219-887-0111

  Gruenenfelder, Jack, PhD, Assoc Prof, Metaph

INDIANA UNIVERSITY, SOUTHEASTERN CAMPUS
  Jeffersonville, Indiana 47130 (N; st; coed; sem; III; 2689) NR

INTERNATIONAL JUNIOR COLLEGE OF BUSINESS
  Fort Wayne, Indiana 46802 (JRCB; p; coed; qr; I; 520) NR

LINCOLNLAND TECHNICAL INSTITUTE, INDIANA VOCATIONAL TECHNICAL COLLEGE
  Evansville, Indiana 47708 (--; st; coed; qr; I; 457) NP

MALLORY TECHNICAL INSTITUTE, INDIANA VOCATIONAL TECHNICAL COLLEGE
  Indianapolis, Indiana 46260 (--; st; coed; qr; I; 1110) NP

MANCHESTER COLLEGE
  North Manchester, Indiana 46962 (N; Ch of Breth; coed; 4-1-4; II; 1410) BA major,
  Dept of Relig and Phil, 219-982-2141 Ext 250

  Rieman, T Wayne, PhD, Prof, Chm, Phil of Relig
  Brown, Kenneth, PhD, Assoc Prof, Ethics, Soc Phil, Logic
  Dell, Robert, PhD, Asst Prof, Hist of Phil

MARIAN COLLEGE
  Indianapolis, Indiana 46222 (N; RC; coed; sem; II; 923) BA major, Dept of Phil,
  317-924-3291 Ext 555

  Doyle, John J, PhD, Prof, Logic
  Kelly, Denis Ryan, MA, Asst Prof, Chm, Logic
  Pedtke, William, MA, Asst Prof, Ethics

MARION COLLEGE
  Marion, Indiana 46952 (N; Wes Meth; coed; sem; II; 829) BA major, Div of Relig and
  Phil, 317-674-6901

  Thompson, R Duane, PhD, Prof, Chm
  Caldwell, Wayne E, ThD, Asst Prof
  Carter, Charles, ThM, Prof, Orient Phil
  Martin, Glenn, MA, Asst Prof, Polit Phil
  Showalter, Jerry, MA, Asst Prof
  Tippey, Byron L, EdD, Prof, Phil of Educ
  Werking, Robert, EdD, Assoc Prof, Phil of Sci
  William, John P, PhD, Asst Prof, Soc Phil

MENNONITE BIBLICAL SEMINARY
  Elkhart, Indiana 46514 (Theol; Menn; coed; 4-1-4; III; 52) NP

NORTH CENTRAL TECHNICAL INSTITUTE, INDIANA VOCATIONAL TECHNICAL COLLEGE
  Kokomo, Indiana 46901 (--; st; coed; qr; I; 544) NP

NORTHWOOD INSTITUTE, INDIANA BRANCH
  West Baden, Indiana 47469 (--; p; coed; qr; II; 322) NP

OAKLAND CITY COLLEGE
  Oakland City, Indiana 47660 (--; Bapt; coed; qr; II; 665) --, Div of Relig Stud,
  812-749-4781 Ext 39

  Smith, Richard B, ThD, Prof, Chm
  Ford, Clifton, STM, Assoc Prof
  Fry, Virgil, ThD, Assoc Prof

PURDUE UNIVERSITY
  Lafayette, Indiana 47907 (N; st; coed; sem; IV; 26,199) PhD major, Dept of Phil,
  317-749-2517

  Grabau, Richard F, PhD, Prof, Head, Exist, German Phil
  Axel, Larry, MA, Instr, Hist and Phil of Relig
  Barbour, Ian, PhD, Visit Lilly Prof in Sci, Theol and Human Values
  Budlong, Theodore W, PhD, Asst Prof, Phil of Lang, Epistem
  Gustason, William W, PhD, Asst Prof, Logic, Phil of Logic
  Kipnis, Kenneth, PhD, Asst Prof, Moral Phil, Theory of Knowl
  McBride, William L, PhD, Assoc Prof, Soc and Polit Phil
  Maitland, Jeffrey A, PhD, Asst Prof, Aes, Phil Psych
  Mitchell, Donald W, PhD, Asst Prof, Comp Phil
  Noble, Cheryl N, PhD, Asst Prof, Amer Phil, Ethics, Hist of Phil
  Rowe, William L, PhD, Prof, Phil of Relig, Metaph
  Schrag, Calvin O, PhD, Prof, Phenomen, Exist, Metaph
  Scott, T Kermit, PhD, Assoc Prof, Med Phil, Soc Phil

Sosensky, Irving, PhD, Assoc Prof, Phil and Hist of Sci, Mod Phil
Stevens, John C, MA, Instr, Phil of Mind, Ethics
Stevenson, John G, MA, Instr, Greek Phil, Metaph
Ulrich, Dolph E, PhD, Assoc Prof, Logic, Phil of Math
Yamamoto, Yutaka, MA, Instr, Ethics, Polit Phil, Legal Phil

Clitheroe, Eric L, PhD, Prof Emer, Comp Phil

Berg, Richard A, MA, Grad Asst	Parker, Steven H, MA, Grad Asst
Clark, David K, BA, Grad Asst	Simons, Margaret, MA, Grad Asst
Christensen, Lawrence, MA, Grad Instr	Smith, James R, BA, Grad Asst
Luegenbiehl, Heinz C, BA, Grad Asst	Smith, Richard A, MA, Grad Instr
McLaughlin, Michael, BA, Grad Asst	Stillwell, Shelley L, BA, Grad Asst
Owens, L Gary, MA, Grad Asst	Thede, Didrik O, BA, Grad Asst

PURDUE UNIVERSITY, CALUMET CAMPUS
Hammond, Indiana 46323 (N; st; coed; sem; III; 5467) BA minor, Dept of Phil, 219-844-0520

Fischer, Gilbert R, PhD, Assoc Prof
Koenig, Thomas, PhD, Asst Prof, Exist, Phenomen

PURDUE UNIVERSITY, FORT WAYNE CAMPUS
Fort Wayne, Indiana 46805 (N; st; coed; sem; III; 2722) MA major, Dept of Phil, 219-482-5638

Schedler, Norbert, PhD, Prof, Chm, Phil of Relig, Phil of Lang
Bruening, William, PhD, Asst Prof, Ethics
Butler, Clark, PhD, Asst Prof, Metaph, Hegel
Durland, William, JD, Assoc Prof, Ethics, Peace Stud
Churchill, James, PhD, Prof, Phenomen
Fairchild, David, PhD, Asst Prof, Logic, Phenomen
Squadrito, Kathleen, PhD, Asst Prof, Mod Phil, Epistem

Fine, Charles	Lezan, William
Gardiner, Sam	Martello, Ernest
Jacobson, David	Peters, Al
Jones, Barbara	Richards, Beverly

PURDUE UNIVERSITY, NORTH CENTRAL CAMPUS
Westville, Indiana 46205 (N; st; coed; sem; III; 1476) Courses with no degree specialization, --, 219-785-2541

ROSE-HULMAN INSTITUTE OF TECHNOLOGY
Terre Haute, Indiana 47803 (N; p; men; qr; III; 1138) NP

SAINT FRANCIS COLLEGE
Fort Wayne, Indiana 46808 (N; RC; coed; sem; III; 2001) BA major, Dept of Phil and Theol, 219-432-3551

Rausch, Ervin J, MA, Act Head
Gehring, Owen, MA
Govert, Mary Evelyn, MA
John, Richard T, MS
Sullivan, Stephen E, MA

SAINT JOSEPH'S COLLEGE
  Rensselaer, Indiana 47978 (N; RC; coed; sem; II; 1236) BA major, Dept of Phil,
  213-866-7111

  Brindley, Donald, MA, Assoc Prof, Ethics, Anal Phil
  Heiman, Ambrose, PhD, Prof, Phil of Relig, Anc Phil, Med Phil
  Kreilkamp, Donald, PhD, Assoc Prof, Phil of Hist, Anc Phil, Med Phil
  McCarthy, Edward, MA, Assoc Prof, Metaph, Ethics, Epistem
  Nichols, John, PhD, Asst Prof, Phil of Sci, Epistem, Contemp Phil
  Ranly, Ernest, PhD, Assoc Prof, Orient Phil, Phil of Man, Metaph, Exist
  Wood, Robert, PhD, Assoc Prof, Metaph, 19th Cent Phil, Phil of Enlightenment, Exist,
     Plato

SAINT JOSEPH'S COLLEGE, CALUMET CAMPUS
  East Chicago, Indiana 46312 (N; RC; coed; sem; II; 1665) BA major, Dept of Phil,
  219-397-9197 Ext 343

  DuFon, Robert D, MA, Assoc Prof, Chm, Exist
  Baer, Campion, PhD, Assoc Prof, Phil of Educ
  VanLoo, Ina Kay, MA, Instr, Phil of Mind

SAINT JOSEPH'S COLLEGE, CAPUCHIN SEMINARY
  Crown Point, Indiana 46307 (N; RC; men; sem; II; 39) NR

SAINT JOSEPH VALLEY TECHNICAL INSTITUTE, INDIANA VOCATIONAL TECHNICAL COLLEGE
  South Bend, Indiana 46619 (--; st; coed; qr; I; 761) NR

SAINT MARY-OF-THE-WOODS COLLEGE
  Saint Mary-of-the-Woods, Indiana 47876 (N; RC; wo; 4-1-4; II; 392) BA minor, Div
  of Human, 812-533-2181 Ext 210

  Collamati, Ernest J, MA, Asst Prof, Area Advisor
  Galvin, James P, PhD, Prof

SAINT MEINRAD COLLEGE
  Saint Meinrad, Indiana 47577 (N; RC; men; sem; II; 259) BA major, Div of Phil, 812-
  357-6558

  Sweeney, Timothy, PhL, Asst Prof, Chm, Logic, Phil of Man
  Colgan, Quentin, MA, Instr, Hist of Phil
  Ring, Gill, MA, Instr, Ethics, Metaph
  Toon, Mark, PhD, Prof, Hist of Phil

  Thomas, Joseph, MA, Prof Emer

SAINT MEINRAD SCHOOL OF THEOLOGY
  Saint Meinrad, Indiana 47577 (Theol; RC; men; sem; II; 150) NP

TAYLOR UNIVERSITY
  Upland, Indiana 46989 (N; p; coed; sem; II; 1414) BA major, Dept of Phil, 317-
  998-2751 Ext 278

  Nygren, E Herbert, PhD, Prof, Chm
  Ellis, M E, AM, Asst Prof
  Wilson, Charles, PhD, Prof

TRI-STATE COLLEGE
  Angola, Indiana 46703 (N; p; coed; qr; II; 1605) Courses with no degree specialization,
  Dept of Socio-Humanistic Stud, 219-665-3141

  Burney, Thomas, MA, Asst Prof
  Lansford, Theron, MA, Assoc Prof

UNIVERSITY OF EVANSVILLE
  Evansville, Indiana 47701 (N; U Meth; coed; qr; III; 5307) BA major, Dept of Phil
  and Relig, 812-477-6241

  Perkins, Wayne R, PhD, Chm, Tillich, Exist
  Connolly, William, Asst Prof, Lewis
  Godbout, Robert, Asst Prof, Greek Phil, Med Phil, Metaph, Epistem, Ethics,
      Collingwood
  Jones, Harry, Visit Asst Prof
  Ott, Philip, PhD, Asst Prof
  Rusk, Jerry, Asst Prof, Ethics, Phil of Hist, Collingwood

  Erickson, Harris, PhD, Prof Emer

UNIVERSITY OF NOTRE DAME
  Notre Dame, Indiana 46556 (N; RC; coed; sem; IV; 8069) PhD major, Dept of Phil, 219-
  283-6471, 219-283-7534

  Delaney, Cornelius, PhD, Assoc Prof, Chm, Amer Phil, Hist of Mod Phil
  Ameriks, Karl, PhD, Asst Prof, Mod Euro Phil, Phil of Mind
  Bobik, Joseph, PhD, Assoc Prof, Metaph, Med Phil
  Boyle, Jerome, PhD, Prof, Metaph
  Brennan, Sheilah, PhD, Assoc Prof, Metaph, Greek Phil
  Burrell, David, PhD, Assoc Prof, Phil of Relig, Theory of Knowl
  Caponigri, Robert A, PhD, Prof, Hist of Mod Phil, Contemp Euro Phil
  Crosson, Frederick, PhD, Prof, Phenomen, Polit Phil
  Evans, Joseph, PhD, Assoc Prof, Soc and Polit Phil, Maritain
  Goodpaster, Kenneth, PhD, Asst Prof, Ethics
  Gutting, Gary, PhD, Asst Prof, Phil of Phys, Hist of Mod Phil
  Johnston, Herbert, PhD, Assoc Prof, Phil of Educ, Soc Ethics
  Küng, Guido, PhD, Assoc Prof, Phenomen, Seman, Soviet Phil
  Larson, Bruce, PhD, Asst Prof, Polit Phil, Marx
  Loux, Michael, PhD, Asst Prof, Phil of Lang, Metaph
  Manier, Edward, PhD, Assoc Prof, Phil of Biology, Sci and Human Values
  McInerny, Ralph, PhD, Prof, Ethics, Med Phil
  McKim, Vaughn, PhD, Assoc Prof, Phil of Mind, Phil of Soc Sci
  McMullin, Ernan, PhD, Prof, Phil and Hist of Sci
  Mellema, Paul, PhD, Asst Prof, Phil of Lang
  Oesterle, John, PhD, Prof, Ethics, Hist of Logic
  Pahi, Biswambhar, PhD, Asst Prof, Sym Logic, Indian Phil
  Reith, Herman, PhD, Assoc Prof, Phil of Man, Aquinas
  Sayre, Kenneth, PhD, Prof, Theory of Knowl, Phil of Artificial Intell, Plato
  Sobocinski, Boleslaw, PHD, Prof, Sym Logic, Found of Math
  Solomon, David, PhD, Asst Prof, Ethics, Phil of Mind
  Sterba, James, PhD, Asst Prof, Polit Phil, Ethics
  Thomas, Ivo, PhD, Prof, Hist of Logic
  Weiher, Charles, PhD, Assoc Prof, Phil of Nature, Metaph

VALPARAISO UNIVERSITY
  Valparaiso, Indiana 46383 (N; Luth Mo Synod; coed; sem; II; 4652) BA major, Dept
  of Phil, 217-462-5111 Ext 373

  Klein, Kenneth H, PhD, Prof, Chm, Phil of Relig

Scheimann, Richard, PhD, Prof, Phenomen
Smith, John L, MA, Asst Prof, Logic, Anc Phil

VINCENNES UNIVERSITY
Vincennes, Indiana 47591 (N; st; coed; sem; I; 3224) Courses with no degree
specialization, Div of Human, 812-882-3350 Ext 480

Galligan, William G, MS, Assoc Prof
Verkamp, Bernard, PhD, Asst Prof

WABASH COLLEGE
Crawfordsville, Indiana 47933 (N; p; men; sem; II; 790) BA major, Dept of Phil,
317-362-1400

Dean, Eric, PhD, Prof, Chm, Hist of Tht
Greene, Jr, David B, PhD, Assoc Prof, Aes
Hackstaff, L H, PhD, Assoc Prof, Logic

Cotton, J Harry, PhD, Prof Emer, Ling Phil

WABASH VALLEY TECHNICAL INSTITUTE, INDIANA VOCATIONAL COLLEGE
Terre Haute, Indiana 47802 (--; st; coed; qr; I; 461) NP

WHITE RIVER VALLEY TECHNICAL INSTITUTE, INDIANA VOCATIONAL COLLEGE
Columbus, Indiana 47201 (--; st; coed; qr; I; 257) NP

IOWA

AQUINAS INSTITUTE OF THEOLOGY
Dubuque, Iowa 52001 (N; RC; coed; 4-1-4; IV; 138) MA major, Dept of Phil, 319-583-
6406

Wilder, Alfred, STL, Chm, Ethics
Ashley, Benedict, PhD, Hist of Phil
Powell, Ralph, PhD, Metaph
Zusy, Dennis, PhD

BRIAR CLIFF COLLEGE
Sioux City, Iowa 51104 (N; RC; coed; --; II; 1096) BA joint or combined major,
Dept of Theol and Phil, 712-279-5486

Ermak, Paul J, BA, Instr

BUENA VISTA COLLEGE
Storm Lake, Iowa 50588 (N U Preb; coed; 4-1-4; II; 884) BA joint or combined major,
Div of Relig and Phil, 712-749-2263

Tollefson, Robert J, PhD, Prof, Chm
Partee, Charles B, PhD, Assoc Prof

CENTRAL UNIVERSITY OF IOWA
Pella, Iowa 50219 (N; Ref; coed; --; II; 1253) BA major, Dept of Phil, 515-628-4151 Ext 243

Paul, William W, PhD, Prof, Chm, Phil of Hist, Ethics
Heerema, Robert P, PhD, Asst Prof, Logic, Phil of Lang
Heideman, Eugene, ThD, Prof, Phil of Relig

CLARKE COLLEGE
Dubuque, Iowa 52001 (N; RC; wo; sem; III; 733) BA minor, Dept of Phil, 319-588-6311, 6317

Garvey, Rita, MA, Instr, Chm
Doering, Mary Louann, MA, Instr

CLINTON COMMUNITY COLLEGE
Clinton, Iowa 52732 (--; st and local; coed; sem; I; 568) NR

COE COLLEGE
Cedar Rapids, Iowa 52402 (N; p; coed; 4-1-4; II; 1164) BA major, Dept of Phil and Relig, 319-364-1511 Ext 297, 298

Peel, Malcolm L, PhD, Assoc Prof, Chm, Phil of Relig
Cox, Ronald, PhD, Asst Prof, Anal and Continen Phil
Kirshbaum, Harold, MA, Instr, Soc Phil

Settle, Edwin T, PhD, Prof Emer, Phil of Relig

COLLEGE OF OSTEOPATHIC MEDICINE AND SURGERY
Des Moines, Iowa 50309 (Osteo; p; coed; sem; V; 398) NP

CORNELL COLLEGE
Mount Vernon, Iowa 52314 (N; p; coed; sem; II; 988) BA major, Dept of Phil, 319-895-8811 Ext 79

Debbins, William, PhD, Prof, Chm, Ethics
Gray, Paul, PhD, Asst Prof, Epistem

DES MOINES AREA COMMUNITY COLLEGE, ANKENY CAMPUS
Ankeny, Iowa 50021 (--; st and local; coed; qr; I; 2273) Courses with no degree specialization, Dept of Gen Educ, 515-964-0651 Ext 388

Jorgensen, Ole, MPhil, Instr

DES MOINES AREA COMMUNITY COLLEGE, BOONE CAMPUS
Boone, Iowa 50036 (--; st; coed; qr; I; 513) Courses with no degree specialization, Div of Gen Human, 515-432-7203

Bodine, Paul E, MA, Instr, Phil of Relig

DIVINE WORD COLLEGE
Epworth, Iowa 52045 (N; RC; men; sem; II; 114) BA major, Dept of Phil and Theol, 319-876-3362

Fitzgibbon, William E, PhD, Prof, Chm, Phil of Sci
Ernest, Stephen T, PhD, Assoc Prof, Amer Phil
Heisig, James W, MA, Asst Prof, Phil of Relig
Wrocklage, Bernard P, MA, Assoc Prof, Exist

DORDT COLLEGE
Sioux Center, Iowa 51250 (N; Chris Ref; coed; sem; II; 970) BA major, --, 712-722-3771

Van Dyk, MA, Asst Prof, Anc and Med Phil
Van Til, Nick R, MA, Prof, Phil of Relig, Ethics
Vander Stelt, John, Doct, Assoc Prof, Mod and Contemp Phil

DRAKE UNIVERSITY
Des Moines, Iowa 50311 (N; p; coed; sem; IV; 7713) MA minor, Dept of Phil and Relig, 515-271-3170

Beardsley, Harry, MA, Lect Part-time, Phil of Relig
Hock, Raymond, PhD, Assoc Prof, Phil of Human Devel
Keyworth, Donald, PhD, Prof, Phil of Relig
Miller, Dale, PhD, Prof, Ethics
Torgeson, Jon, MA, Instr, Phil of Time

EASTERN IOWA COMMUNITY COLLEGE, CLINTON CAMPUS
Clinton, Iowa 52732 (--; st and local; coed; sem; I; 568) NP

EASTERN IOWA COMMUNITY COLLEGE, MUSCATINE CAMPUS
Muscatine, Iowa 52761 (N; st and local; coed; qr; I; 618) NP

ELLSWORTH COMMUNITY COLLEGE
Iowa Falls, Iowa 50126 (N; st and local; coed; sem; I; 1062) NP

FAITH BAPTIST BIBLE COLLEGE
Ankeny, Iowa 50021 (BI; p; coed; sem; II; 426) Courses with no degree specialization, Dept of Gen Educ, 515-964-0601

Kober, Manfred, ThD, Assoc Prof

GRACELAND COLLEGE
Lamoni, Iowa 50140 (N; Reorg LDS; coed; 4-1-4; II; 1349) Courses with no degree specialization, Div of Soc Sci, 515-784-3311 Ext 142

Edwards, Paul M, PhD, Prof, Chm, Epistem
Steele, Dennis, Asst Prof, Logic

GRAND VIEW COLLEGE
Des Moines, Iowa 50140 (N; Luth CA; coed; sem; I; 1214) Courses with no degree specialization, Dept of Relig and Phil, 515-265-4232

Zinger, STM, Assoc Prof, Phil of Relig

GRINNELL COLLEGE
  Centerville, Iowa 52544 (N; p; coed; sem; I; 1304) BA major, Div of Soc Stud,
  515-236-6181

HAWKEYE INSTITUTE OF TECHNOLOGY
  Waterloo, Iowa 50704 (--; st and local; coed; qr; I; 1144) NR

INDIAN HILLS COMMUNITY COLLEGE, CENTERVILLE CAMPUS
  Centerville, Iowa 52544 (--; local; coed; sem; I; 531) Courses with no degree
  specialization, Dept of Soc Sci, 515-856-2143 Ext 56

  Dickerson, Charles, MS

INDIAN HILLS COMMUNITY COLLEGE, OTTUMWA CAMPUS
  Ottumwa, Iowa 52501 (--; st and local; coed; qr; I; 579) NR

IOWA CENTRAL COMMUNITY COLLEGE, EAGLE GROVE CAMPUS
  Eagle Grove, Iowa 50533 (--; local; coed; sem; I; 168) NR

IOWA CENTRAL COMMUNITY COLLEGE, FORT DODGE
  Fort Dodge, Iowa 50501 (--; local; coed; sem; I; 1761) NP

IOWA CENTRAL COMMUNITY COLLEGE, WEBSTER CITY
  Webster City, Iowa 50595 (--; local; coed; sem; I; 231) NP

IOWA LAKES COMMUNITY COLLEGE, NORTH CAMPUS
  Estherville, Iowa 51334 (--; st and local; coed; qr; I; 443) NP

IOWA LAKES COMMUNITY COLLEGE, SOUTH CAMPUS
  Emmetsburg, Iowa 50536 (--; st and local; coed; qr; I; 582) NR

IOWA STATE UNIVERSITY OF SCIENCE AND TECHNOLOGY
  Ames, Iowa 50010 (N; st; coed; qr; IV; 19,790) BA major, Dept of Phil, 515-294-7276

  Van Iten, Richard J, PhD, Prof, Chm
  Alexander, J Davidson, PhD, Asst Prof
  Elrod, John, PhD, Asst Prof
  Harder, Allen, PhD, Asst Prof
  Hollenbach, Paul, PhD, Assoc Prof
  Jobe, Evan, PhD, Asst Prof
  Kottman, Karl, PhD, Asst Prof
  Kupfer, Joseph, PhD, Asst Prof
  Robinson, William, PhD, Asst Prof
  Solomon, Ted, PhD, Assoc Prof

IOWA WESLEYAN COLLEGE
  Mt Pleasant, Iowa 52641 (N; U Meth; coed; 4-1-4; II; 870) BA major, Dept of Relig
  and Phil, 319-385-8021 Ext 255

La More, Jr, George E, ThD, Prof, Chm, Phil of Relig
Kahn, Theodore, PhD, Prof, Metaph
Richards, Jerry, M Div, Asst Prof

IOWA WESTERN COMMUNITY COLLEGE
    Council Bluffs, Iowa 51501 (--; st; coed; qr; I; 1010) --, Dept of Arts and Sci,
    712-328-3831

    Berg, Donald J, MS, Instr

IOWA WESTERN COMMUNITY COLLEGE, CLARINDA CAMPUS
    Clarinda, Iowa 51632 (--; st; coed; qr; I; 396) Courses with no degree specialization,
    --, 712-542-5117

KIRKWOOD COMMUNITY COLLEGE
    Cedar Rapids, Iowa 52406 (N; local; coed; qr; I; 2878) Courses with no degree
    specialization, Dept of Soc Sci, 319-398-5533

    Morse, Mark, MA, Part-time Instr

LORAS COLLEGE
    Dubuque, Iowa 52001 (N; RC; coed; sem; III; 1537) BA major, Dept of Phil, 319-
    588-7100

    Brogan, Harold, MA, Instr, Chm, Contemp Phil
    Chappell, James, MA, Instr
    Howe, Richard, MA, Asst Prof, Marxism, Anc Phil
    Lang, Anthony, PhD, Prof, Metaph, Aes
    Wheeler, Lawrence Wellington, MA, Asst Prof, Ethics

LUTHER COLLEGE
    Decorah, Iowa 52101 (N; Luth; coed; 4-1-4; II; 2036) BA major, Dept of Phil, 319-
    382-3621

    Ylvisaker, Richard, PhD, Prof, Chm, Hist of Phil, Contemp Phil, Metaph, Aes, Bradley
    Linnell, John, PhD, Prof Part-time, Hist of Phil, Logic, Contemp Anal Phil, Locke-
        Berkeley, John Wisdom
    Simmonds, Kent, PhD, Asst Prof, Hist of Phil, Phil of Relig, Ethics, Plato
    Wrightsman, Bruce, PhD, Assoc Prof Part-time, Hist and Phil of Sci, Phil of Relig

MARSHALLTOWN COMMUNITY COLLEGE
    Marshalltown, Iowa 50158 (N; st and local; coed; sem; I; 951) NP

MARYCREST COLLEGE
    Davenport, Iowa 52804 (N; RC; coed; 4-1-4; III; 1080) BA minor, Dept of Phil, 319-
    326-9512

    Buckley, Eugene C, PhD, Asst Prof
    Nahra, Joseph A, MA, Instr

MORNINGSIDE COLLEGE
    Sioux City, Iowa 51106 (N; U Meth; coed; sem; III; 1643) BA major, Dept of Phil,
    712-277-5186

    Lawrence, John, PhD, Assoc Prof, Chm, Soc and Polit Phil
    Gilbert, Thomas, PhD, Asst Prof, Ethics and Soc Phil

MOUNT MERCY COLLEGE
  Cedar Rapids, Iowa 52402 (N; RC; coed; 4-1-4; II; 649) BA minor, Div of Phil and
  Theol, 319-363-8213

  Ryan, Mary Monica, MA, Asst Prof, Chm
  McMaster, Robert K, MA, Instr

MOUNT SAINT CLARE COLLEGE
  Clinton, Iowa 52732 (N; RC; coed; sem; I; 251) Courses with no degree specialization,
  Dept of Phil, 319-242-4023

  McCue, Mary William, MA

MUSCATINE COMMUNITY COLLEGE
  Muscatine, Iowa 52761 (N; st and local; coed; qr; I; 618) NR

NORTHEAST IOWA VOCATIONAL TECHNICAL SCHOOL
  Calmar, Iowa 52132 (--; local; coed; qr; I; 801) NR

NORTHERN IOWA AREA COMMUNITY COLLEGE
  Mason City, Iowa 51041 (N; st and local; coed; sem; I; 1562) NP

NORTHWESTERN COLLEGE
  Orange City, Iowa 51041 (N; Ref; coed; sem; II; 691) BA major, Dept of Phil, 712-
  737-4821 Ext 30

  Tratebas, Edmund W, MA, Assoc Prof, Chm, Hist of Phil, Phil of Relig
  Kennedy, Earl William, ThD, Prof, Phil of Hist

OTTUMWA HEIGHTS COLLEGE
  Ottumwa, Iowa 52501 (N; RC; coed; 4-1-4; I; 348) Courses with no degree
  specialization, Div of Human, 515-682-4551 Ext 26

  Atkin, Eugene L, MA, Ethics

PALMER JUNIOR COLLEGE
  Davenport, Iowa 52501 (--; p; coed; sem; I; 527) Courses with no degree
  specialization, Dept of Phil, 319-324-0835

  Rybka, Hester W, MA, Ethics, Phil of Relig

PARSONS COLLEGE
  Fairfield, Iowa 52803 (N; p; coed; tri; II; 1270) BA major, --, 515-699-8300

  Fulton, Robert B, PhD, Prof
  Huffman, Robert E, MA, Instr
  Snedden, James A, PhD, Prof

SAINT AMBROSE COLLEGE
  Davenport, Iowa 52803 (N; RC; coed; sem; I; 1336) BA major, Dept of Phil, 319-324-
  1681 Ext 252

  Fitzgibbon, John F, PhD, Prof, Chm, Metaph, Ethics, Med Phil
  Dawson, William, PhD, Assoc Prof, Ethics, Logical Anal, Contemp Phil

IOWA

McCaffrey, Joseph, PhD, Assoc Prof, Anc and Mod Phil, Ethics of Sexuality, Epistem
Nahra, Joseph, Lect, Exist, Phenomen

SCOTT COMMUNITY COLLEGE
Davenport, Iowa 52807 (--; st and local; coed; qr; I; 545) NP

SIMPSON COLLEGE
Indianola, Iowa 50125 (N; U Meth; coed; 4-1-4; II; 957) BA major, Dept of Phil,
515-961-6251 Ext 650

Thomas, Norman L, PhD, Prof, Chm, Ethics, Logic
Haddox, M Bruce, PhD, Asst Prof, Epistem
Holder, Fred L, PhD, Assoc Prof, Metaph
Ingram, Paul O, PhD, Assoc Prof, Far East Phil, Relig and Phil

SOUTHEASTERN COMMUNITY COLLEGE, BURLINGTON CAMPUS
West Burlington, Iowa 52655 (--; st and local; coed; qr; I; 952) Courses with no
degree specialization, Dept of Human, 319-752-2731 Ext 29

Haskell, Jonan, MA, Chm
Awbrey, David, MA, Med Phil

SOUTHEASTERN COMMUNITY COLLEGE, SOUTH CAMPUS
Keokuk, Iowa 52632 (--; st and local; coed; qr; I; 435) Courses with no degree
specialization, Dept of Soc Sci, 319-524-3221

Figge, Frederick William, MA, Instr

SOUTHWESTERN COMMUNITY COLLEGE
Creston, Iowa 50801 (--; st; coed; sem; I; 469) NP

UNIVERSITY OF DUBUQUE
Dubuque, Iowa 52001 (N; U Preb; coed; sem; III; 1103) BA major, Dept of Phil, 319-
557-2121

Pease, Kenneth R, MA, Asst Prof, Epistem, Phil of Relig

UNIVERSITY OF IOWA
Iowa City, Iowa 52240 (N; st; coed; sem; IV; 20,981) PhD major, Dept of Phil, 319-
353-5254

Butchvarov, Panayot, PhD, Prof, Chm, Epistem, Metaph
Addis, Laird, PhD, Assoc Prof, Phil of the Soc Sci, Metaph
Bergmann, Gustav, PhD, Prof, Ontology, Phil of Logic
Cummins, Phillip, PhD, Assoc Prof, Hist of Mod Phil
Gram, Moltke, PhD, Assoc Prof, Hist of Mod Phil, Metaph
Duerlinger, James, PhD, Assoc Prof, Hist of Anc Phil
Ostien, Philip, PhD, Asst Prof, Logic, Phil of Sci
Snare, Francis, PhD, Asst Prof, Ethics, Polit Phil

Ahrens, John, BA, Fel
Bradford, Dennis, BA, Grad Asst
Carroll, Michael, MA, Grad Asst
Casullo, Albert, BA, Grad Asst
Dejnozka, Jan, BA, Fel
Fink, Thomas, BA, Grad Asst
Kemerling, Garth, MA, Grad Asst
Kenshur, Deborah, BA, Grad Asst
Kent, Otis, BA, Grad Asst
Konefes, James, BA, Fel
Kovarik, James, BA, Grad Asst
Morse, Mark, MA, Grad Asst

Flage, Daniel, BA, Grad Asst   Spencer, Theodore, BA, Grad Asst
Hickman, David, BA, Grad Asst

UNIVERSITY OF NORTHERN IOWA
   Cedar Falls, Iowa 50613 (N; st; coed; sem; III; 10,234) BA major, Dept of Phil and
   Relig, 319-273-6221

   Thompson, Thomas, PhD, Prof, Head, Hist of Phil, Aes
   Bluhm, David, PhD, Prof, Prag, Phil of Relig
   Crownfield, David, ThD, Prof, Phenomen, Exist
   Fox, Josef, PhD, Prof, Ethics
   Hallberg, Fred, PhD, Assoc Prof, Hist of Phil, Epistem
   Morgan, David, MA, Asst Prof, Logic, Phil of Sci

UPPER IOWA UNIVERSITY
   Fayette, Iowa 52142 (N; p; coed; 4-1-4; II; 1009) BA joint or combined major, Dept
   of Phil and Relig, 319-425-3311

   Wilcox, William, PhD, Prof, Hist of Amer Christ Tht

VENNARD COLLEGE
   University Park, Iowa 52595 (BI; p; coed; sem; III; 187) Courses with no degree
   specialization, Dept of Theol and Phil, 515-673-8391

   Sprunk, Ralph, BD, Assoc Prof, Chm
   Henning, Robert, M Div, Asst Prof

WALDORF COLLEGE
   Forest City, Iowa 50436 (N; Luth; coed; sem; I; 540) Courses with no degree
   specialization, Div of Bib, Phil, and Christ Ed, 515-582-2450 Ext 215

   Hamre, James S, PhD, Assoc Prof, Chm

WARTBURG COLLEGE
   Waverly, Iowa 50677 (N; A Luth; coed; --; II; 1361) BA major, Dept of Phil, 319-
   352-1200 Ext 315

   Gumz, F A, PhD, Prof, Chm, Logic, Epistem, Phil of Sci
   Alexander, R, ThD, Asst Prof, Hist of Relig
   Giess, W, MA, Assoc Prof, Phil of Relig, Orient Phil

WARTBURG THEOLOGICAL SEMINARY
   Dubuque, Iowa 52001 (Theol; Luth; coed; 4-1-4; III; 219) NP

WESTMAR COLLEGE
   LeMars, Iowa 51031 (N; U Meth; coed; 4-1-4; 979) BA minor, Dept of Phil and Relig,
   712-546-7081 Ext 368, 369

   Davis, Merrill C, PhD, Prof, Chm, Metaph, Ethics, Phil of Relig
   Aldana, Manuel, PhD, Assoc Prof, Soc Phil
   Vogel, Dwight W, PhD, Assoc Prof, Axiology

   Thompson, G O, PhD, Prof Emer, Metaph, Phil of Relig

WILLIAM PENN COLLEGE
  Oskaloosa, Iowa 52577 (N; Fr; coed; sem; II; 859) BA minor, Dept of Relig and Phil,
  515-673-8311

  Bowman, Allen, STM, Assoc Prof
  Good, Donald G, PhD, Prof

KANSAS

ALLEN COUNTY COMMUNITY JUNIOR COLLEGE
  Iola, Kansas, 66749 (--; local; coed; sem; I; 512) Courses with no degree
  specialization, Dept of Soc Sci, 316-365-5116

  Tillotson, Elroy E, MA, Instr

BAKER UNIVERSITY
  Baldwin City, Kansas 66006 (N; U Meth; coed; 4-1-4; II; 868) BA major, Dept of
  Relig and Phil, 913-594-6451 Ext 486

  Doudna, John Charles, PhD, Prof
  Rose, Larry, PhD, Assoc Prof
  Ruhlen, Ralph, PhD, Prof

BARTON COUNTY COMMUNITY JUNIOR COLLEGE
  Great Bend, Kansas 67530 (--; local; coed; sem; I; 1153) Courses with no degree
  specialization, Dept of Phil, 316-792-2701 Ext 73

  Biays, Paul M, M Div, Instr, Phil of Relig

BENEDICTINE COLLEGE
  Atchison, Kansas 66002 (N; RC; coed; 4-1-4; II; 1288) BA major, Dept of Phil, 913-
  367-5340 Ext 200

  Horrigan, Kevin, PhL, Asst Prof, Chm, Med Phil, Phil of Nature
  Eggers, John, PhL, Asst Prof, Metaph
  Hubbard, J Macoubrey, PhL, Asst Prof, Phil of Sci
  O'Brien, Joseph, MA, Instr, Ethics
  Scholz, Donald, PhD, Assoc Prof, Phil of Man, Polit Phil

BETHANY COLLEGE
  Lindsborg, Kansas 67456 (N; Luth; coed; 4-1-4; II; 689) BA major, Dept of Relig
  and Phil, 913-227-3312 Ext 60

  Hansen, Carl L, ThM, Assoc Prof
  Swanson, Stanley H, MA, Prof, East Phil

BETHEL COLLEGE
   North Newton, Kansas 67117 (N; Menn; coed; 4-1-4; II; 481) BA major, Dept of Phil,
   316-283-2500

   Gross, Harold H, PhD, Prof, Chm, Ethics, Phil of Relig
   Deckert, Marion, PhD, Prof, Logic, Epistem

BUTLER COUNTY COMMUNITY JUNIOR COLLEGE
   El Dorado, Kansas 67042 (N; local; coed; sem; I; 1724) Courses with no degree
   specialization, Dept of Soc Sci, 316-321-5083

   Kreller, Herbert J, MS

CENTRAL BAPTIST THEOLOGICAL SEMINARY
   Kansas City, Kansas 66102 (Theol; Bapt; coed; 4-1-4; II; 65) Courses with no degree
   specialization, Dept of Theol, 913-371-5313

   Budesheim, Thomas L, ThD, Assoc Prof, Chm

CENTRAL COLLEGE
   McPherson, Kansas 67460 (--; Meth; coed; 4-1-4; I; 184) Courses with no degree
   specialization, Dept of Phil and Relig, 316-241-0723

   Bailey, Robert Q, ThM

CLOUD COUNTY COMMUNITY JUNIOR COLLEGE
   Concordia, Kansas 66901 (--; local; coed; sem; I; 648) Courses with no degree
   specialization, --, 913-243-1435

COFFEYVILLE COMMUNITY JUNIOR COLLEGE
   Coffeyville, Kansas 67337 (N; st and local; coed; sem; I; 768) NP

COLBY COMMUNITY JUNIOR COLLEGE
   Colby, Kansas 67701 (N; st and local; coed; sem; I; 935) NP

COLLEGE OF EMPORIA
   Emporia, Kansas 66801 (N; Preb; coed; sem; II; 600) BA major, Dept of Phil and
   Relig, 316-342-3670

   Broadhurst, Frances N, MA, Asst Prof, Chm
   McCarty, Charles L, MA, Asst Prof

COWLEY COUNTY COMMUNITY JUNIOR COLLEGE
   Arkansas City, Kansas 67005 (--; local; coed; sem; I; 771) Courses with no degree
   specialization, --, 316-442-0430

DODGE CITY COMMUNITY JUNIOR COLLEGE
   Dodge City, Kansas 67801 (N; local; coed; sem; I; 949) NP

DONNELLY COLLEGE
   Kansas City, Kansas 66102(N; RC; coed; sem; I; 627) AA major, Dept of Relig and
   Phil, 913-342-2447

129

Moriones, Francis, STL, Chm
Minton, Virginia, MA, Dean
Oldfield, John J, PhD, Pres, Phil of Man

FORT HAYS KANSAS STATE COLLEGE
Hays, Kansas 67601 (N; st; coed; sem; III; 5246) MA minor, Dept of Phil, 913-628-4000

Hamilton, Sam M, EdD, Prof, Chm
Tramel, Stephen G, PhD, Asst Prof, Logic

FORT SCOTT COMMUNITY JUNIOR COLLEGE
Fort Scott, Kansas 66701 (--; local; coed; sem; I; 601) NP

FRIENDS BIBLE COLLEGE
Haviland, Kansas 67059 (--; p; coed; sem; II; 124) Courses with no degree specialization, Dept of Soc Sci, 316-862-5248

Johnson, Fred R, MS, Asst Prof

FRIENDS UNIVERSITY
Wichita, Kansas 67213 (N; Fr; coed; qr; II; 922) BA joint or combined major, Dept of Phil, 316-263-9131 Ext 262

Nickel, J W, ThD, Prof, Chm, Ethics, Phil of Relig

GARDEN CITY COMMUNITY JUNIOR COLLEGE
Garden City, Kansas 67846 (--; local; coed; sem; I; 784) Courses with no degree specialization, Dept of Psych and Phil, 316-276-7611

Zhiri, Del, PhD, Instr, Chm

HASKELL INDIAN JUNIOR COLLEGE
Lawrence, Kansas 66044 (--; Fed; coed; sem; I; 1316) NR

HESSTON COLLEGE
Hesston, Kansas 67062 (N; Menn; coed; 4-1-4; I; 457) NP

HIGHLAND COMMUNITY JUNIOR COLLEGE
Highland, Kansas 66035 (--; local; coed; sem; I; 613) NR

HUTCHINSON COMMUNITY JUNIOR COLLEGE
Hutchinson, Kansas 67501 (N; st and local; coed; sem; I; 2210) Courses with no degree specialization, Dept of Arts and Human, 316-663-2156 Ext 62

Schinstock, Jim, MA

INDEPENDENCE COMMUNITY JUNIOR COLLEGE
Independence, Kansas 67301 (N; local; coed; sem; I; 576) --, Dept of Soc Sci, 316-331-4100

Foree, Robert L, EdD, Dean

JOHNSON COUNTY COMMUNITY COLLEGE
Overland Park, Kansas 66210 (--; local; coed; sem; I; 3118) Courses with no degree specialization, Div of Human, 913-888-8500 Ext 411, 351

Cunningham, Alan, BA, Instr, Chm, Soc, Polit and Moral Euro Phil
Yeargain, Scott, PhD, Instr, Soc and Polit Phil, Exist, Phil of Relig

KANSAS CITY KANSAS COMMUNITY COLLEGE
Kansas City, Kansas 66112 (N; local; coed; sem; I; 1892) Courses with no degree specialization, Div of Soc Sci, 913-334-1100 Ext 32

Bridges, Ruth, MA, Instr
Clark, Ken, Part-time Instr

KANSAS NEWMAN COLLEGE
Wichita, Kansas 67213 (N; RC; coed; sem; II; 624) Courses with no degree specialization, --, 316-942-4291

Schmidt, Delphine, MA, Asst Prof, Chm, Metaph
Nickel, Jacob, PhD, Prof, Ethics
Soles, David, MA, Instr, Hist of Phil

KANSAS STATE COLLEGE OF PITTSBURG
Pittsburg, Kansas 66762 (N; st; coed; sem; III; 6320) BA joint or combined major, Dept of Soc Sci, 316-231-7000 Ext 251

Stevens, Morris L, PhD, Prof, Chm
Lebrato, C Michael, MA, Asst Prof
Marshall, John M, MA, Asst Prof

KANSAS STATE TEACHERS COLLEGE
Emporia, Kansas 66801 (N; st; coed; sem; III; 7478) BA major, Dept of Phil, 316-343-1200 Ext 461

Roark, Dallas M, PhD, Prof, Chm, Phil of Relig
Dumas, David, MA, Asst Prof

KANSAS STATE UNIVERSITY
Manhattan, Kansas 66506 (N; st; coed; sem; IV; 14,789) PhD minor, Dept of Phil, 913-532-6758

Tilghman, Benjamin R, PhD, Prof, Chm, Aes
Exdell, John B, PhD, Asst Prof, Ethics, Polit Phil
Greenberg, Arthur R, PhD, Asst Prof, Hist of Phil, Phil of Soc Sci
Hamilton, James R, MA, Instr, Phil of Math, Phil of Relig
O'Neil, Michael P, PhD, Asst Prof, Logic, Phil of Sci
Reagan, Charles E, PhD, Assoc Prof, Ethics, Continen Euro Phil
Scheer, Richard K, PhD, Assoc Prof, Logic, Epistem

Miller, Cecil H, MA, Prof Emer

KANSAS TECHNICAL INSTITUTE
Salina, Kansas 67401 (--; st; coed; sem; I; 220) NP

KANSAS WESLEYAN UNIVERSITY
  Salina, Kansas 67401 (N; U Meth; coed; 4-1-4; II; 568) BA major, Div of Human, 913-827-5541

  Durkin, Thomas J, MA, Prof, Aes

  Cassell, Walter E, MA, Prof Emer, Phil of Relig

LABETTE COMMUNITY JUNIOR COLLEGE
  Parsons, Kansas 67357 (--; local; coed; sem; I; 548) Courses with no degree specialization, --, 316-421-6700

  Sullins, Max, MA

MANHATTAN CHRISTIAN COLLEGE
  Manhattan, Kansas 66502 (BI; p; coed; sem; II; 171) Dept of Human, 913-539-3571

  Eggleton, John, PhD, Prof
  Van Buren, James G, PhD, Prof

MARYMOUNT COLLEGE
  Salina, Kansas 67401 (N; RC; coed; sem; II; 571) Courses with no degree specialization, Dept of Phil, 913-823-6317

  Schneider, Monica, PhD, Prof, Chm, Contemp Phil, Metaph
  Schimoler, Robert, Asst Prof, Mod Phil, Ethics

MCPHERSON COLLEGE
  McPherson, Kansas 67460 (N; Ch of Breth; coed; 4-1-4; II; 578) BA joint or combined major, Dept of Phil and Relig, 316-241-0731

  Goldsmith, Dale, PhD, Assoc Prof, Chm
  Lengel, Leland, PhD, Prof

MID-AMERICAN NAZARENE COLLEGE
  Olathe, Kansas 66061 (--; Naz; coed; sem; II; 812) BA minor, Div or Relig and Phil, 913-782-3750

NEOSHO COUNTY COMMUNITY JUNIOR COLLEGE
  Chanute, Kansas 66720 (--; local; coed; sem; I; 514) NP

OTTAWA UNIVERSITY
  Ottawa, Kansas 66067 (N; A Bapt; coed; 4-1-4; II; 759) BA major, Dept of Phil, 913-242-5200 Ext 237

  Meyers, Leonard L, PhD, Assoc Prof, Chm, Ethics, Hist of Phil
  Sandstrom, Peter G, PhD, Asst Prof, Ling Phil, Hist of Phil

PRATT COMMUNITY JUNIOR COLLEGE
  Pratt, Kansas 67124 (--; local; coed; sem; I; 542) NP

SAINT JOHN'S COLLEGE
  Winfield, Kansas 67156 (N; Luth; coed; 4-1-4; I; 283) NP

SAINT MARY COLLEGE
  Leavenworth, Kansas 66048 (N; RC; wo; 4-1-4; II; 602) BA major, --, 913-682-5151

  De Coursey, Mary Edwin, PhD

SAINT MARY OF THE PLAINS COLLEGE
  Dodge City, Kansas 67801 (N; RC; coed; 4-1-4; II; 467) BA minor, Div of Human, 316-225-4171 Ext 63

  Paulie, M Julita, MS, Asst Prof

SEWARD COUNTY COMMUNITY JUNIOR COLLEGE
  Liberal, Kansas 67901 (--; st; coed; sem; I; 532) --, Dept of Educ, 316-624-4481

SOUTHWESTERN COLLEGE
  Winfield, Kansas 67156 (N; U Meth; coed; 4-1-4; II; 611) BA joint or combined major, Dept of Phil and Relig, 316-221-4150 Ext 53

  Gray, Wallace, PhD, Prof, East and West Phil

STERLING COLLEGE
  Sterling, Kansas 67579 (N; U Preb; coed; 4-1-4; II; 524) NP

TABOR COLLEGE
  Hillsboro, Kansas 67063 (N; Menn Breth; coed; 4-1-4; II; 412) BA minor, Dept of Bib and Phil, 316-947-3121

  Clinton, Steve, M Div, Instr, Phil of Relig
  Hiebert, Clarence, PhD, Assoc Prof

UNIVERSITY OF KANSAS
  Lawrence, Kansas 66044 (N; st; coed; sem; IV; 21,232) PhD major, Dept of Phil, 913-864-3131

  Martin, Rex, PhD, Prof, Chm, Polit Phil
  Bricke, John, PhD, Asst Prof, Hume, Phil of Mind
  Brownstein, Donald, PhD, Asst Prof, Metaph
  Cole, Richard, PhD, Prof, Phil of Sci, Logic
  DeGeorge, Richard, PhD, Univ Prof, Soviet Phil, Ethics
  Genova, Anthony, PhD, Prof, Metaph, Hist of Phil,
  Marquis, Donald, PhD, Asst Prof, Phil of Sci, Phil of Hist
  Morse, Warner, PhD, Asst Prof, Ethics, Hist of Phil
  Shapiro, Gary, PhD, Asst Prof, Aes, Prag
  Skidmore, Arthur, PhD, Asst Prof, Logic, Phil of Sci
  Verdu, Alfonzo, PhD, Prof, Orient Phil, Hist of Phil
  Woelfel, James, PhD, Assoc Prof, Phil of Relig
  Young, Michael, PhD, Asst Prof, Kant, Metaph

  Osborne, Clifford, PhD, Prof Emer, Hist of Phil
  Wolf, John, MA, Lect Emer, Hist of Phil

  Cook, James, M Phil, NDEA   McCloud, Lawrence, BA, Grad Asst
  Duda, George, MA, Grad Asst   Nemeth, Thomas, BA, Grad Asst
  George, Timothy, BA, Grad Asst   Schlee, Charles, MA, Grad Asst
  Hall, Robert, BA, Grad Asst   Schmidt, David, BA, Grad Asst
  Hilty, E J, MA, Templin Fel   Ssekasozi, Englebert, MA, Grad Honors Fel
  Johnson, Deborah, BA, NDEA   Tabor, John, MA, Grad Exchange Fel

WASHBURN UNIVERSITY OF TOPEKA
    Topeka, Kansas 66621 (N; local; coed; sem; II; 5196) BA major, Dept of Phil, 913-235-5341 Ext 315

    Shepard, Darrell R, PhD, Assoc Prof, Chm, Hist of Phil, Phil of Hist
    Alksnis, Gunnar, PhD, Asst Prof, Ethics, Phil of Hist
    Homlish, John, PhD, Asst Prof, Phil of Relig
    Nobo, Jorge L, PhD, Asst Prof, Metaph, Amer Phil
    Rood, Harold J, MA, Instr, Logic, Phil of Sci, Aes
    Samuel, Peter, PhD, Asst Prof, Ethics, Phil of Law, Soc and Polit Phil

    French, Merton B, PhD, Prof Emer

WICHITA STATE UNIVERSITY
    Wichita, Kansas 67208 (N; st; coed; sem; IV; 13,034) MA major, Dept of Phil, 316-689-3125

    Paske, Gerald H, PhD, Assoc Prof, Chm
    Fulton, James A, PHD, Asst Prof
    Gotterbarn, Donald, PhD, Asst Prof
    Gross, Damon J, PhD, Asst Prof
    Majors, Troy E, PhD, Assoc Prof
    Mallory, William, PhD, Asst Prof
    Nickel, James W, PhD, Assoc Prof
    Rogers, Ben F, PhD, Assoc Prof
    Soles, Deborah, PhD, Asst Prof

    Chang, Kee Soo, AB, Teach Asst   Peters, Leroy, AB, Teach Asst
    Martinez, Charles, AB, Teach Asst   Tilford, James, AB, Teach Asst
    Paulson, Lawrence, AB, Teach Asst   Wuerch, Robert, AB, Teach Asst

KENTUCKY

ALICE LLOYD COLLEGE
  Pippa Passes, Kentucky 41844 (S; p; coed; --; I; 268) Courses with no degree
  specialization, Dept of Human, 606-368-2101

  Rojas, Billy, MA

ASBURY COLLEGE
  Wilmore, Kentucky 40390 (S; p; coed; qr; II; 1091) BA major, Div of Phil and Relig,
  606-858-3511 Ext 274, 275

  Hamilton, James, PhD, Asst Prof, Ethics, Logic, Phil of Relig
  Hunter, Clarence V, ThD, Prof, Hist of Phil

ASBURY THEOLOGICAL SEMINARY
  Wilmore, Kentucky 40390 (Theol; p; coed; 4-1-4; III; 431) MA joint or combined
  major, Div of Theol and Phil, 606-858-3580 Ext 37

  Kuhn, Harold B, PhD, Prof, Chm, Phil of Relig, Soc Ethics
  Arnett, William M, PhD, Prof, Syst Theol
  Layman, Fred D, ThM, Assoc Prof
  Rose, Delbert R, PhD, Prof

ASHLAND COMMUNITY COLLEGE, UNIVERSITY OF KENTUCKY
  Ashland, Kentuchy 41101 (--; st; coed; sem; I; --) --, --, 606-324-8586

  Goodwin, John, PhD, Instr Part-time

BELLARMINE COLLEGE
  Louisville, Kentucky 40205 (S; RC; coed; sem; I; 1655) BA major, --, 502-452-8011

  Giegerich, Vincent E, PhD, Assoc Prof
  Heckman, John H, PhD, Assoc Prof
  Hendrickson, W Frederick, PhD, Assoc Prof
  Matthews, Paul L, PhD, Assoc Prof

BEREA COLLEGE
  Berea, Kentucky 40403 (S; p; coed; 4-1-4; II; 1449) BA major, Dept of Phil and
  Relig, 606-986-4841

  Parker, George F, PhD, Prof, Chm, Hist of Phil, Phil of Relig
  Ericson, Randall L, PhD, Instr, Logic, Phil of Sci
  Holloway, James Y, PhD, Assoc Prof, Ethics, Polit Phil
  Stassen, Glen, PhD, Asst Prof, Ethics, Exist
  Woodie, Norris B, PhD, Prof, Amer Phil, Phil of Educ

  Noss, George, PhD, Prof Emer, Hist of Phil, Orient Phil
  Ross, W Gordon, PhD, Prof Emer, Epistem, Phil of Man

BRESCIA COLLEGE
    Owensboro, Kentucky 42301 (S; RC; coed; sem; II; 957) --, --, 502-685-3131

    Alvey, Leonard, MA, Instr
    Graney, Marc R, PhD, Asst Prof
    Saffer, Charles A, MS, Assoc Prof

CAMPBELLSVILLE COLLEGE
    Campbellsville, Kentucky 42718 (S; S Bapt; coed; sem; II; 859) Courses with no
    degree specialization, Dept of Bib and Relig Educ, 502-465-8158 Ext 37

    Horner, Paul, ThD, Chm
    Coker, H, E, ThD, Assoc Prof
    Kibbons, Jerry, MA, Asst Prof

CENTRE COLLEGE OF KENTUCKY
    Danville, Kentucky 40422 (S; p; coed; --; II; 726) BA major, --, 606-236-5211

CUMBERLAND COLLEGE
    Williamsburg, Kentucky 40769 (S; S Bapt; coed; sem; II; 1807) Courses with no degree
    specialization, Div of Relig, Bibl Lang and Phil, 606-549-2200

EASTERN KENTUCKY UNIVERSITY
    Richmond, Kentucky 40475 (S; st; coed; sem; III; 11,266) BA major, Dept of Phil,
    606-622-5871

    Harris, R Baine, PhD, Prof, Chm, Anc Phil, Orient Phil, Soc Phil
    Edwards, Kenneth C, MA, Asst Prof, Ethics
    Jones, William F, MA, Asst Prof, Phenomen
    Miller, J Robert, PhD, Assoc Prof, Exist, Hist of Phil
    Nordgulen, George S, PhD, Assoc Prof, Phil of Relig
    Williams, Frank, PhD, Assoc Prof, Phil of Sci, Logic

ELIZABETHTOWN COMMUNITY COLLEGE, UNIVERSITY OF KENTUCKY
    Elizabethtown, Kentucky (ADNUR; st; coed; sem; I; --) NP

GEORGETOWN COLLEGE
    Georgetown, Kentucky (S; S Bapt; coed; 4-1-4; III; 1300) BA major, Dept of Phil,
    502-863-8239

    Gragg, Alan W, PhD, Prof, Chm, Phil of Relig
    Heizer, Ruth B, PhD, Assoc Prof, Epistem

HAZARD COMMUNITY COLLEGE, UNIVERSITY OF KENTUCKY
    Hazard, Kentucky 41701 (S; st; coed; sem; I; --) NP

HENDERSON COMMUNITY COLLEGE, UNIVERSITY OF KENTUCKY
    Henderson, Kentucky 42420 (S; st; coed; sem; I; --) Courses with no degree
    specialization, Div of Human, 502-827-1867

    Marino, John A, PhD, Instr

HOPKINSVILLE COMMUNITY COLLEGE, UNIVERSITY OF KENTUCKY
    Hopkinsville, Kentucky 42240 (S; st; coed; sem; I; --) Courses with no degree
    specialization, Div of Human, 502-886-3921 Ext 44

    Self, E B, PhD, Asst Prof

JEFFERSON COMMUNITY COLLEGE, UNIVERSITY OF KENTUCKY
    Louisville, Kentucky (S; st; coed; sem; I; --) --, Dept of Phil, 584-0181 Ext 231

    Schneiter, Frances, MA, Assoc Prof, Chm, Exist, Spinoza
    Cole, Robert, MA, Instr
    Howard, Raymond, MA, Instr, Anc Phil

KENTUCKY CHRISTIAN COLLEGE
    Grayson, Kentucky 41143 (Bi; Ch of Christ; coed; sem; II; 241) Courses with no
    degree specialization, --, 606-474-6613

    Gresham, Charles R, DEd, Prof, Phil of Relig

KENTUCKY STATE UNIVERSITY
    Frankfort, Kentucky 40601 (S; st; coed; sem; II; 1970) Courses with no degree
    specialization, --, 502-564-6260

    Brewer, Jr, Homer, MA, Part-time Instr

KENTUCKY WESLEYAN COLLEGE
    Owensboro, Kentucky 42301 (S; U Meth; coed; sem; II; 924) Courses with no degree
    specialization, --, 502-684-5261

    Harris, Bond, PhD, Asst Prof
    Rogers, Thomas, ThD, Prof

LEES JUNIOR COLLEGE
    Jackson, Kentucky 41339 (S; Preb; coed; sem; I; 423) --, --, 606-666-7521

LEXINGTON TECHNOLOGICAL INSTITUTE, UNIVERSITY OF KENTUCKY
    Lexington, Kentucky 40506 (S; st; coed; sem; I; --) NP

LEXINGTON THEOLOGICAL SEMINARY
    Lexington, Kentucky 40508 (Theol; Disc of Christ; coed; qr; IV; 115) PhD major,
    --, 606-252-0361

    Barr, William R, PhD, Prof
    Polk, David P, ThM, Asst Prof

LINDSEY WILSON COLLEGE
    Columbia, Kentucky (S; U Meth; coed; sem; I; 324) NP

LOUISVILLE PRESBYTERIAN THEOLOGICAL SEMINARY
    Louisville, Kentucky 40205 (Theol; Preb & U Preb; coed; 4-1-4; III; 192) NR

MADISONVILLE COMMUNITY COLLEGE, UNIVERSITY OF KENTUCKY
Madisonville, Kentucky 42431 (S; st; coed; sem; I; --) Courses with no degree
specialization, Div of Human, 606-821-2250

Chapman, James P, PhD, Asst Prof

MAYSVILLE COMMUNITY COLLEGE, UNIVERSITY OF KENTUCKY
Maysville, Kentucky 41056 (S; st; coed; sem; I; --) NP

MIDWAY COLLEGE
Midway, Kentucky 40347 (S; p; wo; sem; I; 187) Courses with no degree specialization,
--, 606-846-4421

Ward, Thomas Morgan, BD

MOREHEAD STATE UNIVERSITY
Morehead, Kentucky 40351 (S; st; coed; sem; III; 6593) BA major, Dept of Phil, 606-
783-3121

Mangrum, Franklin M, PhD, Prof, Head, Phil of Relig, Metaph, Epistem
Gurley, Betty, MA, Asst Prof, Phenomen, Exist
Luckey, Jr, George M, MA, Assoc Prof, Ethics, Amer Phil

MURRAY STATE UNIVERSITY
Murray, Kentucky 42071 (S; st; coed; sem; III; 7331) MA joint or combined major,
Dept of Phil, 502-762-4489

Sheeks, R W, PhD, Assoc Prof, Chm, Epistem, Greek Phil, Metaph
Kumar, F L, PhD, Assoc Prof, Indian Phil
Robinson, F E, PhD, Assoc Prof, Ethics, Polit Phil

NORTHERN KENTUCKY STATE COLLEGE
Highland Heights, Kentucky 41076 (ADNUR; st; coed; sem; II; 3065) Courses with no
degree specialization, Dept of Soc Sci, 606-781-2600 Ext 188

Lassetter, Clarence R, ThD, Part-time Instr
Richards, Jerald H, PhD, Assoc Prof, Ethics, Soc and Polit Phil, Phil of Relig

PADUCAH COMMUNITY COLLEGE, UNIVERSITY OF KENTUCKY
Paducah, Kentucky 42001 (S; st; coed; sem; I; --) Courses with no degree
specialization, Dept of Soc Sci, 606-442-6131 Ext 22

Vick, O K, MA, Instr

PIKEVILLE COLLEGE
Pikeville, Kentucky 41501 (S; Preb; coed; sem; II; 828) NP

PRESTONSBURG COMMUNITY COLLEGE, UNIVERSITY OF KENTUCKY
Prestonsburg, Kentucky 41653 (S; st; coed; sem; I; --) Courses with no degree
specialization, Div of Soc Sci and Business and Office Educ, 606-886-3863

McAninch, Robert, MA, Asst Prof

SAINT CATHARINE COLLEGE
Saint Catharine, Kentucky 40061 (S; RC; coed; sem; I; 150) --, --, 606-336-3945

Fava, Paul Dominic
Preher, Leo Marie
O'Connor, John

SAINT MARY'S COLLEGE
Saint Mary, Kentucky 40063 (--; RC; men; sem; II; 98) NR

SEMINARY OF SAINT PIUS X
Erlanger, Kentucky 41018 (S; RC; men; sem; II; 44) BA major, Dept of Phil, 606-371-4448

Grosser, Elmer J, PhD, Prof, Head, Anc Phil
Broering, Joseph H, MA, Assoc Prof, Cosmol
Brown, William G, STD, Asst Prof, Epistem
Kettler, Ronald, MA, Visit Asst Prof, Phil of Man
Quill, James E, STD, Prof, Ethics
Twaddell, Gerald E, MA, Asst Prof, Contemp Phil

SOMERSET COMMUNITY COLLEGE, UNIVERSITY OF KENTUCKY
Somerset, Kentucky 42501 (S; st; coed; sem; I; --) --, Dept of Phys Sci and Math, 606-258-9000

Campbell, Gerald P, MS, Asst Prof

SOUTHEAST COMMUNITY COLLEGE, UNIVERSITY OF KENTUCKY
Cumberland, Kentucky 40823 (S; st; coed; sem; I, --) NP

SOUTHEASTERN CHRISTIAN COLLEGE
Winchester, Kentucky 40391 (S; Ch of Christ; coed; sem; I; 122) NP

SOUTHERN BAPTIST THEOLOGICAL SEMINARY
Louisville, Kentucky 40206 (S; S Bapt; coed; 4-1-4; IV; 1073) ThD major, Dept of Christ Phil, 502-897-4606

Rust, Eric C, MA, Prof
Tupper, Frank, ThD, Asst Prof

SPALDING COLLEGE
Louisville, Kentucky 40203 (S; p; coed; sem; III; 1067) BA major, Dept of Phil, 502-585-9372

Eberenz, James H, PhD, Assoc Prof, Chm, Polit Phil, Soc Phil
Basehart, Mary Catharine, PhD, Prof, Phenomen
Crone, Agnes, MA, Asst Prof, Mod Phil

SUE BENNETT COLLEGE
London, Kentucky 40741 (S; U Meth; coed; sem; I; 181) --, Dept of Human, 606-864-2238

Peterson, Jr, J L, MA, Instr Part-time

THOMAS MORE COLLEGE
  Covington, Kentucky 41017 (S; RC; coed; --; II; 1812) BA major, Dept of Phil, 606-341-5800 Ext 63

  Blair, George A, PhD, Assoc Prof
  Cahalan, William, MA, Lect
  Cahill, M Camilla, PhD, Prof
  Ebben, James, MA, Asst Prof
  Garvey, Charles, PhD, Assoc Prof
  Rooks, Charles, MA, Asst Prof

TRANSYLVANIA UNIVERSITY
  Lexington, Kentucky 40508 (S; p; coed; qr; II; 775) BA major, Dept of Phil and Relig, 606-233-8129

  Lewis, Benjamin F, PhD, Prof, Chm, Phil of Cult
  Gobar, Ash, PhD, Assoc Prof, Hist Tht

UNION COLLEGE
  Barbourville, Kentucky 40906 (S; U Meth; coed; sem; III; 902) BA major, Dept of Relig and Phil, 606-546-4151 Ext 143

  Matthews, Robert, PhD, Prof, Chm
  Jones, Royce, PhD, Assoc Prof, Prag

UNIVERSITY OF KENTUCKY
  Lexington, Kentucky 40506 (S; st; coed; sem; IV; 20,455) PhD minor, Dept of Phil, 606-257-1861

  High, Dallas M, PhD, Prof, Chm, Phil of Relig, Contemp Phil, Wittgenstein
  Bayles, Michael D, PhD, Assoc Prof, Ethics, Soc and Polit Phil, Phil of Law
  Breazeale, J Daniel, PhD, Asst Prof, 19th Cent Phil, Phil of Lang, Mod Phil
  Bruzina, Ronald, PhD, Assoc Prof, Phenomen, Soc and Polit Phil, Phil Anthrop
  deBoer, Jesse, PhD, Prof, Anc Phil, Metaph, Phil of Relig
  Fetzer, James H, PhD, Asst Prof, Phil of Sci, Tht of Knowl, Phil of Lang
  Folse, Henry J, PhD, Visit Asst Prof, Phil of Sci, Metaph
  Henley, Kenneth I, PhD, Asst Prof, Ethics, Phil of Mind, Soc and Polit Phil
  Manns, James W, PhD, Asst Prof, Aes, Ethics, Theory of Knowl
  Olshewsky, Thomas M, PhD, Assoc Prof, Phil of Lang, Phil of Mind
  Perreiah, Alan R, PhD, Assoc Prof, Logic, Hist of Logic, Med and Renaissance Phil
  Schankula, Henry A S, MA, Instr, Mod Phil, Theory of Knowl, Phil of Mind

  Kuiper, John, MA, Prof Emer

  Allen, Timothy W, BA, Teach Asst   Peterson, Michael, BA, Grad Fel
  Byassee, William, BA, Teach Asst   Petty, Sam, BA, Teach Asst
  Crunkleton, Martha, BA, Grad Fel   Puhr, Barry, BA, Teach Asst
  Daniels, Richard, BA, Teach Asst   Walsh, John, MA, Teach Asst
  Easton, Raymond, BA, Teach Asst   White, Ronald, BA, Teach Asst

UNIVERSITY OF LOUISVILLE
  Louisville, Kentucky 40208 (S; st; coed; sem; IV; 10,474) MA major, Dept of Phil, 502-636-6111

  Barber, Richard L, PhD, Prof, Metaph, Ethics
  Breslin, Charles F, MA, Asst Prof, Phenomen, Phil of Man
  Flodstrom, John H, PhD, Asst Prof, French Phil, Anc Phil
  Ford, John H, PhD, Lect
  Greer, Melvin E, PhD, Assoc Prof, Ethics, Metaph, Phil of Relig

Gruen, Jr, William C, BA, Lect Part-time
Orr, David A, MA, Instr, Exist, Process Phil
Peak, Ira, BA, Lect Part-time
Schuyler, Jr, William M, MA, Asst Prof, Logic, Phil of Sci, Orient Phil
Smith, Richard Campbell, PhD, Prof, Hist of Phil, Phil of Cult, Metaph, Epistem

WESTERN KENTUCKY UNIVERSITY
    Bowling Green, Kentucky 42101 (S; st; coed; sem; III; 12,002) MA major, Dept of
    Phil and Relig, 502-745-3193

Nash, Ronald H, PhD, Prof, Chm, Hist of Phil, Phil of Hist, Phil of Relig
Howe, Margaret, PhD, Asst Prof, Hellenic Tht
Long, John E, PhD, Asst Prof, Islamic Phil
Mayhew, Larry D, PhD, Asst Prof, Metaph, Epistem, Anal Phil, Logic
Mounce, Robert H, PhD, Prof, Christ Tht
Scott, J Julius, PhD, Assoc Prof, Hellenic Tht
Stahl, John T, PhD, Assoc Prof, Sym Logic, Phil of Sci, Phil of Lang
Tuck, Donald R, PhD, Assoc Prof, Asian Phil
Veenker, Ronald A, PhD, Assoc Prof, Judaic Tht
Vos, Arvin G, PhD, Asst Prof, Med Phil, Phil of Sci, Phil of Mind
Wattles, Jeffrey H, PhD, Asst Prof, Ethics, Phenomen, Hegel

Bowell, James, AB, Grad Asst   Omatze, James, AB, Grad Asst
Geotter, R C, AB, Grad Asst

LOUISIANA

CENTENARY COLLEGE OF LOUISIANA
Shreveport, Louisiana 71104 (S; U Meth; coed; 4-1-4; II; 924) BA major, Dept of
Phil, 318-869-5246

Cox, L Hughes, PhD, Assoc Prof, Chm, Phil Theol
Beaird, Charles T, PhD, Asst Prof, Soc Phil, Phil of Econ

DELGADO VOCATIONAL AND TECHNICAL JUNIOR COLLEGE
New Orleans, Louisiana 70119 (S; st and local; coed; sem; I; 4724) NR

DILLARD UNIVERSITY
New Orleans, Louisiana 70122 (S; mpd; coed; sem; II; 982) BA major, Dept of Phil
and Relig, 504-944-8751

LeFevre, Joseph, MA, Instr

GRAMBLING COLLEGE
Grambling, Louisiana 71245 (S; st; coed; sem; II; 3913) BA minor, --, 318-247-3761

Horton, William H, PhD, Asst Prof, Ethics, Metaph, Afro-American Tht
Payne, Michael A, PhD, Asst Prof, Logic, Hist of Phil, Metaph, Epistem

LOUISIANA COLLEGE
Pineville, Louisiana 71360 (S; Bapt; coed; sem; II; 949) BA minor, Dept of Relig
and Phil, 318-487-7362

Heard, Gerald C, MA, Instr, Phil of Relig

LOUISIANA STATE UNIVERSITY
Baton Rouge, Louisiana 70803 (S; st; coed; sem; IV; 20,536) PhD minor, Dept of
Phil, 504-388-6207

Bigger, C, PhD, Prof, Chm, Plato, Whitehead, Kant, Metaph
Baker, J, PhD, Asst Prof, Logic, Phil of Relig, Anal Phil
Cornay, D, MA, Instr, Phenomen, Hist of Phil, Heidegger
Evans, C, PhD, Assoc Prof, Phil of Mind, Value Theory
Henderson, E, PhD, Assoc Prof, Hist of Phil, Phil Anthrop, Metaph
Shirley, E, PhD, Asst Prof, Phil of Lang, Theory of Truth
Smith, K, PhD, Asst Prof, Polit Phil, German Phil
Utz, S, BA, Instr, Phil of Sci

LOUISIANA STATE UNIVERSITY AT ALEXANDRIA
Alexandria, Louisiana 71303 (S; st; coed; sem; I; 1012) NP

LOUISIANA STATE UNIVERSITY AT EUNICE
Eunice, Louisiana 70535 (S; st; coed; sem; I; 482) Courses with no degree
specialization, Dept of Phil, 318-457-7311 Ext 43

Levy, Gary B, PhD, Instr, Math Logic

LOUISIANA STATE UNIVERSITY AT NEW ORLEANS
New Orleans, Louisiana 70122 (S; st; coed; sem; IV; 12,985) BA major, --, 504-
288-3161

Morillo, Carolyn R, PhD, Assoc Prof, Chm, Epistem, Ethics
Hanks, Donald K, PhD, Asst Prof, Phil of Relig, Metaph, Kant
Jeffries, Stephen, MA, Instr, Phil of Sci, Logic
Nelkin, Norton, PhD, Asst Prof, Phil of Mind, British Empir
Nosich, Gerald M, PhD, Asst Prof, Phil of Lang, Hegel, Kant
Rosen, Deborah, PhD, Asst Prof, Memory, Causality, Phil of Mind
Tice, John K, PhD, Asst Prof, Aes, Ethics, Logic

LOUISIANA STATE UNIVERSITY AT SHREVEPORT
Shreveport, Louisiana 71105 (S; st; coed; sem; IV; 12,985) Courses with no degree
specialization, Dept of Soc Sci, 318-865-7121 Ext 337

LOUISIANA STATE UNIVERSITY MEDICAL CENTER AT NEW ORLEANS
New Orleans, Louisiana 70112 (Med; st; coed; sem; IV; 1079) NR

LOUISIANA STATE UNIVERSITY MEDICAL CENTER AT SHREVEPORT
Shreveport, Louisiana 71133 (Med; st; coed; sem; IV; --) NP

LOUISIANA TECHNOLOGICAL UNIVERSITY
Ruston, Louisiana 71270 (S; st; coed; qr; IV; 8104) NP

LOYOLA CITY COLLEGE, LOYOLA UNIVERSITY
New Orleans, Louisiana 70118 (S; RC; coed; sem; --; --) --, --, 504-866-5471

Clark, John, Asst Prof, MA
Murphy, Edward, Lect, PhD
Waters, Anthony H, Lect, MA

LOYOLA UNIVERSITY
New Orleans, Louisiana 70118 (S; RC; coed; sem; IV; 4981) BA major, Dept of Phil,
504-866-5471 Ext 348

Holloway, Alvin J, PhD, Assoc Prof, Chm, Anc Phil
Boileau, David, PhD, Assoc Prof, Structuralism
Bourgeois, Patrick, PhD, Assoc Prof, Phenomen
Gelpi, Donald, PhD, Assoc Prof, Amer Relig Phil
Herbert, Gary, PhD, Asst Prof, Contemp Phil
Lowry, Jon W, PhD, Asst Prof, Ethics
Montecino, Henry, STL, Prof, Mod Phil
Plamondon, Ann, PhD, Assoc Prof, Logic, Phil of Sci
Rosenthal, Sandra, PhD, Prof, Amer Prag
Watson, James R, PhD, Asst Prof, Exist

MCNEESE STATE UNIVERSITY
Lake Charles, Louisiana 70601 (S; st; coed; sem; IV; 6025) --, Dept of Sco Sci,
318-477-2520 Ext 289

Greenlee, William P, ThD, Assoc Prof

NEW ORLEANS BAPTIST THEOLOGICAL SEMINARY
New Orleans, Louisiana 70126 (S; S Bapt; coed; sem; IV; 582) MA minor, Div of Theol and Hist Stud, 504-282-4455 Ext 52

Humphreys, Fisher, ThD, Asst Prof

NICHOLLS STATE COLLEGE
Thibodaux, Louisiana 70301 (S; st; coed; sem; III; 5411) BA major, --, 504-446-8111

Martin, B Joseph, PhD, Prof, Ethics, Hist of Phil, Soc and Polit Phil

NORTHEAST LOUISIANA UNIVERSITY
Monroe, Louisiana 71201 (S; st; coed; sem; IV; 8810) Courses with no degree specialization, Dept of Hist and Gov, 318-372-2113

Poetker, Joseph L, PhD, Asst Prof, Ethics, Logic

NORTHWESTERN STATE UNIVERSITY
Natchitoches, Louisiana 71457 (S; st; coed; sem; IV; 6268) BA minor, Dept of Soc Sci, 318-357-6361

Snowden, Barnard Fraser, MA, Asst Prof, Phil of Relig, Amer Phil

NOTRE DAME SEMINARY
New Orleans, Louisiana 70118 (S; RC; coed; sem; III; 170) NP

OUR LADY OF HOLY CROSS COLLEGE
New Orleans, Louisiana 70114 (--; RC; coed; sem; II; 287) NP

SAINT BERNARD PARISH COMMUNITY COLLEGE
Chalmette, Louisiana 70043 (--; local; coed; sem; I; 310) NP

SAINT JOSEPH SEMINARY COLLEGE
Saint Benedict, Louisiana 70457 (S; RC; coed; sem; II; 82) BA major, Dept of Phil, 504-892-1800 Ext 9

Jung, Michael, MA, Chm, Mod and Exist Phil
Faraldo, Fernando, PhL, Med Phil, Ethics
Jackman, Francis, PhD
Larman, Marian, MA, Anc and Med Phil

SAINT MARY'S DOMINICAN COLLEGE
New Orleans, Louisiana 70118 (S; RC; wo; sem; II; 859) Courses with no degree specialization, Dept of Phil and Theol, 504-866-5746

Guagliardo, Vincent, MA, Instr, Chm, Metaph

SOUTHEASTERN LOUISIANA UNIVERSITY
Hammond, Louisiana 70401 (S; st; coed; sem; III; 5790) --, Dept of Hist and Gov, 504-345-1400

Jackman, Francis, PhD, Assoc Prof

SOUTHERN UNIVERSITY AGRICULTURAL AND MECHANICAL COLLEGE
Baton Rouge, Louisiana 70813 (S; st; coed; sem; III; 8414) BA major, Dept of Phil,
504-771-3740, 504-771-3741

Lin, Paul J, EdD, Prof, Chm, Orient Phil, Hist of West Phil
Crillie, Hena, MA, Instr
Haynes, L L, ThD, Prof, Phil of Relig, Mod Phil
Marx, Jo Ann, MA, Instr
Perkins, Huel D, PhD, Prof, Dean
White, L L, PhD, Prof, Dean, Phil of Sci

SOUTHERN UNIVERSITY AGRICULTURAL AND MECHANICAL COLLEGE AT NEW ORLEANS
New Orleans, Louisiana (S; st; coed; sem; II; 2134) BA minor, Dept of Human and
and Phil, 504-282-4401 Ext 208

Harvey, Samuel P, MA, Instr, Epistem, Phil of Mind

SOUTHERN UNIVERSITY AGRICULTURAL AND MECHANICAL COLLEGE AT SHREVEPORT
Shreveport, Louisiana 71107 (S; st; coed; sem; I; 744) Courses with no degree
specialization, Dept of English, 318-424-6552 Ext 201

Wiley, Electa C, DEd, Prof

TULANE UNIVERSITY
New Orleans, Louisiana 70118 (S; p; coed; sem; IV; 8732) PhD major, Dept of Phil,
504-865-5305

Reck, Andrew J, PhD, Prof, Chm, Amer Phil
Balinsky, Margaret, PhD, Asst Prof, Greek Phil, Hist of Phil
Ballard, Edward Goodwin, PhD, Prof, Phenomen, Metaph, Hist of Phil
Feibleman, James Kern, Prof, Metaph, Amer Phil
Glenn, Jr, John D, PhD, Asst Prof, Exist, Phil of Relig
Hamburg, Carl H, PhD, Prof, Ethics, Soc Phil
Green, O Harvey, D Phil, Asst Prof, Ethics, Phil of Mind
Lee, Donald Soule, PhD, Assoc Prof, Logic, Phil of Sci
Miller, Larry W, PhD, Asst Prof, Math Logic
Roberts, Louise Nisbet, PhD, Prof, Aes, Med Logic
Whittemore, Robert C, PhD, Prof, Phil of Relig, Indian Phil, Amer Phil

Barton, George Estes, Prof Emer
Lee, Harold Newton, Prof Emer

Ake, Christopher, Teach Fel   St Clair, Judith, Teach Asst
Asadourian, Vazken N, Teach Asst   Summers, James W, Teach Asst
Dugan, D Kerry, Teach Asst   Wallace, Phillip A, Teach Asst
Heim, Michael R, Teach Asst   Zimmerman, Michael, Teach Asst
Miller, Jack E, Teach Asst

UNIVERSITY OF SOUTHWESTERN LOUISIANA
Lafayette, Louisiana 70501 (S; st; coed; sem; IV; 10,654) BA major, Dept of Phil,
318-233-3850 Ext 369

Kirkpatrick, Robert T, PhD, Prof, Head, Phenomen, Exist
Barker, Donald R, PhD, Asst Prof, Phil of Relig, Anal Phil
Vigorito, John V, PhD, Asst Prof, Hist of Phil, Metaph

XAVIER UNIVERSITY OF LOUISIANA
New Orleans, Louisiana 70125 (S; RC; coed; sem; III; 1554) BA major, Dept of Phil,
504-486-7411 Ext 336

Faraldo, Fernando, PhL, Assoc Prof, Chm, Ethics, Logic, Med Phil
Berry, John, MA, Asst Prof, Mod Phil
Kennedy, Edward, PhD, Lect, Black Phil
Olivier, Ann, PhD, Assoc Prof, Logic, Aes
Pelaez, Martha, MA, Instr, Logic, Exist, Phil of Relig
Waters, Anthony, MA, Lect, Exist

MAINE

BANGOR THEOLOGICAL SEMINARY
Bangor, Maine 04401 (E; p; coed; sem; II; 129) Courses with no degree specialization,
Dept of Phil of Relig and Christ Ethics, 207-942-6781

Weber, Stephen L, PhD

BATES COLLEGE
Lewiston, Maine 04240 (E; p; coed; --; II; 1226) BA major, Dept of Phil and Relig,
207-784-9103

D'Alfonso, Joseph, PhD, Prof, Chm, Metaph, Ethics
James, Edward W, PhD, Asst Prof, Ethics, Epistem
Oknent, Mark, PhD, Asst Prof, Metaph, Epistem

BOWDOIN COLLEGE
Brunswick, Maine 04011 (E; p; coed; sem; III; 1034) BA major, --, 207-725-8731

Corish, Denis J, PhD, Asst Prof, Hist of Phil and Sci, Greek Phil
McGee, C Douglas, PhD, Prof, Moral Phil, Epistem
Pols, Edward, PhD, Prof, Metaph

COLBY COLLEGE
Waterville, Maine 04901 (E; p; coed; 4-1-4; III; 1572) BA major, Dept of Phil and
Relig, 207-873-1131

Parker, Francis H, PhD, Prof, Chm, Hist of Phil, Metaph, Theory of Knowl
Hudson, Yeager, PhD, Assoc Prof, Metaph, Phil of Educ
Longstaff, Thomas R W, PhD, Asst Prof
McArthur, Robert P, PhD, Asst Prof, Logic, Anal Phil, Phil of Sci
Reuman, Robert E, PhD, Prof, Ethics, Soc Phil, Mod Phil
Thorwaldsen, Roland W, BD, Asst Prof, Asian Relig, Med Phil
Todrank, Gustave H, PhD, Prof, Phil of Relig, Environmental Ethics

Clark, John A, PhD, Prof Emer, Anc Phil, Soc Phil

EASTERN MAINE VOCATIONAL TECHNICAL INSTITUTE
    Bangor, Maine 04401 (--; st; coed; sem; I; 390) NP

HUSSON COLLEGE
    Bangor, Maine 04401 (SRCB; p; coed; sem; II; 1067) NR

MAINE MARITIME ACADEMY
    Castine, Maine 04421 (E; st; men; sem; II; 338) NP

NASSON COLLEGE
    Springvale, Maine 04083 (E; p; coed; sem; II; 851) BA minor, Div of Human, 207-324-5340

    Aiken, Lillian Woodworth, PhD, Prof, Chm, Ethics, Chinese Phil
    Travers, David, PhD, Asst Prof, Marx, Phil of Sci

RICKER COLLEGE
    Houlton, Maine 04730 (E; p; coed; 4-1-4; II; 541) BA joint or combined major, Div of Human, 207-532-2223 Ext 70

    Atkinson, Barry W, MA, Chm, Ethics
    Bowman, Howard, BD, Phil of Relig

SAINT FRANCIS COLLEGE
    Biddeford, Maine 04005 (E; RC; coed; 4-1-4; II; 716) BA major, Div of Phil and Theol, 207-282-1515 Ext 14

    Giroux, Oscar, LPH, Prof, Ethics, Epistem
    Marcil, George, PhD, Assoc Prof, Phil of Man, Logic

SAINT JOSEPH'S COLLEGE
    North Windham, Maine 04062 (E; RC; coed; sem; II; 347) Courses with no degree specialization, Dept of Phil, 207-892-6766

    Hachey, Mercedes, PhD, Prof, Chm, Hist of Phil, Contemp Phil
    Nargaj, Andrew, PhD, Prof, Phil Psych, Moral Phil

THOMAS COLLEGE
    Waterville, Maine 04901 (E; p; coed; sem; II; 494) Courses with no degree specialization, Dept of Libr Arts, 207-873-0771

    Laws, John W, ThM

UNITY COLLEGE
    Unity, Maine 04988 (--; p; coed; sem; II; 330) BA minor, Dept of Phil, 207-948-3131

    Noonan, Florence, BA, Asst Prof, Chm, Plato

UNIVERSITY OF MAINE AT AUGUSTA
    Augusta, Maine 04330 (E; st; coed; sem; I; 2329) --, Div of Human, 207-622-7131 Ext 40

    Jurenas, Algirdas, ThD, Asst Prof, Phil of Relig, Phenomen, Exist

UNIVERSITY OF MAINE AT FARMINGTON
Farmington, Maine 04938 (E; st; coed; sem; II; 1624) Courses with no degree
specialization, --, 207-778-3501

Stiles, Grace Ellen, PhD, Assoc Prof

UNIVERSITY OF MAINE AT FORT KENT
Fort Kent, Maine 04743 (E; st; coed; sem; II; 608) NP

UNIVERSITY OF MAINE AT MACHIAS
Machias, Maine 04654 (E; st; coed; sem; II; 640) Courses with no degree
specialization, Depts of Educ and Sci, 207-255-3313

Fraenkel-Conrat, Jane, PhD, Assoc Prof
Swadley, Ellis C, MA, Assoc Prof

UNIVERSITY OF MAINE AT ORONO
Orono, Maine 04473 (E; st; coed; sem; IV; 9486) Arts and Sci major, Dept of Phil,
207-581-7167

White, Jefferson, PhD, Prof, Chm, Epistem
Craig, Robert H, MA, Instr
Hjelm, Ralph O, PhD, Prof, Hist of Relig
Skorpen, Erling R, PhD, Prof, Ethics
Tredwell, Robert F, PhD, Prof, Phil of Sci
Weber, Stephen L, PhD, Asst Prof, Greek Phil, Med Phil

UNIVERSITY OF MAINE AT PORTLAND-GORHAM
Portland, Maine 04103 (E; st; coed; sem; III; 6441) BA major, Dept of Phil, 207-
773-2981 Ext 213

Gavin, William Joseph, PhD, Assoc Prof, Chm, Amer Phil
Grange, Joseph, PhD, Assoc Prof, Phenomen
Mackensen, William, MA, Part-time Instr
MacLeod, William, PhD, Prof, Phil of Relig
Pic'l, Ann, MA, Part-time Instr
Schwanauer, Francis, PhD, Prof, Kant, Hegel

UNIVERSITY OF MAINE AT PRESQUE ISLE
Presque Isle, Maine 04769 (E; st; coed; sem; II; 1170) Courses with no degree
specialization, Div of Human, 207-764-0311 Ext 50

UNIVERSITY OF MAINE SCHOOL OF LAW AT PORTLAND
Portland, Maine 04104 (Law; st; coed; sem; III; --) NP

WESTBROOK JUNIOR COLLEGE
Portland, Maine 04103 (E; p; wo; 4-1-4; II; 493) NP

MARYLAND

ALLEGANY COMMUNITY COLLEGE
  Cumberland, Maryland 21502 (M; local; coed; sem; I; 1249) Courses with no degree
  specialization, --, 301-724-7700

  Hazem, George A, MA, Asst Prof

ANNE ARUNDEL COMMUNITY COLLEGE
  Arnold, Maryland 21012 (M; st and local; coed; sem; I; 3784) --, --, 301-647-7100

  Dollar, James L, Assoc Prof, Phenomen

ANTIOCH COLLEGE, WASHINGTON-BALTIMORE CAMPUS
  Baltimore, Maryland 21202 (N; p; coed; qr; TT; 413) NR

BALTIMORE COLLEGE OF COMMERCE
  Baltimore, Maryland 21209 (JRCB; p; coed; sem; II; 665) NR

BALTIMORE HEBREW COLLEGE
  Baltimore, Maryland 21215 (--; p; coed; sem; III; 111) NR

BOWIE STATE COLLEGE
  Bowie, Maryland 20715 (M; st; coed; 4-1-4; III; 2353) NR

CAPITOL INSTITUTE OF TECHNOLOGY
  Kensington, Maryland 20195 (Tech; p; coed; qr; II; 254) NP

CATONSVILLE COMMUNITY COLLEGE
  Catonsville, Maryland (M; local; coed; sem; I; 6199) Courses with no degree
  specialization, Div of Human, 301-747-3220

  Kesmodel, William P, MA, Assoc Prof, Cord, Logic, Gen Phil, Ethics

CECIL COMMUNITY COLLEGE
  North East, Maryland 21901 (--; st and local; coed; sem; I; 513) Courses with no
  degree specialization, Dept of Phil, 301-287-6060

  Keen, Raymond W, MA, Lect,· Anc Phil

CHARLES COUNTY COMMUNITY COLLEGE
  La Plata, Maryland 20646 (M; local; coed; sem; I; 1188) Courses with no degree
  specialization, Div of Human, 301-934-2251 Ext 22

  Fauth, Mae, PhD, Adj Prof

CHESAPEAKE COLLEGE
  Wye Mills, Maryland 21679 (M; st; coed; sem; I; 625) AA major, Dept of Soc Sci,
  301-758-1537

  Callahan, J E, M Div

149

COLLEGE OF NOTRE DAME OF MARYLAND
  Baltimore, Maryland 21210 (M; RC; coed; 4-1-4; II; 733) Courses with no degree
  specialization, --, 301-435-0100

  Rosenberg, Jean, PhD, Chm
  Mark, Stephen A, MA
  Virginia, Mary, PhD

COLUMBIA UNION COLLEGE
  Takoma Park, Maryland 20012 (M; SDA; coed; tri; III; 1010) NP

COMMUNITY COLLEGE OF BALTIMORE
  Baltimore, Maryland 21215 (M; local; coed; sem; I; 9458) Courses with no degree
  specialization, Dept of Soc Sci, 301-462-5800 Ext 230

  Bailey, Charles, MA, Prof, Metaph
  Schecter, Joseph, MA, Part-time Instr

COPPIN STATE COLLEGE
  Baltimore, Maryland 21216 (M; st; coed; sem; III; 2488) --, Dept of Phil, 301-
  383-4542

  Marquandt, James, MA, Asst Prof, Aes
  Myers, John, PhD, Prof
  Schug, Fred, MA, Asst Prof, Phil of Educ

DUNDALK COMMUNITY COLLEGE
  Baltimore, Maryland 21222 (--; local; coed; 4-1-4; I; 503) Courses with no degree
  specialization, Div of Soc Sci, 301-282-6700 Ext 55

  Ravekes, John E, EdD, Prof, Phil of Educ

ESSEX COMMUNITY COLLEGE
  Baltimore, Maryland 21237 (M; local; coed; sem; I; 4604) AA major, Dept of Soc Sci,
  301-262-6800 Ext 268

  Silbermann, Eileen, MA, Asst Prof, Chm, Epistem
  Jensen, Neil, MA, Asst Prof
  Pond, Gardner, PhD, Assoc Prof

FREDERICK COMMUNITY COLLEGE
  Frederick, Maryland 21701 (M; local; coed; sem; I; 1208) --, Dept of Human, 301-
  662-0101

  Rodgers, B W, ThD, Prof, Phil of Relig, Hist of Phil

FROSTBURG STATE COLLEGE
  Frostburg, Maryland 21532 (M; st; coed; sem; III; 2736) BA minor, Dept of Phil,
  301-689-6621

  Machado, Michael A, PhD, Prof, Head, Exist Phenomen, Orient Phil
  Bramann, Jorn K, PhD, Asst Prof, Soc and Polit Phil, Phil of Soc Sci, Wittgenstein
  Bucchino, Angelo A, Asst Prof, Aes, Phil of Relig
  Mappes, Tom, Instr, Ethics, Epistem, Hume

GARRETT COMMUNITY COLLEGE
  McHenry, Maryland 21541 (--; local; coed; sem; I; 100) NP

GOUCHER COLLEGE
  Towson, Maryland, 21204 (M; p; wo; 4-1-4; III; 1050) BA major, Dept of Phil,
  301-825-3300

  Rose, Mary Carman, PhD, Prof, Chm, Phil of Relig, Aes, Phil of Lang, East Phil,
      Greek Phil
  Gossman, Eva Reinitz, PhD, Assoc Prof, Exist
  Martire, Joseph, BA, Asst Prof, Phil of Lang, Wittgenstein
  Morton, Joseph, PhD, Asst Prof, Hist of Ideas, Soc Phil

HAGERSTOWN JUNIOR COLLEGE
  Hagerstown, Maryland 21740 (M; st and local; coed; sem; I; 1355) Courses with no
  degree specialization, Dept of Human, 301-731-2800

  Powell, Allan, MA, Prof, Chm
  Winfrey, David, PhD, Prof

HARFORD COMMUNITY COLLEGE
  Bel Air, Maryland 21014 (M; local; coed; 4-1-4; I; 2339) Courses with no degree
  specialization, Div of Human, 301-838-1000

  O'Sullivan, John, MA, Asst Prof

HOOD COLLEGE
  Frederick, Maryland 21701 (M; p; wo; sem; III; 652) BA major, Dept of Relig and
  Phil, 301-662-3131 Ext 292

  Boston, James, PhD, Assoc Prof, Chm, Asian Phil
  Mehl, Paul, PhD, Assoc Prof, Phil of Relig
  Van Hook, Jay, PhD, Assoc Prof, Hist of Phil

HOWARD COMMUNITY COLLEGE
  Columbia, Maryland 21044 (--; st and local; coed; sem; I; 727) Courses with no
  degree specialization, Dept of Phil, 301-730-8000

  Looney, David B, ThM, Part-time Instr

JOHNS HOPKINS UNIVERSITY
  Baltimore, Maryland 21218 (M; p; coed; sem; IV; 9632) PhD major, Dept of Phil,
  301-366-3300 Ext 426

  Achinstein, Peter, PhD, Prof, Chm, Phil of Sci
  Barker, Stephen, PhD, Prof, Epistem, Phil of Math
  Cummins, Robert, PhD, Asst Prof, Phil of Lang
  Davis, Lawrence, PhD, Asst Prof, Phil of Mind
  Gottlieb, Dale, PhD, Asst Prof, Logic
  Mandelbaum, Maurice, PhD, Mellon Prof, Hist of Mod Phil, Phil Hist
  Price, Kingsley, PhD, Prof, British Phil, Phil of Educ
  Sachs, David, PhD, Prof, Greek Phil, Phil of Mind
  Sturgeon, Nicholas, PhD, Visit Asst Prof, Ethics
  Wilson, George, PhD, Asst Prof, Metaph, Aes of Film

  Boas, George, PhD, Prof Emer, Hist of Phil
  Lowe, Victor, PhD, Prof Emer, Whitehead

KIRKLAND HALL COLLEGE
   Ocean City, Maryland 21842 (--; p; coed; sem; I; 100) --, Dept of Eng and Phil,
   301-289-6181

   Hartnett, Richard, MA, Assoc Prof

LOYOLA COLLEGE
   Baltimore, Maryland 21210 (M; RC; coed; 4-1-4; III; 3468) BA major, Dept of Phil,
   301-323-1010 Ext 325, 326

   Nachbahr, BA, PhD, Prof, Chm, Phil of Relig
   Clark, ME, PhD, Assoc Prof, Metaph, Epistem
   Cunningham, F J, MA, Asst Prof, Plato, Amer Phil
   Madden, A G, PhD, Prof, Phil Psych
   May, T J, BA, Instr
   McAndrews, J F, PhD, Asst Prof, Ethics
   McCormack, J K, PhD, Assoc Prof, Phenomen, Exist
   Stout, F, MA, Instr
   Tassi, A G, PhD, Assoc Prof, Phenomen, Polit Phil

   Higgins, T J, PhD, Prof Emer, Ethics

MARYLAND INSTITUTE, COLLEGE OF ART
   Baltimore, Maryland 21217 (M; p; coed; sem; III; 1050) NP

MONTGOMERY COLLEGE, ROCKVILLE CAMPUS
   Rockville, Maryland 20850 (M; local; coed; sem; I; 6982) Courses with no degree
   specialization, Dept of Eng and Phil, 301-762-7400 Ext 263

   McDowell, Edward A, MA, Assoc Prof
   Peet, James M, MA, Assoc Prof
   White, Robert G, MA, Instr

MONTGOMERY COLLEGE, TAKOMA PARK CAMPUS
   Takoma Park, Maryland 20012 (M; local; coed; sem; I; 2553) --, Dept of Phil, 301-
   587-0415

   Bleich, Harold, Chm
   Wehrly, Jr, W F, Act Chm, Soc Ethics
   Davis, Lewis
   Osheroff, Steven
   Schaaft, Gretchen, MA
   Witkowski, Kenneth, MA

MORGAN STATE UNIVERSITY
   Baltimore, Maryland 21239 (M; st; coed; sem; III; 5743) BA major, Dept of Phil,
   301-323-2270 Ext 247

   Begus, Otto R, PhD, Assoc Prof, Chm, Ontology-Phenomen, Critical Phil
   CheeMooke, Robert, MA, Instr, Phil of Sci, Phil of Lang
   DuRand, Clifford C, MA, Asst Prof, Soc Phil, Epistem
   McKinney, Richard, PhD, Prof, Hist of Phil, Phil of Relig, Exist
   Petersen, Bredahl, PhD, Prof, Phil of Relig
   Taylor, Idel W, MA, Assoc Prof, Ethics, Aes, Logic
   Wilson, Max, PhD, Prof, Phil of Sci, Logic, Latin-American Phil

MOUNT SAINT MARY'S COLLEGE
   Emmitsburg, Maryland 21727 (M; RC; coed; sem; III; 1159) BA major, Dept of Phil,
   301-447-6122 Ext 330

   Winnes, George E, MA, Asst Prof, Chm, Metaph, Polit Phil
   Broussard, Joseph D, PhD, Prof, Phil of Man, Orient Phil
   Fives, Carl J, STL, Assoc Prof, Logic, Ethics
   Kline, Robert R, PhD, Prof, Phil of Sci
   Redmond, Paul V, MA, Assoc Prof, Hist of Phil
   Tollefsen, Olaf P, PhD, Asst Prof, Ethics, Aes

NER ISRAEL RAB COLLEGE
   Baltimore, Maryland 21208 (--; Jewish; men; sem; IV; 315) NR

PEABODY INSTITUTE OF BALTIMORE
   Baltimore, Maryland 21202 (M; p; coed; sem; IV; 428) NP

PRINCE GEORGE'S COMMUNITY COLLEGE
   Largo, Maryland 20870 (M; local; coed; sem; I; 7178) Courses with no degree
   specialization, Dept of Phil, 301-336-6000 Ext 259

   Ebenreck, Clyde, PhD, Assoc Prof, Chm
   Ahlualia, Brij, MA, Instr
   Blecher, Marlene, MA, Assoc Prof
   D'Souza, Anthony, PhD, Instr
   Ebenreck, Sara, MA, Instr
   Gottlieb, Diane, MA, Asst Prof
   Kell, Robin, MA, Instr
   Stelzer, John, PhD, Instr

SAINT JOHN'S COLLEGE
   Annapolis, Maryland 21404 (M; p; coed; sem; III; 357) Courses with no degree
   specialization, --, 301-263-2371

SAINT MARY'S COLLEGE OF MARYLAND
   Saint Mary's City, Maryland 20686 (M; st; coed; 4-1-4; II; 942) BA joint or combined
   major, Div of Human Devel, 301-994-1600 Ext 287

   Martin, Glen O, PhD, Prof, Chm
   Ankner, William, MA, Instr

SAINT MARY'S SEMINARY AND UNIVERSITY
   Baltimore, Maryland 21210 (M; RC; men; sem; IV; 776) NR

SALISBURY STATE COLLEGE
   Salisbury, Maryland 21801 (M; st; coed; sem; III; 1984) --, Dept of Phil, 301-
   749-7191 Ext 284

   Whiteway, Lloyd M, PhD, Assoc Prof, Chm, Ethics, Phil of Relig
   Miller, Jerome A, PhD, Asst Prof, Aes, Hist of Phil
   Moore, Mark A, PhD, Asst Prof, Logic, Phil of Sci

TOWSON STATE COLLEGE
  Baltimore, Maryland 21204 (M; st; coed; 4-1-4; III; 10,065) BA major, Dept of Phil
  and Relig, 301-823-7500 Ext 466, 472

  Eberhardt, Charles R, PhD, Chm
  Baumgarten, Joseph, PhD, Prof
  deBrabander, René F, PhD, Assoc Prof, Metaph, Phil of Relig
  Fuchs, JoAnn, MA, Instr
  Fuchs, Walt, PhD, Asst Prof, Contemp Phil
  Hill, James J, PhD, Assoc Prof, Aes
  Madden, Arthur G, Prof, Logic, Ethics
  Murungi, John, Asst Prof, Contemp Phil, Afr Tht
  Robertson, Bruce, STM, Instr, Comp Relig
  Udoff, Alan, MA, Instr

THE UNITED STATES NAVAL ACADEMY
  Annapolis, Maryland 21402 (M; Nat; men; sem; II; 4310) Courses with no degree
  specialization, Dept of Hist, 301-267-3803

  Johnson, David E, PhD, Asst Prof, Chm, Contemp British Metaph
  Phillips, Anne H, PhD, Asst Prof, Exist

UNIVERSITY OF BALTIMORE
  Baltimore, Maryland 21201 (M; p; coed; sem; II; 4819) Courses with no degree
  specialization, Dept of Phil and Relig, 301-727-6350 Ext 323

  Craig, Daniel B, MA, Assoc Prof, Exist
  Guy, Jr, Alfred H, PhD, Asst Prof, Wittgenstein, Ethics, Metaph

UNIVERSITY OF MARYLAND
  College Park, Maryland 20742 (M; st; coed; sem; IV; 35,261) PhD major, Dept of Phil,
  301-454-2851

  Gorovitz, Samuel, PhD, Prof, Chm, Ethics, Phil Sci
  Brown, John H, PhD, Assoc Prof, Epistem, Ethics
  Burdick, John M, PhD, Visit Asst Prof Part-time, Anc Phil
  Celarier, James L, PhD, Assoc Prof, Greek Phil, Med Phil, Logic
  Curtis, Barry A, AB, Lect Part-time, Ethics, Contemp Phil
  Edlow, R Blair, PhD, Visit Asst Prof Part-time, Anc Phil, Aes
  Gruzalski, Bart K, MA, Instr Part-time, Ethics
  Johnson, Conrad D, PhD, Asst Prof, Phil of Law, Ethics, Polit Phil
  Kress, Jerry R, PhD, Asst Prof, Epistem, Phil of Lang
  Lesher, James H, PhD, Assoc Prof, Anc Phil, Epistem
  Martin, Raymond F, PhD, Assoc Prof, Metaph, Phil of Hist
  Odell, S Jack, PhD, Asst Prof, Epistem, Phil of Mind, Phil of Lang
  Pasch, Alan, PhD, Prof, Metaph, Epsitem
  Perkins, Moreland, PhD, Prof, Phil of Mind, Phil of Lit
  Schlaretzki, W Ernest, PhD, Prof, Ethics, Polit Phil
  Smolko, John F, MA, Lect Part-time, Continen Phil
  Sollazzo, Gary J, PhD, Lect Part-time, Phil of Relig
  Suppe, Frederick R, PhD, Assoc Prof, Phil of Sci, Epistem, Logic Automata Theory
  Svenonius, Diane, MA, Instr Part-time
  Svenonius, Lars S, PhD, Prof, Logic, Phil of Math
  Varnedoe, Samuel L, PhD, Asst Prof, Empir, Prag, Phil of Art

  Anderson, David A, Grad Asst
  Crouse, W Thomas, Grad Asst
  Golash, Deirdre K, Grad Asst
  Hall, Kenneth H, Grad Asst
  Langenbach, John O, Grad Asst

  Lee, C Richard, Grad Asst
  Mathews, Tülin M
  McGee, Karen J, Fel
  Staude, Mitchell, Grad Asst
  Zvara, Andrew A, Grad Asst

UNIVERSITY OF MARYLAND, BALTIMORE COUNTY
Baltimore, Maryland 21228 (M; st; coed; 4-1-4; IV; 3770) BA major, Dept of Phil,
301-455-2103

Levison, Arnold B, PhD, Prof, Chm, Epistem
Barker, Evelyn PhD, Assoc Prof, Exist, Phil of Hist
Barnes, Annette, PhD, Asst Prof, Aes
Benson, Thomas, MA, Instr, Phil of Relig
Braude, Stephen, PhD, Asst Prof, Phil of Lang
Goldberg, Bruce, PhD, Assoc Prof, Phil of Mind
Mayfield, Paul, MA, Lect, Anc Phil
Titchener, John, PhD, Assoc Prof, Ethics
Tormey, Alan, PhD, Prof, Aes, Phil of Mind
Weinstein, Scott, PhD, Asst Prof, Logic

Cote, Maxine, BA Teach Asst

UNIVERSITY OF MARYLAND, BALTIMORE PROFESSIONAL SCHOOL
Baltimore, Maryland 21201 (DH; st; coed; sem; IV; 3521) NP

UNIVERSITY OF MARYLAND, EASTERN SHORE
Princess Anne, Maryland 21853 (M; st; coed; sem; II; 771) Courses with no degree
specialization, --, 301-651-2200

Gordon, Dale H, MA, Instr

VILLA JULIE COLLEGE
Stevenson, Maryland 21153 (M; p; coed; sem; I; 245) Courses with no degree
specialization, Dept of Phil, 301-486-7348

DeBrabender, René, PhD, Lect-Prof, Contemp Phil

WASHINGTON BIBLE COLLEGE
Lanham, Maryland 20801 (BI; p; coed; sem; III; 318) NP

WASHINGTON COLLEGE
Chesterland, Maryland 21620 (M; p; coed; sem; III; 879) BA major, Dept of Phil and
Relig, 301-778-2800 Ext 270

Tapke, Peter F, PhD, Prof, Chm
McDonnell, Kevin, PhD, Asst Prof
Miller, John A, PhD, Asst Prof
Newell, J David, MA, Asst Prof

WESTERN MARYLAND COLLEGE
Westminster, Maryland 21157 (M; U Meth; coed; --; III; 2325) BA major, --, 301-848-
7000 Ext 273, 274, 306, 215

Hartman, Robert H, PhD, Asst Prof, Contemp Phil
Holthaus, Reuben S, PhD, Prof, Asian Stud, Phil of Relig

MASSACHUSETTS

AMERICAN INTERNATIONAL COLLEGE
Springfield, Massachusetts 01109 (E; p; coed; --; III; 2769) BA major, Dept of Phil,
413-737-5331

Baldwin, Robert C, PhD, Prof, Chm, Hist of Phil, Aes
Habermehl, Lawrence L, PhD, Asst Prof, Phil of Relig, Ethics
Provost, Paul E, AB, Asst Prof, Concept Anal

AMHERST COLLEGE
Amherst, Massachusetts 01002 (E; p; men; 4-1-4; III; 1231) BA major, Dept of Phil
and Relig, 413-542-2269

Kennick, William E, PhD, Prof, Chm, Metaph, Aes, Hist of Phil
Epstein, Joseph, PhD, Prof, Phil of Sci, Logic, Prag
Kearns, Thomas R, PhD, Asst Prof, Ethics, Phil of Law
Spelman, Elizabeth Victoria, PhD, Asst Prof, Phil of Mind, Epistem

Lamprecht, Sterling P, PhD, Prof Emer, Metaph, Hist of Phil

ANDOVER NEWTON THEOLOGICAL SCHOOL
Newton Centre, Massachusetts 02159 (Theol; p; coed; sem; IV; 407) PhD major, Dept
of Relig and Society, 617-332-1100

ANNA MARIA COLLEGE FOR WOMEN
Paxton, Massachusetts 01612 (E; RC; wo; 4-1-4; II; 580) --, Dept of Phil, 617-757-
4586 Ext 24

Gagnon, Lorraine Marie, PhD, Assoc Prof, Chm, Moral Phil, Hist of Phil
Belleville, Richard, Asst Prof
Cloutier, Ronald, Asst Prof

AQUINAS JUNIOR COLLEGE
Newton, Massachusetts 02158 (JRCB; RC; wo; sem; I; 158) NP

AQUINAS JUNIOR COLLEGE OF BUSINESS
Milton, Massachusetts 02186 (JRCB; RC; wo; sem; I; 176) NP

ASSUMPTION COLLEGE
Worcester, Massachusetts 01609 (E; RC; coed; sem; III; 1581) BA major, Dept of Phil,
617-752-5615 Ext 359

Fortier, Theodore L, PhD, Assoc Prof, Chm, Ethics
Bauer, Frederick, PhD, Asst Prof, Epistem
Berquist, Duane H, PhD, Assoc Prof, Logic, Phil of Nature, Phil of Sci
Douillard, Paul, MA, Lect, Logic

ATLANTIC UNION COLLEGE
South Lancaster, Massachusetts 01561 (E; SDA; coed; sem; II; 643) Courses with no
degree specialization, Dept of Phil, 617-365-4561

Hauck, Fred, PhD, Prof
Londis, James J, PhD, Assoc Prof
Stafford, Ottilie, PhD, Prof

BABSON COLLEGE
    Babson Park, Massachusetts 02157 (E; p; coed; sem; III; 1756) Courses with no
    degree specialization, --, 617-235-1200

BAY PATH JUNIOR COLLEGE
    Longmeadow, Massachusetts 01106 (E; p; wo; 4-1-4; I; 434) --, --, 413-567-0621

    Batrawi, Salah A, PhD, Prof

BAY STATE JUNIOR COLLEGE OF BUSINESS
    Boston, Massachusetts 02116 (JRCB; p; wo; sem; I; 180) BA minor, Dept of Phil,
    617-266-0220

    Perna, Albert F, MEd, Dir of Phil, Dir of Guidance

BECKER JUNIOR COLLEGE
    Worcester, Massachusetts 01609 (JRCB; p; coed; sem; I; 396) AA major, Dept of Libr
    Stud, 617-791-9241

    Kline, Carl, M Div, Instr

BENTLEY COLLEGE
    Waltham, Massachusetts 02154 (E; p; coed; sem; II; 3331) BA joint or combined major,
    Dept of Phil, 617-891-2204

    Reeves, M Francis, PhD, Prof, Chm, Soc and Moral Phil
    Adelman, Bernard H, AM, Asst Prof, Epistem, Logic
    Brown, Arthur A, MA, Asst Prof, Metaph, Contemp Phil
    Fisher, James V, MA, Lect, Phil of Hist
    Wintersteiner, Gail, PhD, Lect, Phil of Sci

BERKLEE COLLEGE OF MUSIC
    Boston, Massachusetts 02215 (--; p; coed; sem; II; 1422) Courses with no degree
    specialization, --, 617-266-3525

BERKSHIRE CHRISTIAN COLLEGE
    Lenox, Massachusetts 01240 (BI; Ad Chris; coed; sem; II; 155) BA minor, Div of Gen Arts,
    Theol Stud, 413-637-0838

    Dean, David A, ThM, Assoc Prof, Academic Dean, Phil Theol
    Merrill, Janet, EdD, Prof, Phil of Educ
    Northup, A B, MA, Prof, Hist of Phil

BERKSHIRE COMMUNITY COLLEGE
    Pittsfield, Massachusetts 01201 (E; st; coed; sem; I; 2093) Courses with no degree
    specialization, non-dept, 413-499-4660, Ext 351

    Deane, Frank, MA, Prof, Logic
    Lathrop, Donald, MA, Assoc Prof, Soc Ethics

BOSTON COLLEGE
    Chestnut Hill, Massachusetts 02167 (E; RC; coed; sem; IV; 11,111) PhD major, Dept
    of Phil, College of Arts and Sci, Dept of Phil, Grad School of Arts and Sci, 617-
    969-0100 Ext 372, 379, 2534

    Flanagan, Joseph, PhD, Assoc Prof, Chm, Phil of Hist, Hermen, Aes
    Adelmann, Frederick J, PhD, Prof, Marxism

Barrett, Joseph L, STL, Asst Prof, Ethics, Metaph
Blanchette, Oliva, PhD, Assoc Prof, Soc Phil, Polit Phil, Ethics, Metaph
Blakeley, Thomas J, PhD, Prof, Russian Phil, Polit Phil
Casey, Joseph H, PhD, Asst Prof, Phil of Lang, Phil of Relig
Cudahy, Brian J, PhD, Assoc Prof, Whitehead, British Empir, Phil of Relig
Donoghue, John D, STL, Asst Prof, Exist, Ethics
Fuir, Georg R, STL, Asst Prof, Contemp Ethical Theory
Haggerty, William J, PhD, Assoc Prof, Amer Prag, Logic
Kreeft, Peter J, PhD, Assoc Prof, Orient Phil, Phil of Relig
Loughran, Thomas J, PhD, Asst Prof, Logic, Phil of Sci, Ethics
Martin, Stuart B, PhD, Assoc Prof, Anc Phil, Soc Ethics
Molloy, Francis P, STL, Asst Prof, Logic, Exist
Murphy, Richard T, PhD, Assoc Prof, Phenomen, Anal Phil
Navickas, Joseph L, PhD, Assoc Prof, Hegel, 19th Cent German Idealism, Russian Phil
O'Brien, Gerard C, PhD, Asst Prof, Anc Phil, Med Phil
Owens, Thomas J, PhD, Prof, Heidegger, Phenomen, Value Theory
Rasmussen, David M, PhD, Assoc Prof, Phil of Sym, Soc Phil, Structural Ling
Rock, John P, PhD, Assoc Prof, Exist, Metaph, Epistem
Shine, Daniel J, PhD, Assoc Prof, Exist Psych, Phil of Man
Stevens, Richard M, PhD, Asst Prof, Amer Phil, Phil of Sci
Taminiaux, Jacques M, PhD, Prof, Phenomen, Hist of Phil
Toomey, Charles B, AM, Asst Prof, Logic, Ethics
Wells, Norman J, PhD, Prof, Med Phil, Renaissance Phil

Aboulafia, Mitchell S, BA, Grad Asst
Alves, Mary J, BA, Grad Asst
Baillie, Harold W, BA, Teach Fel
Bowers, David W, BA, Teach Fel
Eckstein, Paul, BA, Grad Asst
Egbujie, Innocent I, MA, Teach Fel
Flesche, David E, M Div, Grad Asst
Frontczak, Deirdre, BA, Teach Fel
Gaffney, Richard J, MA, Teach Fel
Gross, Richard, MA, Teach Fel
Hartnett, John K, BA, Grad Asst
Jones, John D, MA, Teach Fel
May, James R, MA, Teach Fel
McAdam, Richard D, BA, Teach Fel
McNally, Patrick H, MA, Teach Fel
Meyer, Theresa A, AB, Teach Fel
Nenon, Thomas J, BA, Grad Asst
O'Connor, Thomas F, AB, Teach Fel
Orgel, Gary S, JD, Teach Fel
Panaro, Gerard P, AB, Teach Fel
Pepper, Michael A, MA, Teach Fel
Polansky, Ronald M, BA, Teach Fel
Robbins, Dennis A, MA, Teach Fel
Santilli, Paul C, AB, Teach Fel
Sevensky, Robert L, MA, Teach Fel
Shenkman, Michael H, BA, Teach Fel
Soo, Francis Y, MA, Grad Asst
Strimple, Patricia A, BA, Grad Asst
Vallicella, William F, BA, Grad Asst
Weinberg, W, BA, Grad Asst
Wieler, Jerome A, AB, Teach Fel
Willenbecher, Thomas C, BA, Grad Asst
Williams, Nedra T, BA, Teach Fel
Wright, Kathleen R, MA, Teach Fel

BOSTON CONSERVATORY OF MUSIC
Boston, Massachusetts 02115 (F; p; coed; sem; III; 530) NP

BOSTON STATE COLLEGE
Boston, Massachusetts 02115 (E; st; coed; sem; III; 8338) BA major, Dept of Phil,
617-731-3300

Colbert, Jr, James G, PhD, Assoc Prof, Chm, Logic, Hist of Greek Phil
Joseph, Stephen G, MA, Asst Prof, Logic, Rationalism, Phil of Relig
Locklin, David K, MA, Instr, Hist of Contemp Phil, Empir
McGregor, James E, MA, Instr, Ethics, Phil of Lang, Metaph
Mellican, R Eugene, PhD, Instr, Phil of Man, Greek Phil
Moore, Robert E, PhD, Assoc Prof, Phil of Educ, Amer Phil
O'Neill, John J, MEd, Assoc Prof, Phil of Educ
O'Sullivan, Joan, PhD, Asst Prof, Exist, Phil of Educ
Scott, Bruce A, AM, Asst Prof, Aes, Orient Phil
Serafini, Jr, Anthony L, PhD, Asst Prof, Epistem, Phil of Lang

BOSTON UNIVERSITY
   Boston, Massachusetts 02215 (E; p; coed; sem; IV; 25,051) PhD major, Dept of Phil,
   617-353-2571, 617-353-2572, 617-353-2573, 617-353-2574

   Lavely, John H, PhD, Prof, Chm, Phil of Relig, Anc Phil
   Agassi, Joseph, PhD, Prof, Phil of Sci
   Bennett, William, PhD, Asst Prof, Polit Phil
   Berry, George, PhD, Prof, Logic, Phil of Sci
   Bertocci, Peter A, PhD, Borden Parker Bowne Prof, Phil of Relig, Metaph
   Burkett, John, PhD, Asst Prof
   Capek, Milic, PhD, Prof, Phil of Sci, Hist of Phil
   Cohen, Robert S, PhD, Prof, Phil of Phys
   Coleman, Francis J, PhD, Assoc Prof, Aes, Ethics
   Elevitch, Bernard, PhD, Assoc Prof, Phil of Psych, Exist
   Findlay, John, PhD, Prof, Metaph, Hist of Phil
   Hullett, James N, PhD, Asst Prof, Epistem, Phil of Educ
   Klein, Barbara, MA, Lect, Logic
   Kohak, Erazim, PhD, Prof, Phenomen, Soc Phil
   Lorenzen, Paul, PhD, Prof, Found of Math
   Martin, Michael, PhD, Assoc Prof, Phil of Soc Sci
   McCarthy, Thomas, PhD, Asst Prof, Phil of Soc Sci
   Morgan, Kathryn, MA, Asst Prof, Phil of Educ
   Rapaport, Elizabeth, PhD, Asst Prof, Ethics, Polit Phil
   Sagal, Paul, PhD, Asst Prof, Med Phil, Phil of Lang
   Shimony, Abner, PhD, Prof, Epistem, Phil of Sci
   Silber, John, PhD, Univ Prof, Hist of Phil, Phil of Law
   Webb, Judson, MA, Asst Prof, Logic, Phil of Mind
   Wartofsky, Marx, PhD, Prof, Aes, Marxism, Phil of Mind

   Allchin, Keith, BA, Teach Asst
   Allen, Michael, MA, Teach Asst
   Boyer, David, BA, Teach Asst
   Buchwalter, Andrew, BA, Teach Asst
   Cerullo, Margaret, BA, Teach Asst
   Fay, Martha, BA, Teach Asst
   Flanagan, Owen, MA, Sr Teach Fel
   Flowers, Peter, MA, Teach Asst
   Fuchs, Jack, BA, Teach Asst
   Garvin, Ned, BA, Teach Asst
   Grim, Patrick, BA, Teach Asst
   Hellenthal, Marc, BA, Teach Asst
   Holman, Elizabeth, BA, Teach Asst
   Hurreh, Ismael, MA, Teach Asst
   Johnson, Galen, MA, Teach Asst
   Kargopoulos, Philip, BA, Teach Asst
   Marshall, Geraldine, BA, Sr Teach Fel

   McCreadie-Albright, Thomas, BA, Teach Asst
   Minch, Larry, BA, Teach Asst
   Nearing, Kathleen, MA, Sr Teach Fel
   Prabhu, Joseph, MA, Teach Asst
   Pruitt, Richard, BA, Teach Asst
   Romanos, George, MA, Teach Asst
   Rothbery, Donald, BA, Teach Asst
   Ryan, Cheyney, MA, Sr Teach Fel
   Sanders, Jack, MA, Sr Teach Fel
   Savage, Terry, BA, Teach Asst
   Sherman, Nancy, BA, Teach Asst
   Simon, Larry, BA, Teach Asst
   Todd, Jennifer, BA, Teach Asst
   von Imhof, Florien, MA, Sr Teach Asst
   Walker, James, BA, Teach Asst
   Webb, Ilona, BA, Sr Teach Fel
   Weightman, Donald, BA, Teach Asst

BRADFORD COLLEGE
   Bradford, Massachusetts 01830 (E; p; coed; sem; II; 324) --, Dept of Phil, Relig
   and Psych, 617-372-7161 Ext 361

   Bowler, T Downing, MA, Chm

BRANDEIS UNIVERSITY
   Waltham, Massachusetts 02154 (E; p; coed; sem; IV; 2994) PhD major, Dept of Phil,
   617-647-2654

   Aiken, Henry D, PhD, Prof, Ethics, Amer Phil, Soc Phil
   Burian, Richard, PhD, Asst Prof, Phil of Sci
   Diamandopoulos, Peter, PhD, Prof, Hist of Anc Phil
   Greenberg, Robert S, PhD, Assoc Prof, Theory of Knowl
   Kvart, Igal, MA, Instr, Epistem, Phil of Sci

159

Sommers, Frederic T, PhD, Prof, Phil of Lang, Metaph, Hist of Phil
van Heijenoort, John, PhD, Prof, Logic, Hist of Logic, Found of Math
Weitz, Morris, PhD, Prof, Phil of Art and Lit, Anal Phil

Brown, Robert A	Lappin, Shalom
Culmer, Charles W	Mallick, Krishna
Elgin, Catherine Z	Rudavsky, Tamar
Gottlieb, Roger	Starr, Zachary
Graham, George A	Wald, Jan David
Juch, William A	

BRIDGEWATER STATE COLLEGE
Bridgewater, Massachusetts 02324 (E; st; coed; sem; III; 6792) MA minor, Dept of
Phil, 617-697-6161 Ext 341

Cheney, David R, PhD, Asst Prof, Chm, 19th Cent Phil, Polit Phil, Aes
Berkson, William, PhD, Asst Prof, Phil of Sci, Logic
Corkery, Joseph, MA, Assoc Prof, Hist of Phil, Metaph
Fitzgibbons, Robert, MA, Assoc Prof, Phil of Educ, Logic
Joyal, Achille, MA, Assoc Prof, Anc and Med Phil, Ethics
Sanders, Steven, PhD, Asst Prof, Ethics, Contemp Anal Phil, Phil of Lang

BRISTOL COMMUNITY COLLEGE
Fall River, Massachusetts 02720 (E; st; coed; sem; I; 3384) NP

BRYANT-STRATTON COMMERCIAL SCHOOL
Boston, Massachusetts 02116 (JRCB; p; coed; sem; I; 1052) NP

BURDETT COLLEGE
Boston, Massachusetts 02116 (JRCB; p; coed; qr; I; 306) NP

CAMBRIDGE JUNIOR COLLEGE
Cambridge, Massachusetts 02140 (--; p; coed; sem; I; 132) Courses with no degree
specialization, Dept of Phil, 617-547-8844

Paley, Bruce, MA

CAPE COD COMMUNITY COLLEGE
West Barnstable, Massachusetts 02668 (E; st; coed; sem; I; 2358) NR

CHAMBERLAYNE JUNIOR COLLEGE
Boston, Massachusetts 02116 (JRCB; p; coed; sem; I; 789) Courses with no degree
specialization, --, 617-536-4500

CLARK UNIVERSITY
Worcester, Massachusetts 01610 (E; p; coed; 4-1-4; IV; 3228) BA major, Dept of Phil,
617-793-7414

Beck, Robert N, PhD, Prof, Chm
Anderson, Albert A, PhD, Assoc Prof
Hollinger, Robert, PhD, Visit Asst Prof
Markle, Gilbert Scott, PhD, Assoc Prof
Overvold, Gary E, PhD, Assoc Prof
Wright, Walter E, PhD, Asst Prof

COLLEGE OF OUR LADY OF ELMS
Chicopee, Massachusetts 01013 (E; RC; wo; sem; II; 482) Courses with no degree
specialization, Dept of Phil, 413-598-8351

Desilets, Donald A, STD, Adj Asst Prof
Johnson, John J, STD, Lect
McCormick, Howard, MA, Lect
Stafford, Robert H, STD, Adj Assoc Prof
Viau, Roger, JCD, Adj Assoc Prof
Ward, Eugene A, PhD, Lect

COLLEGE OF THE HOLY CROSS
Worcester, Massachusetts 01610 (E; RC; coed; sem; III; 2488) BA major, Dept of
Phil, 617-793-2468

DiIanni, Albert R, PhD, Assoc Prof, Chm
Callahan, Francis F, PhD, Asst Prof
Cloeren, Hermann-Josef, PhD, Assoc Prof
Feehan, Thomas D, PhD, Assoc Prof
Hampsch, George H, PhD, Prof
Haran, John P, STD, Prof
Harrington, Eugene J, PhD, Assoc Prof
Herx, Frederick C, PhD, Asst Prof
Hein, Hilde S, PhD, Assoc Prof
Lynch, John J, PhD, Assoc Prof
Pax, Clyde V, PhD, Assoc Prof

CURRY COLLEGE
Milton, Massachusetts 02186 (E; p; coed; sem; II; 957) BA major, Div of Human,
617-333-0500 Ext 333

Anderson, C Alan, PhD, Prof, Chm, Phil of Relig, Metaph
Hahnfeld, John H, PhD, Asst Prof, Phil Theol, Phil of Sci
Kirschenmann, Frederick, PhD, Assoc Prof, Dean
Pregeant, W Russell, PhD, Asst Prof

DEAN JUNIOR COLLEGE
Franklin, Massachusetts 02038 (E; p; coed; sem; I; 964) NR

EASTERN NAZARENE COLLEGE
Wollaston, Massachusetts 02170 (E; Naz; coed; sem; III; 902) BA major, Dept of Phil,
617-773-6350

Kauffman, Alvin H, PhD, Prof
Mullen, Wilbur H, PhD, Prof

EMERSON COLLEGE
Boston, Massachusetts 02116 (E; p; coed; --; III; 1879) --, Dept of Phil and Relig,
617-262-2010

EMMANUEL COLLEGE
Boston, Massachusetts 02115 (E; RC; wo; sem; III; 1342) BA major, Dept of Phil,
617-277-9340

Devettere, Raymond, PhD, Asst Prof, Chm, Exist Phenomen
Kitchel, Mary Jean, MSL, Asst Prof, Med Phil
Kreeft, Peter, PhD, Lect, East Tht
Minichino, Camille, PhD, Lect, Phil of Sci
Wall, Thomas, PhD, Asst Prof, Anglo-Saxon and Amer Phil

ENDICOTT JUNIOR COLLEGE
Beverly, Massachusetts 01915 (E; p; wo; --; I; 804) Courses with no degree specialization, Dept of Phil and Relig, 617-927-0585 Ext 335

Bortzfield, Eric R, MA, Instr

EPISCOPAL THEOLOGICAL SCHOOL
Cambridge, Massachusetts 02138 (Theol; Epis; coed; sem; II; 125) Courses with no degree specialization, --, 617-868-3450

FISHER JUNIOR COLLEGE
Boston, Massachusetts 02116 ((E; p; wo; --; I; 307) NR

FITCHBURG STATE COLLEGE
Fitchburg, Massachusetts 01420 (E; st; coed; sem; III; 5092) BA minor, Dept of Phil, 617-343-6417 Ext 56

Conlon, Michael J, MA, Prof, Phil of Educ
DeCesare, Richard A, PhD, Assoc Prof, Mod Phil
Jeffko, Walter G, PhD, Assoc Prof, Ethics
O'Neill, Reginald F, PhD, Prof, Exist

FORSYTH SCHOOL OF DENTAL HYGIENISTS
Boston, Massachusetts 02115 (DH; p; coed; qr; I; 224) NP

FRAMINGHAM STATE COLLEGE
Framingham, Massachusetts 01701 (E; st; coed; sem; III; 3475) BA major, Dept of Phil, 617-872-3501 Ext 375

Ramsdell, Robert D, PhD, Prof, Chm, Phil of Educ, Contemp Phil, Hist of Mod Phil
Guin, Philip, MA, Asst Prof, Phil of Educ, Aes, Polit Phil
Harris, Robert T, PhD, Prof, Soc Phil, Logic, Anc Phil

FRANKLIN INSTITUTE OF BOSTON
Boston, Massachusetts 02116 (E; local; coed; sem; I; 1110) NP

GARLAND JUNIOR COLLEGE
Boston, Massachusetts 02215 (E; p; wo; sem; I; 308) NP

GORDON COLLEGE
Wenham, Massachusetts 01984 (E; p; coed; qr; II; 813) BA major, Dept of Phil, 617-927-2300 Ext 289

Brushaber, George, PhD, Assoc Prof, Chm, Epistem, Logic, Metaph
Reid, Malcolm A, BA, Asst Prof, Ethics, Phil Theol
Spires, T Grady, STM, Assoc Prof, Aes, Phil of Soc Sci, Phil of Relig

GORDON-CONWELL THEOLOGICAL SEMINARY
South Hamilton, Massachusetts 01982 (Theol; p; coed; sem; III; 407) MA major, Dept of Theol, 617-468-7111 Ext 221

Kalland, Lloyd A, ThD, Prof, Ethics
Roberts, Wesley A, PhD, Asst Prof

GRAHME JUNIOR COLLEGE
Boston, Massachusetts 02215 (JRCB; p; coed; sem; I; 1209) --, School of Libr Arts,
617-536-2050

McCullough, Daniel, MLS

GREENFIELD COMMUNITY COLLEGE
Greenfield, Massachusetts 01301 (E; st; coed; sem; I; 1263) Courses with no degree
specialization, Dept of Human, 413-774-3131 Ext 24

Benander, Donald, Instr

HAMPSHIRE COLLEGE
Amherst, Massachusetts 01002 (--; p; coed; 4-1-4; II; 645) Courses with no degree
specialization, School of Human and Arts, 413-542-4632

Bradt, Raymond K, MA, Asst Prof, Phil of Relig, Chinese Phil
Meagher, Robert E, MA, Asst Prof, Phil of Relig

HARVARD UNIVERSITY
Cambridge, Massachusetts 02138 (E; p; coed; sem; IV; 18,862) PhD major, Dept of
Phil, 617-495-2191

Rawls, John, PhD, Prof, Chm
Cavell, Stanley L, PhD, Prof
Dreben, Burton, AM, Prof, Dean
Firth, Roderick, PhD, Prof
Foy, Linda, PhD, Asst Prof
Friedman, PhD, Asst Prof
Goodman, Nelson, PhD, Prof
Hooker, Michael, PhD, Asst Prof
Irwin, Terence, PhD, Asst Prof
Nozick, Robert, PhD, Prof
Putnam, Hilary, PhD, Prof
Quine, W V, PhD, Prof
Scheffler, Israel, PhD, Prof

Williams, Donald C, PhD, Prof Emer

HEBREW COLLEGE
Brookline, Massachusetts 02146 (E; p; coed; sem; III; 164) MA minor, Dept of Jewish
Tht and Phil, 617-232-8710

Luz, Ehud, MA, Instr
Shapiro, David, MA, Instr
Schimmel, Sol, PhD, Asst Prof

HELLENIC COLLEGE
Brookline, Massachusetts 02146 (--; G Orth; coed; sem; III; 139) BA major, Dept of
Phil and Relig, 617-731-3500

Karahalios, George, PhD, Asst Prof, Act Chm, Early Greek and Byzantine Phil
Proussis, Costas M, PhD, Prof, Early Greek Phil

HOLYOKE COMMUNITY COLLEGE
Holyoke, Massachusetts 01040 (E; st; coed; sem; I; 3599) NR

KATHARINE GIBBS SCHOOL
  Boston, Massachusetts 02116 (JRCB; p; wo; sem; I; 549) NR

LASELL JUNIOR COLLEGE
  Auburndale, Massachusetts 02166 (E; p; wo; sem; I; 789) Courses with no degree
  specialization, --, 617-243-2000

LEICESTER JUNIOR COLLEGE
  Leicester, Massachusetts 01524 (E; p; coed; --; I; 250) Courses with no degree
  specialization, --, 617-892-5511

  Scarborough, John R, MA, Asst Prof

LESLEY COLLEGE
  Cambridge, Massachusetts 02183 (E; p; wo; sem; III; 814) Courses with no degree
  specialization, --, 617-868-9600

  Scofield, Russell G, PhD, Prof

LOWELL STATE COLLEGE
  Lowell, Massachusetts 01854 (E; st; coed; sem; III; 2438) BA major, Dept of Phil,
  617-454-8011 Ext 231

  Smith, P Christopher, PhD, Assoc Prof, Chm, German Phil
  Alexander, Bruce, MA, Instr, Anal Phil
  Innis, Robert, PhD, Asst Prof, Phenomen
  Lyons, Richard, PhD, Assoc Prof, Amer Phil

LOWELL TECHNOLOGICAL INSTITUTE
  Lowell, Massachusetts 01854 (E; st; coed; sem; IV; 6887) Courses with no degree
  specialization, Dept of Lang and Lit, 617-454-7811 Ext 274

  Wiehe, Roger E, PhD, Prof, Phil of Relig

MASSACHUSETTS BAY COMMUNITY COLLEGE
  Watertown, Massachusetts 02172 (E; st; coed; sem; I; 3013) --, Dept of Human,
  617-926-2600 Ext 59

  Goodenough, Irene, MA, Asst Prof

MASSACHUSETTS COLLEGE OF ART
  Boston, Massachusetts 02215 (E; st; coed; sem; III; 1225) Courses with no degree
  specialization, Dept of Critical Stud, 617-742-2345

  McLaughlin, John D, AM, Asst Prof, Aes

MASSACHUSETTS COLLEGE OF OPTOMETRY
  Boston, Massachusetts 02115 (Opt; p; coed; sem; II; 225) NP

MASSACHUSETTS COLLEGE OF PHARMACY
  Boston, Massachusetts 02115 (Phar; p; coed; sem; IV; 640) Courses with no degree
  specialization, --, 617-734-6700

MASSACHUSETTS INSTITUTE OF TECHNOLOGY
Cambridge, Massachusetts 02139 (E; p; coed; 4-1-4; IV; 7698) PhD major, Dept Phil, 617-253-4141

Cartwright, Richard L, PhD, Prof, Chm
Block, Ned J, PhD, Asst Prof
Boolos, George S, PhD, Assoc Prof
Brody, Borch A, PhD, Assoc Prof
Dromberger, Sylvain, PhD, Prof
Fodor, Jerry A, PhD, Prof
Graves, John C, PhD, Assoc Prof
Herman, Barbara, MA, Asst Prof
Horwich, Paul, MA, Asst Prof
Katz, Jerrold J, PhD, Prof
Miller, Izchak, BA, Asst Prof
Morgan, Miles, BA, Instr
Singer, Irving, PhD, Prof
Thomson, James F, MA, Prof
Thomson, Judith J, PhD, Prof

Horowitz, Tamara, Grad Asst   Steinberg, Alan, Grad Asst
Levin, Janet, Grad Asst

MASSACHUSETTS MARITIME ACADEMY
Buzzards Bay, Massachusetts 02532 (--; st; men; qr; II; 333) NP

MASSASOIT COMMUNITY COLLEGE
Brockton, Massachusetts 02402 (E; st; coed; sem; I; 3092) NR

MERRIMACK COLLEGE
North Andover, Massachusetts 01845 (E; RC; coed; sem; II; 2876) BA major, Dept of Phil, 617-683-7111

Meyer, Herbert H, PhD, Chm, Contemp Euro Phil, Ethics
Cahalan, John C, PhD, Asst Prof, Anal Phil, Metaph
Daly, Paul, PhD, Asst Prof, Amer Phil, Anc Phil
Matross, Gerald, PhD, Asst Prof, Polit and Soc Phil
Rickert, Richard, PhD, Asst Prof, Aes, Orient Phil
Sweeney, James J, MA, Asst Prof, Phil of Sci, Phil of Soc Sci
Warren, John, PhD, Asst Prof, Phil of Nature, Ethics, Med Phil

MIDDLESEX COMMUNITY COLLEGE
Bedford, Massachusetts 01730 (XT; st; coed; sem; I; 948) NR

MOUNT ALVERNIA COLLEGE
Newton, Massachusetts 02158 (--; RC; wo; sem; II; 10) NP

MOUNT HOLYOKE COLLEGE
South Hadley, Massachusetts 01075 (E; p; wo; 4-1-4; III; 1919) NR

MOUNT IDA COLLEGE
Newton Centre, Massachusetts (E; p; wo; --; I; 603) AA major, Dept of Phil, 617-969-7000 Ext 14

Glessner, Richard H, BD, Prof

MOUNT WACHUSETT COMMUNITY COLLEGE
　　Gardner, Massachusetts 01440 (E; st; coed; sem; I; 1916) NR

NEWBURY JUNIOR COLLEGE
　　Boston, Massachusetts 02115 (JRCB; p; coed; sem; I; 215) NR

NEW ENGLAND CONSERVATORY OF MUSIC
　　Boston, Massachusetts 02115 (E; p; coed; sem; III; 560) NR

NEW ENGLAND INSTITUTE OF ANATOMY, SANITARY SCIENCE AND EMBALMING
　　Boston, Massachusetts 02215 (--; p; coed; qr; I; 155) Courses with no degree
　　specialization, --, 617-536-6970

　　Reeves, M Francis, PhD

NEW ENGLAND SCHOOL OF LAW
　　Boston, Massachusetts 02180 (Law; p; coed; sem; III; 497) NR

NEWTON COLLEGE OF THE SACRED HEART
　　Newton, Massachusetts 02159 (E; p; wo; 4-1-4; III; 1036) NR

NEWTON JUNIOR COLLEGE
　　Newtonville, Massachusetts 02160 (E; local; coed; sem; I; 472) Courses with no
　　degree specialization, Dept of Soc Sci, 617-969-9570 Ext 45

　　Senior, Robert C, PhD, Assoc Prof

NICHOLS COLLEGE
　　Dudley, Massachusetts 01570 (E; p; coed; sem; II; 707) Courses with no degree
　　specialization, Dept of Human, 617-943-1560

　　Graves, Bernard, PhD, Prof, Chm, Ethics

NORTH ADAMS STATE COLLEGE
　　North Adams, Massachusetts 01247 (E; st; coed; 4-1-4; III; 2485) BA minor, Dept
　　of Phil, 413-663-6582 Ext 250

　　Gomez, Samuel, PhD, Prof, Chm, Value Theory, Phil of Educ, Exist
　　Allmaker, Ali M, PhD, Prof, Metaph, Phil of Sci, Plato, Prag
　　Devine, Philip E, PhD, Asst Prof, Logic, Anal Phil, Epistem
　　Goldstein, Marc A, PhD, Asst Prof, Soc and Polit Phil, 18th and 19th Cent Phil,
　　　　Phil of Hist, Marxism
　　Sullivan, Arthur F, PhD, Prof, Phil of Law, Natur, Anc Phil, Hist of Phil

NORTHAMPTON JUNIOR COLLEGE
　　Northampton, Massachusetts 01060 (JRCB; p; coed; --; I; 444) --, Dept of Libr Arts,
　　413-584-1754

　　Rose, Dudley C, BA, Instr

NORTHEASTERN UNIVERSITY
　　Boston, Massachusetts 02115 (E; p; coed; qr; IV; 34,353) BA major, Dept of Phil
　　and Relig, 617-437-3346

Fogg, Walter L, PhD, Prof, Chm, Hist of Phil
DeAngelis, William J, PhD, Asst Prof, Mod Phil
Hacker, Edward A, PhD, Assoc Prof, Traditional Logic, Phil of Sci
Haule, John, PhD, Asst Prof, Phenomen of Relig
Kovaly, Pavel, PhD, Assoc Prof, Hist of Phil
Lipton, Michael, BS, Instr, Phil Logic
Nathanson, Stephen L, PhD, Asst Prof, Epistem, Phil of Mind
Pruett, Gordon E, PhD, Asst Prof
Wellbank, Joseph H, PhD, Assoc Prof, Ethics

NORTHERN ESSEX COMMUNITY COLLEGE
Haverhill, Massachusetts 01830 (F; st; coed; sem; I; 3563) Courses with no degree
specialization, Dept of Phil and Fine Arts, 617-374-0721 Ext 345

Gustafson, James W, PhD, Assoc Prof, Chm, Metaph
Brown, James W, MA, Asst Prof, Logic

NORTH SHORE COMMUNITY COLLEGE
Beverly, Massachusetts 01915 (E; st; coed; sem; I; 5106) AA major, Dept of Cult
Arts, 617-927-4850

Sullivan, Jr, F Russell, PhD, Prof, Chm, Problems of Phil, Contemp Phil, Phil of
Relig, Logic, Sym Logic
Baker, Robert, MA, Instr, Problems of Phil, Contemp Phil, Phil of Relig

OBLATE COLLEGE AND SEMINARY
Natick, Massachusetts 01760 (--; RC; sem; II; --) BA major, Dept of Phil, 617-
653-0668

Breault, Charles, PhD, Prof, Chm, German Idealism
Beauchesne, Richard, Prof, Phil of Relig
Rocheleau, Maurice, PhL, Prof, Exist

PERRY NORMAL SCHOOL
Milton, Massachusetts 02186 (--; p; coed; sem; I; 178) NR

PINE MANOR JUNIOR COLLEGE
Chestnut Hill, Massachusetts 02167 (E; p; wo; sem; I; 542) --, Dept of Phil and
Relig, 617-731-7073

Thompson, Cameron, MA
Thompson, Stephen, BD, Ethics

QUINCY JUNIOR COLLEGE
Quincy, Massachusetts 02169 (--; local; coed; sem; I; 1752) NR

QUINSIGAMOND COMMUNITY COLLEGE
Worcester, Massachusetts 01606 (E; st; coed; sem; I; 4082) NR

RADCLIFFE COLLEGE
Cambridge, Massachusetts 02138 (E; p; wo; sem; II; 1295) PhD major, Dept of Phil,
Faculty same as Harvard Univ, 617-495-8000

REGIS COLLEGE
    Weston, Massachusetts 02193 (E; p; wo; 4-1-4; II; 849) Courses with no degree
    specialization, --, 617-893-1820

SAINT HYACINTH COLLEGE AND SEMINARY
    Granby, Massachusetts 01033 (E; RC; men; sem; II; 119) Courses with no degree
    specialization, Dept of Phil, 413-467-7180

    Bennett, Owen, PhD, Prof, Chm, Metaph
    Giermek, Joachim, ABD, Instr, Med Phil
    Kane, Louis, STD, Instr, Logic
    Oppitz, Joseph, PhD, Prof, Ethics
    Pietrzak, Daniel, MA, Instr, Phil of Man

SAINT JOHN'S SEMINARY COLLEGE
    Brighton, Massachusetts 02135 (E; RC; men; sem; III; 283) AB major, Dept of Phil,
    617-254-2610 Ext 62

    Noonan, Mark L, PhD, Chm, Process Phil, Phil of Man, Hist of Phil
    Devettere, Raymond, PhD, Exist, Phenomen, Phil of Relig
    McLaughlin, Bernard, MA, Ethics, Polit Phil

SALEM STATE COLLEGE
    Salem, Massachusetts 01970 (E; st; coed; sem; III; 7304) NP

SCHOOL OF THE MUSEUM OF FINE ARTS
    Boston, Massachusetts 02115 (Art; p; coed; sem; III; 654) NR

SCHOOL OF THE WORCESTER ART MUSEUM
    Worcester, Massachusetts 01608 (Art; p; coed; sem; I; 169) NP

SIMMONS COLLEGE
    Boston, Massachusetts 02115 (E; p; wo; sem; III; 2424) BA major, Dept of Phil, 617-
    738-2164

    Bok, Sissela, PhD, Instr Part-time, Polit Phil
    Ochs, Carol, PhD, Assoc Prof, Metaph
    Park, Ynhui, PhD, Asst Prof, Exist
    Rhodes, Margaret, MA, Instr Part-time, Phil of Mind

SIMON'S ROCK
    Great Barrington, Massachusetts 01230 (--; p; coed; 4-1-4; I; 227) Courses with
    no degree specialization, Dept of Soc Stud, 413-528-0771

    Anderson, Graham, BA, Chm, Polit and Econ Phil
    Misch, Edward J, HED, Christ Phil

SMITH COLLEGE
    Northampton, Massachusetts 01060 (E; p; wo; --; IV; 2513) PhD major, Dept of Phil,
    413-584-2700

    Kiteley, Murray, PhD, Prof, Chm, Metaph, Epistem, Object Theory
    Connally, John, PhD, Asst Prof, Phil of Action, Metaph, Soc Phil
    Parsons, Kathryn Pyne, PhD, Assoc Prof, Phil of Sci, Phil of Lang, Ethics
    Smith, Malcolm B E, PhD, Asst Prof, Ethics, Polit Phil, Legal Phil, Aes
    Tymoczko, Thomas, PhD, Asst Prof, Logic, Set Theory, Phil of Lang, Phil of Math

SOUTHEASTERN MASSACHUSETTS UNIVERSITY
North Dartmouth, Massachusetts 02747 (E; st; coed; sem; III; 4961) BA major, Dept of Phil, 617-997-9321

Fitzgerald, John J, PhD, Prof, Chm, Amer Phil
Hogan, Richard, MA, Instr, Anc Phil
Kalikow, Theodora, MA, Instr, Phil of Sci
Place, James, PhD, Asst Prof, Phenomen
Teeter, Lura S, PhD, Prof, Theory of Knowl, Phil of Lang
Wassmer, Thomas A, PhD, Prof, Ethics, Phil of Relig

SPRINGFIELD COLLEGE
Springfield, Massachusetts 01109 (E; p; coed; qr; IV; 2692) BA major, Dept of Relig and Phil, 413-787-2135

Ehman, Mark A, MA, Assoc Prof, Asian Phil
Olds, Mason, PhD, Asst Prof, Phil of Relig
Thomas, Herman E, ThM, Instr, Ethics
Van Derbeck, Holmes, MA, Prof

SPRINGFIELD TECHNICAL COMMUNITY COLLEGE
Springfield, Massachusetts 01105 (E; st; coed; sem; I; 4206) Courses with no degree specialization, Div of Human, 413-781-6470 Ext 32

Lawton, Jr, Philip N, PhD, Asst Prof, Contemp Phil

STONEHILL COLLEGE
North Easton, Massachusetts 02356 (E; RC; coed; sem; II; 1609) Course with no degree specialization, --, 617-238-2052

SUFFOLK UNIVERSITY
Boston, Massachusetts 02114 (E; p; coed; sem; III; 5731) BA major, Dept of Phil, 617-723-4700

Sahakian, William S, PhD, Prof, Chm, Hist of Phil
Outwater, Denis, Asst Prof, Phil of Relig
Pearl, Philip D, PhD, Prof, Orient Phil
Reiche, Harald, PhD, Anc Phil, German Phil
Zuckerstatter, Rudolf, PhD, Assoc Prof, Ethics, Logic

SWAIN SCHOOL OF DESIGN
New Bedford, Massachusetts 02740 (--; p; coed; sem; II; 103) NP

TUFTS UNIVERSITY
Medford, Massachusetts 02155 (E; p; coed; sem; IV; 5560) MA major, Dept of Phil, 617-628-5000 Ext 433, 319

Bedau, Hugo Adam, PhD, Prof, Chm, Soc Phil, Polit Phil, Legal Phil
Cartwright, Helen, PhD, Assoc Prof, Logic, Metaph
Daniels, Norman, PhD, Asst Prof, Phil of Sci, Ethics, Soc Phil
Dennett, Daniel C, DPhil, Deputy Chm, Phil of Mind, Phil of Soc Sci
Israel, David, BA, Instr, Contemp Phil, Epistem
Radden, Jennifer, BPhil, Lect, Phil of Mind, Epistem
Sobel, Jerry, MA, Instr, Phenomen and Exist, Anc Phil

Burch, George Bosworth, PhD, Prof Emer, Med Phil, Orient Phil

UNIVERSITY OF MASSACHUSETTS, AMHERST CAMPUS
Amherst, Massachusetts 01002 (E; st; coed; sem; IV; 23,156) PhD major, Dept of Phil, 413-545-2330

Chappell, Vere, PhD, Prof, Head
Ackermann, Robert, PhD, Prof
Aune, Bruce, PhD, Prof
Bosley, Paul, PhD, Asst Prof
Brentlinger, John, PhD, Assoc Prof
Chisholm, Roderick, PhD, Adj Prof
Ehrlich, Leonard, PhD, Assoc Prof
Feldman, Fred, PhD, Asst Prof
Ferguson, Ann, PhD, Assoc Prof
Foster, Lawrence, PhD, Assoc Prof
Gettier, Edmund, PhD, Prof
Heidelberger, Herbert, PhD, Prof, Dir of Grad Stud
Jubien, Michael, PhD, Asst Prof
Matthews, Gareth, PhD, Prof, Dir of Undergrad Stud
Oppenheim, Felix, PhD, Prof
Parsons, Terence, PhD, Assoc Prof
Partee, Barbara Hall, PhD, Prof
Robison, John, PhD, Assoc Prof, Assoc Head
Sirridge, Mary, PhD, Asst Prof
Sleigh, Robert, PhD, Prof
Wolff, Robert Paul, PhD, Prof

Shute, Clarence, PhD, Prof Emer

Arsenault, Alfred, BA, Teach Asst	McKelligan, Marcia, BA, Teach Asst
Balmer, James, BA, Teach Asst	Mellema, Gregory, BA, Teach Assoc
Benson, Richard, BA, Teach Asst	Nordby, Jon, BA, Teach Asst
Bodanszky, Eva, BA, Teach Asst	Ratzsch, Delvin, BA, Univ Fel
Drager, Kent, BA, Teach Asst	Soderlind, Karen, BA, Teach Assoc
Feldman, Richard, MA, NDEA Fel	Sommer, Stephanie, BA, Teach Asst
Fitch, Gregory, MA, Teach Assoc	Steinbuch, Thomas, BA, Teach Asst
Fried, Dennis, MA, Teach Asst	Stephens, Gayle, BA, Teach Asst
Guiniven, John, MA, NDEA Fel	Stout, Sharon, BA, Teach Asst
Jurkiewicz, Hugh, AB, Teach Asst	Welch, Robert, BA, Res Asst
Markie, Peter, BA, Univ Fel	Wierenga, Edward, MA, Teach Asst

UNIVERSITY OF MASSACHUSETTS MEDICAL SCHOOL AT WORCESTER
Worcester, Massachusetts 01604 (Med; st; coed; sem; IV; 24) NR

UNIVERSITY OF MASSACHUSETTS, BOSTON CAMPUS
Boston, Massachusetts 02116 (E; st; coed; sem; III; 4646) BA major, Dept of Phil, College I, 617-542-6500 Ext 212, 213

Swartz, PhD, Prof, Chm, Theory of Knowl
Andic, Martin, PhD, Asst Prof, Anc Phil
Blum, Lawrence, PhD, Asst Prof, Ethics
Clive, Geoffrey, PhD, Prof, Exist
Cohen, Howard, PhD, Asst Prof, Soc and Polit Phil
Darmstadter, Howard, PhD, Asst Prof, Logic, Phil of Sci
Evans, Clyde, PhD, Asst Prof, Phil of Law
Martin, Jane, PhD, Assoc Prof, Phil of Educ
Shope, Robert K, PhD, Assoc Prof, Phil of Mind, Ethics

WELLESLEY COLLEGE
Wellesley, Massachusetts 02181 (E; p; wo; sem; III; 1872) MA joint or combined major, Dept of Phil, 617-235-0320

Stadler, Ingrid, PhD, Prof, Chm, Kant, 18th Cent Phil, Aes, Contemp Problems
Congleton, Ann, PhD, Assoc Prof, Phil of Lang, Plato, 17th and 18th Cent Phil
Cook, Kathleen, Instr
Menkiti, Ifeani, Instr
Putnam, Ruth Anna, PhD, Assoc Prof, Logic, Ethics, Epistem, Phil of Sci
Shue, Henry G, PhD, Asst Prof, Polit Phil, Ethics, Anc Phil, Contemp Phil

Onderdonk, Virgina, BA, Prof, Emer, Logic, Epistem, 17th Cent Phil
Proctor, Thomas H, PhD, Prof, Emer, Greek Phil, Phil of Relig

WENTWORTH COLLEGE OF TECHNOLOGY
Boston, Massachusetts 02115 (--; p; coed; sem; II; 254) NP

WENTWORTH INSTITUTE
Boston, Massachusetts 02115 (E; p; coed; sem; I; 1662) NR

WESTERN NEW ENGLAND COLLEGE
Springfield, Massachusetts 01119 (E; p; coed; sem; II; 3561) Courses with no degree specialization, Dept of Eng and Human, 413-783-6131

Herman, Steven, MA, Lect
Phillips, R M, PhD, Prof, Metaph
Sheldon, J G, PhD, Prof, Aes, Phil of Relig

WESTFIELD STATE COLLEGE
Westfield, Massachusetts 01085 (E; st; coed; 4-1-4; III; 3667) BA minor, Dept of Phil, 413-568-3311 Ext 219

Foard, Lawrence Clinton, PhD, Assoc Prof, Chm, Phil Theol
McIntire, Mark Dennis, MA, Instr, Phenomen
Tetrault, Gerald Emile, MA, Asst Prof, Phil of Sci

WHEATON COLLEGE
Norton, Massachusetts 02766 (E; p; wo; --; III; 1218) BA major, Dept of Phil, 617-285-7722 Ext 387

Ladd, Rosalind Ekman, PhD, Assoc Prof, Chm, Ethics, Aes
Hazelton, William Dean, PhD, Asst Prof, Metaph, Logic
Winston, Kenneth, PhD, Asst Prof, Phil of Law

Austin, Holcombe Mc, MA, Prof Emer, Aes, Plato

WHEELOCK COLLEGE
Boston, Massachusetts, 02215 (E; p; coed; tri; III; 914) Courses with no degree specialization, --, 617-734-5200

WILLIAMS COLLEGE
Williamstown, Massachusetts 01267 (E; p; coed; 4-1-4; III; 1592) BA major, Dept of Phil, 413-597-2364

Lawrence, Nathaniel, Prof, Chm
Beatty, Joseph W, PhD, Asst Prof

Karelis, Charles H, DPhil, Asst Prof
O'Connor, Daniel D, PhD, Assoc Prof
Versenyi, Laszlo, PhD, Prof

Beals, Lawrence W, PhD, Prof Emer
Miller, John William, PhD, Prof Emer

WORCESTER JUNIOR COLLEGE
   Worcester, Massachusetts 01608 (E; p; coed; sem; I; 925) Courses with no degree
   specialization, Dept of Libr Arts, 617-755-4314

   Stein, Kenneth E, PhD, Prof, Phil of Law, Phil of Relig

WORCESTER POLYTECHNIC INSTITUTE
   Worcester, Massachusetts 01609 (E; p; coed; 4-1-4; IV; 2478) Courses with no degree
   specialization, --, 617-753-1411

WORCESTER STATE COLLEGE
   Worcester, Massachusetts 01602 (E; st; coed; sem; III; 3919) --, Dept of Psych,
   617-756-5121 Ext 280

   Schaff, Dion, PhD, Instr
   Traub, Donald, MA, Asst Prof

MICHIGAN

ADRIAN COLLEGE
   Adrian, Michigan 49221 (N; U Meth; coed; sem; II; 1447) BA major, Dept of Phil and
   Relig, 313-265-5161 Ext 308

   Moulton, Phillips P, PhD, Prof, Ethics
   Spieler, David A, PhD, Asst Prof, Logic

   Emrick, Howard C, PhD, Prof Emer

ALBION COLLEGE
   Albion, Michigan 49224 (N; U Meth; coed; sem; II; 1782) BA major, Dept of Phil,
   517-629-5511

   Padgett, Jack F, PhD, Prof, Chm, Ethics, Phil of Relig, Phil of Person
   Clarke, Desmond, MA, Instr, Hist and Phil of Sci, Logic
   Davis, Ralph, PhD, Assoc Prof, Phil of Mind, Epistem, Phil of Lang
   Munk, Arthur, PhD, Prof, Metaph, Phil of Relig, Phil of Hist, Phil of Educ

ALMA COLLEGE
   Alma, Michigan 48801 (N; p; coed; qr; II; 1328) BA major, Dept of Phil, 517-463-
   2141 Ext 322

Dykstra, Wesley C, BD, Prof, Chm
Haverfield, Roger, MA, Instr

ALPENA COMMUNITY COLLEGE
Alpena, Michigan 49707 (N; local; coed; sem; I; 1044) --, Dept of Fine Arts, 517-356-2247

Hall, Terry A, MA, Instr, Phil of Relig, Ethics

ANDREWS UNIVERSITY
Berrien Springs, Michigan 49104 (N; SDA; coed; qr; III; 2191) Courses with no degree specialization, The Sem and Dept of Relig, 616-471-7771

Vitrano, Steven P, PhD, Prof, Dir, Phil of Relig
Augsburger, Daniel, PhD, Prof, Christ Ethics
Branson, Roy, PhD, Assoc Prof, Christ Ethics

AQUINAS COLLEGE
Grand Rapids, Michigan 49506 (N; RC; coed; sem; III; 1422) BA major, Dept of Phil, 616-459-8281

Houlihan, Teresa, PhD, Assoc Prof, Chm, Phil of Man, Phil of Sci, Exist Phenomen
Boyle, Jr, Joseph, PhD, Asst Prof, Logic, Ethics, Anglo-Amer Phil, Phil of Relig
Rodriguez, V, Prof, Phil of Person, Phil of Relig, Hist of Phil

BAY DE NOC COMMUNITY COLLEGE
Escanaba, Michigan 49829 (--; local; coed; sem; I; 1002) NP

CALVIN COLLEGE
Grand Rapids, Michigan 49506 (N; Chris Ref; coed; 4-1-4; II; 3306) BA major, Dept of Phil, 616-949-4000 Ext 2868

deVos, Peter, MA, Asst Prof, Epistem
Konyndyk, Ken, PhD, Asst Prof, Epistem
Mouw, Richard, PhD, Asst Prof, Ethics
Orlebeke, Clifton, PhD, Prof, Phil of Sci
Plantinga, Alvin, PhD, Prof, Phil of Relig
Prins, Tunis, PhD, Prof, Metaph
Runner, Evan, PhD, Prof, Anc Phil
VanderHoeven, Johann, PhD, Visit Prof, Phenomen
Wolterstorff, Nicholas, PhD, Prof, Aes, Metaph

CALVIN THEOLOGICAL SEMINARY
Grand Rapids, Michigan 49506 (Theol; Chris Ref; coed; qr; III; 144) NR

CENTRAL MICHIGAN UNIVERSITY
Mount Pleasant, Michigan 48858 (N; st; coed; sem; III; 16,961) BA major, Dept of Phil, 517-774-3444

Stengren, George L, PhD, Prof, Chm, Exist, Med Phil, Amer Phil
Gill, John G, PhD, Prof, Ethics, Phil of Relig, Value Theory
Kaiser, Nolan D, PhD, Prof, Polit Phil, Legal Phil
Pillote, Joyce H, PhD, Assoc Prof, Ethics, Soc Phil, Polit Phil, Epistem
Ping, Charles J, PhD, Prof, Prov, Phil of Relig, 19th Cent Phil
Tomsons, Gunars, MA, Instr, Epistem, Phil of Mind, Ethics
Yu, Paul, MA, Instr, Epistem, Phil of Lang

CHARLES STEWART MOTT COMMUNITY COLLEGE
   Flint, Michigan 48503 (N; local; coed; sem; I; 11,951) Courses with no degree
   specialization, Div of Lang, Lit, and Phil, 313-238-1631 Ext 454

   Labiner, Eli, MA
   Wilson, John, MA

CLEARY COLLEGE
   Ypsilanti, Michigan 48197 (JRCB; p; coed; qr; II; 610) Courses with no degree
   specialization, Dept of Gen Educ, 313-483-4400 Ext 21

   Bender, Gerald E, MA

CONCORDIA LUTHERAN JUNIOR COLLEGE
   Ann Arbor, Michigan 48105 (N; Luth Mo Synod; coed; qr; I; 468) NP

CRANBROOK ACADEMY OF ART
   Bloomfield Hills, Michigan 48013 (N; p; coed; sem; III; 154) Courses with no degree
   specialization, --, 313-644-1600

DAVENPORT COLLEGE OF BUSINESS
   Grand Rapids, Michigan 49502 (JRCB; p; coed; qr; I; 1350) NP

DELTA COLLEGE
   University Center, Michigan 48710 (N; local; coed; sem; I; 6250) AA major, Dept of
   Phil, 517-686-0400 Ext 246

   Sanker, Louis M, PhD, Assoc Prof, Chm, Ethics, Exist

DETROIT BIBLE COLLEGE
   Detroit, Michigan 48235 (BI; p; coed; sem; II; 295) Courses with no degree
   specialization, --, 313-864-8400

   Bevier, William A, ThD, Prof
   Cocking, Herbert, MA, Asst Prof
   Hollowman, Henry, ThD

DETROIT COLLEGE OF BUSINESS
   Dearborn, Michigan 48126 (SRCB; p; coed; qr; II; 1262) Courses with no degree
   specialization, Dept of Libr Arts, 313-582-6983

   Beauregard-Bezou, Marion Joseph
   Gnau, Dayton, MA

DETROIT COLLEGE OF LAW
   Detroit, Michigan (Law; p; coed; sem; III; 835) NP

DETROIT INSTITUTE OF TECHNOLOGY
   Detroit, Michigan 48201 (N; p; coed; sem; II; 1139) BA minor, --, 313-962-0830

   La Plante, Harry, MA, Assoc Prof, Hist of Phil

DUNS SCOTUS COLLEGE
   Southfield, Michigan 48075 (N; RC; men; 4-1-4; II; 313) BA major, Dept of Phil,
   313-357-3070

   Effler, Roy R, PhD, Prof, Chm, Metaph, Epistem
   Buescher, Jerome, MA, Anal Phil
   Desch, Paul T, PhD, Prof, Mod Phil, Contemp Phil
   Speier, Thomas O, MA, Assoc Prof, Ethics, Phil of Sci

   Ramstetter, Philibert V, MA, Prof Emer, Metaph

EASTERN MICHIGAN UNIVERSITY
   Ypsilanti, Michigan 48197 (N; st; coed; --; III; 21,466) BA major, Dept of Hist
   and Phil, 313-487-1849

   Anderson, Frederick, PhD, Prof, Chm, Phil of Hist, Amer Phil, Ethics
   Bilsky, Manuel, PhD, Prof, Aes, Plato, Aristotle
   Bufford, Samuel, PhD, Asst Prof, Aes, Phil of Relig, Polit Phil
   Franks, Thomas, PhD, Asst Prof, Exist, Phenomen
   Gendin, Sidney, PhD, Assoc Prof, Epistem, Anal Phil, Phil of Law
   Kamler, Howard, PhD, Asst Prof, Theory of Knowl, Phil of Mind
   MacVey, Wayne, MA, Instr, Phil of Lang, Aes
   Miller, William, PhD, Asst Prof, Hist of Phil, Phil of Kant, Metaph

FERRIS STATE COLLEGE
   Big Rapids, Michigan 49307 (N; st; coed; qr; II; 9162) Courses with no degree
   specialization, Dept of Human, 616-796-9971 Ext 462

   Hanford, Jack T, MA, Asst Prof, Phil of Relig

GENERAL MOTORS INSTITUTE
   Flint, Michigan 48502 (N; p; coed; sem; II; 3075) --, Dept of Human and Soc Sci,
   313-766-9307

GENESEE COMMUNITY COLLEGE
   Flint, Michigan 47503 (N; local; coed; sem; I; 11,951) --, Div of Lang, 313-238-
   1631

   Bigham, Kyle, MA, Instr
   Labiner, Eli, MA, Instr

GLEN OAKS COMMUNITY COLLEGE
   Centreville, Michigan 49032 (N; local; coed; sem; I; 684) NP

GOGEBIC COMMUNITY COLLEGE
   Ironwood, Michigan 49938 (N; local; coed; sem; I; 684) Courses with no degree
   specialization, 905-932-4231

   Grivicich, Donna, MA, Asst Prof, Soc and Phil Found

GRACE BIBLE COLLEGE
   Grand Rapids, Michigan 49509 (BI; p; coed; sem; II; 154) Courses with no degree
   specialization, --, 616-538-2330

GRAND RAPIDS BAPTIST COLLEGE AND SEMINARY
Grand Rapids, Michigan 49505 (Bl; Bapt; coed; sem; II; 694) BA minor, Div of Human, Arts, and Communic, 616-949-5300

Matthews, Victor, STD, Prof, Exist, Augustine
Mayers, Ronald, PhD, Asst Prof, Phil of Relig, Ethics, Amer Phil

GRAND RAPIDS JUNIOR COLLEGE
Grand Rapids, Michigan 49502 (N; local; coed; sem; I; 5568) BA minor, --, 616-456-4895

De Primo, Bernard, MA
Van Dyken, Seymour, ThD

GRAND VALLEY STATE COLLEGE
Allendale, Michigan 49401 (N; st; coed; qr; II; 4174) BA major, Dept of Phil, 616-895-6611 Ext 337

Young, Theodore A, PhD, Prof, Chm, Metaph, Ethics, Phil Anthrop
Cunningham, Thomas J, PhD, Prof, Hist and Phil of Sci
Hoitenga, Dewey, PhD, Prof, Logic, Phil of Relig, Phil of Educ
Jellema, W Harry, PhD, Prof, Hist of Phil, Med Phil
Mugerauer, Robert, PhD, Asst Prof, Aes, Mod Phil
Wasserman, Irving, MA, Asst Prof, Legal Phil, Polit Phil

HENRY FORD COMMUNITY COLLEGE
Dearborn, Michigan 48128 (N; local; coed; sem; I; 10,497) NR

HIGHLAND PARK COMMUNITY COLLEGE
Highland Park, Michigan 48203 (N; local; coed; sem; I; 3597) Courses with no degree specialization, Dept of Soc Stud, 313-868-1264 Ext 309, 304

Kaiser, Donald, MEd, Chm, Educ Phil

HILLSDALE COLLEGE
Hillsdale, Michigan 49242 (N; p; coed; sem; II; 1192) BA major, Dept of Phil and Relig, 517-437-7341 Ext 348

Fallon, Jerome, PhD, Prof
Long, Harry, MA, Asst Prof
Phillips, Leo H, ThD, Prof
Roberts, John, PhD, Prof
Watson, Mark, MA, Asst Prof
Welling, Norman, MA, Assoc Prof

HOPE COLLEGE
Holland, Michigan 49423 (N; p; coed; sem; II; 2111) BA major, Dept of Phil, 616-392-5111 Ext 2270

Dykstra, D Ivan, PhD, Prof, Chm, Hist of Phil, Phil of Sci
Jentz, Jr, Arthur H, PhD, Prof, Ethics, Phil of Relig, Indian Phil

JACKSON BUSINESS UNIVERSITY
Jackson, Michigan 49201 (JRCB; p; coed; qr; I; 451) NP

JACKSON COMMUNITY COLLEGE
    Jackson, Michigan 49201 (N; local; coed; sem; I; 3515) Courses with no degree
    specialization, --, 517-787-0800

    Van Pernis, James

JOHN WESLEY COLLEGE
    Owosso, Michigan 48867 (--; p; coed; --; II; 196) BA joint or combined major, Div
    of Commitment Stud, 517-725-5121

    Farrell, Hobert, PhD
    Knecht, Paul, PhD

KALAMAZOO COLLEGE
    Kalamazoo, Michigan 49001 (N; Bapt; coed; qr; II; 1360) BA major, Dept of Phil,
    616-343-1551

    Start, Lester J, PhD, Prof, Chm, Hist of Phil, Phil of Relig, Exist
    Litke, Robert F, BA, Instr, Ethics
    Scarrow, David S, PhD, Prof, Hist of Phil, Logic, Contemp Phil

KALAMAZOO VALLEY COMMUNITY COLLEGE
    Kalamazoo, Michigan 49001 (N; local; coed; sem; I; 3448) Courses with no degree
    specialization, Dept of Human, 616-375-5000 Ext 364

    Badra, Robert, MA, Prof

KELLOGG COMMUNITY COLLEGE
    Battle Creek, Michigan 49016 (N; local; coed; sem; I; 3314) Courses with no degree
    specialization, Dept of Soc Sci, 616-965-3931 Ext 228

    Schirmer, K E, MA, Instr, Anc Phil, Aes, Phil of Sci

KIRTLAND COMMUNITY COLLEGE
    Roscommon, Michigan 48653 (--; local; coed; sem; I; 585) Courses with no degree
    specialization, Dept of Eng, 517-275-5121

    Fernelius, Carl, PhD, Chm

LAKE MICHIGAN COLLEGE
    Benton Harbor, Michigan 49022 (N; local; coed; sem; I; 3285) Courses with no degree
    specialization, Dept of Eng and Human, 616-927-3571 Ext 210

    Elsner, Gary A, MA, Phil of Relig

LAKE SUPERIOR STATE COLLEGE
    Sault Sainte Marie, Michigan 49783 (N; st; coed; qr; II; 1712) Courses with no
    degree specialization, Dept of Human, 906-632-6841 Ext 275

    Kornmueller, Hellmuth, PhD, Assoc Prof

LANSING COMMUNITY COLLEGE
    Lansing, Michigan 48914 (N; local; coed; qr; I; 7951) AA major, Dept of Human, 517-
    373-7046

Engel, Elfriede, PhD, Assoc Prof, Soc Phil
Omundson, Bruce, MA, Instr

LAWRENCE INSTITUTE OF TECHNOLOGY
    Southfield, Michigan 48075 (N; p; coed; qr; II; 4107) --, Dept of Soc Sci, 313-444-1340

    Read, Ralph H, PhD, Prof

MACOMB COUNTY COMMUNITY COLLEGE, CENTER CAMPUS
    Mount Clemens, Michigan 48043 (N; local; coed; sem; I; 3332) Courses with no degree specialization, Dept of Human, 313-465-2121 Ext 311

    Ihrie, Dale, ThD, Part-time Instr
    Wineman, Saul, MA, Part-time Instr

MACOMB COUNTY COMMUNITY COLLEGE, SOUTH CAMPUS
    Warren, Michigan 48093 (N; local; coed; sem; I; 14,308) --, Div of Human, 313-779-7000

    Panush, Irving, PhD, Div Dir, Value Theory
    Cox, William, MA, Instr, Logic
    Psittas, Nicholas, MA, Instr Part-time
    Wagand, Philip, MA, Assoc Prof, Metaph
    Wineman, Shul, MA, Instr Part-time

MADONNA COLLEGE
    Livonia, Michigan 48150 (N; RC; coed; sem; II; 727) BA joint or combined major, Dept of Phil, 313-425-8000

    Craig, Robert, PhD

MARYGROVE COLLEGE
    Detroit, Michigan 48221 (N; p; coed; --; III; 1102) BA major, Dept of Phil, 313-862-8000 Ext 362

    King, Edward G, PhD, Assoc Prof, Chm, Anal Phil, Ethics
    Hangerman, Sr, Mani Gabriel, PhD, Assoc Prof, Aes
    Peinado, Firmin, LLD, Prof, Polit Phil

MERCY COLLEGE OF DETROIT
    Detroit, Michigan 48219 (N; RC; coed; sem; II; 1618) BA major, Dept of Phil, 313-531-7820

    Yarnevic, Donald, MA, Asst Prof, Chm, Phil of Man, Ethics, Phil of Relig, Aes
    Glazek, Marianne, MA, Part-time, Phil of Educ, Logic
    Schuetzinger, C E, PhD, Prof, Metaph, Epistem, Contemp Euro Phil, Hist of Phil
    Seebaldt, Dorothy, MA, Part-time, Ethics, Phil of Man

MERRILL-PALMER INSTITUTE
    Detroit, Michigan 48202 (--; p; coed; --; V; 84) NR

MICHIGAN CHRISTIAN JUNIOR COLLEGE
    Rochester, Michigan 48063 (--; p; coed; qr; I; 219) NP

MICHIGAN STATE UNIVERSITY
    East Lansing, Michigan 48823 (N; st; coed; qr; IV; 43,888) PhD major, Dept of Phil,
    517-355-4490

    Callaghan, William J, PhD, Prof, Chm
    Asquith, Peter D, PhD, Asst Prof, Phil of Sci
    Benjamin, Martin, PhD, Asst Prof, Phil of Polit
    Bohnert, Herbert G, PhD, Prof, Phil of Sci, Logic
    Cafagna, Albert C, MA, Asst Prof, Polit Phil
    Garelick, Herbert, PhD, Prof, 19th Cent Phil
    Gervasi, Julian A, PhD, Asst Prof, Hegel, Phil of Marx
    Goodfield, June, PhD, Prof, Phil of Sci
    Hall, Richard J, PhD, Assoc Prof, Phil of Sci
    Hanna, Joseph F, PhD, Prof, Phil of Sci
    Hendry, Herbert E, PhD, Assoc Prof, Phil of Sci, Logic
    Hurrell, Paul, PhD, Prof, Phil of Relig
    Kerner, George C, PhD, Prof, Value Theory, Phil of Lang
    Koch, Donald F, PhD, Assoc Prof, Amer Phil, Ethics
    Kotzin, Rhoda H, PhD, Prof, Epistem Metaph
    McCracken, Charles J, PhD, Assoc Prof, Hist of Phil
    Miller, Bruce L, PhD, Asst Prof, Phil of Law, Phil of Polit
    Roper, James E, MA, Asst Prof, Phil of Sci, Logic
    Shepard, Philip T, PhD, Asst Prof, Phil of Sci, Logic
    Staudenbaur, C A, PhD, Assoc Prof, Hist of Phil
    Suter, Ronald, PhD, Assoc Prof, Ethics, Phil of Lang
    Taylor, John F A, PhD, Prof, Aes, Ethics
    Toulmin, Stephen E, PhD, Prof, Phil of Sci
    Walsh, Harold T, PhD, Prof, Hist of Phil
    Wilkinson, Winston, PhD, Asst Prof, Exist, Phenomen
    Zerby, Lewis K, PhD, Prof, Exist, Polit Phil

    Marshall, Donald K, PhD, Assoc Prof Emer, Ethics, Anc Phil

    Andre, Judith, Grad Asst   Kent, Dale, Grad Asst
    Baumgartner, Jorg, Grad Asst   McBeth, Alan, Grad Asst
    Bird, Dennis, Grad Asst   Miller, Arthur, NDEA Fel
    Brody, Leon, EOP Fel   Rosen, Jay, Grad Asst
    Bruce, Charles, Grad Asst   Schick, Lester, Grad Asst
    Callahan, Thomas, Grad Asst   Shanks, James, Grad Asst
    Campana, James, Grad Asst   Smith, Eric, EOP Fel
    Coin, Dianne, NDEA Fel   Smith, Linda, Grad Asst
    Ekstrom, Susan C, Hinman Fel   Starr, Roger, Grad Asst
    Hanink, James, Grad Fel   Tomlinson, Thomas, Grad Asst
    Hart, Allan, Grad Asst   Treloar, John, Grad Asst
    Karega, Chui, Grad Asst   Weaver, Gwendolyn, EOP Fel

MICHIGAN TECHNOLOGICAL UNIVERSITY
    Houghton, Michigan 49931 (N; st; coed; qr; IV; 5002) --, Dept of Human, 906-487-2207

    Mason, Richard G, MA, Assoc Prof, 18th Cent Phil

MID-MICHIGAN COMMUNITY COLLEGE
    Harrison, Michigan 48625 (--; local; coed; sem; I; 701) Courses with no degree
    specialization, --, 517-386-7792

    Streadwick, Robert L

MONROE COUNTY COMMUNITY COLLEGE
Monroe, Michigan 48161 (N; local; coed; sem; I; 1741) Courses with no degree
specialization, Div of Human, 313-242-7300 Ext 235

Holladay, John, EdD, Assoc Prof
Josaitis, Marvin, MA, Assoc Prof, Phil of Relig

MONTCALM COMMUNITY COLLEGE
Sidney, Michigan 48885 (--; local; coed; sem; I; 665) Courses with no degree
specialization, Dept of Human, 517-328-2111 Ext 227

White, R Jerry, MA

MUSKEGON BUSINESS COLLEGE
Muskegon, Michigan 49442 (JRCB; p; coed; qr; I; 429) NP

MUSKEGON COMMUNITY COLLEGE
Muskegon, Michigan 49443 (N; local; coed; sem; I; 3889) Courses with no degree
specialization, Dept of Creative and Performing Arts, 616-773-9131 Ext 273

Halvorson, Phillip, MA, Instr

NAZARETH COLLEGE
Nazareth, Michigan 49074 (N; p; coed; sem; II; 400) Courses with no degree
specialization, Dept of Phil, 616-349-7783 Ext 279

Hang, Paul, MA, Instr, Asst Prof, Berdyaev
McMorrow, George, PhD, Prof, Metaph

NORTH CENTRAL MICHIGAN COLLEGE
Petoskey, Michigan 49770 (N; local; coed; sem; I; 765) NP

NORTHERN MICHIGAN UNIVERSITY
Marquette, Michigan 49855 (N; st; coed; sem; III; 8167) BA major, Dept of Phil,
906-227-1000

Cooper, David E, PhD, Asst Prof, Soc and Polit Phil
Dreisbach, Donald F, PhD, Asst Prof, Phil of Relig, Exist
Greene, James, PhD, Assoc Prof, Phil of Sci, Anal Phil

NORTHWESTERN MICHIGAN COLLEGE
Traverse City, Michigan 49684 (N; st; coed; sem; III; 8167) --, Div of Human, 616-
946-5650 Ext 525

Terdal, Roy, MA, Asst Prof
Terrell, David, MA, Instr

NORTHWOOD INSTITUTE, MAIN CAMPUS
Midland, Michigan 48640 (--; p; coed; qr; II; 2839) --, Dept of Soc Sci, 517-631-
1600 Ext 240, 214, 264

Anker, Willo G, MA, Prof, Mod Phil
Bennett, Thomas E, MA, Asst Prof, Compar Phil
Lloyd, Lewis, PhD, Visit Lect
Watts, V Orval, PhD, Prof, Ethics

OAKLAND COMMUNITY COLLEGE AT AUBURN HILLS
Auburn Heights, Michigan 48057 (N; st and local; coed; tri; I; 4461) Courses with no degree specialization, Dept of Communic and Human, 313-852-1000 Ext 272-5

Hinkins, John P, MA, Asst Prof, Chm
Barthel, Paula, BA, Asst Prof
Harman, Joseph, MA, Assoc Prof

OAKLAND COMMUNITY COLLEGE AT HIGHLAND LAKES
Union Lake, Michigan 48085 (N; st and local; coed; tri; I; 2124) Courses with no degree specialization, --, 313-363-7191

OAKLAND COMMUNITY COLLEGE, ORCHARD RIDGE CAMPUS
Farmington, Michigan 48024 (N; st and local; coed; tri; I; 6253) --, Dept of Math and Phil, 313-476-9400 Ext 321, 322, 323

Henninger, William, Asst Prof Part-time
Ostle, Robert, Part-time
Vendetoulli, James, Part-time

OAKLAND UNIVERSITY
Rochester, Michigan 48063 (N; st; coed; sem; IV; 7088) BA major, Dept of Phil, 313-377-3390

Burke, Richard J, PhD, Prof, Chm, Hist of Phil, Phil of Culture, Phil of Relig
Brooks, Richard W, PhD, Assoc Prof, Indian Phil, Metaph, Parapsych
Cumbee, Jack, BS, Instr, Logic, Phil of Lang, Metaph, Phil Pacifism
Lessing, Alfred, PhD, Assoc Prof, Aes, Ethics, Greek Phil
Morton, Charles E, PhD, Adj Prof, Ethics, Soc and Polit Phil
Weitzenfeld, Julian, MA, Instr, Phil of Mind, Phil of Sci, Epistem

OLIVET COLLEGE
Olivet, Michigan 49076 (N; p; coed; sem; II; 832) BA major, Dept of Phil, 616-749-2111

Mabry, Paul E, PhD, Assoc Prof, Metaph, Epistem, Asian Phil, Phil of Relig

REFORMED BIBLE COLLEGE
Grand Rapids, Michigan 49506 (BI; p; coed; sem; II; 108) NP

SACRED HEART SEMINARY
Detroit, Michigan 48206 (N; RC; men; sem; II; 113) BA major, Dept of Phil, 313-868-2700

Berg, Paul C, PhD, Prof, Chm, Hist of Phil
Carson, Harry A, MA, Assoc Prof, Phil of Relig
Warner, Peter O, PhD, Lect, Phil of Sci

SAGINAW VALLEY COLLEGE
University Center, Michigan 48710 (N; st; coed; tri; II; 2124) BA minor, Dept of Phil, 517-793-9800 Ext 345

Rayfield, David, PhD, Asst Prof, Chm, Phil of Action

SAINT CLAIR COUNTY COMMUNITY COLLEGE
Port Huron, Michigan 48060 (N; local; coed; sem; I; 3139) Courses with no degree
specialization, Dept of Eng, 313-984-3881

Obee, Thomas F, MA, Chm

SAINT MARY'S COLLEGE
Orchard Lake, Michigan 48034 (--; p; coed; sem; II; 98) BA major, Dept of Phil,
313-682-1885

Niedbalski, Terrence, MA, Chm, Metaph
Kosnik, Anthony, STD, Ethics
Torzala, Henry, PhL, Logic

SCHOOLCRAFT COLLEGE
Livonia, Michigan 48151 (N; local; coed; tri; I; 6017) Courses with no degree
specialization, Dept of Phil, 313-591-6400

Chinni, Angelo A, MA, Instr
Lockhart, Walter E, MA, Instr

SHAW COLLEGE OF DETROIT
Detroit, Michigan 48202 (DA; p; coed; qr; II; 810) Courses with no degree
specialization, Dept of Relig and Phil, 313-873-7920

SIENA HEIGHTS COLLEGE
Adrian, Michigan 49221 (N; RC; coed; sem; III; 647) BA major, Dept of Phil, 313-
263-0731 Ext 244, 237

Kramlinger, Thomas, PhD, Asst Prof, Chm
Czerwionka, Felicia, PhD, Asst Prof, Amer Phil

SOCIETY OF ARTS AND CRAFTS
Detroit, Michigan 48202 (Art; p; coed; sem; II; 738) Courses with no degree
specialization, --, 313-872-3118

Hoekstra, Raymond, PhD, Prof

SOUTHWESTERN MICHIGAN COLLEGE
Dowagiac, Michigan 49047 (N; st and local; coed; sem; I; 915) NP

SPRING ARBOR COLLEGE
Spring Arbor, Michigan 49283 (N; Meth; coed; sem; II; 721) BA joint or combined
major, Div of Relig and Phil, 517-750-1200

Campbell, Charles R, MA, Asst Prof
Moore, Darell, MS, Asst Prof

SUOMI COLLEGE
Hancock, Michigan 49930 (N; Luth CA; coed; sem; I; 399) Courses with no degree
specialization, Dept of Relig and Phil, 906-482-5300 Ext 67

Simonson, John F, STM, Chm

UNIVERSITY OF DETROIT
Detroit, Michigan 48221 (N; RC; coed; tri; IV; 9597) MA major, Dept of Phil, 313-342-1000 Ext 285, 601

Vaughn, Adams, MA, Chm, Thomism, Greek Phil, British Empir, Morals
Crawford, David, PhD, Asst Prof, British Idealism, Aes, Phil Anthrop, Phil Psych, Orient Phil, Exist, Kant, Hegel, Wittgenstein, Heidegger, Bradley, Collingwood, Sartre
Donoso, Anton, PhD, Prof, Hist of Amer Phil, Phil of Hist and Culture, Hist of Latin American, Spanish and Portuguese Phil, Prag, Hist of Contemp Phil, Phil Anthrop
Glispin, James, MA, Asst Prof, Thomism, Business Ethics
Grassi, Carlo, PhD, Med Phil, Ethics, Metaph
MacGuigan, Maryellen, MA, Asst Prof, Phenomen, Exist, Hist of Mod Phil
McGlynn, James, PhD, British Empir, Phenomen, Phil of Lit
McGovern, Arthur, PhD, Asst Prof, Marxism, Phil of Soc Change, Phil of Knowl, Hist of Mod Phil
Moeller, Norman, STL, Assoc Prof, Morals, Metaph
Schuett, John T, MA, Asst Prof, Greek Phil, Med Phil, Contemp Phil, Thomism, Exist, Phil of Law, Phil Psych
Turner, Walter H, PhD, Prof, Hist of Greek, Med, Modern and Contemp Phil, Logic, Metaph, Ethics
Vunderink, Ralph, PhD, Asst Prof, Phil of Relig, Hist of Phil
Wallenmaier, Thomas, MA, Asst Prof, Hist of Phil, Phil and Method of Sci, Phil and Method of Biological Sci, Formal Logic, Epistem, Phil of A N Whitehead, Phil of Lang, Soc Aspects of Sci

UNIVERSITY OF MICHIGAN
Ann Arbor, Michigan 48104 (N; st; coed; tri; IV; 36,507) PhD joint or combined major, Dept of Phil, 313-764-1817

Brandt, Richard B, PhD, Prof, Chm, Ethics
Kim, Jaegwon, PhD, Prof, Assoc Chm, Phil of Sci, Logic
Bergmann, Frithjof, PhD, Assoc Prof, Exist, Soc Phil
Bowie, G Lee, PhD, Asst Prof, Logic
Burks, Arthur W, PhD, Prof, Logic, Phil of Communic Sci
Cohen, Carl, PhD, Prof, Soc and Polit Phil
Frankena, William K, PhD, Prof, Ethics, Phil of Educ
Goldman, Alvin I, PhD, Prof, Phil of Mind
Goldman, Holly, PhD, Asst Prof, Ethics
Hart, Wilbur D, PhD, Asst Prof, Logic
Loar, Brian, PhD, Asst Prof
Mavrodes, George I, PhD, Prof, Phil of Relig
Meiland, Jack W, PhD, Assoc Prof, Metaph, Phil of Mind
Munro, Donald J, PhD, Prof, Asian Phil
Sklar, Lawrence, PhD, Assoc Prof, Phil of Sci
Stevenson, Charles L, PhD, Prof, Ethics
Stich, Stephen P, PhD, Assoc Prof, Phil of Lang
Walton, Kendall L, PhD, Assoc Prof, Aes
White, Nicholas P, PhD, Asst Prof

Ball, Steve, Teach Asst
Bartkus, Gytis, Teach Asst
Brown, James, Teach Asst
Brown, Lee, Teach Asst
Ellingboe, John, Teach Asst
Field, Jeffrey, Teach Asst
Hagen, Charles, Teach Asst
Hart, Carl, Teach Asst
Hart, Nancy, Teach Asst
Hartweg, Norman, Teach Asst
Hill, Jerome, Teach Asst
Lovelace, David, Teach Asst
Masson, Keith, Teach Asst
Newman, William, Teach Asst
Overvold, Mark, Teach Asst
Pesca, Dennis, Teach Asst
Polkowski, William, Teach Asst
Poloney, William, Teach Asst
Russell, Michael, Teach Asst
Schmitt, Frederich, Teach Asst
Seldin, Irving, Teach Asst
Shin, Oh Hyun, Teach Asst

Hudelson, Richard, Teach Asst
Ingber, Warren, Teach Asst
Kaplan, Mark, Teach Asst
Knight, Chalmers, Teach Asst
Kolikoff, Fred, Teach Asst
Levy, Sanford, Teach Asst

Thren, Christine, Teach Asst
Tiews, Kenneth, Teach Asst
Wagner, Steve, Teach Asst
White, Patricia, Teach Asst
Wiezel, James, Teach Asst

UNIVERSITY OF MICHIGAN, DEARBORN CAMPUS
Dearborn, Michigan 48128 (N; st; coed; tri; III; 1369) Courses with no degree
specialization, Dept of Human, 313-271-2300

Sayles, Edward M, PhD, Prof, Chm
Mathews, Jr, Bill, MS

UNIVERSITY OF MICHIGAN, FLINT CAMPUS
Flint, Michigan 48503 (N; st; coed; sem; II; 2110) BA major, Dept of Phil, 313-
767-4000 Ext 287

Gull, Richard, PhD, Assoc Prof, Chm, Metaph, Epistem
Cox, Kendall, PhD, Asst Prof, Ethics, Aes
Dunlop, Charles, PhD, Asst Prof, Epistem, Anc Phil
Oaklander, Nathan, MA, Instr, Metaph, Mod Hist of Phil
Peterson, Paul, PhD, Asst Prof, Logic, Phil of Sci

WALSH COLLEGE OF ACCOUNTING AND BUSINESS ADMINISTRATION
Troy, Michigan 48084 (--; p; coed; sem; II; 347) NR

WASHTENAW COMMUNITY COLLEGE
Ann Arbor, Michigan 48107 (DA; local; coed; sem; I; 4024) --, Div of Communic Arts,
313-971-6300 Ext 451

Bollweg, John, MA, Instr
Reuben, Robert, MA, Instr Part-time

WAYNE COUNTY COMMUNITY COLLEGE
Detroit, Michigan 48201 (--; st and local; coed; sem; I; 11,789) Courses with no
degree specialization, --, 313-832-5500

WAYNE STATE UNIVERSITY
Detroit, Michigan 48202 (N; st; coed; qr; IV; 36,765) PhD major, Dept of Phil, 313-
577-2474

Humphries, Barbara, PhD, Assoc Prof, Chm, Phil of Mind, Phil of Lang
Angell, Richard B, PhD, Prof, Logic, Contemp Phil, Phil of Sci
Hadgopoulos, Demetrius
Hall, Richard, PhD, Asst Prof, Ethics, Soc and Polit Phil
Lombard, Lawrence B, AB, Asst Prof, Phil of Lang, Epistem
Morton, Bruce N, PhD, Asst Prof, Aes, Ethics
Powers, Lawrence H, BA, Asst Prof, Metaph
Stine, Gail C, PhD, Assoc Prof, Epistem
Stine, William D, PhD, Assoc Prof, Prag, Amer Phil
Titiev, Robert J, PhD, Asst Prof, Math Logic, Phil of Sci

Hoekstra, Raymond, PhD, Prof, Emer, Aes

Bacon, William, MA, Teach Asst
Baer, Richard, BA, Univ Fel

Kwasniak, Arlene, Univ Fel
Parrish, Thomas, Teach Asst

Bopp, C John, BA, Teach Asst
Demerchant, Blanchard, BA, Teach Asst
Devine, Michael, Teach Asst
Evans, David A, Teach Asst
Freeman, Roderick, MA, NDEA Fel
Hultzen, Carl, BA, Teach Asst

Phillips, Nadine, BA, Teach Asst
Pickard, Sue M, Univ Fel
Seran, William, Univ Fel
Tilson, Lee, Univ Fel
Whipple, Kenneth, Teach Asst
Wider, Kathleen, Teach Asst

WESTERN MICHIGAN UNIVERSITY
Kalamazoo, Michigan 49001 (N; st; coed; tri; IV; 22,971) BA major, Dept of Phil, 616-383-1657, 616-383-1659

Ellin, Joseph, PhD, Assoc Prof, Chm, Ethics, Polit Phil, Phil of Law
Dilworth, John, MA, Asst Prof, Ethics, Metaph
Falk, Arthur, PhD, Assoc Prof, Logic, Phil of Lang
Milton, Donald, MA, Assoc Prof, Anc Phil, Phil of Art
Pritchard, Michael, PhD, Asst Prof, Polit Phil, Ethics
Pulaski, Richard, BA, Asst Prof, Phenomen
Sheridan, Gregory, PhD, Assoc Prof, Logic, Anal Phil, Phil of Mind
Westphal, Dale, MA, Assoc Prof, Anc Phil, Exist Phil
Williams, Harvey, BA, Instr, Kant

WESTERN THEOLOGICAL SEMINARY
Holland, Michigan 49423 (Theol; Ref CA; coed; qr; III; 100) NP

WEST SHORE COMMUNITY COLLEGE
Scottville, Michigan 49454 (--; local; coed; qr; I; 734) Courses with no degree specialization, Div of Human and Fine Arts, 616-845-6211 Ext 245 A

Lehrbass, Judith A, MA, Prof

MINNESOTA

ANOKA-RAMSEY STATE JUNIOR COLLEGE
Coon Rapids, Minnesota 55433 (--; st; coed; qr; I; 2298) Courses with no degree specialization, Dept of Human, 612-427-2600

Skottegaard, Robert C, MA, Ethics

AUGSBURG COLLEGE
Minneapolis, Minnesota 55404 (N; Am Luth; coed; 4-1-4; II; 1616) BA major, Dept of Phil, 612-332-5181 Ext 575

Reichenbach, Bruce R, PhD, Asst Prof, Chm, Phil of Relig, Exist, Phenomen
Benson, John, PhD, Assoc Prof, 19th Cent Phil
Fuehrer, Mark, MA, Instr, Med Phil, Renaissance Phil

AUSTIN STATE JUNIOR COLLEGE
Austin, Minnesota 55912 (N; st; coed; qr; I; 1058) NP

MINNESOTA

BEMIDJI STATE COLLEGE
Bemidji, Minnesota 56601 (N; st; coed; qr; III; 4971) BA major, Dept of Phil, 218-755-3946

Fenske, Albert W, AM, Prof, Chm, Mod Phil, Amer Phil
Lund, David H, PhD, Asst Prof, Phil of Sci, Phil of Mind, Logic
Nasr, Waddah N, AM, Asst Prof, Theory of Knowl
Swanson, Myron R, AM, Prof, Head, Phil of Relig, Exist

BETHANY LUTHERAN COLLEGE
Mankato, Minnesota 56001 (--; Evan Luth; coed; sem; I; 204) Courses with no degree specialization, --, 507-388-2977

Teigen, Bjarne W, MA

BETHEL COLLEGE
St Paul, Minnesota 55112 (N; Bapt; coed; 4-1-4; II; 1044) BA major, Dept of Phil, 612-641-6345

Anderson, Stanley, MA, Assoc Prof, Chm, Ethics, Phil of Educ
Glenn, Alfred A, PhD, Prof, Phil of Relig
Stewart, Melville, MA, Asst Prof, Phil of Relig, Epistem
Smith, W Robert, ThD, Prof, Phil of Relig

BETHEL THEOLOGICAL SEMINARY
St Paul, Minnesota 55112 (Theol; Bapt; coed; qr; III; 229) Courses with no degree specialization, Dept of Interpretation of the Christ Faith, 612-641-6179

Erickson, Millard J, PhD, Prof

BRAINERD STATE JUNIOR COLLEGE
Brainerd, Minnesota 56401 (--; st; coed; qr; I; 621) Courses with no degree specialization, Div of Human, 218-829-4771

Casper, James T, MA, Anc Phil, Mod Phil

CARLETON COLLEGE
Northfield, Minnesota 55057 (N; p; coed; tri; II; 1498) BA major, Dept of Phil, 507-645-4431 Ext 475

Iseminger, Gary, PhD, Prof, Chm, Theory of Knowl, Aes, Logic
Elveton, Roy O, PhD, Assoc Prof, 19th Cent Phil, Phenomen
Lugones, Maria, MA, Instr, Ethics, Soc and Polit Phil, Anc Phil
Mason, P C, PhD, Assoc Prof, Phil of Relig, Theory of Knowl, 18th Cent Phil
Sipfle, David A, PhD, Prof, Process Phil, Ethics, Phil of Sci

Eshleman, Martin, PhD, Prof Emer, Aes, Phenomen

COLLEGE OF SAINT BENEDICT
St Joseph, Minnesota 56374 (N; RC; cord; 4-1-4; II; 927) BA major, Dept of Phil, 612-363-5508

Joyce, Robert E, MA, Assoc Prof, Chm, Metaph
Brinkman, Paul, MA, Asst Prof, Phil of Sci
Lane, Ronald, MA, Asst Prof, Phil of Relig
Schmitt, S Rosina, MA, Asst Prof, Amer Phil
Smith, S Enid, PhD, Prof, Metaph

COLLEGE OF SAINT CATHERINE
    Saint Paul, Minnesota 55105 (N; RC; wo; 4-1-4; II; 1368) BA major, Dept of Phil,
    612-698-5571

    Pampusch, Anita, PhD, Asst Prof, Chm, Logic, Phil of Sci, Contemp Phil
    Freeman, Hilary, PhD, Assoc Prof, Logic, Epistem, Mod Phil
    Fuehrer, Mark, MA, Lect, Phil of Nature
    O'Hara, Mary L, PhD, Prof, Metaph, Phil of Nature
    Olmsted, Richard, MA, Instr, Phil of Relig, Hist of Phil, Phil of Soc Sci
    Stitch, Elizabeth, MA, Lect, Polit Phil
    Wren, David, PhD, Asst Prof, Ethics, Phil of Relig, Wittgenstein

COLLEGE OF SAINT SCHOLASTICA
    Duluth, Minnesota 55811 (N; RC; coed; qr; II; 915) BA joint or combined major,
    Dept of Phil, 218-728-3631 Ext 452

    Nephew, Albert H, PhD, Assoc Prof, Chm, Ethics
    O'Hare, William T, PhD, Asst Prof, Soc and Polit Phil
    Stich, Elizabeth, Soc and Polit Phil

COLLEGE OF SAINT TERESA
    Winona, Minnesota 55987 (N; RC; wo; --; II; 987) BA major, Dept of Phil, 507-454-
    2930 Ext 262

    Bennewitz, Donald, MA, Assoc Prof, Phenomen
    Collins, Robert, PhD, Assoc Prof, Amer Phil

COLLEGE OF SAINT THOMAS
    St Paul, Minnesota 55105 (N; RC; men; sem; III; 2488) BA major, Dept of Phil, 612-
    647-5376

    DuLac, Henri, PhD, Prof, Chm, Logic, Phil Psych
    Austin, Harold J, MA, Asst Prof, Anc Phil, Mod Phil, Ethics
    Berquist, Richard, PhD, Assoc Prof, Phil of Law, Ethics
    Connell, Richard J, PhD, Prof, Phil of Sci, Marxism, Logic
    Flynn, Frederick E, PhD, Prof, Polit Phil, Med Phil
    Rush, Vincent E, PhD, Asst Prof, Aes, Exist
    Stromberg, James S, PhD, Assoc Prof, Ethics, Logic
    Sullivan, Thomas D, PhD, Asst Prof, Metaph, Logic

CONCORDIA COLLEGE
    Moorhead, Minnesota 56560 (N; A Luth; coed; sem; II; 2402) BA major, Dept of Phil,
    218-299-3619

    Christenson, Thomas, PhD, Assoc Prof, Chm, Value Theory
    Anderson, Albert B, PhD, Prof, Phil of Relig
    Farrar, John, MA, Instr, Aes
    Smerud, Warren, PhD, Assoc Prof, Hist of Phil
    Tatalovich, Robert, MA, Instr, Amer Phil

    Thomte, Reidar, PhD, Prof Emer, Phil of Relig

CONCORDIA COLLEGE, SAINT PAUL
    Saint Paul, Minnesota 55104 (N; Luth Mo Synod; coed; qr; II; 714) Courses with no
    degree specialization, --, 612-646-6157

CROSIER SEMINARY
  Onamia, Minnesota 56359 (--; RC; men; sem; I; 29) NP

DR MARTIN LUTHER COLLEGE
  New Ulm, Minnesota 56073 (--; Evan Luth; coed; sem; II; 732) --, --, 507-354-8221

FERGUS FALLS STATE JUNIOR COLLEGE
  Fergus Falls, Minnesota 56539 (N; st; coed; qr; I; 651) NP

GOLDEN VALLEY LUTHERAN COLLEGE
  Minneapolis, Minnesota 55422 (--; p; coed; qr; I; 363) Courses with no degree
  specialization, Dept of Phil and Human, 612-545-0461

GUSTAVUS ADOLPHUS COLLEGE
  St Peter, Minnesota 56082 (N; Luth CA; coed; 4-1-4; II; 1918) BA major, Dept of Phil,
  507-931-4300

  Cady, Duane, PhD, Asst Prof, Epistem
  Jones, Jr, George, PhD, Phil of Sci
  Rosenbaum, Stuart, PhD, Asst Prof, Phil of Mind

HAMLINE UNIVERSITY
  Saint Paul, Minnesota 55104 (N; U Meth; coed; 4-1-4; II; 1274) BA major, Dept of
  Phil, 612-641-2385

  Uemura, Joseph N, PhD, Prof, Chm, Hist of Phil
  D'Onofrio, John, PhD, Asst Prof
  Haas, Kenneth Eugene, PhD, Assoc Prof

HIBBING STATE JUNIOR COLLEGE
  Hibbing, Minnesota 55746 (N; st; coed; qr; I; 772) Courses with no degree
  specialization, Dept of Phil, 218-262-3877 Ext 58

  Longley, Peter, PhD, Instr

INVER HILLS STATE JUNIOR COLLEGE
  Inver Grove Heights, Minnesota 55075 (--; st; coed; qr; I; 979) NP

ITASCA STATE JUNIOR COLLEGE
  Grand Rapids, Michigan 55744 (--; st; coed; qr; I; 563) NR

LAKEWOOD STATE JUNIOR COLLEGE
  White Bear Lake, Minnesota 55110 (--; st; coed; qr; I; 2222) AA major, Dept of
  Human, 612-770-1331 Ext 54

  Ahlstrom, J Millard, JD

LUTHER THEOLOGICAL SEMINARY
St Paul, Minnesota 55108 (Theol; Luth; men; qr; III; 531) Courses with no degree
specialization, Dept of Syst Theol, 612-646-2712

Sponheim, Paul R, PhD, Assoc Prof, Chm, Phil of Relig
Martinson, Paul V, PhD, Asst Prof, World Relig
Quanbeck, Warren A, ThD, Prof
Snook, Lee E, ThD, Assoc Prof

MACALESTER COLLEGE
St Paul, Minnesota 55101 (N; U Preb; coed; 4-1-4; II; 2097) BA major, Dept of Phil,
612-647-6207

Chase, Alston S, PhD, Asst Prof, Chm
Abraham, William E, MA, Visit Prof
Hill, Thomas English, PhD, Prof
West, Henry R, PhD, Assoc Prof
White, David B, PhD, Prof

MANKATO STATE COLLEGE
Mankato, Minnesota 56001 (N; st; coed; qr; III; 13,369) BA major, Dept of Phil, 507-
389-2012

Wallace, Robert, PhD, Assoc Prof, Chm, Phil of Mind, Phil of Relig
Lawson, Jack, MA, Assoc Prof Part-time, Aes, Logic
Paul, Jean, PhD, Asst Prof, Metaph, Contemp Phil, Logic
Rikkers, Robert, MA, Assoc Prof, Hist of Phil, Contem Phil
Taylor, Timothy, MA, Asst Prof Part-time, Phenomen, Exist
Walberg, E H, MA, Asst Prof, Ethics, Phil of Lang, Phil of Mind
Yezzi, Ronald, PhD, Assoc Prof, Phil of Sci, Soc Phil, Polit Phil, Anc Phil

MESABI COMMUNITY COLLEGE
Virginia, Minnesota 55792 (N; st; coed; qr; I; 771) Courses with no degree
specialization, Dept of Soc Sci, 218-741-9200

Tamte, James, PhD

METROPOLITAN STATE JUNIOR COLLEGE
Minneapolis, Minnesota 55403 (--; st; coed; qr; I; 1786) NP

MINNEAPOLIS COLLEGE OF ART DESIGN
Minneapolis, Minnesota 55404 (N; p; coed; sem; II; 590) NR

MINNESOTA BIBLE COLLEGE
Rochester, Minnesota 55901 (BI; Ch of Christ; coed; qr; II; 102) Courses with no
degree specialization, Dept of Arts and Sci, 507-288-4563

Riggin, Donald L, MS, Prof

MINNESOTA METROPOLITAN STATE COLLEGE
St Paul, Minnesota 55101 (--; st; coed; --; II; 330) Courses with no degree
specialization, Libr Arts Conference, 612-296-4461

Lewis, Piers I, PhD, Assoc Prof, Chm
Melton, Richard, MA, Part-time

MOORHEAD STATE COLLEGE
Moorhead, Minnesota 56560 (N; st; coed; qr; III; 5160) BA major, Dept of Phil,
218-236-2294

Magel, Charles R, PhD, Prof, Chm
Chekola, Mark, MA, Asst Prof, Ethics
Johanson, Arnold, PhD, Assoc Prof, Peirce and James
Myers, David, PhD, Asst Prof, Marxism

NORMANDALE STATE JUNIOR COLLEGE
Bloomington, Minnesota 55431 (DH; st; coed; qr; I; 3180) AA major, Dept of Phil,
612-831-5001 Ext 304

Luknic, John, MS
Asp, Waldo, MS

NORTH CENTRAL BIBLE COLLEGE
Minneapolis, Minnesota 55404 (BI; Assem of God; coed; 4-1-4; II; 475) Courses with
no degree specialization, --, 612-332-3491

NORTH HENNEPIN STATE JUNIOR COLLEGE
Brooklyn Park, Minnesota 55445 (N; st; coed; qr; I; 2314) NP

NORTHLAND STATE JUNIOR COLLEGE
Thief River Falls, Minnesota 56701 (--; st; coed; qr; I; 396) Courses with no degree
specialization, --, 218-681-2181

NORTHWESTERN LUTHERAN THEOLOGICAL SEMINARY
St Paul, Minnesota 55108 (Theol; Luth CA; men; tri; III; 185) Courses with no degree
specialization, Dept of Syst Theol, 612-645-6434 Ext 28

Roth, Robert, PhD, Prof, Dean, Chm
Buschmann, Walter, PhD, Assoc Prof, Soc Ethics

RAINY RIVER STATE JUNIOR COLLEGE
International Falls, Minnesota 56649 (--; st; coed; qr; I; 363) Courses with no
degree specialization, Dept of Phil, 218-283-8491

Jerstad, Mark A, D Min

ROCHESTER STATE JUNIOR COLLEGE
Rochester, Minnesota 55901 (N; st; coed; qr; I; 2302) Courses with no degree
specialization, --, 507-288-6101

SAINT CLOUD STATE COLLEGE
St Cloud, Minnesota 56301 (N; st; coed; qr; III; 9965) BA major, Dept of Phil,
612-255-0121

Anderson, Myron, PhD, Prof, Chm, Soc Phil, Polit Phil
Bahde, John, MA, Asst Prof, Anal Phil, Phil of Lang
Corliss, Richard, PhD, Assoc Prof, Phil of Relig, Phil of Lang
Fischmann, Ruel, MA, Asst Prof, Aes
Kohlenberg, Philip, PhD, Asst Prof, Phil of Relig
Phillips, Alan, PhD, Assoc Prof, Plato, Phil of Anthrop

Phillips, John, PhD, Prof, Anal Phil, Phil of Logic
Seran, William, MA, Instr, Contemp Ethical Theory
White, James, PhD, Assoc Prof, Phil of Mind, Phil of Soc Sci
Yoos, George, PhD, Prof, Aes, Phil of Rhet

SAINT JOHN'S UNIVERSITY
  Collegeville, Minnesota 56321 (N; RC; men; 4-1-4; III; 1604) BA major, Dept of Phil,
  612-363-3715

  Joyce, Robert E, MA, Assoc Prof, Chm, Metaph
  Bucher, Vitus, PhD, Prof, Phil Psych
  Eckroth, Richard, MA, Assoc Prof, Logic
  Howard, John, MA, Assoc Prof, Ethics
  McGraw, Rene, PhD, Asst Prof, Phenomen
  Pedrizetti, Raymond, MA, Assoc Prof

  Kilzer, Ernest, PhD, Prof Emer, Hist of Phil

SAINT MARY'S COLLEGE
  Winona, Minnesota 55987 (N; RC; coed; sem; III; 1050) BA major, Dept of Phil, 507-
  452-4430 Ext 261

  Fabian, Andrew, PhL, Asst Prof, Chm, Ethics
  Maher, Michael, Asst Prof, Exist
  Premo, Blanche, Instr, Phil of Sci
  Salzberger, Ronald, Asst Prof, Polit Phil
  Scott, Ulric, PhD, Asst Prof, Hist of Phil

SAINT MARY'S JUNIOR COLLEGE
  Minneapolis, Minnesota 55406 (N; RC; coed; qr; I; 707) NR

SAINT OLAF COLLEGE
  Northfield, Minnesota 55057 (N; A Luth; coed; 4-1-4; II; 2546) BA major, Dept of
  Phil, 507-645-9311 Ext 541

  Stromseth, W A, PhD, Prof, Chm, Phil of Relig
  Fiser, Karen, PhD, Asst Prof, Ethics
  Grandstrand, Karen, PhD, Asst Prof, Ethics
  Hong, Howard, PhD, Prof, Kierkegaard
  Langerak, E, PhD, Asst Prof, Ethics
  Narum, W H K, ThD, Prof, Orient Phil
  Stoutland, F, PhD, Prof, Epistem

SAINT PAUL BIBLE COLLEGE
  Bible College, Minnesota 55375 (BI; Christ and Miss Alliance; coed; II; 409)
  BA major, Dept of Phil, 612-446-1411 Ext 174

  Gates, John F, STD, Prof

SAINT PAUL SEMINARY
  Saint Paul, Minnesota 55101 (N; RC; men; 4-1-4; III; 108) NP

MINNESOTA

SOUTHWEST MINNESOTA STATE COLLEGE
Marshall, Minnesota 56258 (N; st; coed; qr; II; 3272) BA major, --, 507-537-7100

Curtler, Hugh, PhD, Chm, Assoc Prof, Value Theory
Turner, Charles, PhD, Asst Prof, Phil of Relig

UNITED THEOLOGICAL SEMINARY
New Brighton, Minnesota 55112 (Theol; U Ch of Christ; coed; 4-1-4; III; 139) NP

UNIVERSITY OF MINNESOTA
Minneapolis, Minnesota 55455 (N; st; coed; qr; IV; 58,441) PhD major, Dept of Phil,
612-373-3612

Mason, Homer E, PhD, Prof, Chm, Moral and Polit Phil, Phil of Lang
Arnaud, Richard, PhD, Asst Prof, Metaph, Epistem
Brodbeck, May, PhD, Prof, Phil of Soc Sci, Metaph
Dahl, Norman O, PhD, Assoc Prof, Moral Phil, Anc Phil
Dolan, John M, PhD, Assoc Prof, Phil of Lang, Metaph
Earman, John S, PhD, Assoc Prof, Phil of Sci, Metaph
Eaton, Marcia, PhD, Asst Prof, Aes, Phil of Lang
Gunderson, Keith, PhD, Prof, Aes, Phil of Mind
Hanson, William H, PhD, Assoc Prof, Logic, Phil of Logic
Harper, Vicki, MA, Asst Prof, Anc Phil
Hochberg, Herbert, PhD, Prof, Metaph, Phil of Logic
Hopkins, Jasper, PhD, Assoc Prof, Greek Phil, Med Phil, Phil of Relig
Lewis, Douglas, PhD, Assoc Prof, 17th and 18th Cent Phil, Contemp Phil
Meehl, Paul, PhD, Regents' Prof
Maxwell, Grover, PhD, Prof, Phil of Sci, Polit Phil
Peterson, Sandra, PhD, Asst Prof, Anc Phil, Phil of Lang
Root, Michael, PhD, Asst Prof, Phil of Lang, Epistem
Sartorius, Rolf, PhD, Assoc Prof, Phil of Law, Moral and Polit Phil
Savage, C Wade, PhD, Assoc Prof, Perception, Epistem, Phil of Psych
Terrell, D Burnham, PhD, Prof, Hist of Phil, Brentano
Wallace, John R, PhD, Prof, Phil of Lang

Feigl, Herbert, PhD, Prof Emer, Phil of Sci

Brandt, Carl, Grad Teach Asst   McConnell, Terrance, Grad Teach Asst
Brinton, Alan, Grad Teach Asst   McGary, Howard, Grad Teach Asst
Clarke, Richard, Grad Teach Asst   McKenna, Michael, Grad Teach Asst
de la Cova, Alice, Grad Teach Asst   Monical, David, Grad Teach Asst
Dieterle, Richard, Grad Teach Asst   Moody, Thomas, Grad Teach Asst
Gamble, Marilynn, Grad Teach Asst   Smith, James Philip, Grad Teach Asst
Hawthorne, James, Grad Teach Asst   Waithe, Lloyd, Grad Teach Asst
Hoffmaster, Charles Barry, Grad Teach Asst

UNIVERSITY OF MINNESOTA AT DULUTH
Duluth, Minnesota 55812 (N; st; coed; qr; III; 5346) BA major, Dept of Phil, 218-
726-7558

Mayo, David J, Asst Prof, Head, Aes, Axiology
Ehlers, Henry J, PHD, Prof, Phil of Educ, Hist of Phil, Logic
Evans, Robert H, PhD, Assoc Prof, Amer Phil, Phil of Sci

UNIVERSITY OF MINNESOTA AT MORRIS
  Morris, Minnesota 56267 (N; st; coed; qr; II; 1709) BA major, Div of Human, 612-589-4501

  Diehl, John, MA, Instr, Ethics, Epistem
  French, Peter, PhD, Assoc Prof, Phil of Lang
  Uehling, Theodore E, PhD, Prof, Kant

UNIVERSITY OF MINNESOTA, MAYO GRADUATE SCHOOL OF MEDICINE
  Rochester, Minnesota 55901 (N; p; coed; qr; IV; 737) NP

UNIVERSITY OF MINNESOTA TECHNICAL COLLEGE AT WASECA
  Waseca, Minnesota 56093 (N; st; coed; qr; I; 115) NP

UNIVERSITY OF MINNESOTA TECHNICAL INSTITUTE AT CROOKSTON
  Crookston, Minnesota 56716 (N; st; coed; qr; I; 513) NP

VERMILION STATE JUNIOR COLLEGE
  Ely, Minnesota 55731 (N; st; coed; qr; I; 396) NR

WILLIAM MITCHELL COLLEGE OF LAW
  Saint Paul, Minnesota 55105 (Law; p; coed; sem; III; 560) NP

WILLMAR STATE JUNIOR COLLEGE
  Willmar, Minnesota 56201 (N; st; coed; qr; I; 732) Courses with no degree specialization, Dept of Soc Sci, 612-235-2131

  Tintes, Peter, MA, Instr

WINONA STATE COLLEGE
  Winona, Minnesota 55987 (N; st; coed; qr; III; 4261) BA minor, Dept of Phil, 507-457-2046

  Sheehan, Robert, PhD, Prof, Taoism

WORTHINGTON STATE JUNIOR COLLEGE
  Worthington, Minnesota 56187 (--; st; coed; qr; I; 678) Courses with no degree specialization, --, 507-372-2107

  Luknic, Arnold, MA, Chm

MISSISSIPPI

ALCORN AGRICULTURAL AND MECHANICAL COLLEGE
Lorman, Mississippi 39096 (S; st; coed; sem; II; 2677) Courses with no degree
specialization, Dept of Soc Sci, 601-877-3711

Cangemi, Dominic, PhD, Prof, Logic

BELHAVEN COLLEGE
Jackson, Mississippi 39202 (S; Preb; coed; sem; II; 596) BA major, Div II, 601-
352-0013

Wilburn, James R, BD, Asst Prof, Act Chm

BLUE MOUNTAIN COLLEGE
Blue Mountain, Mississippi 38610 (S; S Bapt; wo; sem; II; 293) NR

CLARKE COLLEGE
Newton, Mississippi 39345 (S; S Bapt; coed; sem; I; 252) NP

COAHOMA JUNIOR COLLEGE
Clarksdale, Mississippi 38614 (--; st and local; coed; qr; I; 993) NP

COPIAH-LINCOLN JUNIOR COLLEGE
Wesson, Mississippi 39101 (S; st; coed; sem; I; 1064) NR

DELTA STATE COLLEGE
Cleveland, Mississippi 38732 (S; st; coed; sem; III; 3638) BA minor, Dept of Soc
Sci, 601-843-8139

Pennington, William A, M Div, Asst Prof, Value Theory

EAST CENTRAL JUNIOR COLLEGE
Decatur, Mississippi 39327 (S; local; coed; sem; I; 710) Courses with no degree
specialization, --, 601-635-2111

EAST MISSISSIPPI JUNIOR COLLEGE
Scooba, Mississippi 39358 (S; local; coed; sem; I; 764) --, Dept of Phil and Bib,
601-476-2631

Hughley, Walter C, M Div, Instr, Phil Theol
Winscott, J G, AB, Instr

HINDS JUNIOR COLLEGE
Raymond, Mississippi 39154 (S; st and local; coed; sem; I; 3221) Courses with no
degree specialization, Dept of Phil and Bib, 601-857-5261

HOLMES JUNIOR COLLEGE
Goodman, Mississippi 39079 (S; local; coed; sem; I; 859) NP

ITAWAMBA JUNIOR COLLEGE
   Fulton, Mississippi 38843 (S; local; coed; sem; I; 908) NP

JACKSON STATE COLLEGE
   Jackson, Mississippi 39217 (S; st; coed; qr; III; 5058) Courses with no degree
   specialization, Dept of Soc Sci Educ and Geography, 601-948-8533 Ext 208

   Davison, Roy J, STM, Asst Prof
   Pinter, Alexander E, MA, Asst Prof

JONES COUNTY JUNIOR COLLEGE
   Ellisville, Mississippi 39437 (S; st and local; coed; qr; I; 2209) Courses with no
   degree specialization, Dept of Eng, 601-477-3347

   Kryter, Laurence H, MA, Instr

MARY HOLMES COLLEGE
   West Point, Mississippi 39773 (--; p; coed; sem; I; 618) NP

MERIDIAN JUNIOR COLLEGE
   Meridian, Mississippi 39301 (S; local; coed; sem; I; 1711) Courses with no degree
   specialization, Div of Human, 601-483-8241

MILLSAPS COLLEGE
   Jackson, Mississippi 39210 (S; U Meth; coed; sem; II; 996) BA major, Dept of Phil,
   601-354-5201 Ext 260

   Bergmark, Robert E, PhD, Prof, Chm
   Mitias, Michael H, PhD, Prof

MISSISSIPPI COLLEGE
   Clinton, Mississippi 39058 (S; S Bapt; coed; sem; III; 2414) BA joint or combined
   major, Dept of Phil, 601-924-5131

   Cooper, Joe M, ThD, Prof, Head, Exist, Phil of Relig
   Shurden, Robert, ThD, Asst Prof, Ethics

MISSISSIPPI DELTA JUNIOR COLLEGE
   Moorhead, Mississippi 38761 (S; local; coed; sem; I; 1138) Courses with no degree
   specialization, Dept of Phil and Bib, 601-246-7811

MISSISSIPPI GULF COAST JUNIOR COLLEGE, JACKSON COUNTY CAMPUS
   Gautier, Mississippi 39553 (S; local; coed; sem; I; 905) --, Dept of Soc Stud,
   601-762-0975

   Strahan, Archie, MS, Instr

MISSISSIPPI GULF COAST JUNIOR COLLEGE, JEFFERSON DAVIS CAMPUS
   Handsboro, Mississippi 39554 (S; local; coed; sem; I; 1338) --, Dept of Soc Stud,
   601-864-7156

   Shows, Charles R, PhD

MISSISSIPPI GULF COAST JUNIOR COLLEGE, PERKINSTON CAMPUS
    Perkinston, Mississippi 39573 (S; local; coed; sem; I; 768) Courses with no degree
    specialization, Dept of Soc Stud, 601-928-7211 Ext 71

    Rominger, Robert, MA, Instr

MISSISSIPPI INDUSTRIAL COLLEGE
    Holly Springs, Mississippi 38635 (--; CME; coed; sem; II; 285) BA major, Dept of
    Relig and Phil, 601-252-3411

    Stewart, P A G, BD, Prof

MISSISSIPPI STATE COLLEGE FOR WOMEN
    Columbus, Mississippi 39701 (S; st; wo; sem; II; 2591) BA major, Dept of Phil and
    Relig, 601-328-4628

    Roach, Dewey R, ThD, Prof, Head, Phil of Relig
    Prout, William E, ThD, Assoc Prof

MISSISSIPPI STATE UNIVERSITY
    State College, Mississippi 39762 (S; st; coed; sem; IV; 10,068) PhD minor, --, 601-
    325-3221

    Sutphin, John E, ThD, Prof, Head, Phil of Relig
    Keehley, Jay T, MA, Asst Prof, Phil of Sci
    Murphree, Wallace, MA, Asst Prof, Whitehead
    Vardaman, E Jerry, ThD, Act Prof

MISSISSIPPI VALLEY STATE COLLEGE
    Itta Bena, Mississippi 38941 (S; st; coed; sem; II; 2410) Courses with no degree
    specialization, --, 601-254-2321

NATCHEZ JUNIOR COLLEGE
    Natchez, Mississippi 39120 (--; Bapt; coed; qr; I; 125) NR

NORTHEAST MISSISSIPPI JUNIOR COLLEGE
    Booneville, Mississippi 38829 (S; st and local; coed; sem; I; 1216) NP

NORTHWEST MISSISSIPPI JUNIOR COLLEGE
    Senatobia, Mississippi 38668 (S; st; coed; sem; I; 1749) NP

PEARL RIVER JUNIOR COLLEGE
    Poplarville, Mississippi 39470 (S; st and local; coed; sem; I; 1210) NP

PRENTISS NORMAL AND INDUSTRIAL INSTITUTE
    Prentiss, Mississippi 39474 (--; p; coed; qr; I; 319) NP

REFORMED THEOLOGICAL SEMINARY
    Jackson, Mississippi 39209 (--; p; coed; qr; II; 95) Courses with no degree
    specialization, Dept of Doctrinal Theol, 601-922-4988

    Killen, Allen, ThD, Prof

RUST COLLEGE
Holly Springs, Mississippi 38635 (S; U Meth; coed; sem; I; 747) BA joint or combined minor, Dept of Phil and Relig, 601-252-4661

Williams, Newton, BA, Instr

SAINTS COLLEGE
Lexington, Mississippi 39095 (--; Ch of God in Christ; coed; sem; I; 155) NP

SOUTHEASTERN BAPTIST COLLEGE
Laurel, Mississippi 39440 (--; Bapt; coed; qr; I; 118) NR

SOUTHWEST MISSISSIPPI JUNIOR COLLEGE
Summit, Mississippi 39666 (S; local; coed; sem; I; 852) NP

TOUGALOO COLLEGE
Tougaloo, Mississippi 39174 (S; p; coed; 4-1-4; II; 750) BA joint or combined major Dept of Phil and Relig, 601-956-4941 Ext 43

Johnson, Richard C, MA, Asst Prof, Chm, Ethics, Black Phil
Johnson, Larry, M Div, Part-time

UNIVERSITY OF MISSISSIPPI
University, Mississippi 38677 (S; st; coed; sem; IV; 7822) MA major, Dept of Phil and Relig, 601-232-7211

Flynn, Thomas J, PhD, Prof, Chm, Hist of Phil
Furr, W Hal, PhD, Assoc Prof, Ethics, Phi of Relig
Harrington, Michael, PhD, Asst Prof, Phil of Sci
Shepard, Nolan, PhD, Asst Prof, Orient Phil

UNIVERSITY OF MISSISSIPPI MEDICAL CENTER
Jackson, Mississippi 39216 (S; st; coed; qr; IV; 714) NR

UNIVERSITY OF SOUTHERN MISSISSIPPI
Hattiesburg, Mississippi 39401 (S; st; coed; qr; IV; 11,686) BA major, Dept of Anthrop, Phil and Relig, 601-266-7173

Nau, John F, PhD, Prof, German Idealism, German Phil
Thomas, James A, PhD, Assoc Prof, Amer Mil Tht, Soc and Polit Phil
Wood, Jr, Forrest, ThD, Assoc Prof, Phil of Relig

UTICA JUNIOR COLLEGE
Utica, Mississippi 39175 (--; st; coed; sem; I; 714) NP

WHITWORTH COLLEGE
Brookhaven, Mississippi 39601 (--; p; coed; sem; II; 117) --, --, 601-833-4311

Howard, Ivan, PhD

WILLIAM CAREY COLLEGE
Hattiesburg, Mississippi 39401 (S; S Bapt; coed; sem; III; 916) BA minor, Dept of
Relig and Phil, 601-582-5051 Ext 67

Oswalt, Jerry, ThD, Assoc Prof

WOOD JUNIOR COLLEGE
Mathiston, Mississippi 39752 (S; U Meth; coed; sem; I; 283) Courses with no degree
specialization, Dept of Phil and Relig, 601-263-5352

Fulton, Travis, M Div, Chm
Sowell, Jesse J, BD

MISSOURI

AVILA COLLEGE
Kansas City, Missouri 64145 (N; RC; coed; 4-1-4; II; 754) BA minor, Dept of Theol
and Phil, 816-942-3204

Bryde, George, MA, Assoc Prof, Metaph
Stuckel, Ruth, Instr, Anal Phil, Logic

Beck, Florence, Prof Emer

CALVARY BIBLE COLLEGE
Kansas City, Missouri 64111 (BI; p; coed; sem; III; 384) Courses with no degree
specialization, Dept of Soc Sci, 816-753-4511

Andrus, Michael P, MA, Logic, Ethics

CARDINAL GLENNON COLLEGE
St Louis, Missouri 63119 (N; RC; men; sem; II; 174) BA major, Dept of Phil, 314-
644-0266

Persich, Harold B, PhD, Prof, Div Chm, Metaph, Epistem, Mod Phil
Beuttenmuller, Paul, PhD, Asst Prof, Hist of Mod Phil, Moral Phil
Brannan, Patrick T, PhD, Asst Prof, Hist of Anc Phil
Kane, Frances, PhD, Instr, Metaph, Mod Phil
Schneebeck, Paul O, MA, Assoc Prof

CENTRAL BIBLE COLLEGE
Springfield, Missouri 65802 (BI; Prot; coed; sem; II; 901) Courses with no degree
specialization, Dept of Phil, 417-833-2551 Ext 9

Johns, Donald F, PhD, Prof

CENTRAL INSTITUTE OF TECHNOLOGY
Kansas City, Missouri 64108 (Tech; p; coed; qr; II; 478) NR

CENTRAL METHODIST COLLEGE
Fayette, Missouri 65248 (N; U Meth; coed; 4-1-4; II; 806) BA major, Dept of Phil,
816-248-3391

Hix, Jr, C Eugene, PhD, Prof, Head
Koch, Melville L, MA, Instr

CENTRAL MISSOURI STATE UNIVERSITY
Warrensburg, Missouri 64093 (N; st; coed; qr; III; 12,572) BA minor, Dept of Phil,
816-429-4782

Jent, H Clay, PhD, Prof, Head, Polit Phil, Epistem, Ethics, Phil of Sci
Sides, Chery, MA, Asst Prof, Hist of Phil, Aes, Logic
Tickemyer, Garland E, PhD, Prof, Phil of Relig

COLUMBIA COLLEGE
Columbia, Missouri 65201 (N; p; coed; sem; I; 756) --, Dept of Phil, 314-449-0531
Ext 336

Drennan, Eldon

CONCEPTIONS SEMINARY COLLEGE
Conception, Missouri 64433 (N; RC; men; sem; II; 119) BA major, Dept of Phil, 816-
944-2211 Ext 29, 33

True, Isaac D, PhD, Chm, Process Phil
Falk, Conrad, PhD, Hist of Phil
Hanu-s, Jerome, PhD, Ethics
Weierich, Andre J, PhD, Phil of Sci, Chardin

CONCORDIA SEMINARY
St Louis, Missouri 63105 (Theol; Luth; coed; qr; IV; 792) Courses with no degree
specialization, Dept of Syst Theol, 314-721-5934

Bertram, Robert W, PhD, Prof, Chm
Klann, Richard, PhD, Assoc Prof
Lueker, Erwin L, PhD, Prof
Piepkorn, Arthur C, PhD, Prof
Preus, Robert D, PhD, Prof

COTTEY COLLEGE
Nevada, Missouri 64772 (N; p; wo; sem; I; 288) --, Dept of Phil and Relig, 417-
667-2016

Byer, Inez, PhD, Prof
Gregory, Henry, ThD, Prof

COVENANT THEOLOGICAL SEMINARY
St Louis, Missouri 63141 (--; Ref Preb; coed; sem; III; 112) Courses with no degree
specialization, Dept of Syst Theol and Apologetics, 314-434-4044

Jones, David C, ThD, Asst Prof, Chm, Ethics
Reymond, Robert L, PhD, Assoc Prof

CROWDER COLLEGE
  Neosho, Missouri 64850 (--; local; coed; sem; I; 587) Courses with no degree
  specialization, --, 417-451-3223

  Orr, Alexander R, MS

CULVER-STOCKTON COLLEGE
  Canton, Missouri 63435 (N; Disc Christ; coed; 4-1-4; II; 682) BA joint or combined
  major, --, 314-288-5221

  Sawyer, Edward H, ThD, Assoc Prof, Phil of Relig

DRURY COLLEGE
  Springfield, Missouri 65802 (N; p; coed; sem; III; 2469) BA major, Dept of Phil
  and Relig, 417-865-8731 Ext 314

  Eikner, Allen, PhD, Prof, Contemp British Phil, Contemp Euro Phil
  McKay, Clifford, PhD, Asst Prof, Hist of Phil, East Phil
  Smith, III, Samuel D, PhD, Prof, Amer Phil, Ethics

EAST CENTRAL MISSOURI JUNIOR COLLEGE
  Union, Missouri 63084 (--; local; coed; sem; I; 660) Courses with no degree
  specialization, Dept of Phil, 314-583-5193

  Landers, Billy L, MA

EDEN THEOLOGICAL SEMINARY
  Webster Groves, Missouri 63119 (Theol; Ch of Christ; coed; 4-1-4; IV; 233) NP

EVANGEL COLLEGE
  Springfield, Missouri 65802 (N; Assem of God; coed; 4-1-4; II; 1228) BA joint or
  combined major, Dept of Bibl Stud and Phil, 417-865-2811 Ext 53

  Baldwin, Donald, MA, Asst Prof
  Campbell, Malcolm, ThM, Asst Prof
  Williams, Ward, PhD, Prof

FLORISSANT VALLEY COMMUNITY COLLEGE
  St Louis, Missouri 63135 (N; local; coed; sem; I; 6251) Courses with no degree
  specialization, Dept of Phil, 314-524-2020

FONTBONNE COLLEGE
  St Louis, Missouri 63105 (N; RC; wo; 4-1-4; II; 738) --, Dept of Phil, 314-862-
  3456 Ext 214

  Connelly, Robert J, PhD, Asst Prof
  Kane, Frances, PhD, Prof

FOREST PARK COMMUNITY COLLEGE
  St Louis, Missouri 63110 (N; local; coed; sem; I; 6823) Courses with no degree
  specialization, Dept of Phil, 314-644-3300

  Helbig, Ed, MA, Assoc Prof, Act Head
  Jackoway, Malkom, MA, Assoc Prof, Hist of Phil

HARRIS TEACHERS COLLEGE
St Louis, Missouri 63103 (N; local; coed; sem; II; 1026) Courses with no degree
specialization, Dept of Soc Sci, 314-533-3366

Ferguson, Edward E, MA, Instr, Ethics

JEFFERSON COLLEGE
Hillsboro, Missouri 63050 (N; st and local; coed; sem; I; 1069) Courses with no
degree specialization, Div of Human, 314-789-2693

Hopkins, Robert M, MA, Instr
Manley, Michael, PhD, Instr

KANSAS CITY ART INSTITUTE
Kansas City, Missouri 64111 (N; p; coed; sem; II; 868) NR

KANSAS CITY COLLEGE OF OSTEOPATHIC MEDICINE
Kansas City, Missouri 64124 (Osteo; p; coed; tri; IV; 463) NP

KEMPER MILITARY SCHOOL AND COLLEGE
Boonville, Missouri 65233 (N; p; men; sem; I; 129) NP

KENRICK SEMINARY
St Louis, Missouri 63119 (--; RC; men; sem; III; 102) NR

KIRKSVILLE COLLEGE OF OSTEOPATHIC MEDICINE
Kirksville, Missouri 63501 (Osteo; p; coed; qr; IV; 433) NP

LINCOLN UNIVERSITY
Jefferson City, Missouri 65101 (N; st; coed; sem; III; 2620) BA major, Dept of
Phil, 314-751-2325 Ext 249

Mattingly, Susan S, PhD, Assoc Prof, Head, Metaph, Epistem
Ticac, Wayne, BA, Asst Instr

THE LINDENWOOD COLLEGES
St Charles, Missouri 63301 (N; U Preb; coed; 4-1-4; II; 651) BA major, Dept of Phil
and Relig, 314-723-7152 Ext 215

Crenshaw, Mary Lupton, MA, Asst Prof
Thomas, William West, PhD, Assoc Prof, Phil Theol

Conover, C Eugene, PhD, Prof Emer

LONGVIEW COMMUNITY COLLEGE
Lee's Summit, Missouri 64063 (N; local; coed; sem; I; 2689) NR

MAPLE WOODS COMMUNITY COLLEGE
Kansas City, Missouri 64156 (N; local; coed; sem; I; 1731) AA major, Dept of Soc
Sci, 816-436-6500 Ext 70

Denning, LaVerne J, MPhil, Instr, Contemp Phil

MARILLAC COLLEGE
    St Louis, Missouri 63121 (N; RC; wo; 4-1-4; II; 321) BA minor, Dept of Phil and
    Theol, 314-385-8400

    Beuttenmuller, Paul, PhD, Asst Prof, Metaethics
    Burns, Josephine, Assoc Prof
    Coerver, Robert, Lect Part-time
    DeVrees, Bernard, Lect Part-time
    Foley, Helen, Lect Part-time
    Kryger, Henry, Assoc Prof
    Moran, Judith, Lect Part-time
    Quigley, James, Lect Part-time
    Sinz, Eugene, Lect
    Vitt, Margaret Marie, Lect Part-time

MARYVILLE COLLEGE
    St Louis, Missouri 63141 (N; RC; coed; 4-1-4; II; 658) BA major, Dept of Phil,
    314-434-4100

    Reitzner, Melvin R, PhD, Assoc Prof, Chm, Ethics, Phil of Relig, Comp Phil
    Lee, Bernard J, PhD, Asst Prof, Process Phil, Prag
    Martinez, Marie Louise, PhD, Prof, Contemp Phil, Amer Phil
    Reitzner, Melvin K, PhD, Assoc Prof, Ethics, Phil of Relig, Comp Phil
    Smith, Edward G, MA, Asst Prof, Phil of Man, Mod Phil, Logic, Phenomen
    Wickersham, John P, MA, Asst Prof, Metaph, Med Phil, Plato, Aristotle

MERAMEC COMMUNITY COLLEGE
    St Louis, Missouri 36122 (N; local; coed; sem; I; 8138) AA major, Dept of Phil,
    314-966-3402 Ext 363, 366

    Machin, Jr, Harry, MA, Assoc Prof, Chm, Epistem, Metaph, Phil of Lang
    Gamble, Harold, MA, Instr, Logic, Phil of Mind
    Illert, W Paul, MA, Assoc Prof, Ethics, Aes, Hist of Phil
    Soccio, Douglas, MA, Instr, Aes, Ethics, Hist of Phil

MIDWESTERN BAPTIST THEOLOGICAL SEMINARY
    Kansas City, Missouri 64118 (N; S Bapt; coed; --; III; 254) Courses with no degree
    specialization, Dept of Theol, 816-453-4600

    McCarty, Doran, ThD, Prof, Phil of Relig

MINERAL AREA COLLEGE
    Flat River, Missouri 63601 (N; local; coed; sem; I; 1051) NP

MISSOURI BAPTIST COLLEGE, HANNIBAL CAMPUS
    Hannibal, Missouri 63401 (N; S Bapt; coed; sem; I; 413) AA major, Dept of Relig,
    314-221-3675

    Burns, John, ThD, Prof, Chm, Phil of Relig

MISSOURI BAPTIST COLLEGE, SAINT LOUIS CAMPUS
    St Louis, Missouri 63141 (N; S Bapt; coed; sem; II; 444) BA minor, Div of Human,
    314-434-1115 Ext 56

    Roark, William Wallace, ThD, Asst Prof, Phil of Relig
    Sutherland, Robert S, EdD, Prof, Phil of Educ

MISSOURI SOUTHERN STATE COLLEGE
Joplin, Missouri 64801 (N; st and local; coed; sem; II; 3158) Courses with no degree specialization, Dept of Lang and Lit, 417-624-8100 Ext 221

McCormick, Bernard P, MA, Asst Prof, Part-time, Hist of Phil

MISSOURI VALLEY COLLEGE
Marshall, Missouri 65340 (N; A Preb; coed; sem; II; 838) BA joint or combined major, Dept of Relig and Phil, 816-886-7491

Rabe, Virgil W, ThD, Prof, Chm, Hist of Phil, Ethics, Logic
Nelson, Tim B, M Div, Instr, Ethics

MISSOURI WESTERN COLLEGE
St Joseph, Missouri 64507 (N; st and local; coed; sem; II; 3151) Courses with no degree specialization, --, 816-233-7192

Harris, Charles Moore, MA, Instr, Metaph

Meyer, Myron, DD, Prof Emer

MOBERLY JUNIOR COLLEGE
Moberly, Missouri 65270 (--; local; coed; sem; I; 571) Courses with no degree specialization, Dept of Soc Sci, 816-263-4110

Doctorian, David, MA, Chm

NAZARENE THEOLOGICAL SEMINARY
Kansas City, Missouri 64131 (Theol; Naz; coed; sem; II; 280) Courses with no degree specialization, Dept of Relig and Christ Ethics, 816-333-6254

Reed, Oscar F, PhD, Prof, Chm, Phil of Relig

NORTHEAST MISSOURI STATE UNIVERSITY
Kirksville, Missouri 63501 (N; st; coed; sem; III; 6819) BA major, Dept of Soc Sci, 816-665-5171 Ext 3340

Smits, Henry, PhD, Asst Prof, Chm, Metaph, Logic, Phil of Relig
Blair, Kathryn, PhD, Asst Prof, Ethics, Soc and Polit Phil

NORTHWEST MISSOURI STATE UNIVERSITY
Maryville, Missouri 64468 (N; st; coed; sem; III; 5632) BA major, Dept of Human and Phil, 816-582-2120, 816-582-4500

Davis, Gary, PhD, Assoc Prof, Chm, Phil of Relig
Gnagy, Allen S, MA, Asst Prof, Hist of Phil, Latin American Phil
Nagle, Robert, MA, Asst Prof, Ethics, C S Peirce
Weierich, Andre, PhD, Asst Prof, Phil of Sci

NOTRE DAME COLLEGE
St Louis, Missouri 63125 (N; RC; wo; sem; II; 340) Courses with no degree specialization, Dept of Phil, 314-544-0455

Hotze, Mary H, MA, Assoc Prof, Act Chm, Ethics
Wildt, Carol Marie, PhD, Instr, Phil of Sci

PARK COLLEGE
   Kansas City, Missouri 64152 (N; Preb; coed; sem; II; 604) BA major, Dept of Phil
   and Relig, 816-741-2000 Ext 270

   Proudfoot, Charles Merrill, PhD, Prof, Chm, Phil of Relig, Phil of Educ, Hist of Phil
   Bailey, Robert E, PhD, Assoc Prof, Hist of Phil
   Nickell, James, PhD, Assoc Prof, Polit Phil
   Sibley, Francis, PhD, Assoc Prof, Aes, Ethics

PARKS COLLEGE OF AERONAUTICAL TECHNOLOGY, SAINT LOUIS UNIVERSITY
   Via Cahokia, Illinois 62206 (N; RC; coed; tri; II; 670) Courses with no degree
   specialization, Dept of Phil, 314-436-1695

   Claseman, Francis Adrian, MS, Instr, Phil of Soc Sci

PENN VALLEY COMMUNITY COLLEGE
   Kansas City, Missouri 64111 (N; local; coed; sem; I; 4674) Courses with no degree
   specialization, Dept of Soc Sci, 816-756-2800

   Muhrer, Verle, MA, Instr, Logic, Soc Phil
   Neuschaefer, Wolfgang, MA, Instr, Hist of Phil, Ethics

ROCKHURST COLLEGE
   Kansas City, Missouri 64110 (N; RC; coed; sem; II; 2415) BA major, Dept of Phil,
   816-363-4010

   Brady, Jules M, PhD, Prof, Chm
   Bedell, Gary, PhD, Asst Prof, Bradley
   Barber, Michael, MA, Instr, Ockham
   Daues, Vincent, MA, Assoc Prof, Epistem
   Kennedy, Samuel, PhD, Prof, Med Phil
   Freeman, Joseph, MA, Prof, Ethics
   LaCroix, William, MA, Instr, Ethics
   Rossner, William, PhD, Prof, Phil of Love

SAINT LOUIS COLLEGE OF PHARMACY
   St Louis, Missouri 63110 (N; p; coed; sem; II; 625) NR

SAINT LOUIS INSTITUTE OF MUSIC
   St Louis, Missouri 63141 (Mus; p; coed; sem; III; 104) NP

SAINT LOUIS UNIVERSITY
   St Louis, Missouri 63103 (N; RC; coed; sem; IV; 9158) PhD major, Dept of Phil, 314-
   535-3300 Ext 506

   Thro, Linus J, PhD, Prof, Chm, Theory of Knowl, Anc Phil
   Barth, Louis A, PhD, Assoc Prof, Marxism, Orient Phil
   Berger, Carol A, PhD, Lect
   Beuttenmuller, Paul, PhD, Lect
   Blackwell, Richard J, PhD, Prof, Phil of Sci, Greek Phil
   Bourke, Vernon J, PHD, Prof, Ethics, Med Phil
   Bushman, Rita Marie, PhD, Lect
   Carlson, John W, PhD, Asst Prof, Phil of Lang, Phil of Relig
   Charron, William C, PhD, Assoc Prof, Amer Phil, Phil of Mind
   Childress, Marianne, PhD, Assoc Prof, Ethics, Metaph
   Collins, James D, PhD, Prof, Mod Phil

Doyle, John P, PhD, Prof, Ethics, Metaph
Ermatinger, Charles J, PhD, Prof, Med Phil, Sym Logic, Seman
Eslick, Leonard J, PhD, Prof, Greek Phil, Contemp Phil
Foote, Edward T, PhD, Assoc Prof, Med Phil, Phil of Sci
Marsh, James L, PhD, Asst Prof, Polit Phil, Exist, Phenomen
O'Keefe, Martin D, PhD, Asst Prof, Greek Phil
Punzo, Vincent C, PhD, Prof, Ethics, Mod Phil, Amer Phil
Reagan, James T, PhD, Prof, Metaph, Greek Phil
Rossner, William L, PhD, Visit Prof
Rubin, Alvan D, MHL, Ad Asst Prof
Weiler, William J, MA, Asst Prof, Ethics
Wilson, Barrie A, MA, Instr, Logic, Anal Phil

Mueller, Joseph P, MA, Prof Emer
Ziegelmeyer, Edmund, PhD, Prof Emer

Balestra, Dominic J, AB, Asst
Beaulieu, Richard J, AB, Asst
Cruz, Feodor F, MA, Asst
Dahlstrom, Daniel O, Ph Lic, Asst
Daniel, Stephen H, AB, Asst
Dunphy, Richard, MA, Asst
Eichhoefer, Gerald W, AB, Asst
Gilroy, Jr, John D, AB, Fel

Griesemer, Mary F, AB, Asst
Murray, J Patrick, AB, Asst
Phelps, Mary, MA, Asst
Roman, Mark D, AB, Fel
Seidler, Michael J, AB, Fel
Talmage, Ronald R, AB, Asst
Wildt, Carol M, AB, Asst

SAINT MARY'S COLLEGE
O'Fallon, Missouri 63366 (N; RC; coed; sem; I; 353) AA major, Dept of Human, 314-272-3500

Wiederholt, Marie Frances, MA, Chm, Instr

SAINT MARY'S SEMINARY COLLEGE
Perryville, Missouri 63775 (N; RC; men; 4-1-4; II; 89) BA major, Dept of Phil, 314-547-6533

Bagen, John J, PhD, Prof
Schneebeck, Paul, MA, Asst Prof
Stakelum, James W, PhD, Prof

SAINT PAUL SCHOOL OF THEOLOGY
Kansas City, Missouri 65726 (Theol; U Meth; coed; 4-1-4; IV; 162) Courses with no degree specialization, --, 816-483-9600

SAINT PAUL'S COLLEGE
Concordia, Missouri 64020 (N; Luth; coed; qr; I; 156) NP

SCHOOL OF THE OZARKS
Point Lookout, Missouri 65726 (N; p; coed; tri; II; 1114) BA joint or combined major, Dept of Phil and Relig, 417-334-3101

Stone, Frank F, ThD, Prof, Chm
Quiko, Eduard, PhD, Asst Prof

SOUTHEAST MISSOURI STATE COLLEGE
Cape Girardeau, Missouri 63701 (N; st; coed; sem; III; 7554) BA major, Dept of
Eng, Phil and Jour, 314-334-8211 Ext 255

Hamby, James H, PhD, Asst Prof, Phil of Educ
Metzger, Kenneth H, PhD, Asst Prof, British Empir
Seidensticker, William D, PhD, Asst Prof, Plato

SOUTHWEST BAPTIST COLLEGE
Bolivar, Missouri 65613 (N; S Bapt; coed; sem; II; 1159) BA minor, Dept of Phil,
417-326-5281

Cochran, Dan W, ThD, Assoc Prof, Chm

SOUTHWEST MISSOURI STATE UNIVERSITY
Springfield, Missouri 65802 (N; st; coed; sem; III; 9795) BA major, Dept of Polit
Sci and Phil, 417-831-1561 Ext 251

Brown, William R, PhD, Assoc Prof
Helm, Bertrand, PhD, Assoc Prof
Jaquette, William, PhD, Asst Prof
McKay, Clifford, PhD, Supply Instr
Moran, Jan, PhD, Asst Prof

STATE FAIR COMMUNITY COLLEGE
Sedalia, Missouri 65301 (--; local; coed; sem; I; 890) NP

STEPHENS COLLEGE
Columbia, Missouri 65201 (N; p; wo; sem; II; 2095) BA major, Dept of Relig and
Phil, 314-442-2211

Gelwick, Richard L, ThD, Prof, Chm, Phil of Knowl
Bates, Leslie, M, PhD, Prof, Metaph
Conn, Joann, MA, Asst Prof, Amer Phil
Crosby, Isaac, ThD, Asst Prof, Phil of Relig
Waddell, James E, DPhil, Assoc Prof, Phil of Lang
Whitehill, James D, PhD, Assoc Prof, Orient Phil

TARKIO COLLEGE
Tarkio, Missouri 64491 (N; U Preb; coed; 4-1-4; II; 671) BA joint or combined
major, Dept of Phil and Relig, 816-736-4131 Ext 366

Guinn, Ralph A, PHD, Prof, Chm

THREE RIVERS COMMUNITY COLLEGE
Poplar Bluff, Missouri 63901 (--; st; coed; sem; I; 1009) Courses with no degree
specialization, Dept of Eng, Jour, and Phil, 314-785-7794

Coats, James B, MTh, Instr

TRENTON JUNIOR COLLEGE
Trenton, Missouri 64683 (--; local; coed; sem; I; 406) NP

UNIVERSITY OF MISSOURI AT COLUMBIA
Columbia, Missouri 65201 (N; st; coed; sem; IV; 22,892) PhD major, Dept of Phil,
314-882-2871

Wilcox, William, PhD, Assoc Prof, Chm, Logic, Epistem
Berndtson, Arthur, PhD, Prof, Aes, Metaph
Bien, Joseph, PhD, Assoc Prof, Phenomen, Marxism
Bondeson, William, PhD, Assoc Prof, Anc Phil, Med Phil
Chandler, Kenneth, PhD, Asst Prof, Hist of Phil, Amer Phil
Cremer, Peter, PhD, Asst Prof, Soc Phil, Ethics
Kultgen, John, PhD, Prof, Phil of Sci, Phil of Soc Sci
Sievert, Donald, PhD, Assoc Prof, Anal Phil, Phil of Mind

Oliver, W Donald, PhD, Prof Emer, Epistem, Hist of Phil

Bales, Eugene, MA, Teach Asst
Baumli, Francis, MA, Teach Asst
Danner, Robert, MA, Teach Asst
Georgacarakos, George, MA, Teach Asst
Gibson, Roger, BA, Teach Asst
Hargrove, Eugene, MA, Teach Asst
Hays, Bill, BA, Teach Asst
Heatherly, Cheryl, BA, Teach Asst
Herman, Carl, MA, Teach Asst
Huff, Douglas, MA, Teach Asst
MacAlmon, Edward, BA, Teach Asst
Raines, Douglas, BA, Teach Asst
Shudy, John, MA, Teach Asst
Silverblatt, Barry, BA, Teach Asst
Tritschler, Alan, MA, Teach Asst
Uebelhoer, Jane, MA, Teach Asst

UNIVERSITY OF MISSOURI AT KANSAS CITY
Kansas City, Missouri 64110 (N; st; coed; sem; IV; 9894) BA major, Dept of Phil,
816-276-1331

Levy, Solomon, PhD, Prof, Chm, Phil of Sci
Andriopoulos, Dimitri, PhD, Asst Prof, Greek Phil
Baker, Bruce, PhD, Assoc Prof, Phil of Educ
Bubacz, Bruce, PhD, Asst Prof, Hist of Mod Phil
Frankel, Henry, Instr, Phil of Sci
Gale, George, PhD, Asst Prof, Phil of Sci
Levit, Martin, PhD, Prof, Phil of Educ
Minton, Arthur, Instr, Phil of Lang
Uffelmann, Hans, PhD, Prof, Phenomen, Exist
Walter, Edward, PhD, Assoc Prof, Ethics

Buschman, Harold, PhD, Prof Emer

UNIVERSITY OF MISSOURI AT ROLLA
Rolla, Missouri 65401 (N; st; coed; sem; IV; 5829) BA major, Dept of Human, 314-
341-4631

Cogell, Wayne, PhD, Assoc Prof, Aes, Phenomen, Exist
Miller, Richard W, PhD, Asst Prof, Logic, Phil of Sci
Oakes, Robert A, PhD, Assoc Prof, Phil of Relig, Epistem
Smith, Carol Ann, PhD, Asst Prof, Anal Phil

UNIVERSITY OF MISSOURI AT SAINT LOUIS
St Louis, Missouri 63121 (N; p; coed; sem; IV; 11,221) BA major, Dept of Phil, 314-
453-5631

Munson, J Ronald, PhD, Assoc Prof, Chm
Clifford, John E, PhD, Asst Prof
Conway, David A, PhD, Asst Prof
Costello, Edward B, PhD, Assoc Prof

Doyle, James F, PhD, Assoc Prof
Fuss, Peter, PhD, Assoc Prof
Gomberg, Paul R, PhD, Asst Prof
Gordon, Robert M, PhD, Assoc Prof
Griesedieck, David J, MA, Instr
Harris, Will C, MA, Instr
Lehocky, Daniel L, PhD, Visit Asst Prof
Norris, Stephen E, PhD, Asst Prof
Shapiro, Henry L, PhD, Asst Prof
Walters, James H, PhD, Asst Prof

WASHINGTON UNIVERSITY
St Louis, Missouri 63130 (N; p; coed; sem; IV; 11,221) PhD major, Dept of Phil,
314-863-0100, Ext 4907, 4908, 4909

Barrett, Robert B, PhD, Prof, Chm, Logic, Phil of Sci, Polit Phil
Blanchard, Eric, MA, Instr, Soc and Polit Phil, Phil of Sci, Judaic Phil
Gass, William H, PhD, Prof, Aes, Anc Phil, Ethics
Levi, Albert William, PhD, Prof, Contemp Continen Phil, Hist of Phil
McClennen, Edward, PhD, Assoc Prof, Ethics, Game Theory
Oppacher, Franz, PhD, Asst Prof, Phil of Sci
Popkin, Richard H, PhD, Prof, Hist of Phil, Hist of Ideas, Judaic Phil
Rudner, Richard S, PhD, Prof, Phil of Sci, Epistem
Schiller, Jerome P, PhD, Assoc Prof, Class Phil, Hist of Phil, Aes
Schwarzschild, Steven S, DHL, Prof, Hist of Phil, Phil of Relig, Judaic Phil
Stenner, Alfred J, PhD, Assoc Prof, Phil of Sci, Epistem
Trebilcot, Joyce, PhD, Asst Prof, Ethics
Ullian, Joseph S, PhD, Prof, Logic
Watson, Richard A, PhD, Assoc Prof, Hist of Phil, Descartes, Cartesianism, Epistem
Wellman, Carl P, PhD, Prof, Ethics

Spiegelberg, Herbert, PhD, Prof Emer, Phenomen

Bridgewater, Bradley S, BA, Univ Fel
Browne, Helen C, MA, Teach Asst
Colavita, Lawrence J, BA, Teach Asst
Conradi, J Christian, BA, NDEA Fel
Dunlavey, James L, BA, Teach Asst
Feleppa, Robert, BA, Univ Fel
Fleming, Patricia A, BA, Res Asst
Force, James E, BA, Res Asst
Gaa, James C, BA, Teach Asst
Gresham, Robert W, BA, Teach Asst
Hamilton, William F, BA, Univ Fel
Hughes, Steven P, M Div, Teach Asst
Lucas, Karen G, BA, Univ Fel
Mannoia, V James, BS, Teach Asst
Mayhall, Jr, James W, BA, Univ Fel
Mixson, Jr, William C, BA, Teach Asst
Riggs, Michael D, BA, Teach Asst
Rubin, Richard M, MA, Univ Fel
Schuler, Jeanne A, BA, Univ Fel
Schwartz, Robert J, BA, Teach Asst
Sklar, Judith B, BA, Univ Fel
Wawrytko, Sandra A, BA, Teach Asst

WEBSTER COLLEGE
St Louis, Missouri 63119 (N; p; coed; sem; III; 1665) BA major, Dept of Phil, 314-
968-0500 Ext 403

Sandler, Arthur M, MA, Asst Prof, Chm
Corbett, Robert, MA, Asst Prof
Evans, James, PhD, Asst Prof
Zinner, Jacqueline, MA, Instr

WENTWORTH MILITARY ACADEMY
Lexington, Missouri 64067 (N; p; men; sem; I; 128) NP

WESTMINSTER COLLEGE
    Fulton, Missouri 65251 (N; Preb; men; --; II; 687) BA major, Dept of Phil, 312-642-3361 Ext 255

    Mattingly, Richard E, PhD, Assoc Prof, Epistem

WILLIAM JEWELL COLLEGE
    Liberty, Missouri 64068 (N; Bapt; coed; sem; II; 1089) BA major, Dept of Phil, 816-781-3806 Ext 234, 294

    Trotter, Robert S, PhD, Prof, Chm
    David, Keith R, PhD, Assoc Prof

WILLIAM WOODS COLLEGE
    Fulton, Missouri 65251 (N; p; wo; --; II; 1224) BA major, Dept of Phil, 314-642-2251 Ext 323

    Atkinson, Gary Michael, PhD, Asst Prof, Assoc Chm, Ethics, Logic

MONTANA

CARROLL COLLEGE
  Helena, Montana 59601 (NW; RC; coed; sem; II; 1079) BA major, Dept of Phil, 406-442-3450

  Wiegenstein, Francis J, MA, Assoc Prof, Head, Metaph
  Kelly, Cornelius J, PhD, Assoc Prof, Logic, Phil of Nature
  Lambert, Richard T, PhD, Instr, Med Phil

COLLEGE OF GREAT FALLS
  Great Falls, Montana 59401 (NW; RC; coed; 4-1-4; II; 1031) BA major, Dept of
  Phil and Relig Stud, 406-761-8210 Ext 234

  Fox, Robert James, PhD, Prof, Chm, Ethics
  Dobbin, Jay Dee, STD, Assoc Prof
  Foley, Cornelius, MA, Assoc Prof, Metaph
  Pecharromen, Ovid, PhD, Assoc Prof
  Verhalen, Philip, STD, Asst Prof

DAWSON COLLEGE
  Glendive, Montana 59330 (NW; local; coed; qr; I; 693) NP

EASTERN MONTANA COLLEGE
  Billings, Montana 59101 (NW; st; coed; qr; III; 3466) BA minor, Div of Human, 406-657-2305

  Johnson, Glen, PhD, Prof, Ethics, Phil of Educ
  Leland, James, MA, Asst Prof, Action Theory

FLATHEAD VALLEY COMMUNITY COLLEGE
  Kalispell, Montana 59901 (NW; local; coed; qr; I; 952) --, Div of Soc Sci, 406-752-3411

  Cunningham, Bruce, MA, Instr, Ethics
  Forester, Timothy D, MA

MILES COMMUNITY COLLEGE
  Miles City, Montana 59301 (NW; local; coed; qr; I; 413) NP

MONTANA COLLEGE OF MINERAL SCIENCE AND TECHNOLOGY
  Butte, Montana 59701 (NW; st; coed; sem; III; 899) --, Dept of Human and Soc Sci,
  406-792-8321

  Lester, Tom, MS, Asst Prof

MONTANA STATE UNIVERSITY
  Bozeman, Montana 59715 (NW; st; coed; qr; IV; 8113) BA major, Dept of Hist, Gov,
  and Phil, 406-994-3945

  Hausser, Harry, PhD, Prof, Chm, Ethics, Aes
  Brittan, Gordon, PhD, Assoc Prof, Phil of Sci
  Marshall, Norman, PhD, Asst Prof, Phil of Lang

NORTHERN MONTANA COLLEGE
Havre, Montana 59501 (NW; st; coed; qr; III; 1583) Courses with no degree specialization, Dept of Lang and Lit, 406-265-7821 Ext 267

Thackeray, Jr, William W, MA, Assoc Prof, Hist of Phil, Ethics

ROCKY MOUNTAIN COLLEGE
Billings, Montana 59102 (NW; Interdenom; coed; 4-1-4; II; 546) BA major, Dept of Phil, 406-245-6151 Ext 270

Murphy, Clifford H, PhD, Prof, Ethics

UNIVERSITY OF MONTANA
Missoula, Montana 59801 (NW; st; coed; qr; IV; 9313) MA major, Dept of Phil, 406-243-2171

Huff, Thomas P, PhD, Assoc Prof, Chm
Birch, Thomas, PhD, Asst Prof
Black, Bryan T, PhD, Asst Prof
Borgmann, Albert, PhD, Prof
Bugbee, Henry G, PhD, Prof
Fandozzi, Phillip, MA, Instr
Lanfear, Ray, PhD, Assoc Prof
Lawry, John F, PhD, Prof
McGlynn, Fred, MA, Instr
Perrin, Ronald, PhD
Schuster, Cynthia A, PhD, Prof
Townsend, Burke, PhD, Asst Prof
Walton, Richard, MA, Instr
Whited, Gary, PhD, Asst Prof

Marvin, E L, MA, Prof Emer

Dakin, Marion
Horlick, Robert
Imhoff, Christine

Kemmis, Daniel
Konigsberg, Jan
Mahlum, Ed

WESTERN MONTANA COLLEGE
Dillon, Montana 59725 (NW; st; coed; qr; III; 1008) Courses with no degree specialization, Dept of Educ, 406-683-5332

Newlon, Robert E, PhD, Assoc Prof, Phil of Educ

NEBRASKA

BELLEVUE COLLEGE
  Bellevue, Nebraska 68005 (--; p; coed; sem; II; 1026) BA major, Dept of Phil, 402-291-8102

  Stites, Del E, MA, Asst Prof, Head, Phil of Relig, Hume, Swedenborg, Hist of Phil
  Paulsen, David, PhD, Instr, Phil of Lang, Logic, Human
  Shaw, John, MRE, Instr, Phil of Relig, Ethics
  Witt, Richard, MA, Instr, Metaph, Epistem, Ethics

CENTRAL NEBRASKA TECHNICAL COLLEGE
  Hastings, Nebraska 68901 (DA; local; coed; qr; I; 1438) NP

CHADRON STATE COLLEGE
  Chadron, Nebraska 69337 (N; st; coed; sem; III; 2428) BA minor, Dept of Phil, 308-432-4451 Ext 3

  Graves, Dorset, PhD, Prof

COLLEGE OF SAINT MARY
  Omaha, Nebraska 68124 (N; RC; wo; sem; II; 560) BA minor, Dept of Phil, 402-393-8800 Ext 34

  Graham, Mary Jude, MA, Assoc Prof, Chm, Metaph, Phil of Relig, Amer Phil, Exist

CONCORDIA TEACHERS COLLEGE
  Seward, Nebraska 68434 (N; Luth; coed; 4-1-4; III; 1737) Courses with no degree specialization, Dept of Theol, 402-643-3651

  Meyer, David P, STM, Asst Prof

CREIGHTON UNIVERSITY
  Omaha, Nebraska 68178 (N; RC; coed; sem; IV; 4172) MA minor, Dept of Phil, 402-536-2834

  Donahue, Eugene L, PhD, Asst Prof, Chm, Hegel, Phil of Relig
  Apostol, Robert Z, PhD, Prof, Exist, Marxism
  Datko, James L, PhD, Assoc Prof, Ethics, Logic
  George, Francis E, PhD, Asst Prof, Amer Phil, Soc Phil
  Haley, Mary Alice, PhD, Asst Prof, Leibniz, Med Phil
  Jelinek, John P, PhD, Prof, Thomistic Phil, Ethics
  Muse, Kenneth, AM, Instr, Ethics and Soc, Soc Phil
  Peterkin, John M, AM, Asst Prof, Phil of Relig
  Richards, Robert J, PhD, Asst Prof, Phil Psych, Phenomen
  Selk, Eugene E, PhD, Asst Prof, Phil of Sci, Sym Logic
  Vaske, Martion O, AM, Prof, Metaph

DANA COLLEGE
  Blair, Nebraska 68008 (N; Amer Luth; coed; 4-1-4; II; 848) BA major, Dept of Phil, 402-426-4101 Ext 245

  Hanson, Clifford, PhD, Prof, Ethics
  Nielsen, John, BD, Assoc Prof
  Northwall, John, PhD, Assoc Prof, Phil of Communic

DOANE COLLEGE
Crete, Nebraska 68333 (N; U Ch of Christ; coed; 4-1-4; II; 711) Courses with no degree specialization, Dept of Phil and Relig, 402-826-2161

Williams, Daryl E, PhD, Prof, Phil of Relig
Ferrell, Donald R, STM, Asst Prof

GRACE BIBLE INSTITUTE
Omaha, Nebraska 68108 (BI; p; coed; sem; II; 525) Courses with no degree specialization, Dept of Gen Educ, 402-342-3377

Quinnelly, James D, ThM

HASTINGS COLLEGE
Hastings, Nebraska 68901 (BI; p; coed; sem; II; 525) BA major, Dept of Phil, 402-463-2402

Walker, James S, PhD, Prof, Chm, Phil of Relig
Underhill, PhD, Prof, Phil of Relig

JOHN F KENNEDY COLLEGE
Wahoo, Nebraska 68066 (--; p; coed; sem; II; 311) BA joint or combined major, --, 402-433-4171

Anderson, William D, MA, Assoc Prof, Dean
Dillow, Ted, MA, Assoc Prof
Myer, Rawley, PhD, Assoc Prof

KEARNEY STATE COLLEGE
Kearney, Nebraska 68847 (N; st; coed; sem; III; 5783) Courses with no degree specialization, Dept of Hist and Phil, 308-236-4141

Holmgren, Philip S, PhD, Prof, Chm

MCCOOK COLLEGE
McCook, Nebraska 69001 (--; local; coed; sem; I; 349) Courses with no degree specialization, --, 308-345-6303

MIDLAND LUTHERAN COLLEGE
Fremont, Nebraska 68025 (N; Luth Ch Amer; coed; 4-1-4; II; 867) BA major, Dept of Phil, 402-721-5480

Egertson, Erick R, ThD, Asst Prof, Chm

NEBRASKA SOUTHERN COMMUNITY COLLEGE
Fairbury, Nebraska 68352 (--; local; coed; sem; I; 473) Courses with no degree specialization, Dept of Human, 402-729-6148

Jackson, Gilbert, M Div, Phil of Relig

NEBRASKA WESLEYAN UNIVERSITY
Lincoln, Nebraska 68504 (N; p; coed; sem; II; 1177) BA major, --, 402-466-2371
Ext 377

Walker, John Mark, PhD, Asst Prof, Head, Aes
Pfeffer, William, MA, Asst Prof, Ethics

NEBRASKA WESTERN COLLEGE
Scottsbluff, Nebraska 69361 (--; local; coed; sem; I; 863) NP

NORTH PLATTE COLLEGE
North Platte, Nebraska 69101 (--; local; coed; sem; I; 499) NP

NORTHEASTERN NEBRASKA COLLEGE
Norfolk, Nebraska 68701 (--; local; coed; sem; I; 729) NP

PERU STATE COLLEGE
Peru, Nebraska 68421 (N; st; coed; sem; II; 1001) Courses with no degree
specialization, Dept of Hist and Soc Sci, 402-872-3815

PLATTE JUNIOR COLLEGE
Columbus, Nebraska 68601 (--; local; coed; sem; I; 770) Courses with no degree
specialization, Dept of Lang and Lit, 402-564-7132

Hanson, Luther C, MA

PLATTE VALLEY BIBLE COLLEGE
Scottsbluff, Nebraska 69361 (--; Ch of Chris; coed; sem; II; 81) Courses with no
degree specialization, Div of Gen Educ, 308-632-6933

UNION COLLEGE
Lincoln, Nebraska 68506 (N; SDA; coed; sem; II; 808) Courses with no degree
specialization, Dept of Relig, 402-488-2331

UNIVERSITY OF NEBRASKA
Lincoln, Nebraska 68502 (N; st; coed; sem; IV; 21,541) PhD major, Dept of Phil,
402-472-2425

Dewey, Robert E, PhD, Prof, Chm, Ethics, Amer Phil
Anderson, Robert F, PhD, Assoc Prof, Metaph, Hist of Phil
Audi, Robert N, PhD, Assoc Prof, Metaph, Epistem
Becker, Edward F, PhD, Asst Prof, Epistem, Logic
Carpenter, Elizabeth, PhD, Asst Prof Part-time, Logic
Eddy, Lyle K, MA, Prof Part-time, Ethics, Amer Phil
Erlandson, Douglas, PhD, Asst Prof, Phil of Relig, Ethics
Evans, Cedric A, PhD, Asst Prof, Ethics, Polit Phil
Hubbart, James R, MA, Instr, Hist of Phil
Hurlbutt, III, Robert H, PhD, Prof, Aes, Phil of Hist
Leinfellner, Werner H, PhD, Prof, Phil of Sci
Potter, Nelson T, PhD, Asst Prof, Hist of Phil, Aes
Sayward, Jr, Charles W, PhD, Assoc Prof, Logic, Phil of Lang
Schneider, Hubert H, PhD, Assoc Prof Part-time, Logic

Bouwsma, Oets K, PhD, Prof Emer, Phil of Lang
Patterson, Charles H, PhD, Prof Emer, Ethics, Phil of Relig

Basinger, David, BA, Teach Asst
Berghel, Harold L, BA, Teach Asst
Day, Michael A, BS, Teach Asst
Hansen, Michael M, BA, Teach Asst
Lillegard, Norman S, MA, Teach Asst
Manig, Thomas O, BA, Teach Asst
Moats, Gail, BA, NDEA

Olson, Carl W, BA, Teach Asst
Paas, David E, BA, Teach Asst
Phelps, John J, BA, Teach Asst
Prater, Francine, BA, Teach Asst
Rickertsen, Bryan C, BA, Teach Asst
Shaw, John P, BA, Teach Asst

UNIVERSITY OF NEBRASKA AT OMAHA
Omaha, Nebraska 68132 (N; st; coed; sem; III; 12,711) BA major, Dept of Phil and
Relig, 402-554-2628

Anderberg, Clifford, Prof, Chm, Mod Phil, Amer Phil
Blizek, William, PhD, Assoc Prof, Aes, Phil of Justice
Blum, Gary, Asst Prof, Logic, Ethics
Gillespie, Michael, Asst Prof, Exist, Phil of Hist
Willard, L Duane, Instr, Class Ethical Theories

UNIVERSITY OF NEBRASKA MEDICAL CENTER
Omaha, Nebraska 68105 (Med; st; coed; qr; IV; 1054) NP

WAYNE STATE COLLEGE
Wayne, Nebraska 68787 (N; st; coed; tri; III; 2668) Courses with no degree
specialization, Dept of Eng, 402-375-2200 Ext 218

Butler, Katherine, PhD, Assoc Prof, Ethics
Lewis, Katherine, PhD, Assoc Prof, Logic

YORK COLLEGE
York, Nebraska 68467 (N; p; coed; sem; I; 343) NP

NEVADA

CLARK COUNTY COMMUNITY COLLEGE
   Las Vegas, Nevada 89101 (--; st; coed; sem; I; 402) Courses with no degree specialization,
   Dept of Phil, 702-385-5595 Ext 13

   Isham, George Frederick, PhD, Instr, Med Phil, Marxism

ELKO COMMUNITY COLLEGE
   Elko, Nevada 89801 (--; st; coed; sem; I; 494) NP

SIERRA NEVADA COLLEGE
   Incline Village, Nevada 89450 (--; p; coed; qr; II; 99) Courses with no degree
   specialization, Dept of Human, 702-831-1314

UNIVERSITY OF NEVADA AT LAS VEGAS
   Las Vegas, Nevada 89154 (NW; st; coed; sem; III; 5707) BA major, Dept of Phil,
   702-739-3433

   Travis, Janet L, PhD, Assoc Prof, Chm, Phil of Biological Sci, Epistem, Phil of
      Relig, Anc Egyptian Theol
   Finocchiaro, Maurice A, PHD, Asst Prof, Logic, Phil of Sci
   Pasterk, Cyrill, PhD, Asst Prof, Phenomen, Exist, Idealism
   Tominaga, Thomas T, PhD, Asst Prof, Wittgenstein, Anal Phil, Phil of Lang, Phil of
      Mind
   Walton, Craig, PhD, Assoc Prof, Hist of Phil, Renaissance Phil, Soc Phil, Amer Phil

UNIVERSITY OF NEVADA AT RENO
   Reno, Nevada 89507 (NW; st; coed; sem; IV; 7631) PhD minor, Dept of Phil, 702-
   784-6846

   Kelly, Jack, PhD, Assoc Prof, Chm, Ethics, Phil of Mind
   Halberstadt, W H, PhD, Prof, Aes, Logic
   Hirschmann, David, BA, Visit Lect, Phil Psych, Phil Biology
   Lucash, Frank S, PhD, Asst Prof, Contemp Phil, Phil of Lang
   Petock, Stuart J, PhD, Asst Prof, Aes
   Roelofs, Robert T, PhD, Prof, Phil Ecology
   Theophanous, Andrew, BA, Res Assoc, Kant, Phil of Sci

   Etchemendy, John, BA, Grad Fel   Peterson, Rolf, BA, Grad Asst

WESTERN NEVADA COMMUNITY COLLEGE
   Carson City, Nevada 89701 (--; st; coed; sem; I; 705) Courses with no degree
   specialization, --, 702-882-8477

   Fry, George F, ThM, Instr

NEW HAMPSHIRE

BELKNAP COLLEGE
Center Harbor, New Hampshire 03226 (--; p; coed; 4-1-4; II; 444) BA major, Dept of Phil, 603-279-4576

Shenk, J Paul, PhD, Prof, Chm, Phil of Relig, Metaph
Chalmers, A Burns, BD, Lect, Phil of Relig
Casey, John, MA, Asst Prof, Amer Phil, Metaph
Casey, Susan, Asst Prof, Amer Phil, Phil of Biology, Metaph
Frye, Royal M, PhD, Chancellor, Phil of Sci

CANAAN COLLEGE
Canaan, New Hampshire 03741 (--; p; coed; sem; II; 92) BA major, --, 603-523-7700

Smith, Peter Fox, PhD

COLBY JUNIOR COLLEGE FOR WOMEN
New London, New Hampshire 03257 (JE; p; wo; 4-1-4; II; 577) Courses with no degree specialization, Dept of Phil and Relig, 603-526-6455

Jensen, Jack W, PhD, Assoc Prof, Ethics
Swanson, Lynn, PhD, Asst Prof, Phil of Ling

DARTMOUTH COLLEGE
Hanover, New Hampshire 03755 (E; p; coed; --; IV; 3792) BA major, Dept of Phil, 603-646-2386

Gert, Bernard, PhD, Prof, Chm, Rationality
Doney, Willis, PhD, Prof, Hist of Phil, Descartes
Duggan, Timothy J, PhD, Prof, British Empir
Fried, Marlene G, PhD, Asst Prof, Phil of Hist, Marxism
Gramlich, Francis W, PhD, Prof
Menza, Victor G, PhD, Asst Prof, Greek Phil
Moor, James H, PhD, Asst Prof, Phil of Sci
Scott-Craig, T S K, PhD, Prof, Aes

FRANCONIA COLLEGE
Franconia, New Hampshire 03580 (--; p; coed; sem; II; 389) Courses with no degree specialization, --, 603-823-8086

Congdon, William, STB
Corsi, Jerome, PhD
Howe, Nicholas, BA

FRANKLIN PIERCE COLLEGE
Rindge, New Hampshire 03461 (E; p; coed; 4-1-4; II; 1077) Courses with no degree specialization, Dept of Phil and Relig, 603-899-5111 Ext 251

Polan, Stanley M, SSL, Asst Prof, Act Chm
Chatalian, George, PhD, Assoc Prof, Buddhism
Valakis, Apollon, MA, Prof, Aes

KEENE STATE COLLEGE, UNIVERSITY OF NEW HAMPSHIRE
Keene, New Hampshire 03431 (E; st; coed; sem; III; 2837) --, Dept of Soc Sci, 603-352-1310 Ext 209

Hornbeck, Charles E, Instr

MOUNT SAINT MARY COLLEGE
Hooksett, New Hampshire 03106 (E; p; wo; 4-1-4; II; 247) Courses with no degree specialization, Div of Human, 603-485-9536

Gurczak, Francis, MA, Lect
Vaccarest, Anne, MA, Asst Prof

NATHANIEL HAWTHORNE COLLEGE
Antrim, New Hampshire 03440 (E; p; coed; sem; II; 716) BA major, Dept of Phil, 603-588-6341

Stahl, Roland C, PhD, Assoc Prof, Chm
Umen, Samuel, ThD, Lect Part-time

NEW ENGLAND AERONAUTICAL INSTITUTE
Nashua, New Hampshire 03060 (--; p; coed; tri; I; 411) Courses with no degree specialization, --, 603-883-3556

NEW ENGLAND COLLEGE
Henniker, New Hampshire 03242 (E; p; coed; 4-1-4; II; 1190) BA major, Div of Human, 603-428-2211

Jaffe, Erwin A, PhD, Dean, Polit Phil
Anthony, Clifford H, MA, Asst Prof
Bailey, Joan, PhD, Asst Prof
Sylvester, R P, PhD, Ethics, Anal Phil

NEW HAMPSHIRE COLLEGE
Manchester, New Hampshire 03104 (SRCB; p; coed; sem; II; 1407) Courses with no degree specialization, Dept of Human, 603-668-2211 Ext 246

Commenator, George E, PhD, Assoc Prof, Phenomen

NEW HAMPSHIRE TECHNICAL INSTITUTE AT CONCORD
Concord, New Hampshire 03301 (E; st; coed; qr; I; 496) Courses with no degree specialization, Dept of Eng and Soc Sci, 603-271-2531 Ext 0

Duclos, Marcel A, MTh, Assoc Prof

NOTRE DAME COLLEGE
Manchester, New Hampshire 03104 (E; RC; wo; 4-1-4; II; 439) Courses with no degree specialization, Div of Human, 603-623-1846

O'Hara, John J, MA, Prof, Chm, Ethics

PLYMOUTH STATE COLLEGE, UNIVERSITY OF NEW HAMPSHIRE
Plymouth, New Hampshire 03264 (E; st; coed; sem; III; 2637) BA minor, Dept of Phil, 603-536-1550 Ext 314

O'Neill, Robert E, MA, Asst Prof, Chm
Haight, David F, PhD, Asst Prof, Ethics, Metaph
Leibowitz, Constance, PhD, Asst Prof, Anc Phil, Exist, Phil of Relig
Otto, Herbert R, PhD, Assoc Prof, Logic, Phil of Sci, Phil of Lang

RIVIER COLLEGE
Nashua, New Hampshire 03060 (E; p; wo; 4-1-4; III; 825) Courses with no degree specialization, Dept of Phil, 603-888-1311

Debrock, Guy, PhD, Assoc Prof, Chm, Hegel
Landry, Jacqueline, Asst Prof, Ethics, Phil of Ricoeur

SAINT ANSELM'S COLLEGE
Manchester, New Hampshire 03102 (E; RC; men; sem; II; 1674) BA major, Dept of Phil, 603-669-1030

Augros, Robert, MA, Instr, Phil of Man
Collins, George, MA, Asst Prof, Mod Phil, Marx, Hegel
Gahringer, Robert, PhD, Assoc Prof, Mod Phil, Ethics, Kant, Logic
McDonald, Joseph, PhD, Prof, Class Phil, Schol Phil
O'Rourke, James, MA, Asst Prof, Metaph, Logic, Marx, Phenomen
Regan, Anselm, PhD, Prof, Ethics, Theol, Schol Phil
Robinson, Andrew, PhD, Assoc Prof, Phil of Nature, Anc Phil, Med Phil
Ryan, John J, BA, Prof, Phil of Art

UNIVERSITY OF NEW HAMPSHIRE
Durham, New Hampshire 03824 (E; st; coed; sem; IV; 10,527) BA major, Dept of Phil, 603-862-1040

Bangs, Judith Lundsford, MA, Instr
Birmingham, Frank, PhD, Asst Prof
Brockelman, Paul T, PhD, Assoc Prof
Dusek, R V, PhD, Asst Prof
Moore, Asher, PhD, Babcock Prof
Scharff, Robert C, PhD, Asst Prof
Whittier, Duane H, PhD, Assoc Prof

WHITE PINES COLLEGE
Chester, New Hampshire 03036 (--; p; coed; sem; I; 96) Courses with no degree specialization, --, 603-887-4401

Holmberg, Fred B, STB

NEW JERSEY

ALMA WHITE COLLEGE
    Zarephath, New Jersey 08890 (--; Prot; coed; sem; II; 86) Courses with no degree
    specialization, --, 201-356-1646

    Mienert, R W, MA, Head
    Economos, Homer, MA

ALPHONSUS COLLEGE
    Woodcliff Lake, New Jersey 07675 (--; RC; wo; sem; I; 296) AA major, Div of Human,
    201-391-8550

    Galgan, Gerald J, PhD, Asst Prof, Amer Phil, Hist of Mod Phil

ASSUMPTION COLLEGE FOR SISTERS
    Mendham, New Jersey 07945 (M; RC; wo; sem; I; 37) Courses with no degree
    specialization, --, 201-543-4672

    Heinen, Julitta, Chm, Ethics
    Klauder, Francis, PhD

ATLANTIC COMMUNITY COLLEGE
    Mays Landing, New Jersey 08330 (M; local; coed; sem; I; 3044) Courses with no degree
    specialization, Dept of Behavior Sci, 609-625-1111 Ext 270

    Missiras, Andrew, MS, Assoc Prof
    Sollish, Martin, MA, Assoc Prof

BERGEN COMMUNITY COLLEGE
    Paramus, New Jersey 07652 (M; st and local; coed; sem; I; 4539) AA major, Dept of
    Soc Sci, 201-447-1500 Ext 526

    Cronk, George F, PhD, Asst Prof, Amer Phil
    Klein, Sherwin, MA, Adj Faculty

THE BERKELEY SCHOOL
    East Orange, New Jersey 07017 (JRCB; p; wo; qr; I; 520) NP

BETH MEDRASH GOVOHA
    Lakewood, New Jersey 08701 (--; Jewish; men; sem; III; 520) NR

BLOOMFIELD COLLEGE
    Bloomfield, New Jersey 07003 (M; U Preb; coed; 4-1-4; II; 1698) BA major, Dept of
    Phil, 201-748-9000

    Stein, George P, PhD, Prof, Chm, Aes, Ethics
    Bell, James, PhD, Asst Prof, Ethics, Phil of Sci
    Brown, Stephen, Asst Prof, Phil of Relig
    Teschner, George, Asst Prof, Phenomen, Hist of Phil

BROOKDALE COMMUNITY COLLEGE
  Lincroft, New Jersey 07738 (M; st and local; coed; 4-1-4; I; 5295) --, Dept of
  Phil, Human Affairs Inst, 201-849-1900 Ext 310

  Halberstam, Joshua, DD, Instr, Chm
  Goodman, Steve, MA, Part-time
  Pence, Greg, Part-time

BURLINGTON COUNTY COLLEGE
  Pemberton, New Jersey 08068 (M; st and local; coed; --; I; 2513) AA major, Dept of
  Human, 609-894-9311 Ext 371

  Williams, George, PhD, Prof, Phil of Mind

CALDWELL COLLEGE
  Caldwell, New Jersey 07006 (M; RC; wo; sem; II; 829) BA minor, --, 210-228-4424

  Konecsni, Johnemery, MA, Instr, Phil of Sci
  Lichtenberg, Benjamin, MA, Asst Prof, Phil Psych
  Peal, Janet, PhD, Prof, Ethics
  Smith, Philip, MA, Instr, Ethics

CAMDEN COUNTY COLLEGE
  Blackwood, New Jersey 08012 (M; st and local; coed; sem; I; 4242) Courses with no
  degree specialization, --, 609-227-7200

  Krakow, Irving, MA, Assoc Prof

CENTENARY COLLEGE FOR WOMEN
  Hackettstown, New Jersey 07840 (JM; p; wo; sem; II; 590) AA major, Dept of Phil
  and Relig, 201-852-1400 Ext 8

  Orr, William M, M Div, Prof, Chm, Phil of Relig
  Knott, Moses A, M Div

COLLEGE OF SAINT ELIZABETH
  Convent Station, New Jersey 07961 (M; RC; wo; sem; II; 685) BA major, Dept of Phil,
  201-539-1600 Ext 309

  Roche, Thérèse Aquinas, PhD, Prof, Chm, Phil of Sci
  Richey, Francis Augustine, PhD, Prof
  Rueshoff, Agnes Vincent, MA, Asst Prof

COUNTY COLLEGE OF MORRIS
  Randolph, New Jersey 07801 (M; st; coed; sem; I; 5200) Courses with no degree
  specialization, Area of Phil, 201-361-5000 Ext 289

  Murray, John, MA, Asst Prof, Logic
  Warganz, Joseph F, PhD, Prof, Anc Phil, Phil of Man, Phil of Relig

CUMBERLAND COUNTY COLLEGE
  Vineland, New Jersey 08360 (M; st and local; coed; sem; I; 1517) Courses with no
  degree specialization, Dept of Human, 609-691-8600 Ext 60

  Horbach, C Frederick, PhD, Assoc Prof

DON BOSCO COLLEGE
  Newton, New Jersey 07860 (M; RC; men; sem; II; 118) BA major, Dept of Phil, 201-383-3900

  Klauder, Francis J, PhD, Prof, Dean, Schol Phil, Med Phil, Teilhard de Chardin
  Occhio, Joseph M, PhD, Prof, Ethics, Orient Phil
  Zuliani, Vincent A, PhD, Prof, Mod Phil, Contemp Phil

DREW UNIVERSITY
  Madison, New Jersey 07940 (M; p; coed; sem; IV; 1691) BA major, Dept of Phil, 201-377-3000

  Knox, Jr, John, PhD, Prof, Chm, Theory of Knowl, Metaph
  Copeland, John Wilson, PhD, Prof, Act Chm, Ethics, Soc and Polit Phil
  Courtney, Charles, PhD, Assoc Prof, Phil of Relig
  Gonzalez-Cobarrubias, Juan J, MA, Instr Part-time, Theory of Knowl, Phil of Sci
  Herberg, Will, PhD, Prof, Phil of Culture
  Morsink, Johannes, MA, Instr, Hist of Phil
  Pain, James H, DPhil, Assoc Prof, Russian Phil
  Riemer, Neal, PhD, Prof, Polit Phil

  Kimpel, Benjamin F, PhD, Prof Emer, Hist of Phil

ENGLEWOOD CLIFFS COLLEGE
  Englewood Cliffs, New Jersey 07632 (--; RC; coed; 4-1-4; I; 868) Courses with no
  degree specialization, Dept of Phil and Relig Stud, 201-568-7730

  O'Connor, Catherine Regina, PhD, Chm
  Kramnick, Thomas, MA, Instr
  O'Toole, Edward J, MA, Prof

ESSEX COUNTY COLLEGE
  Newark, New Jersey 07102 (ADNUR; st; coed; sem; I; 4862) AA major, Dept of Educ,
  Phil and Relig, 201-621-2200 Ext 250

  MacBryde, Duncan, PhD, Assoc Prof
  Wilson, Ned M, PhD, Assoc Prof

FAIRLEIGH DICKINSON UNIVERSITY, EDWARD WILLIAMS CAMPUS
  Hackensack, New Jersey 07601 (M; p; coed; 4-1-4; I; 669) NR

FAIRLEIGH DICKINSON UNIVERSITY, MADISON CAMPUS
  Madison, New Jersey 07940 (M; p; coed; sem; IV; 4969) BA major, Dept of Hist and
  Phil, 201-377-4700 Ext 231

  Buchanan, Emerson, PhD, Prof, Anc Phil
  Hall, Patrick, MA, Instr
  Mechanic, Janevive, PhD, Asst Prof, Phil of Sci

FAIRLEIGH DICKINSON UNIVERSITY, RUTHERFORD CAMPUS
  Rutherford, New Jersey 07070 (M; p; coed; sem; IV; 4969) NR

FAIRLEIGH DICKINSON UNIVERSITY, TEANECK CAMPUS
  Teaneck, New Jersey 07666 (M; p; coed; sem; IV; 10,221) BA major, --, 201-836-6300

  Humbert, Earl R, PhD, Assoc Prof, Chm, Metaethics, Phil of Sci
  Lahood, Gabriel, PhD, Instr, Aes
  Milmed, Bella, PhD, Instr, Kant
  Sher, George, BA, Instr,

  Hart, Samuel L, PhD, Prof Emer, Ethics, Aes

FELICIAN COLLEGE
  Lodi, New Jersey 07644 (--; RC; wo; sem; II; 505) --, Dept of Phil and Theol, 201-778-1190

  Beebe, William, PhD, Asst Prof
  Figurski, Leshak, MA, Instr

GEORGIAN COURT COLLEGE
  Lakewood, New Jersey 08701 (M; RC; wo; sem; II; 730) Courses with no degree
  specialization, Dept of Phil, 201-364-2200 Ext 44

  Driscoll, Edward A, MA, Assoc Prof, Chm, 17th and 18th Cent Phil
  Witman, Edward P, MA, Instr, Process Phil

  Ferguson, Jane Frances, PhD, Prof Emer

GLASSBORO STATE COLLEGE
  Glassboro, New Jersey 08028 (M; st; coed; sem; III; 11,290) BA minor, Dept of Phil
  and Relig, 609-445-5273

  Whitcraft, John E, STM, Assoc Prof, Chm, Phil of Lang
  Cell, Howard R, MA, Asst Prof, Soc Ethics
  Grace, James H, ThM, Asst Prof, Contemp Relig Tht
  MacIntire, Gordon P, MA, Asst Prof, Phil of Relig
  Shaw, Albert C, MA, Prof, Plato
  Sizemore, Warner, MA, Asst Prof
  Tong, Paul K K, PhD, Assoc Prof, East Relig

GLOUCESTER COUNTY COLLEGE
  Sewell, New Jersey 08080 (--; st and local; coed; sem; I; 1700) AA major, Div of
  Human, 609-468-5000 Ext 209

  Fischer, Jan B, PhD, Prof, Chm, Ethics
  Harrison, Edward H, EdD, Assoc Prof, Relig of the World
  Sullivan, Henry B, EdD, Asst Prof

IMMACULATE CONCEPTION SEMINARY
  Darlington, New Jersey 07430 (--; RC; men; sem; II; 150) Courses with no degree
  specialization, Dept of Phil, 201-327-0300

  Feehan, Stephen S, PhD, Assoc Prof, Chm, Hist of Phil
  Liddy, Richard M, PhD, Assoc Prof, Phil of Relig
  O'Brien, John F, STL, Prof, Syst Phil

JERSEY CITY STATE COLLEGE
Jersey City, New Jersey 07305 (M; st; coed; sem; III; 9967) BA major, Dept of Phil and Relig, 201-547-3431

Karnoutsos, George, EdD, Prof, Chm
Brown, James, MST, Asst Prof, Contemp Phil
Daley, Leo C, MA, Assoc Prof, Phil of Relig
Emmons, Donald, PhD, Asst Prof
Grosso, Michael, PhD, Instr, Metaph
Huang, Edward, PhD, Asst Prof, Orient Relig
McGowan, John, MA, Adj Prof
Sasso, James, PhD, Asst Prof, Exist, Great Philosophers
Schapker, Howard, PhD, Asst Prof, Comp Relig
Schievella, P S, PhD, Assoc Prof, Phil of Sci

KATHARINE GIBBS SCHOOL
Montclair, New Jersey 07042 (JRCB; p; wo; sem; I; 328) NR

LUTHER COLLEGE
Teaneck, New Jersey 07666 (--; p; coed; qr; I; 132) AA major, Dept of Relig and Phil, 201-836-3426

Moellering, H Armin, PhD, Phil of Relig
Daib, Walter, M Div

MERCER COUNTY COMMUNITY COLLEGE
Trenton, New Jersey 08690 (M; local; coed; sem; I; 5288) Courses with no degree specialization, Dept of Soc Sci, 609-396-9241 Ext 320, 328

Goldwasser, Saul, MA, Assoc Prof

MIDDLESEX COUNTY COLLEGE
Edison, New Jersey 08817 (M; local; coed; sem; I; 7134) --, Dept of Human, 201-548-6000 Ext 275

Smith, Ian, Asst Prof

MONMOUTH COLLEGE
West Long Branch, New Jersey 07764 (M; p; coed; sem; III; 5768) BA major, Dept of Psych and Phil, 201-222-6600

Ficca, S Charles, PhD, Prof, Chm
Darnoi, Dennis N K, PhD, Prof, Epistem, Metaph, Hist of Phil
Fell, Gilbert S, PhD, Assoc Prof, Amer Phil, Logic, Phil of Relig
Oakes, Guy B, PhD, Assoc Prof, Method, Phil of Natural and Soc Sci, Polit Phil
Short, Morris R, PhD, Prof, Aes, Anal Phil, Ethics

MONTCLAIR STATE COLLEGE
Upper Montclair, New Jersey 07043 (M; st; coed; sem; III; 13,472) BA major, Dept of Phil and Relig, 201-893-5144

Brantl, George, PhD, Prof, Chm, Anc Phil, Med Phil, Orient Phil
Aman, Kenneth, PhD, Asst Prof, Phil of Relig, Soc and Polit Phil
Benfield, David, PhD, Asst Prof, Logic, Ethics, Epistem

Bridges, Thomas, PhD, Asst Prof, Phil of Lang, Metaph, Phenomen, Exist
Lipman, Matthew, PhD, Prof, Aes, Amer Phil
Richardson, Thomas H, EdD, Dist Service Prof, Phil of Educ
Stanton, William L, MA, Asst Prof, Logic, Phil of Mind, Epistem

NEW BRUNSWICK THEOLOGICAL SEMINARY
New Brunswick, New Jersey 08901 (Theol; Ref; coed; sem; III; 65) Courses with no
degree specialization, Dept of Syst Theol, 201-247-5241

Fries, Paul, Doctorundus Theol, Asst Prof, Chm

NEWARK COLLEGE OF ENGINEERING
Newark, New Jersey 07102 (M; st and local; coed; sem; IV; 4755) Courses with no
degree specialization, Dept of Human, 201-645-5220

Crater, Warren H, MA, Prof, Ethics, Phil of Relig
Hodge, Elizabeth J, MA, Asst Prof, Ethics

NEWARK STATE COLLEGE
Union, New Jersey 07083 (M; st; coed; 4-1-4; III; 12,361) --, Dept of Phil, 201-
527-2311, 201-527-2312

Burtt, George T, EdD, Prof, Soc Phil, Phil of Educ
Catalano, Joseph S, PhD, Assoc Prof, Exist, Phil of Sci
Fethe, Charles B, PhD, Asst Prof
Pezzolo, Peter E, MPh, Asst Prof, Soc Phil, Polit Phil, 19th Cent Phil
Stern, H Willard, EdD, Assoc Prof, Ling Phil

NORTHEASTERN COLLEGIATE BIBLE INSTITUTE
Essex Fells, New Jersey 07021 (BI; Interdenom; coed; sem; II, 270) Courses with no
degree specialization, --, 201-226-1074

Bjornstad, James, PhD, Prof, Metaph
Olson, Gordon, ThM, Assoc Prof, Ethics

OCEAN COUNTY COLLEGE
Toms River, New Jersey 08753 (M; local; coed; sem; I; 3193) --, Dept of Human,
201-255-4000

Kavalec, Norman, MA, Assoc Prof

PASSAIC COUNTY COMMUNITY COLLEGE
Paterson, New Jersey 07505 (--; local; coed; sem; I; 372) NR

PRINCETON THEOLOGICAL SEMINARY
Princeton, New Jersey 08540 (M; U Preb; coed; sem; IV; 548) PhD major, Dept
of Theol, 609-921-8300

West, Charles C, PhD, Prof, Chm, Ethics
Allen, Diogenes, PhD, Assoc Prof, Contemp Phil
Dowey, Edward A, PhD, Prof
Kerr, Hugh T, PhD, Prof
Migliore, Daniel L, PhD, Assoc Prof

PRINCETON UNIVERSITY
  Princeton, New Jersey 08540 (M; p; coed; sem; IV; 5421) PhD major, Dept of Phil, 609-452-4289

  Vlastos, Gregory, PhD, Prof, Chm, Anc Phil
  Benacerraf, Paul, PhD, Prof, Phil of Math
  Davidson, Donald, PhD, Visit Lect-Prof, Phil of Lang
  Field, Hartry, PhD, Asst Prof, Metaph
  Glymour, Clark, PhD, Assoc Prof, Phil of Sci
  Grandy, Richard, PhD, Asst Prof, Phil of Math
  Harman, Gilbert, PhD, Prof, Theory of Knowl
  Hoy, David, PhD, Asst Prof, 19th and 20th Cent Continen Phil
  Jones, Barrington, BPhil, Asst Prof, Greek Phil
  Kaufmann, Walter, PhD, Prof, Hist of Ideas
  Kripke, Saul, BA, Visit Lect-Assoc Prof, Metaph
  Lewis, David, PhD, Prof, Metaph
  Morton, John Adam, PhD, Asst Prof, Logic
  Nagel, Thomas, PhD, Prof, Phil of Mind
  Pitcher, George, PhD, Prof, Vice-Chm, Phil of Mind
  Rorty, Richard, PhD, Prof, Hist of Phil
  Scanlon, Jr, Thomas M, PhD, Assoc Prof, Polit Phil
  Smith, James Ward, PhD, Prof, Polit Phil
  Sukale, Michael, PhD, Asst Prof, Contemp Euro Phil
  Szathmary, Arthur, PhD, Prof, Aes
  Wilson, Margaret, PhD, Assoc Prof, Mod Phil

  Hempel, Carl G, PhD, Prof Emer, Phil of Sci

RAMAPO COLLEGE
  Mahwah, New Jersey 07430 (--; st; coed; --; II; 1526) BA major, School of Amer Stud, School of Human Gov, School of Intercultural Stud, 201-825-2800

  Radest, Howard, PhD, Prof, Dir, Soc and Polit Phil
  Bond, Richard, PhD, Assoc Prof, Ethics
  Brady, Ronald, PhD, Asst Prof
  Cassidy, John Robert, PhD, Vice Pres, Logic, Ethics
  Murnion, William, PhD, Assoc Prof
  Weiss, Larry, PhD, Assoc Prof

RIDER COLLEGE
  Trenton, New Jersey 08602 (M; p; coed; 4-1-4; III; 5981) BA major, Dept of Phil, 609-896-0800 Ext 339

  Stroh, Guy, PhD, Prof, Chm, Amer Phil, Ethics
  Iorio, Dominick, PhD, Assoc Prof, Med Phil, Malebranche
  Sweeney, John, PhD, Asst Prof, 20th Cent British Phil
  Vail, Loy, PhD, Assoc Prof, Heidegger
  Walther, Sandra, PhD, Assoc Prof, Phil of Art

RUTGERS, THE STATE UNIVERSITY, CAMDEN CAMPUS
  Camden, New Jersey 08102 (Law; st; coed; sem; II; 2822) NR

RUTGERS, THE STATE UNIVERSITY, NEW BRUNSWICK CAMPUS
  New Brunswick, New Jersey 08903 (M; st; coed; sem; IV; 27,298) PhD major, Dept of Phil, 201-247-1766

  Smullyan, Arthur F, PhD, Prof, Chm, Dir of Grad Program, Logic, Kant, Epistem

Gilchrist, Shelley, BA, Teach Asst   Rosen, Jeffrey, AB, Teach Asst
McEnerney, David, BA, Teach Asst   Stool, Matthew, BA, Teach Asst

RUTGERS, THE STATE UNIVERSITY, NEW BRUNSWICK CAMPUS, DOUGLASS COLLEGE
New Brunswick, New Jersey 08903 (M; st; coed; sem; IV; --) BA major, Dept of
Phil, 201-247-1766 Ext 1352

Henson, Richard G, PhD, Prof, Chm, Ethics, Phil of Mind
Alston, William P, PhD, Prof, Phil of Mind, Phil of Lang, Phil of Psych
Bloustein, Edward J, Pres, PhD, Prof, Phil of Law
Frank, Karl D, BA, Lect, Epistem, Hist of Phil
Greenaway, Malcolm, BA, Lect, Ethics, Soc Phil
Magid, Carolyn, BA, Lect, Epistem, Soc Phil
Shehadi, Fadlou, PhD, Prof, Aes, Islamic Phil, Exist

Klein, Dianna, BA, Teach Asst   Silverman, Robert, BA, Teach Asst

RUTGERS, THE STATE UNIVERSITY, NEW BRUNSWICK CAMPUS, LIVINGSTON COLLEGE
New Brunswick, New Jersey 08903 (M; st; coed; sem; IV; --) BA major, Dept of Phil,
201-932-3109

Blumberg, Albert E, PhD, Prof, Chm, Phil of Logic, Soc Phil
Bolton, Martha Brandt, PhD, Asst Prof, Hist of Mod Phil, Epistem, Metaph
Dorsey, William R, BA, Asst Prof, Polit Phil, Logic
Flynn, John D, PhD, Asst Prof, Phil of Soc Sci, Phil of Mind
Gibson, Mary, BA, Asst Prof, Soc and Polit Phil
Klein, Peter D, PhD, Assoc Prof, Theory of Knowl
Maloney, Charles, MA, Asst Prof, Phil of Relig
Martin, Robert L, PhD, Assoc Prof, Phil of Lang, Logic
Murph, Dwight, BA, Polit Phil, Afr Phil, Ethics
Rorty, Amelie Oksenberg, PhD, Assoc Prof, Theory of Value, Phil Psych
Smith, Willie J, PhD, Assoc Prof, Phil of Relig, Black Tht in America

Tisdale, Noel, BA, Teach Asst

RUTGERS, THE STATE UNIVERSITY, NEW BRUNSWICK CAMPUS, RUTGERS COLLEGE
New Brunswick, New Jersey 08903 (M; st; coed; sem; IV; --) BA major, Dept of Phil,
201-247-1766 Ext 6638

Feldman, Seymour, PhD, Assoc Prof, Chm, Med Phil, Phil of Hist, Jewish Phil
Bolton, Robert, PhD, Asst Prof, Greek Phil, Phil of Lang
Kempner, Martin, PhD, Asst Prof, Ethics
Neyer, Joseph, PhD, Prof, Polit Phil, 19th Cent Phil, Ethics
Schick, Frederic, PhD, Prof, Induc Logic, Decision Theory, Anal Phil, Phil of Soc Sci
Stern, Laurent, PhD, Prof, Aes, Phenomen, 19th Cent Phil
Weber, Renée, PhD, Assoc Prof, Exist, Phil in Lit
Weingard, Robert, PhD, Asst Prof, Phil of Sci, Logic, Metaph

Nagle, Linda AB, Teach Asst

RUTGERS, THE STATE UNIVERSITY, UNIVERSITY COLLEGE
New Brunswick, New Jersey 08903 (M; st; coed; sem; IV; --) BA major, Dept of Phil,
201-247-1766

Wilshire, Bruce W, PhD, Assoc Prof, Chm, Hist of Phil, Phil of Mind
Belaief, Gail A, PhD, Assoc Prof, Metaph, Ethics
Bennett, James D, BA, Coadj Instr Part-time
Lam, Philip, MFA, Coadj Instr Part-time

Lenkowski, W Jon, MA, Instr, Greek Phil, German Idealism
Tillmann, George D, BS, Coadj Instr Part-time
Wadia, Pheroze S, PhD, Assoc Prof, Phil of Relig, Phil of Mind, Ethics

RUTGERS, THE STATE UNIVERSITY, NEWARK CAMPUS
Newark, New Jersey 07102 (M; st; coed; sem; III; 6749) BA major, Dept of Phil, 201-648-5178

Kivy, Peter, PhD, Assoc Prof, Chm, Aes
Berlinski, David, PhD, Asst Prof, Theory of Knowl, Phil of Mind
Biederman, Charles, MA, Prof, Contemp Phil, Metaph
Dalrymple, Stuart, MA, Instr, 19th Cent Phil
Lindermayer, Eric, MA, Instr, Exist
Rohr, Michael, BA, Instr, Anc Phil
Sweet, Albert, PhD, Assoc Prof, Logic, Phil of Sci

SAINT MICHAELS PASSIONIST MONASTERY
Union City, New Jersey 07087 (--; RC; men; sem; III; 30) NR

SAINT PETER'S COLLEGE
Jersey City, New Jersey 07306 (M; RC; coed; sem; II; 4561) BA major, --, 201-333-4400 Ext 314

Amberg, John V, MA, Adj Instr
Blake, Arthur J, JD, Adj Asst Prof
Cassidy, Laurence L, PhD, Asst Prof, Idealism
Caulfield, Joseph R, PhD, Assoc Prof
Cousineau, Robert H, DEd, Adj Asst Prof, Process Phil
Dates, Ralph O, MA, Prof, Mod Phil
Foley, John P, MA, Adj Instr
Grimaldi, Leonard N, MA, Adj Instr
Kelleher, Thomas B, MA, Asst Prof
Kiernan, William E, PhD, Asst Prof, Amer Natur
McGann, Thomas F, PhD, Assoc Prof, Ethics
McGlinchy, Edward H, PhL, Asst Prof, Amer Phil
McGraw, John B, PhL, Asst Prof, Metaph
O'Grady, Dennis J, MA, Adj Asst Prof
Papay, Joseph L, PhD, Prof, Med Phil
Rooney, Matthew A, PhD, Prof, Ling Anal
Strong, John V, MA, Adj Instr
Walsh, Joseph M, PhD, Asst Prof, Personalism
Welch, John J, MA, Asst Prof, Ethics

SALESIAN COLLEGE
North Haledon, New Jersey 07508 (--; RC; wo; sem; I; 63) --, Dept of Phil, 201-742-6200

Younge, Edith, MA, Prof

SETON HALL UNIVERSITY
South Orange, New Jersey 07079 (M; RC; coed; sem; IV; 9628) BA major, --, 201-762-9000

Smith, William A, PhD, Prof, Chm, Italian Idealism, Amer Phil
Anderson, John, PhD, Assoc Prof, Phil of Sci
Barral, Mary Rose, PhD, Prof, Phenomen, Exist
Caminiti, Francis, PhD, Assoc Prof, Polit Phil
Dalcourt, Gerard, PhD, Assoc Prof, Ethics

Helewa, John, MA, Adj Asst Prof
Herrera, Robert, MA, Asst Prof, Spanish Phil, Phil of Relig
Hsiang, Paul, STD, Assoc Prof, Orient Phil
Luisi, Miriam, MA, Adj Asst Prof, Amer Phil, Logic
Radtke, William, MA, Asst Prof, Logic
White, George, MA, Adj Assoc Prof, Phil of Relig

Pollock, Robert, PhD, Adj Prof Emer, Amer Phil

SOMERSET COUNTY COLLEGE
    Somerville, New Jersey 08876 (M; local; coed; sem; I; 1361) AA major, Dept of Arts, Human, and Soc Sci, 201-526-1200 Ext 295

    Fink, Rychard, PhD, Prof

STEVENS INSTITUTE OF TECHNOLOGY
    Hoboken, New Jersey 07030 (M; p; coed; sem; IV; 2340) NP

STOCKTON STATE COLLEGE
    Pomona, New Jersey 08244 (--; st; coed; --; II; 1035) BA major, Phil of Relig Program, 609-646-7575 Ext 251

    Lacy, Allen, PhD, Assoc Prof, Cord, Phil of Relig
    Manley, James, PhD, Asst Prof, Aes, Ethics
    Maultsby, Hubert, STB, Asst Prof, Anc Near East Tht
    Walsh, Joseph, MA, Asst Prof, Soc Phil

TOMBROCK COLLEGE
    West Paterson, New Jersey 07424 (--; RC; wo; sem; I; 436) Courses with no degree specialization, Dept of Phil, 201-345-2020

    de Vinck, José M, LLD, Prof, Med Phil-St Bonaventure, Christ Exist, Phil of Marriage

TRENTON STATE COLLEGE
    Trenton, New Jersey 08625 (M; st; coed; sem; III; 10,929) BA major, Dept of Phil and Relig, 609-771-2458

    Barnes, Gerald, PhD, Assoc Prof, Chm, Ethics
    Clouser, Roy, PhD, Assoc Prof, Metaph, Logic
    Cummings, Philip, PhD, Asst Prof, Hist of Phil, Epistem, Phil of Lang
    Gotthelf, Allan, MA, Asst Prof, Anc Phil
    Owen, Dennis, MA, Asst Prof, Exist
    Smith, Robert, DST, Asst Prof, Phil of Relig

    Hirsch, Elizabeth, PhD, Prof Emer, Exist, Polit Phil

UNION COLLEGE
    Cranford, New Jersey 07016 (M; p; coed; sem; I; 3624) Courses with no degree specialization, Dept of Hist, 201-276-2600 Ext 285

    Schmeltekopf, Donald, PhD, Asst Prof, Soc Phil, Ethics

UPSALA COLLEGE
    East Orange, New Jersey 07019 (M; Luth Ch; coed; sem; II; 2027) BA major, Dept of Phil and Relig, 201-266-7147, 201-266-7233

Stam, James H, PhD, Assoc Prof, Act Chm, Greek Phil, German Phil, Phil of Lang
Allen, Joseph, BD, Lect Part-time
Elias, William, MA, Lect Part-time
Pauly, Herta, PhD, Prof, Med Phil, Aes
Wallhausser, John, PhD, Assoc Prof, German Phil, Contemp Phil and Relig
Zucker, Wolfgang Max, PhD, Prof, Heidegger, Phil of Hist, Phil of Lang

WILLIAM PATERSON COLLEGE OF NEW JERSEY

Wayne, New Jersey 07470 (M; st; coed; sem; III; 5594) BA major, Dept of Phil, 201-881-2173

Juffras, Angelo, PhD, Assoc Prof, Chm, 18th Cent Phil, David Hume, Meaning
Choi, Sung, PhD, Assoc Prof, Hist of Phil
Friquegnon, Marie-Louise, PhD, Asst Prof, Phil of Relig, Ethics
Hailparn, Michael, EdD, Assoc Prof, Phil of Educ, Hist of Phil
Myatt, Rodney, EdD, Asst Prof, Ethics, Phil of Ed
Noah, Aris, PhD, Instr, Phil of Logic, Anc Greek Phil
Siegel, Kenneth, MA, Instr, Metaph, Orient Phil
Strahl, Paula, MA, Asst Prof, Polit Phil, Exist
Teghrarian, Souren, PhD, Asst Prof, Phil of Lang, Logic

WESTMINSTER CHOIR COLLEGE

Princeton, New Jersey 08540 (M; p; coed; sem; III; 411) NR

NEW MEXICO

COLLEGE OF SANTA FE

Santa Fe, New Mexico 87501 (N; RC; coed; sem; II; 1264) BA minor, Dept of Human, 505-982-6101

Kleitz, Philip Rex, PhD, Assoc Prof, Chm
Dybowski, Brian, PhD, Asst Prof, Ethics
Harriman, Charles J, PhD, Asst Prof, Phil of Lang
McEvilly, Wayne, PhD, Asst Prof, Metaph

EASTERN NEW MEXICO UNIVERSITY

Portales, New Mexico 88130 (N; st; coed; 4-1-4; III; 4298) Courses with no degree specialization, Dept of Relig, 505-562-2121

Eckstein, Stephen, PhD, Prof
Eggleton, John, PhD, Assoc Prof
McCoy, Glenn, BD, Asst Prof
McMillion, Phil, STB, Asst Prof
Woodward, Al, ThD, Asst Prof

EASTERN NEW MEXICO UNIVERSITY, ROSWELL CAMPUS

Roswell, New Mexico 88201 (N; st; coed; sem; I; 992) NR

NEW MEXICO HIGHLANDS UNIVERSITY
    Las Vegas, New Mexico 87701 (N; st; coed; qr; III; 2669) MA minor, Dept of Phil,
    505-425-7511 Ext 272

    Wilson, Helen G, PhD, Assoc Prof, Chm, Mod Phil, Phil of Sci
    Conkling, Mark L, MA, Asst Prof, Exist
    García, Jesús A, MA, Instr, German Idealism
    Triplett, Janet C, PhD, Asst Prof, Amer Phil

NEW MEXICO INSTITUTE OF MINING AND TECHNOLOGY
    Socorro, New Mexico 87801 (N; st; coed; sem; IV; 1004) NR

NEW MEXICO JUNIOR COLLEGE
    Hobbs, New Mexico 88240 (N; local; coed; sem; I; 1079) Courses with no degree
    specialization, Div of Arts, Business and Human, 505-392-6526

    Hatch, Orin Walker, MA, Prof

NEW MEXICO MILITARY INSTITUTE
    Roswell, New Mexico, 88201 (N; st; men; sem; I; 249) Courses with no degree
    specialization, Dept of Eng, 505-622-6250 Ext 27

    Granzow, James R, PhD, Asst Prof

NEW MEXICO STATE UNIVERSITY
    Las Cruces, New Mexico 88003 (N; st; coed; sem; IV; 9485) BA major, Dept of Gov
    and Phil, 505-646-4935

    Paul, Wilford N, PhD, Assoc Prof, Phil of Relig
    Korsak, Ronald, PhD, Asst Prof, Logic
    Keaton, Alvin, PhD, Assoc Prof, Anal Phil

NEW MEXICO STATE UNIVERSITY, AT ALAMOGORDO
    Alamogordo, New Mexico 88310 (N; st; coed; sem; I; 741) Courses with no degree
    specialization, --, 505-437-6860

    Blair, Alexander, BD

NEW MEXICO STATE UNIVERSITY, AT CARLSBAD
    Carlsbad, New Mexico 88220 (N; st; coed; sem; I; 405) NP

NEW MEXICO STATE UNIVERSITY, AT GRANTS
    Grants, New Mexico 87020 (N; st; coed; sem; I; 174) NP

NEW MEXICO STATE UNIVERSITY, AT SAN JUAN
    Farmington, New Mexico 87401 (N; st; coed; sem; I; 549) NR

SAINT JOHN'S COLLEGE OF SANTA FE
    Santa Fe, New Mexico 87501 (N; p; coed; sem; III; 260) MA major, --, 505-982-3691

UNIVERSITY OF ALBUQUERQUE
  Albuquerque, New Mexico 87120 (N; RC; coed; sem; II; 2521) Courses with no degree
  specialization, --, 505-243-9461

  Desaulniers, Lawrence, MA, Assoc Prof
  Dorsel, Thomas N, MS, Part-time
  Gibson, Joan, MA, Part-time
  Piché, Donald R, MA, Part-time
  Schneider, Paul Marcian, MA, Asst Prof

UNIVERSITY OF NEW MEXICO
  Albuquerque, New Mexico 87106 (N; st; coed; sem; IV; 20,137) PhD major, Dept of
  Phil, 505-277-2405

  Schmidt, Paul F, PhD, Prof, Chm, Exist, Phil of Relig
  Alexander, Hubert G, PhD, Prof, Aes, Phil of Lang
  Casalis, Matthieu, PhD, Asst Prof, Phil of Relig
  Eilstein, Helena, PhD, Assoc Prof, Phil of Sci
  Evans, Melborne G, PhD, Prof, Logic, Phil of Sci
  Goodman, Russell B, PhD, Asst Prof, Phil of Lang, Epistem
  Lee, Donald C, PhD, Asst Prof, Soc and Polit Phil
  McDermott, Charlene, PhD, Assoc Prof, Logic, Med Phil, East Phil
  O'Neil, Brian E, PhD, Asst Prof, Epistem, Hist of Phil
  Schueler, G Frederic, PhD, Asst Prof, Ethics
  Stern, Carl, MA, Asst Prof, Kant, 19th Cent Phil
  Tuttle, Howard N, PhD, Assoc Prof, Phenomen, Phil of Hist

  Bahm, Archie, PhD, Prof Emer, Asian Phil, Metaph
  Knode, Jay Carroll, PhD, Prof Emer, Dean of Arts and Sci College

  Chung, Bong, MA, Grad Asst   Grieg, James A, MA, Teach Asst
  Cooperstein, Paul, MA, Teach Asst   Hostetler, Barbara, BA, Teach Asst
  DeMay, William, BA, Grad Asst   Smith, William G, MA, Grad Asst

UNIVERSITY OF NEW MEXICO, GALLUP BRANCH
  Gallup, New Mexico 87301 (N; st; coed; sem; I; 422) NR

WESTERN NEW MEXICO UNIVERSITY
  Silver City, New Mexico 88061 (N; st; coed; sem; III; 1505) NP

NEW YORK

ACADEMY OF AERONAUTICS
  Flushing, New York 11371 (M; p; coed; tri; I; 1304) NR

ADELPHI UNIVERSITY
  Garden City, New York 11530 (M; p; coed; sem; IV; 7882) BA major, Dept of Phil,
  516-294-8700 Ext 7258, 7259

  Allen, Harold J, PhD, Prof, Chm, Hist of Phil

Curello, Anthony, PhD, Instr Part-time, Phil Psych
DeLange, David L, PhD, Asst Prof, Epistem, Polit Phil
Helmers, Frederick J, MA, Instr Part-time, Human Phil
Jamali, Naseem Z, MA, Instr Part-time, Logic, Phil of Sci
Knight, Thomas S, PhD, Prof, Phenomen, Exist
Olsen, Richard E, PhD, Asst Prof, Logic, Phil of Sci
Pashman, Susan, MA, Instr Part-time, Ethics
Pasotti, Robert N, PhD, Assoc Prof, Aes, Phil of Hist
Valenti, Frederick, BA, Instr Part-time, Phil of Lit

ADIRONDACK COMMUNITY COLLEGE, STATE UNIVERSITY
Glens Falls, New York 12801 (M; st and local; coed; sem; I; 1385) BA minor, --, 518-793-4491

Loper, Joseph N, PhD, Prof, Soc Phil

AGRICULTURAL AND TECHNICAL COLLEGE AT ALFRED, STATE UNIVERSITY OF NEW YORK
Alfred, New York 14802 (M; st; coed; qr; I; 3889) AA major, Dept of Eng and Human, 607-871-6301

Bouck, Warren L, Doct, Prof

AGRICULTURAL AND TECHNICAL COLLEGE AT CANTON, STATE UNIVERSITY OF NEW YORK
Canton, New York 13617 (M; st; coed; sem; I; 2282) NR

AGRICULTURAL AND TECHNICAL COLLEGE AT COBLESKILL, STATE UNIVERSITY OF NEW YORK
Cobleskill, New York 12043 (M; st; coed; sem; I; 2164) Courses with no degree specialization, --, 518-234-5011

AGRICULTURAL AND TECHNICAL COLLEGE AT DELHI, STATE UNIVERSITY OF NEW YORK
Delhi, New York 13753 (M; st; coed; sem; I; 2443) Courses with no degree specialization, Dept of Human, 607-746-4375

Ruggiero, Vincent Ryan, MA, Prof, Chm, Ethics
Smith, Camilla, MA, Asst Prof

AGRICULTURAL AND TECHNICAL COLLEGE AT FARMINGDALE, STATE UNIVERSITY OF NEW YORK
Farmingdale, New York 11735 (M; st; coed; sem; I; 11,815) Courses with no degree specialization, Dept of Eng, 516-420-2000

Deland, Peter, MA, Prof, Metaph, Epistem
Friel, James, MA, Asst Prof, Hist of Phil, Polit Phil, Ethics, Phil of Relig, Greek Phil, Phil of Sci
Phelan, Gerard, MA, Asst Prof, Phil of Relig, Ethics
De Falco, Joseph, MA, Prof, Amer Phil, Euro Phil

AGRICULTURAL AND TECHNICAL COLLEGE AT MORRISVILLE, STATE UNIVERSITY OF NEW YORK
Morrisville, New York 13408 (M; st; coed; sem; I; 2760) Courses with no degree specialization, Depts of Soc Sci, and Eng, 315-684-7081

Huntley, Taze, MA, Prof, Chm, Comp Polit Phil
Nelson, Paul, MA, Assoc Prof

ALBANY COLLEGE OF PHARMACY
Albany, New York 12208 (Phar; p; coed; sem; II; 480) NP

ALBANY LAW SCHOOL
    Albany, New York 12208 (Law; p; coed; sem; III; 609) NP

ALBANY MEDICAL COLLEGE
    Albany, New York 12208 (Med; p; coed; --; IV; 349) NP

ALFRED UNIVERSITY
    Alfred, New York 14802 (M; p; coed; 4-1-4; IV; 2170) BA major, Div of Human Stud,
    607-871-2218

    Cairns, John B, BA, Instr, Logic
    Gilmour, John C, PhD, Assoc Prof, Metaph
    Sibley, Myron K, STM, Prof

AMERICAN ACADEMY OF DRAMATIC ARTS
    New York, New York 10016 (--; p; coed; sem; I; 267) NR

AUBURN COMMUNITY COLLEGE, STATE UNIVERSITY OF NEW YORK
    Auburn, New York 13021 (M; st and local; coed; sem; I; 3002) Courses with no degree
    specialization, Dept of Soc Sci, 315-253-9107

    Richards, David H, MA, Instr

BANK STREET COLLEGE OF EDUCATION
    New York, New York 10027 (M; p; coed; sem; III; 1036) NP

BARD COLLEGE
    Annandale-on-Hudson, New York 12504 (M; p; coed; sem; II; 772) BA major, --, 914-
    758-6072

    Griffith, William James, MA, Asst Prof
    Lensing, William E, PhD

BARNARD COLLEGE, COLUMBIA UNIVERSITY
    New York, New York 10027 (M; p; wo; sem; II; 1909) NR

BE'ER SHMUEL TALMUDICAL ACADEMY
    Brooklyn, New York 11219 (--; Jewish; men; sem; III; 190) NR

BENNETT COLLEGE
    Millbrook, New York 12545 (M; p; wo; 4-1-4; I; 666) AA major, Dept of Behavior and
    Soc Sci, 914-677-3441

    Moody, F Kennen, MA, Instr, Ethics

BERNARD BARUCH COLLEGE, CITY UNIVERSITY OF NEW YORK
    New York, New York 10010 (M; local; coed; sem; IV; 12,251) BA major, Dept of Phil,
    212-673-8169

    McDermott, Robert, PhD, Assoc Prof, Chm, Indian Phil
    Green, Murray, PhD, Assoc Prof, Hegel
    Kahane, Howard, PhD, Assoc Prof, Phil of Sci, Logic
    Lackey, Douglas, Asst Prof, Bertrand Russell

234

Morewedge, Parvis, Asst Prof, Islamic Phil
Munitz, Milton, PhD, Dist Univ Prof, Cosmology
Wyschogrod, Michael, PhD, Prof, Phil of Relig, Exist

BETH JACOB HEBREW TEACHERS COLLEGE
   New York, New York 10002 (--; Jewish; wo; sem; II; 244) NR

BOBOVER YESH BNEI ZION
   Brooklyn, New York 11219 (--; Jewish; men; tri; III; 273) NR

BOROUGH OF MANHATTAN COMMUNITY COLLEGE, CITY UNIVERSITY OF NEW YORK
   New York, New York 10019 (M; st and local; coed; sem; I; 9516) Courses with no degree
   specialization, Dept of Soc Sci, 212-262-5460

   Kasachkoff, Tziporad, PhD, Asst Prof, Ethics

BRIARCLIFF COLLEGE
   Briarcliff Manor, New York 10510 (M; p; wo; 4-1-4; II; 397) BA joint or combined
   major, Dept of Hist and Phil, 914-941-6400

   Boyer, Lynn, MA, Asst Prof
   Munitz, Lenore B, PhD, Assoc Prof, Ethics

BRONX COMMUNITY COLLEGE, CITY UNIVERSITY OF NEW YORK
   Bronx, New York 10468 (M; st and local; coed; sem; I; 11,756) --, Dept of Soc Sci,
   212-960-8808

   Trusis, Aivars, MA

BROOKLYN COLLEGE, CITY UNIVERSITY OF NEW YORK
   Brooklyn, New York 11210 (M; local; coed; sem; IV; 29,451) MA major, Dept of Phil,
   212-780-5311

   Sprague, Elmer, PhD, Prof, Act Chm
   Brown, Malcolm, PhD, Assoc Prof
   Caffentzis, C George, BA, Instr
   Cannavo, Salvator, PhD, Assoc Prof
   Edwards, Paul, PhD, Prof
   Ezorsky, Gertrude, PhD, Prof
   Funk, Nanette, BA, Lect
   Jones, Jere, PhD, Asst Prof
   Kent, Edward, PhD, Asst Prof
   Korn, Frederick, PhD, Instr
   Koslow, Arnold, PhD, Prof
   Lean, Martin, PhD, Prof
   Levy, Donald, BA, Lect
   Massie, David, PhD, Asst Prof
   Michael, Emily, PhD, Asst Prof
   Portnoy, Julius, PhD, Prof
   Rosenthal, Abigail, PhD, Asst Prof
   Schwartz, Robert, PhD, Asst Prof
   Sprague, Elmer, PhD, Prof
   Smithurst, Michael, BPhil, Asst Prof
   Steinberg, Eric, BA, Instr
   Taylor, Paul, PhD, Prof
   Wiseman, Mary, Instr

   Altman, Ira, BA, Adj Lect

235

Brody, Alan, BA, Adj Lect
Cohen, Eli, BA, Adj Lect
Daher, Adel, PhD, Adj Lect
Feinstein, Sherryl, BA, Adj Lect
Fontana, Thomas, MA, Adj Lect
Jefka, Myron, BA, Adj Lect
Matics, Marion, PhD, Adj Lect
Morritt, Ronald, MA, Adj Lect
Obstfeld, Kaila, BA, Adj Lect
Reich, Stephen, BA, Adj Lect
Sfekas, Stanely, BA, Adj Lect

Cerf, Walter, Prof Emer
Kretschmann, Phillip, Prof Emer
Van Rensselaer, Wilson H, Prof Emer

BROOKLYN LAW SCHOOL
Brooklyn, New York 11201 (Law; p; coed; sem; III; 1289) NP

BROOME COMMUNITY COLLEGE, STATE UNIVERSITY OF NEW YORK
Binghamton, New York 13902 (M; st and local; coed; qr; I; 4444) AA major, Dept of
Human, 607-772-5092

Chambers, Paul A, MEd, Chm
Boyden, James E, MA, Asst Prof
Cappellucci, Gabriel, MA, Assoc Prof,
Croll, Charles, MS, Asst Prof
Korducavich, Stephen A, MS, Prof

CANISIUS COLLEGE
Buffalo, New York 14208 (M; p; coed; sem; III; 4162) BA major, Dept of Phil, 716-
883-7000 Ext 760

Lavere, George J, PhD, Assoc Prof, Chm, Ethics, Polit Phil, Med Phil
Braun, Francis R, PhD, Lect, Logic
Clark, Joseph T, PhD, Prof, Logic, Phil of Sci
Harris, Benedict O, MA, Asst Prof, Exist
Joly, Ralph P, PhD, Assoc Prof, Metaph, Marxism
Juhasz, Ladislaus F, PhD, Asst Prof, Phil of Man, St Augustine
Kelly, John E, PhD, Assoc Prof, Metaph, Hegel
Murray, Clayton J, PhD, Prof, Metaph, Anc Phil
Nelson, Herbert J, PhD, Asst Prof, Metaph, Phil of Relig
Piggush, James R, MA, Asst Prof, Phil of Man, Soc Phil
Roth, Joseph S, PhD, Assoc Prof, Neo-Freudian Soc Phil
Stevens, Edward V, PhD, Assoc Prof, Phil of Relig, East Phil
Vodraska, Stanley L, PhD, Assoc Prof, Aes, Phil of Sci

CATHEDRAL COLLEGE OF THE IMMACULATE CONCEPTION
Douglaston, New York 11362 (M; RC; men; sem; II; 311) BA major, Dept of Phil, 212-
631-4600

Dietz, Conrad R, PhD, Chm, Epistem, Metaph
Casey, Donald P, PhD, Asst Prof, Ethics, Mod Phil
Grace, James P, PhD, Asst Prof, Anc Phil, Med Phil
Lauder, Robert E, PhD, Asst Prof, Phil of Man, Continen Phil
Smith, Robert S, MA, Lect, Anc Phil, Med Phil

CAZENOVIA COLLEGE
Cazenovia, New York 13035 (M; p; wo; --; I; 477) Courses with no degree specialization, Dept of Lang and Lit, 315-655-3466 Ext 229

Penfield, Katharine S, MA, Lect, Phil of Relig

CEN YESH TOM TMIMIM LUBVZ
Brooklyn, New York 11230 (--; Jewish; men; sem; IV; 321) NR

CITY COLLEGE, CITY UNIVERSITY OF NEW YORK
New York, New York 10031 (M; local; coed; sem; III; 20,459) MA major, Dept of Phil, 212-621-2291

Saunders, Jason Lewis, PhD, Prof, Chm, Hist of Phil
Bayley, James E, PhD, Asst Prof, Hist of Phil
Cohen, Maurice, PhD, Asst Prof, Hist of Phil
Collins, Arthur W, PhD, Prof, Epistem
Elias, Julius, PhD, Prof, Aes
Evans, Charles, PhD, Asst Prof, Epistem
Grewe, Rudolf, PhD, Asst Prof, Logic
Hutcheon, Willard, MA, Lect, Hist of Phil
Irani, K D, LLB, Prof, Phil of Sci
Kantor, Jay, MA, Lect Part-time
Karp, Barrie, BA, Lect Part-time
Kornfeld, Theodore, BS, Adj Lect
Levin, Michael, PhD, Asst Prof, Logic
Lipman, Matthew, PhD, Adj Assoc Prof, Aes
Magid, Henry M, PhD, Prof, Polit Phil
Marti, Oscar, BA, Lect Part-time
Ratowsky, Henry, BA, Lect Part-time
Stern, Lawrence I, PhD, Asst Prof, Ethics, Soc Phil
Tamny, Martin, MA, Lect, Phil of Sci
Thayer, H S, PhD, Prof, Hist of Phil
Weissman, David, PhD, Assoc Prof, Contemp Phil

Krikorian, Yervant, PhD, Prof Emer
Wiener, Philip P, PhD, Prof Emer

CLARKSON COLLEGE OF TECHNOLOGY
Potsdam, New York 13676 (M; p; coed; sem; IV; 2608) Courses with no degree specialization, Dept of Human, 714-268-6485

Porter, Fred Steven, MA, Instr, Metaph, Phil of Sci, Phil of Mind

CLINTON COMMUNITY COLLEGE, STATE UNIVERSITY OF NEW YORK
Plattsburgh, New York 12901 (--; st and local; coed; sem; I; 765) Courses with no degree specialization, --, 518-561-6650

COLGATE UNIVERSITY
Hamilton, New York 13346 (M; p; coed; --; III; 2304) MA major, Dept of Phil and Relig, 315-824-1000 Ext 324

Smith, Robert V, PhD, Prof, Chm, Phil of Relig
Agonito, Rosemary, MA, Lect Part-time
Arentz, Donald, MA, Lect Part-time
Aronovitch, Hilliard, MA, Instr, Marxist Tht
Balmuth, Jerome, MA, Prof, Lang Anal
Berry, Donald L, PhD, Prof

Blum, Roland P, PhD, Assoc Prof, French Phil
Breslauer, Daniel, MHL, Instr, Jewish Phil
Brown, Coleman, BD, Instr
Carter, John, PhD, Asst Prof, Asian Phil
Gagnon, Laurence, MA, Instr, Logic, Semantics, Med Phil
Hammitt, Virginia, PhD, Lect Part-time
Hartshorne, M Holmes, ThD, Prof, Exist
Martin, Guy V, MA, Instr Part-time
Morgan, Kenneth, STB, Prof, Asian Phil
Morris, John S, PhD, Prof, British Empir
Roberts, Kline, BD, Lect Part-time
Spitzer, Adele, PhD, Assoc Prof, Greek Phil, Prag
Terrell, Huntington, PhD, Prof, Ethics
Waldman, Elliott, MHL, Lect Part-time

Brautigam, Herman A, PhD, Prof Emer

COLGATE-BEXLEY-CROZER DIVINITY SCHOOLS
   Rochester, New York 14620 (Theol; p; coed; sem; III; 206) Courses with no degree
   specialization, --, 716-271-1320

   Belk, Leotis S, PhD, Assoc Prof, Chm, Phil and Theol Ethics
   Cauthen, Kenneth, PhD, Prof, Phil of Sci
   Taylor, Richard, PhD, Prof Part-time, Epistem

COLLEGE AT BROCKPORT, STATE UNIVERSITY OF NEW YORK
   Brockport, New York 14420 (M; st; coed; sem; III; 10,023) MA major, Dept of Phil,
   716-395-2420

   Stack, George J, PhD, Prof, Chm, Hist of Phil, Exist Phenomen
   Catan, John, PhD, Assoc Prof, Anc Phil, Med Phil
   Clements, Tad, PhD, Prof, Phil of Sci
   Dicker, Georges, PhD, Assoc Prof, Epistem, Amer Phil
   Donaghy, Kevin, PhD, Asst Prof, Ethics
   Gilbert, Joseph, PhD, Assoc Prof, Contemp Phil
   Glickman, Jack, PhD, Asst Prof, Aes, Phil of Lang
   Greenstein, Harold, PhD, Assoc Prof, Phil of Hist, Phil of Soc Sci
   Hartnack, Justus, D Phil, Dist Univ Prof, Anal Phil, Hist of Phil
   Kiefer, Howard, EdD, Dean, Hist of Phil, Phil of Educ
   Mathur, Dinesh, PhD, Prof, Amer Phil, Indian Phil
   McGuire, Richard, MA, Instr, Contemp Phil
   Morrison, Paul, PhD, Prof, Phil of Sci, Logic

   Callen, Donald, BA, Grad Asst   Shaikun, Glenn, BA, Grad Asst

COLLEGE AT BUFFALO, STATE UNIVERSITY OF NEW YORK
   Buffalo, New York 14222 (M; st; coed; sem; III; 10,895) BA major, Dept of Phil,
   716-862-5136

   Minahan, John P, PhD, Assoc Prof, Chm, Metaph
   Balowitz, Victor H, PhD, Assoc Prof, Phil Logic
   Carbonara, John C, PhD, Assoc Prof, Anc Phil
   Grunebaum, James O, PhD, Asst Prof, Polit Phil
   Hole, George T, PhD, Asst Prof, Ethics
   La Croix, Richard R, PhD, Asst Prof, Med Phil
   Paterson, Antoinette M, PhD, Prof, Hist of Phil
   Pollock, Lansing, PhD, Asst Prof, Ethics
   Roblin, Ronald E, PhD, Assoc Prof, Phenomen, Exist
   Vannoy, Russell C, PhD, Asst Prof, Aes

COLLEGE AT CORTLAND, STATE UNIVERSITY OF NEW YORK
Cortland, New York 13045 (M; st; coed; sem; III; 5565) BA major, Dept of Phil, 607-753-2727

Ashley, Lawrence, PhD, Asst Prof, Chm, Aes, Phil of Mind
Barr, William, PhD, Assoc Prof, Logic, Phil of Sci, Phil of Soc Sci
Bennett, Philip, PhD, Asst Prof, Phil of Mind, Phil of Relig
Mayeroff, Milton, PhD, Prof, Exist, Phenomen, Phil of Relig
Schwager, Robert L, PhD, Assoc Prof, Ethics, Soc Phil, Phil of Law

COLLEGE AT FREDONIA, STATE UNIVERSITY OF NEW YORK
Fredonia, New York 14063 (M; st; coed; sem; III; 5129) MA minor, Dept of Phil, 716-673-3111

Schagrin, Morton L, PhD, Assoc Prof, Chm, Phil of Sci
Bryant, David C, AM, Instr, Phil of Mind, Phil of Relig
Kohl, Marvin, PhD, Assoc Prof, Ethics, Phil of Lang
Lucey, Kenneth, PhD, Asst Prof, Epistem, Phil of Mind
MacDonald, Lauchlin D, PhD, Prof, Logic, Phil of Sci
Machan, Tibor R, PhD, Asst Prof, Soc and Polit Phil
Palmer, R David, PhD, Asst Prof, Metaph, Hist of Phil
Remick, Oscar E, PhD, Prof, Phil of Relig

COLLEGE AT GENESEO, STATE UNIVERSITY OF NEW YORK
Geneseo, New York 14454 (M; st; coed; sem; III; 5905) BA major, Dept of Phil, 716-245-5231

Wilbur, James B, PhD, Prof, Chm, Hist of Phil
Blackman, Larry, MA, Instr, Phil of Lang
Cox, Gary, PhD, Assoc Prof, Phil of Educ
Edgar, William, PhD, Asst Prof, Phil of Mind
Laszlo, Ervin, PhD, Prof, Systems Phil
Schiff, Daniel, PhD, Asst Prof, Metaph
Umphrey, Stewart, PhD, Asst Prof, Anc Phil

COLLEGE AT HERKMER-ROME-UTICA, STATE UNIVERSITY OF NEW YORK
Utica, New York 13502 (--; st; coed; sem; III; 576) NR

COLLEGE AT NEW PALTZ, STATE UNIVERSITY OF NEW YORK
New Paltz, New York 12561 (M; st; coed; sem; III; 7880) BA major, Dept of Phil, 914-257-2696

Blankenship, J David, PhD, Asst Prof
Chakravarty, Amiya, PhD, Univ Prof
Charlson, Price, PhD, Prof
Gould, Carol, MPhil, Asst Prof
Holmes, Larry, PhD, Prof
Kirk, John, PhD, Prof
Kuykendall, Eleanor, PhD, Assoc Prof
Newburger, Stanley, PhD, Prof

COLLEGE AT OLD WESTBURY, STATE UNIVERSITY OF NEW YORK
Old Westbury, New York 11568 (--; st; coed; sem; II; 571) Courses with no degree specialization, Comp Hist, Ideas and Cultures Program

Adams, Anne Donchin, PhD, Assoc Prof, Epistem

COLLEGE AT ONEONTA, STATE UNIVERSITY OF NEW YORK
Oneonta, New York 13820 (M; st; coed; sem; III; 5893) BA major, Dept of Phil, 607-431-3500

Collins, Paul W, PhD, Prof, Chm, Phil of Sci
Malhotra, Ashok, PhD, Assoc Prof, Orient Phil
Roda, Anthony, PhD, Assoc Prof, Soc and Polit Phil
Shandalow, Neil, MA, Asst Prof, Phil of Soc Sci, Amer Phil

COLLEGE AT OSWEGO, STATE UNIVERSITY OF NEW YORK
Oswego, New York 13126 (M; st; coed; sem; III; 8528) BA major, Dept of Phil, 315-341-2500

Ruf, Henry L, PhD, Assoc Prof, Chm, Metaph
Byrne, Rodney P, PhD, Asst Prof, Phil of Soc Sci
Carnes, Robert D, PhD, Assoc Prof, Phil of Lang
Eaker, Charles E, PhD, Asst Prof, Phil of Educ
Echelbarger, Charles G, PhD, Asst Prof, Phil of Mind
Eisenhower, Michael C, MA, Asst Prof, Phil of Marxism
Friedman, Kenneth S, PhD, Asst Prof, Phil of Sci
Harbert, David L, MA, Asst Prof, Exist
Pierce, Christine M, PhD, Asst Prof, Phil of Law
Steinkraus, Warren E, PhD, Prof, Hist of Phil

COLLEGE AT PLATTSBURGH, STATE UNIVERSITY OF NEW YORK
Plattsburgh, New York 12901 (M; st; coed; sem; III; 5754) BA major, Dept of Phil, 518-564-2180

Yardan, John L, PhD, Prof, Chm, Phil of Relig, Ethics, Orient Phil
Goldthwait, John T, PhD, Prof, Aes, Kant, Hist of Phil
Krecz, Charles, BA, Instr, Metaph, Ethics
Mowry, David, PhD, Instr, Phil of Mind, Anal Phil
Newgarden, Arthur, PhD, Assoc Prof, Phenomen, Aes, Soc and Polit Phil
Rottschaefer, William, PhD, Asst Prof, Epistem, Phil of Sci, Metaph

COLLEGE AT POTSDAM, STATE UNIVERSITY OF NEW YORK
Potsdam, New York 13676 (M; st; coed; 4-1-4; III; 4844) BA major, Dept of Phil, 315-268-2849

Brouwer, Fred, PhD, Prof, Chm, Ethics, Polit Phil
Bertman, Martin, PhD, Asst Prof, Metaph
Digiovanna, Joseph, PhD, Asst Prof, Contemp British Phil
Tartaglia, Philip, PhD, Assoc Prof, Logic
Thompson, William, PhD, Asst Prof, Phil of Relig

COLLEGE AT PURCHASE, STATE UNIVERSITY OF NEW YORK
Purchase, New York 10577 (--; st; coed; --; II; 778) BA major, Phil Board of Study, 914-253-5045 Ext 45

Neville, Robert, PhD, Assoc Prof, Cord, Amer Phil, Phil of Relig, Metaph, Ethics, Hist of Phil
Cavell, Marcia, PhD, Asst Prof, Phil of Psych, Phil of Lit, Phil of Art, Phil of Relig
Gettner, Alan, PhD, Asst Prof, Ethics, Phil of Sci, Epistem
Grontkowski, Christine, PhD, Visit Asst Prof, Phil of Sci, Phenomen, 19th Cent Phil

COLLEGE FOR HUMAN SERVICES
New York, New York 10014 (--; p; coed; --; I; 168) NR

THE COLLEGE OF INSURANCE
   New York, New York 10038 (M; p; coed; tri; III; 1572) Courses with no degree
   specialization, Div of Libr Arts, 212-962-4111 Ext 225

   Bilik, Laurie, MA, Adj Asst Prof
   Helmers, Fred, MA, Adj Asst Prof

COLLEGE OF MOUNT SAINT VINCENT
   Riverdale, New York 10471 (M; p; cord; sem; II; 1042) BA major, Dept of Phil, 212-
   549-8000

   Hunt, Marion, PhD, Assoc Prof, Chm
   Brady, Mary L, PhD, Prof
   Brennan, Mary Alethea, PhD, Assoc Prof

COLLEGE OF NEW ROCHELLE
   New Rochelle, New York 10801 (M; p; wo; sem; III; 965) NR

COLLEGE OF SAINT ROSE
   Albany, New York 12203 (M; p; coed; 4-1-4; III; 1512) NR

THE COLLEGE OF WHITE PLAINS
   White Plains, New York 10603 (M; p; coed; 4-1-4; II; 479) Courses with no degree
   specialization, Dept of Phil, 914-949-9494

   Vallone, Gerard, MA, Asst Prof, Chm, Ethics, Phil of Man

COLUMBIA UNIVERSITY
   New York, New York 10027 (M; p; coed; sem; IV; 15,315) PhD major, Dept of Phil,
   212-280-3196

   Levi, Isaac, PhD, Prof, Chm, Induc Logic, Epistem, Phil of the Soc Sci
   Berofsky, Bernard, PhD, Assoc Prof, Phil of Mind, Metaph
   Cauman, Leigh S, PhD, Lect, Logic
   Cumming, Robert D, PhD, Prof, Hist of Polit Theory, Exist, Phenomen
   Danto, Arthur C, PhD, Prof, Phil of Mind, Phil of Art, Anal Phil
   Frankel, Charles, PhD, Prof, Ethics, Soc Phil, Amer Phil
   Geuss, Raymond, PhD, Asst Prof, Continen Phil
   Henrich, Dieter, PhD, Visit Prof, German Phil, 19th Cent Phil
   Higginbotham, James, PhD, Asst Prof, Phil of Lang
   Hyman, Arthur, PhD, Visit Prof, Jewish Phil, Islamic Phil
   Kuhns, Richard F, PhD, Prof, Aes
   Malino, Jonathan, BA, Instr, Phil of Lang
   Morgenbesser, Sidney, PhD, Prof, Phil of Sci, Phil of the Soc Sci, Moral Phil,
      Polit Phil
   Parsons, Charles D, PhD, Prof, Logic, Kant
   Sidorsky, David, PhD, Prof, Moral Phil, Polit Phil, Amer Phil
   Stein, Howard, PhD, Prof, Phil of Sci
   Steiner, Mark, PhD, Asst Prof, Logic
   Teitelman, Michael, PhD, Asst Prof, Moral Phil, Polit Phil
   Walsh, James J, PhD, Prof, Med Phil

   Friess, Horace L, Prof Emer
   Gutmann, James, Prof Emer
   Kristeller, Paul O, Prof Emer, Spec Lect
   Nagel, Ernest, Univ Prof Emer, Spec Lect
   Randall, John H, Prof Emer
   Schneider, Herbert W, Prof Emer

Ackermann, David, Preceptor
Caplan, Arthur, Preceptor
Ebisch, Glen, Preceptor
Fehler, J Richard, Preceptor
Greene, Richard, Preceptor
Hagius, Hugh, Preceptor
Lieberson, Jonathan, Preceptor
Meyerson, Barbara, Preceptor

Miller, Franklin, Preceptor
Payer, Mary, Preceptor
Rajchman, John, Preceptor
Rapaczynski, Andrzej, Preceptor
Rumsey, William, Preceptor
Wagner, Douglas, Preceptor
Willner, David, Preceptor
Wytwycky, Bohdan, Preceptor

COLUMBIA UNIVERSITY, BARNARD COLLEGE
New York, New York 10027 (M; p; wo; sem; II; 1909) NR

COLUMBIA UNIVERSITY, COLLEGE OF PHARMACEUTICAL SCIENCES
New York, New York 10027 (Phar; p; coed; sem; IV; 500) --, --, 212-787-0600

Belaief, Lynne, PhD, Asst Prof, Ethics, Phil of Relig
Lipman, Matthew, PhD, Prof, Polit Phil, Aes
Lucas, Gerald, PhD, Adj Asst Prof, Phil of Sci, Phil Psych

COLUMBIA UNIVERSITY, TEACHERS COLLEGE
New York, New York 10027 (M; p; coed; sem; IV; 5487) PhD major, Dept of Phil and
the Soc Sci, 212-870-4185

Greene, Maxine, PhD, Prof, Aes, Phil of Educ
Phenix, Philip, PhD, Prof, Phil of Relig, Phil of Educ
Soltis, Jonas, EdD, Prof, Phil of Mind, Phil of Educ

Childs, John, PhD, Prof Emer, Phil of Educ
Raup, Bruce, PhD, Prof Emer, Phil of Educ

COLUMBIA-GREENE COMMUNITY COLLEGE
Athens, New York 12015 (--; st and local; coed; 4-1-4; I; 506) NR

CONCORDIA COLLEGE
Bronxville, New York 10708 (M; Luth; coed; 4-1-4; II; 442) Courses with no degree
specialization, Dept of Phil, 914-337-9300 Ext 40, 42

Timm, Roger E, MA, Asst Prof, Chm, Phil of Relig, Anal Phil, Metaph
Schnabel, Robert V, PhD, Prof, Hist of Phil, Phil of Educ, Axiology

COOPER UNION
Cooper Square, New York 10003 (M; p; coed; sem; IV; 1452) Courses with no degree
specialization, Dept of Human, 212-254-6300

Arato, Andrew, MA, Asst Prof, Soc Phil

CORNELL UNIVERSITY
Ithaca, New York 14850 (M; p; coed; sem; IV; 11,094) PhD major, Sage School of Phil,
607-256-5000, 607-256-3687

Kretzmann, Norman, PhD, Prof, Chm
Black, Max, PhD, Prof
Boyd, Richard, PhD, Assoc Prof
Chateaubriand, Oswaldo, PhD, Asst Prof
Dancy, Russell, PhD, Assoc Prof
Fischler, Paul, MA, Instr
Ginet, Carl, PhD, Assoc Prof

Lyons, David, PhD, Prof
Malcolm, Norman, PhD, Prof
Miller, Richard, MA, Asst Prof
Shoemaker, Sydney, PhD, Prof
Stalnaker, Robert, PhD, Assoc Prof
Sturgeon, Nicholas, BA, Asst Prof
Wood, Allen, PhD, Assoc Prof

Burtt, Edwin A, PhD, Prof Emer
Smart, Harold R, PhD, Prof Emer

CORNING COMMUNITY COLLEGE, STATE UNIVERSITY OF NEW YORK
    Corning, New York 14830 (M; st and local; coed; sem; I; 2778) Courses with no degree
    specialization, Div of Human, 607-962-9238

    Bennett, Henry G, MA, Asst Prof, Phil of Mind, Value Theory

DOMINICAN COLLEGE OF BLAUVELT
    Blauvelt, New York 10913 (M; p; coed; sem; II; 616) Courses with no degree
    specialization, Dept of Phil, 914-359-3400

    Hurst, William J, MA, Asst Prof, Chm
    Twohill, M Dominic, PhD, Prof

DOWLING COLLEGE
    Long Island, New York 11769 (M; p; coed; 4-1-4; II; 1574) BA major, Div of Human,
    516-589-6100 Ext 276

    Baron, Harold, PhD, Adj Asst Prof
    Gschwendtner, John V G, PhD, Prof
    Mizzi, Charles E, MS, Lect
    Mullen, John D, MA, Instr
    Pfeffer, Rose, PhD, Assoc Prof

DOWNSTATE MEDICAL CENTER, STATE UNIVERSITY OF NEW YORK
    Brooklyn, New York 11203 (M; st; coed; sem; IV; 1240) NP

DUTCHESS COMMUNITY COLLEGE, STATE UNIVERSITY OF NEW YORK
    Poughkeepsie, New York 12601 (M; st and local; coed; sem; I; 4200) --, Dept of Hist,
    Econ, and Polit Sci, 914-471-4500 Ext 201

    Ross, Walter B, MA, Prof, Phil of Hist
    Skelton, Kenneth T, PhD, Part-time, Phil of Relig

D'YOUVILLE COLLEGE
    Buffalo, New York 14201 (M; p; coed; sem; II; 1161) BA major, Div of Human, 716-
    886-8100 Ext 318

    Hallborg, Robert, MA, Instr, Logic, Continen Phil, British and Amer Phil
    Nielsen, Robert L, MA, Asst Prof, Ethics, East Phil

EISENHOWER COLLEGE
    Seneca Falls, New York 13148 (--; p; coed; 4-1-4; II; 769) BA major, Div of Human,
    315-568-2032

    Campbell, James I, PhD, Prof, Dir, 20th Cent English Phil, Phil of Relig
    Barnett, Robert A, PhD, Assoc Prof, Phil Theol

Chan, Wing-Ming, MA, Asst Prof, Exist, Orient Phil
Mack, Eric, PhD, Asst Prof, Phil of Rights
McDermott, John, PhD, Asst Prof, Amer Phil, Phil of Mind
Walsh, George V, PhD, Prof, 20th Cent Phil, Polit and Soc Phil

ELIZABETH SETON COLLEGE
Yonkers, New York 10701 (M; p; coed; sem; I; 373) Courses with no degree specialization, Dept of Phil, 914-969-4000

Paderon, Eduardo S, PhD, Assoc Prof, Chm, Phil of Man
O'Sullivan, Maureen, PhD, Asst Prof, Ethics

ELMIRA COLLEGE
Elmira, New York 14901 (M; p; coed; --; III; 3266) BA major, --, 607-734-3911 Ext 247, 209

Johnson, Howard R, ThD, Assoc Prof, Exist Phil, Phil of Relig, Comp Ontology
McLaughlin, John, PhD, Asst Prof, Phil of Logic, Phil of Lang, Phil of Law

EMPIRE STATE COLLEGE, STATE UNIVERSITY OF NEW YORK
Saratoga Springs, New York 12866 (--; st; coed; --; II; 120) BA major, --, 518-587-2100

Davis, Forest K, STB, Prof
Drury, George F, PhD, Prof
Flynn, Bernard C, PhD, Asst Prof
Jacobson, John, PhD, Prof
Neumaier, John, PhD, Prof
Parker, Bernard S, PhD, Asst Prof
Zaslow, Robert J, PhD, Asst Prof

ERIE COMMUNITY COLLEGE, STATE UNIVERSITY OF NEW YORK
Buffalo, New York 14221 (M; st and local; coed; sem; I; 7552) AA major, Dept of Human, 716-634-0800 Ext 341

McNabb, James R, PhD, Instr
Ricci, Louis M, PhD, Asst Prof, Epistem

FASHION INSTITUTE OF TECHNOLOGY, STATE UNIVERSITY OF NEW YORK
New York, New York 10001 (M; st and local; coed; sem; I; 5020) NP

FINCH COLLEGE
New York, New York 10021 (M; p; wo; 4-1-4; II; 354) Courses with no degree specialization, --, 212-288-8450

FINGER LAKES COMMUNITY COLLEGE
Canandaigua, New York 14424 (--; st and local; coed; sem; I; 1330) Courses with no degree specialization, Dept of Human, 315-394-3500

Pennock, Robert E, ThD, Phil of Relig

FORDHAM UNIVERSITY
Bronx, New York 10458 (M; p; coed; sem; IV; 13,841) PhD major, Dept of Phil, 212-933-2233 Ext 323

Potter, Vincent G, PhD, Assoc Prof, Chm, Amer Prag, Peirce

Bacon, John, PhD, Asst Prof, Logic, Phil Applications of Logic
Chethimattam, John B, PhD, Assoc Prof, Indian Phil, Phil of Man
Clarke, Norris W, PhD, Prof, Metaph, Med Phil
Cooke, Vincent M, PhD, Asst Prof, Wittgenstein, Ling Anal
Dolan, Joseph, PhD, Assoc Prof, Ethics, Phil of Law
Donnelly, John, PhD, Asst Prof, Contemp Anal Phil, Phil of Mind
Feldstein, Leonard, PhD, Assoc Prof, Phil of the Person, Metaph
Helbig, Frederick, JD, Asst Prof, Ethics, Business Ethics
Gallagher, Kenneth, PhD, Prof, Phenomen, Epistem
Grontkowski, Raymond, PhD, Assoc Prof, Mod Class Phil, Phil of Sci
Johann, Robert O, PhD, Prof, Phil of Value, Morality, Transcendent Method
Kelbley, Charles, PhD, Assoc Prof, Contemp French Phil, Phil of Soc Sci
Kraus, Elizabeth, PhD, Asst Prof, Amer Phil, Whitehead
Lauer, J Quentin, PhD, Prof, 19th Cent Phil, Anc Phil
McCool, Gerald A, PhD, Prof, Thomism, Phil of Relig
O'Connell, Robert J, PhD, Prof, St Augustine, Platonic Tradition
Richardson, William, PhD, Prof, Exist Phil
Roth, Robert J, PhD, Prof, Amer Prag, Natur, Phil of Man
Riordan, Joseph D, PhD, Asst Prof, Med Phil, Islamic Phil
Sadowsky, James, STL, Asst Prof, Logic, Ling Anal
Smith, Gerrit, PhD, Asst Prof, Phil of Sci, Phil of Space and Time
Varga, Andrew C, PhD, Asst Prof, Ethics, Marxism

Donceel, Joseph F, PhD, Prof Emer, Phil of Man, Teilhard de Chardin
Salmon, Elizabeth G, PhD, Prof Emer, Cartesianism, British Empir

Banja, John, Teach Fel
Ambrosio, Francis J, Grad Asst
Clay, Christopher Clay, Grad Asst
Conway, Gertrude, Grad Asst
De Angelis, Roger, Grad Asst
De Carlo, Ralph, Grad Asst
Ellison, Marjorie, Grad Asst

Eveleth, Lois, Teach Fel
Greene, Joseph, Teach Fel
Hatab, Lawrence, Teach Fel
Matthis, Michael J, Grad Asst
Mosca, Amedio, Teach Fel
Reisig, Joseph, Teach Fel
Wargo, Donald, Grad Asst

FRIENDS WORLD COLLEGE
  Westbury, New York 11590 (--; p; coed; sem; II; 115) NR

FULTON-MONTGOMERY COMMUNITY COLLEGE, STATE UNIVERSITY OF NEW YORK
  Johnstown, New York 12095 (M; st and local; coed; sem; I; 1295) AA major, Dept of
  Human, 518-829-6201 Ext 321, 323

  Rambush, Arlene, MA, Asst Prof

GENERAL THEOLOGICAL SEMINARY
  New York, New York 10011 (Theol; PE; coed; 4-1-4; IV; 144) NP

GENESEE COMMUNITY COLLEGE, STATE UNIVERSITY OF NEW YORK
  Batavia, New York 14020 (M; st and local; coed; sem; I; 1720) NP

GEORGE MERCER JUNIOR MEMORIAL SCHOOL OF THEOLOGY
  Garden City, New York 11530 (--; Prot Epis; coed; tri; III; 33) Courses with no
  degree specialization, --, 516-248-4800

THE GRADUATE SCHOOL AND UNIVERSITY CENTER, CITY UNIVERSITY OF NEW YORK
  New York, New York 10036 (M; local; coed; sem; IV; 2421) PhD major, PhD Program
  in Phil, 212-790-4246, 212-790-4247

  Koslow, Arnold, PhD, Executive Officer, Logic, Phil of Sci

Baumrin, Bernard H, PhD, Ethics, Phil of Law
Brown, Malcolm S, PhD, Greek Phil
Caws, Peter J, PhD, Phil of Sci
Cohen S, Marshall, MA, Legal and Polit Phil, Aes, Criticism
Collins, Arthur W, PhD, Anal Phil
Elias, Julius, PhD, Aes
Ezorsky, Gertrude, PhD, Ethics, Polit Phil, Soc Phil
Gildin, Hilail, PhD, Polit Phil, Anc Phil
Golding, Martin, PhD, Phil of Law
Greene, Murray, PhD, Hist of Phil
Grewe, Rudolf, PhD, Logic, Hist of Phil, Phil of Sci
Held, Virginia, PhD, Ethics, Soc and Polit Phil
Irani, K D, LLB, Phil of Sci
Kahane, Howard, PhD, Logic, Phil of Sci
Krzywicki-Herburt, PhD, Phil of Sci, Contemp Phil
Landesman, Jr, Charles, PhD, Metaph, Phil of Mind
Lange, John F, PhD, Contemp Phil
Lango, John W, PhD, Metaph
Lean, Martin E, PhD, Anal Phil
Levin, Michael, PhD, Phil of Sci
Magid, Henry, PhD, Polit Phil
Massie, David, PhD, Logic, Phil of Sci
McAlister, Linda, PhD, Hist of Phil, Ethics
McDermott, John, PhD, Amer Phil
McLaughlin, Andrew, PhD, Phil of Sci, Soc Phil
Myers, Gerald E, Phil of Mind
Orenstein, Alex, PhD, Logic, Phil of Sci
Pohle, William B, PhD, Hist of Phil
Rosenthal, David, PhD, Phil of Mind, Phil of Lang, Epistem
Saunders, Jason Lee, PhD, Anc Phil
Sherover, Charles, PhD, Mod Euro Phil, Amer Phil
Sleeper, Ralph W, PhD, Ethics
Spielman, Stephen, PhD, Logic, Phil of Sci
Sprague, Elmer, PhD, British Empir
Stolnitz, Jerome, PhD, Ethics, Aes
Taylor, Paul, PhD, Ethics
Thayer, H Standish, PhD, Hist of Phil
Weissman, David, PhD, Metaph
Wertheimer, Roger, PhD, Ethics, Phil of Lang
Wyschogrod, Michael, PhD, Phenomen, Exist

HAMILTON COLLEGE
Clinton, New York 13323 (M; p; men; 4-1-4; II; 932) BA major, Dept of Phil, 315-859-7110

Blackwood, Russell T, PhD, Prof, Chm, Phil of Relig
Bowie, Norman E, PhD, Asst Prof, Soc Phil
Duncan, A R C, MA, Truax Visit Prof, Ethics
Ring, Elizabeth M, MA, Lect, Epistem
Simon, Robert L, PhD, Assoc Prof, Polit Phil

HARRIMAN COLLEGE
Harriman, New York 10926 (--; RC; wo; sem; I; 168) --, Div of Human, 914-782-8136

McMahon, Joseph, MA, Assoc Prof

HARTWICK COLLEGE
Oneonta, New York 13820 (M; p; coed; --; II; 1682) BA major, Dept of Phil and Relig, 607-432-4200 Ext 254

Burrington, Dale E, PhD, Prof, Chm, Phil of Mind

Konecky, Stanley J, PhD, Asst Prof, Exist
Wisan, Richard N, PhD, Prof, Ethics

HEALTH SCIENCE CENTER AT BUFFALO, STATE UNIVERSITY OF NEW YORK
   Buffalo, New York 14214 (Med; st; coed; sem; IV; 2065) NR

HEALTH SCIENCE CENTER AT STONY BROOK, STATE UNIVERSITY OF NEW YORK
   Stony Brook, New York 11790 (Med; st; coed; --; IV; 402) NR

HEBREW UNION COLLEGE, NEW YORK BRANCH
   New York, New York 10023 (M; Jewish; coed; sem; IV; 321) NR

HERKIMER COUNTY COMMUNITY COLLEGE, STATE UNIVERSITY OF NEW YORK
   Herkimer, New York 13350 (M; st and local; coed; --; I; 1091) Courses with no degree
   specialization, Div of Human, 315-866-0300 Ext 51

   Pring, Robert K, MA, Asst Prof, Clsm

HILBERT COLLEGE
   Hamburg, New York 14075 (--; p; coed; sem; I; 619) Courses with no degree
   specialization, Dept of Relig Stud and Phil, 716-649-7900

   Swol, Gabriel, MA, Chm
   Marcia, Sister
   Edmunette, Sister, PhD

HOBART AND WILLIAM SMITH COLLEGES
   Geneva, New York 14456 (M; p; coed; --; II; 1658) BA major, Dept of Phil, 315-
   789-5500

   Oliver, G Benjamin, PhD, Assoc Prof, Chm, Phil of Lang
   Bär, Eugen S, PhD, Asst Prof, Act Chm, Semiotics
   Daise, Benjamin, PhD, Asst Prof, Kierkegaard
   McDonald, Durstan R, PhD, Asst Prof Part-time, Epistem
   Payne, Perrell F, MA, Asst Prof, Logic

HOFSTRA UNIVERSITY
   Hempstead, New York 11550 (M; p; coed; sem; IV; 12,616) BA major, Dept of Phil,
   516-560-3381

   LaLumia, J, PhD, Prof, Chm, Phil of Sci
   Cernic, David, PhD, Asst Prof, Hist of Phil
   Garrett, Richard, PhD, Asst Prof, Hist of Phil
   Inman, Floyd, PhD, Asst Prof, Logic, Epistem
   Kelly, Derek, PhD, Asst Prof, Phenomen, Epistem
   McKwen, W P, PhD, Prof, Phil of the Soc Sci
   Pearl, Leon, PhD, Assoc Prof, Anal Phil
   Shirk, Evelyn, PhD, Prof, Ethics, Aes

HOLY TRINITY ORTHODOX SEMINARY
   Jordanville, New York 13361 (--; Russian Orth; men; sem; II; 38) NR

HOSTOS COMMUNITY COLLEGE, STATE UNIVERSITY OF NEW YORK
   Bronx, New York 10451 (--; st and local; coed; qr; I; 1107) Courses with no degree
   specialization, --, 212-993-8000

HOUGHTON COLLEGE
Houghton, New York 14744 (M; Wes; coed; sem; II; 1219) BA major, Dept of Relig and Phil, 716-567-2211 Ext 250

Reist, Irwin, ThM, Assoc Prof, Act Chm
Mullen, Lawrence, MA, Assoc Prof, Hist of Phil, Ethics
Wood, Laurence, PhD, Assoc Prof, Phil of Relig

HUDSON VALLEY COMMUNITY COLLEGE, STATE UNIVERSITY OF NEW YORK
Troy, New York 12180 (M; st and local; coed; sem; I; 6075) Courses with no degree specialization, Dept of Phil, 518-283-1100 Ext 365

Marsh, Joseph, MA, Assoc Prof, Logic, Hist of Phil

HUNTER COLLEGE, CITY UNIVERSITY OF NEW YORK
New York, New York 10021 (M; local; coed; sem; III; 24,962) MA major, Dept of Phil, 212-360-2427

Sherover, Charles, PhD, Prof, Chm
Banu, Beatrice, MA, Adj Lect
Binswanger, Harry, PhD, Adj Assoc Prof
Blom, John, MA, Instr
Bryar, William, PhD, Prof
Caws, Peter, PhD, Prof
Cohen, Mark, BA, Lect Part-time
De Simone, Robert, BA, Adj Lect
Di Lascia, Alfred, PhD, Adj Prof
Farkas, Livia, BA, Lect Part-time
Finch, Henry Le Roy, PhD, Visit Prof
Funk, Warren, BA, Adj Lect
Garrett, Lester, BA, Adj Lect
Harrison, Joan, BA, Adj Lect
Held, Virginia, PhD, Assoc Prof
Jourdain, Alice, PhD, Prof
Landesman, Charles, PhD, Prof
Lango, John, PhD, Asst Prof
Martin, Glen, BA, Adj Lect
McGeough, Joseph, BA, Adj Lect
McKinney, Daphne, BA, Lect Part-time
Mellinger, Matthew, BA, Adj Lect
Muyskens, James, PhD, Asst Prof
Shapiro, Daniel, BA, Lect Part-time
Shapley, Susan, BA, Adj Lect
Shea, Dennis, BA, Adj Lect
Stambaugh, Joan, PhD, Assoc Prof
Weinberg, Sue, BA, Adj Lect
Weinstein, Mark, BA, Instr

IMMACULATE CONCEPTION SEMINARY
Troy, New York 12180 (--; RC; men; sem; II; 47) --, Dept of Phil, 518-273-8422

Di Pasquale, Ralph, PhD
Gulley, Anthony, PhD
Tormey, Anthony, MA

INSTITUTE OF ADVANCE STUDIES IN HUMANITIES
New York, New York 10027 (--; p; coed; sem; IV; 420) NR

IONA COLLEGE
New Rochelle, New York 10801 (M; p; coed; sem; III; 3954) BA major, Dept of Phil, 914-636-2100 Ext 254

Currey, E Kilian, PhD, Assoc Prof, Chm, Contemp Ethical Theory
Azar, Lawrence, PhD, Prof, Thomism, Phil Psych
Bradley, John, MA, Instr
Donovan, Rickart, PhD, Asst Prof, Amer Phil
Giles, James, PhD, Asst Prof, Amer Phil
O'Neill, Peter, PhD, Assoc Prof, Ling Phil
O'Neill, William, PhD, Asst Prof, Phil of Sci
Pepper, George, PhD, Prof, Phil Anthrop
Quinn, Wilfred, MA, Asst Prof, Med Phil

ITHACA COLLEGE
Ithaca, New York 14850 (M; p; coed; sem; III; 4220) BA major, Dept of Phil and Relig, 607-274-3200

Richards, Benjamin A, PhD, Assoc Prof, Chm, Polit Phil
Elbrecht, Joyce, PhD, Prof, Phenomen
Creel, Richard, PhD, Assoc Prof, Value Theory
Finlay, Linda, MA, Asst Prof, Exist
Goldstein, Alex, MA, Asst Prof, Phil of Sci
Hoffmann, William, PhD, Asst Prof, Epistem
Kates, Carol, PhD, Assoc Prof, Aes
Schwartz, Stephen, PhD, Asst Prof, Phil of Mind, Phil of Action

JAMESTOWN COMMUNITY COLLEGE, STATE UNIVERSITY OF NEW YORK
Jamestown, New York 14701 (M; st and local; coed; sem; I; 2566) Courses with no degree specialization, Dept of Phil, 716-665-5220

Eckstrand, B R, MA, Prof, Aes
McCabe, James, MA, Instr, Soc Phil

JEFFERSON COMMUNITY COLLEGE, STATE UNIVERSITY OF NEW YORK
Watertown, New York 13601 (M; st and local; coed; sem; I; 1520) AA major, Div of Libr Arts, 315-782-5250

Curtin, Brendan, MA, Assoc Prof

THE JEWISH THEOLOGICAL SEMINARY OF AMERICA
New York, New York 10027 (M; Jewish; coed; sem; IV; 405) PhD joint or combined major, Dept of Phil of Relig, 212-749-8000

Heschel, Abraham J, PhD, Prof, Phil of Relig
Rothschild, Fritz A, DHL, Assoc Prof, Phil of Relig
Silverman, David W, MHL, Instr, Phil of Relig
Siegel, Seymour, DHL, Prof

JOHN JAY COLLEGE OF CRIMINAL JUSTICE, CITY UNIVERSITY OF NEW YORK
New York, New York 10010 (M; local; coed; sem; III; 5554) NR

THE JUILLIARD SCHOOL
New York, New York 10023 (M; p; coed; sem; IV; 1122) NP

KEHILATH YAKOV RABBINICAL SEMINARY
Brooklyn, New York 11211 (--; p; men; sem; II; 204) NR

KEUKA COLLEGE
Keuka Park, New York 14478 (M; p; wo; qr; II; 769) BA joint or combined major,
Dept of Phil and Relig, 315-536-4411

Stephens, Walter S, PhD, Assoc Prof, Chm

KINGSBOROUGH COMMUNITY COLLEGE, STATE UNIVERSITY OF NEW YORK
Brooklyn, New York 11235 (M; st and local; coed; sem; I; 7058) AA major, Dept of
Hist and Polit Sci, 212-769-9200 Ext 445, 446

Kluback, William, PhD, Assoc Prof, Metaph

KING'S COLLEGE
Briarcliff Manor, New York 10510 (M; p; coed; sem; II; 736) BA major, Dept of Phil,
914-941-7200

Worrad, Jr, Lewis H, BA, Instr, Chm
Collord, Paul D, PhD, Visit Prof

KIRKLAND COLLEGE
Clinton, New York 13323 (--; p; coed; 4-1-4; II; 592) BA major, Div of Human, 315-
859-7291

Laslie, Adele, BA, Instr, Phil of Sci
Morris, Phyllis S, PhD, Asst Prof, Exist, Phil of Mind
Roelofs, Richard, PhD, Assoc Prof, Ethics, Phil of Relig

LA SALETTE SEMINARY
Altamont, New York 12009 (--; RC; men; sem; I; 40) NR

LADYCLIFF COLLEGE
Highland Falls, New York 10928 (M; p; wo; 4-1-4; II; 469) Courses with no degree
specialization, Dept of Phil and Relig Stud, 914-446-4747 Ext 46

Gibbons, Joseph P, PhD, Asst Prof, Chm, Phil of Relig
Breidenbach, Francis J, PhD, Prof, Anc Phil

LE MOYNE COLLEGE
Syracuse, New York 13214 (M; RC; coed; sem; II; 1561) BA major, Dept of Phil, 315-
446-2882

Campbell, Daniel, MA, Asst Prof, Chm, Epistem, Exist
Curley, Thomas V, PhD, Assoc Prof, Amer Phil, Phil of Educ
Ewens, Thomas, PhD, Asst Prof, Freud, Phenomen
Flower, Robert, PhD, Asst Prof, Anal Phil, Anc Phil
Giegengack, Mary, PhD, Asst Prof, Phil of Relig, Hocking
Grimm, Randolph, MA, Instr, Nietzsche, Phil Anthrop
Hanley, Katharine Rose, PhD, Assoc Prof, Metaph, Marcel, Exist Phenomen
Harrison, Stanley, PhD, Asst Prof, Amer Phil, Peirce, Phil Anthrop
Kelly, Charles, PhD, Asst Prof, Logic, Anal Phil
Kent, Thomas, PhL, Asst Prof, Logic, Aes, Ethics
Madigan, Patrick, PhD, Asst Prof, German Enlightenment

LEHMAN COLLEGE, CITY UNIVERSITY OF NEW YORK
Bronx, New York 10468 (M; local; coed; sem; IV; 12,508) BA major, Dept of Phil,
212-960-8292

Pohle, William, PhD, Asst Prof, Chm
Barmrin, Bernard, PhD, Prof
Dunmore-Leibor, Justin, PhD, Asst Prof
Gould, Carol, PhD, Asst Prof
Kolitch, Dean, BA, Lect Part-time
McLaughlin, Andrew, PhD, Asst Prof
Mendelsohn, Richard, BA, Lect
Raju, P T, Visit Prof
Rosenthal, David, PhD, Asst Prof
Schwartz, Lewis, PhD, Assoc Prof
Spielman, Stephen, PhD, Asst Prof
Stolnitz, Jerome, PhD, Prof
Weinstock, Jerome, PhD, Asst Prof
Wettstein, Howard, BA, Lect Part-time

LONG ISLAND UNIVERSITY, BROOKLYN CENTER
Brooklyn, New York 11201 (M; p; coed; sem; IV; 7533) BA major, Dept of Phil, 212-834-6240

Hirsch, Eli, PhD, Asst Prof, Chm, Metaph
Bandman, Bertram, PhD, Prof, Ethics, Phil of Law, Phil of Educ
Earle, William J, PhD, Asst Prof Part-time, Metaph, Amer Phil
Horowitz, Louise S, PhD, Assoc Prof, Phil of Mind, Orient Phil, Aes
Ley, Michael, MA, Instr Part-time, Logic, Orient Phil
Longacre, Lawson, MA, Instr Part-time
Olson, Robert G, PhD, Prof, Ethics, Polit and Soc Phil
Pashman, Jon, PhD, Asst Prof Part-time, Theory of Man
Reis, Lincoln, PhD, Univ Prof, Phil of Law, Metaph, Hist of Phil
Struhl, Karsten J, MA, Instr, Soc and Polit Phil, Phenomen
West, Elinor J M, PhD, Assoc Prof, Exist, Greek Phil

LONG ISLAND UNIVERSITY, BROOKLYN COLLEGE OF PHARMACY
Brooklyn, New York 11216 (M; p; coed; sem; III; 513) Courses with no degree specialization, Dept of Human, 212-622-4040 Ext 28

Riess, Chester L, PhD, Chm
Bernstein, Michael, PhD

LONG ISLAND UNIVERSITY, C W POST COLLEGE
Greenvale, New York 11548 (M; p; coed; --; III; 11,211) BA major, Dept of Phil, 516-299-2341

Skelly, Alan, MA, Asst Prof, Chm, Phil of Relig, Aes
Berleant, Arnold, PhD, Prof, Aes
Brier, Robert, PhD, Asst Prof, Phil of Sci, Phil and Parapsychology
Hassol, Milton, PhD, Assoc Prof, Phil and Psychoanalysis, Ethics
Hobbs, Hoyt, PhD, Assoc Prof, Logic, Epistem
Hoffman, Lester, PhD, Asst Prof, Phil of Sci, Phil of Educ, Phil of Mind
Lothstein, Arthur, MA, Instr, Radical Phil
Paulidis, John, MA, Instr, Anc Phil, Ethics
Press, Howard, PhD, Assoc Prof, Marxism, Aes
Schmidt-Raghavan, M, PhD, Assoc Prof, Phil of Sci, Indian Phil, Logic, Ethics
Stone, Robert, PhD, Asst Prof, Phenomen
Sprintzen, David, PhD, Assoc Prof, Soc Phil, Amer Phil
Walther, Eric, PhD, Assoc Prof, Hist of Phil, Metaph, Logic

LONG ISLAND UNIVERSITY, SOUTHAMPTON COLLEGE
Southampton, New York 11968 (M; p; coed; 4-1-4; II; 1416) BA major, Div of Human, 516-283-4000 Ext 244

NEW YORK

García-Gómez, Jorge, PhD, Assoc Prof, Chm, Phenomen, Exist
Gormley, William, PhD, Assoc Prof, Ethics, Phil of Relig

MANHATTAN COLLEGE
Riverdale, New York 10471 (M; p; men; sem; III; 4431) BA major, Dept of Phil, 212-548-1400 Ext 326

Trant, Edward J, PhD, Assoc Prof, Chm, Contemp Ethics, Phil of Soc Sci
Ansbro, John J, PhD, Assoc Prof, Exist
Daher, Adel H, PhD, Asst Prof, Phil of Relig, Sym Logic
DiLascia, Alfred P, PhD, Prof, Mod Phil
Halpin, John, MA, Asst Prof, Soc Phil
Hashimoto, Rentaro, PhD, Assoc Prof, Orient Phil
James, Theodore E, PhD, Prof, Late Med Phil
McCormick, William R, MA, Asst Prof, Marxism
Moran, John H, PhD, Assoc Prof, Ling Phil
Reilly, William F, PhD, Assoc Prof, Amer Phil

Ryan, Bernard M, PhD, Prof Emer, Phil of Sci

MANHATTAN SCHOOL OF MUSIC
New York, New York 10027 (M; p; coed; sem; III; 1027) NR

MANHATTANVILLE COLLEGE
Purchase, New York 10577 (M; p; coed; sem; III; 1465) MA minor, Dept of Phil, 914-946-9600

Clark, Mary T, PhD, Prof, Chm, Plotinus-Augustine, Med Phil, Metaph
Colburn, Brooks, MA, Asst Prof, Phil of Sci, Phenomen, Logic
Langley, Raymond J, PhD, Assoc Prof, 19th Cent Phil, Exist, Hume, Hegel

MANNES COLLEGE OF MUSIC
New York, New York 10021 (--; p; coed; sem; II; 184) Courses with no degree specialization, --, 212-737-0700

Dunham, Barrows, PhD

MARIA COLLEGE OF ALBANY
Albany, New York 12208 (--; p; coed; sem; I; 450) --, --, 518-438-3111

Wieboldt, Barbara, MA, Instr

MARIA REGINA COLLEGE
Syracuse, New York 13208 (M; p; wo; sem; I; 608) Courses with no degree specialization, Dept of Relig Stud, 315-474-4891 Ext 22

Ball, M Tarcisia, PhD, Prof, Ethics
Mohr, Simon, STL, Asst Prof, Hist of Phil

MARIST COLLEGE
Poughkeepsie, New York 12601 (M; p; coed; sem; III; 1823) BA minor, Dept of Phil, 914-471-3240 Ext 273

Drennen, D A, PhD, Prof, Chm, Phil of Hist, Islamic Phil, Phil of Relig
Benin, Italo, PhD, Asst Prof, Marxism, Exist
Casey, Thomas, MA, Asst Prof, Amer Phil
Donohue, Kevin E, MA, Asst Prof, Aes, Phil of Soc
Ryan, Xavier, PhD, Asst Prof, Systems Phil

MARITIME COLLEGE, STATE UNIVERSITY OF NEW YORK
  Bronx, New York 10465 (M; st; men; sem; III; 768) NP

MARYKNOLL SEMINARY
  Maryknoll, New York 10545 (M; RC; men; sem; III; 67) Courses with no degree
  specialization, Theol Program, 914-941-7590 Ext 409

  Chang, Peter, PhD, Asst Prof, Feuerbach, Marx
  Keegan, John, MA, Asst Prof

MARYMOUNT COLLEGE
  Tarrytown, New York 10591 (M; p; wo; sem; II; 950) BA major, Dept of Phil, 914-
  631-3200 Ext 398

  Nordstrom, Louis, PhD, Asst Prof, Chm, East Phil, Metaph
  Keane, Ellen Marie, PhD, Assoc Prof, Exist, Kierkegaard
  Strath, Frederick, PhL, Assoc Prof, William James, Phil of Hist, Phil of Culture

MARYMOUNT MANHATTAN COLLEGE
  New York, New York 10021 (M; p; wo; 4-1-4; II; 988) BA major, Dept of Phil, 212-
  861-4200 Ext 53

  Baker, Peter H, MA, Asst Prof, Chm
  Keyes, Marie St Timothy, MA, Asst Prof

MATER DEI COLLEGE
  Ogdensburg, New York 13669 (--; RC; coed; sem; I; 124) --, Div of Human, 315-393-
  5930

  Davis, Robert B, MA, Instr

MEDAILLE COLLEGE
  Buffalo, New York 14214 (M; p; coed; sem; II; 497) Courses with no degree
  specialization, Dept of Human, 716-884-2231

  Ransom, Kevin T, EdM, Asst Prof

MEDGAR EVERS COLLEGE, CITY UNIVERSITY OF NEW YORK
  Brooklyn, New York 11225 (--; local; coed; sem; II; 1080) NR

MERCY COLLEGE
  Dobbs Ferry, New York 10522 (M; p; coed; sem; II; 1316) Courses with no degree
  specialization, Div of Phil and Relig Stud, 914-693-4500

  Gannon, Joseph F, MA, Assoc Prof
  Grow, Ann E, PhD, Assoc Prof

MES TORAH VODAATH SEMINARY
  Brooklyn, New York 11218 (--; Jewish; men; sem; III; 687) NR

MESIVTA EASTERN PARKWAY RABBINICAL SEMINARY
  Brooklyn, New York 11203 (--; Jewish; men; sem; III; 130) NR

MESIVTHA TIFERETH JER AMR
   New York, New York 10002 (--; Jewish; men; sem; III; 130) NR

MILLS COLLEGE OF EDUCATION
   New York, New York 10011 (M; p; wo; sem; II; 353) NR

MIRRER YESHIVA CENTRAL INSTITUTE
   Brooklyn, New York 11223 (--; Jewish; men; sem; III; 351) NR

MOHAWK VALLEY COMMUNITY COLLEGE, STATE UNIVERSITY OF NEW YORK
   Utica, New York 13501 (M; st; coed; qr; I; 4845) Courses with no degree specialization,
   Dept of Gen Educ, 315-735-7511

   Mussman, Emanuel, MA, Assoc Prof

MOLLOY COLLEGE FOR WOMEN
   Rockville Centre, New York 11570 (M; RC; wo; sem; II; 1125) BA major, Dept of Phil,
   516-678-5000 Ext 54

   Maher, Paul J, STD, Asst Prof, Chm, Phil of Relig
   Espina, Jose R, MA, Asst Prof,
   Halpin, Marlene, PhD, Prof, Metaph
   Fitzgerald, Janet, PhD, Assoc Prof, Phil of Sci
   Losasso, Rosemarie, PhD, Asst Prof, Phil of Human Person
   Reilly, William F, PhD, Adj Prof, Ethics

MONROE COMMUNITY COLLEGE, STATE UNIVERSITY OF NEW YORK
   Rochester, New York 14623 (M; st and local; coed; sem; I; 8280) --, Dept of Eng and
   Human, 716-442-9950 Ext 520

   Blomgren, Fred J, MA, Assoc Prof
   McMurry, Moreland, MA, Asst Prof
   Pennock, Robert E, ThD, Adj Assoc Prof

MOUNT SAINT ALPHONSUS SEMINARY
   Esopus, New York 12429 (M; RC; men; sem; III; 110) NP

MOUNT SAINT MARY COLLEGE
   Newburgh, New York 12550 (M; p; coed; sem; II; 743) --, Div of Phil and Relig Stud,
   914-561-0800

   Lindemann, Kathryn, MA, Instr
   Mahoney, Mary Eleanor, PhD, Prof
   Stankiewicz, Ann, MA, Instr

MOUNT SINAI SCHOOL OF MEDICINE, CITY UNIVERSITY OF NEW YORK
   New York, New York 10021 (Med; local; coed; 4-1-4; IV; 178) NR

NASSAU COMMUNITY COLLEGE, STATE UNIVERSITY OF NEW YORK
   Garden City, New York 11530 (M; st and local; coed; sem; I; 18,092) Courses with no
   degree specialization, Dept of Phil, 516-742-0600 Ext 440

   Lataner, Albert, MPhil, Prof, Chm, Hist of Phil, Amer Phil
   Edwards, James, MA, Asst Prof, Exist, Orient Phil
   Mooney, Christopher, MA, Instr, Aes, Amer Phil
   Stanton, William, MA, Assoc Prof, Soc Phil, Phil of Relig

NAZARETH COLLEGE OF ROCHESTER
Rochester, New York 14610 (M; p; coed; --; III; 1682) BA major, Dept of Phil, 716-586-2525 Ext 303

Koenen, Jane, PhD, Prof, Chm, Exist, Phil of Psych, Med Phil
Curtin, J Claude, PhD, Asst Prof, Phenomen, Hist of Phil
Dwyer, Helene, MA, Asst Prof, Phil of Art, Phil of Lang
Miller, Robert J, PhD, Prof, Contemp Phil, Exist, East Tht

NEW SCHOOL FOR SOCIAL RESEARCH
New York, New York 10003 (M; p; coed; sem; IV; 3765) PhD major, Dept of Phil, 212-675-2700 Ext 250, 258

Jonas, Hans, PhD, Alvin Johnson Prof, Chm, Anc Phil, Metaph
Abel, Reuben, PhD, Adj Prof, Anal Phil
Arendt, Hannah, PhD, Univ Prof, Polit Phil
Benardete, Seth, PhD, Visit Lect, Anc Phil
Dove, Kenley, PhD, Assoc Prof, Polit Phil, German Phil
Kuehl, James R, PhD, Asst Prof, Exist
Mohanty, J N, PhD, Visit Prof, Phenomen
Wellmer, Albrecht, PhD, Assoc Prof, Soc Phil
Vollrath, Ernst, PhD, Visit Prof, Metaph

Kallen, Horace M, PhD, Prof Emer

Bruehl, Elizabeth, MA, Teach Asst   McKenna, William, MA, Dept Asst
Kohn, Jerome, MA, Teach Asst

NEW YORK CITY COMMUNITY COLLEGE, CITY UNIVERSITY OF NEW YORK
Brooklyn, New York 11201 (M; st and local; coed; sem; I; 15,233) Courses with no degree specialization, Dept of Human, 212-643-8482

Blumberg, David, PhD, Asst Prof, Phil of Law, Ethics, Polit Phil
Harrington, R Ward, MA, Prof
Mohl, Oscar, DD, Asst Prof, Exist, Phil of Relig

NEW YORK COLLEGE OF PODIATRIC MEDICINE
New York, New York 10035 (Pod; p; coed; sem; IV; 203) NP

NEW YORK INSTITUTE OF TECHNOLOGY, NEW YORK CAMPUS
New York, New York 10019 (M; p; coed; sem; III; 1676) Courses with no degree specialization, Dept of Soc Sci, 212-582-8080 Ext 49

Erdos, Edward, AB, Adj Instr

NEW YORK INSTITUTE OF TECHNOLOGY, OLD WESTBURY CAMPUS
Old Westbury, New York 11568 (M; p; coed; sem; III; 3233) Courses with no degree specialization, Dept of Soc Sci, 516-626-3400 Ext 223

Kelly, Eugene, PhD, Adj Asst Prof, German Phil
Lancia, Elaine, MA, Instr, Ordinary Lang Anal
Navia, Luis E, PhD, Asst Prof, Kant

NEW YORK LAW SCHOOL
New York, New York 10013 (Law; p; coed; sem; II; 788) NP

NEW YORK MEDICAL COLLEGE
New York, New York 10029 (Med; p; coed; sem; IV; 677) NP

NEW YORK STATE COLLEGE OF AGRICULTURE AND LIFE SCIENCES AT CORNELL UNIVERSITY
Ithaca, New York 14850 (LDAR; st; coed; sem; IV; 3522) NR

NEW YORK STATE COLLEGE OF CERAMICS AT ALFRED UNIVERSITY
Alfred, New York 14802 (Art; st; coed; 4-1-4; IV; 585) NR

NEW YORK STATE COLLEGE OF HUMAN ECOLOGY AT CORNELL UNIVERSITY
Ithaca, New York 14850 (M; st; coed; sem; IV; 1288) NR

NEW YORK THEOLOGICAL SEMINARY
New York, New York 10017 (Theol; p; coed; sem; III; 228) NR

NEW YORK UNIVERSITY
New York, New York 10003 (M; p; coed; sem; IV; 30,818) PhD major, Dept of Phil,
212-598-3262

Barrett, William C, PhD, Prof, Chm, Exist, Phil of Art
Abelson, Raziel, PhD, Prof, Phil Psych, Epistem
Atherton, Margaret, PhD, Asst Prof, Phil Psych, Anc Phil
Downes, Chauncey, PhD, Assoc Prof, Phenomen, Polit Phil
Gurland, Robert, PhD, Assoc Prof, Logic, Prag
Hambourger, Robert, BA, Asst Prof, Metaph, Epistem, Ethics
Lockwood, Michael, DPhil, Asst Prof, Phil Logic, Soc Ethics
McLendon, Hiram, PhD, Assoc Prof, Hist of Phil
Ruddick, William, PhD, Assoc Prof, Phil of Sci, Metaph
Singer, Peter, MA, Visit Asst Prof, Polit Phil, Ethics
Taurek, John, PhD, Assoc Prof, Ethics, Hist of Mod Phil
Unger, Peter, DPhil, Assoc Prof, Epistem, Phil of Lang

Hook, Sidney, PhD, Prof Emer, Polit Phil, Metaph
Knox, Israel, PhD, Prof Emer, Phil of Relig

NIAGARA COUNTY COMMUNITY COLLEGE, STATE UNIVERSITY OF NEW YORK
Niagara Falls, New York 14303 (M; st and local; coed; sem; I; 3192) Courses with no
degree specialization, Div of Human, 716-731-3271 Ext 256

Warthling, William G, STL, Asst Prof, Chm, Phil Theol
Dagley, Hansa, MA, Instr, Orient Phil
Schmidke, Charles, PhD, Instr, Phil of Relig
Thomas, Edmund, MA, Prof, Phil of Ling

NIAGARA UNIVERSITY
Niagara University, New York 14109 (M; RC; coed; sem; III; 3344) MA major,
Dept of Phil, 716-285-1212

Breen, Joseph S, PhD, Prof, Chm, Syst and Soc Phil
Bennett, Lewis F, JCD, Prof, Ethics
Bonnette, Dennis, PhD, Assoc Prof, Metaph
Fleckenstein, Marilynn, MA, Asst Prof, Phil of Man, Phil of Sci
Fitts, M Pauline, PhD, Prof, Phil of the Person, Contemp Phil, Amer Phil

Gannon, William T, MA, Asst Prof, Phil Anthrop
Heiser, John H, PhD, Assoc Prof, Hist of Phil, Anc and Med Phil
Masiello, Ralph J, PhD, Prof, Metaph, Amer Phil
Munday, Daniel P, PhD, Prof, Phil of Man, Ethics
Popik, Kristin P, MA, Instr, Metaph, Phil of Hist, Phil of Culture
Slattery, Kenneth F, PhD, Prof, Phil Psych, Ethics
Sullivan, Robert P, MA, Asst Prof, Ethics, Metaph, Logic
Sylvester, C Bernard, MA, Asst Prof, Ethics, Hist of Mod and Contemp Phil

Burns, John V, PhD, Prof Emer, Ethics, Soc Phil

Weigan, Burt, BA, Dept Asst

NORTH COUNTRY COMMUNITY COLLEGE, STATE UNIVERSITY OF NEW YORK
Saranac Lake, New York 12983 (--; st and local; coed; sem; I; 1001) Courses with
no degree specialization, Div of Human, 518-891-2915 Ext 40

Maat, Howard, MA, Asst Prof

NYACK COLLEGE
Nyack, New York 10931 (M; Chris and Miss All; coed; sem; II; 591) BA major, Dept
of Phil, 914-358-1710 Ext 295

Miller, Myron, MA, Assoc Prof, Head, Phil of Sci, Phil of Lang
Bailey, Thomas, MA, Prof, World Relig
Collord, Paul, PhD, Prof, Phil of Relig
Mapstone, Jay, MA, Asst Prof
Shelly, Harold, PhD, Assoc Prof, Soc and Polit Theory

ONONDAGA COMMUNITY COLLEGE, STATE UNIVERSITY OF NEW YORK
Syracuse, New York 13215 (M; st and local; coed; sem; I; 4697) Courses with no
degree specialization, Dept of Soc Sci, 315-469-7741 Ext 5301

MacMillan, Claude V, MA, Asst Prof, Metaph
Muir, David G, PhD, Asst Prof, Hist of Phil
Schofeild, James L, BA, Asst Prof, Epistem

ORANGE COUNTY COMMUNITY COLLEGE, STATE UNIVERSITY OF NEW YORK
Middletown, New York 10940 (M; st and local; coed; sem; I; 3663) Courses with no
degree specialization, Div of Human, 914-343-1121 Ext 224

Langan, Hubert E, PhD, Prof, Phil of Educ

PACE COLLEGE
New York, New York 10038 (M; p; coed; sem; IV; 7876) BA joint or combined major,
Dept of Soc Sci, 212-285-3000

Brennan, Bernard P, PhD, Prof
Brown, Harold, AB, Instr
Feingold, Elliot, BA, Instr
Luisi, Miriam, MA, Instr
Pollock, Robert C, PhD, Adj Prof

PACE COLLEGE, WESTCHESTER CAMPUS
Pleasantville, New York 10570 (M; p; coed; sem; III; 2537) --, Dept of Psych and
Soc Sci, 914-769-3200

Kraus, Richard, PhD, Adj Asst Prof, Logic
Shanker, George, PhD, Prof, Hist of Phil
Sherman, Ernest, Instr, Hist of Phil

PARSONS SCHOOL OF DESIGN
New York, New York 10011 (Art; p; coed; sem; II; 593) Courses with no degree specialization, --, 212-759-2214

THE PASSIONIST MONASTIC SEMINARY
Jamaica, New York 11432 (--; RC; men; sem; II; 51) NP

PAUL SMITH'S COLLEGE OF ARTS AND SCIENCE
Paul Smith's, New York 12970 (--; p; coed; sem; I; 1123) Courses with no degree specialization, Dept of Libr Arts, 518-327-6223

Loder, Lester E, M Div, Assoc Prof, Phil of Soc Sci

POLYTECHNIC INSTITUTE OF BROOKLYN
Brooklyn, New York 11201 (M; p; coed; sem; IV; 3841) BA minor, Dept of Eng, 212-643-8833

Peikoff, Leonard, PhD, Assoc Prof

PRATT INSTITUTE
Brooklyn, New York 11205 (M; p; coed; sem; III; 4552) Courses with no degree specialization, Dept of Soc Sci, 212-636-3485

Cobitz, Joseph, PhD, Prof
Feingold, Elliot, BA, Part-time

QUEENS COLLEGE, CITY UNIVERSITY OF NEW YORK
Flushing, New York 11367 (M; local; coed; sem; III; 28,370) MA major, Dept of Phil, 212-445-7500 Ext 368
    520-7368 — JOHN McDERMOTT
Burstein, Harvey, Lect
Capaldi, Nicholas, PhD, Assoc Prof
Dwyer, John, Lect
Fontinell, Eugene, PhD, Prof
Gildin, Hilail, PhD, Assoc Prof
Hallstein, Joseph, Lect
Jordan, James, PhD, Asst Prof
Krzywicki-Herburt, George, PhD, Assoc Prof
Lange, John, PhD, Assoc Prof
Leites, Edmund, PhD, Asst Prof
Manicas, Peter T, PhD, Assoc Prof
McArdle, Ann, Lect
McDermott, John J, PhD, Prof
Mullally, Joseph P, PhD, Prof
Myers, Gerald, PhD, Prof
Noone, John B, PhD, Prof
Orenstein, Alex, PhD, Asst Prof
Purnell, Frederick, PhD, Asst Prof
Sleeper, Ralph, PhD, Prof
Schwarcz, Ernest, PhD, Prof
Taylor, Darrell, PhD, Assoc Prof
Wolz, Henry, PhD, Prof
Wyschogrod, Edith, PhD, Asst Prof

QUEENSBOROUGH COMMUNITY COLLEGE, STATE UNIVERSITY OF NEW YORK
New York, New York 11364 (M; st and local; coed; sem; I; 12,813) Courses with no
degree specialization, --, 212-631-6262

Seltzer, Edward, PhD, Asst Prof, Phenomen
Stabile, Katina, MA, Asst Prof, Class Phil
White, Frank, PhD, Assoc Prof

RABBI JACOB JOSEPH RABBINICAL COLLEGE AT NEW YORK
New York, New York 10002 (--; Jewish; men; sem; IV; 302) NR

RABBINICAL ACADEMY, MESIVTA RABBI CHAIM BERLIN
Brooklyn, New York 11230 (--; Jewish; men; sem; III; 723) MA minor, Dept of Jewish
Phil, 212-253-5682

Davis, Avrohom, MA, Assoc Prof, Ethics
Friedman, Mosheh, MA, Prof, Phil of Hist

RABBINICAL COLLEGE AT LONG ISLAND
Long Beach, New York 11561 (--; p; men; tri; III; 100) NR

RABBINICAL COLLEGE OF C CH'SAN SOFER AT NEW YORK
Brooklyn, New York 11204 (--; Jewish; men; sem; IV; 234) NR

RABBINICAL COLLEGE OF KAMENITZ YESHIVA
Brooklyn, New York 11219 (--; Jewish; men; sem; III; 595) NR

RABBINICAL SEMINARY NETZACH ISR RAM
Brooklyn, New York 11213 (--; Jewish; men; sem; III; 224) NR

RABBINICAL SEMINARY OF AMERICA
New York, New York 11375 (--; Jewish; men; sem; III; 151) Courses with no degree
specialization, Dept of Phil, 212-268-2986

RCA INSTITUTES
New York, New York 10001 (Tech; p; coed; qr; I; 3500) NP

RENSSELAER POLYTECHNICAL INSTITUTE
Troy, New York 12181 (M; p; coed; sem; IV; 4719) MA major, Dept of Phil, 518-270-
6526

Wieck, David T, PhD, Prof, Chm, Aes, Soc Phil
Baum, Robert J, PhD, Assoc Prof, Phil of Sci, Ethics, Logic
Flores, Albert W, MA, Instr, Epistem, Ethics
Hammer, Louis Z, PhD, Assoc Prof, Aes, Exist
Koller, John M, PhD, Assoc Prof, Orient Phil, Phil of Relig
Schumacher, John A, MS, Instr, Phil of Mind, Phil of Psych
Thomas, Deborah R, PhD, Asst Prof, Metaph, Phil of Mind, Logic
Zenzen, Michael J, PhD, Asst Prof, Phenomen, Exist, Phil of Sci

Colovos, Polygnotos H, MS, Teach Asst   Stavros, Peter, BS, Teach Asst
Duquette, David A, BA, Teach Asst   Thomas-Moore, Gar, BA, Teach Asst

RICHMOND COLLEGE, CITY UNIVERSITY OF NEW YORK
Staten Island, New York 10301 (M; local; coed; sem; III; 3080) BA major, Div of Human, 212-448-8433

Cohen, Marshall, MA, Prof, Polit Phil, Aes
Hemmendinger, David, PhD, Instr, Phenomen, Phil of Sci

ROBERTS WESLEYAN COLLEGE
Rochester, New York 14624 (M; Meth; coed; tri; II; 654) BA minor, Dept of Phil, 716-594-9471

Ahern, Alvin A, PhD, Prof, Hist of Phil

ROCHESTER INSTITUTE OF TECHNOLOGY
Rochester, New York 14623 (M; p; coed; qr; III; 10,674) Courses with no degree specialization, Col of Gen Stud, 716-464-2468

Gordon, Dane, MA, Assoc Prof, Phil of Relig
Hamblin, Frances M, PhD, Prof, Ethics

THE ROCKEFELLER UNIVERSITY
New York, New York 10021 (--; p; coed; --; IV; 100) PhD major, Dept of Phil, 212-360-1325

Feinberg, Joel, PhD, Prof, Chm, Ethics, Soc Phil
Davidson, Donald, PhD, Prof, Phil of Lang, Phil of Mind
Frankfurt, Harry, PhD, Prof, Hist of Mod Phil, Phil of Mind
King, John, PhD, Asst Prof, Theory of Knowl, Phil of Sci
Kripke, Saul, PhD, Prof, Logic, Phil of Lang

Berger, Alan, BA
Bratman, Michael, BA
Burdick, Howard, BA
Lear, Jonathon, BA
Malament, David, BA

Reiss, Richard, BA
Ryan, Allison, BA
Schwartz, Adina, BA
Weinstein, Scott, BA
Yoder, Jesse, BA

ROCKLAND COMMUNITY COLLEGE, STATE UNIVERSITY OF NEW YORK
Suffern, New York 10901 (M; st and local; coed; sem; I; 5495) Courses with no degree specialization, Dept of Eng, 914-356-4650 Ext 330

Delfini, Alexander, MA, Cult Phil
Johnson, Frederick, M Div
Woodhouse, Robert, MA, Prof, Ethics

ROSARY HILL COLLEGE
Buffalo, New York 14226 (M; p; coed; sem; II; 1249) Courses with no degree specialization, --, 716-839-3600

O'Leary, James F, PhD, Asst Prof, Chm, Aes, Anc Phil, Phil of Relig
Hooper, Rachel, PhD, Prof, Metaph, Med Phil
Moran, James, PhD, Asst Prof, Ethics, Soc Phil, Exist
Welch, Mary F, Asst Prof, Mod Phil

RUSSELL SAGE COLLEGE
Troy, New York 12180 (M; p; coed; 4-1-4; III; 3813) BA major, Dept of Phil, 518-270-2336

Porter, Burton, PhD, Assoc Prof, Chm, Exist, Anal Phil, Phil in Lit

Ahlers, Rolf, ThD, Reynolds Prof, Biomedical Ethics, Hist of Phil
Hetko, Alex, PhD, Assoc Prof, Phil of Relig, Ethics

RUSSELL SAGE JUNIOR COLLEGE OF ALBANY
Albany, New York 12208 (M; p; coed; sem; I; 632) NR

SAINT BERNARD'S SEMINARY
Rochester, New York 14612 (Theol; RC; men; sem; III; 110) NR

SAINT BONAVENTURE UNIVERSITY
St Bonaventure, New York 14778 (M; RC; coed; sem; IV; 2685) BA major, Dept of Phil, 716-372-0300 Ext 308

Dooley, Patrick K, PhD, Assoc Prof, Chm, Amer Phil
Brown, Mary Anthony, PhD, Prof, Med Logic
Chiariello, Michael V, PhD, Asst Prof, Marx
Fay, Cornelius, PhD, Assoc Prof, Thomistic Phil
Geller, Leonard, PhD, Asst Prof, Exist
Hughes, Roderick, PhD, Asst Prof, Kierkegaard
Hunter, John, PhD, Asst Prof, Anal Phil
Kearney, Francis William, PhD, Prof, Med Phil
Lhota, Brian, PhD, Prof, Logic
Redlon, Reginald, PhD, Prof, Metaph
Reilly, Richard, PhD, Asst Prof, Ethics

SAINT FRANCIS COLLEGE
Brooklyn, New York 11201 (M; RC; coed; sem; II; 2624) BA major, --, 212-522-2300

SAINT JOHN FISHER COLLEGE
Rochester, New York 14618 (M; p; coed; sem; II; 1349) BA major, Dept of Phil, 716-586-4140

Carrington, William, MA, Instr, Metaph, Ethics
LaCentra, Walter, PhD, Assoc Prof, Theory of Knowl
McLaughlin, Robert J, PhD, Assoc Prof, Anc Phil, Med Phil, Polit Phil
Miller, Robert G, PhD, Prof, Med Phil, Contemp Phil
Williams, Clifford, BA, Instr, Phil of Time, Anal Phil

SAINT JOHN VIANNEY SEMINARY
East Aurora, New York 14052 (--; RC; men; sem; III; 97) BA major, Undergrad Dept, 716-652-8900

Belzer, Paul, MA
Caligiuri, Angelo, PhD, Ethics
Leising, Fred, MA
Weil, H Gil, PhD, Hist of Phil

SAINT JOHN'S UNIVERSITY
Jamaica, New York 11432 (M; RC; coed; sem; IV; 13,622) BA major, --, 212-969-8000

SAINT JOHN'S UNIVERSITY, STATEN ISLAND CAMPUS
Staten Island, New York 10301 (M; RC; coed; sem; IV; --) BA minor, Div of Human, 212-447-4343

Houchin, Thomas, PhD, Prof, Chm

Farrell, Edward P, PhD, Prof
Weeks, Louis, MA, Assoc Prof

SAINT JOSEPH'S COLLEGE
Brooklyn, New York 11205 (M; p; coed; sem; II; 616) NR

SAINT JOSEPH'S SEMINARY AND COLLEGE
Yonkers, New York 10704 (M; RC; men; sem; III; 79) Courses with no degree
specialization, Dept of Syst Theol, 914-968-6200

Imbelli, Robert P, PhD, Asst Prof, Amer Relig Phil
Komonchak, Joseph A, STM, Asst Prof, Phil of Man

SAINT LAWRENCE UNIVERSITY
Canton, New York 13617 (M; p; coed; 4-1-4; III; 2492) BA major, Dept of Phil, 315-
379-5456

Carmichael, Douglas, PhD, Prof, Chm
Crimmel, Henry H, PhD, Prof
Johnson, Bayler L, BA, Instr
Kirby, Brian S, PhD, Asst Prof

SAINT THOMAS AQUINAS COLLEGE
Sparkill, New York 10976 (M; p; coed; 4-1-4; II; 660) BA minor, Dept of Phil, 914-
359-1279

Biller, Mary Ann, PhD, Prof
Burunat, Julio, MA, Instr
Hurst, William, MA, Instr
McDonald, Robert, MA, Instr

SAINT VLADIMIR'S ORTHODOX THEOLOGICAL SEMINARY
Crestwood, New York 10707 (--; p; coed; sem; III; 76) NP

SARAH LAWRENCE COLLEGE
Bronxville, New York 10708 (M; p; coed; sem; III; 842) --, Dept of Phil, 914-337-
0700 Ext 403

SCHENECTADY COUNTY COMMUNITY COLLEGE, STATE UNIVERSITY OF NEW YORK
Schenectady, New York 12305 (--; st and local; coed; qr; I; 2014) Courses with no
degree specialization, Dept of Gen Educ, 518-346-6211 Ext 270, 271

Bryant, Paul, MA, Asst Prof
Buckhout, Gerard, PhD, Prof

SCHOOL OF INDUSTRIAL AND LABOR RELATIONS AT CORNELL UNIVERSITY
Ithaca, New York 14850 (M; st; coed; sem; IV; 605) NR

SIENA COLLEGE
Loudonville, New York 12211 (M; p; coed; sem; II; 1906) BA major, Dept of Phil,
518-785-8511

Davies, Julian A, PhD, Asst Prof, Head, Ordinary Lang Phil
Fitzpatrick, Noel A, PhD, Assoc Prof, Phenomen

Meilach, Michael, PhD, Asst Prof, Whitehead, Process Tht
Mooney, Donald, MA, Asst Prof, Stoics
O'Connor, Richard, MA, Prof, Hist of Phil
Roche, Evan, PhD, Prof, Med Phil
Van Hook, John, MA, Asst Prof, Phil of Mind

SKIDMORE COLLEGE
Saratoga Springs, New York 12866 (M; p; coed; 4-1-4; II; 2009) BA major, Dept of
Phil, 518-584-5000 Ext 394

Prosch, Harry, PhD, Prof, Chm, Ethics, Soc Phil, Polanyi
Dornenburg, Noreen, MPhil, Instr, Aes
Hockenos, Warren J, PhD, Assoc Prof, Logic, Phil of Sci
Honeywell, J Arthur, PhD, Prof, Compar Phil, Metaph
Rucker, Darnell, PhD, Prof, Amer Prag, Mead, Dewey
Waldrop, Charles, BD, Instr, Theol, Phil of Relig
Weller, Eric J, PhD, Assoc Prof Part-time, Lang Anal

STATE UNIVERSITY AT ALBANY, STATE UNIVERSITY OF NEW YORK
Albany, New York 12203 (M; st; coed; sem; IV; 13,905) PhD major, Dept of Phil, 518-
457-3433

Reese, William L, PhD, Prof, Chm, Metaph
Brunius, Teddy, PhD, Visit Prof, Aes
Bynum, Terrell W, MA, Asst Prof, Hist of Logic, Metaphil, Phil of Sci
Cadbury, Warder H, MA, Asst Prof, Ethics, Soc Tht, Hist of Greek Phil
Creegan, Robert F, PhD, Prof, Epistem, Soc Tht
Deitsch, Martin, PhD, Asst Prof, Phil of Mind, Phil of Lang, Epistem
Fullinwider, Robert K, PhD, Asst Prof, Ethics, Polit Phil
Garvin, Robert M, PhD, Asst Prof, Phil of Relig, Phil Anthrop, Ethics
Gould, Josiah B, PhD, Assoc Prof, Greek Phil, Phil Logic
Grimes, William V, PhD, Asst Prof, Theory of Value, Aes, Epistem
Howard, Michael S, AB, Lect, Soc Phil, Marxism
Leue, William H, PhD, Assoc Prof, Metaph, Hist of Phil
Martland, T R, PhD, Assoc Prof, Prag, Phil of Relig, Aes
Meyers, Robert G, PhD, Assoc Prof, Theory of Knowl, Amer Phil
Meyn, Henning L, PhD, Asst Prof, Phenomen, Phil of Lang
Morick, Harold, PhD, Assoc Prof, Phil of Mind, Epistem
Stern, Kenneth, PhD, Assoc Prof, Phil of Lang, Epistem, Phil of Sci
Thomas, James A, MA, Lect, Logic, Phil of Lang, Phil of Math

STATE UNIVERSITY AT BINGHAMTON, STATE UNIVERSITY OF NEW YORK
Binghamton, New York 13901 (M; st; coed; sem; IV; 7604) PhD major, Dept of Phil,
607-798-2655

Mischel, Theodore, PhD, Prof, Chm, Phil of Psych, Hist and Phil of Sci, Epistem
Ager, Tryg, PhD, Asst Prof, Kant, Epistem
Aronson, Jerrold L, PhD, Assoc Prof, Phil of Sci
Dillon, Martin C, PhD, Asst Prof, Exist, Phenomen, Hist of Phil
Duda, William L, PhD, Prof, Logic, Phil of Sci
Goldstein, Leon J, PhD, Prof, Phil of Hist, Phil of Soc Sci, Epistem
Haver, Ronald J, PhD, Visit Asst Prof, Greek Phil
Jameton, Andrew L, PhD, Visit Asst Prof, Medical Ethics, Epistem
Kaminsky, Jack, PhD, Prof, Seman Anal, Phil of Logic
Pizante, William, PhD, Asst Prof, Ethics, Metaph
Preus, Anthony, PhD, Assoc Prof, Anc Greek Phil
Roberts, Lawrence D, PhD, Asst Prof, Ethics, Hist of Med Phil
Roma, III, Emilio, PhD, Assoc Prof, Aes, Metaph, Epistem, Soc Phil
Ross, Stephen D, PhD, Prof, Ethics, Metaph
Sinisi, Vito F, PhD, Prof, Phil of Logic, Contemp Polish Logic and Phil

Thomas, Jr, Sid B, PhD, Assoc Prof, Ethics, Phil of Relig
Tonelli, Giorgio, PhD, Prof, 17th and 18th Cent Phil
Weiss, Donald D, PhD, Asst Prof, Polit Phil
Wilcox, John T, PhD, Assoc Prof, Contemp Ethical Theory, Hist of British Ethics,
    Nietzsche

Brown, Helen C, Grad Asst
Cabral, Susan C, Grad Asst
Griffin, Jr, Judson S, Grad Asst
King, Jeffrey H, Grad Asst
Martin, Kenneth F, Grad Asst
Mauldin, Denise E, Grad Asst
Monroe, Craig J, Grad Asst
Pass, Harry B, Grad Asst
Popich, Michael A, Grad Asst
Prokopczyk, Czeslaw

Ringle, Martin, Grad Asst
Rothbart, Daniel, Grad Asst
Russello, James J, Grad Asst
Schwartz, Robert D, Grad Asst
Seiz, Mark A, Grad Asst
Singer, Linda, Grad Asst
Steiner, Kenneth M, Grad Asst
Silver, Mitchel H, Grad Asst
Toole, Robert J, Grad Asst
Wassner, Gary A, Grad Asst

STATE UNIVERSITY AT BUFFALO, STATE UNIVERSITY OF NEW YORK
Amherst, New York 14226 (M; st; coed; sem; IV; 22,321) PhD major, Dept of Phil,
716-831-1331

Hare, Peter H, PhD, Prof, Chm
Barber, Kenneth F, PhD, Assoc Prof
Barker, Peter, Part-time Instr
Baumer, William H, PhD, Prof
Brady, James B, PhD, Assoc Prof
Brown, Ludlow, Part-time Instr
Cho, Kah-Kyung, PhD, Prof
Corcoran, John P, PhD, Prof
Diesing, Paul R, PhD, Prof
Dryden, Lee, Part-time Instr
Eddins, Berkley B, PhD, Prof
Farber, Marvin, PhD, Dist Prof
Franklin, Mitchell, JD, Prof
Gallagher, Cornelius, BA, Asst Prof
Garver, Newton, PhD, Prof
Gracia, Jorge J, PhD, Asst Prof
Handy, Rollo L, PhD, Prof
Hourani, George F, PhD, Prof
Hull, Richard T, PhD, Asst Prof
Inada, Kenneth K, PhD, Prof
Kearns, John T, PhD, Assoc Prof
Koehl, Richard A, PhD, Assoc Prof
Korsmeyer, Carolyn W, PhD, Asst Prof
Kurtz, Paul W, PhD, Prof
Lambros, Charles, PhD, Asst Prof
Lawler, James, PhD, Asst Prof
Madden, Edward H, PhD, Prof
Moser, Shia, PhD, Prof
Parry, William T, PhD, Prof
Perry, Thomas D, PhD, Assoc Prof
Radner, Daisie, PhD, Asst Prof
Riepe, Dale M, PhD, Prof
Robertson, Ann, Part-time Instr
Rose, Lynn E, PhD, Prof
Varney, Mary, PhD, Asst Prof
Wood, Susan, Part-time Instr
Zimmerman, Marvin, PhD, Prof

Boger, George, Grad Asst
Chakrabarti, Chandana, Grad Asst
Chakrabarti, Kisor, Grad Asst

Lachenman, Daniel, Grad Asst
Light, Lissa, Grad Asst
Lion, Roberta, Grad Asst

Choi, Chang-Han, Grad Asst
Corson, Lawrence, Grad Asst
DiFilippo, Terry, Grad Asst
Dolinsky, Paul, Grad Asst
Elkatip, Sule, Grad Asst
Finsen, Lawrence, Grad Asst
Garrison, George, Grad Asst
Giacaman, George, Grad Asst
Giuffrida, Robert, Grad Asst
Kahn, Steven, Grad Asst

Malia, Mary, Grad Asst
Nutter, Terry, Grad Asst
Oursler, Barney, Grad Asst
Peters, Haven, Grad Asst
Peterson, Richard, Grad Asst
Simpson, Walter, Grad Asst
Snyder, Lee, Grad Asst
Soble, Alan, Grad Asst
Tye, Michael, Grad Asst
Zeltner, Philip, Grad Asst

STATE UNIVERSITY AT STONY BROOK, STATE UNIVERSITY OF NEW YORK

Stony Brook, New York 11790 (M; st; coed; sem; IV; 11,413) PhD major, Dept of Phil, 516-246-6561, 516-246-6560

Heelan, Patrick, PhD, Prof, Chm, Phil of Sci
Ackley, Sheldon, PhD, Asst to Pres, Phil of Law
Allison, David, PhD, Asst Prof, Phenomen, Exist
Buchler, Justus, PhD, Dist Prof, Syst Phil
Dallery, Arleen, PhD, Asst Prof, Phenomen, Phil of Environ
Dallery, Carleton, PhD, Asst Prof, Phil and Medicine
deNicolas, Antonio, PhD, Assoc Prof, Indian Phil
Dilworth, David, PhD, Assoc Prof, Chinese Phil, Japanese Phil
Erwin, Edward, PhD, Asst Prof, Epistem, Phil of Mind
Federici, Sylvia, PhD, Visit Asst Prof, Soc Phil, Marxism
Gelber, Sidney, PhD, Academic Vice Pres, Polit Phil
Hill, Patrick, PhD, Assoc Prof, Dir Masters Program, Phil of Communic
Howard, Richard, PhD, Asst Prof, Soc Phil
Ihde, Don, PhD, Prof, Dir Grad Stud, Phenomen
Miller, Clyde Lee, PhD, Lect, Hist of Phil
Slote, Michael, PhD, Assoc Prof, Metaph, Epistem
Spector, Marshall, PhD, Assoc Prof, Phil of Sci
Sternfeld, Robert, PhD, Prof, Logical Theory
Tejera, Victor, PhD, Prof, Aes
Watson, Walter, PhD, Assoc Prof, Hist of Phil
Welton, Donn, PhD, Asst Prof, Phenomen
Zemach, Eddy, PhD, Assoc Prof, Epistem, Aes
Zyskind, Harold, PhD, Prof, Phil Rhet

Bell, Roger, Grad Asst
Bunch, Robert, Grad Asst
Byrne, Patrick, Grad Asst
Cohen, Richard, Grad Asst
Cote, Richard, Grad Asst
Duchon, Steve, Grad Asst
Esposito, Joan, Grad Asst
Essman, Shirley, Grad Asst
Faulkner, Charles, Grad Asst
Fiore, William, Grad Asst
Gavroglu, Kosta, Grad Asst
Glass, Elyse, Grad Asst
Gold, Jonathan, Grad Asst
Gross, Bennett, Grad Asst

Hart, Richard, Grad Asst
Johnson, Charles, Grad Asst
Kupers, Lawrence, Grad Asst
Mac Rae, Mairi, Grad Asst
Miller, Marjorie, Grad Asst
Morrison, Linda, Grad Asst
Newton, Tika, Grad Asst
Pinkard, Terry, Grad Asst
Pritchard, Ilona, Grad Asst
Rosen, Ira, Grad Asst
Savas, Sazan, Grad Asst
Slaughter, Tom, Grad Asst
Sluiter, Paul, Grad Asst

STATEN ISLAND COMMUNITY COLLEGE, STATE UNIVERSITY OF NEW YORK

Staten Island, New York 10301 (M; st and local; coed; sem; I; 8559) Courses with no degree specialization, Dept of Econ, Polit Sci and Phil, 212-390-7605

Belaief, Lynne, PhD, Assoc Prof, Ethics

Natanson, Harvey, PhD, Prof, Soc Phil
Roy, Subodh, PhD, Assoc Prof, Orient Phil

SUFFOLK COUNTY COMMUNITY COLLEGE, STATE UNIVERSITY OF NEW YORK
Selden, New York 11784 (M; st and local; coed; sem; I; 10,818) --, Dept of Music,
Fine Arts and Phil, 516-732-1600

Arcario, Peter, MA, Part-time
Kleinman, Lowell, MA, Asst Prof
Lichenstein, Sandra, MA, Instr
Whitely, Robert, MA, Asst Prof, Orient Phil

SULLIVAN COUNTY COMMUNITY COLLEGE, STATE UNIVERSITY OF NEW YORK
Loch Sheldrake, New York 12779 (M; st and local; coed; 4-1-4; I; 1238) AA major,
Dept of Human, 914-434-5750

Magana, Richard, PhD, Prof, Phil of Theol

SYRACUSE UNIVERSITY
Syracuse, New York 13210 (M; p; coed; sem; IV; 23,431) PhD major, Dept of Phil,
315-423-2045

Thau, Stewart, PhD, Assoc Prof, Chm, Phil of Lang, Anal Phil
Benardete, José, PhD, Prof, Metaph, Phil of Math, Anc Phil
Brown, Mark, PhD, Asst Prof, Logic, Found of Logic and Math
Denise, T C, PhD, Prof, Logic, Phil of Logic, Hist of Logic
Green, Thomas F, Adj Prof, Phil of Educ
Hardin, C L, PhD, Assoc Prof, Phil of Sci
Kidder, Joel, PhD, Asst Prof, Moral and Polit Phil
Lachterman, David, BA, Lect, Anc Phil, German Phil, Metaph
Lord, Catherine, PhD, Prof, Aes
McKay, Thomas, PhD, Asst Prof, Logic, Epistem
Meiklejohn, Donald, PhD, Prof, Polit and Soc Phil, Phil of Law
Molina, Fernando, PhD, Prof, Exist, Phil of Mind
Olscamp, Paul, PhD, Prof, Mod Phil, Moral Phil
Peterfreund, Sheldon, PhD, Prof, Moral Phil, Amer Phil
Peterson, Phillip, PhD, Assoc Prof, Phil of Lang, Epistem
Robinson, J Alan, Adj Prof, Proof Theory
Smith, Huston, Adj Prof, Phil of Relig, East Phil
van Inwagen, Peter, PhD, Asst Prof, Metaph, Logic

Anderson, James
Cahill, Christopher
Campbell, Thomas
Chakravarti, Sitansu
Cowley, Barbara
Fleming, Derwood

Gibian, Barbara
Harbison, Warren
Lewis, Jonathan
Manolakos, Peter
Schoenhofen, Darr
Stewart, Roderick

TOMPKINS-CORTLAND COMMUNITY COLLEGE, STATE UNIVERSITY OF NEW YORK
Groton, New York 13073 (--; st and local; coed; sem; I; 1331) Courses with no
degree specialization, Dept of Human, 607-898-5825 Ext 44

TOURO COLLEGE
New York, New York 10036 (--; p; men; sem; II; 35) NR

TROCAIRE COLLEGE
Buffalo, New York 14220 (XT; RC; coed; sem; I; 436) Courses with no degree
specialization, Dept of Phil, 716-826-1200

Maloney, Joseph Marie, MA, Chm
Mitchell, Thomas, MA

ULSTER COUNTY COMMUNITY COLLEGE, STATE UNIVERSITY OF NEW YORK
Stone Ridge, New York 12484 (M; st and local; coed; sem; I; 2129) Courses with
no degree specialization, Div of Human, 914-687-7621

UNION COLLEGE
Schenectady, New York 12308 (M; p; coed; --; IV; 3145) BA major, Dept of Phil, 518-
370-6214

Ludwig, Jan K, PhD, Asst Prof, Act Chm, Phil of Sci, Anal Phil
Baker, Robert B, PhD, Asst Prof, Value Theory
Elliston, Frederick A, MA, Instr, Phenomen, Exist
Enteman, Willard F, PhD, Assoc Prof, Prov, Phil of the Soc Sci
Peterson, Sven R, PhD, Prof, Hist of Phil
Tolan, Edwin K, PhD, Prof, Med Phil
Vetterling, Mary K, MA, Visit Instr, Hist of Phil, Phil of Soc Sci

Larrabee, Harold A, PhD, Prof Emer

UNION THEOLOGICAL SEMINARY
New York, New York 10027 (M; p; coed; sem; IV; 427) PhD major, Dept of Phil of
Relig, 212-662-7100

Martin, J Alfred, PhD, Prof, Phil of Relig
Williams, Daniel D, PhD, Prof, Phil of Relig, Process Phil

UNITED STATES MERCHANT MARINE ACADEMY
Kings Point, New York 11024 (M; Fed; men; qr; II; 1000) NP

UNITED STATES MILITARY ACADEMY
West Point, New York 10996 (M; Fed; men; sem; II; 4095) Courses with no degree
specialization, Dept of Eng, 914-938-4337

Matthews, Lloyd J, PhD, Assoc Prof, Dir, Phil in Lit
Bergen, John D, MA, Instr
Dowling, Dean E, PhD, Asst Prof
Haack, Duane G, MA, Instr
Hartle, Anthony E, MA, Instr
Ivey, Herman V, MA, Instr
Kelly, Jr, Arthur M, MA, Asst Prof
Lazarus, Francis M, PhD, Asst Prof, Class Phil
Peterson, James C, MA, Asst Prof
Smith, Daniel M, MA, Instr, Phil in Lit
Weems, Jr, Kelly G, MA, Instr

UNIVERSITY OF ROCHESTER
Rochester, New York 14627 (M; p; coed; sem; IV; 8631) PhD major, Dept of Phil,
716-275-4105

Kyburg, Jr, Henry E, PhD, Prof, Chm, Phil of Sci
Beck, Lewis W, PhD, Prof, Mod Phil
Eberle, Rolf, PhD, Assoc Prof, Logic
Holcomb, Harmon R, BD, Prof, Phil of Relig
Holmes, Robert L, PhD, Prof, Ethics
Jones, S Milton, BA, Asst Prof, Metaph

Lehrer, Keith, PhD, Prof, Theory of Knowl
Pollock, John, PhD, Assoc Prof, Epistem
Shaw, James R, PhD, Asst Prof, Anc Phil, Med Phil
Taylor, Richard, PhD, Prof, Metaph
Turbayne, Colin M, PhD, Prof, Metaph

Jones, Alfred H, PhD, Prof Emer

Ackerman, Terrence
Carr, James E
Cassidy, John H
Franzwa, Gregg
Gietz, William
Greene, Jesse A
Hamblin, Peter D
Haver, Richard

Krenis, Joel H
Lockhart, Ted W
McIntire, Stephan J
Mirarchi, Lawrence
Rotondo, Joseph T
Stulberg, Joseph B
Werner, Richard

UPSTATE MEDICAL CENTER, STATE UNIVERSITY OF NEW YORK
Syracuse, New York 13210 (M; st; coed; sem; IV; 830) NP

VASSAR COLLEGE
Poughkeepsie, New York 12601 (M; p; coed; sem; III; 2130) BA major, Dept of Phil,
914-452-7000 Ext 112

Weingartner, Rudolph H, PhD, Prof, Chm, Phil of Hist, Plato
Frankfurt, Harry, PhD, Visit Prof Part-time, Phil of Mind
Grontkowski, Christine, PhD, Asst Prof Part-time, Phil of Sci
Hoagland, Sarah, BA, Instr, Theory of Knowl
Kalin, Jesse, PhD, Asst Prof, Ethics, Soc Phil, Polit Phil
Kitcher, Philip, BA, Instr, Phil of Sci, Logic
McCarthy, Michael, PhD, Asst Prof, Phil of Lang, Hist of Phil
Miller, Mitchell, PhD, Asst Prof, Class Phil, German Phil, Hist of Phil
Murray, Michael, PhD, Assoc Prof, Exist, Phenomen, Aes
Tillman, Frank, PhD, Prof, Phil of Mind, Aes
Vander Veer, Garrett, PhD, Assoc Prof, Metaph, Theory of Knowl

Venable, Vernon, PhD, Prof Emer, Ethics, Theories of Human Nature

VILLA MARIA COLLEGE OF BUFFALO
Buffalo, New York 14225 (M; p; coed; 4-1-4; I; 517) Courses with no degree
specialization, Dept of Relig Stud, 716-896-0700 Ext 315

Long, James, M Div, Instr

WADHAMS HALL SEMINARY-COLLEGE
Ogdensburg, New York 13669 (M; RC; men; sem; I; 103) BA major, Phil Teach Area,
315-393-4231

Joly, Paul T, MA, Prof
Keene, J Calvin, PhD, Visit Prof
Poissant, Leeward J, PhD, Instr
Riani, Peter R, STD, Prof

WAGNER COLLEGE
Staten Island, New York 10301 (M; Luth; coed; sem; III; 3298) BA major, Dept of
Phil, 212-390-3179

Gardner, Romaine, Prof, Chm, Ethics, Polit Phil
Benson, Robert, BD, Instr, 19th Cent Exist

Lynes, Jack, PhD, Asst Prof, Mod Phil, Phil of Action
Unhjem, Arne, PhD, Prof, Orient Phil, Phil of Relig

WEBB INSTITUTE OF NAVAL ARCHITECTURE
Glen Cove, New York 11542 (M; p; men; sem; II; 83) NR

WELLS COLLEGE
Aurora, New York 13026 (M; p; wo; 4-1-4; III; 602) BA major, Dept of Phil, 315-364-7161 Ext 313

Brown, Peter I, PhD, Assoc Prof, Chm, Hist of Phil, Value Theory
Jaffe, Raymond, PhD, Prof, Soc Phil, Value Theory
Litzenburg, Jr, Thomas V, PhD, Assoc Prof, Phil of Relig, Phil of Mind

WESTCHESTER COMMUNITY COLLEGE, STATE UNIVERSITY OF NEW YORK
Valhalla, New York 10595 (M; st and local; coed; sem; I; 5813) Courses with no degree specialization, Dept of Human, 914-946-1616 Ext 208

Behr, Stanley M, AM, Assoc Prof, British Empir

WOODSTOCK COLLEGE
New York, New York 10027 (M; RC; men; sem; IV; 128) NR

YESH BETH SHEARM RABBINICAL INSTITUTE
Brooklyn, New York 11204 (--; Jewish; men; sem; III; 205) NR

YESHIVA UNIVERSITY
New York, New York 10033 (M; p; coed; sem; IV; 3495) BA major, Dept of Phil, 212-568-8400 Ext 313

Hyman, Arthur, PhD, Univ Prof, Chm, Hist of Phil, Med Phil, Early Mod Phil
Roth, Sol, PhD, Visit Asst Prof, Logic, Phil of Sci, Epistem
Schnall, Ira, BA, Visit Lect, Logic, Metaph
Shmidman, Joshua, BA, Visit Lec, Phil of Relig
Wurzburger, Walter, PhD, Visit Assoc Prof, Ethics, Soc Phil, Exist, Phenomen

YORK COLLEGE, CITY UNIVERSITY OF NEW YORK
Jamaica, New York 11432 (M; local; coed; sem; II; 2707) BA major, Dept of Human, 212-969-4040

Gross, Barry R, PhD, Asst Prof, Phil of Mind, Epistem, Metaph
Hartenberg, Sam, PhD, Asst Prof, Ethics, Soc Phil, Polit Phil
Hoffman, Robert, PhD, Asst Prof, Phil of Lang, Phil of Art, Phil of Relig
Ruttenberg, Howard, MA, Lect, Soc Phil, Polit Phil

NORTH CAROLINA

ANSON TECHNICAL INSTITUTE
Ansonville, North Carolina 28007 (--; st and local; coed; qr; I; 278) NR

APPALACHIAN STATE UNIVERSITY
Boon, North Carolina 28607 (S; st; coed; qr; III; 7668) MA minor, --, 704-264-8871

Stines, James W, PhD, Assoc Prof, Chm, Exist, Phenomen
Humphrey, Richard A, PhD, Prof, Med Stud
Richter, Mary Ann, PhD, Asst Prof, Contemp Stud
Ruble, Raymond S, PhD, Asst Prof, British Empir, German Ideal
van der Bogert, Frans, PhD, Asst Prof, Logic

ASHEVILLE BUNCOMBE TECHNICAL INSTITUTE
Asheville, North Carolina 28801 (S; st; coed; qr; I; 1184) NR

ATLANTIC CHRISTIAN COLLEGE
Wilson, North Carolina 27893 (S; Chris; coed; sem; II; 1794) BA minor, Dept of
Relig and Phil, 919-237-3161 Ext 218

Purcell, Jr, E G, M Div, Assoc Prof, Phil of Relig

BARBER SCOTIA COLLEGE
Concord, North Carolina 28025 (S; Preb; coed; sem; II; 550) Courses with no degree
specialization, --, 704-786-5171

BEAUFORT COUNTY TECHNICAL INSTITUTE
Washington, North Carolina 27889 (--; st and local; coed; qr; I; 461) NP

BELMONT ABBEY COLLEGE
Belmont, North Carolina 28012 (S; RC; coed; sem; II; 718) Courses with no degree
specialization, Dept of Phil, 704-825-3711

Coggin, Walter A, PhD, Prof, Chm, Metaph
Camele, Anthony M, PhD, Instr Part-time, Ethics

BENNETT COLLEGE
Greensboro, North Carolina 27420 (S; U Meth; wo; sem; II; 582) Courses with no
degree specialization, Div of Human, 919-275-9791 Ext 25

Goldstein, Signe Burke, PhD, Asst Prof, Marxist Phil, Phil Anthrop
Lucier, Ruth Miller, PhD, Asst Prof, Epistem, Soc and Polit Phil

BLADEN TECHNICAL INSTITUTE
Dublin, North Carolina 28332 (--; st; coed; qr; I; 146) NR

BLUE RIDGE TECHNICAL INSTITUTE
Hendersonville, North Carolina 28739 (--; st and local; coed; qr; I; 211) NP

BREVARD COLLEGE
   Brevard, North Carolina 28712 (S; U Meth; coed; sem; I; 546) NR

CALDWELL COMMUNITY COLLEGE AND TECHNICAL INSTITUTE
   Lenoir, North Carolina 28645 (S; local; coed; qr; I; 812) AA major, Dept of Human
   and Soc Sci, 704-728-4323

   Morgan, Metaleen, MA
   Pittman, David, PhD

CAMPBELL COLLEGE
   Buie's Creek, North Carolina 27506 (S; S Bapt; coed; sem; II; 2401) BA major, Dept
   of Phil, 919-893-4111 Ext 268

   Newman, Stewart A, ThD, Prof, Chm
   Hester, Joseph P, PhD, Asst Prof, Ethics

CAPE FEAR TECHNICAL INSTITUTE
   Wilmington, North Carolina 28401 (S; st and local; coed; qr; I; 647) NP

CARTERET TECHNICAL INSTITUTE
   Morehead City, North Carolina 28557 (--; st and local; coed; qr; I; 305) NP

CATAWBA COLLEGE
   Salisbury, North Carolina 28144 (S; U Ch of Christ; coed; qr; I; 1132) BA major,
   Dept of Relig and Phil, 704-636-5311

   Brown, J Daniel, PhD, Assoc Prof
   McClatchey, John, PhD, Asst Prof, Logic, Epistem

CATAWBA VALLEY TECHNICAL INSTITUTE
   Hickory, North Carolina 28601 (S; st and local; coed; qr; I; 1073) NR

CENTRAL CAROLINA TECHNICAL INSTITUTE
   Sanford, North Carolina 27330 (--; st and local; coed; qr; I; 653) NP

CENTRAL PIEDMONT COMMUNITY COLLEGE
   Charlotte, North Carolina 28204 (S; st and local; coed; qr; I; 14,618) --, Dept
   of Human, 704-372-2590 Ext 317

   Rouzer, Nancy C

CHOWAN COLLEGE
   Murfreesboro, North Carolina 27855 (S; S Bapt; coed; sem; I; 1545) Courses with
   no degree specialization, Dept of Relig and Phil, 919-398-4101

   Parker, Earl H, PhD, Prof

CLEVELAND COUNTY TECHNICAL INSTITUTE
   Shelby, North Carolina 28150 (--; st and local; coed; qr; I; 359) NP

COASTAL CAROLINA COMMUNITY COLLEGE
   Jacksonville, North Carolina 28540 (--; st; coed; qr; I; 984) --, --, 919-455-
   1221

Pierson, Eilene C, BA

COLLEGE OF THE ALBEMARLE
Elizabeth City, North Carolina 27909 (S; st; coed; qr; I; 946) NR

CRAVEN TECHNICAL INSTITUTE
Newbern, North Carolina 28560 (S; st and local; coed; qr; I; 380) NR

DAVIDSON COLLEGE
Davidson, North Carolina 28036 (S; Preb; coed; --; II; 1087) BA major, Dept of Phil,
704-892-8021

Abernethy, George L, PhD, Prof, Chm, Phil of Relig, Compar Relig, Polit Phil
MacCormac, Earl L, PhD, Prof, Phil of Sci, Phil of Relig, Phil of Lang
Thomas, William, PhD, Visit Asst Prof, Logic, Phil of Sci
Young, John, PhD, Asst Prof, Anal Phil, Logic

DAVIDSON COUNTY COMMUNITY COLLEGE
Lexington, North Carolina 27292 (S; local; coed; qr; I; 5605) Courses with no degree
specialization, Dept of Human, 704-249-8186

Helm, Paul, PhD
Jarvis, Dwight C, PhD, Assoc Dean, Ethics

DUKE UNIVERSITY
Durham, North Carolina 27706 (S; p; coed; sem; IV; 8217) PhD major, Dept of Phil,
919-684-3838

Welsh, Paul, PhD, Prof, Chm, Aes, Ethics, Phil of Lang
Aquila, Richard, PhD, Asst Prof, Hist of Phil, Kant, Phil of Mind
Benditt, Theodore, PhD, Asst Prof, Moral Phil, Phil of Law
Coder, David, PhD, Asst Prof, Phil of Mind, Phil of Lang, Logic
Dray, William H, PhD, Prof, Phil of Hist
Mahoney, Edward, PhD, Assoc Prof, Late Anc Phil, Med and Renaissance Phil
Negley, Glenn R, PhD, Prof, Polit Phil
Peach, Bernard, PhD, Prof, 18th and 20th Cent Phil, Anglo-Amer Moral Phil
Roberts, George W, PhD, Assoc Prof, Ethics, Hist of Phil, Phil of Relig
Ross, David, PhD, Asst Prof, Logic, Phil of Sci, Metaph
Sanford, David, PhD, Assoc Prof, Causation and Conditions

DURHAM COLLEGE
Durham, North Carolina 27707 (JRCB; p; coed; qr; I; 450) NR

DURHAM TECHNICAL INSTITUTE
Durham, North Carolina 27703 (S; st and local; coed; qr; I; 1038) NR

EAST CAROLINA UNIVERSITY
Greenville, North Carolina 27834 (S; st; coed; qr; III; 11,067) MA minor, Dept of
Phil, 919-758-6121

Kozy, Jr, John, PhD, Chm, Prof, Metaph
Gibbons, Alan C, PhD, Asst Prof, Phenomen
Gross, Dwayer D, PhD, Assoc Prof
Ingardia, Richard, PhD, Asst Prof, 19th Cent Phil
Koller, Alice, PhD, Asst Prof, Phil of Lang
Marshall, Ernest C, PhD, Assoc Prof, Phil of Mind

Murphy, Frank J, PhD, Asst Prof, Ethics
Nedzynski, Thomas G, MA, Asst Prof, Logic
Ross, Gregory A, PhD, Asst Prof, Epistem
Ryan, Eugene E, PhD, Assoc Prof, Anc and Med Phil
Smith, James L, PhD, Asst Prof, Aes, Polit Phil

EAST CAROLINA UNIVERSITY AT CHERRY POINT
Cherry Point, North Carolina 28533 (S; st; coed; qr; I; 114) NR

EAST CAROLINA UNIVERSITY AT LEJEUNE
Camp Lejeune, North Carolina 28542 (S; st; coed; qr; I; 316) NP

EDGECOMBE TECHNICAL INSTITUTE
Tarboro, North Carolina 27886 (--; st and local; coed; qr; I; 1464) NP

ELIZABETH CITY STATE UNIVERSITY
Elizabeth City, North Carolina 27909 (S; st; coed; sem; II; 1084) --, Dept of Soc
Sci, 919-335-0551 Ext 339

Nadeau, Louis V, PhD, Prof, Syst Phil

ELON COLLEGE
Elon College, North Carolina 27244 (S; U Ch of Christ; coed; 4-1-4; II; 1836) BA
major, Dept of Phil, 919-584-9711 Ext 217

Sullivan, John G, JCD, Asst Prof, Chm
Reynolds, Ferris E, PhD, Prof

FAYETTEVILLE STATE UNIVERSITY
Fayetteville, North Carolina 28301 (S; st; coed; sem; II; 1490) Courses with no
degree specialization, Area of Phil and Relig, 919-483-6144 Ext 258

Thomas, C C, PhD, Prof, Phil of Relig
Miller, J C, MTh, Instr

FAYETTEVILLE STATE UNIVERSITY AT FORT BRAGG
Fort Bragg 28307 (S; st; coed; --; II; 1061) NR

FAYETTEVILLE TECHNICAL INSTITUTE
Fayetteville, North Carolina 28303 (S; st; coed; qr; I; 1118) Courses with no
degree specialization, Dept of Soc Sci, 919-484-4121

Moore, Anne R, MA, Instr

FORSYTH TECHNICAL INSTITUTE
Winston-Salem, North Carolina 27103 (S; st; coed; qr; I; 1051) NP

GARDNER-WEBB COLLEGE
Boiling Springs, North Carolina 28017 (S; S Bapt; coed; sem; II; 1420) Courses with
no degree specialization, Dept of Relig Stud and Phil

Hewitt, Thomas Furman, ThD, Assoc Prof, Phil of Relig

GASTON COLLEGE
    Dallas, North Carolina 28034 (S; st; coed; qr; I; 5116) NP

GREENSBORO COLLEGE
    Greensboro, North Carolina 27420 (S; U Meth; coed; sem; II; 590) BA joint or
    combined major, --, 919-272-7102

GUILFORD COLLEGE
    Greensboro, North Carolina 27410 (S; Fr; coed; sem; II; 1740) BA major, Dept of
    Phil, 919-292-5511 Ext 68

    Kent, E Daryl, PhD, Prof, Chm, Hist of Phil, Ethics
    Beidler, William, PhD, Assoc Prof, East Phil
    Feagins, Carroll, PhD, Prof, Aes
    Millholland, Donald, PhD, Assoc Prof, Mod Euro Phil

GUILFORD TECHNICAL INSTITUTE
    Jamestown, North Carolina 27282 (S; st; coed; qr; I; 1761) NP

HALIFAX COUNTY TECHNICAL INSTITUTE
    Weldon, North Carolina 27890 (--; st and local; coed; qr; I; 406) NP

HAYWOOD TECHNICAL INSTITUTE
    Clyde, North Carolina 28721 (--; st; coed; qr; I; 421) NP

HIGH POINT COLLEGE
    High Point, North Carolina 27262 (S; U Meth; coed; sem; II; 1060) BA major, Dept
    of Relig and Phil, 919-885-5101 Ext 34

    Crow, Earl, PhD, Prof
    Davis, E Vance, PhD, Asst Prof, Ethics
    Weatherly, Owen M, PhD, Prof

ISOTHERMAL COMMUNITY COLLEGE
    Spindale, North Carolina 28160 (S; st and local; coed; qr; I; 273) NP

JAMES SPRUNT INSTITUTE
    Kenansville, North Carolina 28398 (--; st; coed; qr; I; 427) Courses with no
    degree specialization, Dept of Gen Educ, 919-293-4591

    Remington, David, MA

JOHNSON C SMITH UNIVERSITY
    Charlotte, North Carolina 28216 (S; Preb; coed; sem; II; 1036) BA major, Dept of
    Phil and Relig, 704-372-2370 Ext 241

    Bohn, Ralph P, PhD, Prof, Chm, West Myst, Phil of Communic
    Coleman, Sr, Winson R, PhD, Prof, Polit Phil
    Counts, Herman L, AM, Prof

KING'S COLLEGE
    Charlotte, North Carolina 28204 (JRCB; p; coed; qr; I; 538) NP

KITTRELL COLLEGE
   Kittrell, North Carolina 27544 (--; AME; coed; sem; I; 554) Courses with no degree
   specialization, Dept of Human, 919-492-2131 Ext 31

   Ragland, O J, MA, Prof, Chm

LEES-MCRAE COLLEGE
   Banner Elk, North Carolina 28604 (S; Preb; coed; sem; I; 670) Courses with no
   degree specialization, Div of Relig, Phil and Fine Arts, 704-898-5241

   Farley, Ben, ThM

LENOIR COMMUNITY COLLEGE
   Kinston, North Carolina 28501 (S; st and local; coed; qr; I; 1547) NR

LENOIR-RHYNE COLLEGE
   Hickory, North Carolina 28601 (S; Luth CA; coed; 4-1-4; II; 1395) BA major, Dept
   of Phil, 704-328-1741

   McDaniel, Michael C D, MA, Asst Prof
   von Dohlen, Richard, BD, Asst Prof

LIVINGSTONE COLLEGE
   Salisbury, North Carolina 28144 (S; AMEZ; coed; sem; II; 754) Courses with no
   degree specialization, --, 704-633-7960

   Spaulding, Oliva Turrentine, MRE, Prof

LOUISBURG COLLEGE
   Louisburg, North Carolina 27549 (S; U Meth; coed; sem; I; 773) AA major, Dept of
   Relig and Phil, 919-496-4101 Ext 24

   Farmer, Charles J, MEd, Prof, Chm
   Stafford, Sidney, M Div, Prof

MARS HILL COLLEGE
   Mars Hill, North Carolina 28754 (S; S Bapt; coed; 4-1-4; II; 1467) Courses with no
   degree specialization, Dept of Relig and Phil, 704-689-1216

   Leininger, C Earl, ThD, Assoc Prof, Phil of Relig

MARTIN TECHNICAL INSTITUTE
   Williamston, North Carolina 27892 (--; st; coed; qr; I; 286) Courses with no degree
   specialization, --, 919-792-5033

MCDOWELL TECHNICAL INSTITUTE
   Marion, North Carolina 28752 (--; st; coed; qr; I; 245) NP

MEREDITH COLLEGE
   Raleigh, North Carolina 27611 (S; S Bapt; wo; sem; II; 1291) --, Dept of Relig and
   Phil, 919-833-6461 Ext 290

   Littleton, Jr, Harold E, MA, Asst Prof

METHODIST COLLEGE
   Fayetteville, North Carolina 28301 (S; U Meth; coed; sem; II; 1496) BA minor,
   Area II - Relig and Phil, 919-488-7110 Ext 264

   Plyler, Lorenzo P, PhD, Assoc Prof, Chm, Hist of Phil, Ethics, Phil of Relig
   Sarenac, Veselin, ThD, Assoc Prof, Logic, Contemp Phil, Hist of Phil, Mod Phil

MITCHELL COLLEGE
   Statesville, North Carolina 28677 (S; p; coed; 4-1-4; I; 576) NP

MONTREAT-ANDERSON COLLEGE
   Montreat, North Carolina 28757 (S; Preb; coed; sem; I; 320) NR

MOUNT OLIVE COLLEGE
   Mount Olive, North Carolina 28365 (S; F Will Bapt; coed; sem; I; 328) Courses with
   no degree specialization, Dept of Soc Sci, 919-658-2502

NASH TECHNICAL INSTITUTE
   Rocky Mount, North Carolina 27801 (--; st and local; coed; qr; I; 185) NR

NORTH CAROLINA AGRICULTURAL AND TECHNICAL STATE UNIVERSITY
   Greensboro, North Carolina 27411 (S; st; coed; sem; III; 4445) NP

NORTH CAROLINA CENTRAL UNIVERSITY
   Durham, North Carolina 27707 (S; st; coed; sem; IV; 3723) BA major, Dept of Phil
   and Latin, 919-682-2171 Ext 425

   Clack, R Jerold, PhD, Assoc Prof, Chm, Phil of Lang, Metaph
   Marlette, Wade, MA, Asst Prof, Soc and Polit Phil

NORTH CAROLINA SCHOOL OF THE ARTS
   Winston-Salem, North Carolina 27107 (S; st; coed; tri; II; 328) Courses with no
   degree specialization, Dept of Academic Stud, 919-784-7170

   Miller, Richard Harry, BA, Instr, Med Phil

NORTH CAROLINA STATE UNIVERSITY
   Raleigh, North Carolina 27607 (S; st; coed; sem; IV; 13,483) BA major, Dept of
   Phil and Relig, 919-737-2477

   Bryan, Robert S, PhD, Prof, Chm, Ethics, Phil of Educ
   Bredenberg, Paul A, PhD, Prof, Aes
   Carter, W R, PhD, Asst Prof, Phil of Mind
   Fitzgerald, W Curtis, BD, Asst Prof, Exist
   Gillmor, Wiley G, BA, Instr, Found of Math
   Lear, George A, PhD, Asst Prof, Ethics
   Levin, Harold D, BS, Instr, Phil of Lang
   Metzger, Robert S, PhD, Assoc Prof, Phil of Sci
   Nagel, Richard I, AB, Instr, Phil of Sci
   Regan, Thomas H, PhD, Assoc Prof, Ethics
   Stalnaker, C L, MA, Instr, Phil of Relig
   VanDeVeer, A Donald, PhD, Asst Prof, Phil of Mind, Polit Phil

   Hicks, William N, Prof Emer

NORTH CAROLINA WESLEYAN COLLEGE
Rocky Mount, North Carolina 27801 (S; U Meth; coed; --; II; 617) BA major, Dept of
Phil and Relig, 919-442-7121

Hailey, James R, PhD, Prof, Chm
Haggard, Frank P, PhD, Asst Prof, Med Phil
James, Ralph E, PhD, Assoc Prof, Process Phil
Moore, Jack W, PhD, Prof, Ethics

PEACE COLLEGE
Raleigh, North Carolina 27602 (S; Preb; wo; sem; I; 509) NP

PEMBROKE STATE UNIVERSITY
Pembroke, North Carolina 28372 (S; st; coed; sem; II; 2078) Courses with no
degree specialization, Dept of Phil and Relig, 919-521-4214

Gustafson, Robert, ThD, Prof, Chm, Amer Intell Tht
Guerry, Herbert, PhD, Asst Prof, Logic
Studdard, Albert, ThD, Assoc Prof, Phil of Relig

PFEIFFER COLLEGE
Misenheimer, North Carolina 28109 (S; U Meth; coed; sem; II; 1088) BA major, Dept
of Phil, 704-463-3111

Beyer, E, MA, Assoc Prof, Chm, Hist of Phil
Thomas, C T, PhD, Prof, Asian Phil

PIEDMONT BIBLE COLLEGE
Winston-Salem, North Carolina 27101 (BI; p; coed; sem; II; 385) Courses with no
degree specialization, --, 919-725-8344 Ext 68

Patterson, Richard, PhD, Chm
Le Grand, M David, MRE, Phil and Christ Educ

PIEDMONT TECHNICAL INSTITUTE
Roxboro, North Carolina 27573 (--; st and local; coed; qr; I; 1015) NR

PITT TECHNICAL INSTITUTE
Greenville, North Carolina 27834 (S; st; coed; qr; I; 672) NP

QUEENS COLLEGE
Charlotte, North Carolina 28207 (S; Preb; wo; 4-1-4; II; 673) BA minor, Dept of
Phil, 704-332-7121 Ext 242

Lange, Ann E, MA, Asst Prof, Chm, Aes, Exist
Crosthwaite, Jane, PhD, Asst Prof, Ethics

RANDOLPH TECHNICAL INSTITUTE
Asheboro, North Carolina (--; st and local; coed; qr; I; 356) NR

RICHMOND TECHNICAL INSTITUTE
Hamlet, North Carolina 28345 (S; st and local; coed; qr; I; 480) NP

ROANOKE-CHOWAN TECHNICAL INSTITUTE
    Ahoskie, North Carolina 27910 (--; st and local; coed; qr; I; 272) NP

ROBESON TECHNICAL INSTITUTE
    Saint Pauls, North Carolina 28384 (--; st and local; coed; qr; I; 1061) NR

ROCKINGHAM COMMUNITY COLLEGE
    Wentworth, North Carolina 27375 (S; st and local; coed; qr; I; 1244) NR

ROWAN TECHNICAL INSTITUTE
    Salisbury, North Carolina 28144 (S; st; coed; qr; I; 758) NP

SACRED HEART COLLEGE
    Belmont, North Carolina 28012 (S; RC; wo; sem; II; 318) --, Dept of Integrated
    Stud, 704-825-3932

    Camele, Anthony M, Asst Prof
    Donovan, Edward L, PhD, Assoc Prof

SAINT ANDREWS PRESBYTERIAN COLLEGE
    Laurinburg, North Carolina 28352 (S; Preb; coed; 4-1-4; II; 892) BA joint or combined
    major, Div of Relig and Phil, 919-276-3652

    Alexander, William M, PhD, Prof, Chm, Hist of Phil, Phil of Relig
    Crossley, Ronald C, PhD, Assoc Prof, Hist of Relig, Hindu Relig and Phil
    Ludlow, L Spencer, M Div, Asst Prof, Phil of Relig, Ethics, Logic
    Prust, Richard C, PhD, Asst Prof, Contemp Phil, Phenomen, Exist

SAINT AUGUSTINE'S COLLEGE
    Raleigh, North Carolina 27611 (S; Prot Epis; coed; sem; II; 1284) NR

SAINT MARY'S JUNIOR COLLEGE
    Raleigh, North Carolina 27611 (S; Prot Epis; wo; sem; I; 341) NP

SALEM COLLEGE
    Winston-Salem, North Carolina 27108 (S; Morav; wo; 4-1-4; II; 530) Courses
    with no degree specialization, Dept of Relig and Phil, 919-723-7961 Ext 218

    Hill, Mary Stewart, PhD, Prof, Chm, Phil of Relig, Ethics

SAMPSON TECHNICAL INSTITUTE
    Clinton, North Carolina 28328 (--; st and local; coed; qr; I; 279) NR

SANDHILLS COMMUNITY COLLEGE
    Southern Pines, North Carolina 28387 (S; st; coed; qr; I; 1393) NR

SHAW UNIVERSITY
    Raleigh, North Carolina 27602 (S; p; coed; tri; II; 1061) BA major, Area of Phil
    and Relig, 919-755-4815

    Barker, Jr, Orus C, PhD, Prof, Cord, Heidegger, Contemp German and French Phil
    Hunt, James D, PhD, Assoc Prof, Ghandi, Hist of Relig

SOUTHEASTERN BAPTIST THEOLOGICAL SEMINARY
Wake Forest, North Carolina 27587 (Theol; S Bapt; coed; sem; IV; 552) D Min major,
Dept of Theol, 919-556-3101 Ext 21

Hollon, Jr, Ellis W, PhD, Prof, Phil of Relig

SOUTHEASTERN COMMUNITY COLLEGE
Whiteville, North Carolina 28472 (S; st; coed; qr; I; 1299) Courses with no degree
specialization, --, 919-642-7141

SOUTHWESTERN TECHNICAL INSTITUTE
Sylva, North Carolina 28779 (S; st; coed; qr; I; 464) NP

SOUTHWOOD COLLEGE
Salemburg, North Carolina 28385 (S; p; coed; sem; I; 197) --, Dept of Relig and
Phil, 919-525-4144

Marshburn, Robert F, PhD
Wood, Pearle S, MA

SURRY COMMUNITY COLLEGE
Dobson, North Carolina 27017 (S; st; coed; qr; I; 745) Courses with no degree
specialization, Dept of Phil, 919-386-8121

Fink, James R, ThM, Phil of Relig

TECHNICAL INSTITUTE OF ALAMANCE
Burlington, North Carolina 27215 (S; st and local; coed; qr; I; 935) NP

TRI-COUNTY TECHNICAL INSTITUTE
Murphy, North Carolina 28906 (--; st; coed; qr; I; 288) Courses with no degree
specialization, Dept of Human, 704-837-6810

McGraw, Minerva San Juan, MA, Instr, Chm, Ethics, Epistem

UNIVERSITY OF NORTH CAROLINA AT ASHEVILLE
Asheville, North Carolina 28801 (S; st; coed; sem; II; 1107) NR

UNIVERSITY OF NORTH CAROLINA AT CHAPEL HILL
Chapel Hill, North Carolina 27514 (S; st; coed; sem; IV; 19,160) PhD major, Dept
of Phil, 919-933-7291

Falk, W D, PhD, Prof, Chm, Ethics, Value Theory
Adams, E M, PhD, Prof, Epistem, Metaph
Darwall, Stephen L, PhD, Asst Prof, Ethics, Polit Phil
English, Jane, PhD, Asst Prof, Phil of Sci
Galligan, Edward M, PhD, Assoc Prof, Anc and Med Phil
Heintz, John, PhD, Assoc Prof, Logic, Phil of Math, Metaph
Kuflik, Arthur, PhD, Asst Prof, Ethics, Polit Phil
Long, Douglas C, PhD, Assoc Prof, Phil of Mind, Ethics
Munsat, Stanley, PhD, Prof, Phil of Mind, Epistem
Nolan, Rita, PhD, Assoc Prof, Phil of Lang, Theory of Knowl
Resnik, Michael D, PhD, Assoc Prof, Logic, Phil of Math
Rosenberg, Jay F, PhD, Assoc Prof, Epistem, Metaph, Recent Anal Phil
Schlesinger, George, PhD, Prof, Phil and Hist of Sci
Smyth, Richard A, PhD, Assoc Prof, Hist of Mod Phil, Logic of Sci

Vance, Robert D, PhD, Asst Prof, Phil of Mind, Hist of Mod Phil
Zaffron, Richard H, PhD, Asst Prof, Phil of Soc Sci
Ziff, Paul, PhD, Prof, Aes, Phil of Lang

Arkin, Marc
Baley, James M
Ball, Patricia G
Bjurloff, Thomas A
Blanchard, John P
Branham, Barry H
Buchanan, Allen
Christopher, Dennis
Coyne, Anthony M
Dornan, Kevin
Goble, Jonathan C
Hardy, Louise S
Hart, Donald B
Hill, Judith M
Hobbs, William G
Hudson, Stephen D
Jamieson, Dale W
Kaufman, Paul S

Kelley, Leigh B
Kolb, Robert W
Kussack, Alan A
May, H Cleveland
Moore, Terry
Nixon, Mark R
Nord, Warren A
Rosenberg, Fred C
Smythe, Jeanne P
Stalker, Douglas F
Sullivan, Jay L
Tarr, Patrick H
Teutsch, Ralph J
Torppa, Alan J
Vreeland, Robert G
Waller, Bruce N
Weiss, Bruce S

UNIVERSITY OF NORTH CAROLINA AT CHARLOTTE
Charlotte, North Carolina 28213 (S; st; coed; sem; III; 4676) MA minor, Dept of
Phil, 704-597-2161

Shumaker, James D, PhD, Assoc Prof, Chm, Aes
Cook, Thomas, MA, Instr, Logic, Phil of Sci
Fishman, Stephen M, PhD, Assoc Prof, Phil of Mind
Lincourt, John M, PhD, Asst Prof, Amer Phil
Presler, Judith L, PhD, Asst Prof, Anc Phil
Toenjes, Richard H, MA, Asst Prof, Soc and Polit Phil

Corkey, W B H, MA, Asst Prof Emer, Amer Phil

UNIVERSITY OF NORTH CAROLINA AT GREENSBORO
Greensboro, North Carolina 27412 (S; st; coed; sem; IV; 6983) BA major, Dept of
Phil, 919-379-5144

Rosthal, Robert, PhD, Assoc Pof, Chm, Phil of Mind, Contemp Euro Phil
Ashby, Warren, PhD, Prof, Ethics
Hoffman, Joshua, PhD, Lect, Phil of Mind, Aes, Logic
Kent, Daryl, PhD, Part-time Lect, Hist of Phil
Kort, Louis, BPhil, Asst Prof, Contemp Ethics, Metaph
Leplin, Jarrett, PhD, Asst Prof, Logic, Phil of Sci
Newman, Charles, MA, Lect, Soc and Polit Phil, Phil of Law
Smythe, Thomas, PhD, Asst Prof, Phil Psych, Phil of Soc Sci

UNIVERSITY OF NORTH CAROLINA AT WILMINGTON
Wilmington, North Carolina 28401 (S; st; coed; sem; II; 2014) BA major, --, 919-
791-4330 Ext 276

Hall, B Frank, ThD, Prof, Chm, Hist of Phil
Dankel, S, MA, Part-time Instr, Aes, Logic
Duckett, R E E, Instr, Anal Phil, Ethics
Garnier, Francois, PhL, Visit Prof
McGowan, James K, PhD, Assoc Prof, Exist
Shinn, Gerald H, PhD, Assoc Prof, Aristotle, Phil of Relig

VANCE COUNTY TECHNICAL INSTITUTE
    Henderson, North Carolina 27536 (--; st and local; coed; qr; I; 171) NR

W W HOLDING TECHNICAL INSTITUTE
    Raleigh, North Carolina 27603 (S; st and local; coed; qr; I; 848) NR

WAKE FOREST UNIVERSITY
    Winston-Salem, North Carolina 27109 (S; Bapt; coed; 4-1-4; IV; 3738) BA major, Dept
    of Phil, 919-725-9711 Ext 424, 209

    Pritchard, Gregory D, PhD, Assoc Prof, Chm, Ethics, Hist of Phil
    Helm, Robert M, PhD, Prof, Logic, Mod Phil
    Hester, Marcus B, PhD, Assoc Prof, Aes, Contemp Phil
    Lewis, Charles M, PhD, Asst Prof, Phil of Relig, Mod Phil
    Vorsteg, Robert H, PhD, Asst Prof, Phil of Sci, Contemp Phil

    Reid, Albert C, PhD, Prof Emer

WARREN WILSON COLLEGE
    Swannanoa, North Carolina 28778 (S; U Preb; coed; sem; II; 360) BA minor, Dept of
    Phil, 704-298-3325

    Scott, George E, PhD

WAYNE COMMUNITY COLLEGE
    Goldsboro, North Carolina 27530 (S; st and local; coed; qr; I; 1680) NR

WESTERN CAROLINA UNIVERSITY
    Cullowhee, North Carolina 28723 (S; st; coed; qr; III; 5660) BA minor, Dept of
    Relig and Phil, 704-293-7160

    Bennett, John B, PhD, Prof, Epistem
    Swanson, Reuben J, PhD, Prof

WESTERN PIEDMONT COMMUNITY COLLEGE
    Morganton, North Carolina 28655 (S; st; coed; qr; I; 1076) Courses with no degree
    specialization, Dept of Phil and Relig, 704-437-8688

WILKES COMMUNITY COLLEGE
    Wilkesboro, North Carolina 28697 (S; st; coed; qr; I; 992) Courses with no degree
    specialization, Dept of Human, 919-667-7136 Ext 33

    Wingard, II, Gordon G, PhD, Anc and Med Phil

WILSON COUNTY TECHNICAL INSTITUTE
    Wilson, North Carolina 27893 (S; st; coed; qr; I; 597) NP

WINGATE COLLEGE
    Wingate, North Carolina 28174 (S; S Bapt; coed; sem; I; 1703) Courses with no degree
    specialization, Dept of Relig and Phil, 704-233-4121

    Surratt, Jerry L, PhD, Academic Dean, Phil

NORTH CAROLINA

WINSTON-SALEM STATE UNIVERSITY
   Winston-Salem, North Carolina 27102 (S; st; coed; sem; II; 1623) Courses with no
   degree specialization, Dept of Soc Sci, 919-725-3563

NORTH DAKOTA

BISMARCK JUNIOR COLLEGE
   Bismarck, North Dakota 58501 (N; local; coed; sem; I; 1453) Courses with no degee
   specialization, Dept of Human, 701-223-4500 Ext 58

   Stenerson, Orville, MA, Chm

DICKINSON STATE COLLEGE
   Dickinson, North Dakota 58601 (N; st; coed; qr; II; 1457) Courses with no degree
   specialization, Dept of Lit and Lang, 701-227-2124

   Fleming, William, MA, Assoc Prof

JAMESTOWN COLLEGE
   Jamestown, North Dakota 58401 (N; Preb; coed; 4-1-4; II; 1072) BA joint or combined
   major, Dept of Phil, 701-252-4331 Ext 500

   Starkey, Lawrence H, PhD, Assoc Prof, Chm, Phil of Sci, Phil of Relig

LAKE REGION JUNIOR COLLEGE
   Devils Lake, North Dakota 58301 (--; local; coed; sem; I; 680) Courses with no
   degree specialization, --, 701-662-4951

MARY COLLEGE
   Bismarck, North Dakota 58501 (N; RC; coed; 4-1-4; II; 658) Courses with no degree
   specialization, Div of Phil and Theol, 701-255-4681

   Maloney, Daniel, MA, Asst Prof, Chm, Logic
   Spain, Arnold, BA, Lect, Ethics

MAYVILLE STATE COLLEGE
   Mayville, North Dakota 58257 (N; st; coed; qr; II; 708) NP

MINOT STATE COLLEGE
   Minot, North Dakota 58701 (N; st; coed; qr; III; 3657) Courses with no degree
   specialization, Div of Soc Sci, 701-838-6101 Ext 231

   Morrison, Paul W, PhD, Chm
   Heide, Philip, MA, Ethics

NORTH DAKOTA STATE SCHOOL OF SCIENCE
Wahreton, North Dakota 58075 (N; st; coed; qr; I; 3047) NP

NORTH DAKOTA STATE UNIVERSITY
Fargo, North Dakota 58102 (N; st; coed; qr; IV; 7118) MA joint or combined major, Dept of Phil, 701-237-7020

Brkić, Jovan, PhD, Prof, Chm, Logic, Ethics, Phil of Law
Roach, Corwin, PhD, Prof, Hist of Phil

NORTH DAKOTA STATE UNIVERSITY, BOTTINEAU CAMPUS
Bottineau, North Dakota 58318 (N; st; coed; qr; I; 529) Courses with no degree specialization, Div of Arts, Human, and Soc Sci, 701-228-2278

NORTHWEST BIBLE COLLEGE
Minot, North Dakota 58701 (--; Ch of God; coed; sem; II; 119) Courses with no degree specialization, Dept of Bib and Theol, 701-839-5920 Ext 39

Breckenridge, James F, M Div, Asst Prof

UNIVERSITY OF NORTH DAKOTA
Grand Forks, North Dakota 58201 (N; st; coed; sem; IV; 8823) PhD minor, Dept of Phil, 701-777-4236, 701-777-4237

Voskuil, Duane, Asst Prof, Chm
Glassheim, Patricia, Assoc Prof
Messenger, Theodore, Assoc Prof
Mullins, Robert, Asst Prof
Pearce, Donald, Assoc Prof Part-time
Ring, Benjamin, Assoc Prof

UNIVERSITY OF NORTH DAKOTA, WILLISTON BRANCH
Williston, North Dakota 58801 (N; st; coed; sem; I; 480) NP

VALLEY CITY STATE COLLEGE
Valley City, North Dakota 58072 (N; st; coed; qr; II; 1204) NP

OHIO

AIR FORCE INSTITUTE OF TECHNOLOGY
Wright-Patterson AFB Dayton, Ohio 45433 (N; Fed; coed; qr; IV; 621) NR

ANTIOCH COLLEGE
Yellow Springs, Ohio 45387 (N; p; coed; qr; III; 2795) BA major, Dept of Phil and Relig, 513-767-7331

Atkins, Robert A, MA, Asst Prof

Denman, Alvin L, PhD, Assoc Prof
Geiger, George Raymond, PhD, Prof
Love, Jr, Charles E, MA, Asst Prof
McGary, Keith, PhD, Prof
Qureshi, Tufail, MA, Asst Prof
Walden, Phyllis, MA, Asst Prof

ART ACADEMY OF CINCINNATI
    Cincinnati, Ohio 45202 (Art; p; coed; sem; V; 107) NP

ASHLAND COLLEGE
    Ashland, Ohio 44805 (N; Breth; coed; sem; III; 2841) BA major, --, 419-324-4561

    Acuña, Juna J, STM, Assoc Prof
    Braby, Robert D, PhD, Asst Prof
    Ferm, Vergilius, PhD, Prof
    Stark, Bruce C, ThD, Prof
    Witte, Wayne W, ThD, Prof

THE ATHENAEUM OF OHIO
    Cincinnati, Ohio 45230 (N; RC; men; qr; III; 270) MA major, Faculty of Libr Arts,
    513-231-2223

    Hater, Robert J, PhD, Assoc Prof, Chm, Personalism, Phil of Sci
    Beatty, Michael, MA, Instr, Exist, Marxism
    Dumont, Richard, PhD, Visit Prof, Metaph, Med Phil
    Gendreau, Bernard, PhD, Visit Prof, Personalism, Metaph
    Hogan, Donald, MA, Visit Prof, Axiology
    Jones, William, PhD, Visit Prof, Amer Phil
    Roedel, Francis, MA, Part-time, Anc and Med Phil
    Voellmecke, Francis W, PhD, Instr, Phil of Lang, Ethics
    Wessling, John E, STD, Prof, Phil of God, Mod Phil

BALDWIN-WALLACE COLLEGE
    Berea, Ohio 44017 (N; U Meth; coed; qr; II; 2982) BA major, Dept of Phil, 216-826-
    2277

    Garrett, Roland W, PhD, Asst Prof, Chm, Amer Phil, Metaph
    Iverson, Sherwin L, PhD, Assoc Prof, Logic
    Lingswiler, Robert D, ThD, Assoc Prof, Phil of Relig, Phil of Sci, Polit and Soc Phil
    Noragon, Patricia A, PhD, Asst Prof, Ethics
    Watts, Donald F, MA, Assoc Prof, Hist of Phil, Aes

BELMONT TECHNICAL COLLEGE
    St Clairsville, Ohio 43950 (--; st; coed; qr; I; 257) NP

BLISS COLLEGE
    Columbus, Ohio 43215 (JRCB; p; coed; qr; I; 525) NR

BLUFFTON COLLEGE
    Bluffton, Ohio 45817 (N; Menn; coed; --; II; 697) BA major, Dept of Phil, 419-358-
    8015

    Neufeld, Elmer, PhD, Assoc Prof, Chm, Ethics

BORROMEO SEMINARY OF OHIO
   Wickliffe, Ohio 44092 (N; RC; men; sem; II; 100) BA major, Dept of Phil, 216-943-3888

   Minoggio, Ferrando, PhD, Prof, Chm, Metaph
   Bode, Hugh H, MA, Prof, Phil of Man
   Murphy, John F, PhD, Prof, Ethics
   Monroe, Lee J, MA, Visit Instr, Contemp Phil

BOWLING GREEN STATE UNIVERSITY
   Bowling Green, Ohio 43403 (N; st; coed; qr; IV; 15,313) MA major, Dept of Phil,
   419-372-2117

   Facione, Peter, PhD, Asst Prof, Chm, Logic, Phil of Lang
   Attig, Thomas, MA, Instr, Phenomen, Exist, Hist of Mod Phil
   Bradie, Michael, PhD, Asst Prof, Logic, Phil of Sci, Far East Phil
   Cormier, Ramona, PhD, Prof, Phil of Hist, Aes
   Daye, Douglas, PhD, Asst Prof, Far East Phil
   Goodwin, Robert, PhD, Prof, Metaph, Med Phil, Amer Phil
   Katzner, Louis, PhD, Assoc Prof, Soc Phil, Polit Phil
   Kauber, Peter, PhD, Asst Prof, Amer Phil, Ethics, Epistem
   Lineback, Richard, PhD, Prof, Ethics
   Littlefield, Loy, PhD, Asst Prof, Metaph, Phenomen
   Miller, Fred, PhD, Asst Prof, Greek Phil, Metaph
   Robins, Michael, PhD, Asst Prof, Ethics
   Scherer, Donald, PhD, Assoc Prof, Phil of Relig, Ling Anal
   Stuart, James, PhD, Asst Prof, Hist of Phil, Metaph

   Tuttle, Thomas, PhD, Prof Emer, Neo-Platonic Tht

   DeCarolis, Arnold, BA   Rappaport, Mark, BA
   Foote, Charles, BA   Rosenthal, Charles, BA
   Greene, Stephanie, BA   Swartz, Thomas, BA
   Holzaepfel, Todd, BA   Triebewasser, Harold, BA
   Lahood, Gabriel, BA   Ward, Michael, BA
   Latkewicz, John, BA

BOWLING GREEN STATE UNIVERSITY, FIRELANDS BRANCH
   Huron, Ohio 44839 (N; st; coed; qr; I; 796) AA major, Dept of Phil, 419-433-5560

   Schnetzer, O Dale, MA, Instr, Phil of Relig

CAPITAL UNIVERSITY
   Columbus, Ohio 43209 (N; Amer Luth; coed; --; II; 2276) BA major, Dept of Phil,
   614-236-6595

   Hackmann, E Edward, PhD, Prof, Chm, Phil of Relig, Hist of Phil
   Beversluis, Eric, PhD, Asst Prof, Phil of Educ, Ethics
   Straumanis, Eric, PhD, Asst Prof, Phil of Educ

CASE WESTERN RESERVE UNIVERSITY
   Cleveland, Ohio 44106 (N; p; coed; 4-1-4; IV; 9209) PhD major, Dept of Phil, 216-
   368-2810

   Kadish, Mortimer, PhD, Prof, Chm, Aes, Legal Phil, Polit Phil
   Creary, Lewis, PhD, Asst Prof, Phil of Sci, Logic
   Kim, Chin-Tai, PhD, Assoc Prof, Epistem, Metaph
   Long, Herbert, PhD, Prof, Greek Phil, Hellenistic Phil
   Macklin, Ruth, PhD, Assoc Prof, Anal Phil, Phil Psych
   McIntyre, Ronald, PhD, Asst Prof, Phenomen, Phil of Lang
   Nelson, Raymond, PhD, Prof, Logic, Phil of Math

O'Connor, John, PhD, Assoc Prof, Ethics, Phil of Mind
Waldner, Ilmar, PhD, Asst Prof, Phil of Soc Sci

CEDARVILLE COLLEGE
Cedarville, Ohio 45314 (--; Bapt; coed; qr; II; 970) BA minor, Dept of Bibl Educ, 513-766-2211 Ext 287

Grier, James M, ThM, Asst Prof, Christ Phil

CENTRAL STATE UNIVERSITY
Wilberforce, Ohio 45384 (N; st; coed; qr; I; 2525) NR

CHATFIELD COLLEGE
St Martin, Ohio 45170 (N; RC; coed; sem; I; 176) Courses with no degree specialization, --, 513-875-4101

THE CINCINNATI BIBLE SEMINARY
Cincinnati, Ohio 45204 (BI; Ch of Christ; coed; sem; III; 692) Courses with no degree specialization, Dept of Phil, 513-471-4800 Ext 62

Karns, C Franklin, PhD, Prof

CINCINNATI TECHNICAL INSTITUTE
Cincinnati, Ohio 45223 (--; st; coed; --; I; 1149) NR

CLARK TECHNICAL COLLEGE
Springfield, Ohio 45501 (--; st; coed; qr; I; 958) --, Dept of Gen Educ, 513-325-0691 Ext 70

Monnin, Lloyd N, PhD, Assoc Prof, Chm
Murray, John P, MA, Instr
Kolasny, Joseph A, MA, Asst Prof

CLEVELAND INSTITUTE OF ART
Cleveland, Ohio 44106 (N; p; coed; sem; II; 796) Courses with no degree specialization, Dept of Academic Stud, 216-421-4322

Sperd, Shubert, PhD, Lect Part-time, Phil of Relig, Ethics, Aes

CLEVELAND INSTITUTE OF MUSIC
Cleveland, Ohio 44106 (Mus; p; coed; sem; IV; 300) Courses with no degree specialization, --, 216-791-5165

CLEVELAND STATE UNIVERSITY
Cleveland, Ohio 44115 (N; st; coed; qr; III; 15,201) MA major, Dept of Phil, 216-687-2000

Armour, Leslie, PhD, Prof, Chm, Metaph, Ethics
Bartlett, III, Edward T, PhD, Asst Prof, Phil of Mind, Aes
Brimmer, Harvey H, Asst Prof, Metaph, French Tht, Process Phil
DeMarco, Joseph P, PhD, Asst Prof, Soc and Polit Phil, Black Tht
Fox, Richard M, PhD, Assoc Prof, Ethics
McIntyre, Jane L, PhD, Asst Prof, Epistem, Logic
Moutafakis, Nicholas J, PhD, Assoc Prof, Phil Logic, Anc Phil

Pole, Nelson, PhD, Asst Prof, Phil of Sci, Logic
Richmond, Samuel A, PhD, Assoc Prof, Ethics, Epistem
Shmueli, Efraim, PhD, Prof, Phenomen, Metaph, Hist of Phil
Werth, Lee F, PhD, Asst Prof, Metaph, Phil of Sci

COLLEGE OF MOUNT SAINT JOSEPH
Mount St Joseph, Ohio 45051 (N; RC; wo; sem; II; 793) BA major, Dept of Phil, 513-244-4856

Gloekner, Martha, Lic Phil, Instr, Chm, Phil of Sci
Adams, Pedro, PhD, Asst Prof, Metaph

THE COLLEGE OF STEUBENVILLE
Steubenville, Ohio 43952 (N; RC; coed; sem; II; 1304) BA major, Dept of Phil, 614-283-3771 Ext 250

Spinnenweber, Andrew E, PhD, Assoc Prof, Act Chm, Process Tht
Hall, Robert, PhD, Assoc Prof, Soc Phil
Schlegel, Edward R, MA, Asst Prof, Kant

COLLEGE OF WOOSTER
Wooster, Ohio 44691 (N; p; coed; qr; III; 1881) BA major, Dept of Phil, 216-264-1234 Ext 485

Fry, Thomas, Instr, Metaph, Franz Brentano
Haden, James, PhD, Prof, Hist of Phil, Aes, Kant Stud
Hustwit, Ronald, PhD, Asst Prof, Anal Phil, Kierkegaard Stud
Jackson, Darrell, PhD, Asst Prof, Class Phil, Patristics, Hist of Phil
Medlock, Gordon, Asst Prof, Amer Phil, Phil of Educ

COLUMBUS COLLEGE OF ART AND DESIGN
Columbus, Ohio 43215 (--; p; coed; sem; II; 602) Courses with no degree specialization, --, 614-224-9101

COLUMBUS TECHNICAL INSTITUTE
Columbus, Ohio 43215 (--; st and local; coed; qr; I; 1839) --, Dept of Behavior Stud, 615-221-6743 Ext 60

Malin, John, MS
Parr, Wilma R

CUYAHOGA COMMUNITY COLLEGE, METROPOLITAN CAMPUS
Cleveland, Ohio 44115 (N; local; coed; qr; I; 11,985) Courses with no degree specialization, Area of Phil, 216-241-5966

Lightbody, Thomas P, MA, Instr
McLellan, John M, BA, Assoc Prof

CUYAHOGA COMMUNITY COLLEGE, WESTERN CAMPUS
Parma Height, Ohio 44130 (N; local; coed; qr; I; 6356) AA major, Dept of Human, 216-845-4000 Ext 302, 308

Crane, John D, MA, Asst Prof
Spencer, James C, MA, Instr

OHIO

DAVIS JUNIOR COLLEGE
   Toledo, Ohio 43624 (JRCB; p; coed; qr; I; 229) NP

DEFIANCE COLLEGE
   Defiance, Ohio 43512 (N; U Ch of Christ; coed; 4-1-4; II; 1043) BA major, Dept of
   Phil and Relig, 419-784-4010 Ext 273

   Luchies, John E, PhD, Prof, Chm, Phil of Relig, Ethics
   Hayes, Victor, PhD, Assoc Prof, Hist of Mod Tht
   Strupl, Milos, PhD, Asst Prof, Hist of Chirst Phil

DENISON UNIVERSITY
   Granville, Ohio 43023 (N; p; coed; 4-1-4; II; 2132) BA major, Dept of Phil, 614-
   582-9181 Ext 319

   Friedman, Marilyn, MA, Asst Prof, Phil of Action, Metaph, Hist of Mod Phil
   Goldblatt, David A, PhD, Asst Prof, Ethics, Soc Phil, Epistem
   Hepp, Maylon H, PhD, Prof, Chinese Phil, Hist of Phil
   Lisska, Anthony J, PhD, Asst Prof, Med Phil, Natural Law
   Santoni, Ronald E, PhD, Prof, Phil of Relig, Soc and Polit Phil, Exist
   Straumanis, Joan, MA, Asst Prof, Phil of Sci, Logic
   Titus, Harold H, PhD, Prof, Ethics, Soc Phil

DYKE COLLEGE
   Cleveland, Ohio 44114 (SRCB; p; coed; tri; II; 734) BA minor, Dept of Human, 216-
   696-9000

   Grdina, Frank, MA, Assoc Prof
   Sosna, Norman, BA, Assoc Prof

EDGECLIFF COLLEGE
   Cincinnati, Ohio 45206 (N; RC; coed; sem; II; 800) BA major, Dept of Phil, 513-
   961-3770 Ext 275

   Buse, Robert O, MA, Prof, Chm, Epistem, Metaph
   Magno, Joseph, MA, Assoc Prof, Ethics

EVANGELICAL LUTHERAN THEOLOGICAL SEMINARY
   Columbus, Ohio 43209 (Theol; A Luth; coed; qr; III; 237) NR

FINDLAY COLLEGE
   Findlay, Ohio 45840 (N; Ch of God, coed; --; II; 1175) BA major, Dept of Phil and
   Relig, 419-422-8313 Ext 314

   Hamilton, Wayne, PhD, Asst Prof, Act Chm, Exist, Phenomen, Phil of Relig
   Kern, Richard, PhD, Prof, Ethics
   Wallen, Raeburn, MA, Asst Prof

FRANKLIN UNIVERSITY
   Columbus, Ohio 43215 (--; p; coed; tri; II; 3420) Courses with no degree specialization,
   --, 614-224-6237

   Kocher, James C, MA

HEBREW UNION COLLEGE
   Cincinnati, Ohio 45220 (N; Jewish; coed; sem; IV; 286) --, --, 513-221-1875

   Reines, Alvin, PhD, Prof, Med Jewish Phil

HEIDELBERG COLLEGE
   Tiffin, Ohio 44883 (N; U Ch of Christ; coed; sem; II; 1240) BA major, Dept of Phil,
   419-448-2188

   Muska, Rudolph, PhD, Prof, Chm
   Keen, Tom, PhD, Assoc Prof
   Putnam, Leon, PhD, Prof

HIRAM COLLEGE
   Hiram, Ohio 44234 (N; p; coed; qr; II; 1284) BA major, Dept of Phil, 216-569-3211
   Ext 231

   Peters, Eugene H, PhD, Prof, Chm, Metaph, Phil of Relig, Hartshorne, Whitehead
   Hoffman, W Michael, PhD, Asst Prof, Ethics, Hist of Phil, Kant

HOCKING TECHNICAL COLLEGE
   Nelsonville, Ohio 45764 (--; st; coed; qr; I; 1029) NP

JEFFERSON COUNTY TECHNICAL INSTITUTE
   Steubenville, Ohio 43952 (--; st; coed; qr; I; 627) NP

JOHN CARROLL UNIVERSITY
   University Heights, Ohio 44118 (N; RC; coed; sem; III; 3964) BA major, Dept of Phil,
   216-491-4375

   Pratt, Ronald L, PhD, Assoc Prof, Chm
   Bichl, William M, MA, Asst Prof
   Boatright, John R, MA, Asst Prof
   Buckley, Joseph A, PhD, Assoc Prof
   Bukala, Casimir R, PhD, Asst Prof
   Hay, Gerald C, PhD, Assoc Prof
   Horvath, Nicholas A, PhD, Prof
   Pugh, John K, MA, Asst Prof
   Schell, Joseph O, MA, Prof
   Sweeney, Robert D, PhD, Prof
   Thirlkel, W Edmund, MA, Assoc Prof
   Tomasic, Thomas M, PhD, Assoc Prof

KENT STATE UNIVERSITY
   Kent, Ohio 44242 (N; st; coed; qr; IV; 22,012) MA major, Dept of Phil, 216-672-2315

   Moulds, George H, PhD, Prof, Chm, Value Theory
   Bickley, Theodore, PhD, Asst Prof, Phil of Relig
   Burlingame, Charles E, PhD, Asst Prof, Phil of Art, Phil of Mind
   Dickoff, James W, PhD, Prof, Norm Phil
   Dyal, Robert A, PhD, Asst Prof, Phil of Art, Phil of Relig, Phenomen
   James, Patricia A, PhD, Prof, Norm Phil
   Lee, Kwang-Sae, PhD, Asst Prof, Phil of Sci, Contemp Metaph, Kant
   Lyle, William E, MA, Asst Prof

Papageorgopoulos, Nenos A, PhD, Asst Prof, Aes, Hist of Phil, Greek Phil
Parmenter, James, MA, Asst Prof
Steel, Margaret, MA, Instr, Phil of Lang
Washell, Richard, PhD, Asst Prof, Phil of Culture, Phil of Communic, Anc and Med
    Phil
Wheeler, Arthur M, PhD, Prof, Phil of Relig, Epistem, Ethics
Zellner, Harold, PhD, Asst Prof, Ethics, Soc and Polit Phil

Baum, Maurice, PhD, Prof Emer, Aes, Prag
Politella, Joseph, PhD, Prof Emer, Anc Phil, Phil of Myst, East Relig

Bobinski, John, Grad Asst	Krumroy, Karl, Grad Asst
Bozick, Lawrence M, Grad Asst	Lewis, Gregory E, Grad Asst
Couch, Bonita H, Grad Asst	Miller, William M, Grad Asst
Dietrich, Gary J, Grad Asst	Pendleton, Gene, Grad Asst
Geeroms, Claude R, Grad Asst	Sandrock, Marque, Grad Asst
Gill, Kermode F, Grad Asst	Susak, Michael, Grad Asst

KENT STATE UNIVERSITY, ASHTABULA CAMPUS
    Ashtabula, Ohio 44004 (N; st; coed; qr; I; 957) Courses with no degree specialization,
    Dept of Phil, 216-963-2624

    Zellner, Harold, PhD, Asst Prof, Metaph, Epistem

KENT STATE UNIVERSITY, EAST LIVERPOOL CAMPUS
    East Liverpool, Ohio 43920 (N; st; coed; qr; I; 593) --, Dept of Phil, 216-385-3805

    Washell, Richard F, PhD, Asst Prof

KENT STATE UNIVERSITY, SALEM CAMPUS
    Salem, Ohio 44460 (N; st; coed; qr; I; 766) Courses with no degree specialization,
    --, 216-332-0361

KENT STATE UNIVERSITY, STARK COUNTY CAMPUS
    North Canton, Ohio 44720 (N; st; coed; qr; I; 2579) --, Dept of Phil, 216-499-9600
    Ext 271

    Bickley, Theodore G, PhD, Asst Prof, Metaph
    Parmenter, James, MA, Asst Prof, Phil of Relig

KENT STATE UNIVERSITY, TRUMBULL CAMPUS
    Warren, Ohio 44483 (N; st; coed; qr; I; 1128) AA major, Dept of Phil and Relig,
    216-963-2624

    Zellner, Harold, PhD, Asst Prof, Ethics

KENT STATE UNIVERSITY, TUSCARAWS COUNTY CAMPUS
    New Philadelphia, Ohio 44663 (N; st; coed; qr; I; 889) BA major, --, 216-364-5561

KENYON COLLEGE
    Gambier, Ohio 43022 (N; PE; coed; sem; II; 1294) BA major, Dept of Phil, 614-427-
    2244

    Kading, Daniel, PhD, Prof, Chm, Ethics
    Banning, Cyrus, PhD, Assoc Prof, Phil of Sci
    McLaren, Ronald, PhD, Assoc Prof, Metaph, Logic

Schermer, Marsha, MA, Asst Prof, Aes, Phenomen
Short, Thomas, BA, Asst Prof, Hist of Phil, Logic

KETTERING COLLEGE OF MEDICAL ARTS
Kettering, Ohio 45429 (MT; SDA; coed; sem; I; 274) Courses with no degree
specialization, Dept of Relig and Ethics, 513-298-0144

LAKE ERIE COLLEGE
Painesville, Ohio 44077 (N; p; coed; tri; III; 760) BA major, Dept of Phil, 216-
352-3361 Ext 277

Adams, John Stokes, PhD, Prof, Aes
Todd, James A, PhD, Asst Prof

Ruddick, C T, PhD, Prof Emer, Phil of Sci

LAKELAND COMMUNITY COLLEGE
Mentor, Ohio 44060 (--; local; coed; qr; I; 3303) --, Dept of Human, 216-951-1000
Ext 342

Conrath, Richard, MA, Instr
Parsisson, Donald, MA, Instr

LIMA TECHNICAL COLLEGE
Lima, Ohio 45804 (--; st and local; coed; qr; I; 467) NR

LORAIN COUNTY COMMUNITY COLLEGE
Elyria, Ohio 44035 (N; st and local; coed; qr; I; 3892) --, Dept of Lang and Human,
216-365-4191

Jacobozzi, Elio, MA, Instr Part-time

LOURDES COLLEGE
Sylvania, Ohio 43560 (N; RC; wo; sem; I; 41) Courses with no degree specialization,
Div of Phil and Relig Stud, 419-882-2016

Kirtland, Robert, MA, Assoc Prof, Phil of Law
Steinle, James, MA, Assoc Prof

MALONE COLLEGE
Canton, Ohio 44709 (N; Fr; coed; --; II; 836) BA joint or combined major, Div of
Relig and Phil, 216-454-3011

Hess, Weldon Robert, PhD, Prof, Asian Phil
Johnson, Robert L, PhD, Prof, Stoicism, Hist of Phil

MARIETTA COLLEGE
Marietta, Ohio 45750 (N; p; coed; sem; II; 2175) BA major, Dept of Phil, 614-373-
4643

Wilbanks, Jan J, PhD, Prof, Chm
Harris, James R, PhD, Asst Prof
Metrick, Dennis L, PhD, Asst Prof

Johnson, J Glover, PhD, Prof Emer

MARION TECHNICAL COLLEGE
Marion, Ohio 43302 (--; st; coed; qr; I; 187) NR

MARY MANSE COLLEGE
Toledo, Ohio 43620 (N; RC; coed; tri; II; 600) BA minor, Area One: Man the Interpreter, 419-243-9241 Ext 70

Fiscella, Joan, MA, Asst Prof, Ethics, Class and Contemp Phil
Simon, St Simon, MA, Asst Prof, Logic, Metaph

MEDICAL COLLEGE OF OHIO
Toledo, Ohio 43614 (Med; st; coed; qr; III; 113) NP

METHODIST THEOLOGICAL SCHOOL IN OHIO
Delaware, Ohio 43015 (Theol; U Meth; coed; qr; III; 215) Courses with no degree specialization, Dept of Theol Stud, 614-363-1146

MIAMI-JACOBS JUNIOR COLLEGE OF BUSINESS
Dayton, Ohio 45402 (JRCB; p; coed; qr; I; 487) NP

MIAMI UNIVERSITY
Oxford, Ohio 45056 (N; st; coed; qr; IV; 13,131) MA major, Dept of Phil, 513-529-5712, 513-529-5713

Kane, G Stanley, PhD, Assoc Prof, Chm, Phil of Relig, Hist of Phil
Goldman, Michael, PhD, Asst Prof, Phil of Sci
Momeyer, Richard, PhD, Asst Prof, Moral Phil, Phil of Educ, Polit Phil
Rama Rao, P S S, PhD, Asst Prof, Ethics, Phil of Law, East Phil
Schuller, Peter, MA, Instr, 19th Cent Phil, Marxism, Soc and Polit Phil
Seidel, Asher, PhD, Asst Prof, Logic, Metaph, Anal Phil
Smoot, II, William R, PhD, Post-Doct Teach Fel, Aes, Phenomen, Exist
Wilder, Hugh T, PhD, Asst Prof, Phil of Lang, Anal Phil

MIAMI UNIVERSITY, HAMILTON BRANCH
Hamilton, Ohio 45011 (N; st; coed; qr; I; 1592) Courses with no degree specialization, Dept of Phil, 513-529-5712, 513-529-5713

MIAMI UNIVERSITY, MIDDLETOWN BRANCH
Middletown, Ohio 45052 (N; st; coed; qr; I; 2114) Courses with no degree specialization, Dept of Phil, 513-529-5712, 513-529-5713

MICHAEL J OWENS TECHNICAL COLLEGE
Perrysburg, Ohio 43551 (--; st; coed; qr; I; 811) Courses with no degree specialization, Dept of Gen Educ, 419-666-0580

Long, Janele Baker, BA, Instr

MOUNT UNION COLLEGE
Alliance, Ohio 44601 (N; U Meth; coed; qr; II; 1325) BA major, Dept of Relig and Phil, 216-821-5320

Buckey, Donald R, PhD, Asst Prof, Phil of Relig
Thomas, George H, PhD, Prof, Berkeley

MOUNT VERNON NAZARENE COLLEGE
Mount Vernon, Ohio 43050 (N; Naz; coed; qr; I; 532) Courses with no degree
specialization, Div of Relig and Phil, 614-397-1244 Ext 147

Cubie, David L, PhD, Chm

MUSKINGUM AREA TECHNICAL COLLEGE
Zanesville, Ohio 43701 (--; st; coed; qr; I; 1015) NP

MUSKINGUM COLLEGE
New Concord, Ohio 43762 (N; U Preb; coed; 4-1-4; II; 1268) BA major, Dept of Phil
and Relig, 614-826-8120

McClelland, William L, PhD, Prof, Chm, Med and Renaissance Phil
Barrett, J Edward, PhD, Assoc Prof
Elkins, J B, PhD, Assoc Prof, East Phil, Exist, Process Phil
Gepford, William G, STD, Lect
Hutchison, Russell S, PhD, Prof
McKenney, John L, PhD, Assoc Prof, Ethics, Logic

NORTH CENTRAL TECHNICAL COLLEGE
Mansfield, Ohio 44906 (--; st; coed; qr; I; 505) NR

NORTHWEST TECHNICAL COLLEGE
Archbold, Ohio 43502 (--; st; coed; qr; I; 282) NP

NOTRE DAME COLLEGE
South Euclid, Ohio 44121 (N; RC; wo; sem; II; 605) BA joint or combined major,
Dept of Phil, 216-381-1680

Finn, Mary LeRoy, MA, Asst Prof, Chm, Ethics
Peters, Mary Nivard, MA, Instr

Crawford, John E, BA, Lect Emer

OBERLIN COLLEGE
Oberlin, Ohio 44074 (N; p; coed; 4-1-4; III; 2710) MA major, Dept of Phil, 216-774-
1221 Ext 3165

Grimm, Robert H, PhD, Assoc Prof, Chm, Metaph, Phil of Logic, Logic, Hist of Phil,
    Theory of Knowl
Care, Norman S, PhD, Assoc Prof, Moral Phil, Polit Phil, Theory of Action
MacKay, Alfred F, PhD, Assoc Prof, Phil of Lang, Phil Logic, Ethics, Contemp Anal
    Phil
Merrill, Daniel D, PhD, Assoc Prof, Logic, Phil of Sci, Hist of Phil, Epistem, Metaph,
    Phil of Relig
Love, David A, MA, Instr, Hist of Mod Phil, Ethics, Polit Phil, Soc Phil, Phil of
    Hist, Phil of Law, Phil of Lang
Trelogan, Thomas K, MA, Instr, Phil Stud of Man, Theory of Knowl, Phil of Art,
    Husserl, Heidegger, Merleau-Ponty, Sartre, Nietzsche, Kant, Hegel

OHIO COLLEGE OF PODIATRIC MEDICINE
Cleveland, Ohio 44106 (Pod; p; coed; sem; I; 370) NR

OHIO DOMINICAN COLLEGE
   Columbus, Ohio 43219 (N; RC; coed; sem; II; 965) BA major, Dept of Phil, 614-253-2741

   Garry, Martin, PhD, Prof, Chm, Amer Phil
   Caspar, Ruth, PhD, Assoc Prof, Phil of Relig
   Franks, Joan, MA, Asst Prof, Logic

OHIO INSTITUTE OF TECHNOLOGY
   Columbus, Ohio 43209 (Tech; p; coed; qr; II; 1269) NR

OHIO NORTHERN UNIVERSITY
   Ada, Ohio 45810 (N; U Meth; coed; qr; III; 2450) BA major, Dept of Phil and Relig, 419-634-3015

   Hinderliter, Harold H, PhD, Prof, Chm
   Benson, Ronald E, PhD, Assoc Prof, Logic, Ethics
   Priley, Jeanne M, PhD, Asst Prof, Aes, Exist

OHIO STATE UNIVERSITY
   Columbus, Ohio 43210 (N; st; coed; qr; IV; 46,882) PhD major, Dept of Phil, 614-422-7914, 614-422-7915

   Turnbull, Robert G, PhD, Prof, Chm, Anc Greek Phil, Metaph
   Anderson, Wallace, PhD, Assoc Prof, Hist of Mod Phil, Amer Phil
   Boer, Steven E, PhD, Asst Prof, Logic, Epistem
   Boh, Ivan, PhD, Prof, Med Phil, Hist of Logic
   Farrell, Daniel M, PhD, Asst Prof, Polit Phil, Phil of Law, Phil of Soc Sci
   Fox, Marvin, PhD, Prof, Anc Greek Phil, Med Phil, Jewish Phil
   Garner, Richard T, PhD, Prof, Phil Logic, Phil of Lang, Aes
   Hausman, Alan, PhD, Assoc Prof, Hist of Mod Phil, Logic, Metaph
   Hinshaw, Jr, Virgil, PhD, Prof, Phil of Sci, Epistem, Phil of Hist
   Kielkopf, Charles F, PhD, Assoc Prof, Logic, Phil of Logic and Math
   Laymon, Ronald E, MA, Asst Prof, Phil and Hist of Sci, Epistem
   Lycan, William G, PhD, Assoc Prof, Phil of Mind, Epistem, Phil Logic
   Machamer, Peter K, PhD, Assoc Prof, Phil and Hist of Sci, Epistem, Aes
   Oldenquist, Andrew G, PhD, Prof, Ethics, Phil of Mind, Phil of Law
   Pappas, George S, PhD, Asst Prof, Hist of Mod Phil, Epistem
   Robison, Wade L, PhD, Asst Prof, Phil of Law, Hist of Mod Phil, Epistem
   Rosen, Bernard, PhD, Assoc Prof, Ethics, Epistem, Amer Phil
   Scanlan, James P, PhD, Prof, Hist of Russian Phil, Polit Phil
   Schumm, George F, MA, Asst Prof, Logic, Epistem
   Swain, Marshall W, PhD, Assoc Prof, Inductive Logic, Epistem

   Evans, Luther D, PhD, Prof Emer
   Nelson, Everett J, PhD, Prof Emer, Logic, Metaph
   Reither, William H, PhD, Assoc Prof Emer

   Baron, Bat-Ami, MA, Grad Asst
   Blake, Betsy A, BA, Grad Asst
   Blickle, Thomas, BA, Grad Asst
   Brechbill, Timothy, BA, Grad Asst
   Brummet, Robert, MA, Grad Asst
   D'Amore, Michael, MA, Grad Asst
   Edelstein, Roy S, BA, Grad Asst
   Franz, Lawrence, BA, Fel
   Gold, Jeffrey, BA, Fel
   Georghring, George, BA, Grad Asst
   Heller, Lorraine, BA, Grad Asst,
   Holt, David, BA, Grad Asst
   Josephson, John, BA, Grad Asst
   Loose, Patrice, MA, Grad Asst
   Lunsford, Stephen, BA, Fel
   Makruski, Edward, BA, Grad Asst
   Nusenoff, Ronald, BA, Grad Asst
   Parker, Eugene, BA, Grad Asst
   Schweickart, Charles, PhD, Grad Asst
   Sherouse, Mark, MA, Grad Asst
   Shih, Yuang-Kang, BA, Grad Asst
   Shonsheck, Jonathan C, BA, Grad Asst
   Spitzig, Norman, BA, Fel
   St Clair, Ute H, MA, Grad Asst
   Stough, Robert, BA, Fel
   Sutula, John, BA, Grad Asst

Josephson, Susan, MA, Grad Asst
King, Guy O'Gorman, BA, Grad Asst
Kirk, Samuel A, BA, Grad Asst
Lichtblau, Dale, MA, Grad Asst
Lloyd, Thomas, MA, Grad Asst

Turner, Dan, BA, Fel
Udell, Irwin L, MA, Grad Asst
Ulm, Melvin, MA, Grad Asst
Vanaman, Stehen, MA, Grad Asst

OHIO STATE UNIVERSITY, LIMA BRANCH
Lima, Ohio 45804 (N; st; coed; qr; I; 1197) --, --, 419-228-2641

Kantor, Samuel, PhD

OHIO STATE UNIVERSITY, MANSFIELD BRANCH
Mansfield, Ohio 44906 (N; st; coed; qr; I; 1113) Courses with no degree specialization, --, 419-747-6561

Pasquarello, Anthony, MA, Instr

OHIO STATE UNIVERSITY, MARION BRANCH
Marion, Ohio 43302 (N; st; coed; qr; I; 749) Courses with no degree specialization, --, 614-389-2361

McFarland, James, LLB, Lect

OHIO STATE UNIVERSITY, NEWARK BRANCH
Newark, Ohio 43055 (N; st; coed; qr; I; 863) Courses with no degree specialization, Dept of Phil, 614-366-3321 Ext 273

Hall, Michael, PhD, Asst Prof, Greek Phil, Anal Phil

OHIO UNIVERSITY
Athens, Ohio 45701 (N; st; coed; qr; IV; 15,944) MA major, Dept of Phil, 614-594-4168

Grean, Stanley, PhD, Prof, Chm, Phil of Relig
Stewart, J David, PhD, Asst Prof, Asst Chm, Contemp French Phil
Blocker, H Gene, PhD, Assoc Prof, Aes
Borchert, Donald M, PhD, Assoc Prof, Marxism, Phil of Relig
Butrick, Richard P, PhD, Assoc Prof, Logic, Phil of Lang
Cheng, Hsueh-li, MA, Instr, Chinese Phil and Relig
Corrado, Michael, PhD, Asst Prof, Metaph, Logic
Goldman, Alan H, PhD, Visit Asst Prof, Phil Psych
Lincicome, David, PhD, Asst Prof, Logic, Phil of Lang
Lal, Purshotam, R L Morton Visit Prof, Indian Literature and Tht
Mickunas, Algis, PhD, Asst Prof, Phenomen
Murphree, Idus L, PhD, Prof, Amer Phil, Soc Phil
Organ, Troy W, PhD, Dist Prof, Anc Phil, Orient Phil
Perotti, James, PhD, Asst Prof, Asst Dean, Contemp Euro Phil
Ruchti, Warren, PhD, Prof, Phil of Sci
Saydah, J Roger, PhD, Assoc Prof, Ethics, Polit Phil
Smith, Elizabeth, PhD, Asst Prof, Anal Phil
Trevas, Robert, PhD, Asst Prof, Ethics, Phil of Mind
Weckman, George, PhD, Assoc Prof, Hist of Relig
Wieman, Robert, PhD, Prof, Assoc Dean, Hist of Phil

Jeffers, James, Grad Asst
Jones, Glynis, Grad Asst
Patti, Doris E, Grad Asst

Phillips, John F, Grad Asst
Pocklington, Stephen L, Grad Asst

OHIO UNIVERSITY, BELMONT COUNTY BRANCH
Saint Clairsville, Ohio 43950 (N; st; coed; qr; I; 247) NR

OHIO UNIVERSITY, CHILLICOTHE BRANCH
Chillicothe, Ohio 45601 (N; st; coed; qr; I; 184) NR

OHIO UNIVERSITY, IRONTON BRANCH
Ironton, Ohio 45638 (N; st; coed; qr; I; 55) NP

OHIO UNIVERSITY, LANCASTER BRANCH
Lancaster, Ohio 43130 (N; st; coed; qr; I; 1214) Courses with no degree specialization,
Div of Human, 614-654-6711

Groby, Gordon L, MA, Instr, Chm

OHIO UNIVERSITY, PORTSMOUTH BRANCH
Portsmouth, Ohio 45662 (N; st; coed; qr; I; 85) Courses with no degree specialization,
--, 614-354-3205

OHIO UNIVERSITY, ZANESVILLE BRANCH
Zanesville, Ohio 43701 (N; st; coed; qr; I; 170) Courses with no degree specialization,
Dept of Phil, 614-594-4168

Arnold, John J, PhD, Assoc Prof

OHIO WESLEYAN UNIVERSITY
Delaware, Ohio 43105 (N; U Meth; coed; qr; II; 2543) BA major, Dept of Phil, 614-
363-1261 Ext 225

Easton, Loyd D, PhD, Prof, Chm, Amer Phil, Hegel, Marx
Anderson, Daniel, PhD, Assoc Prof, Greek Phil, Aes
Murchland, Bernard, PhD, Assoc Prof, Exist
Waber, William, PhD, Assoc Prof, British Phil

OTTERBEIN COLLEGE
Westerville, Ohio 43081 (N; U Meth; coed; --; II; 1356) BA major, Dept of Relig and
Phil, 614-882-3601 Ext 348

Amy, William, ThD, Assoc Prof, Chm, Metaph
Ackert, Paul, PhD, Prof, Logic
Chaney, Norman, MA, Asst Prof
Redditt, Paul, PhD, Asst Prof
Recob, James, ThD, Asst Prof, Ethics

PONTIFICAL COLLEGE JOSEPHINUM
Worthington, Ohio 43085 (Theol; RC; men; sem; III; 188) BA major, Div of Phil, 614-
888-6862

Schubert, Robert J, PhD, Prof, Chm, Schol Phil
Semeraro, Richard P, MA, Assoc Prof, Schol Phil, Contemp Phil

RABBINICAL COLLEGE OF TELSHE
Wickliffe, Ohio 44092 (--; Jewish; men; qr; III; 273) NR

RIO GRANDE COLLEGE
Rio Grande, Ohio 45674 (N; p; coed; sem; II; 750) BA minor, Dept of Art, Professional Educ, and Sci, 614-245-5353

Palmer, Jr, T Vail, PhD, Assoc Prof, Ethics and Society

SAINT JOHN COLLEGE OF CLEVELAND
Cleveland, Ohio 44114 (N; RC; coed; sem; III; 849) Courses with no degree specialization, --, 216-771-2388

Carney, Francis W, STD, Prof
Iezzi, Anthony J, PhD, Assoc Prof
Picard, Emy, MA, Assoc Prof

SAINT MARY SEMINARY
Cleveland, Ohio 44108 (Theol; RC; men; qr; III; 148) NP

SCHOOL OF DAYTON ART INSTITUTE
Dayton, Ohio 45405 (Art; p; coed; sem; II; 318) NP

SCIOTO COUNTY TECHNICAL INSTITUTE
Lucasville, Ohio 45648 (--; st; coed; qr; I; 324) NR

SINCLAIR COMMUNITY COLLEGE
Dayton, Ohio 45402 (N; local; coed; qr; I; 4746) Courses with no degree specialization, Dept of Human, 513-226-2831

Hickey, John T, MA, Assoc Prof, Chm, Greek and Med Phil
Burnside, Ronald L, MA, Instr, Ethics, Anal Phil
Klein, Mary K, PhD, Instr Part-time
Seman, Paul, MA, Instr Part-time
Von der Embse, Allecia, MA, Instr Part-time

STARK STATE TECHNICAL INSTITUTE
Canton, Ohio 44720 (--; st; coed; qr; I; 125) NR

TIFFIN UNIVERSITY
Tiffin, Ohio 44883 (SRCB; p; coed; sem; II; 519) NP

UNION EXPERIMENTING COLLEGE AND UNIVERSITY
Yellow Springs, Ohio 45387 (--; p; coed; --; II; 730) NR

UNITED THEOLOGICAL SEMINARY
Dayton, Ohio 45406 (Theol; U Meth; coed; qr; III; 249) --, --, 513-278-5817

UNIVERSITY OF AKRON
Akron, Ohio 44325 (N; st; coed; qr; IV; 19,674) MA major, Dept of Phil, 216-375-7094, 216-375-7095

Uhlinger, Paul J, PhD, Prof, Head, Aes, Phil of Relig
Buchanan, James H, PhD, Asst Prof, Phenomen, Exist
Cox, David, PhD, Assoc Prof, Ethics, Soc Phil, Polit Phil
Hart, Alan, PhD, Assoc Prof, Hist of Mod Phil, Plato
Hood, Michael, MA, Part-time

McMahon, William E, PhD, Asst Prof, Logic
Paige, R Douglas, PhD, Asst Prof, Phil of Law, Theory of Knowl, Amer Phil, Contemp Phil

Patrick, Walter T, BA, Grad Asst   Urbas, Michael J, BA, Grad Asst

UNIVERSITY OF CINCINNATI
Cincinnati, Ohio 45221 (N; st and local; coed; qr; IV; 32,751) PhD major, Dept of Phil, 513-475-6324, 513-475-2155

McMicken College of Arts and Sciences, Department of Phil

Gustafson, Donald F, PhD, Prof, Chm, Phil of Mind
Crockett, Campbell, PhD, Prof, Aes, Phil and Psychiatry
Faaborg, Robert W, PhD, Asst Prof, Ontology, Hist of Phil
Jaggar, Alison, PhD, Asst Prof, Anal Phil, Soc and Polit Phil
Jost, Lawrence J, MA, Asst Prof, Ethics, Greek Phil
Long, Thomas A, PhD, Assoc Prof, Phil of Relig, Phil of Law
Martin, John N, MA, Asst Prof, Formal Seman, Logic
McEvoy, John G, MA, Asst Prof, Hist and Phil of Sci
Miller, George, PhD, Prof, Hist of Phil, Kantian Stud
Morris, William E, MA, Asst Prof, Epistem, Phil Logic
Mullane, Harvey P, PhD, Assoc Prof, Phil of Mind, Phil and Psychiatry
Robinson, Jenefer M, MA, Visit Lect, Aes
Simons, Leo, PhD, Prof, Logic, Med Phil
Todd, William L, PhD, Prof, Phil of Ling, Phil of Lang
Workman, Rollin W, PhD, Prof, Moral and Polit Phil, Metaph

Ames, Van Meter, PhD, Prof Emer, Ethics
Browne, Samuel S S, PhD, Prof Emer, Logic, Ethics, Hist of Mod Phil

Brooks, James, Grad Asst   Mirvish, Adrian, Grad Asst
Coffman, Frederick, Grad Asst   Olson, George, Grad Asst
Dougherty, Thomas, Grad Asst   Popp, Michele, Grad Asst
Fessler, Kathryn, Grad Asst   Ray, Kenneth, Grad Asst
Glosser, Lawrence, Grad Asst   Rechtin, Lisbeth, Grad Asst
Hagner, David, Grad Asst   Russell, William, Grad Asst
Hart, John, Grad Asst   Santos, Antonio, Grad Asst
Iyer, Rojam, Grad Asst   Trowbridge, Mark, Grad Asst
Kosted, Paul, Grad Asst

University College, Department of Phil

Burks, Thompson, MA, Assoc Prof, Phil of Sci, Ordinary Lang Logic
Bradford, James, MA, Instr, 20th Cent Phil
Davidoff, Allen, MA, Asst Prof, Ordinary Lang Phil
Levine, Maurie, MA, Asst Prof, Phil of Psych
Sutton, Jr, Paul W, PhD, Prof, Hist of West Phil, Logic
Umbenhauer, William Peter, MA, Instr, Hist of Phil, Phil Method
Wilson, Arnold, MA, Instr, Epistem, Logic

UNIVERSITY OF CINCINNATI, RAYMOND WALTERS COLLEGE
Blue Ash, Ohio 45236 (N; st and local; coed; qr; I; 1902) AA major, Dept of Phil, 513-793-6010

Sullivan, William A, BA, Asst Prof

UNIVERSITY OF CINCINNATI TRI-COUNTY ACADEMIC CENTER
Macon, Ohio 45143 (N; st and local; coed; qr; --; --) NR

UNIVERSITY OF DAYTON
Dayton, Ohio 45469 (N; RC; coed; tri; IV; 8713) MA major, Dept of Phil, 513-229-2933

Herbenick, Raymond M, PhD, Assoc Prof, Chm
Baker, Richard R, PhD, Prof
Cartagenova, Gonzalo, PhD, Assoc Prof
Dieska, Joseph L, PhD, Prof
Edelenyi, Achilles, PhD, Asst Prof
Greene, Robert, MA, Asst Prof
Kunkel, Joseph C, PhD, Assoc Prof
Monasterio, Xavier O, PhD, Assoc Prof
Nersoyan, H James, PhD, Assoc Prof
Quinn, John F, MA, Asst Prof
Rhodes, Edmund M, MA, Asst Prof
Richards, William M, PhD, Asst Prof
Rinderly, Allen V, MA, Asst Prof
Thompson, John G, MA, Asst Prof
Ulrich, Lawrence P, PhD, Assoc Prof
Wening, Gerald G, MA, Asst Prof
Tibbetts, Paul, PhD, Asst Prof

Brezna, George
Cicantelli, Patricia
Dombrowiak, David
Dwyer, Charles
Ertel, Philip
Himes, Cynara
Hyland, Richard
Kanatsky, Christopher
Wilk, Gregory

Knight, Kirby
Kraft, Charles
McCusker, Owen
Miller, Thomas
Sedhi, Ziaollah
Strong, Carson
Vail, Alice
Viskovick, Frederick

UNIVERSITY OF TOLEDO
Toledo, Ohio 43606 (N; st; coed; qr; IV; 14,903) PhD minor, Dept of Phil, 419-531-5711 Ext 2619

Dewey, Ernest W, PhD, Prof, Chm, Value Theory, Soc Phil, Polit Phil, Amer Phil
Daley, James, PhD, Assoc Prof, Aes, Phil of Mind, Phil of Hist
Delattre, Edwin, PhD, Asst Prof, Epistem, Amer Phil, Ethics
Guthrie, George, PhD, Prof, Mod Phil, Ontology, Phenomen, Exist
Mayberry, Thomas, PhD, Prof, Anal Phil, Epistem, Phil of Mind
Mortimer, Roderick, Visit Instr
Pickard, Richard D, MA, Instr, Mod Phil, Contemp Phil, Metaph, Ethics
Puligandla, Ramakrishna, PhD, Prof, Logic, Phil of Sci, East Phil
Taylor, Stephen, PhD, Asst Prof, Ethics, Metaph, British Empir
Tigner, Steven, PhD, Assoc Prof, Greek Phil, Ethics, Phil of Relig

Coffin, Mary S, BA, Grad Asst
Dianda, James J, BA, Grad Asst
Drew, John M, BA, Grad Asst
Henderson, James, BA, Grad Asst
Koepp, Cynthia J, BA, Grad Asst

MacDowell, Mark E, BA, Grad Asst
Trundle, Robert C, BA, Grad Asst
Wilson, Thomas A, BA, Grad Asst
Zaciek, Alan J, BA, Grad Asst

URBANA COLLEGE
Urbana, Ohio 43078 (--; p; coed; qr; II; 731) BA joint or combined major, Dept of Phil of Relig, 513-652-1301 Ext 325

Klein, J Theodore, PhD, Asst Prof, Phil of Persons, Metaph, Phil of Educ
Klein, Mary K, PhD, Lect Part-time, Soc Phil, Phil of Sci

URSULINE COLLEGE
    Cleveland, Ohio 44124 (N; p; wo; sem; II; 400) BA major, Dept of Phil, 216-449-4200

    Kelly, James Therese, PhD, Prof, Chm
    O'Keefe, Lucienne, MA, Assoc Prof

VANGUARD TECHNICAL INSTITUTE
    Fremont, Ohio 43420 (--; st; coed; qr; I; 668) NR

WALSH COLLEGE
    Canton, Ohio 44720 (N; RC; coed; sem; II; 899) Courses with no degree specialization,
    Dept of Phil, 216-499-7090 Ext 24

    Stergiades, John W, Asst Prof, Chm, Ethics, Epistem
    Francoeur, Robert A, PhD, Prof, Logic, Aes

THE WESTERN COLLEGE
    Oxford, Ohio 45056 (N; p; coed; --; II; 351) Courses with no degree specialization,
    --, 513-529-8024

    Sommer, John, PhD, Prof, Ethics, Aes
    Sturm, Fred Gilette, PhD, Prof, Phenomen, Phil of Relig, Chinese Phil, Latin
        American Phil

WILBERFORCE UNIVERSITY
    Wilberforce, Ohio 45384 (N; AME; coed; tri; II; 1328) BA joint or combined major,
    --, 513-376-2911

    Gillespie, Malcolm, MA, Assoc Prof, Chm, Greek Phil
    Barranda, Natividad, PhD, Assoc Prof, Far East Relig
    Foster, James, M Div, Asst Prof
    Hansen, Clifford, PhD, Prof
    Reeves, Gene, PhD, Prof, Process Phil, Logic

WILMINGTON COLLEGE
    Wilmington, Ohio 45177 (N; Fr; coed; qr; II; 996) BA major, Dept of Relig and Phil,
    513-382-0951 Ext 37, 38

    Van Nuys, Kelvin, PhD, Prof, Head, Phil of Relig, Value Theory
    Hanson, Philip, MA, Asst Prof, Phenomen, Orient Tht
    Jones, T Canby, PhD, Prof, Quaker Tht

    Stanfield, Jesse A, DD, Asst Prof Emer

WITTENBERG UNIVERSITY
    Springfield, Ohio 45501 (N; Luth CA; coed; --; III, 3262) BA major, Dept of Phil,
    513-327-7633

    Long, Robert O, MA, Prof, Chm, Contemp Phil
    Gray, Philip, AB, Instr, Ethics
    Klive, Visvaldis, PhD, Assoc Prof, Phil of Relig
    Levy, Robert, PhD, Asst Prof, Phil of Sci
    Remsberg, Robert, PhD, Prof, 17th Cent Continen Phil

WRIGHT STATE UNIVERSITY
    Dayton, Ohio 45431 (N; st; coed; qr; III; 11,624) BA major, Dept of Phil, 513-426-
    6650 Ext 597, 598

Hough, Ronald F, PhD, Assoc Prof, Chm, Phil of Sci
Beelick, Donald J, PhD, Asst Prof, Ethics
Power, Robert J, PhD, Assoc Prof, Logic
Walters, William, MA, Instr, Phil of Lang

WRIGHT STATE UNIVERSITY, WESTERN OHIO BRANCH
Celina, Ohio 45822 (N; st; coed; qr; III; 725) --, --, 419-586-2379

Tomlinson, Arline, MA

XAVIER UNIVERSITY
Cincinnati, Ohio 45207 (N; RC; coed; sem; III; 5964) MA major, Dept of Phil, 513-745-3629

Schmidt, Robert W, PhD, Prof, Chm, Epistem, Metaph, Phil of Man
Bado, Walter J, MA, Instr, Phil of Man, Mod Phil, Kant
Blair, Elena, MA, Asst Prof, Phil of Man, Metaph
Bonvillain, Richard H, PhD, Asst Prof, Metaph, Ethics, Soc Phil, Contemp Phil
Charlton, Terrence P, MA, Instr, Phil of Man, Metaph
Curran, George A, PhD, Prof, Ethics, Soc Phil, Medical Ethics, Business Ethics
Dumont, Richard E, PhD, Prof, Metaph, Phil of God, Epistem, Contemp Phil
Foley, Daniel P, PhD, Prof, Phil of Man
Gendreau, Bernard A, PhD, Prof, Metaph, Med Phil, Contemp Phil
Hogan, Donald J, MA, Lect Part-time, Ethics, Soc Phil
Jones, William A, PhD, Assoc Prof, Ethics, Soc Phil, Amer Phil
Marrero, Alvin C, MA, Asst Prof, Phil of Nature, Logic, Phil of Sci, Phil of Man
Mercurio, Frank X, AB, Lect Part-time, Logic, Metaph
Moorman, Joseph G, MA, Lect Part-time, Ethics
Mulligan, Robert W, PhD, Prof, Phenomen, Anal Phil
Oppenheim, Frank M, PhD, Assoc Prof, Mod Phil, Amer Phil, Ethics, Soc Phil
Somerville, James M, PhD, Prof, Ethics, Phil of Man, Phil of God
Tillman, Stanley C, PhD, Prof, Metaph, Phil of Man

Viragh, Andrew S, PhD, Prof Emer, Ethics, Soc Phil
Wuellner, Bernard J, PhD, Prof Emer, Metaph, Phil of God

YOUNGSTOWN STATE UNIVERSITY
Youngstown, Ohio 44503 (N; st; coed; qr; III; 14,588) BA major, Dept of Phil and Relig Stud, 216-746-1851 Ext 475, 476

Greenman, Martin A, PhD, Prof, Chm, Exist, Phenomen
Belsan, Richard C, BD, Instr, Ethics
Cohen, Barry F, PhD, Asst Prof, Phil of Sci
Eminhizer, Earl Eugene, ThD, Asst Prof, Logic
Lucas, Joseph R, PhD, Prof, Phil of Relig
Reid, Charles L, PhD, Assoc Prof, Anal Phil
Riley, Bruce T, PhD, Prof, Hist of Phil
Shipka, Thomas A, PhD, Asst Prof, Soc Phil
Skodacek, August A, ThD, Instr, Phil of Relig

OKLAHOMA

ALTUS JUNIOR COLLEGE
Altus, Oklahoma 73521 (--; st; coed; sem; I; 777) Courses with no degree specialization, --, 405-482-5696

Frederick, Joe B, BD, Instr

AMERICAN CHRISTIAN COLLEGE
Tulsa, Oklahoma 74129 (--; Prot; coed; --; II; 88) BA minor, Div of Human, 918-836-1692

Wheeler, William, PhD, Prof, Chm
Noebel, David, MA, Asst Prof, Ethics

BACONE COLLEGE
Bacone, Oklahoma 74420 (N; Bapt; coed; sem; I; 568) --, --, 918-683-2921

Ferree, Robert F, EdD, Assoc Prof, Aes

BARTLESVILLE WESLEYAN COLLEGE
Bartlesville, Oklahoma 74003 (--; Wes; coed; sem; II; 203) Courses with no degree specialization, Dept of Phil, 918-333-6151

Mueller, Donald, MA, Part-time

BETHANY NAZARENE COLLEGE
Bethany, Oklahoma 73008 (N; Naz; coed; sem; III; 1704) MA minor, --, 405-789-6400

Rothwell, Mel Thomas, PhD, Chm, Epistem, Metaph, Phil of Sci, Soc Phil
Griffin, Robert M, EdD, Ethics, Phil of Educ
Hall, John, AM, Contemp Phil, Logic, Hist of Phil
Reed, Oscar E, PhD

CAMERON COLLEGE
Lawton, Oklahoma 73501 (ADNUR; st; coed; sem; II; 3866) Courses with no degree specialization, Dept of Soc Sci, 405-248-2200 Ext 53

Andrus, Charles E, PhD, Asst Prof, Ethics

CARL ALBERT JUNIOR COLLEGE
Poteau, Oklahoma 74953 (--; local; coed; sem; I; 429) Courses with no degree specialization, Dept of Phil, 918-647-3514

Garrett, Brad, EdD, Instr

CENTRAL STATE UNIVERSITY
Edmond, Oklahoma 73034 (N; st; coed; sem; III; 10,678) BA major, Dept of Phil, 405-341-2980 Ext 2636

Prewett, Aris, MA, Asst Prof, Chm, Hist of Phil, Ethics, Phil of Relig
Parker, Clarence M, PhD, Asst Prof, Latin American Phil, Mod Phil, Logic, Phil of Relig

CLAREMORE JUNIOR COLLEGE
Claremore, Oklahoma 74017 (N; st; coed; sem; I; 950) Courses with no degree

specialization, Dept of Soc Sci, 918-341-7510 Ext 33

Goodman, Carter, MS

CONNORS STATE COLLEGE
Warner, Oklahoma 74469 (N; st; coed; sem; I; 919) NP

EAST CENTRAL STATE COLLEGE
Ada, Oklahoma 74820 (N; st; coed; sem; III; 3092) NP

EASTERN OKLAHOMA STATE COLLEGE
Wilburton, Oklahoma 74578 (N; st; coed; sem; I; 1536) NP

EL RENO JUNIOR COLLEGE
El Reno, Oklahoma 73036 (--; local; coed; sem; I; 502) --, Dept of Phil and Hist,
405-262-2552

Beavers, Tedd D, MS, Prof, Chm
Coleman, A W, DD, Instr
Harrison, A R, PhD, Pres

HILLSDALE FREE WILL BAPTIST COLLEGE
Moore, Oklahoma 73160 (--; Fr Will Bapt Ch; coed; sem; I; 94) Courses with no degree
specialization, Dept of Relig, 405-794-6446

LANGSTON UNIVERSITY
Langston, Oklahoma 73050 (N; st; coed; sem; II; 1236) NR

MURRAY STATE COLLEGE
Tishomingo 73460 (N; st; coed; sem; I; 869) NP

NORTHEASTERN OKLAHOMA AGRICULTURAL AND MECHANICAL COLLEGE
Miami, Oklahoma 74354 (N; st; coed; sem; I; 2316) Courses with no degree specialization,
Div of Soc Sci, 918-542-8441

Anderson, Robert M, MA

NORTHEASTERN STATE COLLEGE
Tahlequah, Oklahoma 74464 (N; st; coed; sem; III; 5582) Courses with no degree
specialization, --, 918-456-5511

Jarrell, James A, PhD, Asst Prof

NORTHERN OKLAHOMA COLLEGE
Tonkawa, Oklahoma 74653 (N; st; coed; sem; I; 1453) NP

NORTHWESTERN STATE COLLEGE
Alva, Oklahoma 73717 (N; st; coed; sem; III; 2258) --, --, 405-327-0196

Arthurs, Marie, PhD, Prof
Sibley, S Floyd, MA, Instr

OKLAHOMA

OKLAHOMA BAPTIST UNIVERSITY
    Shawnee, Oklahoma 74801 (N; S Bapt; coed; 4-1-4; II; 1587) BA major, Dept of Phil,
    405-275-2850 Ext 231

    Clarke, Robert E, ThD, Prof, Anc Phil, Metaph, Phenomen, Exist, Phil of Relig
    Wester, Donald G, MA, Asst Prof, Mod Phil, Logic, Epistem, Anal Phil, Phil of Mind

OKLAHOMA CHRISTIAN COLLEGE
    Oklahoma City, Oklahoma 73111 (N; p; coed; tri; II; 1140) NP

OKLAHOMA CITY COLLEGE
    Oklahoma City, Oklahoma 73106 (N; U Meth; coed; sem; III; 2471) BA major, Dept of
    Phil, 405-525-5461

    Novak, David, PhD, Assoc Prof
    Wells, Stephen, MA, Assoc Prof
    Werneke, Leo, MA, Asst Prof

OKLAHOMA COLLEGE OF LIBERAL ARTS
    Chickasha, Oklahoma 73018 (N; st; coed; tri; II; 1015) Courses with no degree
    specialization, Dept of Phil and Relig Tht, 405-224-3140 Ext 275

    Sikes, Doug, MA, Asst Prof, Ethics, Logic, Phil of Educ and Relig

OKLAHOMA PANHANDLE STATE COLLEGE
    Goodwell, Oklahoma 73939 (N; st; coed; sem; II; 1268) Courses with no degree
    specialization, Dept of Human, 405-349-2611

    Libbey, Edwin B, MA, Prof, Head

OKLAHOMA SCHOOL OF BUSINESS, ACCOUNTING, LAW AND FINANCE
    Tulsa, Oklahoma 74119 (JRCB; p; coed; tri; I; 525) NR

OKLAHOMA STATE UNIVERSITY
    Stillwater, Oklahoma 74074 (N; st; coed; sem; IV; 19,935) PhD joint or combined
    major, Dept of Phil, 405-372-6211 Ext 447

    Scott, Walter G, PhD, Assoc Prof, Chm, Phil of Relig
    Bosworth, John R, MA, Asst Prof, Phil of Sci
    Bush, Richard C, PhD, Prof, Orient Phil
    Eggerman, Richard, PhD, Asst Prof, Ethics
    Lawry, Edward G, PhD, Asst Prof, Exist, Aes
    Luebke, Neil R, PhD, Assoc Prof, Soc and Mod Phil
    Radford, Robert T, PhD, Assoc Prof, Phil of Mind
    Susky, John E, EdD, Assoc Prof, Phil of Educ

    Hall, Terry R, BA, Grad Asst   McMurry, William L, BA, Grad Asst

OKLAHOMA STATE UNIVERSITY AT OKLAHOMA CITY
    Oklahoma City, Oklahoma 73107 (N; st; coed; sem; I; 1362) NP

ORAL ROBERTS UNIVERSITY
    Tulsa, Oklahoma 74105 (N; p; coed; sem; II; 1334) NP

OSCAR ROSE JUNIOR COLLEGE
    Midwest City, Oklahoma 73110 (--; st; coed; sem; I; 3021) NP

PHILLIPS UNIVERSITY
    Enid, Oklahoma 73701 (N; Disc Chirst; coed; sem; IV; 1361) BA major, Div of Relig
    and Phil, 405-237-4433, Ext 229, 319, 214

    Simpson, Robert L, PhD, Chm, Amer Phil, Aes
    Connor, William, PhD, Ethics
    Moore, J T, PhD, Hist of Phil

SAINT GREGORY'S COLLEGE
    Shawnee, Oklahoma 74801 (N; RC; coed; sem; I; 510) Courses with no degree
    specialization, Div of Human, Phil Section, 405-273-9870 Ext 527

    Statham, Denis, STD, Chm, Anc and Med Phil
    Roberts, Victor, PhD, Mod Phil
    Seneschal, Theodore, Mag Div, Phil of Relig

SAYRE JUNIOR COLLEGE
    Sayre, Oklahoma 73662 (MLT; st and local; coed; sem; I; 317) --, --, 405-928-3053

    Guinn, Toney, MA, Instr

SEMINOLE JUNIOR COLLEGE
    Seminole, Oklahoma 74868 (--; st and local; coed; sem; I; 705) Courses with no
    degree specialization, Dept of Human, 405-382-9950

SOUTH OKLAHOMA CITY JUNIOR COLLEGE
    Oklahoma City, Oklahoma 73159 (--; local; coed; --; I; 1100) AA major, Inst of
    Human Affairs, 405-682-1611

    Sapp, Charles Leon, DEd, Prof, Contemp Phil

SOUTHEASTERN STATE COLLEGE
    Durant, Oklahoma 74701 (N; st; coed; sem; III; 3793) NP

SOUTHWESTERN COLLEGE
    Oklahoma City, Oklahoma 73127 (--; Pent Hol; coed; sem; I; 1213) Courses with no
    degree specialization, Dept of Phil, 405-947-2331

SOUTHWESTERN STATE COLLEGE
    Weatherford, Oklahoma 73096 (N; st; coed; sem; III; 5482) BA minor, Dept of Gen
    Educ, 405-772-6611

    Sill, James D, ThD, Prof, Chm, Phil of Relig, Contemp Phil
    Abel, John W, ThD, Assoc Prof, Logic, Ethics

TULSA JUNIOR COLLEGE
    Tulsa, Oklahoma 74119 (--; st; coed; sem; I; 3923) --, Dept of Cult and Soc Services,
    918-587-6561 Ext 256

    Owen, Robert, MA, Instr

UNIVERSITY OF OKLAHOMA
Norman, Oklahoma 73069 (N; st; coed; sem; IV; 20,854) PhD major, Dept of Phil, 405-325-6324

Shahan, Robert W, PhD, Assoc Prof, Chm, Exist, 20th Cent Continen Phil, Ethics
Berenda, Carlton W, PhD, Prof, Phil of Sci
Boyd, Tom W, PhD, Asst Prof, Phil of Relig, Ethics
Cook, Monte L, PhD, Asst Prof, Phil Anal, Continen Ration
Clay, Marjorie A, Instr, Ethics, Phil Anal
Cromwell, William E, MA, Instr, Phil Anal, Phil of Relig
Feaver, J Clayton, PhD, Prof, Phil of Relig, Ethics
Hadgopoulos, Demetrius, Visit Asst Prof, Anc Phil
Horosz, William, PhD, Prof, Ethics, Soc Phil, Polit Phil
Kovach, Francis J, PhD, Prof, Med Phil, Aes
Merrill, Kenneth R, PhD, Assoc Prof, Logic, Mod Ration, Process Phil
Mohanty, Jitendra N, PhD, Res Prof, Phenomen, 19th and 20th Cent Phil
Willcox, David E, PhD, Visit Asst Prof, Phil of Logic, Phil of Sci

Mueller, Gustav E, PhD, Prof Emer

Calvert, Robert M, MA, Grad Assoc
Constantikes, John J, BA, Kingfisher Fel
DePlois, Barbara C, MA, Teach Asst
Feezell, Larry, BA, Teach Asst
Feezell, Randolph M, BA, Grad Assoc
Hutcheson, Peter W, BA, Teach Asst
Kagan, Connie B, MA, Grad Assoc
Longley, Dianne, MA, Kingfisher Fel
McDowell, Elwood, MA, Teach Asst
Ozmun, Letitia J, MA, Kingfisher Fel
Pappin, III, Joseph L, MA, Teach Asst
Pence, Carol L, BA, Grad Assoc
Schaefer, Michael P, BA, NDEA Fel
Stacy, James W, MA, Teach Asst
Tate, Donald S, MA, Teach Asst
Wood, Carol, BA, Teach Asst

UNIVERSITY OF OKLAHOMA HEALTH SCIENCE CENTER
Oklahoma City, Oklahoma 73104 (Med; st; coed; sem; IV; 1227) NR

UNIVERSITY OF TULSA
Tulsa, Oklahoma 74104 (N; p; coed; sem; IV; 6194) BA major, Dept of Phil, 918-939-6351 Ext 255

Brown, Paul L, ThD, Prof, Phil of Relig, Logic
Gibson, Leonard, PhD, Asst Prof, Exist, Whitehead
Lind, Richard, PhD, Asst Prof, Aes, Phenomen
Reed, Margaret, PhD, Asst Prof, Value Theory

OREGON

BLUE MOUNTAIN COMMUNITY COLLEGE
Pendleton, Oregon 97801 (NW; st and local; coed; qr; I; 462) NR

CENTRAL OREGON COMMUNITY COLLEGE
Bend, Oregon 97701 (NW; local; coed; qr; I; 978) NR

CHEMEKETA COMMUNITY COLLEGE
    Salem, Oregon 97303 (--; local; coed; qr; I; 4407) NP

CLACKAMAS COMMUNITY COLLEGE
    Oregon City, Oregon 97045 (NW; local; coed; qr; I; 3298) AA major, Dept of Phil,
    503-656-2631

    Roy, Mayo Rae, MA, Instr, Ideas and Methods

CLATSOP COMMUNITY COLLEGE
    Astoria, Oregon 97103 (NW; local; coed; qr; I; 1896) Courses with no degree
    specialization, Dept of Soc Sci, 503-325-0910 Ext 227

    Hauser, John David, PhD, Phil of Sci, Phil of Myst

COLUMBIA CHRISTIAN COLLEGE
    Portland, Oregon 97220 (--; p; coed; qr; II; 204) Courses with no degree specialization,
    Div of Human, 503-255-7060

    Danner, Dan, PhD, Chm
    Sanders, J P, PhD

CONCORDIA COLLEGE
    Portland, Oregon 97211 (NW; Luth Mo Synod; coed; qr I; 152) NP

EASTERN OREGON COLLEGE
    La Grande, Oregon 97850 (NW; st; coed; qr; III; 1628) NR

GEORGE FOX COLLEGE
    Newberg, Oregon 97132 (NW; Fr; coed; qr; II; 443) BA joint or combined major, Div
    of Relig, 503-538-2101

    Roberts, Arthur O, PhD, Prof

JUDSON BAPTIST COLLEGE
    Portland, Oregon 97220 (--; Bapt; coed; qr; I; 132) AA major, Dept of Phil, 503-
    252-5563

    Hampton, Mariel, MA, Assoc Prof, Chm

LANE COMMUNITY COLLEGE
    Eugene, Oregon 97405 (NW; local; coed; qr; I; 5445) Courses with no degree
    specialization, Dept of Soc Sci, 503-747-4501 Ext 240

    Molenkamp, Harold, MA, Asst Prof

LEWIS AND CLARK COLLEGE
    Portland, Oregon 97219 (NW; p; coed; qr; III; 2443) BA major, Dept of Phil, 503-
    244-6161 Ext 595

    Harrington, John, PhD, Prof, Chm, Phil of Relig
    Hirschbein, Sevin, PhD, Asst Prof, 19th Cent Phil and Culture
    Morgareidge, Clayton, PhD, Assoc Prof

LINFIELD COLLEGE
McMinnville, Oregon 97128 (NW; A Bapt; coed; sem; III; 1085) BA major, Dept of Phil, 503-472-4121 Ext 216

Fost, Frederic F, PhD, Prof, Phil of Relig, Metaph, Asian Phil
Nelson, Francis G, MA, Asst Prof, Hist of Phil, Ethics, Value Theory

LINN-BENTON COMMUNITY COLLEGE
Albany, Oregon 97321 (ADNUR; st; coed; qr; I; 2002) Courses with no degree specialization, Dept of Human, 503-928-2361

Crawford, Jr, Edwin E, MA

MARYLHURST COLLEGE
Marylhurst, Oregon 97036 (NW; p; wo; sem; III; 529) BA minor, Dept of Phil and Relig Stud, 503-636-8141

McInnis, S Peter Mary, MA, Asst Prof, Chm
Madden, S Frances, PhD, Prof, Hist of Phil
Orange, S Donna, MA, Instr

MOUNT ANGEL COLLEGE
Mt Angel, Oregon 97362 (NW; p; coed; qr; II; 276) BA joint or combined major, Dept of Human, 503-845-2234 Ext 22

Micallef, John, PhD, Assoc Prof, Chm, Exist
Winstin, Reid, MA, Asst Prof, Contemp Phil

MOUNT ANGEL SEMINARY
St Benedict, Oregon 97373 (--; local; coed; qr; I; 8904) BA major, Dept of Phil, 503-845-2221

Feiss, Hugh, PhD, Chm, Phil of Relig, Anc Phil
Kohls, John, MA, Mod Phil, Phenomen
Lawrence, Philip, MA, Logic, Phil of Sci
Pollard, Martin, PhD, Schol Phil

MOUNT HOOD COMMUNITY COLLEGE
Gresham, Oregon 97030 (--; local; coed; qr; I; 8904) AA major, Div of Soc Sci, 503-666-1561 Ext 294

Casey, Michael M, MA

MULTNOMAH SCHOOL OF BIBLE
Portland, Oregon 97220 (BI; p; coed; sem; II; 680) NP

MUSEUM ART SCHOOL
Portland, Oregon 97205 (JNW; p; coed; sem; II; 150) NP

NORTHWESTERN CHRISTIAN COLLEGE
Eugene, Oregon 97401 (NW; Disc of Christ; coed; qr; II; 435) Courses with no degree specialization, --, 503-343-1641

Boosinger, John W, MA, Prof, Hist of Phil

OREGON COLLEGE OF EDUCATION
    Monmouth, Oregon 97361 (NW; st; coed; qr; III; 3975) BA joint or combined major,
    Dept of Human, 503-838-1220 Ext 408

    Moore, John, CPhil, Asst Prof, 19th and 20th Cent Phil
    Tompkins, Robert, PhD, Assoc Prof, Metaph, Orient Phil

OREGON GRADUATE CENTER
    Beaverton, Oregon 97005 (--; p; coed; tri; IV; 19) NR

OREGON STATE UNIVERSITY
    Corvallis, Oregon 97331 (NW; st; coed; qr; IV; 15,532) PhD minor, Dept of Phil,
    503-754-2955

    Harris, Frederick P, PhD, Prof, Chm, Asian Phil, Phil of Educ, Hist of Phil
    Anton, Peter, PhD, Prof, Contemp Anal Phil
    Dale, Robert D, PhD, Asst Prof, Contemp Anal Phil
    Frank, William F, MA, Instr, Logic, Phil of Sci, Phil of Ling
    List, Peter C, PhD, Asst Prof, Ethics, Amer Phil

OREGON TECHNICAL INSTITUTE
    Klamath Falls, Oregon 97601 (JNW; st; coed; qr; II; 1598) NP

PACIFIC UNIVERSITY
    Forest Grove, Oregon 97116 (NW; p; coed; sem; III; 1236) MA major, Dept of Phil,
    503-357-6151 Ext 351

    Reif, Walter F, PhD, Chm, Hist of Phil, Aes, Anal Phil
    Reynolds, Jr, Levering, PhD, Exist, Ethics
    Shishido, Miles, PhD, Phil of Relig, Logic, Marx

PORTLAND COMMUNITY COLLEGE, CASCADE CAMPUS
    Portland, Oregon 97219 (NW; local; coed; qr; I; --) AA major, Dept of Soc Sci, 503-
    244-6111, 503-283-2541

    Simmons, Valerie, A, MA, Instr

PORTLAND COMMUNITY COLLEGE, MOUNT SYLVANIA CAMPUS
    Portland, Oregon 97219 (NW; local; coed; qr; I; 12,225) Courses with no degree
    specialization, Dept of Soc Sci, 503-244-6111 Ext 271

    Carey, Steve, MA, Instr, Phil of Logic, Phil of Lang
    Hagensick, Paul, PhD, Instr
    Jolin, F R, PhD, Instr
    Rathman, Steve, MA, Instr, Phil of Mind, Phil Psych

PORTLAND STATE UNIVERSITY
    Portland, Oregon 97207 (NW; st; coed; qr; IV; 14,497) BA major, Dept of Phil, 503-
    229-3524

    Bowlden, Larry S, PhD, Asst Prof, Chm
    Adami, Richard R, MA, Asst Prof
    Blank, John S, MA, Asst Prof
    Buchanan, Rupert A, PhD, Asst Prof
    Conroy, Graham P, PhD, Assoc Prof
    Dexter, Roger, M Phil, Asst Prof
    Haines, Byron L, PhD, Asst Prof

Hammond, John L, PhD, Assoc Prof
Moor, Donald R, BA, Asst Prof
Newhall, David H, PhD, Prof
Passell, Dan, PhD, Asst Prof
Philips, Michael L, PhD, Asst Prof
Polonoff, Irving I, PhD, Prof
Williams, Robert L, BA, Instr
Wolfe, H Kirke, MA, Asst Prof

REED COLLEGE
Portland, Oregon 97202 (NW; p; coed; sem; III; 1316) BA major, --, 503-771-1112

Paul, Robert, MA, Assoc Prof, Ethics, Phil of Mind
Athay, Michael, BA, Asst Prof, Metaph, Epistem
Beauregard, Laurent, MS, Asst Prof, Phil of Sci
Levich, Marvin, BA, Prof, Phil of Hist, Aes
Peck, William, BA, Assoc Prof, Euro Phil

ROGUE COMMUNITY COLLEGE
Grants Pass, Oregon 97526 (--; local; coed; qr; I; 846) NR

SOUTHERN OREGON COLLEGE
Ashland, Oregon 97520 (NW; st; coed; qr; III; 4758) BA joint or combined major,
Div of Human, 503-482-6291

Kreisman, Arthur, PhD, Prof, Chm, Orient Phil
Alexander, David, MA, Asst Prof, Phil of Educ
Alexander, John, PhD, Asst Prof, Epistem, Axiology
Volkomener, Helen, PhD, Assoc Prof, Metaph, Axiology

SOUTHWESTERN OREGON COMMUNITY COLLEGE
Coos Bay, Oregon 97420 (NW; local; coed; qr; I; 2198) Courses with no degree
specialization, Dept of Eng, 503-888-3234

Swearinger, Jack, PhD, Prof

TREASURE VALLEY COMMUNITY COLLEGE
Ontario, Oregon 97914 (NW; local; coed; qr; I; 1193) NP

UMPQUA COMMUNITY COLLEGE
Roseburg, Oregon 97470 (NW; local; coed; qr; I; 1178) Courses with no degree
specialization, Dept of Soc Sci, 503-672-5571

Moisan, James V, MA

UNIVERSITY OF OREGON
Eugene, Oregon 97403 (NW; st; coed; qr; IV; 15,249) PhD major, Dept of Phil, 503-
686-4847

Zweig, Arnulf, PhD, Prof, Head, Hist of Phil, Phil of Law, Ethics
Alexander, Henry A, PhD, Assoc Prof, Epistem, Hist of Phil
Cook, John W, PhD, Prof, Wittgenstein, Phil of Soc Sci
Davie, William E, PhD, Asst Prof, Ethics, Hist of Phil
Ebersole, Frank B, PhD, Prof, Phil of Lang, Phil of Mind
Geddes, Leonard, PhD, Asst Prof, Ethics, Hist of Phil
Herbert, Robert T, PhD, Assoc Prof, Phil of Relig, Aes

Levi, Don S, PhD, Assoc Prof, Phil of Math, Contemp Soc and Moral Tht
Wisdom, A John, MA, Prof, Phil Methods

Harrington, John, BA, Grad Teach Fel   Schneider, Paul A, MA, Grad Teach Fel
Meyer, Jeffrey N, MA, Grad Teach Fel   Walker, Robert A, Grad Teach Fel
Thomas, John C, BA, Grad Teach Fel

UNIVERSITY OF OREGON DENTAL SCHOOL
    Portland, Oregon 97201 (Dent; st; coed; qr; IV; 418) NR

UNIVERSITY OF OREGON MEDICAL SCHOOL
    Portland, Oregon 97201 (Med; st; coed; qr; IV; 944) NP

UNIVERSITY OF PORTLAND
    Portland, Oregon 97203 (NW; p; coed; sem; IV; 1945) BA major, Dept of Phil, 503-283-
    7144, 503-283-7223

    Faller, Thompson Mason, PhD, Assoc Prof, Chm, Ethics, Aes
    Bill, Thomas L, PhD, Assoc Prof, Metaph
    Hund, William B, PhD, Asst Prof, Phil Anthrop
    Jolin, Stephen T, PhD, Asst Prof, Exist
    Mayr, Franz K, PhD, Assoc Prof, Hist of Phil, Phil of Relig

    Dum, George L, MA, Adj Assoc Prof Emer, Epistem
    McAvoy, Bernard L, MA, Adj Assoc Prof Emer, Metaph

WARNER PACIFIC COLLEGE
    Portland, Oregon 97215 (NW; Ch of God; coed; qr; II; 468) Courses with no degree
    specialization, Dept of Relig, 503-775-4368

    Monroe, Warner, PhD, Prof, Ethics

WESTERN BAPTIST BIBLE COLLEGE
    Salem, Oregon 97302 (NW; Bapt; coed; qr; II; 447) Courses with no degree specialization,
    Dept of Arts and Human, 503-581-8600

WESTERN CONSERVATIVE BAPTIST THEOLOGICAL SEMINARY
    Portland, Oregon 97215 (NW; p; coed; qr; III; 264) NP

WILLAMETTE UNIVERSITY *
    Salem, Oregon 97301 (NW; p; coed; sem; IV; 1707) BA major, Dept of Phil, 503-370-
    3638

    Hunnex, Milton D, PhD, Prof, Chm, Phil of Relig
    Canning, Jerry, PhD, Assoc Prof, Phil of Sci
    Talbott, Thomas, PhD, Instr, Metaph

PENNSYLVANIA

ACADEMY OF THE NEW CHURCH
Bryn Athyn, Pennsylvania 19009 (M; Ch of N Jeru; coed; qr; III; 128) BA joint or combined major, --, 215-947-4200

Allen, Edward F, AM, Prof
Cole, Charles, AM, Prof

ALBRIGHT COLLEGE
Reading, Pennsylvania 19604 (M; U Meth; coed; 4-1-4; II; 1593) BA major, Dept of Phil, 215-921-2381 Ext 245

Haskell, Ellery B, PhD, Prof, Head, Phil of Hist, Hist of Phil
Barth, Eugene H, PhD, Prof, Phil of Relig, Ethics
McBride, Robert E, PhD, Prof

ALLEGHENY COLLEGE
Meadville, Pennsylvania 16335 (M; p; coed; --; III; 1713) BA major, Dept of Phil and Relig, 814-724-3366

Sheridan, James F, PhD, Prof, Chm, Contemp Euro Phil
Bywater, William, PhD, Asst Prof, Aes, Metaph
Day, James, PhD, Prof, Ethics, Phil of Relig

ALLENTOWN COLLEGE OF SAINT FRANCIS DE SALES
Center Valley, Pennsylvania 18034 (M; RC; coed; sem; II; 638) Courses with no degree specialization, Div of Phil and Theol, 215-282-1000

Larkin, Ronald, PhD, Asst Prof, Chm, Epistem
Sullivan, William, PhD, Soc Phil

ALLIANCE COLLEGE
Cambridge Springs, Pennsylvania 16403 (M; p; coed; sem; II; 580) --, Dept of Math and Phys, 814-398-4611

Caiazza, John, MA, Instr, Phil of Sci

ALVERNIA COLLEGE
Reading, Pennsylvania 19607 (M; RC; wo; sem; II; 189) BA minor, --, 215-777-5411

Jacinta, Mary, Prof, Chm, Plato
Accursia, Mary, PhD, Prof, Med Phil
Villareal, James, PhB, Asst Prof, Contemp Phil

BAPTIST BIBLE COLLEGE
Clarks Summit, Pennsylvania 18411 (BI; Bapt; coed; sem; II; 603) Courses with no degree specialization, Dept of Apologetics, 717-587-1172 Ext 260

Thomas, Thomas A, MA, Assoc Prof, Hist of Phil, Phil Apologetics for Chirst

BEAVER COLLEGE
Glenside, Pennsylvania 19038 (M; Preb; wo; sem; II; 802) BA major, Dept of Phil, 215-884-3500 Ext 321

Huang, Siu-chi, PhD, Prof, Chm, Chinese Phil, Comp Phil, Ethics
O'Connor, Finbarr W, LPh, Asst Prof, Phil of Sci, Logic, Contemp Phil
McWhinney, Russell, MA, Asst Prof Part-time

BLOOMSBURG STATE COLLEGE
Bloomsburg, Pennsylvania 17815 (M; st; coed; sem; III; 4956) BA major, Dept of Phil,
717-389-2500

Carlough, William L, PhD, Prof, Chm, Phil of Relig
Brook, Richard J, PhD, Assoc Prof, Mod Phil, Phil of Sci
Larmi, Oliver J, PhD, Assoc Prof, Anc Phil
Schwimmer, Seymour, MA, Assoc Prof, Ethics

BRYN MAWR COLLEGE
Bryn Mawr, Pennsylvania 19010 (M; p; wo; sem; IV; 1421) PhD major, --, 215-525-1000

Ferrater-Mora, J, PhL, Prof, Chm, Contemp Phil, Epistem, Hist of Concepts
Kline, George L, PhD, Prof, Russian Phil, Hegel, Mod Phil
Krausz, M, PhD, Asst Prof, Phil of Hist, Epistem, Anal Phil
Mulhern, John, PhD, Lect, Greek Phil, Anal Phil
Potter, Jean, PhD, Prof, Med Phil, Phil of Relig
Stearns, Isabel, PhD, Prof, Metaph, Amer Phil
Weaver, George, PhD, Asst Prof, Logic, Phil of Math

De Laguna, Grace A, PhD, Prof Emer
Nahm, Milton C, PhD, Prof Emer

Logan, Michael   Wallace, Carol

BUCKNELL UNIVERSITY
Lewisburg, Pennsylvania 17837 (M; p; coed; sem; III; 2962) MA major, Dept of Phil,
717-524-3461

Martin, F David, PhD, Prof, Chm, Aes
Brockhaus, Richard, PhD, Asst Prof, Phil of Sci
Fell, Joseph P, PhD, Prof, Phenomen
Hochberg, Gary H, PhD, Asst Prof, Ethics
Wilson, Jr, Francis E, PhD, Instr, Anal Phil

Warren, W Preston, PhD, Prof Emer

BUCKS COUNTY COMMUNITY COLLEGE
Newtown, Pennsylvania 18940 (M; local; coed; sem; I; 5165) Courses with no degree
specialization, Dept of Phil, 215-968-4261 Ext 433

DeMarco, Elaine Choate, MA, Assoc Prof, Chm, Ethics, Logic, Anal Phil

BUTLER COUNTY COMMUNITY COLLEGE
Butler, Pennsylvania 16001 (M; local; coed; sem; I; 1808) Courses with no degree
specialization, Dept of Human, 412-287-8711 Ext 143

Pohmea, Tim, MDiv, Asst Prof

CABRINI COLLEGE
Radnor, Pennsylvania 19087 (M; RC; coed; sem; II; 395) BA major, --, 215-687-2100

Giorgi, Louis P, MA, Assoc Prof, Epistem
Kearns, Thomas J, PhD, Lect, Phil of Sci
Marshall, David, PhD, Lect, German Phil
Romane, Joseph J, PhD, Prof, Greek Phil
Shwarze, Sharon, MA, Instr, Metaph of Space and Time

313

CALIFORNIA STATE COLLEGE
   California, Pennsylvania 15419 (M; st; coed; tri; III; 6505) BA major, Dept of
   Phil, 412-938-2281 Ext 305, 306

CARLOW COLLEGE
   Pittsburgh, Pennsylvania 15213 (M; RC; wo; sem; II; 1045) BA major, Dept of Phil,
   412-683-4800 Ext 281

   McMillan, Elizabeth, PhD, Asst Prof, Ethics, Phil of Relig
   Tybor, Arthur, PhD, Assoc Prof, Hist of Phil, Metaph

CARNEGIE-MELLON UNIVERSITY
   Pittsburgh, Pennsylvania 15213 (M; p; coed; sem; IV; 4540) BA major, Dept of Hist
   and Phil, 412-661-2600 Ext 487

   Schwartz, Thomas, PhD, Assoc Prof, Chm, Polit Phil, Soc Choice Theory, Ethics
   Carrier, David, PhD, Asst Prof, Aes, Phil of Mind
   Covey, Preston, MA, Instr, Phil in Lit, Ethics, Phil of Relig
   Pottinger, Garrel, PhD, Asst Prof, Math Logic, Phil of Math, Hist of Phil
   Wojick, David, PhD, Asst Prof, Phil of Tech, Phil of Sci, Marx and Hegel

CEDAR CREST COLLEGE
   Allentown, Pennsylvania 18104 (M; U Ch of Christ; wo; 4-1-4; II; 774) BA major,
   Dept of Phil, 215-437-4471 Ext 226

   Coffin, Peter, PhD, Prof, Chm, 19th and 20th Cent Phil
   Avlick, Lynn, AB, Instr, Greek Phil, Logic

CHATHAM COLLEGE
   Pittsburgh, Pennsylvania 15232 (M; p; wo; 4-1-4; II; 640) BA major, Dept of Phil
   and Relig, 412-441-8200

   Arnett, Willard E, PhD, Prof, Chm, Hist of Phil, Aes
   Chan, Wing-tsit, PhD, Prof, Oreint Phil
   Crumbine, Nancy Jay, PhD, Asst Prof, Exist
   Kaplan, Solomon M, MHL, Adj Assoc Prof, Judaism
   Morrill, Richard L, PhD, Asst Prof, Mod Relig Tht
   Nicholson, Susan T, BA, Instr, Ethics, Logic

CHESTNUT HILL COLLEGE
   Philadelphia, Pennsylvania 19118 (M; RC; wo; sem; II; 1128) BA major, Dept of Phil,
   215-247-4212

   Kearns, Thomas J, PhD, Assoc Prof, Chm
   Mary, Gerald, MA, Lect
   Touey, John V, MA, Asst Prof

CHEYNEY STATE COLLEGE
   Cheyney, Pennsylvania 19319 (M; st; coed; sem; III; 2362) NR

CLARION STATE COLLEGE
   Clarion, Pennsylvania 16214 (M; st; coed; sem; III; 3979) BA major, Dept of Soc Sci,
   814-226-6000 Ext 207

   Bertsch, Jack H, PhD, Assoc Prof, Phil of Sci, Logic
   Takei, Franklin S, PhD, Prof, Phil of Relig

Zallys, Richard, MA, Assoc Prof, Aes

CLARION STATE COLLEGE, VENANGO CAMPUS
Oil City, Pennsylvania 16301 (M; st; coed; sem; I; 382) NR

COLLEGE MISERICORDIA
Dallas, Pennsylvania 18612 (M; RC; wo; --; II; 919) --, Dept of Phil, 717-675-2181
Ext 227

Cronk, George, PhD, Asst Prof
Inverso, Donald, MA, Asst Prof
Kozel, Constance, PhD, Asst Prof
Latarewicz, Edward, MA, Asst Prof

COMMUNITY COLLEGE OF ALLEGHENY COUNTY, ALLEGHENY CAMPUS
Pittsburgh, Pennsylvania 15212 (M; local; coed; sem; I; 6120) Courses with no
degree specialization, Dept of Foreign Lang, Educ and Phil, 412-321-0192

Eskridge, John, MA, Asst Prof, Phenomen
James, Robert, MEd, Assoc Prof

COMMUNITY COLLEGE OF ALLEGHENY COUNTY, BOYCE CAMPUS
Monroeville, Pennsylvania 15146 (M; local; coed; sem; I; 4430) AA major, Dept of
Phil and World Cultures, 412-327-1327

Edelson, Zvi, MA, Assoc Prof

COMMUNITY COLLEGE OF ALLEGHENY COUNTY, SOUTH CAMPUS
West Mifflin, Pennsylvania 15219 (--; local; coed; sem; I; 2870) Courses with no
degree specialization, --, 412-462-1808

COMMUNITY COLLEGE OF BEAVER COUNTY
Monaca, Pennsylvania 15061 (M; st and local; coed; sem; I; 1627) NR

COMMUNITY COLLEGE OF PHILADELPHIA
Philadelphia, Pennsylvania 19107 (M; local; coed; sem; I; 5963) Courses with no
degree specialization, Dept of Hist and Phil, 215-569-3680 Ext 272

Berger, Jeffrey, MA, Asst Prof
Katen, Tom, MA, Assoc Prof
Spear, Martin, MA, Asst Prof

CURTIS INSTITUTE OF MUSIC
Philadelphia, Pennsylvania 19103 (--; p; coed; sem; III; 187) NR

DELAWARE COUNTY COMMUNITY COLLEGE
Media, Pennsylvania 19063 (M; local; coed; sem; I; 2313) Courses with no degree
specialization, --, 215-459-4800

Marron, John, MA, Assoc Prof, Ethics

DELAWARE VALLEY COLLEGE OF SCIENCE AND AGRICULTURE
Doylestown, Pennsylvania 18901 (M; p; coed; sem; II; 1224) --, Div of Gen Stud, 215-
345-1500 Ext 250

Lawrence, Edwin, MA, Instr
O'Brien, Edward, MA, Instr

DICKINSON COLLEGE
Carlisle, Pennsylvania 17013 (M; p; coed; sem; II; 1639) BA major, Dept of Phil, 717-243-5121

Allan, George, PhD, Prof, Chm, Soc Phil
Dwiggins, W Cyril, MA, Asst Prof, Phenomen
Ferré, Frederick, PhD, Prof, Phil of Relig, Phil of Sci

Gould, William Drum, PhD, Prof Emer, Orient Phil

DICKINSON SCHOOL OF LAW
Carlisle, Pennsylvania 17013 (Law; p; coed; sem; III; 432) NP

DIVINITY SCHOOL OF THE PROTESTANT EPISCOPAL CHURCH
Philadelphia, Pennsylvania 19104 (Theol; PE; coed; sem; III; 78) Courses with no degree specialization, Dept of Theol, 215-386-7475

Skinner, John E, STD, Prof, Phil Theol

DREXEL UNIVERSITY
Philadelphia, Pennsylvania 19104 (M; p; coed; qr; IV; 8622) BA joint or combined major, Dept of Lit and Lang, 215-895-2431

Ginsburg, Robert, PhD, Adj Assoc Prof, Polit and Soc Phil
McCord, Joan, PhD, Assoc Prof
Montgomery, Martha B, PhD, Asst Prof, Ethics, 20th Cent Phil, Logic
Shapiro, Vivian M, PhD, Asst Prof, Hist of Ideas

THE DROPSIE UNIVERSITY
Philadelphia, Pennsylvania 19132 (M; p; coed; sem; IV; 110) PhD major, Dept of Comp Relig and Phil, 215-229-0110

Agus, Jacob, PhD, Visit Prof, Mod Phil
Efros, Israel, PhD, Prof, Anc and Med Phil

DUQUESNE UNIVERSITY
Pittsburgh, Pennsylvania 15219 (M; RC; coed; sem; IV; 8427) PhD major, Dept of Phil, 412-434-6500

Schuwer, André, PhD, Prof, Chm, Phenomen, Marxism, Phil of Relig
Allen, Jeffner, MA, Part-time Instr
Berreckman, Carleton, PhD, Asst Prof, Phenomen, Anal Phil
Collins, Maurice, MA, Part-time Instr
Daniel, James, MA, Part-time Instr
Davis, Steven, MA, Part-time Instr
Gelblum, Edward L, MA, Asst Prof, Greek Phil, Phenomen
Holveck, Eleanore, PhD, Asst Prof, Phenomen, Anal Phil
Keyes, Charles D, PhD, Assoc Prof, Phenomen, Med Phil, Phil of Relig
Luzitano, George, MA, Part-time Instr
Madden, Robert E, MA, Instr, Phenomen, Phil of Knowl
Madsen, Peter, MA, Part-time Instr
Maschner, Horst G, PhD, Prof, 19th Cent German Phil
Puccetti, Peter, MA, Assoc Prof, Ethics, Thomism
Ramirez, J Roland, PhD, Prof, Med Phil, Contemp British and Amer Ethics, Orient Phil
Sallis, John C, PhD, Prof, Kant, German Phil, Phenomen

Scanlon, John D, PhD, Assoc Prof, Phenomen, German Phil
Schürmann, Reiner, PhD, Asst Prof, Contemp Continen Phil, Polit Phil
Shaver, John, MA, Part-time Instr
Strasser, Michael W, PhD, Prof, German Phil, Med Phil
Torinsky, Norman, MA, Part-time Instr
Vielkind, John, MA, Part-time Instr

Berube, Edward, MA, Teach Fel
Brogan, Walter, MA, Grad Asst
Buehner, Thomas, MA, Grad Asst
Cannon, Thomas, BA, Grad Asst
Friedlander, Bruce, BA, Grad Asst
Harris, Gregory, MA, Teach Fel
Scott, Edward, BA, Grad Asst
Strang, John, MA, Grad Asst
Sullivan, Mary Jane, BA, Grad Asst
Wyatt, Stephen, MA, Grad Asst

EAST STROUDSBURG STATE COLLEGE
East Stroudsburg, Pennsylvania 18301 (M; st; coed; sem; III; 3400) BA major, Dept
of Phil, 717-424-3603

Forth, David, PhD, Prof, Chm, British Empir, Phil of Value
Allen, Paul, MA, Assoc Prof, Kant, Ethics
Thompson, George, MA, Asst Prof

EASTERN BAPTIST THEOLOGICAL SEMINARY
Philadelphia, Pennsylvania 19151 (M; Bapt; coed; 4-1-4; III; 198) Courses with
no degree specialization, Dept of Theol, 215-877-4200

Bender, Thorwald W, ThD, Prof, Chm
Henry, Carl F H, PhD, Prof, Phil of Relig

EASTERN COLLEGE
Saint Davids, Pennsylvania 19087 (M; A Bapt; coed; sem; II; 592) BA major, Dept of
Phil, 215-688-3300 Ext 342

Genco, Peter, PhD, Assoc Prof, Phil of Relig, Phil of Sci
Shinn, Robert W, ThD, Prof, Phil of Relig, Phil of Hist

EDINBORO STATE COLLEGE
Edinboro, Pennsylvania 16412 (M; st; coed; sem; III; 7156) BA major, Dept of Phil,
814-734-1671 Ext 490

Holloway, Maurice, PhD, Prof, Chm, Phil of Relig
Abegg, Edmund, PhD, Assoc Prof, Phil of Hist
Cogan, Robert, PhD, Assoc Prof, Logic
Drane, James, PhD, Prof, Ethics
Haber, Ted, PhD, Assoc Prof, Polit Phil
Martinson, Paul, MA, Asst Prof, Phil of Educ
Munro, James, MA, Asst Prof, Phil of Sci
Richardson, David, PhD, Prof, Phil of Culture
Sauer, Harold, MA, Asst Prof, Phenomen
Schattle, Bryant, MA, Asst Prof, Amer Phil
Sherlock, Maureen, MA, Asst Prof, Aes

ELIZABETHTOWN COLLEGE
Elizabethtown, Pennsylvania 17022 (M; Ch of Breth; coed; sem; II; 2059) BA joint
or combined major, Dept of Relig and Phil, 717-367-1151

Snowden, Armon, BD, Prof, Chm
Clemens, Eugene P, MEd, Assoc Prof
Puffenberger, William V, PhD, Assoc Prof

317

Ritterspach, Austin D, PhD, Assoc Prof
Sutphin, Stanley T, ThD, Prof
Zeigler, Carl W, BD, Prof

ELLEN CUSHING JUNIOR COLLEGE
Bryn Mawr, Pennsylvania 19010 (--; Bapt; wo; qr; I; 108) AA major, Dept of Phil
and Relig, 215-525-6373

Thomas, John W, PhD, Prof, Chm, Phil of Relig

FAITH THEOLOGICAL SEMINARY
Elkins Park, Pennsylvania 19117 (--; p; coed; sem; III; 31) NP

FRANKLIN AND MARSHALL COLLEGE
Lancaster, Pennsylvania 17604 (M; p; coed; sem; III; 2608) BA major, Dept of Phil,
717-393-3621 Ext 270, 271, 272

Binkley, Luther J, PhD, Prof, Chm, Value Theory, Contemp British Phil
Galis, Leon, PhD, Assoc Prof, Soc Phil
Hopson, Ronald C, PhD, Asst Prof, Logic, Phil of Sci
Lewis, Earl E, PhD, Prof, British Empir
Roth, Michael, PhD, Assoc Prof, Anc Phil, Epistem
Meier, Carl, PhD, Asst Prof, Kant, Metaph

Noss, John B, PhD, Prof Emer, Hist and Phil of Relig

GANNON COLLEGE
Erie, Pennsylvania 16501 (M; RC; coed; 4-1-4; III; 3568) BA major, Dept of Phil,
814-456-7523 Ext 241

Minkiel, Stephen, PhD, Asst Prof, Chm, Phil of God, Amer Phil, Logic
Acri, Michael, Asst Prof, Mod Phil, Communism
Crispo, Alphonse, PhD, Prof, Anc Phil, Med Phil, Mod and Contemp Phil, Phil of Hist
Dipre, Gilio, PhD, Asst Prof, Ling Anal, Logic
Kelvington, James, PhD, Asst Prof, Phil of Sci, Ethics, Mod Phil
Montanari, Giovanni, PhD, Assoc Prof, Phil of Man, Phil of God, Aes
Prah, John, STD, Asst Prof, Ethics, Phil of Man

GENEVA COLLEGE
Beaver Falls, Pennsylvania 15010 (M; Ref Preb; coed; sem; II; 1591) BA minor, Dept
of Bib, Relig Educ and Phil, 412-846-5100

Steen, Peter, ThD, Asst Prof

GETTYSBURG COLLEGE
Gettysburg, Pennsylvania 17325 (M; p; coed; 4-1-4; II; 1906) BA major, Dept of Phil,
717-334-4331 Ext 210

Richardson, Norman E, PhD, Prof, Chm, 19th Cent Phil, Phil of Relig
Coulter, Chan, PhD, Assoc Prof, Anal Phil
Schubart, W Richard, MA, Assoc Prof, Ethics, Aes

GRATZ COLLEGE
Philadelphia, Pennsylvania 19141 (M; p; coed; sem; II; 418) Courses with no degree
specialization, --, 215-329-3363

Kurlana, Samuel, PhD, Prof Emer

GROVE CITY COLLEGE
Grove City, Pennsylvania 16127 (M; p; coed; sem; II; 2114) BA major, Dept of Phil and Relig, 412-458-6600

Bowne, Dale R, ThD, Prof, Chm, Ethics
Bremer, Paul, M Div, Asst Prof
Foster, Ross A, BD, Asst Prof, Phil of Relig
Hoffecker, Andrew, PhD, Asst Prof
Liggitt, O Eugene, M Div, Prof, Ethics
MacKenzie, Charles S, ThD, Prof, 18th and 19th Cent Phil
Trammell, Richard L, PhD, Asst Prof, Contemp Phil

GWYNEDD-MERCY COLLEGE
Gwynedd Valley, Pennsylvania 19437 (M; p; coed; sem; II; 1111) Courses with no degree specialization, --, 215-646-7300 Ext 269

Ruggeri, John, MA, Asst Prof
Young, Thomas, MA, Asst Prof, Metaph

HAHNEMANN MEDICAL COLLEGE AND HOSPITAL
Philadelphia, Pennsylvania 19102 (Med; p; coed; qr; IV; 956) NP

HARCUM JUNIOR COLLEGE
Bryn Mawr, Pennsylvania 19010 (M; p; wo; sem; I; 954) Courses with no degree specialization, Dept of Soc Sci, 215-525-4100 Ext 226

Duzy, Michael, PhD, Prof, Pres

HARRISBURG AREA COMMUNITY COLLEGE
Harrisburg, Pennsylvania 17110 (M; st and local; coed; sem; I; 4232) AA major, Dept of Communic and the Arts, 717-236-9533 Ext 317

Carrick, Paul, MA, Instr, Soc and Polit Phil
DeLuca, Emeric, MA, Asst Prof
Smith, Roger, MA, Asst Prof

HAVERFORD COLLEGE
Haverford, Pennsylvania 19041 (M; p; men; sem; II; 720) BA major, Dept of Phil, 215-659-9600

Desjardins, Jr, Paul, PhD, Prof, Act Chm, Class Greek Phil, 17th and 18th Cent Phil, Orient Phil
Bernstein, Richard J, PhD, Prof, Contemp Phil, Metaph, Polit Phil
Gangadean, Asoka, PhD, Asst Prof, Phil of Logic, Phil of Lang, Metaph, West and Indian Phil
Kosman, L Aryeh, PhD, Prof, Class Phil, Anal Phil
Thompson, Josiah D, PhD, Assoc Prof, 19th and 20th Cent Exist, Phenomen

HOLY FAMILY COLLEGE
Philadelphia, Pennsylvania 19114 (M; RC; coed; sem; II; 752) Courses with no degree specialization, Dept of Phil, 215-637-7700

Hobaugh, Regina, MA, Instr, Act Chm
Grugan, Arthur, PhD, Asst Prof, Heidegger

IMMACULATA COLLEGE
    Immaculata, Pennsylvania 19345 (M; RC; wo; sem; II; 1473) Courses with no degree
    specialization, Dept of Phil, 215-647-4400

    Strom, Elisabeth A, PhD, Asst Prof, Chm, Ethics, Process Phil, Epistem, Polit and
        Soc Phil, Aes, Phil of Relig, Symbolic Logic
    Evans, Joseph, MA, Instr, Phil of Lit, Exist
    Malloy, John, MA, Asst Prof, Phil of Educ, Exist
    Sesek, Raphael, STD, Assoc Prof, 19th Cent German Phil, Greek and Roman Phil,
        Thomistic Phil

INDIANA UNIVERSITY OF PENNSYLVANIA
    Indiana, Pennsylvania 15701 (M; st; coed; sem; IV; 9742) BA major, Dept of Phil,
    412-357-2310, 412-357-2311

    Hermann, Robert M, PhD, Chm, Ethics, Polit Phil
    Boone, Daniel, PhD, Assoc Prof, Anal Phil, Logic
    Chan, Benjamin, PhD, Prof
    Ferrara, Vincent, PhD, Prof, Euro Phil
    Kannwisher, Arthur, PhD, Prof, Hist of Phil
    Lin, Tian-mein, PhD, Asst Prof
    Montgomery, Sharon, PhD, Assoc Prof, Phil of Lang
    Schaub, Thomas, PhD, Asst Prof

INDIANA UNIVERSITY OF PENNSYLVANIA, ARMSTRONG COUNTY CAMPUS
    Kittanning, Pennsylvania 16201 (M; st; coed; sem; I; 504) BA major, Dept of Phil,
    412-542-1411

    Hermann, Robert M, PhD
    Kannwisher, Arthur, PhD

INDIANA UNIVERSITY OF PENNSYLVANIA, PUNXSUTAWNEY CAMPUS
    Punxsutawney, Pennsylvania 15767 (M; st; coed; sem; I; 243) NP

JUNIATA COLLEGE
    Huntingdon, Pennsylvania 16652 (M; p; coed; --; II; 1222) BA major, Dept of Phil
    814-643-4310 Ext 78

    Wagoner, Robert E, PhD, Prof, Chm, Phil of Relig, Exist
    Hartman, Donald T, PhD, Asst Prof, Logic, Phil of Sci
    Lewis, Janet R, MA, Asst Prof, Metaph, Ethics

KEYSTONE JUNIOR COLLEGE
    La Plume, Pennsylvania 18440 (M; p; coed; sem; I; 1153) Courses with no degree
    specialization, Div of Human, 717-945-5141 Ext 69

    Brahinsky, David, MA
    Brown, Edward, BA
    Fairbanks, Matthew, PhD
    Mac Kay, Charles, PhD

KING'S COLLEGE
    Wilkes Barre, Pennsylvania 18711 (M; p; coed; sem; II; 2666) BA major, Dept of Phil,
    717-824-9931 Ext 386

    Visgilio, III, Thomas, MA, Asst Prof, Chm, Amer Phil, Epistem, Logic
    Belford, Charles E, MA, Instr, Anal Phil, Logic
    Drumin, William A, PhD, Asst Prof, Phil of Sci, Hist of Phil, Metaph

Desharnais, Richard, PhD, Prof, Med Phil, Phil of Man
Haas, James A, MA, Asst Prof, Anc Phil, Sym Logic
Nardone, Henry F, PhD, Assoc Prof, Ethics, Aes

KUTZTOWN STATE COLLEGE
   Kutztown, Pennsylvania 19530 (M; st; coed; sem; III; 5030) BA major, Dept of Soc
   Sci, 215-683-3511 Ext 317

   Lucas, Jr, Raymond E, PhD, Prof, Anal Phil, Plato
   Shackelford, III, E A, MA, Assoc Prof, Logic, Phil of Sci
   Watkins, Charles, MA, Asst Prof, Phil of Relig
   Zusin, Elizabeth, MA, Instr, Ethics, Process Phil

LA ROCHE COLLEGE
   Pittsburgh, Pennsylvania 15237 (--; RC; coed; sem; II; 400) BA major, Div of Human,
   412-931-4312 Ext 46

   Lauer, Eugene F, STD, Prof, Chm
   Gratz, Robert, MA, Asst Prof

LA SALLE COLLEGE
   Philadelphia, Pennsylvania 19141 (M; RC; coed; sem; III; 7165) BA major, Dept of
   Phil, 215-848-8300 Ext 217

   Kerlin, Michael J, PhD, Assoc Prof, Chm, Phil of Relig
   Allen, Carl J, MA, Asst Prof, East Phil
   Aylward, William, MA, Lect, Ethics
   Ballisty, Aloysius, MA, Lect, Anthrop
   Fallon, James C, BS, Asst Prof, Metaph
   Fay, Florence, MA, Lect, Ethics
   Fitzgerald, Eugene J, BA, Assoc Prof, Aes
   Gibbons, John F, PhL, Assoc Prof, Logic
   Janik, Allan, PhD, Asst Prof, Marxism
   Janik, Linda, PhD, Lect, Hist of Phil
   Lashchyk, Eugene, PhD, Asst Prof, Phil of Sci
   Lowry, Atherton C, PhD, Asst Prof, Phenomen
   Macoretta, Ormand, MA, Asst Prof, Ethics
   Malloy, John F, MA, Lect, Anthrop
   Mihalich, Joseph C, PhD, Prof, Metaph
   Mullen, Philip, MA, Lect, Logic
   Murawski, E, BA, Lect, Logic
   Naughton, E Russell, PhD, Prof, Phil of Relig
   Phillips, Thomas R, MA, Asst Prof, Amer Phil
   Pierzchalski, Raymond J, PhD, Assoc Prof, Business Ethics
   Strosser, Richard F, MA, Assoc Prof, Hist of Phil

LACKAWANNA JUNIOR COLLEGE
   Scranton, Pennsylvania 18503 (JRCB; p; coed; sem; I; 402) Courses with no degree
   specialization, --, 717-342-7679

LAFAYETTE COLLEGE
   Easton, Pennsylvania 18042 (M; Preb; coed; sem; II; 2212) BA major, Dept of Phil,
   215-253-6281 Ext 310

   Losee, John P, PhD, Assoc Prof, Act Head, Phil of Sci
   Clark, George A, PhD, Prof, Amer Phil
   Slaght, Ralph, PhD, Asst Prof, Epistem
   Rabinowitz, Rea, AB, Instr, Aes

LANCASTER SCHOOL OF BIBLE
Lancaster, Pennsylvania 17601 (BI; p; coed; sem; II; 225) NR

LEBANON VALLEY COLLEGE
Annville, Pennsylvania 17003 (M; U Meth; coed; sem; II; 1254) BA major, Dept of Phil, 717-867-3561 Ext 283

Thompson, Warren K A, MA, Asst Prof, Chm, Ethics, Phil of Relig
Ehrhart, Carl Y, PhD, Act Chm, Dean
Heffner, John H, AM, Instr, Logic, Metaph, Phil of Sci

LEHIGH COUNTY COMMUNITY COLLEGE
Schnecksville, Pennsylvania 18078 (M; local; coed; sem; I; 2351) Courses with no degree specialization, Dept of Lang Arts, 215-799-2121 Ext 186

Clewell, Richard, MA, Instr
Sell, Jr, Ralph W, MA, Asst Prof

LEHIGH UNIVERSITY
Bethlehem, Pennsylvania 18015 (M; p; coed; sem; IV; 5283) BA major, Dept of Phil, 215-691-7000 Ext 257

Lindgren, J Ralph, PhD, Assoc Prof, Chm, Soc Phil, Hist of Phil
Barnes, Robert F, PhD, Assoc Prof, Logic, Phil of Math
Haynes, Thomas M, PhD, Prof, Ethics, Value Theory
LaPava, Nicholas A, PhD, Asst Prof, Logic, Phil of Sci
Melchert, Norman P, PhD, Assoc Prof, Phil of Mind, Hist of Phil

LINCOLN UNIVERSITY
Lincoln University, Pennsylvania 19352 (M; st; coed; 4-1-4; II; 1067) BA major, Dept of Phil, 215-932-8300 Ext 201

Hurwitz, Gerald Q, PhD, Assoc Prof, Chm, Kant, Gandhi, Moral Group Politics
Levinson, Joel, PhD, Instr, Marxism, Phil Anal

LOCK HAVEN STATE COLLEGE
Lock Haven, Pennsylvania 17745 (M; st; coed; sem; II; 2387) BA major, Dept of Eng and Phil, 717-748-5351 Ext 246

Dayananda, James Y, PhD, Prof, Chm
Congdon, Howard K, PhD, Asst Prof, Phil of Relig
Irwin, John P, PhD, Prof, Epistem
Redpath, Peter A, MA, Asst Prof, Med Phil
Silberg, Jack, MA, Assoc Prof, Santayana

LUTHERAN THEOLOGICAL SEMINARY AT GETTYSBURG
Gettysburg, Pennsylvania 17325 (M; Luth; coed; 4-1-4; III; 219) NP

LUTHERAN THEOLOGICAL SEMINARY AT PHILADELPHIA
Philadelphia, Pennsylvania 19119 (M; Luth; coed; sem; III; 171) MA joint or combined major, Dept of Syst Theol, 215-242-3555

Lundeen, Lyman, ThD, Assoc Prof, Chm, Phil of Relig

LUZERNE COUNTY COMMUNITY COLLEGE
Wilkes-Barre, Pennsylvania 18711 (--; local; coed; sem; I; 1656) Courses with no degree specialization, Dept of Human, 717-825-7594

Kelleher, John R, MA, Asst Prof
Talarsky, Joseph W, MA, Prof

LYCOMING COLLEGE
Williamsport, Pennsylvania 17701 (M; U Meth; coed; sem; II; 1635) BA major, Dept of Phil, 717-326-1951

Griffith, Stephen R, PhD, Asst Prof
Herring, Owen F, Asst Prof
Schoeman, Ferdinand D, PhD, Asst Prof
Whelan, John M, Asst Prof

Faus, W Arthur, PhD, Prof Emer

MANOR JUNIOR COLLEGE
Jenkintown, Pennsylvania 19046 (M; p; wo; sem; I; 180) Courses with no degree specialization, Dept of Phil, 215-885-2360

Murphy, James J, MA, Lect

MANSFIELD STATE COLLEGE
Mansfield, Pennsylvania 16933 (M; st; coed; sem; III; 3215) BA major, Dept of Phil, 717-662-2114 Ext 267

Sefler, George, PhD, Asst Prof, Chm, Phil of Lang, Exist, Metaph, Hist of Phil
Bickham, Stephen, PhD, Asst Prof, Anal Phil, Epistem, Metaph
Newman, Ira, ABD, Asst Prof, Exist, Soc and Polit Phil, Phil of Lit, Phil Psych

MARY IMMACULATE SEMINARY AND COLLEGE
Northampton, Pennsylvania 18067 (M; RC; men; 4-1-4; III; 60) NP

MARYWOOD COLLEGE
Scranton, Pennsylvania 18509 (M; p; coed; 4-1-4; III; 2216) BA joint or combined major, Dept of Phil, 717-343-6521 Ext 314, 315

Haney, Dorothy A, PhD, Asst Prof, Chm, Phil of Hist
Borja, Francisco, MA, Assoc Prof, Phil of Art, Phil of Relig
Jacobson, Paul, MA, Instr, Phenomen
Mohan, William, MA, Asst Prof, Ethics
Snyder, John, MA, Asst Prof, Phil Anthrop

THE MEDICAL COLLEGE OF PENNSYLVANIA
Philadelphia, Pennsylvania 19129 (Med; p; coed; tri; IV; 411) NP

MERCYHURST COLLEGE
Erie, Pennsylvania 16501 (M; RC; coed; tri; II; 954) --, Dept of Phil, 814-864-0681

Cisek, Robert, MA, Asst Prof, Dir, Hist of Phil
Gwaltney, Marilyn, MA, Asst Prof, Exist, Marxism

323

MESSIAH COLLEGE

Grantham, Pennsylvania 17027 (M; Breth in Christ; coed; sem; II; 800) BA major, Div of Relig and Phil, 717-766-2511

MILLERSVILLE STATE COLLEGE

Millersville, Pennsylvania 17551 (M; st; coed; sem; III; 5634) BA major, Dept of Phil, 717-872-5411

Fischer, Kurt R, PhD, Prof, Chm, Hist of Recent Phil
Kenig, Howard, AB, Asst Prof, Phil of Sci
Miller, Leon, AB, Assoc Prof, Logic
Sarracino, Mia, MA, Asst Prof, Ethics
Winter, John E, PhD, Prof, Phil Anthrop

MONTGOMERY COUNTY COMMUNITY COLLEGE

Blue Bell, Pennsylvania 19422 (M; local; coed; sem; I; 3326) Courses with no degree specialization, Dept of Soc Relations, 215-643-6000 Ext 253

Snowden, Thomas G, PhD, Assoc Prof, Phil of Relig, Comp Relig

MOORE COLLEGE OF ART

Philadelphia, Pennsylvania 19103 (M; p; wo; 4-1-4; II; 202) NR

MORAVIAN COLLEGE

Bethlehem, Pennsylvania 18018 (M; Morav; coed; 4-1-4; II; 1725) BA major, Dept of Phil, 215-865-0741 Ext 349

Russell, Christopher W, AM, Asst Prof, Chm, Logic
McConnell, Jr, Frederick, PhD, Assoc Prof, Ethics

MOUNT ALOYSIUS JUNIOR COLLEGE

Cresson, Pennsylvania 16630 (M; RC; coed; sem; I; 485) Courses with no degree specialization, Dept of Soc Sci, 814-886-4131

Gallagher, William, MA, Asst Prof
Florentine, Thomas, MA, Asst Prof

MUHLENBERG COLLEGE

Allentown, Pennsylvania 18104 (M; p; coed; sem; II; 1885) BA major, Dept of Phil, 215-433-3191 Ext 209

Reed, David A, PhD, Assoc Prof, Head
Howell, David, PhD, Asst Prof
Schlecht, Ludwig, PhD, Asst Prof

NORTHAMPTON COUNTY AREA COMMUNITY COLLEGE

Bethlehem, Pennsylvania 18017 (M; st and local; coed; sem; I; 2869) --, Dept of Phil, 215-865-5351 Ext 277

Voight, Richard C, MA, Asst Prof, Ethics

NORTHEAST BIBLE INSTITUTE

Green Lane, Pennsylvania 18054 (BI; Assem of God; coed; 4-1-4; I; 211) --, Dept of Gen Educ, 215-234-4503

Roberson, C C, MEd

NORTHEASTERN CHRISTIAN JUNIOR COLLEGE
  Villanova, Pennsylvania 19085 (--; Ch of Christ; coed; tri; I; 158) NP

OUR LADY OF ANGELS COLLEGE
  Aston, Pennsylvania 19014 (M; p; wo; sem; I; 290) NR

PEIRCE JUNIOR COLLEGE
  Philadelphia, Pennsylvania 19102 (M; p; coed; sem; I; 1802) AA major, Dept of Human
  215-545-6400 Ext 275

  Uberti, J Richard, PhD, Assoc Prof, Chm, Amer Phil

PENN HALL JUNIOR COLLEGE
  Chambersburg, Pennsylvania 17201 (--; p; coed; sem; I; 93) NP

PENNSYLVANIA COLLEGE OF OPTOMETRY
  Philadelphia, Pennsylvania 19141 (M; p; coed; sem; III; 452) NP

PENNSYLVANIA COLLEGE OF PODIATRIC MEDICINE
  Philadelphia, Pennsylvania 19107 (Pod; p; coed; sem; III; 206) NP

PENNSYLVANIA STATE UNIVERSITY
  University Park, Pennsylvania 16802 (M; st; coed; --; IV; 38,448) PhD major, Dept
  of Phil, 814-865-6397

  Hausman, Carl R, PhD, Prof, Chm, Aes, Value Theory, Phil of Creativity
  Anderson, John M, PhD, Prof, Lang and Logic, Aes, Polit Phil
  Druckman, Aaron, BA, Assoc Prof
  Flay, Joseph C, PhD, Assoc Prof, Metaph, Hist of Mod Phil
  Ford, Lewis S, PhD, Assoc Prof, Phil of Relig, Whitehead
  Goldman, Steven, PhD, Asst Prof, Phil of Sci
  Gotshalk, Richard A, PhD, Assoc Prof, Orient Phil, Hist of Phil, Metaph
  Johnstone, Henry W, PhD, Prof, Metaphil, Logic, Metaph
  Kennington, Richard H, PhD, Assoc Prof, Polit Phil, Greek Phil, Hist of Mod Phil
  Kockelmans, Joseph J, PhD, Prof, Phil of Sci, Mod Phil, Contemp Phil
  Lingis, Alphonso F, PhD, Assoc Prof, Ontology, Hist of Mod Phil, Phenomen, Exist
  Orianne, Andre P, PhD, Asst Prof, Phil of Lang, Polit and Contemp Phil
  Press, Gerald, MA, Instr, Hist of Phil, Phil of Culture
  Price, Robert G, PhD, Assoc Prof, Phil of Lang, Phil of Logic, Greek Phil, Value Theory
  Rosen, Stanley, PhD, Prof, Greek Phil, Metaph, Phil of Hist
  Rothenberg, Albert, MD, Adj Assoc Prof, Phil of Psych, Phenomen
  Seebohm, Thomas M, PhD, Prof, Hist of Phil, Hermen, Phenomen
  Tsugawa, Albert, PhD, Assoc Prof, Value Theory, Phil of Art, Anal Phil, British
    Moral Phil
  Vaught, Carl G, PhD, Assoc Prof, Metaph, Phil of Relig
  Verene, Donald P, PhD, Assoc Prof, Phil of Culture, 19th Cent Phil

  Freund, E Hans, PhD, Prof Emer
  Mourant, John A, PhD, Prof Emer

  Anderson, William R, BA, Teach Asst   Lundgren, Gerald, MA, Teach Asst
  Cater, Robert M, BA, Teach Asst   Lynch, Raymond, BA, Teach Asst
  Christopherson, Rosemarie, BA, Teach   Martine, Brian, BA, Teach Asst
    Asst   Pippin, Robert, MA, Fel
  Cuneo, John, BA, Teach Asst   Rethy, Robert, BA, Teach Asst
  Davis, Michael, MA, Fel   Sacks, Joe, MA, Fel
  Dostal, Robert, MA, Teach Asst   Sandberg, Eric, BA, Teach Asst
  Dufee, Richard, BA, Teach Asst   Sitte, Martin, MA, Fel

Ess, Charles, BA, Teach Asst
Faulconer, James, BA, Teach Asst
Gram, Richard, BA, Teach Asst
Griswold, Charles, BA, Teach Asst
Karnos, David, BA, Teach Asst
Krois, John, MA, Teach Asst

Stripling, Scott, MA, Teach Asst
Surber, Jere, MA, Fel
Unger, Susan, BA, Teach Asst
Velkley, Richard, BA, Teach Asst
Wharton, Christine, BA, Teach Asst
Wright, Abbott, MA, Fel

PENNSYLVANIA STATE UNIVERSITY, ALLENTOWN CAMPUS
Allentown, Pennsylvania 18051 (M; st; coed; 4-1-4; I; 169) NP

PENNSYLVANIA STATE UNIVERSITY, ALTOONA CAMPUS
Altoona, Pennsylvania 16003 (M; st; coed; 4-1-4; I; 2274) NR

PENNSYLVANIA STATE UNIVERSITY, BEAVER CAMPUS
Monaca, Pennsylvania 15061 (M; st; coed; 4-1-4; I; 1402) BA major, Dept of Phil,
412-775-8830 Ext 52

Park, Il C, PhD, Asst Prof, Phenomen

PENNSYLVANIA STATE UNIVERSITY, BEHREND CAMPUS
Erie, Pennsylvania 16510 (M; st; coed; 4-1-4; II; 1875) BA joint or combined major,
Dept of Phil, 814-899-3101 Ext 266

Iobst, Philip, MA, Instr, Prag, Aes, Humanism
Mester, Richard, PhD, Asst Prof, Amer Phil, Pierce, Aristotle

PENNSYLVANIA STATE UNIVERSITY, BERKS CAMPUS
Reading, Pennsylvania 19608 (M; st; coed; 4-1-4; I; 1402) Courses with no degree
specialization, Dept of Phil, 215-375-4211

Yee, Stevan, MA, Instr, Chm

PENNSYLVANIA STATE UNIVERSITY, CAPITOL CAMPUS
Middletown, Pennsylvania 17057 (M; st; coed; 4-1-4; III; 2001) BA major, Dept of
Human, 717-787-7952

Brewster, Leonard E, PhD, Asst Prof, Logic, Metaph

PENNSYLVANIA STATE UNIVERSITY, DELAWARE COUNTY CAMPUS
Media, Pennsylvania 19063 (M; st; coed; 4-1-4; I; 1117) BA major, Dept of Phil
215-565-3300

Cox, Robert, MA, Instr
Ginsberg, Robert, PhD, Assoc Prof, Polit Phil, Soc Phil, Aes

PENNSYLVANIA STATE UNIVERSITY, DUBOIS CAMPUS
Dubois, Pennsylvania 15801 (Tech; st; coed; 4-1-4; I; 617) AA major, Dept of Phil,
814-371-2800

Morgan, James S, MA, Instr

PENNSYLVANIA STATE UNIVERSITY, FAYETTE CAMPUS
Uniontown, Pennsylvania 15401 (M; st; coed; 4-1-4; I; 1070) AA major, Dept of Phil,

412-437-2801

Townsley, Gale A, PhD, Asst Prof, Contemp Anal Phil

PENNSYLVANIA STATE UNIVERSITY, HAZLETON CAMPUS
   Hazleton, Pennsylvania 18201 (Tech; st; coed; 4-1-4; I; 1106) Courses with no
   degree specialization, Dept of Phil, 717-454-8731

   Campbell, Richard, MA, Instr, Exist
   Santulli, Michael, DEd, Asst Prof, Phil of Sci

PENNSYLVANIA STATE UNIVERSITY, HERSHEY MEDICAL CENTER
   Hershey, Pennsylvania 17033 (Med; st; coed; qr; IV; 314) Courses with no degree
   specialization, Dept of Human, 717-534-8778

   Clouser, K Danner, PhD, Assoc Prof, Medical Ethics, Phil of Medicine, Phil of Psych
   Zucker, Arthur, MA, Res Assoc, Medical Ethics, Phil of Biology

PENNSYLVANIA STATE UNIVERSITY, KING OF PRUSSIA GRADUATE CENTER
   King of Prussia, Pennsylvania 19406 (M; st; coed; qr; III; 375) NR

PENNSYLVANIA STATE UNIVERSITY, MCKEESPORT CAMPUS
   McKeesport, Pennsylvania 15132 (M; st; coed; 4-1-4; I; 1478) BA minor, --, 412-678-
   9501

   Colucci, Robert, PhD, Asst Prof
   Gavrilis, Nicholas, MA, Asst Prof

PENNSYLVANIA STATE UNIVERSITY, MONT ALTO CAMPUS
   Mont Alto, Pennsylvania 17237 (M; st; coed; 4-1-4; I; 756) --, Dept of Phil, 717-
   749-3111

   Rensma, Patricia, PhD, Asst Prof, Orient Phil, Mod Phil, Phenomen, Exist

PENNSYLVANIA STATE UNIVERSITY, NEW KENSINGTON CAMPUS
   New Kensington, Pennsylvania 15068 (Tech; st; coed; 4-1-4; I; 1209) Courses with
   no degree specialization, Dept of Phil, 412-339-1031

   Croake, Lawrence E, AB, Instr

PENNSYLVANIA STATE UNIVERSITY, OGONTZ CAMPUS
   Abington, Pennsylvania 19001 (M; st; coed; 4-1-4; I; 1669) NR

PENNSYLVANIA STATE UNIVERSITY, SCHUYLKILL CAMPUS
   Schuylkill Haven, Pennsylvania 17972 (M; st; coed; 4-1-4; I; 1019) Courses with
   no degree specialization, Dept of Phil, 717-385-4500 Ext 56

   Lindenmuth, Donald C, MA, Instr, Chm, Anc Phil

PENNSYLVANIA STATE UNIVERSITY, SHENANGO VALLEY CAMPUS
   Sharon, Pennsylvania 16146 (M; st; coed; 4-1-4; I; 677) Courses with no degree
   specialization, Dept of Libr Arts and Soc Stud, 412-981-1640

   Riforgiato, Leonard R, PhD, Asst Prof

PENNSYLVANIA STATE UNIVERSITY, WILKES-BARRE CAMPUS
    Wilkes-Barre, Pennsylvania 18708 (M; st; coed; 4-1-4; I; 458) NR

PENNSYLVANIA STATE UNIVERSITY, WORTHINGTON SCRANTON CAMPUS
    Dunmore, Pennsylvania 18512 (M; st; coed; 4-1-4; I; 930) Courses with no degree
    specialization, Dept of Phil, 717-961-4757 Ext 53

    Hopkins, Jr, Clyde L, MA, Asst Prof, Contemp Phil, Hist of Phil

PENNSYLVANIA STATE UNIVERSITY, YORK CAMPUS
    York, Pennsylvania 17403 (M; st; coed; 4-1-4; I; 803) --, --, 717-846-8828

    Neville, Michael R, PhD, Asst Prof

PHILADELPHIA COLLEGE OF ART
    Philadelphia, Pennsylvania 19102 (M; p; coed; sem; III; 1822) Courses with no degree
    specialization, Dept of Libr Arts, 215-546-0545 Ext 230, 231

    Webster, William E, PhD, Asst Prof, Aes

PHILADELPHIA COLLEGE OF BIBLE
    Philadelphia, Pennsylvania 19103 (M; p; coed; sem; II; 653) --, Dept of Environ
    Stud, 215-564-4820 Ext 274

    Peterson, Gilbert, EdD, Prof, Phil of Relig
    Stewart, Mae, MA, Asst Prof

PHILADELPHIA COLLEGE OF OSTEOPATHIC MEDICINE
    Philadelphia, Pennsylvania 19131 (Osteo; p; coed; qr; III; 575) NP

PHILADELPHIA COLLEGE OF PHARMACY AND SCIENCE
    Philadelphia, Pennsylvania 19104 (M; p; coed; sem; IV; 949) NP

PHILADELPHIA COLLEGE OF TEXTILES AND SCIENCE
    Philadelphia, Pennsylvania 19144 (M; p; coed; sem; II; 2156) NP

PHILADELPHIA MUSICAL ACADEMY
    Philadelphia, Pennsylvania 19107 (M; p; coed; sem; III; 293) Courses with no degree
    specialization, --, 215-735-9635

PINEBROOK JUNIOR COLLEGE
    East Stroudsburg, Pennsylvania 18301 (--; Prot; coed; sem; I; 56) Courses with no
    degree specialization, Dept of Human, 717-421-3633

    Cassel, Carl, MA, Dean

PITTSBURGH THEOLOGICAL SEMINARY
    Pittsburgh, Pennsylvania 15206 (M; U Preb; coed; sem; III; 333) Courses with no
    degree specialization, Div of the Church and Ministry, 412-362-5610

    Baid, John M, ThM, Assoc Prof, Christ Ethics
    Stone, Ronald H, PhD, Prof, Soc Ethics
    Wiest, Walter E, PhD, Prof, Phil of Relig

POINT PARK COLLEGE
Pittsburgh, Pennsylvania 15222 (M; p; coed; 4-1-4; II; 2584) BA major, Dept of
Human, 412-391-4100

Taylor, Thelma W, Chm, Hist of Phil, Exist
Broido, J, MA, Instr Part-time, Metaph
Hopkins, John, PhD, Act Pres, Med Phil, Logic

READING AREA COMMUNITY COLLEGE
Reading, Pennsylvania 19605 (--; local; coed; sem; II; 314) AA major, --, 215-921-
2361

Morgan, J, MA, Adj Instr, Phil of Relig

REFORMED PRESBYTERIAN THEOLOGICAL SEMINARY
Pittsburgh, Pennsylvania 15208 (--; Ref Preb; men; qr; III; 19) NP

ROBERT MORRIS COLLEGE
Coraopolis, Pennsylvania 15108 (M; p; coed; sem; II; 4176) Courses with no degree
specialization, Dept of Human, 412-264-9300 Ext 247

Mistro, Angel, PhD, Assoc Prof

ROSEMONT COLLEGE
Rosemont, Pennsylvania 19010 (M; p; wo; sem; II; 723) BA major, Div of Human, 215-
527-0200 Ext 286

Carney, Thomas Lee, MA, Assoc Prof, Cord, Med Phil
Duska, Ronald F, PhD, Assoc Prof, Ethical Theory, Aristotle
Glackin, John J, MA, Asst Prof, Ethical Theory, Nietzsche
Healy, Margaret, PhD, Assoc Prof, Polit Phil, Anc Phil, Mod Phil
Moss, Henry, MA, Instr, 19th Cent Phil

SAINT CHARLES BORROMEO SEMINARY
Philadelphia, Pennsylvania 19151 (M; RC; men; sem; III; 305) BA major, Dept of
Phil, 215-839-3760

Helduser, Frederick J, PhD, Assoc Prof, Hist of Phil
Foley, John P, Asst Prof, Ethics, Metaph
Rodgers, Arthur E, PhD, Asst Prof, Phil of Man, Thomism
McKenzie, Leo, PhD, Lect, Aes

SAINT FIDELIS COLLEGE
Herman, Pennsylvania 16039 (M; RC; men; sem; II; 74) BA major, Dept of Phil, 412-
287-4794

Rohr, Vincent, MA, Assoc Prof, Chm, Ethics
Elerding, MA, Instr
Fey, William, MA
Luzitano, George, MA, Instr
Russman, Thomas, MA

SAINT FRANCIS COLLEGE
Loretto, Pennsylvania 15940 (M; RC; coed; sem; III; 1660) BA major, --, 814-472-
7000 Ext 261

Burke, James P, MA, Assoc Prof, Chm, Phil of Man

Bradley, Raymond, MA, Assoc Prof, Moral Phil
Cain, Gervase, MA, Assoc Prof, Phil of Communic
Oei, Lee, MA, Asst Prof, Metaph, Orient Phil
Shuman, Kilian, MA, Asst Prof, Phil of Nature
Waldron, James, MA, Asst Prof, Phil of Knowl

SAINT FRANCIS SEMINARY
    Loretto, Pennsylvania 15940 (--; RC; men; sem; II; 82) NR

SAINT JOSEPH'S COLLEGE
    Philadelphia, Pennsylvania 19131 (M; RC; coed; sem; III; 7042) BA major, Dept of
    Phil, 215-879-1000 Ext 269

    Homann, Frederick A, PhD, Act Chm, Neoplatonism
    Ecsodi, John, PhD, Assoc Prof, Aes
    Hayden, Vincent, MA, Asst Prof, Thomism
    Jacklin, John, MA, Assoc Prof, Ethics
    Kearney, John, PhD, Asst Prof, Kant
    Keller, John, MA, Instr, Anc Phil
    Marshall, David, PhD, Asst Prof, Anal Phil
    McKinnon, Lawrence, MA, Asst Prof, Med Phil
    Renz, Francis, MA, Prof, Metaph
    Wallner, Frank, MA, Assoc Prof

    Blee, Michael, PhD, Prof Emer, Medical Ethics
    Guthrie, Hunter, PhD, Prof Emer, Metaph

SAINT VINCENT COLLEGE
    Latrobe, Pennsylvania 15650 (M; RC; men; sem; II; 1027) BA major, Dept of Phil, 412-
    539-9761 Ext 358

    Nolan, Justin, PhD, Assoc Prof, Chm, Anc Phil, Phil of Man
    Meny, James, MA, Asst Prof, Anc Phil, Mod Phil
    O'Neill, Patrick, MA, Asst Prof, Mod Phil, Epistem
    Quinn, Dennis, PhD, Assoc Prof, Anc Phil, Logic
    Ryer, Joseph, MA, Assoc Prof, Metaph
    Samay, Sebastian, PhD, Assoc Prof, Mod Phil, Epistem

SAINT VINCENT SEMINARY
    Latrobe, Pennsylvania 15650 (M; RC; men; sem; II; 74) NR

SETON HILL COLLEGE
    Greensburg, Pennsylvania 15601 (M; RC; wo; sem; II; 786) BA major, Dept of Phil,
    412-834-2200

    Bleyer, John Francis, EdD, Asst Prof
    Jacoby, Paul Joseph, PhD, Prof

SHIPPENSBURG STATE COLLEGE
    Shippensburg, Pennsylvania 17257 (M; st; coed; sem; III; 5276) Courses with no
    degree specialization, --, 717-532-9121

    Dako, Martin, MA, Asst Prof, Epistem, Logic
    Winter, Kenneth, MA, Asst Prof, Ethics

    Zogby, James, Asst Prof Emer

SLIPPERY ROCK STATE COLLEGE
Slippery Rock, Pennsylvania 16057 (M; st; coed; sem; III; 6020) BA major, Dept of
Phil, 412-794-7322

Macoskey, Robert A, PhD, Assoc Prof, Chm, Value Theory
Fuksa, Michael, MA, Asst Prof Part-time, Phil Anal
Kneupper, Theodore, PhD, Asst Prof, Phil of Sci, Logic
Larsen, Allan, PhD, Assoc Prof, Exist, Phenomen
Oman, William, MA, Instr, Soc and Polit Phil
Rohr, Vincent, MA, Asst Prof Part-time, Ethics
Taylor, Robert, MA, Asst Prof Part-time, Phil of Relig
Wells, E Frank, PhD, Assoc Prof, Metaph

SPRING GARDEN COLLEGE
Chestnut Hill, Pennsylvania 19118 (Tech; p; coed; 4-1-4; II; 1051) --, Dept of Eng
and Gen Stud, 215-242-3700 Ext 203, 212

Murphy, James, MA, Asst Prof

SUSQUEHANNA UNIVERSITY
Selinsgrove, Pennsylvania 17870 (M; Luth CA; coed; --; II; 1501) BA major, Dept
of Phil, 717-374-2345 Ext 343

Hunt, C Murray, PhD, Asst Prof, Ethics
Kamber, Richard, BA, Asst Prof, Aes
Livernois, Thomas, MA, Instr, Relig
Reimherr, Otto, PhD, Prof, Hist of Phil

SWARTHMORE COLLEGE
Swarthmore, Pennsylvania 19081 (M; p; coed; sem; III; 1170) MA major, Dept of Phil,
215-544-7900 Ext 332

Bennett, Daniel
Henke, Uwe
Lacey, Hugh M
Oberdiek, Hans
Raff, Charles
Schuldenfrei, Richard
Sharvy, Richard
Stott, Gilmore

Moore, John, PhD, Prof Emer

TEMPLE UNIVERSITY
Philadelphia, Pennsylvania 19122 (M; st; coed; sem; IV; 28,967) PhD major, Dept of
Phil, 215-787-8292

Leblanc, Hugues, PhD, Prof, Chm
Atwell, John, PhD, Assoc Prof
Axinn, Sidney, PhD, Prof
Beardsley, Elizabeth, PhD, Prof
Beardsley, Monroe, PhD, Prof
Dyke, Charles, PhD, Asst Prof
Fisher, John, PhD, Prof
Fitzgerald, Paul, PhD, Visit Asst Prof
Greenlee, Douglas, PhD, Assoc Prof
Hathaway, Ronald, PhD, Asst Prof
Margolis, Joseph, PhD, Prof
McClintock, Thomas, PhD, Asst Prof
Moulton, Janice, PhD, Visit Asst Prof

Nelson, John, PhD, Asst Prof
Snyder, D Paul, PhD, Assoc Prof
Tormey, Judith, PhD, Asst Prof
Vision, Gerald, PhD, Asst Prof
Welker, David, PhD, Asst Prof
White, Alan, PhD, Visit Prof
Wisdom, William, PhD, Assoc Prof

Wiener, Philip, PhD, Prof Emer

TEMPLE UNIVERSITY, AMBLER CAMPUS
  Ambler, Pennsylvania 19002 (M; st; coed; sem; I; 716) NR

THEOLOGICAL SEMINARY OF THE REFORMED EPISCOPAL CHURCH
  Philadelphia, Pennsylvania 19104 (--; Ref Epis; coed; sem; III; 111) NP

THIEL COLLEGE
  Greenville, Pennsylvania 16125 (M; Luth; coed; 4-1-4; IV; 1580) BA major, --, 412-
  588-7770

  Koehler, Conrad J, PhD, Assoc Prof, Chm
  Reese, George C, MA, Prof
  Shearin, Jesse E, PhD, Asst Prof

THOMAS JEFFERSON UNIVERSITY
  Philadelphia, Pennsylvania 19107 (Med; p; coed; qr; IV; 1580) NP

UNITED WESLEYAN COLLEGE
  Allentown, Pennsylvania 18103 (Bl; Wes; coed; sem; II; 112) NR

UNIVERSITY OF PENNSYLVANIA
  Philadelphia, Pennsylvania 19174 (M; p; coed; sem; IV; 19,397) PhD major, Dept of
  Phil, 215-594-8563

  Jeffrey, Richard, PhD, Prof, Chm, Logic, Phil of Sci
  Anscombe, G E M, PhD, Adj Prof
  Cornman, James W, PhD, Prof
  Chellas, Brian, PhD, Asst Prof, Logic
  Domotor, Zolton, PhD, Asst Prof, Phil of Sci
  Flower, Elizabeth, PhD, Assoc Prof, Amer Phil
  Garson, James, PhD, Asst Prof, Phil of Math
  Geach, Peter, PhD, Adj Prof
  Hartman, Edwin, PhD, Asst Prof
  Kahn, Charles, PhD, Prof, Class Phil
  Mondadori, Fabrizio, PhD, Asst Prof
  Ross, James F, PhD, Prof, Phil of Relig, Phil of Law
  Sagoff, Mark, PhD, Asst Prof
  Watson, Gary, PhD, Asst Prof

  Swain, Marshall, PhD, Assoc Prof Emer, Phil of the Mind

UNIVERSITY OF PITTSBURGH
  Pittsburgh, Pennsylvania 15260 (M; st; coed; tri; IV; 27,453) PhD major, Dept of
  Phil, 412-624-5774

  Massey, Gerald J, PhD, Prof, Chm, Logic, Phil of Sci
  Anderson, Alan Ross, PhD, Prof, Logic, Phil of Soc Sci

Baier, Annette, BPhil, Assoc Prof, Phil of Mind, Hist of Phil, Phil of Lang
Baier, Kurt E, DPhil, Prof, Ethics, Phil of Law, Soc and Polit Phil
Bartley, III, W W, PhD, Prof, Phil of Relig
Belnap, Jr, Nuel D, PhD, Prof, Logic, Phil of Soc Sci
Camp, Jr, Joseph, PhD, Assoc Prof, Metaph
Cooper, John M, PhD, Assoc Prof, Greek Phil
Foa, Pamela, PhD, Asst Prof, Epistem
Frye, Marilyn, PhD, Asst Prof, Phil of Lang
Gale, Richard, PhD, Prof, Metaph
Gibbard, Alan F, PhD, Visit Assoc Prof, Ethics
Grünbaum, Adolf, PhD, Andrew Mellon Prof, Phil of Sci, Phil of Phys
Guyer, Paul D, MA, Visit Asst Prof, Hist of Phil
Hansen, Chad, PhD, Asst Prof, Chinese Phil
Hill, Christopher, PhD, Mellon Post-Doc Fel, Phil of Lang, Phil of Mind
Laudan, Laurens, PhD, Prof, Hist and Phil of Sci
McCall, Storrs, DPhil, Assoc Prof, Logic, Metaph
McGuire, James E, PhD, Prof, Hist and Phil of Sci
Meyer, Robert, PhD, Visit Assoc Prof, Logic
Nehamas, Alexander, PhD, Asst Prof, Greek Phil, Phil of Lang, Exist, Aes
Posy, Carl J, PhD, Asst Prof, Phil of Math, Logic, Phenomen
Rescher, Nicholas, PhD, Univ Prof, Epistem, Logic, Metaph, Phil of Sci, Hist of
   Phil, Value Theory, Arabic Logic
Schaffner, Kenneth, PhD, Prof, Hist and Phil of Sci
Schneewind, Jerome, PhD, Prof, Ethics, Hist of Phil
Schultz, Robert, PhD, Asst Prof, Aes, Ethics
Sellars, Wilfrid, MA, Univ Prof, Epistem, Metaph, Phil of Sci
Sherover, Erica, MA, Instr, 19th Cent Phil
Thomason, Richmond, PhD, Assoc Prof, Phil of Lang, Logic
Zilonis, Jr, Walter A, MA, Visit Instr, Phil of Law

Reiser, Oliver L, PhD, Prof Emer

UNIVERSITY OF PITTSBURGH, BRADFORD CAMPUS
   Bradford, Pennsylvania 16701 (M; st; coed; tri; I; 514) Courses with no degree
   specialization, Dept of Phil, 814-362-3801

   Fohr, Samuel D, PhD, Asst Prof

UNIVERSITY OF PITTSBURGH, GREENSBURG CAMPUS
   Greensburg, Pennsylvania 15601 (M; st; coed; tri; I; 957) Courses with no degree
   specialization, Div of Human, 412-837-7040

   Gaughan, Norbert, PhD, Asst Prof

UNIVERSITY OF PITTSBURGH, JOHNSTOWN CAMPUS
   Johnstown, Pennsylvania 15904 (M; st; coed; tri; II; 2518) Courses with no degree
   specialization, Div of Human, 814-266-5841 Ext 378

   Ochoco, Severino M, MA, Asst Prof, Logic, Ethics, Hist of Phil, Probs of Phil

UNIVERSITY OF PITTSBURGH, TITUSVILLE CAMPUS
   Titusville, Pennsylvania 16354 (M; st; coed; tri; I; 320) Courses with no degree
   specialization, Dept of Phil, 814-825-3246

   Galbraith, Winslow H, BS, Adj Asst Prof

UNIVERSITY OF SCRANTON
  Scranton, Pennsylvania 18510 (M; RC; men; sem; III; 3312) BA major, Dept of Phil,
  717-347-3321 Ext 280

  Fairbanks, Matthew, PhD, Prof, Chm, Phil of Sci
  Capestany, Edward, PhD, Assoc Prof, Phil of Law
  Devlin, William, PhL, Prof, Ethics
  Fleming, Leo, MA, Asst Prof, Ethics
  Gannon, Edward, PhD, Prof, Phenomen
  Garrett, Thomas, PhD, Prof, Business Ethics
  Jarvis, Edward, PhD, Assoc Prof, Phil of Relig
  McGinley, John, PhD, Asst Prof, Phenomen
  Narbutas, Jonas, PhD, Asst Prof, Exist
  Nordberg, Kevin, BA, Asst Prof, Phil of Man
  Suppé, Bernard, PhL, Prof, Camus

URSINUS COLLEGE
  Collegeville, Pennsylvania 19426 (M; p; coed; sem; II; 1869) BA joint or combined
  major, Dept of Phil and Relig, 215-489-4111

  Williamson, William Bedford, EdD, Prof, Chm, Anal Phil
  Creager, Alfred Leon, DD, Assoc Prof Part-time
  Hardman, Keith Jordan, PhD, Asst Prof
  Zakydalsky, Taras Danxlo, MA, Instr, Logic, Phil of Sci

VALLEY FORGE MILITARY JUNIOR COLLEGE
  Wayne, Pennsylvania 19087 (M; p; men; sem; I; 110) NP

VILLA MARIA COLLEGE
  Erie, Pennsylvania 16505 (M; RC; wo; 4-1-4; II; 733) Courses with no degree
  specialization, Dept of Relig Stud and Phil, 814-838-1966

  Galla, Jane Ellen, AMR, Instr, Metaph
  Onofrio, Teresina, MA, Assoc Prof, Logic, Ethics

VILLANOVA UNIVERSITY
  Villanova, Pennsylvania 19085 (M; RC; coed; sem; IV; 9993) MA major, Dept of Phil,
  215-527-2100 Ext 394, 395

  Caputo, John D, PhD, Assoc Prof, Chm, German Phil
  Betz, Joseph M, MA, Asst Prof, Amer Phil
  Busch, Thomas W, PhD, Assoc Prof, Exist, Phenomen
  Doody, John A, MA, Instr, Phil of Soc Sci, Phil of Phys Sci
  Fielder, John H, PhD, Asst Prof, Anal Phil
  Goff, Edwin L, MA, Instr, Moral Phil
  Immerwahr, John, PhD, Asst Prof, Mod Phil
  Kondoleon, Theodore J, PhD, Assoc Prof, St Thomas Aquinas
  Losoncy, Thomas A, PhD, Asst Prof, Med Phil
  McFadden, Charles J, PhD, Prof, Moral Phil, Phil of Communism
  Nwodo, Christopher S, MA, Instr, Aes
  O'Brien, James F, PhD, Prof, Phil of Nature, Phil of Sci
  O'Neil, Charles J, PhD, Prof, Moral Theory, Hist of Metaph
  Paparella, Benedict A, PhD, Prof, Moral Phil, Soc and Polit Phil
  Regan, Daniel T, MA, Asst Prof, Soc and Polit Phil
  Russell, Robert P, PhD, Prof, St Augustine, Plotinus
  Slattery, Michael P, PhD, Prof, Anal Phil, Metaph
  Stepelevich, Lawrence S, PhD, Assoc Prof, Bergson, Marxism
  Tich, John G, MA, Asst Prof, Greek Phil, Indian Phil
  Van Fleteren, Frederick E, PhD, Asst Prof, St Augustine

Wall, Barbara E, MA, Instr, Communism, Phil of the Person
Woodring, Kenneth J, MA, Instr, Logic

Corwell, George, Grad Asst
Edler, Maris, Grad Asst
Husson, Kathleen, Grad Asst
Labor, Suzanne, Grad Asst

Liero, Steven, Grad Asst
Myers, William, Grad Asst
Stack, John, Grad Asst
Twomey, Donald, Grad Asst

WASHINGTON AND JEFFERSON COLLEGE
Washington, Pennsylvania 15301 (M; p; coed; 4-1-4; II; 1094) BA major, Dept of Phil,
412-222-4400

Dukelow, Oven W, PhD, Assoc Prof, Chm, Phil of Hist, Phil of Man, Ethics
Hellegers, Frederick, ThD, Prof, Phil of Relig
Jacobson, John, M Div, Asst Prof, Hist of Phil
McDonald, John William, PhD, Asst Prof, Polit Phil
Mitchell, R Lloyd, MA, Asst Prof, Phenomen, Exist, Logic

WAYNESBURG COLLEGE
Waynesburg, Pennsylvania 15370 (M; U Preb; coed; sem; II; 1081) Courses with no
degree specialization, Dept of Phil and Relig, 412-627-8191 Ext 275

Vaska, Vootele, PhD, Prof, 19th Cent Phil, German Phil

WEST CHESTER STATE COLLEGE
West Chester, Pennsylvania 19380 (M; st; coed; sem; III; 8106) MA major, Dept of
Phil, 215-436-2841

Claghorn, George S, PhD, Prof, Chm, Greek Phil, Amer Phil
Banyacski, Paul, BA, Assoc Prof, Logic, Contemp Phil
Croddy, W Stephen, PhD, Assoc Prof, Phil of Lang, Epistem
Platt, Thomas W, PhD, Prof, Phil of Sci, Ethics
Riukas, Stanley, PhD, Prof, Hist of Mod Phil, Phil of Mind
Streveler, Paul, PhD, Asst Prof, Med Phil, Anc Phil, Wittgenstein
Struckmeyer, Frederick R, PhD, Prof, Phil of Relig, Orient Phil, Soc Phil
Williams, Edwin L, BA, Assoc Prof, Logic, Phil of Hist

WESTMINSTER COLLEGE
New Wilmington, Pennsylvania 16142 (M; U Preb; coed; 4-1-4; III; 2010) BA major,
Dept of Relig and Phil, 412-946-6710 Ext 20

Cadwallader, Eva H, PhD, Asst Prof, 19th Cent Phil, Phil of Sci
Gregory, Thomas M, PhD, Prof, Phil of Relig, Hist of Phil, Exist

WESTMINSTER THEOLOGICAL SEMINARY
Philadelphia, Pennsylvania 19118 (M; p; men; sem; IV; 166) Courses with no degree
specialization, Field of Theol Stud, 215-887-5511

Frame, John McElphatrick, MPhil, Assoc Prof
Knudsen, Robert Donald, PhD, Assoc Prof

WESTMORELAND COUNTY COMMUNITY COLLEGE
Youngwood, Pennsylvania 15697 (--; local; coed; sem; I; 1042) Courses with no
degree specialization, Dept of Human, 412-836-1600

Prosperi, A O, MA, Asst Prof, Chm
Finn, J, MA, Asst Prof

WIDENER COLLEGE
  Chester, Pennsylvania 19013 (M; p; coed; 4-1-4; III; 3105) Courses with no degree
  specialization, Dept of Human, 215-876-5551 Ext 249

  Cottee, William L, MA, Prof, Logic
  Logan, Eleanor, MA, Prof, Phil of Relig
  Nearing, Homer, PhD, Prof, Hist of Phil
  Sophocles, Sophocles, PhD, Prof, Ethics

WILKES COLLEGE
  Wilkes Barre, Pennsylvania 18703 (M; p; coed; sem; III; 3436) BA major, Dept of
  Phil and Relig Stud, 717-824-4651

  Vujica, Stanko M, PhD, Prof, Chm, Compar Relig, Metaph
  Barras, Abraham D, DHL, Adj Prof
  Henson, Donald A, PhD, Asst Prof, Epistem, Phil of Relig
  Jardine, John G, MA, Asst Prof, Soc Phil, Polit Phil, Amer Phil
  Kay, Stanley B, PhD, Assoc Prof, Phil of Sci, Kant
  Williams, Roy E, PhD, Assoc Prof, Phil of Relig

WILLIAMSPORT AREA COMMUNITY COLLEGE
  Williamsport, Pennsylvania 17701 (M; local; coed; sem; I; 2928) Courses with no
  degree specialization, Dept of Eng, 717-326-3761 Ext 203

  Holdstock, Roger, PhD, Instr, Med Phil

WILSON COLLEGE
  Chambersburg, Pennsylvania 17201 (M; p; wo; sem; II; 455) BA major, Dept of Phil,
  717-264-4141

  Platt, David Sellers, PhD, Prof, Chm, Class Amer Phil, Phil of Relig
  Nordquist, Roger Frank, PhD, Asst Prof, Exist, Hist of Phil-Descartes thru Hegel

YORK COLLEGE OF PENNSYLVANIA
  York, Pennsylvania 17405 (JM; p; coed; sem; II; 2514) BA joint or combined major,
  Dept of Human, 717-843-8891

  Papacostas, George A, PhD, Prof, Phil of Educ

PUERTO RICO

ANTILLIAN COLLEGE
  Mayaguez, Puerto Rico 00708 (--; SDA; coed; sem; II; 438) NP

CARIBBEAN CENTER FOR ADVANCED STUDIES, PSYCHOLOGICAL INSTITUTE OF PUERTO RICO
  Carolina, Puerto Rico 00630 (--; p; coed; sem; IV; 101) NP

CATHOLIC UNIVERSITY OF PUERTO RICO
Ponce, Puerto Rico 00731 (M; RC; coed; sem; III; 6997) BA major, Dept of Phil, 809-842-4150

Buxó, Arturo M, PhD, Chm, Mod Phil
Benavides, Manuel, PhD
De Armas, Alexio, MA, Metaph, Med Phil
Echevarría, José R, PhD, Logic, Phil of Sci
Estrada, Manuel, MA, Ethics
Gómez, Néstor, MA, Schol Phil
Nadal, Juan, MA, Anc Phil
Rojas Ossorio, Carlos, MA, Latin American Phil
Rojo Seijas, José L, PhD, Aes
Salgado, José, MA, Schol Phil
Santacruz, Benedicto, MA, Schol Phil
Vilaró, Narciso, MA, Phil Anthrop

COLLEGE OF THE SACRED HEART
Santurce, Puerto Rico 00914 (M; no; wo, sem; II; 1472) BA minor, Dept of Human, 809-724-7800

González de la Fuente, Angel, MA
González-Cobarrubias, María Juana
Leiva, Emilio, MA
Montalvo, Josefina, MA
Mora, Antonia, MA
Samaranch, Francisco, PhD

CONSERVATORY OF MUSIC OF PUERTO RICO
Hato Rey, Puerto Rico 00918 (--; st; coed; sem; II; 328) NP

INTERAMERICAN UNIVERSITY OF PUERTO RICO, AGUADILLA BRANCH
Aguadilla, Puerto Rico 00603 (M; p; coed; sem; I; 859) NR

INTERAMERICAN UNIVERSITY OF PUERTO RICO, ARECIBO BRANCH
Arecibo, Puerto Rico 00612 (M; p; coed; sem; I; 1197) NR

INTERAMERICAN UNIVERSITY OF PUERTO RICO, BARRANQUITAS BRANCH
Barranquitas, Puerto Rico 00618 (M; p; coed; sem; I; 600) NR

INTERAMERICAN UNIVERSITY OF PUERTO RICO, BAYAMON BRANCH
Bayamon, Puerto Rico 00619 (M; p; coed; sem; I; 1717) NR

INTERAMERICAN UNIVERSITY OF PUERTO RICO, HATO REY CAMPUS
Hato Rey, Puerto Rico 00919 (M; p; coed; sem; IV; 3327) Courses with no degree specialization, --, 809-765-3765

Jimenez, Tomás M, MA, Asst Prof
Maldonado, José M, MA, Instr
Oliveros, Antonio, PhD, Instr
Quiñones, Leoncio, EED, Asst Prof

INTERAMERICAN UNIVERSITY OF PUERTO RICO, PONCE BRANCH
Ponce, Puerto Rico 00731 (M; p; coed; sem; I; 949) --, Dept of Phil and Relig, 809-843-3825

Fosela, Mariano, BA, Asst Prof
Quiros, Carlos S, BS, Asst Prof

INTERAMERICAN UNIVERSITY OF PUERTO RICO, RAMEY COLLEGE
Ramey AFB, Puerto Rico 00604 (M; p; coed; sem; I; --) Courses with no degree
specialization, Dept of Phil, 809-891-1510 Ext X6197 IAU

McNeil, Thomas, ThD, Prof, Hist of Phil

INTERAMERICAN UNIVERSITY OF PUERTO RICO, SAN GERMAN CAMPUS
San German, Puerto Rico 00753 (M; p; coed; sem; III; 2362) NR

PUERTO RICO JUNIOR COLLEGE
Rio Piedras, Puerto Rico 00928 (M; p; coed; sem; I; 4764) NR

UNIVERSITY OF PUERTO RICO, ARECIBO REGIONAL COLLEGE
Arecibo, Puerto Rico 00612 (M; st; coed; sem; I; --) Courses with no degree
specialization, Dept of Human, 809-878-2830 Ext 212

García Marchand, Juan, MA, Instr, Chm

UNIVERSITY OF PUERTO RICO, CAYEY UNIVERSITY COLLEGE
Cayey, Puerto Rico 00633 (M; st; coed; sem; II; 2224) BA minor, Dept of Human, 809-
738-2162

García Cabán, Ebenezer, MA, Instr, Phil of Hist, Exist

UNIVERSITY OF PUERTO RICO, HUMACAO REGIONAL CAMPUS
Humacao, Puerto Rico 00661 (M; st; coed; sem; I; --) NR

UNIVERSITY OF PUERTO RICO, MAYAGUEZ CAMPUS
Mayaguez, Puerto Rico 00708 (M; st; coed; sem; III; 9069) BA major, Dept of Human
809-832-4040 Ext 422

Owen, William A, PhD, Prof, Chm
Cisneros, Marcelino, PhD, Assoc Prof
Fiala, Dorit, PhD, Asst Prof
García Herrera, Emilio, MA, Asst Prof
Lugo, Elena, PhD, Assoc Prof
Owen, William A, PhD, Prof
Rojo Seijas, Luis, PhD, Assoc Prof
Ruano, Argimiro, PhD, Prof
Sánchez, Halley, PhD, Instr
Stern, Alfred, PhD, Prof

UNIVERSITY OF PUERTO RICO MEDICAL SCIENCES
San Juan, Puerto Rico 00905 (Med; st; coed; sem; IV; 1427) NP

UNIVERSITY OF PUERTO RICO, PONCE REGIONAL COLLEGE
Ponce, Puerto Rico 00731 (M; st; coed; sem; I; --) AA major, Dept of Human, 809-
843-6262 Ext 215

Pijnenburg, Petrus, MA, Instr
Ramos, Carlos, MA, Instr
Ruiz Cordobés, Salvador, MA, Lect

UNIVERSITY OF PUERTO RICO, RIO PIEDRAS REGIONAL CAMPUS
Rio Piedras, Puerto Rico 00931 (M; st; coed; sem; IV; 25,889) MA major, Dept of
Phil, 809-765-0415

Gómez, Luis O, PhD, Assoc Prof, Dir, Orient Phil, Buddhism, Phil of Relig
Casares, Angel J, PhD, Prof, Contemp Phil, Heidegger
Castilla-Lázaro, Ramón, PhD, Prof, Contemp Phil
Chiesa, Ernesto, MA, Adj Instr, Logic
Cordúa de Torretti, Carla, MA, Adj Assoc Prof, Contemp Phil
Delacre, Georges, PhD, Prof, Phil of Sci
Echeverria, José R, PhD, Prof, Phil of Law
Enjuto-Bernal, Jorge R, PhD, Prof, Contemp Phil, Whitehead
Fromm, Georg, PhD, Assoc Prof, Hegel, Marxism
González-Cobarrubias, Juan J, MA, Asst Prof, Anal Phil, Logic
Kerkhoff, Manfred, PhD, Prof, Anc Phil, Mod Phil, Nietzsche
Mojica, Aguedo, MA, Instr, Mod Phil
Pérez-Marchand, Monelisa, PhD, Prof, Aes, Phil of Hist
Schajowicz, Ludwig, PhD, Prof, Phil of Art
Soto, Carlos, MA, Adj Instr, Anal Phil
Tollinchi, Esteban, PhD, Assoc Prof, Ethics, Mod Phil, Hegel
Torretti, Roberto, PhD, Prof, Logic, Phil of Sci

Soto, Juan B, Prof Emer

WORLD UNIVERSITY
Hato Rey, Puerto Rico 00917 (--; p; coed; qr; III; 1592) NR

RHODE ISLAND

BARRINGTON COLLEGE
Barrington, Rhode Island 22806 (E; p; coed; 4-1-4; II; 597) BA major, Dept of
Phil, 401-246-1200 Ext 211

Gregory, Carlton H, PhD, Prof, Chm, Ethics
Crum, Terrelle B, LLD, Prof, Phil of Relig
Geehan, E Robert, PhD, Asst Prof, Metaph
Young, William, PhD, Prof, Phil of Educ

BROWN UNIVERSITY
Providence Rhode Island 02912 (E; p; coed; sem; IV; 5789) PhD major, Dept of Phil,
401-863-2718

Sosa, Ernest, PhD, Prof, Chm
Brock, Dan W, PhD, Asst Prof
Chisholm, Roderick M, PhD, Prof
Ladd, John, PhD, Prof

Leeds, Stephen, PhD, Asst Prof
Lenz, John W, PhD, Prof
Luschei, Eugene C, PhD, Assoc Prof
Quinn, Philip L, PhD, Assoc Prof
Schmitt, Richard, PhD, Prof
Tomas, Vincent, PhD, Prof

Boon, Kevin, MA, Grad Asst
Carson, Thomas, BA, Grad Asst
Covey, Judith, MA, Grad Asst
Cusmariu, Arnold, BA, Grad Asst
Delaurentis, Michael, BA, Grad Asst
Foley, Richard, MA, Grad Asst
Galbreath, Bruce, MA, Grad Asst

Gorr, Michael, MA, Grad Asst
McLean, Charles J, MA, Grad Asst
Neilson, Bryan, MA, Grad Asst
Preacher, Thomas, BA, Grad Asst
Rosenkrantz, Gary, BA, Grad Asst
Scher, Stephen, MA, Grad Asst
Sheridan, Diane, BA, Grad Asst

BRYANT COLLEGE OF BUSINESS ADMINISTRATION
Providence, Rhode Island 02906 (E; p; coed; sem; III; 4053) Courses with no degree
specialization, Dept of Human, 401-231-1200

JOHNSON AND WALES COLLEGE
Providence, Rhode Island 02903 (JRCB; p; coed; tri; II; 1287) Courses with no
degree specialization, --, 401-331-3915

MOUNT SAINT JOSEPH COLLEGE
Wakefield, Rhode Island 02879 (--; RC; wo; sem; II; 233) --, --, 401-789-0809

PROVIDENCE COLLEGE
Providence, Rhode Island 02919 (E; RC; coed; sem; IV; 3644) BA major, Dept of Phil,
401-865-2335

Kenny, John P, PhD, Prof, Chm, Medical Ethics
Concordia, George L, PhD, Assoc Prof, Ethics
Cunningham, John F, PhD, Prof, Mod Phil
Danilowicz, Richard D, MA, Assoc Prof, Metaph
Devine, Robert V, MA, Instr, Amer Phil
Fay, Benjamin U, PhL, Assoc Prof, Ethics
Haladus, Jerome J, PhD, Asst Prof, Metaph
Jackson, Arthur, PhD, Asst Prof
Kane, Dennis C, PhD, Prof, Logic
Kelly, James P, PhD, Assoc Prof
Langton, Bernard F, MA, Instr, Greek and Med Phil
McAvey, James R, PhL, Assoc Prof, Metaph
Morry, Matthew F, STD, Assoc Prof, Hist of Phil
Peterson, Thomas R, PhD, Assoc Prof, Orient Phil
Robillard, George M, STL, Assoc Prof, Phil of Sci

RHODE ISLAND COLLEGE
Providence, Rhode Island 02908 (E; st; coed; sem; III; 7534) BA major, Dept of
Phil and Found of Educ, 401-831-6600

Houghton, Raymond, PhD, Prof, Chm
Hoy, Daniel J, Asst Prof, Phenomen, Exist, Epistem

RHODE ISLAND JUNIOR COLLEGE
Providence, Rhode Island 02908 (E; st; coed; sem; I; 3743) Courses with no degree
specialization, Dept of Soc Sci, 401-825-2169

Dean, Lloyd, PhD, Prof
Kinnaman, William, MA, Asst Prof

RHODE ISLAND SCHOOL OF DESIGN
Providence, Rhode Island 02903 (E; p; coed; sem; III; 1250) NP

ROGER WILLIAMS COLLEGE
Bristol, Rhode Island 02809 (E; p; coed; sem; II; 1507) BA major, Area of Phil,
401-255-2139

Blackburn, Robert J, MA, Chm
Hebert, Rodolphe-Louis, PhD
Jones, Martin M, PhD
Kowall, Thomas W, MA

SALVE REGINA COLLEGE
Newport, Rhode Island 02040 (E; RC; wo; 4-1-4; II; 1357) BA minor, Reflective Area,
401-847-6650 Ext 53

Hersh, William James, MA, Asst Prof, Anc Greek Phil, Orient Phil

SEMINARY OF OUR LADY OF PROVIDENCE
Warwick, Rhode Island 02889 (E; RC; men; sem; II; 96) BA major, Dept of Phil, 401-
739-6850

Blain, Lionel A, PhD, Prof, Dean, Mod Phil, Continen Phil, Epistem
Inman, David, PhD, Asst Prof, Anc Phil, Sartre, Heidegger
Kehew, Donal R, PhD, Asst Prof, Logic, Marx, Phil of Relig
Simas, Edward, MA, Asst Prof, Epistem, Ethics, Metaph

Cox, John F, PhD, Prof Emer, Metaph, Ethics

UNIVERSITY OF RHODE ISLAND
Kingston, Rhode Island 02881 (E; st; coed; sem; IV; 15,450) MA major, Dept of Phil,
401-792-2418

Freeman, David H, PhD, Prof, Chm, Phil of Relig, Logic, Dooyeweerd
Fedoryka, Damian P, PhD, Asst Prof, Phil of Psych, Exist, Polit Phil
Hanke, John W, PhD, Asst Prof, Metaph, Aes, Hist of Phil
Kim, Yong Choon, PhD, Asst Prof, Orient Phil, Phil of Relig
Kowalski, James G, MA, Instr, Phil of Sci, Logic
Martin, William Oliver, PhD, Prof, Phil of Educ, Realism, Polit Phil
Pauley, Edward H, PhD, Asst Prof, Epistem, Ling Phil, Anal Phil
Peterson, John F, PhD, Asst Prof, Epistem, Phil Logic
Schwarz, Stephen D, PhD, Asst Prof, Exist, Ethics, Metaph, Phenomen
Young, William, ThD, Assoc Prof, Hist of Phil, Logic, Epistem, Wittgenstein, Hegel
Zeyl, Donald J, PhD, Asst Prof, Class Phil, Plato

Boatright, L	Messier, R
Bower, K	Roberts, M
Glasson, J	Robinson, B
Higgins, W	Tsakaris, A
Jenner, T	

SAMOA

COMMUNITY COLLEGE OF AMERICAN SAMOA
Pago Pago, American Samoa 96799 (--; st; coed; sem; I; 632) NP

SOUTH CAROLINA

AIKEN TECHNICAL EDUCATION CENTER
Aiken, South Carolina 29801 (--; st; coed; qr; I; 39) NP

ALLEN UNIVERSITY
Columbia, South Carolina 29204 (--; AME; coed; sem; II; 456) NP

ANDERSON COLLEGE
Anderson, South Carolina 29621 (S; S Bapt; coed; sem; I; 456) NP

BAPTIST COLLEGE AT CHARLESTON
Charleston, South Carolina 29411 (S; S Bapt; coed; 4-1-4; II; 1918) BA major, Dept
of Phil, 803-553-5110 Ext 2212

Barry, Jr, John A, ThD, Prof, Phil of Relig
Haight, E F, ThD, Prof, Hist of Phil

BENEDICT COLLEGE
Columbia, South Carolina 29204 (S; p; coed; sem; II; 1487) BA joint or combined
major, Dept of Relig and Phil, 803-779-4930

BERKELEY-CHARLESTON-DORCHESTER TECHNICAL EDUCATION CENTER
North Charleston, South Carolina 29405 (S; st and local; coed; qr; I; 1222) NR

BOB JONES UNIVERSITY
Greenville, South Carolina 29614 (--; p; coed; sem; IV; 3770) --, Dept of Phil,
803-242-5100

Jantz, Albert Elmer, MEd

CENTRAL WESLEYAN COLLEGE
Central, South Carolina 29630 (--; Wes Meth; coed; sem; II; 33) Courses with no
degree specialization, --, 803-639-2453

Bross, James B, PhD, Asst Prof
Foutz, Kenneth, MA, Assoc Prof

CHESTERFIELD-MARLBORO TECHNICAL EDUCATION CENTER
    Cheraw, South Carolina 29520 (--; st; coed; qr; I; 231) NP

THE CITADEL MILITARY COLLEGE OF SOUTH CAROLINA
    Charleston, South Carolina 29409 (S; st; coed; sem; III; 2768) Courses with no
    degree specialization, --, 803-723-0611

CLAFLIN UNIVERSITY
    Orangeburg, South Carolina 29115 (S; U Meth; coed; sem; II; 795) BA joint or combined
    major, Dept of Relig and Phil, 803-534-2710 Ext 78

    Johnson, Douglas W, PhD, Assoc Prof, Chm, Hist of Christ Tht, Augustine, Hist of
        West Tht
    Gregg, W R, STM, Part-time, Phil of Relig

CLEMSON UNIVERSITY
    Clemson, South Carolina 29631 (S; st; coed; sem; IV; 8416) BA minor, Dept of Hist
    and Phil, 803-656-3153

    McCollough, J L, PhD, Asst Prof, Ethics, Metaph
    Pharr, Jr, Walter M, MA, Instr, Logic, Anal Phil
    White, Jr, David F, MA, Asst Prof, Ethics, Epistem

CLEMSON UNIVERSITY, GREENVILLE BRANCH
    Greenville 29606 (S; st; coed; sem; I; 244) NP

CLEMSON UNIVERSITY, SUMTER BRANCH
    Sumter, South Carolina 29150 (S; st; coed; sem; I; 230) NR

COKER COLLEGE
    Hartsville, South Carolina 29550 (S; p; coed; qr; II; 409) NR

THE COLLEGE OF CHARLESTON
    Charleston, South Carolina 29401 (S; st; coed; sem; III; 2252) BA major, Dept of
    Phil, 803-722-0181 Ext 253

    Browning, Lorin, PhD, Asst Prof, Chm, Logic, Recent Phil
    Abbott, James, MA, Asst Prof, Ethics, Polit Theory, Phil of Relig
    Petrick, Eileen, PhD, Part-time, Phenomen, Hist of Phil
    Petrick, Joseph, PhD, Asst Prof, Metaph, Epistem, Amer Phil

COLUMBIA BIBLE COLLEGE
    Columbia, South Carolina 29203 (BI; p; coed; qr; III; 569) Courses with no degree
    specialization, Dept of Gen Educ, 803-754-4100

    McCallister, Albert, MA

COLUMBIA COLLEGE
    Columbia, South Carolina 29203 (S; U Meth; wo; sem; II; 970) Courses with no degree
    specialization, Dept of Human Relations, 803-754-1100 Ext 353

    Butler, William W, PhD, Prof, Dean, Christ Ethics
    Chandler, George P, PhD, Assoc Prof, Phil of Relig

CONVERSE COLLEGE
    Spartanburg, South Carolina 29301 (S; p; wo; 4-1-4; III; 804) Courses with no degree
    specialization, Div of Human, 803-585-6421 Ext 385

    Schmitz, Alfred O, PhD, Prof, Exist

ERSKINE COLLEGE
    Due West, South Carolina 29639 (S; Prot; coed; 4-1-4; II; 746) --, Dept of Phil,
    803-379-2131

    Stevenson, Don R, MA, Instr, Phil Theol

FLORENCE-DARLINGTON TECHNICAL EDUCATION CENTER
    Florence, South Carolina 29501 (S; st and local; coed; qr; I; 813) NP

FRANCIS MARION COLLEGE
    Florence, South Carolina 29501 (--; st; coed; sem; II; 1443) BA minor, Dept of
    Soc and Phil, 803-669-4121

    Hall, Ronald, PhD, Asst Prof, Phil of Mind, Ethics, Phil of Relig
    Von Frank, James, PhD, Asst Prof, Metaph, Epistem, Hist of Phil

FRIENDSHIP JUNIOR COLLEGE
    Rock Hill, South Carolina 29730 (--; Bapt; coed; sem; I; 201) NR

FURMAN UNIVERSITY
    Greenville, South Carolina 29613 (S; S Bapt; coed; --; III; 2245) BA major, Dept
    of Phil, 803-246-3550

    Buford, Thomas, PhD, Assoc Prof, Chm, Epistem, Phil of Educ, Plato
    Edwards, James C, PhD, Asst Prof, Epistem, Ethics, Phil of Sci, Wittgenstein
    MacDonald, Douglas M, PhD, Asst Prof, Ethics, Metaph, Phil of Relig, Santayana

GREENVILLE TECHNICAL EDUCATION CENTER
    Greenville, South Carolina 29606 (S; st; coed; qr; I; 1843) NP

HORRY-GEORGETOWN TECHNICAL EDUCATION CENTER
    Conway, South Carolina 29526 (--; st; coed; qr; I; 408) NP

LANDER COLLEGE
    Greenwood, South Carolina 29646 (S; local; coed; sem; II; 986) Courses with no
    degree specialization, --, 803-229-5521

LIMESTONE COLLEGE
    Gaffney, South Carolina 29340 (S; p; coed; 4-1-4; II; 589) Courses with no degree
    specialization, Dept of Relig and Phil, 803-489-7151 Ext 76

    Bassett, Frederick W, PhD, Prof, Chm, Relig
    Taylor, S Wallace, PhD, Dean, Relig

LUTHERAN THEOLOGICAL SEMINARY
    Columbia, South Carolina 29203 (Theol; Luth CA; coed; qr; III; 133) NP

MEDICAL UNIVERSITY OF SOUTH CAROLINA
 Charleston, South Carolina 29401 (S; st; coed; sem; IV; 1252) Courses with no degree
 specialization, --, 803-792-0211

MIDLANDS TECHNICAL EDUCATION CENTER
 Columbia, South Carolina 29205 (S; local; coed; qr; I; 1444) Courses with no degree
 specialization, Dept of Human, 803-782-5471 Ext 305

 Reed, Sylvia, MA, Phil of Ling

MORRIS COLLEGE
 Sumter, South Carolina 29150 (--; Bapt; coed; sem; II; 520) NR

NEWBERRY COLLEGE
 Newberry, South Carolina 29108 (S; Luth; coed; 4-1-4; II; 804) BA joint or combined
 major, Dept of Relig and Phil, 803-276-5010 Ext 270

 Crenshaw, Floyd D, PhD, Assoc Prof, Phil of Relig
 Peters, Theodore F, PhD, Asst Prof

NORTH GREENVILLE JUNIOR COLLEGE
 Tigerville, South Carolina 29688 (S; S Bapt; coed; sem; I; 610) NP

ORANGEBURG CALHOUN TECHNICAL EDUCATION CENTER
 Orangeburg, South Carolina 29115 (S; st; coed; qr; I; 822) Courses with no degree
 specialization, Dept of Eng, 803-536-0311

PALMER COLLEGE
 Charleston, South Carolina 29401 (S; p; coed; qr; I; 605) Courses with no degree
 specialization, Dept of Gen Educ, 803-722-0531

 Moseley, Matilda H, AB
 Murchison, Anna, AB

PALMER COLLEGE AT COLUMBIA
 Columbia, South Carolina 29201 (S; p; coed; qr; I; 602) Courses with no degree
 specialization, Dept of Gen Educ, 803-253-9456

 Lever, Oscar W, PhD, Chm, Ethics

PIEDMONT TECHNICAL EDUCATION CENTER
 Greenwood, South Carolina 29646 (--; st; coed; qr; I; 662) NP

PRESBYTERIAN COLLEGE
 Clinton, South Carolina 29325 (S; Preb; coed; tri; II; 857) BA joint or combined
 major, Dept of Phil and Relig, 803-833-2820

 Moorefield, David R, PhD, Prof, Ethics, Phil Theol, Hist of Phil

SOUTH CAROLINA STATE COLLEGE
 Orangeburg, South Carolina 29115 (S; st; coed; sem; III; 2383) NR

SPARTANBURG COUNTY TECHNICAL EDUCATION CENTER
Spartanburg, South Carolina 29303 (S; st; coed; qr; I; 875) NP

SPARTANBURG JUNIOR COLLEGE
Spartanburg, South Carolina 29301 (S; U Meth; coed; --; I; 1111) NP

SUMTER AREA TECHNICAL EDUCATION CENTER
Sumter, South Carolina 29150 (S; st; coed; qr; I; 540) NP

TRI-COUNTY TECHNICAL EDUCATION CENTER
Pendleton, South Carolina 29670 (S; st; coed; qr; I; 662) NP

UNIVERSITY OF SOUTH CAROLINA
Columbia, South Carolina 29208 (S; st; coed; sem; IV; 16,615) MA major, Dept of
Phil, 803-777-4166

Long, Eugene T, PhD, Prof, Chm, Phenomen, Exist, Phil of Relig
Dematteis, Philip B, PhD, Asst Prof, Soc and Polit Phil, Ethics
DuBose, L Shannon, PhD, Assoc Prof, Hist of Phil, Anc Phil
Goode, Terry M, PhD, Asst Prof, Phil of Hist, Logic
Hunter, David A, MA, Instr, Hist and Phil of Sci
Loewer, Barry M, MA, Instr, Phil of Lang, Logic
Matsen, Herbert S, PhD, Assoc Prof, Med Phil, Renaissance Phil, Metaph
Mulvaney, Robert J, PhD, Assoc Prof, 17th Cent Phil, Phil of Educ
Oliver, James W, PhD, Prof, Logic, Theory of Knowl
Panish, Theodore M, PhD, Asst Prof, Phenomen, Phil of Art
Rosenkrantz, Roger D, PhD, Assoc Prof, Logic, Decision Theory
Salomon, Hilel B, PhD, Asst Prof, Chinese Phil
Skrupskelis, Ignas K, PhD, Assoc Prof, Mod Phil, Amer Phil
Sprague, Rosamond K, PhD, Prof, Anc Phil
Stiver, James L, PhD, Asst Prof, Phil of Lang, Ethics, Logic
Sullivan, Roger J, PhD, Asst Prof, Ethics, Theory of Action
Tait, Foster E, PhD, Assoc Prof, British Empir, Theory of Knowl, Phil of Sci
Wettersten, John R, PhD, Asst Prof, Phil of Soc Sci

Clark, Kevin M, BA, Grad Asst	Liszka, James A, BA, Grad Asst
Dixon, Paul R, BA, Grad Asst	Shinn, Earl W, BA, Grad Asst
Greene, Jeffrey P, BA, Grad Asst	Skadden, Stuart B, BA, Grad Asst
Havey, William B, BA, Grad Asst	Steen, Frederick R, BA, Grad Asst
Loewer, Marjorie A, BA, Grad Asst	Sullivan, William C, BA, Grad Asst

UNIVERSITY OF SOUTH CAROLINA AT AIKEN
Aiken, South Carolina 29801 (S; st; coed; sem; I; 695) Courses with no degree
specialization, Div of Human, 803-648-6851 Ext 38

Franz, Harold J, PhD, Assoc Prof, Phil of Educ

UNIVERSITY OF SOUTH CAROLINA AT ALLENDALE
Allendale, South Carolina 29810 (S; st; coed; sem; I; 170) NR

UNIVERSITY OF SOUTH CAROLINA AT BEAUFORT
Beaufort, South Carolina 29902 (S; st; coed; sem; I; 336) --, Dept of Phil, 803-
524-7112

Bowen, Noran Kizer, MA, Instr

UNIVERSITY OF SOUTH CAROLINA AT CONWAY
    Conway, South Carolina 29526 (S; st; coed; sem; I; 773) BA major, Dept of Phil,
    803-347-3161

    Robinson, R N, PhD, Asst Prof, Greek Phil, Moral Phil, Hist of Tht
    Sullivan, Neal, PhD, Prof, Logic, Polit Phil

UNIVERSITY OF SOUTH CAROLINA AT LANCASTER
    Lancaster, South Carolina 29720 (S; st; coed; sem; I; 496) BA major, --, 803-283-
    8478

UNIVERSITY OF SOUTH CAROLINA AT SPARTANBURG
    Spartanburg, South Carolina 29303 (S; st; coed; sem; I; 688) NR

UNIVERSITY OF SOUTH CAROLINA AT UNION
    Union, South Carolina 29379 (S; st; coed; sem; I; 236) NP

VOORHEES COLLEGE
    Denmark, South Carolina 29042 (S; Prot Epis; coed; sem; II; 736) --, Dept of Phil,
    803-793-3346 Ext 9

    Clarke, Shelton, MA, Instr
    Jackson, James C, BTh, Instr

WINTHROP COLLEGE
    Rock Hill, South Carolina 29730 (S; st; coed; sem; III; 3879) BA major, Dept of
    Phil and Relig, 803-323-2129

    Jacobson, Nolan P, PhD, Prof, Chm, Buddhist Phil, Phil of Relig
    Craighead, Houston, PhD, Assoc Prof, Phil of Relig
    Daniel, William W, PhD, Prof, Contemp Phil

WOFFORD COLLEGE
    Spartanburg, South Carolina 29301 (S; U Meth; coed; 4-1-4; II; 1030) BA major,
    Dept of Phil, 803-585-4821 Ext 245

    Keller, James A, PhD, Asst Prof, Chm, Phil of Relig, Phil of Sci
    Hendricks, M Elton, PhD, Asst Prof
    Hudgins, Walter E, PhD, Assoc Prof, Ethics

YORK COUNTY TECHNICAL EDUCATION CENTER
    Rock Hill, South Carolina 29730 (S; st; coed; qr; I; 347) NP

AUGUSTANA COLLEGE
Sioux Falls, South Dakota 57102 (N; Luth; coed; 4-1-4; III; 2078) BA major, Dept of Phil, 605-336-5492

Bowles, George, PhD, Asst Prof, Greek Phil
Pederson, LaMoyne, PhD, Asst Prof, Ethics

BLACK HILLS STATE COLLEGE
Spearfish, South Dakota 57783 (N; st; coed; sem; III; 3135) NP

DAKOTA STATE COLLEGE
Madison, South Dakota 57042 (N; st; coed; sem; II; 1208) NP

DAKOTA WESLEYAN UNIVERSITY
Mitchell, South Dakota 57301 (N; U Meth; coed; 4-1-4; II; 549) BA joint or combined major, Dept of Phil and Relig, 605-996-6511 Ext 250

Miller, Marv H, ThD, Assoc Prof, Chm
Rice, Dan, M Div, Asst Prof

FREEMAN JUNIOR COLLEGE
Freeman, South Dakota 57029 (--; Menn; coed; 4-1-4; I; 56) NR

HURON COLLEGE
Huron, South Dakota 57350 (N; U Preb; coed; 4-1-4; II; 730) BA major, Dept of Phil, 605-352-8721

Rila, James S, PhD, Assoc Prof, Phil of Relig, Phil of Lang, Phil of Educ
Sherman, Merton E, ThD, Prof

MOUNT MARTY COLLEGE
Yankton, South Dakota 57078 (N; RC; coed; 4-1-4; II; 524) BA joint or combined major, Dept of Relig Stud and Phil, 605-668-1507

Imming, Donald, MA, Lect, Ethics, Hist of Phil, Metaph
Kilzer, Philomene, PhL, Assoc Prof, Phil of Man, Hist of Phil, Metaph, Phil of Sci

NATIONAL COLLEGE OF BUSINESS
Rapid City, South Dakota 57701 (SRCB; p; coed; qr; II; 960) Courses with no degree specialization, Div of Arts and Sci, 605-348-1200 Ext 79

Houska, R B, PhD, Assoc Prof, Chm, Metaph
Jarman, John, PhD, Asst Prof, Ethics, Logic

NORTH AMERICAN BAPTIST SEMINARY
Sioux Falls, South Dakota 57105 (Theol; Bapt; coed; 4-1-4; II; 51) D Min major, Div of Heritage and Tht, 605-336-6588

Powell, Ralph E, ThD, Prof, Chm, Phil of Relig, Ethics
Borchert, Gerald L, PhD, Prof, Dean
Dunger, George A, PhD, Prof, Non-Christ Phil

NORTHERN STATE COLLEGE
    Aberdeen, South Dakota 57401 (N; st; coed; --; III; 3000) BA minor, Dept of Soc Sci
    605-622-2602

    Tillery, Thomas D, MA, Asst Prof, Ethics

PRESENTATION COLLEGE
    Aberdeen, South Dakota 57401 (N; RC; coed; 4-1-4; I; 359) Courses with no degree
    specialization, Dept of Phil, 605-225-0420

    Bordenkircher, Robert, MA, Chm

SIOUX FALLS COLLEGE
    Sioux Falls, South Dakota 57101 (N; A Bapt; coed; 4-1-4; II; 755) BA major, Dept
    of Phil, Relig, and Christ Educ, 605-336-2850 Ext 132

    Ferly, Firman A, ThD, Prof, Chm, Phil of Relig
    Bowden, Larry R, M Div, Instr, Phil of Relig
    Nickel, Walter R, MA, Assoc Prof, Moral Phil
    Wells, Ronald V, PhD, Prof, Amer Phil

SOUTH DAKOTA SCHOOL OF MINES AND TECHNOLOGY
    Rapid City, South Dakota 57701 (N; st; coed; sem; IV; 1595) Courses with no degree
    specialization, Dept of Lang and Soc Sci, 605-394-2481

    Robinson, Blaine B, MA, Asst Prof

SOUTH DAKOTA STATE UNIVERSITY
    Brookings, South Dakota 57006 (N; st; coed; sem; IV; 7057) Courses with no degree
    specialization, Dept of Phil and Relig, 605-688-4825

    Nelson, David S, PhD, Assoc Prof, Head
    Kedl, Kent, PhD, Asst Prof, Epistem

UNIVERSITY OF SOUTH DAKOTA
    Vermillion, South Dakota 57069 (N; st; coed; sem; IV; 6854) MA minor, Dept of Phil,
    605-677-5486

    Schmucker, Larry A, PhD, Assoc Prof, Chm, Wittgenstein, Phil Anal
    Kiesau, Robert F, PhD, Asst Prof, Metaph, Anc Phil
    Skeen, Nancy N, AM, Asst Prof, Ethics, Amer Phil, Phil Psych

    Drummond, Douglas, BA, Grad Teach Asst

YANKTON COLLEGE
    Yankton, South Dakota 57078 (N; p; coed; --; II; 502) NP

349

TENNESSEE

AMERICAN BAPTIST THEOLOGICAL SEMINARY
  Nashville, Tennessee 37207 (BI; Bapt; coed; sem; II; 123) BA major, Dept of Phil,
  615-228-7877

  McCoy, D B, ThD, Prof, Comp Relig
  Douglas, N E, M Div, Asst Prof, Christ Tht
  Earl, R R, M Div, Asst Prof, Ethics
  Phelps, H L, MS, Asst Prof
  Powell, J L, MED, Assoc Prof

AQUINAS JUNIOR COLLEGE
  Nashville, Tennessee 37205 (S; RC; coed; 4-1-4; I; 302) NR

AUSTIN PEAY STATE UNIVERSITY
  Clarksville, Tennessee 37040 (S; st; coed; qr; III; 3822) BA major, Dept of Phil,
  615-648-7417

  Forderhase, Duane, PhD, Assoc Prof, Chm, Phil of Relig, Ethics
  Randall, Albert, PhD, Asst Prof, Exist, Logic

BELMONT COLLEGE
  Nashville, Tennessee 37203 (S; S Bapt; coed; sem; II; 882) BA major, Dept of Relig
  and Phil, 615-383-7001 Ext 238

  Awalt, Houston Mike, Assoc Prof, Phil of Relig

BETHEL COLLEGE
  McKenzie, Tennessee 38201 (S; Preb; coed; qr; II; 465) BA minor, Div of Relig and
  Phil, 901-353-3055

  Morrow, Hubert W, PhD, Prof, Chm, Ethics

BRYAN COLLEGE
  Dayton, Tennessee 37321 (S; p; coed; sem; II; 455) Courses with no degree specialization,
  Div of Bibl Stud and Phil, 615-775-2041

  Anderson, John, ThD, Prof, Phil of Relig
  Richardson, Brian, EdD, Assoc Prof, Phil of Christ Educ

CARSON-NEWMAN COLLEGE
  Jefferson City, Tennessee 37760 (S; S Bapt; coed; sem; II; 1748) BA major, Dept of
  Phil, 615-475-9061 Ext 288

  Brewer, Paul D, ThD, Prof, Head
  Patteson, Drury, ThD, Assoc Prof

CHATTANOOGA STATE TECHNICAL COMMUNITY COLLEGE
  Chattanooga, Tennessee 37406 (S; st; coed; qr; I; 1204) Courses with no degree
  specialization, Div of Basic Stud, 615-698-8681 Ext 21

  Arendale, Marirose, MA, Assoc Prof

CHRISTIAN BROTHERS COLLEGE
Memphis, Tennessee 38104 (S; RC; coed; sem; II; 864) NP

CLEVELAND STATE COMMUNITY COLLEGE
Cleveland, Tennessee 37311 (S; st; coed; qr; I; 2190) NP

COLUMBIA STATE COMMUNITY COLLEGE
Columbia, Tennessee 38401 (S; st; coed; qr; T; 1444) Courses with no degree
specialization, Div of Human, 615-388-0120 Ext 242

Neale, Philip, MA, Part-time Instr

CUMBERLAND COLLEGE OF TENNESSEE
Lebanon, Tennessee 37087 (S; p; coed; 4-1-4; I; 356) Courses with no degree
specialization, Dept of Human, 615-444-2562

Brown, Harvey, MA

DAVID LIPSCOMB COLLEGE
Nashville, Tennessee 37203 (S; Ch of Christ; coed; qr; II; 2196) Courses with no
degree specialization, --, 615-269-5661

Choate, Jr, J E, PhD, Prof

DYERSBURG STATE COMMUNITY COLLEGE
Dyersburg, Tennessee 38024 (S; st; coed; qr; I; 779) Courses with no degree
specialization, Dept of Human, 901-285-6910

Fowler, J M, MA, Asst Prof

EAST TENNESSEE STATE UNIVERSITY
Johnson City, Tennessee 37601 (S; st; coed; qr; IV; 9610) MA major, Dept of Phil,
615-929-4425

Mielke, Robert H E, PhD, Prof, Head, Phil of Relig
Botkin, Robert, PhD, Prof, Exist
Hackler, Chris, MA, Asst Prof, Anal Phil
Rogers, Kim, PhD, Assoc Prof, Phenomen
White, Stephen W, PhD, Asst Prof, Anal Phil

FISK UNIVERSITY
Nashville, Tennessee 37203 (S; p; coed; 4-1-4; III; 1413) BA major, Dept of Relig
and Phil, 615-244-3580 Ext 213

Schrag, O Oswald, PhD, Chm
Outlaw, I Lucius T
Welch, Wilson Q, BD

Cady, Lyman V, ThD, Prof Emer

FREED-HARDEMAN COLLEGE
Henderson, Tennessee 38348 (S; Ch of Christ; coed; sem; I; 851) --, Dept of Bib,
901-989-4611

Woodson, William, MTh

FREE WILL BAPTIST BIBLE COLLEGE
Nashville, Tennessee 37205 (BI; Bapt; coed; sem; II; 474) Courses with no degree
specialization, Dept of Phil and Comp Relig, 615-297-4676

Picirilli, Robert E, PhD

GEORGE PEABODY COLLEGE FOR TEACHERS
Nashville, Tennessee 37203 (S; p; coed; sem; IV; 1993) NP

HIWASSEE COLLEGE
Madisonville, Tennessee 37354 (S; U Meth; coed; qr; I; 614) NP

JACKSON STATE COMMUNITY COLLEGE
Jackson, Tennessee 38301 (S; st; coed; qr; I; 1351) --, Div of Soc Stud and Educ,
901-424-3520 Ext 283

McHan, George L, MAT, Instr

JOHN A GUPTON COLLEGE
Nashville, Tennessee 37920 (S; p; coed; qr; I; 57) Courses with no degree specialization,
Dept of Human, 615-291-6891

Fulton, III, Charles N, BA, Ethics

JOHNSON BIBLE COLLEGE
Knoxville, Tennessee 37920 (BI; p; coed; sem; II; 285) Courses with no degree
specialization, --, 615-573-4519

Lowe, John M, MA

KING COLLEGE
Bristol, Tennessee 37620 (S; Preb; coed; 4-1-4; II; 326) BA minor, Dept of Phil and
Christ Tht, 615-968-1187 Ext 78

Ramsay, William M, PhD, Prof, Chm, Hist of Phil, Phil of Relig
Jackson, M B, ThD, Asst Prof

KNOXVILLE COLLEGE
Knoxville, Tennessee 37921 (S; Preb; coed; --; II; 1039) Courses with no degree
specialization, Dept of Hist, Relig, and Phil, 615-546-0751 Ext 212

Grohman, Donald D, ThD, Assoc Prof

LAMBUTH COLLEGE
Jackson, Tennessee 38301 (S; U Meth; coed; 4-1-4; II; 787) BA major, Dept of Relig
and Phil, 901-427-6743

McIntire, Russell M, PhD, Asst Prof
Wilkerson, J Kenneth, PhD, Assoc Prof, Amer Phil

LANE COLLEGE
Jackson, Tennessee 38301 (S; CME; coed; sem; II; 921) Courses with no degree
specialization, Div of Soc Sci, 901-424-4600 Ext 76

Cunningham, Ronald, Chm

LEE COLLEGE
Cleveland, Tennessee 37311 (S; Ch of God; coed; 4-1-4; II; 1093) Courses with no degree specialization, Dept of Bibl and Hist Stud, 615-472-2111

Sims, John, Asst Prof

LE MOYNE-OWEN COLLEGE
Memphis, Tennessee 38126 (S; Prot, coed; sem; II; 712) BA minor, Dept of Phil and Relig, 901-948-6626

Hayes, Paul, ThD, Prof, Chm, Phil of Relig
Green, Reuben, STM, Asst Prof Part-time

LINCOLN MEMORIAL UNIVERSITY
Harrogate, Tennessee 37752 (S; p; coed; qr; II; 634) Courses with no degree specialization, --, 615-869-3622

West, Charles E, BD, Ethics

MARTIN COLLEGE
Pulaski, Tennessee 38478 (S; U Meth; coed; sem; I; 386) Courses with no degree specialization, Dept of Relig, 615-363-1567

Alford, Ben Robert, M Div, Instr, Chm
Taylor, William Garie, M Div, Instr

MARYVILLE COLLEGE
Maryville, Tennessee 37801 (S; U Preb; coed; --; II; 833) Courses with no degree specialization, Dept of Phil and Relig, 615-982-6912

Cartlidge, David R, ThD, Assoc Prof
Stewart, Claude, M Div, Asst Prof

MEHARRY MEDICAL COLLEGE
Nashville, Tennessee 37208 (Med; p; coed; 4-1-4; IV; 571) NR

MEMPHIS ACADEMY OF ARTS
Memphis, Tennessee 38112 (S; p; coed; sem; II; 217) NP

MEMPHIS STATE UNIVERSITY
Memphis, Tennessee 38152 (S; st; coed; sem; IV; 19,700) MA major, Dept of Phil, 901-321-1535

James, Gene G, PhD, Assoc Prof, Act Chm, Polit Phil, Logic
Barton, William B, PhD, Prof, Theory of Knowl, Phil of Relig
Bowman, Carroll R, PhD, Prof, Metaph, Phil of Relig
Epp, Ronald H, PhD, Asst Prof, Class Phil, Aes
Hiley, David R, PhD, Asst Prof, Phil of Sci, Phil of Mind
Simco, Nancy D, PhD, Assoc Prof, Ontology, Logic

Austin, James, BS, Grad Asst   Childers, Ginger H, BA, Grad Asst
Barton, Charles J, BA, Grad Asst   Thompson, Robert F, BA, Grad Asst

MEMPHIS THEOLOGICAL SEMINARY
Memphis, Tennessee 38104 (--; Preb; coed; 4-1-4; III; 76) NR

MIDDLE TENNESSEE STATE UNIVERSITY
Murfreesboro, Tennessee 37130 (S; st; coed; sem; IV; 8646) BA major, Dept of Phil, 615-898-2300

Parker, Harold L, PhD, Assoc Prof
Wellwood, David, MA, Asst Prof

MID-SOUTH BIBLE COLLEGE
Memphis, Tennessee 38112 (BI; p; coed; sem; II; 116) NR

MILLIGAN COLLEGE
Milligan College, Tennessee 37682 (S; p; coed; sem; II; 785) BA major, Area of Humane Learning, 615-928-1165 Ext 55

Phillips, G R, PhD, Assoc Prof, Dir, Ethics, Hist of Phil, Phil of Relig
Mayfield, William, PhD, Part-time Instr
Wetzel, C R, PhD, Assoc Prof, Logic, Ordinary Lang Anal

MORRISTOWN COLLEGE
Morristown, Tennessee 37814 (S; U Meth; coed; sem; I; 150) Courses with no degree specialization, --, 615-586-5262

MOTLOW STATE COMMUNITY COLLEGE
Tullahoma, Tennessee 37388 (S; st; coed; qr; I; 861) NP

NASHVILLE STATE TECHNICAL INSTITUTE
Nashville, Tennessee 37209 (--; st; coed; qr; I; 475) NP

ROANE STATE COMMUNITY COLLEGE
Harriman, Tennessee 37748 (--; st; coed; qr; I; 324) NR

SCARRITT COLLEGE OF CHRISTIAN WORKERS
Nashville, Tennessee 37203 (S; U Meth; coed; sem; III; 149) Courses with no degree specialization, Dept of Christ Life and Tht, 615-327-1311

White, David C, PhD, Prof

SHELBY STATE COMMUNITY COLLEGE
Memphis, Tennessee 38111 (--; st; coed; qr; I; 1070) AA major, Dept of Human, 901-323-6444

Coomber, David A, MA, Asst Prof

SOUTHERN COLLEGE OF OPTOMETRY
Memphis, Tennessee 38104 (S; p; coed; qr; III; 501) NP

SOUTHERN MISSIONARY COLLEGE
Collegedale, Tennessee 37315 (S; SDA; coed; sem; II; 1412) --, --, 615-396-2111

Chambers, Alma C, PhD, Chm of Behavior Sci, Assoc Prof
Kennedy, K M, EdD, Chm of Educ, Prof
Lamb, Edward, MSW, Asst Prof
Lee, Wilton, MSW, Lect

Payne, La Veta, PhD, Prof
Rolfe, Rhea, MA, Lect

SOUTHWESTERN AT MEMPHIS
Memphis, Tennessee 38112 (S; Preb; coed; 4-1-4; II; 1037) BA major, Dept of Phil,
901-274-1800 Ext 281

Jobes, James W, PhD, Assoc Prof, Chm, Anal Phil, Greek Phil, Med Phil, Aes
Lacy, William Larry, PhD, Prof, Phil of Relig, Ethics, Exist
Llewellyn, Robert R, PhD, Asst Prof, Phil of Sci, Hist of Phil
McLain, F Michael, PhD, Assoc Prof, Phil Theol, Ethics

STATE TECHNICAL INSTITUTE AT MEMPHIS
Memphis, Tennessee 38128 (S; st; coed; qr; I; 1515) NP

STEED COLLEGE
Johnson City, Tennessee 37601 (JRCB; p; coed; qr; I; 148) NR

TENNESSEE STATE UNIVERSITY
Nashville, Tennessee 37203 (S; st; coed; qr; III; 4576) Courses with no degree
specialization, Dept of Speech and Drama, 615-329-9500 Ext 414

Countess, Robert H, PhD, Asst Prof
Simmons, William J, MA, Prof, Ethics

TENNESSEE TECHNOLOGICAL UNIVERSITY
Cookeville, Tennessee 38501 (S; st; coed; qr; IV; 6312) BA minor, Dept of Soc and
Phil, 615-528-3437

Diemer, Richard, PhD, Prof, Chm
Dykes, Donna, MA, Asst Prof, Part-time
Henry, Wesley, MA, Asst Prof, Phil of Relig, Hist of Phil

Sharpe, Charles, MA, Prof Emer, World Religions

TENNESSEE TEMPLE COLLEGE
Chattanooga, Tennessee 37404 (--; Bapt; coed; sem; II; 1284) NR

TENNESSEE WESLEYAN COLLEGE
Athens, Tennessee (S; U Meth; coed; 4-1-4; II; 691) BA joint or combined major,
Dept of Relig and Phil, 615-745-9320

Kay, Toomb, PhD, Prof
Tidwell, Jacqueline, MA, Asst Prof
Wilson, Jack, PhD, Prof

TREVECCA NAZARENE COLLEGE
Nashville, Tennessee 37210 (S; Naz; coed; qr; II; 760) BA minor, Dept of Relig
and Phil, 615-244-6000 Ext 265

Strickland, William J, PhD, Chm, Prof
Dunning, H Roy, PhD, Prof, Ethics
Wynkoop, Mildred, ThD, Prof

TUSCULUM COLLEGE
  Greeneville, Tennessee 37743 (S; U Preb; coed; qr; II; 588) BA major, Div of Hist,
  Phil and Relig Stud, 615-639-2171

  Barnett, Samuel, Asst Prof, Phenomen, Exist
  Paton, Thomas, MPhil, Asst Prof, Phil of Reformation

  Keller, Paul, PhD, Prof Emer

UNION UNIVERSITY
  Jackson, Tennessee 38301 (S; Bapt; coed; sem; II; 862) BA joint or combined major,
  Dept of Relig and Phil, 901-422-2576 Ext 58

  Tilley, W Clyde, ThD, Assoc Prof, Ethics

THE UNIVERSITY OF THE SOUTH
  Sewanee, Tennessee 37375 (S; Prot Epis; coed; sem; III; 998) BA major, Dept of Phil,
  615-598-5983

  Caldwell, Hugh H, PhD, Prof, Metaph, Phil of Sci, Phil of Math
  Garland, William J, PhD, Asst Prof, Ethics, Metaph, Amer Phil
  Mullen, Michael J, MA, Instr, Aes

  Marshall, John S, PhD, Prof Emer, Aristotle, Hooker, Phil Theol

UNIVERSITY OF TENNESSEE
  Knoxville, Tennessee 37916 (S; st; coed; qr; IV; 26,620) PhD major, Dept of Phil,
  615-974-3255

  Davis, John W, PhD, Prof, Head, Axiology, Ethics, Amer Phil
  Bennett, James O, PhD, Asst Prof, Epistem, Phil of Sci, Ethics
  Bowman, Peter A, PhD, Asst Prof, Phil of Sci
  Brenkert, George G, PhD, Asst Prof, Ethics, Soc Phil, Continen Phil
  Cebik, LeRoy B, PhD, Assoc Prof, Phil of Hist, Phil of Soc Sci
  Cohen, Sheldon M, PhD, Asst Prof, Anal Phil
  Davis, Richard S, PhD, Asst Prof, Aes, Metaph
  Edwards, Rem B, PhD, Prof, Metaethics, Phil of Relig
  Graber, Glenn C, PhD, Asst Prof, Ethics, Phil of Relig
  Gravander, Jerry W, AB, Instr, Phil of Sci
  Hamlin, Howard P, PhD, Asst Prof, Phil of Relig, Phil of Lit
  Hardwig, John R, BA, Instr, Ethics, Soc Phil
  Herrmann, Rolf-Dieter, PhD, Prof, Aes, Mod Phil
  Latta, Betsy C, PhD, Asst Prof, Logic, Phil of Sci
  Osborne, Martha L, MA, Instr, Hist of Phil, Logic
  Van de Vate, Dwight, PhD, Prof, Phil of Mind, Soc Phil

  Moore, Merritt H, PhD, Prof Emer

UNIVERSITY OF TENNESSEE AT CHATTANOOGA
  Chattanooga, Tennessee 37401 (S; st; coed; sem; III; 4873) BA major, Dept of Phil
  and Relig, 615-755-4334, 615-755-4169, 615-755-4334, 615-755-4488

  Mildram, Robert C, PhD, Prof, Chm, Hist of Relig, Phenomen
  Burhenn, Jr, Herbert W, PhD, Asst Prof, Hist of Phil, Phil of Sci, Phil of Hist
  Hall, Thor, PhD, Dist Prof, Phil of Relig and Theol
  Klinefelter, Donald S, PhD, Assoc Prof, Phil Theol and Human, Ethics
  Weisbaker, Donald R, PhD, Assoc Prof, Phil Theol, Exist

UNIVERSITY OF TENNESSEE AT MARTIN
  Martin, Tennessee 38237 (S; st; coed; qr; III; 4907) BA minor, Dept of Psych and
  Relig Stud, 901-587-7736

  Mauldin, Frank Louis, ThD, Asst Prof, Phil of Relig, Metaph

UNIVERSITY OF TENNESSEE AT MEMPHIS
  Memphis, Tennessee 38103 (S; st; coed; qr; IV; 1784) NP

UNIVERSITY OF TENNESSEE AT NASHVILLE
  Nashville, Tennessee 37203 (S; st; coed; qr; III; 2945) NR

VANDERBILT UNIVERSITY
  Nashville, Tennessee 37235 (S; p; coed; sem; IV; 6678) PhD major, Dept of Phil,
  615-322-2637

  Sherburne, Donald W, PhD, Prof, Chm
  Compton, John J, PhD, Prof
  Dore, Clement J, PhD, Prof
  Ehman, Robert R, PhD, Assoc Prof
  Hodges, Michael P, PhD, Assoc Prof
  Lachs, John, PhD, Prof
  Post, John F, PhD, Assoc Prof
  Scott, Charles E, PhD, Assoc Prof
  Tlumak, Jeffrey, PhD, Asst Prof
  Williams, Robert C, PhD, Visit Assoc Prof

  Bugg, Eugene, PhD, Prof Emer

  Aiken, William H, BA, Teach Fel   Neale, Philip, BA, Teach Fel
  Bond, Steve, BA, Teach Fel   Redman, Delmar R, BA, Teach Fel
  Erickson, Glenn, BA, Teach Fel   Rouse, David, BA, Teach Fel
  Hooker, John, BA, Teach Fel   Slivinski, Dennis, BA, Teach Fel
  Katt, Robert, BA, Teach Fel   Smith, Charles, BA, Teach Fel
  Mandt, Almer J, BA, Teach Fel   Valentine, John, BA, Teach Fel
  Moulton, Eben, BA, Teach Fel   Wright, Michael, BA, Teach Fel

VOLUNTEER STATE COMMUNITY COLLEGE
  Gallatin, Tennessee 37066 (--; st; coed; qr; I; 585) Courses with no degree
  specialization, Div of Human, 615-452-8600

  Herrmann, Richard E, PhD, Assoc Prof

WALTERS STATE COMMUNITY COLLEGE
  Morristown, Tennessee 37814 (--; st; coed; qr; I; 1153) NR

TEXAS

ABILENE CHRISTIAN COLLEGE
   Abilene, Texas 79601 (S; p; coed; sem; III; 3372) Courses with no degree specialization,
   Bib Dept, 915-677-1911

   Thomas, J D, PhD, Prof, Chm, Hist of Phil
   Olbricht, T H, PhD, Prof, Phil of Relig

ALVIN JUNIOR COLLEGE
   Alvin, Texas 77511 (S; local; coed; sem; I; 1808) NR

AMARILLO COLLEGE
   Amarillo, Texas 79105 (S; local; coed; sem; I; 3472) --, Dept of Soc Sci, --, 806-
   376-5641

   Ellis, R L, MA, Assoc Prof

ANGELINA COLLEGE
   Lufkin, Texas 75901 (S; st and local; coed; sem; I; 1026) NP

ANGELO STATE UNIVERSITY
   San Angelo, Texas 76901 (S; st; coed; sem; III; 3892) Courses with no degree
   specialization, Dept of Mod Lang, 915-942-2244

   Martinez, H S, PhD, Assoc Prof, Phil of Hist

AUSTIN COLLEGE
   Sherman, Texas 75090 (S; Preb; coed; --; III; 1143) BA major, Dept of Relig and
   Phil, 214-892-9101 Ext 361

   Nuckols, Thomas W, PhD, Assoc Prof, Chm, Relig Ethics
   Hinkle, Gerald, PhD, Assoc Prof, Contemp Phil
   Ware, James, PhD, Prof, Hist of Phil, Asian Phil
   Willmann, James, MA, Instr, Ethics

AUSTIN PRESBYTERIAN THEOLOGICAL SEMINARY
   Austin, Texas 78705 (Theol; Amer Preb; coed; sem; III; 87) Courses with no degree
   specialization, Dept of Theol and Hist, 512-472-6736

   Dunn, Ross Denison, BD, Asst Prof, Chm, Christ Ethics
   Heyer, Jr, George Stuart, PhD, Assoc Prof

BAYLOR COLLEGE OF DENTISTRY
   Dallas, Texas 75226 (Dent; p; coed; qr; IV; 532) NR

BAYLOR COLLEGE OF MEDICINE
   Houston, Texas 77025 (S; p; coed; qr; IV; 533) NP

BAYLOR UNIVERSITY
   Waco, Texas 76703 (S; Bapt; coed; sem; IV; 7051) PhD minor, --, 817-755-1611

Kilgore, William J, PhD, Prof, Chm, Metaph, Hist of Phil, Phil of Relig, Latin
   American Phil
Baird, Robert M, PhD, Assoc Prof, Ethics, Hist of Phil, Soc Phil
Cooper, William F, PhD, Prof, Continen Euro Phil, Seman, Latin American Phil
Duncan, Elmer H, PhD, Prof, Aes, Phil Anal, Value Theory
Toland, William G, PhD, Prof, Asst Prov, Epistem, Phil Anal, Phil of Hist

BEE COUNTY COLLEGE
   Beeville, Texas 78102 (S; local; coed; sem; I; 1097) Courses with no degree
   specialization, --, 512-358-3130

BISHOP COLLEGE
   Dallas, Texas 75241 (S; Bapt; coed; sem; II; 1561) BA major, Dept of Relig and
   Phil, 214-376-4311 Ext 257

BLINN COLLEGE
   Brenham, Texas 77833 (S; st and local; coed; sem; I; 1717) Courses with no degree
   specialization, Dept of Eng and Phil, 713-836-9311

   Hohlt, David T, MA

BRAZOSPORT COLLEGE
   Lake Jackson, Texas 77566 (S; local; coed; sem; I; 1601) NR

CENTRAL TEXAS COLLEGE
   Killeen, Texas 76541 (S; local; coed; sem; I; 4011) NP

CISCO JUNIOR COLLEGE
   Cisco, Texas 76437 (S; st; coed; sem; I; 951) NP

CLARENDON COLLEGE
   Clarendon, Texas 79226 (S; local; coed; sem; I; 423) Courses with no degree
   specialization, Div of Soc Sci, 806-874-3571

COLLEGE OF THE MAINLAND
   Texas City, Texas 77590 (S; local; coed; sem; I; 1335) Courses with no degree
   specialization, --, 713-938-1211

CONCORDIA LUTHERAN COLLEGE
   Austin, Texas 78705 (S; Luth Mo Synod; coed; sem; I; 263) AA major, Div of Relig
   and Soc Sci, 512-452-7661

   Stringer, Varnes, EdS, Assoc Prof

COOKE COUNTY JUNIOR COLLEGE
   Gainesville, Texas 76240 (S; local; coed; sem; I; 1916) NP

DALLAS BAPTIST COLLEGE
   Dallas, Texas 75211 (S; S Bapt; coed; sem; II; 1339) BA minor, Div of Relig and
   Phil, 214-331-8311 Ext 278

   Boles, Joe R, ThD, Prof, Phil of Relig

DALLAS BIBLE COLLEGE
  Dallas, Texas 75228 (BI; p; coed; sem; II; 204) NR

DALLAS THEOLOGICAL SEMINARY GRADUATE SCHOOL
  Dallas, Texas 75204 (S; p; men; sem; IV; 432) --, Dept of Syst Theol, 214-824-3094

  Hoak, H Phillip, ThD, Asst Prof
  Witmer, John A, ThD, Asst Prof

DEL MAR COLLEGE
  Corpus Christi, Texas 78404 (S; local; coed; sem; I; 5842) Courses with no degree specialization, Dept of Eng, 512-882-6231

  Williams, Patricia, PhD

DEVRY INSTITUTE OF TECHNOLOGY
  Dallas, Texas 75235 (--; p; coed; qr; I; 412) NR

DOMINICAN COLLEGE
  Houston, Texas 77021 (S; RC; wo; sem; II; 366) Courses with no degree specialization, Dept of Phil and Theol, 713-747-2700

  De la Torre, Teodoro, PhD, Assoc Prof, Chm, Hist of Phil, Ethics
  Reardon, Joseph, MA, Lect, Logic, Metaph
  Wakefield, Donam H, PhD, Lect, Phil of Relig, Orient Phil
  Wood, Marianne, MA, Lect, Phil of Relig

EAST TEXAS BAPTIST COLLEGE
  Marshall, Texas 75670 (S; Bapt; coed; sem; II; 730) Courses with no degree specialization, --, 214-935-7963

  Atkinson, Franklin, ThD, Asst Prof

EAST TEXAS STATE UNIVERSITY
  Commerce, Texas 75428 (S; st; coed; sem; IV; 8801) BA minor, --, 214-468-2212

  Hunak, Miroslov John, PhD, Assoc Prof, 19th Cent Vital, Schopenhauer, Nietzsche, Bergson, Hegel, Exist

EASTFIELD COLLEGE
  Dallas, Texas 75149 (--; st and local; coed; sem; I; 5902) BA minor, Div of Human, 214-746-3132

  Henson, Jerry, MA, Instr, Logic, Phil of Relig
  Solganick, Harvey, MA, Instr, Ethics, Exist

EL CENTRO COLLEGE
  Dallas, Texas 75202 (S; st and local; coed; sem; I; 7119) AA major, Div of Soc Sci, 214-746-2360

  Bennett, Robert C, MA, Chm, Anc Phil
  Elkins, Dexter, BA, Part-time Instr, Epistem
  Thompson, Dora J, MA, Instr, Relig Phil

EL PASO COMMUNITY COLLEGE
El Paso, Texas 79904 (--; local; coed; sem; I; 915) Courses with no degree specialization, Div of Human, 915-568-2854

Cummings, Nancy Pekin, Instr, Phil of Lang

EPISCOPAL THEOLOGICAL SEMINARY OF THE SOUTHWEST
Austin, Texas 78767 (Theol; PE; coed; sem; III; 40) --, Dept of Theol, 512-472-6808

Green, William Baillie, DPhil, Assoc Prof, Chm, Phil Theol

FRANK PHILLIPS COLLEGE
Borger, Texas 79007 (S; local; coed; sem; I; 562) --, --, 806-274-5311

Younce, Richard Dale, ThD, Instr

GALVESTON COLLEGE
Galveston, Texas 77550 (S; st; coed; sem; I; 1330) NR

GRAYSON COUNTY JUNIOR COLLEGE
Denison, Texas 75020 (S; local; coed; sem; I; 2795) NP

GULF COAST BIBLE COLLEGE
Houston, Texas 77008 (BI; Ch of God; coed; sem; II; 301) --, Dept of Phil, 713-862-3800

Brumfield, Donald R, M Div, Asst Prof
Carver, Everett I, MA, Assoc Prof

HARDIN-SIMMONS UNIVERSITY
Abilene, Texas 79601 (S; Bapt; coed; sem; III; 1610) BA minor, Dept of Bib and Phil, 915-677-7281 Ext 719

Dunagan, Clinton, PhD, Asst Prof
Hurst, Clyde, ThD, Prof

HILL JUNIOR COLLEGE
Hillsboro, Texas 76645 (S; local; coed; sem; I; 760) NP

HOUSTON BAPTIST COLLEGE
Houston, Texas 77036 (S; Bapt; coed; 4-1-4; II; 1126) Courses with no degree specialization, Dept of Christ and Phil, 713-774-7661 Ext 287

Cain, Glen T, PhD, Prof, Chm

HOUSTON COMMUNITY COLLEGE
Houston, Texas 77027 (--; st; coed; sem; I; 10,600) NR

HOWARD COMMUNITY JUNIOR COLLEGE
Big Spring, Texas 79720 (S; local; coed; sem; I; 1070) Courses with no degree specialization, Dept of Soc Sci, 915-267-6311

Smith, Bobby L, MS, Chm

HOWARD PAYNE COLLEGE
  Brownwood, Texas 76801 (S; S Bapt; coed; sem; III; 1391) BA minor, Dept of Phil,
  915-646-2502

  Tracy, Nat, PhD, Prof, Head
  Shields, James, PhD, Prof

HUSTON-TILLOTSON COLLEGE
  Austin, Texas 78702 (S; Prot; coed; sem; II; 717) BA joint or combined major, Dept
  of Phil and Relig, 512-476-7421 Ext 44

  Grant, Hector J, STB, Instr, Hist of Phil, Ethics

INCARNATE WORD COLLEGE
  San Antonio, Texas 78209 (S; RC; coed; sem; III; 1529) BA major, Dept of Phil,
  512-826-1261 Ext 260

  Burke, Sean, PhD, Assoc Prof, Logic, Metaph
  Leonard, Richard, PhL, Instr

JACKSONVILLE COLLEGE
  Jacksonville, Texas 75766 (--; Bapt; coed; sem; I; 158) NP

JARVIS CHRISTIAN COLLEGE
  Hawkins, Texas 75765 (S; Disc of Christ; coed; sem; II; 645) NR

KILGORE COLLEGE
  Kilgore, Texas 75662 (S; local; coed; sem; I; 2664) NP

LAMAR UNIVERSITY
  Beaumont, Texas 77710 (S; st; coed; sem; IV; 10,440) Courses with no degree
  specialization, Dept of Soc, 713-838-8316

  Wall, George B, PhD, Assoc Prof, Ethics

LAREDO JUNIOR COLLEGE
  Laredo, Texas 78040 (S; local; coed; sem; I; 2194) NP

LEE COLLEGE
  Baytown, Texas 77520 (S; st and local; coed; sem; I; 3401) NP

LETOURNEAU COLLEGE
  Longview, Texas 75601 (S; p; coed; sem; II; 762) Courses with no degree specialization,
  Div of Human and Soc Stud, 214-753-0231 Ext 56

  Stuber, John W, PhD, Assoc Prof, Phil of Relig

LON MORRIS COLLEGE
  Jacksonville, Texas 75766 (S; U Meth; coed; sem; I; 412) Courses with no degree
  specialization, Dept of Relig, 214-586-2471

LUBBOCK CHRISTIAN COLLEGE
  Lubbock, Texas 79407 (JS; Ch of Christ; coed; sem; II; 1045) NP

MARY HARDIN-BAYLOR COLLEGE
  Belton, Texas 76513 (S; S Bapt; coed; sem; II; 953) NP

MCLENNAN COMMUNITY COLLEGE
  Waco, Texas 76703 (S; local; coed; sem; I; 2448) Courses with no degree specialization,
  Div of Human, 817-756-6551

  Walker, Dan, MA, Instr, Phil of Relig

MCMURRY COLLEGE
  Abilene, Texas 79605 (S; U Meth; coed; 4-1-4; II; 1700) BA major, Dept of Phil,
  915-692-4130 Ext 296

  Stamey, Joseph D, PhD, Assoc Prof, Chm, Ethics
  Affleck, Bert, PhD, Prof, Hist of Tht

MIDWESTERN UNIVERSITY
  Wichita Falls, Texas 76308 (S; st; coed; sem; III; 4100) BA minor, Dept of Hist and
  Phil, 817-692-6611

  Hendrickson, Jr, Kenneth E, PhD, Prof, Chm
  Rockwell, Paul Hunter, MA, Asst Prof

MOUNTAIN VIEW COLLEGE
  Dallas, Texas 75211 (--; st and local; coed; sem; I; 4545) AA major, Dept of Phil,
  214-746-4171

  Paroski, Mary, MA, Instr

NAVARRO JUNIOR COLLEGE
  Corsicana, Texas 75110 (S; local; coed; sem; I; 1094) NP

NORTH TEXAS STATE UNIVERSITY
  Denton, Texas 76203 (S; st; coed; sem; IV; 15,129) PhD minor, Dept of Phil, 817-788
  2266

  Gunter, Pete A Y, PhD, Prof, Chm, Bergson, Phil of Sci
  Barnhart, J E, PhD, Assoc Prof, Phil of Mind
  Leggett, Richard C, MA, Instr, Fichte
  Miller, III, John F, PhD, Assoc Prof, Phil of Relig
  Owsley, Richard M, PhD, Prof, Phenomen
  Yaffe, Martin D, PhD, Asst Prof, Anc Phil

NORTHWOOD INSTITUTE, TEXAS BRANCH
  Cedar Hill, Texas 75104 (--) Courses with no degree specialization, --, 214-291-1541

  Ryker, Kenneth W, Academic Dean, Phil of Business, Phil of Gov

OBLATE COLLEGE OF THE SOUTHWEST
  San Antonio, Texas 78216 (S; RC; coed; sem; III; 38) NP

363

ODESSA COLLEGE
  Odessa, Texas 79760 (S; local; coed; sem; I; 2769) Courses with no degree
  specialization, Dept of Soc Sci, 915-337-5381 Ext 213

  Hilliard, Truett L, MA, Assoc Prof

ODESSA COLLEGE, MIDLAND CAMPUS
  Midland, Texas 79701 (S; local; coed; sem; I; 1065) NR

OUR LADY OF THE LAKE COLLEGE
  San Antonio, Texas 78285 (S; RC; coed; 4-1-4; III; 2018) BA major, Dept of Phil,
  512-434-6711 Ext 141

  Lonergan, J, PhD, Prof, Chm, Aristotle, Aquinas, Locke, Hume
  Kippes, A, PhD, Asst Prof, Aristotle, Aquinas
  Morkovsky, Mary, PhD, Assoc Prof, Bergson

PAN AMERICAN UNIVERSITY
  Edinburg, Texas 78539 (S; st; coed; sem; III; 6217) BA minor, Dept of Behavior Sci,
  512-381-3321

  Clark, Theodore R, ThD, Prof

PANOLA JUNIOR COLLEGE
  Carthage, Texas 75633 (S; local; coed; sem; I; 743) Courses with no degree
  specialization, Dept of Soc and Behavior Sci, 214-693-3837

  Hough, Joe, MA

PARIS JUNIOR COLLEGE
  Paris, Texas 75460 (S; st and local; coed; sem; I; 1140) NP

PAUL QUINN COLLEGE
  Waco, Texas 76703 (--; Afr Meth Epis; coed; sem; II; 457) --, Dept of Relig and
  Phil, 817-753-6417

  Anderson, James, MA, Instr
  Lester, Russell, PhD, Prof
  Wood, L C, PhD, Prof

PRAIRIE VIEW AGRICULTURAL AND MECHANICAL COLLEGE
  Prairie View, Texas 77445 (S; st; coed; sem; III; 4115) NP

RANGER JUNIOR COLLEGE
  Ranger, Texas 76470 (S; local; coed; sem; I; 442) NP

RICE UNIVERSITY
  Houston, Texas 77001 (S; p; coed; sem; IV; 3231) PhD major, Dept of Phil, 713-528-
  4141 Ext 563

  Fulton, J S, PhD, Prof, Chm, Prof, Phenomen, Hist of Phil
  Angene, Lyle, PhD, Asst Prof, Epistem, Metaph, Ethics
  Burch, R W, PhD, Asst Prof, Phil of Mind, Ethics
  Giannoni, C B, PhD, Assoc Prof, Logic, Phil of Sci
  Kolenda K, PhD, Prof, Ethics, Phil of Mind

Sclafani, R J, PhD, Asst Prof, Aes, Metaph
Vendler, Zeno, PhD, Prof, Phil of Lang, Epistem

Tsanoff, R A, PhD, Prof Emer, Hist of Phil

Diombala, A P, Fel

Pavlik, R M, Fel
Joynton, O H, Fel   Rodriguez, F C, Fel
Mosley, J L, Fel   Zaciek, A J, Fel
Naugle, M H, Fel

RICHLAND COLLEGE
    Dallas, Texas 75202 (--; st and local; coed; sem; I; 3500) Courses with no degree
    specialization, Div of Human, 214-746-4550

    Chapman, Sidney, MA
    Garrett, Leroy, PhD, Part-time
    Graham, Steve, BA, Part-time

SAINT EDWARD'S UNIVERSITY
    Austin, Texas 78704 (S; p; coed; 4-1-4; III; 1236) BA major, --, 512-444-2621

    Brady, Dominic, PhD, Assoc Prof
    Celestian, George, MA, Assoc Prof
    Kinsella, Arthur, PhD, Prof
    Ruane, Ed, MA, Instr
    Wise, Neil, MA, Instr

SAINT MARY'S UNIVERSITY
    San Antonio, Texas 78228 (S; RC; coed; sem; III; 3977) BA major, Dept of Phil, 512-
    433-2311 Ext 251

    Knodell, Jr, Preston, PhD, Assoc Prof, Chm, Logic, Phil of Sci, Ethics
    Blasen, Charles, MA, Assoc Prof, Metaph, Ethics, Hist of Phil
    Dreisoerner, Charles, PhD, Prof, Logic
    Kaczkowski, Conrad, PhD, Assoc Prof, Hist of Phil
    Kusman, Stanley, MA, Assoc Prof, Ethics, Metaph
    Pousson, Leon, PhD, Prof, Phil of Man
    Schorp, Franz, PhD, Asst Prof, Contemp Phil, Logic, Epistem
    Shiao, Louis, PhD, Asst Prof, Orient Phil, Soc Phil
    Totten, John, MA, Assoc Prof, Metaph, Phil of Relig

SAINT PHILLIP'S COLLEGE
    San Antonio, Texas 78203 (S; local; coed; sem; I; 3122) NP

SAM HOUSTON STATE UNIVERSITY
    Huntsville, Texas 77340 (S; st; coed; sem; IV; 11,843) BA joint or combined major,
    Dept of Phil, 713-295-6211 Ext 2866

    Cording, Richard, PhD, Prof, Chm, Exist, Phenomen, Phil of Mind
    Fair, Frank, PhD, Asst Prof, Epistem, Phil of Sci
    Satre, Thomas, PhD, Assoc Prof, Logic, Hist of Phil

SAN ANTONIO COLLEGE
    San Antonio, Texas 78284 (S; local; coed; sem; I; 15,582) AA major, Dept of Phil,
    512-734-7311 Ext 273

    Hoyt, Harold B, PhD, Prof, Chm, Hist of Phil, Value Theory

Bender, Fred A, MA, Assoc Prof, Anc Phil
Law, David A, MA, Asst Prof, Ethics, Value Theory
Oliver, Richard L, MA, Instr, Hist of Phil, Exist
Shirahama, Yukio, MA, Asst Prof, Orient Phil, Soc and Polit Phil

SAN JACINTO COLLEGE
Pasadena, Texas 77505 (S; local; coed; sem; I; 6995) NP

SCHREINER INSTITUTE
Kerrville, Texas 78028 (S; Preb; coed; sem; I; 283) NP

SOUTH PLAINS COLLEGE
Levelland, Texas 79336 (S; st; coed; sem; I; 1739) Courses with no degree specialization,
Dept of Soc Sci, 806-894-4921 Ext 226

Cooper, James G, MA, Asst Prof
Stephenson, Weldon Lee, MA, Assoc Prof, Aes

SOUTH TEXAS COLLEGE OF LAW
Houston, Texas 77002 (Law; p; coed; sem; III; 756) NP

SOUTH TEXAS JUNIOR COLLEGE
Houston, Texas 77002 (S; p; coed; sem; I; 4318) Courses with no degree specialization,
Div of Human and Fine Arts, 713-225-2151

Levy, Sylvia, MA, Prof
Wathen, James, MA, Prof

SOUTHERN METHODIST UNIVERSITY
Dallas, Texas 75222 (S; U Meth; coed; sem; IV; 10,016) MA major, Dept of Phil, 214-692-2118

Zaner, Richard M, PhD, Prof, Chm, Phenomen, Phil of the Soc Sci
Almquist, Calvin B, MA, Instr, Epistem
Hausman, David B, PhD, Asst Prof, Contemp Phil, Phil of Sci
Hicks, Joe H, PhD, Assoc Prof, Mod Phil, Kant
Kappler, A Serge, MA, Asst Prof, Anc Phil
Lamb, James W, PhD, Asst Prof, Logic, Metaph
Petty, Benjamin A, PhD, Assoc Prof, Phil of Relig, Exist
Quinn, Michael S, MA, Instr, Ethics, Phil in Lit
Wiggins, Jr, Osborne P, MA, Instr, Phenomen

Mahan, Walter B, PhD, Prof Emer

Drake, Alice Lynn   Hunter, Mary Susan, BA

SOUTHWEST TEXAS JUNIOR COLLEGE
Uvalde, Texas 78801 (S; local; coed; sem; I; 1274) Courses with no degree
specialization, Dept of Human, 512-278-7901

Tumlinson, Don, MEd, Instr, Phil of Relig

SOUTHWEST TEXAS STATE UNIVERSITY
San Marcos, Texas 78666 (S; st; coed; sem; III; 11,620) BA minor, Dept of Eng and

Phil, 512-245-2285

Lovin, Keith H, PhD, Asst Prof, Chm, Phil of Relig, Law, Ethics
Fulmer, Gilbert, PhD, Asst Prof, Epistem, Hist of Phil
Geuras, Dean, PhD, Asst Prof, Contemp Phil, Hist of Phil
Joy, Glenn C, PhD, Asst Prof, Phil of Sci, Logic
O'Brien, Louis D, MA, Instr
Orenduff, Jess M, PhD, Asst Prof, Sym Logic, Metaph
Treanor, James, MA, Instr, Aes

Tampke, Robert A, Prof Emer

SOUTHWESTERN ASSEMBLIES OF GOD COLLEGE
Waxahachie, Texas 75165 (BI; Assem of God; coed; sem; II; 621) Courses with no
degree specialization, Dept of Christ Ministry, 214-937-4010

Moon, Jesse K, D Min, Chm

SOUTHWESTERN BAPTIST THEOLOGICAL SEMINARY
Fort Worth, Texas 76122 (S; S Bapt; coed; sem; IV; 1920) Courses with no degree
specialization, --, 817-923-1921

Newport, John, PhD, Prof, Phil of Relig
Woodfin, Yandall, PhD, Prof, Phil of Relig

SOUTHWESTERN CHRISTIAN COLLEGE
Terrell, Texas 75160 (--; Ch of Christ; coed; sem; I; 241) NP

SOUTHWESTERN UNION COLLEGE
Keene, Texas 76059 (S; SDA; coed; qr; II; 555) NP

SOUTHWESTERN UNIVERSITY
Georgetown, Texas 78626 (S; p; coed; sem; II; 862) BA major, Dept of Relig and
Phil, 512-863-6511 Ext 309

Steelman, Edmund H, PhD, Prof, Chm, Hist of Phil
Score, II, John N R, PhD, Prof, Ethics
Watts, Harvey D, MA, Assoc Prof

STEPHEN F AUSTIN STATE UNIVERSITY
Nacogdoches, Texas 75961 (S; st; coed; sem; III; 10,212) BA major, Dept of Eng
and Phil, 713-569-2101

Giese, Albrecht, PhD, Asst Prof, Ethics
Lower, Richard, MA, Asst Prof, Logic, Metaph
Magruder, James, PhD, Asst Prof, Amer Phil, Logic

SUL ROSS STATE UNIVERSITY
Alpine, Texas 79839 (S; st; coed; sem; III; 2537) NP

TARLETON STATE UNIVERSITY
Stephenville, Texas 76401 (S; st; coed; sem; III; 3181) Courses with no degree
specialization, Dept of Soc Sci, 817-968-2196

Walton, Hal, MA, Instr

TARRANT COUNTY JUNIOR COLLEGE, NORTHEAST CAMPUS
  Hurst, Texas 76053 (DH; st and local; coed; sem; I; 5185) Courses with no degree
  specialization, --, 817-281-7860

  Lyda, Hap, PhD, Assoc Prof, Phil of Relig
  Petrusz, Gustav W, MA, Asst Prof

TARRANT COUNTY JUNIOR COLLEGE, SOUTH CAMPUS
  Fort Worth, Texas 76102 (S; st and local; coed; sem; I; 6938) Courses with no
  degree specialization, Dept of Behavior Sci, 817-534-4861 Ext 413

  Platt, Robert M, EdD, Prof, Chm, Phil of Sci
  Lyda, Hap, PhD, Assoc Prof, Phil of Relig

TEMPLE JUNIOR COLLEGE
  Temple, Texas 76501 (S; local; coed; sem; I; 1206) NP

TEXARKANA COLLEGE
  Texarkana, Texas 75501 (S; local; coed; sem; I; 2189) NP

TEXAS AGRICULTURAL AND INDUSTRIAL UNIVERSITY
  Kingsville, Texas 78363 (S; st; coed; sem; III; 8437) BA minor, Dept of Phil, 512-
  595-2111 Ext 1171

  Davidson, Robert Burns, PhD, Asst Prof, Hist of Phil

TEXAS A & M UNIVERSITY
  College Station, Texas 77843 (S; st; coed; sem; IV; 14,932) PhD minor, Dept of Phil
  and Human, 713-845-5723

  Davenport, Manuel M, PhD, Prof, Head, Value Theory
  Alsmeyer, Jr, Henry L, MA, Asst Prof
  Becka, Richard, PhD, Assoc Prof, Phil of Mind
  Boone, Robert L, MA, Asst Prof
  Carpenter, Stanley R, PhD, Asst Prof, Phil of Sci
  Harris, Jr, C Edwin, PhD, Asst Prof, Contemp Phil
  McCann, Jr, Hugh J, PhD, Asst Prof, Action Theory
  Riley, Jr, Thomas D, MA, Lect, Soc Phil
  Stadelman, Richard W, M Div, Asst Prof, Phil of Relig

TEXAS A & M MARITIME ACADEMY
  Galveston, Texas 77550 (S; st; men; sem; II; 91) NR

TEXAS CHRISTIAN UNIVERSITY
  Fort Worth, Texas 76129 (S; Disc of Christ; coed; sem; IV; 6537) PhD minor, Dept
  of Phil, 817-926-2461 Ext 205

  Klein, Jr, Ted E, PhD, Assoc Prof, Chm, Phenomen, Exist, Phil of Relig
  O'Connor, Robert F, Instr, Amer Phil, Metaph, Phil of Sci
  Senter, Nell W, PhD, Asst Prof, Soc and Polit Phil, Legal and Moral Phil
  Wertz, Spencer K, PhD, Asst Prof, Phil of Hist, Anal Phil, Logic

  Banks, Jerry E, Grad Asst   Sinatra, Richard L, Grad Asst
  Johnson, John F, Grad Asst   Walsh, Philip F, Grad Asst
  LeFlore, Ralph Bunche, Grad Asst   Zucco, Jane, Grad Asst

TEXAS COLLEGE
  Tyler, Texas 75701 (S; CME; coed; sem; II; 511) Courses with no degree specialization,
  Div of Educ, Phys Educ, Health and Recreation, 214-597-3200

TEXAS COLLEGE OF OSTEOPATHIC MEDICINE
  Fort Worth, Texas 76107 (Osteo; p; coed; sem; III; 51) NR

TEXAS LUTHERAN COLLEGE
  Seguin, Texas 78155 (S; Luth; coed; 4-1-4; II; 1071) BA major, Dept of Theol and
  Phil, 512-379-4161 Ext 22

  Enquist, Roy J, ThD, Assoc Prof, Chm, Phil of Relig
  Gilbertson, Mark, BA, Instr, Hist of Phil
  Wilkens, Thomas G, PhD, Assoc Prof

TEXAS SOUTHERN UNIVERSITY
  Houston, Texas 77004 (S; st; coed; sem; IV; 6174) BA minor, Dept of Psych and Phil,
  713-528-0611 Ext 204

  Adams, Anne Donchin, PhD, Asst Prof, Epistem
  McElvain, Thomas, MA, Instr, Phil of Mind

TEXAS SOUTHMOST COLLEGE
  Brownsville, Texas 78520 (S; st and local; coed; sem; I; 1856) NP

TEXAS STATE TECHNICAL INSTITUTE, JAMES CONNALLY CAMPUS
  Waco, Texas 76705 (S; st; coed; tri; I; 1781) NP

TEXAS STATE TECHNICAL INSTITUTE, MID-CONTINENT CAMPUS
  Amarillo, Texas 79105 (S; st; coed; tri; I; 357) NR

TEXAS STATE TECHNICAL INSTITUTE, RIO GRANDE CAMPUS
  Harlingen, Texas 78550 (S; st; coed; tri; I; 650) NR

TEXAS TECH UNIVERSITY
  Lubbock, Texas 79409 (S; st; coed; sem; IV; 21,547) PhD minor, Dept of Phil,
  806-742-2272

  Hardwick, Charles S, PhD, Prof, Chm, Epistem
  Cortes, Alberto, PhD, Asst Prof, Phil of Sci, Logic
  Ketner, Kenneth L, PhD, Asst Prof, Phil of Soc Sci, Amer Phil
  Little, Ivan L, PhD, Prof, Soc Phil
  Nathan, Daniel O, MA, Asst Prof, Ethics, Aes
  Werness, George S, PhD, Visit Asst Prof, Aes, Soc and Polit Phil

  Waters, Thomas B, PhD, Prof Emer

TEXAS WESLEYAN COLLEGE
  Fort Worth, Texas 76105 (S; Meth; coed; sem; II; 1874) BA minor, Div of Phil and
  Relig, 817-534-0251

  Wonders, Alice W, EdD, Prof, Chm
  LaFon, James, PhD, Assoc Prof

TEXAS WOMAN'S UNIVERSITY
  Denton, Texas 76201 (S; st; wo; sem; IV; 5810) BA minor, Dept of Phil and Psych,
  817-387-1322

  Sibley, Jack, PhD, Asst Prof

TRINITY UNIVERSITY
  San Antonio, Texas 78284 (S; p; coed; sem; III; 3106) MA major, --, 512-736-4141

  Kimmel, Larry D, PhD, Assoc Prof, Chm, Exist Phil, Soc and Polit Phil
  Chinn, Ewing Y, PhD, Assoc Prof, Logic, Phil of Sci
  Duce, Leonard A, PhD, Prof, Dean, Hist of Phil
  Erde, Edmund L, PhD, Asst Prof, Epistem, Phil of Lang
  Hunt, Terence J, PhD, Asst Prof, Ethics, Hist of Phil
  Marshall, John P, PhD, Asst Prof, Hist of Phil, Phil of Educ
  Nyman, James, PhD, Asst Prof, Soc and Polit Phil
  Thorn, Laurlee, MA, Asst Prof, Aes

TYLER JUNIOR COLLEGE
  Tyler, Texas 75701 (S; local; coed; sem; I; 3882) NP

UNIVERSITY OF CORPUS CHRISTI
  Corpus Christi, Texas 78411 (S; Bapt; coed; sem; II; 560) NR

UNIVERSITY OF DALLAS
  Irving, Texas 75062 (S; RC; coed; sem; IV; 1403) PhD joint or combined major, Dept
  of Phil, 214-253-1123 Ext 258

  Hardy, Gilbert G, PhD, Assoc Prof, Chm, Mod Phil, Recent Phil, Phil of Relig, Phil
    of Man
  Balas, David, PhD, Prof, Anc Phil, Mod Phil
  Cain, Thomas, PhD, Assoc Prof, Anc Phil, Med Phil, Metaph
  Crosby, John, PhD, Asst Prof, Phenomen, Husserl, Marxism, Phil of Man
  Daboub, Anthony, MA, Instr, Anc Phil
  Fenton, Norman, PhD, Asst Prof, Mod Phil, 17th Cent Phil, Metaph, Phil of Man
  Rabay, Christopher, PhD, Assoc Prof, Metaph
  Seifert, Josef, PhD, Asst Prof, Dir of Grad Stud, Epistem, Phil of Man, Recent Phil
  Wilhelmsen, Frederick, PhD, Prof, Metaph, Epistem, Aes, Anc Phil, Med Phil, Phil
    of Media and Communic

UNIVERSITY OF HOUSTON
  Houston, Texas 77004 (S; st; coed; sem; IV; 26,475) MA major, Dept of Phil, 713-
  749-4991

  Yoes, Jr, M G, PhD, Assoc Prof, Chm, Phil of Logic
  Austin, Page I, MA, Instr, Med Phil
  Becnel, Edwin R, BA, Lect Part-time, Phil of Black Movement
  Howard, Wendell T, PhD, Asst Prof, Amer Phil
  Johnsen, Bredo C, PhD, Asst Prof, Epistem
  Klenk, Virginia H, PhD, Asst Prof, Logic, Phil of Sci
  Nelson, William N, PhD, Asst Prof, Ethics, Polit Phil
  Pozzi, Hector R, PhL, Instr, Logic, Phil of Lang
  Shuford, Haywood R, PhD, Prof, Epistem

  Chambers, Jeffrey J, Teach Fel   Rios, Roberto, Teach Fel
  Cornwell, Sandra G, Teach Fel   Rogers, David L, Teach Fel

UNIVERSITY OF PLANO
   Plano, Texas 75074 (--; p; coed; 4-1-4; II; 183) NR

UNIVERSITY OF SAINT THOMAS
   Houston, Texas 77006 (S; RC; coed; sem; III; 1483) BA major, Dept of Phil, 713-522-7911

   Brezik, Victor B, PhD, Prof, Chm, Mod Phil, Ethics
   Dunne, Mary Rachel, PhD, Asst Prof, Contemp Phil, Orient Phil
   Garvey, Edwin C, PhD, Prof, Contemp Phil, Soc Phil, Polit Phil
   Gieselman, Richard W, MA, Assoc Prof, Metaph, Epistem
   Graham, Joseph M, PhD, Prof, Mod Phil, Phil of Sci
   Inglis, Brian D, PhD, Asst Prof, Greek Phil, Med Phil
   Keon, James J, MA, Assoc Prof, Greek Phil, Med Phil

UNIVERSITY OF TEXAS AT ARLINGTON
   Arlington, Texas 76010 (S; st; coed; sem; IV; 13,569) BA major, Dept of Hist and Phil, 817-273-2861

   Dalrymple, Houghton B, PhD, Assoc Prof, Ethics, Logic, Anal Phil
   King, Thomas W, PhD, Asst Prof, Phenomen, Exist, 19th Cent Phil, Phil of Hist
   Odschlaeger, Max F, PhD, Asst Prof, Phil of Hist
   Townsend, Jr, Dabney, PhD, Asst Prof, Aes, Phil in Lit
   Weiss, Donald H, PhD, Adj Prof Part-time, Soc and Polit Phil

UNIVERSITY OF TEXAS AT AUSTIN
   Austin, Texas 78712 (S; st; coed; sem; IV; 40,000) PhD major, Dept of Phil, 512-471-1919

   Browning, Douglas, PhD, Prof, Chm, Metaph, Ethics
   Allaire, Edwin B, PhD, Prof, Metaph, Theory of Knowl
   Angelelli, Ignazio, PhD, Prof, Hist and Phil of Logic
   Blumenfeld, Jean, PhD, Asst Prof, Epistem, Phil of Mind
   BonJour, Laurence, PhD, Asst Prof, Epistem
   Bouwsma, O K, PhD, Prof, Ling Anal, Contemp Phil
   Causey, Robert L, PhD, Assoc Prof, Phil of Sci, Value Theory
   Cooney, Brian, PhD, Asst Prof, Hist of Mod Phil
   Desani, G V, Prof, Buddhism, Phil of Relig
   Gillespie, Norman C, PhD, Asst Prof, Ethics, Phil of Law
   Hartshorne, Charles, PhD, Prof, Metaph, Phil of Relig
   Hickman, Larry, PhD, Asst Prof, Hist of Logic
   Jones, Hardy E, PhD, Asst Prof, Ethics, Soc Phil
   Kane, Robert H, PhD, Asst Prof, Phil of Mind, Phil of Sci
   Katz, Bernard, BA, Instr, Metaph, Phil of Lang
   Kellner, Douglas, PhD, Asst Prof, Continen Phil, Polit Phil
   Lieb, Irwin C, PhD, Prof, Metaph, Phil of Logic
   Mackey, Louis H, PhD, Prof, Med Phil, Aes
   Martin, Norman M, PhD, Prof, Logic, Computer Theory
   Martinich, Aloysius, PhD, Asst Prof, Med Phil, Continen Phil
   Miller, David L, PhD, Prof, Epistem, Phil of Sci
   Mourelatos, Alexander P D, PhD, Prof, Hist of Anc Phil
   Murphy, John P, PhD, Asst Prof, Continen Phil, Logic
   Palter, Robert, PhD, Prof, Hist and Phil of Sci
   Perlmutter, Martin, MA, Asst Prof, Epistem, Phil of Mind
   Pincoffs, Edmund L, PhD, Prof, Ethics, Phil of Educ, Phil of Law
   Raja Rao, Prof, Hinduism, Buddhism
   Solomon, Robert, PhD, Assoc Prof, Exist, Continen Phil
   Seung, Thomas K, PhD, Prof, Phil of Cult, Phil of Art, Metaph
   von Schoenborn, Alexander, PhD, Asst Prof, Kant, Phenomen, Continen Phil
   Woodruff, Paul, PhD, Asst Prof, Greek Phil

Brogan, A P, PhD, Prof Emer, Anc Phil, Logic
Gentry, George, PhD, Prof Emer, Epistem, Theory of Signs

Akers, Lawrence Keith, BA, Ext Lect
Andrews, Frank Edwin, BA, Teach Asst
Balto, David Alan, BA, Teach Asst
Beauchamp, Emmette William, BA, Teach Asst
Brady, Feurman Neil, BA, Teach Asst
Byrtus, Paul Hunter, BA, Teach Asst
Craft, Jimmy, BA, Teach Asst
Culbreth, John Maxwell, MA, Teach Asst
Curran, William Stephen, MA, Asst Instr
Davison, Daniel, MA, Teach Asst
Diaz, Manuel Richard, BA, Teach Asst
Dudik, Evan Matthew, BA, Teach Asst
Fischer, Thomas Grier, BA, Asst Instr
Granger, Edgar Herbert, BA, Teach Asst
Hagen, John, BA, Teach Asst
Hanlon, Thomas Joseph, BA, Teach Asst
Haynes, Marc, BA, Teach Asst
Hickman, Randall Clark, MA, Teach Asst
Hiltz, Stephen Charles, BA, Teach Asst
Hinckley, Diane, MA, Teach Asst
Hirsch, Edward William, BA, NDEA Fel
Holley, David Marlin, BA, Teach Asst
Hoormann, Cyril, BA, NDEA Fel
Johnson, Stephen, BA, Teach Asst
Jones, Steven Charles, BA, Teach Asst
Jordan, Cherie, BA, Teach Asst
Justice, John, BA, Ext Lect
Levenson, Bruce Edward, BA, Teach Asst
Lewis, Randy, BA, Ext Lect

Magilow, Molly Ruth, BA, Teach Asst
McClelland, Charles, BA, Teach Asst
McCullough, Laurence, BA, Teach Asst
McInerney, Peter, BA, Teach Asst
Mee, Thomas Alan, BA, Teach Asst
Meierding, Loren, BA, Teach Asst
Moes, Mark Matthew, BA, Teach Asst
Moskop, John Charles, BA, Teach Asst
Ost, David, MA, Teach Asst
Prior, William James, BA, Univ Fel
Ross, David Anthony, BA, Ext Lect
Rossi, Philip Joseph, BA, Ext Lect
Rude, Richard, MA, Teach Asst
Sanderson, Donald, MA, Teach Asst
Schouborg, Gary Robert, MA, Ext Lect
Sensat, Julius, BA, Ext Lect
Spector, Jonathan Micahel, BA, Teach Asst
Starks, Michael W, BA, Ext Lect
Stone, John David, BA, Univ Fel
Stuhr, John Jeremy, BA, Teach Asst
Thompson, Edward, JD, Asst Instr
Vickers, Dennis Walter, MA, Teach Asst
Wallick, Merritt, BA, Teach Asst
Wear, Stephen, BA, Teach Asst
Wilhoit, Lawrence Randolph, BA, Teach Asst
Winkler, Kenneth, BA, NDEA, Fel
Woodward, James, BA, Ext Lect
Wu, Laurence, MA, Teach Asst

UNIVERSITY OF TEXAS AT DALLAS
    Dallas, Texas 75230 (S; st; coed; sem; IV; 70) NR

UNIVERSITY OF TEXAS AT EL PASO
    El Paso, Texas 79968 (S; st; coed; sem; III; 11,348) BA major, Dept of Phil, 915-747-5213

    Springer, William, PhD, Assoc Prof, Chm, Exist Phenomen
    Briones, Ernesto, MA, Instr
    Cummings, Nancy, PhD, Part-time Instr
    Haddox, Jack, PhD, Prof, Latin American Phil
    Hall, David, PhD, Assoc Prof, Whitehead, Phil of Cult

    Romanell, Patrick, PhD, Prof Emer, Natur, Mexican Phil, Locke

UNIVERSITY OF TEXAS DENTAL BRANCH
    Houston, Texas 77025 (Dent; st; coed; sem; III; 552) NP

UNIVERSITY OF TEXAS GRADUATE SCHOOL OF BIOMEDICAL SCIENCES
    Houston, Texas 77025 (--; st; coed; qr; IV; 153) NR

UNIVERSITY OF TEXAS MEDICAL BRANCH AT GALVESTON
    Galveston, Texas 77550 (Med; st; coed; --; III; 827) NR

UNIVERSITY OF TEXAS MEDICAL SCHOOL AT DALLAS
Dallas, Texas 75235 (Med; st; coed; sem; IV; 507) NP

UNIVERSITY OF TEXAS MEDICAL SCHOOL AT HOUSTON
Houston, Texas 77025 (Med; st; coed; qr; III; 51) NR

UNIVERSITY OF TEXAS MEDICAL SCHOOL AT SAN ANTONIO
San Antonio, Texas 78229 (Med; st; coed; --; III; 420) NP

UNIVERSITY OF TEXAS SCHOOL OF NURSING
Austin, Texas 78712 (NURSW; st; coed; sem; III; 996) NP

THE UNIVERSITY OF TEXAS SCHOOL OF PUBLIC HEALTH
Houston, Texas 77025 (Ph; st; coed; qr; IV; 218) NP

VERNON REGIONAL JUNIOR COLLEGE
Vernon, Texas 76384 (--; st and local; coed; sem; I; 608) NR

VICTORIA COLLEGE
Victoria, Texas 77901 (S; local; coed; sem; I; 1745) NP

WAYLAND BAPTIST COLLEGE
Plainview, Texas 79072 (S; S Bapt; coed; 4-1-4; II; 761) BA joint or combined major,
Dept of Phil, 806-296-5521 Ext 72

Kirkpatrick, David, ThD, Asst Prof, Phil of Relig
Olive, Don H, PhD, Assoc Prof, Epistem, Ethics

WEATHERFORD COLLEGE
Weatherford, Texas 76086 (S; local; coed; sem; I; 1104) NP

WEST TEXAS STATE UNIVERSITY
Canyon, Texas 79015 (S; st; coed; sem; III; 7351) BA minor, Dept of Hist, 806-656-
2178

Johnson, Arthur, MA, Asst Prof, Hist of Phil, Ethics

WESTERN TEXAS COLLEGE
Snyder, Texas 79549 (--; st and local; coed; sem; I; 649) --, Dept of Communic and
Letters, 915-573-8511

Long, Jesse C, MA, Assoc Prof, Epistem, British Empir, 18th Cent Phil

WHARTON COUNTY JUNIOR COLLEGE
Wharton, Texas 77488 (S; local; coed; sem; I; 2017) Courses with no degree
specialization, Div of Soc Sci, 713-532-4560

WILEY COLLEGE
Marshall, Texas 75670 (S; U Meth; coed; sem; II; 510) BA joint or combined major,
Dept of Relig and Phil, 214-938-8341 Ext 55

Love, Charles B, PhD, Assoc Prof, Chm
Jenkins, I D, MA, Assoc Prof
Miller, T H, D Min, Assoc Prof, Ethics

UTAH

BRIGHAM YOUNG UNIVERSITY
Provo, Utah 84601 (NW; LDS; coed; --; IV; 26,616) PhD minor, Dept of Phil, 801-374-1211 Ext 3276

Reynolds, Noel B, PhD, Asst Prof, Chm, Legal Phil, Polit Phil, Epistem, Plato
Bradford, M Gerald, MA, Instr, Phil of Relig
Carter, K Codell, PhD, Assoc Prof, Logic, Polit Phil
Griggs, C Wilfred, MA, Asst Prof, Greek Phil
Madsen, Truman G, PhD, Prof, Contemp Phil, Phil of Lang, Phil of Relig
Paulsen, David L, JD, Instr, Phil of Relig
Rasmussen, Dennis F, PhD, Asst Prof, Metaph, Aes
Riddle, Chauncey C, PhD, Prof, Phil of Sci
Warner, C Terry, PhD, Assoc Prof, Phil Psych, Phil of Lang
Yarn, David H, EdD, Prof, Hist of Phil

COLLEGE OF EASTERN UTAH
Price, Utah 84501 (NW; st; coed; qr; I; 898) NP

DIXIE COLLEGE
Saint George, Utah 84700 (NW; st; coed; qr; I; 1145) Courses with no degree specialization, --, 801-673-4811

Dalton, Robert O, MA, Prof

LATTER-DAY SAINTS BUSINESS COLLEGE
Salt Lake City, Utah 84111 (JRCB; LDS; coed; qr; I; 1068) NP

SNOW COLLEGE
Ephraim, Utah 84627 (NW; st; coed; qr; I; 813) --, Dept of Phil, 801-283-4611

SOUTHERN UTAH STATE COLLEGE
Cedar City, Utah 84720 (NW; st; coed; qr; II; 1939) Courses with no degree specialization, Dept of Phil, 801-586-4411 Ext 227

Woolf, Eugene T, PhD, Prof

STEVENS HENAGER COLLEGE
Salt Lake City, Utah 84102 (JRCB; p; coed; qr; I; 803) NR

STEVENS HENAGER COLLEGE AT OGDEN
  Ogden, Utah 84401 (JRCB; p; coed; qr; I; 385) NP

UNIVERSITY OF UTAH
  Salt Lake City, Utah 84112 (NW; st; coed; qr; IV; 22,204) PhD major, Dept of Phil,
  801-581-8161

  Reed, T M, PhD, Assoc Prof, Chm, Ethics, Epistem
  Aldrich, Virgil C, PhD, Adj Prof, Aes, Epistem, Phil of Mind
  Appleby, Peter C, PhD, Assoc Prof, Phil of Relig, Exist
  Bennett, David W, PhD, Prof, Found of Math, Phil of Sci
  Cohen, Mendel F, PhD, Prof, Ethics, Epistem
  Haanstad, Paul J, MA, Instr, Phenomen, Metaph
  Hagen, Fred W, PhD, Prof, Phil of Mind, Anal Phil
  Johnston, Pat L, PhD, Asst Prof, Phil of Lang, Logic
  Kachi, Yukio, PhD, Assoc Prof, Anc Phil, Metaph
  Kourany, Janet A, BA, Instr, Phil of Sci, Prag
  Landesman, Bruce M, PhD, Asst Prof, Polit Phil, Phil of Mind
  Mangon, Charles H, PhD, Prof, Phil of Educ, Polit Phil
  Oguah, Benjamin E, BPhil, Visit Assoc Prof, Epistem, Afr Phil
  Rogers, Lewis M, PhD, Prof, Hist of Relig, Comp Relig
  Tanner, Obert C, MA, Prof, Hist of Phil, Phil of Relig
  Tapscott, Bangs L, PhD, Assoc Prof, Phil of Lang, Phil of Logic
  Watson, Roy M, MA, Instr, Value Theory, Metaph
  Whisner, William N, PhD, Asst Prof, Ethics, Aes
  Windt, Peter Y, PhD, Assoc Prof, Phil Method, Value Theory

  Read, Waldemer P, PhD, Prof Emer, Polit Phil, Soc Phil, Phil of Relig

  Cook, Jeffrey S, Teach Fel   Ransom, Gene, Teach Fel
  Haines, Sharon, Teach Fel   Tibolla, Patricia, Teach Fel
  Lanning, Gregory J, Teach Fel   Utsman, Robert S, Teach Fel
  Nutting, Kurt, Teach Fel   Woolf, Thomas H, Teach Fel
  Randle, D Craig, Teach Fel

UTAH STATE UNIVERSITY
  Logan, Utah 84322 (NW; st; coed; qr; IV; 9554) BA major, Dept of Lang and Phil, 801-
  752-4100 Ext 7451

  Robson, Kent E, PhD, Asst Prof, Assoc Head, Phil of Hist, Ethics, Hist of Phil
  Beyers, John M, MA, Assoc Prof, Aes
  Crawford, A Berry, PhD, Assoc Prof, Soc Phil
  Johnson, Charles W, PhD, Asst Prof, Logic, Concept of Mind

UTAH TECHNICAL COLLEGE AT PROVO
  Provo, Utah 84601 (NW; st; coed; qr; I; 2747) NP

UTAH TECHNICAL COLLEGE AT SALT LAKE CITY
  Salt Lake City, Utah 84107 (NW; st; coed; qr; I; 3976) NP

WEBER STATE COLLEGE
  Ogden, Utah 84403 (NW; st; coed; qr; II; 9818) BA minor, Dept of Polit Sci and Phil,
  801-399-5941 Ext 160, 161

  Evans, L C, PhD, Prof, Chm, Hist of Phil, Aes, Phil and Lit
  Glidden, J C, PhD, Assoc Prof, Phil of Soc Sci, Epistem, Ethics
  Olson, J G, EdD, Prof, Phil of Relig, Ethics
  Rolston, J S, MA, Asst Prof, Logic, Ethics, Metaph

WESTMINSTER COLLEGE
Salt Lake City, Utah 84105 (NW; Prot; coed; 4-1-4; II; 837) BA major, Dept of Phil
and Relig, 801-484-7651 Ext 56

Johnston, Dale A, PhD, Asst Prof, Chm, Amer Phil, Phil of Relig, Phil of Cult
Boyack, Alice, PhD, Asst Prof, Phil of Relig
Boyack, James D, PhD, Prof, Metaph, Hist of Phil, Whitehead

VERMONT

BENNINGTON COLLEGE
Bennington, Vermont 05201 (E; p; coed; sem; III; 600) BA major, Dept of Soc Sci,
802-442-5401

Lackowski, Peter, PhD, Phil of Ling
Harris, Steven, BA
Schlabach, Anne V, PhD

CASTLETON STATE COLLEGE
Castleton, Vermont 05735 (E; st; coed; sem; III; 1543) Courses with no degree
specialization, Div of Human, 802-468-5611 Ext 235

Jardine, Joseph, PhD, Assoc Prof

CHAMPLAIN COLLEGE
Burlington, Vermont 05401 (--; p; coed; sem; I; 908) Courses with no degree
specialization, Dept of Arts and Sci, 802-658-0800

Peden, James B, M Div

COLLEGE OF SAINT JOSEPH THE PROVIDER
Rutland, Vermont 05701 (--; p; coed; sem; II; 195) Courses with no degree
specialization, --, 802-775-0806

Miglorie, Jr, Frank S, BA, Instr

GODDARD COLLEGE
Plainfield, Vermont 05667 (E; p; coed; tri; III; 1599) BA joint or combined major,
--, 802-454-8311 Ext 344

Holm, Brian, MA, Hist and Phil of Sci
Thomas, Carla R, PhD, Hist of Phil, German Phil, Phil Anthrop

GREEN MOUNTAIN COLLEGE
Poultney, Vermont 05764 (E; p; wo; 4-1-4; I; 626) NP

JOHNSON STATE COLLEGE
    Johnson, Vermont 05656 (E; st; coed; sem; II; 1123) BA joint or combined major,
    --, 802-635-2356

    Hundley, Robert, M Div, Instr, Phil of Relig
    Miller, Herschel, M Div, Asst Prof, Hist of Phil
    Sapadin, Eugene, PhD, Hume

LYNDON STATE COLLEGE
    Lyndonville, Vermont 05851 (E; st; coed; sem; II; 768) Courses with no degree
    specialization, --, 802-626-3335

    Vos, Kenneth D, PhD, Assoc Prof

MARLBORO COLLEGE
    Marlboro, Vermont 05344 (E; p; coed; tri; II; 225) BA major, Dept of Phil, 802-
    254-2393

    Weiner, Neal O, PhD, Greek Phil, Hist of Phil

MIDDLEBURY COLLEGE
    Middlebury, Vermont 05753 (E; p; coed; 4-1-4; IV; 1891) BA major, Dept of Phil, 802-
    388-7024

    Bates, Stanley, PhD, Asst Prof, Chm, Ethics
    Bigelow, Leslie Cole, PhD, Prof, Ethics
    O'Brien, George, Dennis, PhD, Prof, Dean, Phil of Hist
    Temin, Marc, PhD, Instr, Phil of Lang

    Andrews, John Thayer, MA, Prof Emer

NORWICH UNIVERSITY
    Northfield, Vermont 05663 (E; p; coed; sem; III; 1036) BA major, Dept of Phil,
    Relig and Fine Arts, 802-485-5011 Ext 64

    Sutfin, Edward, PhD, Prof, Chm, Hist of Phil
    Birney, George H, PhD, Assoc Prof, Ethics
    Pelon, Michael P, MA, Instr, Med Phil

SAINT JOSEPH COLLEGE
    Old Bennington, Vermont 05201 (--; p; coed; sem; I; 167) NR

SAINT MICHAEL'S COLLEGE
    Winooski, Vermont 05404 (E; RC; coed; sem; III; 1424) BA major, Dept of Phil, 802-
    655-2000 Ext 346

    VanderWeel, Richard L, PhD, Prof, Chm, Greek Phil, Logic
    Case, James J, LMS, Assoc Prof, Ethics, Phil of Art
    Dupont, Gerald E, PhD, Prof, Phil of Man, Polit Phil
    Hanagan, John J, MA, Assoc Prof, Ethics, Med Phil
    MacDonald, Daniel F, MA, Prof, Phil of Sci, Mod Phil
    Zeno, Carl A, MA, Asst Prof, Metaph, Contemp Phil

SCHOOL FOR INTERNATIONAL TRAINING
    Brattleboro, Vermont 05301 (--; p; coed; qr; III; 425) NR

TRINITY COLLEGE
  Burlington, Vermont 05401 (E; RC; wo; sem; II; 500) Courses with no degree
  specialization, Dept of Phil, 802-862-8326

  Steady, Leo J, PhD, Prof, Chm, Metaph
  Beary, Thomas, ThD, Prof
  Davis, Oren, MA, Asst Prof, Exist

UNIVERSITY OF VERMONT
  Burlington, Vermont 05401 (E; st; coed; sem; IV; 9650) MA major, Dept of Phil, 802-
  656-3080

  Cahn, Steven, PhD, Prof, Chm, Phil of Relig, Phil of Educ
  Anderson, Gerald, MA, Instr, Soc Phil
  Beckett, William, PhD, Asst Prof, Anal Phil
  Corcoran, James, MA, Instr, 19th Cent Phil
  Hall, Robert W, PhD, Prof, Plato, Phil of Art and Relig
  Miller, Willard, PhD, Asst Prof, Amer Phil
  Moneta, Giuseppina, PhD, Assoc Prof, Phenomen
  Paskow, Alan, PhD, Asst Prof, Phenomen
  Rice, Robert, PhD, Asst Prof, Hist of Ideas
  Sugarman, Richard, MA, Instr, Phenomen
  Swanson, Gerald, MA, Instr, Orient Phil

  Dykhuizen, George, Prof Emer

VERMONT COLLEGE
  Montpelier, Vermont 05602 (E; p; cord; sem; II; 349) NR

VERMONT TECHNICAL COLLEGE
  Randolf Center, Vermont 05061 (E; st; coed; sem; I; 456) Courses with no degree
  specialization, --, 802-728-3391

WINDHAM COLLEGE
  Putney, Vermont 05346 (E; p; coed; sem; II; 877) BA major, Dept of Phil, 802-387-
  5511 Ext 264

  Robinson, John Mansley, PhD, Prof, Chm, Greek Phil, Metaph
  Carter, Richard, PhD, Assoc Prof
  Gans, Steven, PhD, Asst Prof, Phenomen

VIRGIN ISLANDS

COLLEGE OF THE VIRGIN ISLAND
  Saint Thomas, Virgin Island 00801 (N; st; coed; sem; II; 471) BA joint or combined
  major, --, 809-774-1252

  Escardo, Mauricio E, PhD, Prof, Chm
  Barac, Vladimir, PhD, Asst Prof

COLLEGE OF THE VIRGIN ISLANDS, SAINT CROIX CAMPUS
    Saint Croix, Virgin Islands 00850 (N; st; coed; sem; II; --) NR

VIRGINIA

AVERETT COLLEGE
    Danville, Virginia 24541 (S; Bapt; coed; --; II; 889) BA joint or combined major,
    --, 703-793-7811

    Godsey, R Kirby, PhD, Dean
    Mills, Watson E, ThD, Dir of Admis

BLUE RIDGE COMMUNITY COLLEGE
    Weyers Cave, Virginia 24486 (S; st; coed; qr; I; 1263) AA major, Dept of Phil and
    Relig, 703-234-2461 Ext 26

    Bailey, David L, MA, Asst Prof, Comp Relig
    McKnight, David A, M Div, Asst Prof

BLUEFIELD COLLEGE
    Bluefield, Virginia 24605 (S; S Bapt; coed; sem; I; 285) Courses with no degree
    specialization, Dept of Relig and Phil, 304-327-7137

BRIDGEWATER COLLEGE
    Bridgewater, Virginia 22812 (S; Ch of the Breth; coed; --; II; 876) BA joint or
    combined major, Dept of Phil and Relig, 703-828-2051

    Watson, Steve, Asst Prof

CENTRAL VIRGINIA COMMUNITY COLLEGE
    Lynchburg, Virginia 24502 (S; st; coed; qr; I; 1687) Courses with no degree
    specialization, Dept of Phil, 703-239-0321 Ext 235

    Seward, Robert, MA, Assoc Prof, Chm
    Gilpatrick, Jean, M Div, Lect

CHRISTOPHER NEWPORT COLLEGE
    Newport News, Virginia 23606 (S; st; coed; sem; II; 1987) BA major, Dept of Phil,
    703-596-7611 Ext 256

    Nauman, Jr, St Elmo, PhD, Assoc Prof, Chm, Exist
    Hoaglund, John, PhD, Asst Prof, Kant

CLINCH VALLEY COLLEGE, UNIVERSITY OF VIRGINIA
    Wise, Virginia 24293 (S; st; coed; sem; II; 781) Courses with no degree specialization,
    Dept of Human, 703-328-2431 Ext 257

    Lewis, Judd W, MA, Prof, Chm, Logic, Hist of Phil

379

COLLEGE OF WILLIAM AND MARY
  Williamsburg, Virginia 23185 (S; st; coed; sem; IV; 5443) BA major, Dept of Phil,
  703-229-3000 Ext 260

  Jones, David H, PhD, Prof, Chm, Phil of Mind
  Bohl, Jr, F Robert, PhD, Asst Prof, Phil of Lang
  Cobb, Jr, William S, PhD, Assoc Prof, Exist, Phenomen
  Foster, Jr, Lewis A, PhD, Assoc Prof, East Phil
  Fuchs, Alan E, PhD, Asst Prof, Ethics
  Hearn, Jr, Thomas K, PhD, Assoc Prof, Phil of Educ
  MacDonald, Frank A, MA, Prof, Theory of Knowl
  McLane, H Earl, PhD, Assoc Prof, Logic
  Reed, Elizabeth S, PhD, Assoc Prof, Phil of Relig

DABNEY LANCASTER COMMUNITY COLLEGE
  Clifton Forge, Virginia 24422 (S; st; coed; qr; I; 676) Courses with no degree
  specialization, --, 703-862-4246

DANVILLE COMMUNITY COLLEGE
  Danville, Virginia 24541 (S; st; coed; qr; I; 1824) AA major, --, 703-797-3553
  Ext 74

  Holley, Robert F, M Div, Lect
  Jones, W George, ThM, Asst Prof

EASTERN MENNONITE COLLEGE
  Harrisonburg, Virginia 22801 (S; Menn; coed; --; III; 994) Courses with no degree
  specialization, Dept of Bib and Phil, 703-433-2771 Ext 356

  Wenger, Linden, MTh, Assoc Prof

EASTERN SHORE COMMUNITY COLLEGE, UNIVERSITY OF VIRGINIA
  Wallops Island, Virginia 23337 (--; st; coed; qr; I; 107) Courses with no degree
  specialization, --, 301-957-1388

  McGee, Harold F, STM, Lect, Chm

EASTERN VIRGINIA MEDICAL SCHOOL
  Norfolk, Virginia 23507 (Med; p; coed; --; III; --) NP

EMORY AND HENRY COLLEGE
  Emory, Virginia 24327 (S; U Meth; coed; --; II; 799) BA major, Dept of Relig and
  Phil, 703-944-3121 Ext 211

  Damer, T Edward, PhD, Assoc Prof, Chm, Ethics, Phil of Relig
  O'Neil, Richard A, PhD, Asst Prof, Polit Phil, Metaethics

FERRUM COLLEGE
  Ferrum, Virginia 24088 (S; U Meth; coed; sem; I; 1174) --, Div of Human, 703-365-
  2121

  Chang, Key H, BTh, Assoc Prof

GEORGE MASON UNIVERSITY
  Fairfax, Virginia 22030 (S; st; coed; sem; III; 3140) BA major, --, 703-591-4600

McFarlane, William H, PhD, Prof, Chm, Metaph, Logic
Bergoffen, Debra B, MA, Instr, Exist
Fletcher, James, MA, Act Asst Prof, Aes
Holman, Emmett, PhD, Instr, Anal Phil
Houlgate, Laurence, PhD, Assoc Prof, Legal Phil
Kreilkamp, Karl, PhD, Assoc Prof, Phil of Sci
McDermott, Michael, MA, Assoc Prof, Class Phil
Pielke, Robert G, PhD, Asst Prof, Ethics, Polit Phil
Sinks, John, MA, Lect, Logic

GERMANNA COMMUNITY COLLEGE
Fredericksburg, Virginia 22401 (--; st; coed; qr; I; 863) Courses with no degree
specialization, Dept of Human, 703-825-2120 Ext 282

Mackenzie, John S, MA, Asst Prof

HAMPDEN-SYDNEY COLLEGE
Hampden-Sydney, Virginia 23943 (S; Preb; men; sem; II; 693) BA major, Dept of Phil,
804-223-4381 Ext 42

Iverson, Vincent A, PhD, Asst Prof, Chm
Hinchcliff, John, PhD, Asst Prof
Schrag, Brian, MA, Asst Prof

Allan, D Maurice, PhD, Prof Emer

HAMPTON INSTITUTE
Hampton, Virginia 23368 (S; p; coed; 4-1-4; III; 2587) BA major, Dept of Phil and
Relig, 703-727-5000

de la Torre, Armando, MA, Asst Prof
Kiker, Frank, BD, Lect
Kollmann, Edward C, PhD, Prof Part-time

HOLLINS COLLEGE
Hollins College, Virginia 24020 (S; p; wo; 4-1-4; III; 1133) BA major, Dept of
Phil and Relig, 703-362-6353

Becker, Lawrence C, PhD, Assoc Prof, Chm, Moral Phil
Crosby, Jr, H Lamar, PhD, Prof, Anc Phil, Aes
Frazier, A M, PhD, Assoc Prof, Phil of Relig
Zeldin, Mary-Barbara, PhD, Prof, Kant, Russian Phil, Metaph

INSTITUTE OF TEXTILE TECHNOLOGY
Charlottesville, Virginia 22902 (--; p; men; sem; IV; 22) NP

J SARGEANT REYNOLDS COMMUNITY COLLEGE
Richmond, Virginia 23230 (--; st; coed; qr; I; 600) NR

JOHN TYLER COMMUNITY COLLEGE
Chester, Virginia 23831 (S; st; coed; qr; I; 2016) NP

LONGWOOD COLLEGE
Farmville, Virginia 23901 (S; st; wo; sem; III; 2373) Courses with no degree
specialization, Dept of Eng and Phil, 804-392-4139

Daubner, Edith, PhD, Assoc Prof, Ethics, Aes
Frank, William, PhD, Prof
Savage, Helen, MA, Assoc Prof

LORD FAIRFAX COMMUNITY COLLEGE
Middletown, Virginia 22645 (--; st; coed; qr; I; 801) NP

LUTHER RICE COLLEGE
Alexandria, Virginia 22310 (--; p; coed; sem; II; 127) NR

LYNCHBURG COLLEGE
Lynchburg, Virginia 24504 (S; p; coed; sem; III; 2046) BA major, Dept of Phil, 804-845-9071

Scudder, Jr, John R, EdD, Prof, Phil of Educ, Phil of Hist
Kelly, James Patrick, MA, Asst Prof, Hist of Phil, Phil of Relig
Martin, Ronald E, MLA, Asst Prof, Phil of Sci, Aes
Spader, Peter H, PhD, Assoc Prof, Phenomen

Morgan, Raymond E, PhD, Prof Emer

MADISON COLLEGE
Harrisonburg, Virginia 22801 (S; st; coed; sem; III; 4582) BA major, Dept of Phil and Relig, 703-433-6394

Callahan, William E, ThD, Prof, Head, Greek Phil, Ethics, Phil of Relig
Brickhouse, Thomas, MA, Instr Part-time, Contemp Ling Phil
O'Meara, William M, PhD, Assoc Prof, Amer Phil, Soc Phil
Sweigart, John, PhD, Prof, Logic, Epistem, Phil of Sci
Thomas, William W, PhD, Prof, Phil Theol
Wiles, Ann McCoy, MA, Asst Prof, Anc Greek Phil, Logic, Epistem

MARY BALDWIN COLLEGE
Staunton, Virginia 24401 (S; Amer Preb; wo; sem; II; 712) BA major, Dept of Relig and Phil, 703-885-0811

Baker, Lynne R, PhD, Asst Prof, Anal Phil
Chambers, Marjorie B, PhD, Prof
Edwards, Carl N, BD, Asst Prof
McAllister, James L, PhD, Prof

MARY WASHINGTON COLLEGE
Fredericksburg, Virginia 22401 (S; st; coed; sem; II; 2111) BA major, Dept of Phil, 703-373-7250 Ext 351

Van Sant, George M, PhD, Prof, Chm, Contemp Phil, Phil of Sci, Hist of Phil
Bonyhard, Janet F, MA, Asst Prof, Ethics, Aes
Snyder, Peter V, PhD, Asst Prof, Logic, Epistem

MARYMOUNT COLLEGE OF VIRGINIA
Arlington, Virginia 22207 (S; RC; wo; sem; I; 580) Courses with no degree specialization, Dept of Phil and Relig, 703-524-2500

Campbell, Gerald Lee, MA, Instr
Didoha, Michael, PhD, Assoc Prof
Draghi, Robert Alfred, PhD, Assoc Prof

MOUNTAIN EMPIRE COMMUNITY COLLEGE
   Big Stone Gap, Virginia 24219 (--; st; coed; qr; I; 530) NP

NATIONAL BUSINESS COLLEGE
   Roanoke, Virginia 24009 (JRCB; p; coed; qr; I; 247) NP

NEW RIVER COMMUNITY COLLEGE
   Dublin, Virginia 24084 (--; st; coed; qr; I; 1006) Courses with no degree
   specialization, Dept of Human, 703-674-2611

   Dawson, Jr, William J, EdD, Assoc Prof
   Hobbs, Nancy, BA, Lect Part-time

NORFOLK STATE COLLEGE
   Norfolk, Virginia 23504 (S; st; coed; sem; II; 5678) --, Dept of Hist and Geography,
   703-627-4371 Ext 242

   Butts, William H, PhD, Soc Phil, Phil of Relig

NORTHERN VIRGINIA COMMUNITY COLLEGE, ALEXANDRIA CAMPUS
   Alexandria, Virginia 22311 (S; st; coed; qr; I; --) Courses with no degree
   specialization, Div of Human, 703-323-4242

   Niner, Elaine C, PhD, Prof, Chm, Phil of Man
   Harrison, Elizabeth, MA, Instr, Ethics, Logic
   Trudinger, Paul, PhD, Assoc Prof, Phil of Relig

NORTHERN VIRGINIA COMMUNITY COLLEGE, ANNANDALE CAMPUS
   Annandale, Virginia 22003 (S; st; coed; qr; I; 12,047) AA major, Dept of Phil, 703-
   280-4000

   Gregory, Donald R, PhD, Instr, Chm, Anal Phil
   Gregory, Mary S, MA, Instr Part-time, Aes
   Piscitelli, Emile, MA, Asst Prof, Phil of Relig

OLD DOMINION UNIVERSITY
   Norfolk, Virginia 23508 (S; st; coed; sem; IV; 9903) BA major, Dept of Phil, 804-
   489-8000

   Brenner, William H, PhD, Asst Prof, Phil of Relig
   Buxton, James H, PhM, Instr, Logic
   McCleary, Richard C, PhD, Assoc Prof, Exist Phil

   Tunyogi, Andrew C, PhD, Prof Emer

PAUL D CAMP COMMUNITY COLLEGE
   Franklin, Virginia 23851 (--; st; coed; qr; I; 426) NR

PATRICK HENRY COMMUNITY COLLEGE
   Martinsville, Virginia 24112 (--; st; coed; qr; I; 449) --, Dept of Phil and Relig,
   703-638-8777 Ext 17

   Anderson, II, Clarence A, MA, Assoc Prof

PIEDMONT VIRGINIA COMMUNITY COLLEGE
    Charlottesville, Virginia 22903 (--; st; coed; qr; I; 425) Courses with no degree
    specialization, Div of Human, 804-977-3900

    Krinsky, Raymond, MHL
    St Clair, Reginald, MA

PRESBYTERIAN SCHOOL OF CHRISTIAN EDUCATION
    Richmond, Virginia 23227 (S; Preb; coed; 4-1-4; III; 106) NP

PROTESTANT EPISCOPALIAN THEOLOGICAL SEMINARY IN VIRGINIA
    Alexandria, Virginia 22304 (Theol; Prot Epis; coed; 4-1-4; III; 179) NP

RADFORD COLLEGE
    Radford, Virginia 24141 (S; st; coed; qr; III; 3860) BA major, Dept of Phil and
    Relig, 703-731-5313

    Taylor, Charles D, ThD, Prof, Chm, Phil of Relig
    Peery, Rebecca S, MA, Asst Prof, Ethics, Aes, Exist
    Vengrin, Michael, MA, Asst Prof, Phil of Sci, Logic, Epistem

RANDOLPH-MACON COLLEGE
    Ashland, Virginia 23005 (S; U Meth; coed; 4-1-4;· II; 784) BA major, Dept of Phil,
    703-798-8372

    Lilienkamp, Paul, PhD, Asst Prof, Soc Phil, Polit Phil
    Pannill, H Burnell, PhD, Prof, Amer Phil

RANDOLPH-MACON WOMAN'S COLLEGE
    Lynchburg, Virginia 24504 (S; U Meth; wo; sem; III; 774) BA major, Dept of Phil,
    804-846-7392 Ext 431

    Cornett, Robert, PhD, Prof, Chm, Ethics, Soc Phil
    Heil, John, PhD, Asst Prof, Logic, Phil of Ling, Phil of Sci

RAPPAHANNOCK COMMUNITY COLLEGE
    Glenns, Virginia 23149 (--; st; coed; qr; I; 435) Courses with no degree specialization,
    Dept of Biology and Phil, 703-758-5324

    Andrews, Allan, MS, Asst Prof

RICHARD BLAND COLLEGE OF WILLIAM AND MARY
    Petersburg, Virginia 23803 (S; st; coed; sem; I; 669) Courses with no degree
    specialization, Dept of Phil and Relig, 703-732-0111 Ext 232

    Smith, Jr, Paul E, MA, Asst Prof, Chm

ROANOKE COLLEGE
    Salem, Virginia 24153 (S; Luth CA; coed; 4-1-4; II; 1355) BA major, Dept of Phil
    and Relig, 703-389-2351 Ext 350

    Jordahl, V Truman, PhD, Assoc Prof, Chm, Anc and Contemp Phil
    Bent, R S, MA, Asst Prof, Phil of Relig
    Hinshaw, W B, MA, Instr, Ling Phil
    Keister, J D, M Div, Instr
    Ritter, G A, M Div, Assoc Prof

SAINT PAUL'S COLLEGE
   Lawrenceville, Virginia 23868 (S; Prot Epis; coed; sem; II; 512) Courses with no
   degree specialization, Dept of Eng and Human, 703-848-2636

SHENANDOAH COLLEGE AND CONSERVATORY OF MUSIC
   Winchester, Virginia 22601 (JS; U Meth; coed; sem; II; 537) NR

SOUTHERN SEMINARY JUNIOR COLLEGE
   Buena Vista, Virginia 24416 (S; p; wo; sem; I; 289) --, Div of Libr Arts, 703-261-
   3752

   Patteson, Jr, Roy K, PhD, Pres

SOUTHSIDE VIRGINIA COMMUNITY COLLEGE
   Alberta, Virginia 23821 (--; st; coed; qr; I; 749) Courses with no degree
   specialization, Div of Human, 703-949-2411 Ext 27

   Halbrooks, G Thomas, PhD, Assoc Prof
   Ogden, Marguerite, MA, Instr

SOUTHWEST VIRGINIA COMMUNITY COLLEGE
   Richlands, Virginia 24641 (S; st; coed; qr; I; 1007) --, Dept of Soc Sci, 703-964-
   4028

   Barlow, Daniel L, EdD, Prof, Phil Psych, Phil Theol, Phil of Educ
   Compton, Stafford, MA, Assoc Prof, Soc Phil

STRATFORD COLLEGE
   Danville, Virginia 24541 (S; p; wo; 4-1-4; II; 590) Courses with no degree
   specialization, Dept of Phil, 703-792-1852

SULLINS COLLEGE
   Briston, Virginia 24201 (S; p; wo; sem; I; 302) NP

SWEET BRIAR COLLEGE
   Sweet Briar, Virginia 24521 (S; p; wo; 4-1-4; II; 731) BA major, --, 703-381-5521

   Wentworth, Elizabeth C, PhD, Assoc Prof, Chm

THOMAS NELSON COMMUNITY COLLEGE
   Hampton, Virginia 23366 (S; st; coed; qr; I; 2303) NP

TIDEWATER COMMUNITY COLLEGE
   Portsmouth, Virginia 23703 (S; st; coed; qr; I; 2899) Courses with no degree
   specialization, Dept of Human and Soc Sci, 703-484-2121 Ext 70

   Ashenfelder, John, MTh, Lect

UNION THEOLOGICAL SEMINARY IN VIRGINIA
   Richmond, Virginia 23227 (S; Preb; coed; qr; IV; 244) Courses with no degree
   specialization, Dept of Theol, 703-355-0671

   Dawe, Donald G, ThD, Prof, Chm

UNIVERSITY OF RICHMOND
  Richmond, Virginia 23173 (S; Bapt; coed; sem; II; 4747) MA minor, Dept of Phil, 703-285-6391

  Mucklow, Neale H, PhD, Assoc Prof, Chm, Ethics, Polit Phil
  Brockway, George, ABD, Asst Prof, 17th and 18th Cent Phil
  Hall, James H, PhD, Assoc Prof, Phil of Relig, Epistem
  McGhan, Barbara, ABD, Part-time Instr, 20th Cent Phil

UNIVERSITY OF VIRGINIA
  Charlottesville, Virginia 22903 (S; st; coed; sem; IV; 12,351) PhD major, Corcoran Dept of Phil, 703-924-3535

  Thomas, George B, PhD, Assoc Prof, Chm, Phil of Mind
  Cargile, James T, DPhil, Assoc Prof, Logic
  Devereux, Daniel T, PhD, Asst Prof, Anc Phil
  Diamond, Cora, BPhil, Assoc Prof, Wittgenstein
  Goosens, William K, PhD, Asst Prof, Logic, Phil of Sci
  Hammond, Lewis M, PhD, Prof, Anc Phil
  Heath, Peter L, BA, Prof
  Mallett, Marcus B, PhD, Assoc Prof, Ethics, Polit Phil
  Marshall, John, PhD, Asst Prof, Ethics
  Woozley, Anthony D, MA, Prof, Legal Phil
  Yalden-Thomson, D C, PhD, Assoc Prof, Epistem

  Buckalew, Charles, MA   Lucas, Barbara, MA
  Cooke, Lee, BA   Meyer, Leroy, MA
  Fleming, Robin, MA   Mills, Stephen, MA
  Howe, Roger, BA   Nigreen, William, BA
  Jezierski, Carol, MA   Ryan, Andrew, BA
  Keating, Bernard, BA   Spier, Carl, MA

VIRGINIA COLLEGE
  Lynchburg, Virginia 24501 (--; Bapt; coed; sem; I; 91) NR

VIRGINIA COMMONWEALTH UNIVERSITY
  Richmond, Virginia 23220 (S; st; coed; sem; IV; 15,067) BA major, Dept of Phil and Relig Stud, 804-770-6518, 804-770-6519

  Hall, Jr, Thomas O, ThD, Prof, Chm
  Berman, Myron, PhD, Part-time
  Coleman, Earle J, PhD, Asst Prof, Aes, Exist
  Crim, Keith R, ThD, Assoc Prof
  Deane, Brian C, MA, Part-time
  Edwards, Clifford W, PhD, Part-time
  Freasier, Sr, Barney R, ThD, Assoc Prof, Greek Phil
  Friedman, William H, PhD, Asst Prof, Logic, Contemp Phil
  Leith, John, PhD, Part-time
  Lilienkamp, Paul, PhD, Part-time
  Lindsey, Jr, James E, ThD, Asst Prof, Metaph, Phil of Sci
  Lonnes, Jerome L, PhD, Asst Prof, Ethics, Hist of Phil
  Mallory, Fred C, ThD, Part-time
  McGhan, Barbara, MA, Part-time
  McGhan, Harlan P, MA, Asst Prof, Phil of Sci, Logic
  Ragen, David, MA, Part-time
  Robinson, William, Part-time
  Spiro, Jack D, PhD, Part-time
  Talbert, Robert M, PhD, Asst Prof

VIRGINIA HIGHLANDS COMMUNITY COLLEGE
  Abingdon, Virginia 24210 (--; st; coed; qr; I; 808) NP

VIRGINIA INTERMONT COLLEGE
  Bristol, Virginia 24201 (JS; S Bapt; wo; sem; II; 544) BA minor, --, 703-669-6101

  Taylor, Louis H, PhD, Prof, Chm, Metaph, Logic
  Tuck, William P, PhD, Instr, Ethics

VIRGINIA MILITARY INSTITUTE
  Lexington, Virginia 24450 (S; st; men; sem; II; 1154) Courses with no degree
  specialization, Dept of Phil and Psych, 703-463-6233

  Carlsson, P Allan, PhD, Prof, Hist of Phil, Phil of Relig, Ethics
  Wilson, Robert K, MA, Lect, Ethics, Comp Relig

VIRGINIA POLYTECHNIC INSTITUTE AND STATE UNIVERSITY
  Blacksburg, Virginia 24061 (S; st; coed; qr; IV; 13,292) PhD minor, Dept of Phil
  and Relig, 703-951-5118

  Grover, Norman L, PhD, Prof, Chm, Ethics
  Cardwell, Charles E, PhD, Asst Prof, Phil of Sci, Logic
  Edwards, Richard A, PhD, Assoc Prof
  Hammond, Guyton B, PhD, Prof, Phil of Relig, Contemp Relig Tht
  Kennedy, Charles A, PhD, Assoc Prof, Asian Relig
  Manor, Ruth, PhD, Asst Prof, Logic
  McCabe, Russell T, PhD, Asst Prof, Mod Phil, Metaph, Epistem
  Miller, Harlan B, PhD, Asst Prof, Phil of Mind, Anc Phil
  Neumann, Franke J, PhD, Asst Prof, Hist and Phenomen of Relig
  Pitt, Joseph C, PhD, Asst Prof, Phil of Sci, Phil of Law
  Talbutt, Jr, Palmer C, PhD, Assoc Prof, Metaph, Phil of Relig
  Williams, William H, MA, Asst Prof, Epistem, Moral Phil, Polit Phil

VIRGINIA STATE COLLEGE
  Petersburg, Virginia 23803 (S; st; coed; sem; III; 3684) BA major, Dept of Phil,
  703-526-5111 Ext 237

  Greenland, Virginia Beth, MA, Asst Prof, Ethics, Logic

VIRGINIA UNION UNIVERSITY
  Richmond, Virginia 23220 (S; Bapt; coed; sem; III; 107) Courses with no degree
  specialization, Dept of Human, 703-359-9331

VIRGINIA WESLEYAN COLLEGE
  Norfolk, Virginia 23502 (S; U Meth; coed; sem; II; 637) BA major, Dept of Phil
  and Relig, 804-464-6291

  Hultgren, Lawrence, MA, Asst Prof, Exist, Phenomen Phil
  Sturm, William, DPhil, Prof, Hist of Phil

VIRGINIA WESTERN COMMUNITY COLLEGE
  Roanoke, Virginia 24015 (S; st; coed; qr; I; 3164) Courses with no degree
  specialization, Dept of Human, 703-344-2031

  Pullen, Paul T, PhD, Assoc Prof, Chm
  Smith, Milton S, PhD, Prof

WASHINGTON AND LEE UNIVERSITY
Lexington, Virginia 24450 (S; p; men; --; II; 1610) BA major, Dept of Phil, 703-463-9111 Ext 353

Pemberton, Harrison, PhD, Prof, Chm, Plato, Phenomen
Boggs, Charles, MA, Instr, Wittgenstein, Neitzche, Phil of Mind
Martin, Ramsey, PhD, Assoc Prof, British Phil, Logic
Sessions, Lad, PhD, Asst Prof, Metaph, Phil of Sci, Amer Phil, Phil of Relig

WYTHEVILLE COMMUNITY COLLEGE
Wytheville, Virginia 24382 (S; st; coed; qr; I; 1014) AA major, Div of Human, 703-228-5541

Price, Kenneth, BD, Asst Instr

WASHINGTON

BELLEVUE COMMUNITY COLLEGE
Bellevue, Washington 98007 (NW; st; coed; qr; I; 3563) --, --, 206-641-0111

Mayer, Dalmen, MA, Instr
Wulff, Jon V, MA, Instr

BIG BEND COMMUNITY COLLEGE
Moses Lake, Washington 98837 (NW; st; coed; qr; I; 1184) --, Dept of Phil, 509-765-7821 Ext 222

Wolff, David R, MA, Instr

CENTRAL WASHINGTON STATE COLLEGE
Ellensburg, Washington 98926 (NW; st; coed; qr; III; 11,719) BA major, --, 509-963-1818

Keller, Chester Z, PhD, Prof, Act Chm, Phil of Educ, Phil of Relig
Bachrach, Jay E, PhD, Assoc Prof, Aes
Burkholder, Peter M, PhD, Assoc Prof, Ethics, Epistem
Goedecke, W Robert, PhD, Prof, Phil of Law
Harris, H John, MA, Asst Prof, Phenomen
Hood, Webster F, PhD, Assoc Prof, Exist, Phil of Tech
Nadler, Charles H, AB, Asst Prof, Phil of Sci
Utzinger, John G, PhD, Assoc Prof, Ethics, Soc Phil

CENTRALIA COLLEGE
Centralia, Washington, 98531 (NW; st; coed; qr; I; 2974) AA major, Dept of Phil, 206-736-9391 Ext 253

Lord, Arthur, LTh, Chm

CLARK COLLEGE
Vancouver, Washington 98663 (NW; st; coed; qr; I; 4200) Courses with no degree

specialization, Dept of Phil, 206-694-6521 Ext 268

Epton, Charles, MA, Prof, Chm, Logic, Phil Psych
Apsler, Alfred, PhD, Prof, Phil of Relig
Gomez, Jose, MA, Part-time, Logic, Phil of Relig

COLUMBIA BASIN COLLEGE
Pasco, Washington 99301 (NW; st and local; coed; qr; I; 3680) Courses with no degree
specialization, Dept of Human, 509-547-0511

Commeree, Noel, MA, Chm

EASTERN WASHINGTON STATE COLLEGE
Cheney, Washington 99004 (NW; st; coed; qr; III; 6618) BA major, Dept of Phil, 509-
359-2405

Gibbons, Theodore, MS, Assoc Prof, Dir, Phil of Lang
Kuo, David, PhD, Asst Prof, Orient Phil
Raley, Adam, STD, Asst Prof, Phil of Relig
Rottmayer, William, PhD, Asst Prof, Phil of Sci
Scott, Steven, PhD, Asst Prof, Ontology

EDMONDS COMMUNITY COLLEGE
Lynnwood, Washington 98036 (--; st; coed; qr; I; 3180) --, Div of Soc Sci, 206-
775-3511 Ext 36

Meacham, Marion, MA, Instr Part-time

EVERGREEN STATE COLLEGE
Olympia, Washinton 98505 (--; st; coed; qr; II; 1178) NR

EVERETT COMMUNITY COLLEGE
Everett, Washington 98201 (NW; st; coed; qr; I; 5867) AA major, Div of Soc Sci
206-259-7151 Ext 211, 218

Houghtaling, David N, MA

FORT STEILACOOM COMMUNITY COLLEGE
Tacoma, Washington 98499 (--; st; coed; qr; I; 3193) --, Dept of Phil, 206-588-3623
Ext 20

Kalles, John D, MA

FORT WRIGHT COLLEGE OF THE HOLY NAMES
Spokane, Washington 99204 (NW; RC; wo; 4-1-4; III; 410) Courses with no degree
specialization, --, 509-328-2970

GONZAGA UNIVERSITY
Spokane, Washington 99202 (NW; RC; coed; sem; III; 2873) MA major, Dept of Phil,
509-328-4220 Ext 281

Royce, Thomas R, PhD, Assoc Prof, Chm, Ethics
Abel, Donald, MA, Instr, Exist
Bjelland, Andrew, PhD, Assoc Prof, Greek Phil
Carney, William, PhD, Prof, Metaph

Gilmore, Thomas, MA, Assoc Prof, Phil Anthrop
Gjording, Christopher, MA, Lect, Amer Phil
Kennard, George, Lect, Anal Phil
Kohls, Gerald, PhD, Asst Prof, Phil Anthrop
Kossel, Clifford, PhD, Prof, Med Phil
Rukavina, Thomas, PhD, Prof, Mod Phil
Ryan, William, PhD, Asst Prof, Epistem
Tyrrell, Bernard, PhD, Asst Prof, Phil of God
Chang, Matthew, PhD, Asst Prof, Phenomen
Ste Marie, Louis, PhD, Prof, Phil of Art

Wolf, Theodore, PhD, Prof Emer, Ethics

Buhrer, Richard, Teach Asst, Logic

GRAYS HARBOR COLLEGE
Aberdeen, Washington 98520 (NW; st and local; coed; qr; I; 2298) Courses with no
degree specialization, --, 206-532-9020

Stensager, Eugene F, MA

GREEN RIVER COMMUNITY COLLEGE
Auburn, Washington 98002 (NW; st; coed; qr; I; 5154) --, Div of Human, 206-833-9111

Van Ry, Meredith, MA, Instr

HIGHLINE COMMUNITY COLLEGE
Midway, Washington 98031 (NW; st; coed; qr; I; 6424) Courses with no degree
specialization, Dept of Human, 206-878-3710 Ext 281

Jones, Donald F, MA

LOWER COLUMBIA COLLEGE
Longview, Washington 98632 (NW; st; coed; qr; I; 2569) AA major, Dept of Soc Sci,
206-425-6500 Ext 72

Kelley, Dick
Mashinter, Harvey, MA

NORTHWEST COLLEGE
Kirkland, Washington 98033 (BI; Assem of God; coed; qr; II; 513) Courses with no
degree specialization, --, 206-822-8266

Hagen, Loren, Part-time

OLYMPIC COLLEGE
Bremerton, Washington 98310 (NW; st; coed; qr; I; 3804) Courses with no degree
specialization, Dept of Soc Sci, 206-478-4633

Norton, Richard H, MA

PACIFIC LUTHERAN UNIVERSITY
Tacoma, Washington 98447 (NW; Amer Luth; coed; 4-1-4; III; 3038) MA joint or combined
major, Dept of Phil, 206-531-6900 Ext 257

Arbaugh, George E, PhD, Prof, Chm, Ethics, Theory of Value, Exist

Huber, Curtis, PhD, Prof, Epistem, Metaph, Phil of Relig
Menzel, Paul, PhD, Asst Prof, Ethics, Phil of Law
Myrbo, Gunnulf, PhD, Asst Prof, Decision Theory, Game Theory, Contemp Phil

PENINSULA COLLEGE
Port Angeles, Washington 98362 (NW; st and local; coed; qr; I; 1420) AA major, Div of Human, 206-452-9277 Ext 26

Brauninger, R Kent, MS, Asst Prof, Logic
Evans, John F, PhD, Asst Prof, Logic
Quast, Werner C, PhD, Asst Prof, Polit Theory, Ethics

SAINT MARTIN'S COLLEGE
Olympia, Washington 98503 (NW; RC; coed; sem; II; 574) BA major, Dept of Phil, 206-491-4700

Seidel, George J, PhD, Prof, Chm, Contemp Phil, Metaph
Parker, Joseph, MA, Lect, Ethics, Logic

Osqniach, Augustine, PhD, Prof Emer, Polit and Soc Phil

SEATTLE CENTRAL COMMUNITY COLLEGE
Seattle, Washington 98122 (NW; st; coed; qr; I; 6228) AA major, Dept of Soc Sci, 206-587-4164

Anderson, Paul B L, MA, Instr
Fox, John H, Instr Part-time
Keller, Richard P, MA, Instr

SEATTLE PACIFIC COLLEGE
Seattle, Washington 98119 (NW; RC; coed; qr; III; 3170) BA major, School of Human, 206-281-2036

Johnson, Walter, ThD, Prof, Ethics
Macdonald, Michael, MA, Asst Prof, German Idealism
Wells, Raymond, PhD, Prof, Aes

SEATTLE UNIVERSITY
Seattle, Washington 98122 (NW; RC; coed; qr; III; 3170) MA major, Dept of Phil, 206-626-6890

Reichmann, James B, PhD, Prof, Chm, Metaph, Med Phil, 19th Cent Phil
Axer, Engelbert, PhD, Assoc Prof, Ethics
Burke, John Patrick, Asst Prof, Phenomen, Phil of Hist, Aes
Garvin, Thomas, PhD, Asst Prof, Amer Phil, Phil of Sci
Harkins, Vernon, STL, Assoc Prof, Ethics
Kaufman, Leo, PhD, Prof, Plato, Phil of Lang
Kohls, Harry, PhD, Assoc Prof, Aristotle, Lonergan
McMahon, Roberta, PhD, Assoc Prof, Process Phil
Morton, Edmund, PhD, Prof, Greek Phil, Med Phil
Riley, James, PhD, Asst Prof, Phenomen
Toulouse, Michael, MA, Asst Prof, Ethics
Trainor, Rosaleen, PhD, Assoc Prof, Soc and Polit Phil

Bussy, J Gerard, PhD, Prof Emer, Ethics, Exist
McGuigan, James, MA, Assoc Prof Emer, Med Phil

SHORELINE COMMUNITY COLLEGE
  Seattle, Washington 98133 (NW; local; coed; qr; I; 6383) --, --, 206-546-4101

  Heick, Cecil, MA, Assoc Prof, Logic, Aes
  McClure, Steve, MA, Instr, Ethics, Phil of Sci
  Patrick, Forrest, MA, Prof, Euro Phil
  Riordan, Tim, MA, Instr, Logic

SKAGIT VALLEY COLLEGE
  Mount Vernon, Washington 98273 (NW; local; coed; qr; I; 3432) AA major, Dept of
  Phil, 206-424-1031

  Coole, Walter A, MA, Instr, Chm, Logic, Phil of Sci
  Larson, John B, Adj Instr, Phil of Tech
  Vasarada, Hemlata N, MA, Adj Instr, Asian Phil

SPOKANE FALLS COMMUNITY COLLEGE
  Spokane, Washington 99202 (NW; st; coed; qr; I; 2303) Courses with no degree
  specialization, Dept of Soc Sci, 509-456-2862

  Baldusty, Richard, MA, Part-time Instr
  Hollowell, Rex, MA, Instr, Phil of the Soc Sci
  Lagault, Francis, BA, Instr

SULPICIAN SEMINARY OF THE NORTHWEST
  Kenmore, Washington 98028 (NW; RC; men; qr; III; 96) NR

TACOMA COMMUNITY COLLEGE
  Tacoma, Washington 98465 (NW; st; coed; qr; I; 3871) AA major, Dept of Eng and
  Phil, 206-564-7200

  Edrington, Devon, MA, Epistem
  Evans, John, MA, Part-time, Logic

UNIVERSITY OF PUGET SOUND
  Tacoma, Washington 98416 (NW; U Meth; coed; 4-1-4; II; 3652) BA major, Dept of
  Phil, 206-756-3290

  Magee, John B, PhD, Prof, Chm, Phil of Values, Ethics, Aes, East and West Relig
  Kunze, Robert W, PhD, Asst Prof, Phil of Sci, Phenomen
  Langbauer, Delmar Neil, PhD, Asst Prof, Phil of Relig, Asian Phil

UNIVERSITY OF WASHINGTON
  Seattle, Washington 98195 (NW; st; coed; qr; IV; 33,089) PhD major, Dept of Phil
  206-543-5855

  Keyt, David, PhD, Prof, Chm, Anc Phil, Comtemp Phil
  Boler, John F, PhD, Assoc Prof, Med Phil, Amer Phil
  Burke, John P, MA, Act Asst Prof, Phenomen, 19th Cent Phil, Soc and Polit Phil
  Clatterbaugh, Kenneth C, PhD, Assoc Prof, Phil of Sci, Anc Phil, Continen Ration
  Coburn, Robert C, PhD, Prof, Metaph, Soc Phil
  Cohen, S Marc, PhD, Assoc Prof, Anc Phil, Phil of Mind
  Crocker, J Lawrence, PhD, Asst Prof, Soc and Polit Phil, Phil of Sci
  Dietrichson, Paul, PhD, Prof, Phil of Relig, Metaph
  Kirk, Robert E, PhD, Asst Prof, Logic, Phil of Math, Phil of Lang
  Lucian, Miriam, PhD, Asst Prof, Logic, Set Theory
  Marks, Charles, PhD, Asst Prof, Contemp Phil, British Empir, Continen Ration

Marks, Sandra, MA, Visit Lect, Phil of Film, Phil of Lang, Logic
Mish'Alani, James, PhD, Asst Prof, Ethics, Phil Psych
Potter, Karl, PhD, Prof, Indian Phil, Epistem
Richman, Robert J, PhD, Prof, Contemp Phil, Epistem
Siegler, Frederick A, PhD, Assoc Prof, Phil of Mind, Ethics
Small, Kenneth, MA, Lect, Phil of Lang, Epistem, Logic
Thomas, Stephen N, PhD, Asst Prof, Anal Phil, Phil of Mind

Rader, Melvin, PhD, Prof Emer, Aes, Phil of Hist

WALLA WALLA COLLEGE
College Place, Washington 99324 (NW; SDA; coed; qr; III; 1820) NR

WALLA WALLA COMMUNITY COLLEGE
Walla Walla, Washington 99362 (NW; st; coed; qr; I; 1515) AA major, Dept of Phil,
509-529-0670

Richardson, Henry V M, PhD, Prof, Chm, Christ Exist

WASHINGTON STATE UNIVERSITY
Pullman, Washington 99163 (NW; st; coed; sem; IV; 14,539) MA major, Dept of Phil,
509-335-8611

Broyles, James E, PhD, Assoc Prof, Chm, Logic, Phil of Math
Bishop, Donald H, PhD, Prof, Phil of Relig, Orient Relig
Carloye, Jack C, PhD, Assoc Prof, Epistem, Metaph, Phil of Sci
Lilje, Gerald W, PhD, Asst Prof, Logic, Phil of Lang, Phil of Behavior Sci
Neville, Michael, PhD, Asst Prof, Exist, Phil of Lit, Aes
Silverstein, Harry S, PhD, Assoc Prof, Logic, Ethics

Hobson, Mary Stiles, Teach Asst   Rickert, Trudy, Teach Asst
Jones, David, Teach Asst

WENATCHEE VALLEY COLLEGE
Wenatchee, Washington 98801 (NW; st and local; coed; qr; I; 2002) Courses with no
degree specialization, Div of Lang Arts, 509-663-5126

WESTERN WASHINGTON STATE COLLEGE
Bellingham, Washington 98225 (NW; st; coed; qr; III; 10,853) BA major, Dept of Phil,
206-676-3859

Daugert, Stanley, PhD, Prof, Chm, Phil of Hist
Downing, Thomas, PhD, Asst Prof, Phil of Lang
Fleetwood, Hugh, PhD, Assoc Prof, Phil of Relig
Karason, Halldor, PhD, Assoc Prof, Phil of Educ
Landrum, George, PhD, Asst Prof, Metaph, Epistem
Montague, Phillip, PhD, Assoc Prof, Ethics, Aes
Morrow, Frank, PhD, Asst Prof, Ethics, Phil of Law
Purtill, Richard, PhD, Prof, Logic, Metaph

WHATCOM COMMUNITY COLLEGE
Ferndale, Washington 98248 (--; st; coed; qr; I; 387) Courses with no degree
specialization, --, 206-676-3062

Magnano, Paul, MA

WHITMAN COLLEGE
    Walla Walla, Washington 99362 (NW; p; coed; sem; II; 1071) BA major, Dept of Phil,
    509-529-5100 Ext 242

    Brown, Geoffrey Wallace, PhD, Asst Prof, Value Theory
    Maier, Joseph John, BD, Asst Prof, Phil of Sci
    Soper, William Wayne, PhD, Prof, Phenomen

WHITWORTH COLLEGE
    Spokane, Washington 99251 (NW; p; coed; 4-1-4; III; 1640) BA major, Dept of Phil,
    509-489-3550 Ext 273

    Krebbs, Norman A, PhD, Assoc Prof, Head, Greek Phil, Hist of Phil
    Redmond, Howard A, PhD, Prof, Aes, Augustine
    Yates, Lawrence E, ThD, Prof, Prag

YAKIMA VALLEY COLLEGE
    Yakima, Washington 98902 (NW; st; coed; qr; I; 3200) NR

WEST VIRGINIA

ALDERSON BROADDUS COLLEGE
    Philippi, West Virginia 26416 (N; Bapt; coed; --; II; 1067) BA major, Dept of Phil
    and Relig, 304-457-1700

    Unger, Daniel, PhD, Assoc Prof, Chm
    Fowler, Bill G, ThD, Asst Prof, Phil of Relig

APPALACHIAN BIBLE INSTITUTE
    Bradley, West Virginia 25818 (BI; p; coed; sem; II; 181) Courses with no degree
    specialization, --, 304-877-6428

    Beukema, Cal C, MA

BECKLEY COLLEGE
    Beckley, West Virginia 25801 (--; p; coed; sem; I; 1380) NP

BETHANY COLLEGE
    Bethany, West Virginia 26032 (N; p; coed; sem; II; 1138) BA major, Dept of Phil,
    304-829-7121

    Myers, Robert E, PhD, Assoc Prof, Chm, Ethics, Exist, Phenomen, Phil of Relig,
        Phil of Man and Culture, Amer Phil, Mod Phil
    Garrison, Gary L, BA, Instr, Phil and Psych, 19th Cent Phil, Anal Phil, Anc Phil,
        Med Phil, Logic
    Gresham, Perry E, PhD, Dist Prof, Anc Phil, Amer Prag, Polit and Soc Phil

BLUEFIELD STATE COLLEGE
    Bluefield, West Virginia 24701 (N; st; coed; sem; II; 1177) --, Dept of Soc Sci,
    304-325-7102 Ext 312

    Yates, Louise, MA, Asst Prof

CONCORD COLLEGE
    Athens, West Virginia 24712 (N; st; coed; sem; II; 1986) BA minor, Dept of Phil,
    304-384-3115

    McMichael, Jack R, PhD, Assoc Prof, Ethics, Soc Phil, Phil of Relig

DAVIS AND ELKINS COLLEGE
    Elkins, West Virginia 26241 (N; Prot; coed; 4-1-4; II; 815) BA joint or combined
    major, Dept of Relig and Phil, 304-636-1900 Ext 35

    Phipps, William E, PhD, Prof, Hist of Phil
    Walter, Donald, PhD, Assoc Prof, Ethics

FAIRMONT STATE COLLEGE
    Fairmont, West Virginia 26554 (N; st; coed; sem; II; 3681) BA minor, Div of Soc Sci,
    304-363-4000 Ext 341

    Pulsifer, Jack R, MA, Assoc Prof, Hist of Phil
    Springer, Hugh B, PhD, Asst Prof, Phil of Educ

GLENVILLE STATE COLLEGE
    Glenville, West Virginia 26351 (N; st; coed; sem; II; 1469) Courses with no degree
    specialization, --, 304-462-7361

    Gay, Ralph, BD, Instr

MARSHALL UNIVERSITY
    Huntington, West Virginia 25701 (N; st; coed; sem; III; 9944) MA minor, Dept of Phil,
    304-696-6739

    Slaatte, Howard Alexander, PhD, Prof, Chm, Exist, Phil of Relig
    Mininni, Frank J, PhD, Assoc Prof, Ethics, Phil of Relig
    Plott, John Culpepper, PhD, Assoc Prof, Orient Phil

MORRIS HARVEY COLLEGE
    Charleston, West Virginia 25304 (N; p; coed; sem; II; 3094) BA joint or combined
    major, Dept of Relig and Phil, 304-346-9471 Ext 286

    Newman, Robert G, PhD, Prof, Head, Exist, Hist of Phil
    Daugherty, Mary L, MA, Part-time
    Kirkland, William, PhD, Part-time, Hist of Tht
    Miller, Jr, C T, M Div, Asst Prof, Logic

OHIO VALLEY COLLEGE
    Parkersburg, West Virginia 26101 (--; Ch of Christ; coed; sem; I; 144) Courses with
    no degree specialization, Dept of Soc Sci, 304-485-7384

PARKERSBURG COMMUNITY COLLEGE
Parkersburg, West Virginia 26101 (N; st; coed; sem; I; 2256) AA major, Div of Soc Sci, 304-485-7961 Ext 229

Allen, Bernard L, PhD, Asst Prof, John Dewey, Phil of Hist
Harford, Samuel A, STB, Act Dean
McLendon, Vonceil, PhD, Asst Prof, Hist of Phil
Reyes, Raul, MA, Asst Prof

POTOMAC STATE COLLEGE
Keyser, West Virginia 26726 (N; st; coed; sem; I; 766) Courses with no degree specialization, --, 304-788-3011

Plumley, Boyd, MS, Instr

SALEM COLLEGE
Salem, West Virginia 26426 (N; p; coed; sem; II; 1475) BA joint or combined major, Dept of Relig and Phil, 304-782-5393

Nida, Melvin, ThD, Prof
Stroud, William, ThD, Assoc Prof, Phil of Relig, Ethics

SALEM COLLEGE AT CLARKSBURG
Clarksburg, West Virginia 26301 (N; p; coed; sem; I; 163) NR

SHEPHERD COLLEGE
Shepherdtown, West Virginia 25443 (N; st; coed; sem; II; 2054) Courses with no degree specialization, Div of Soc Sci, 304-876-2511 Ext 332

Hanak, Walter K, PhD, Asst Prof, Hist of Phil

SOUTHERN WEST VIRGINIA COMMUNITY COLLEGE AT LOGAN
Logan, West Virginia 25601 (N; st; coed; sem; I; 599) Courses with no degree specialization, Div of Human, 304-752-5900

Bartlett, James, MA, Instr
Stock, Jerold, MA, Instr

SOUTHERN WEST VIRGINIA COMMUNITY COLLEGE
Williamson, West Virginia 25661 (N; st; coed; sem; I; 379) Courses with no degree specialization, Div of Human, 304-235-2800

WEST LIBERTY STATE COLLEGE
West Liberty, West Virginia 26074 (N; st; coed; sem; II; 3551) BA minor, Dept of Phil and Relig, 304-336-8098

Cayard, W Wallace, PhD, Prof, Chm, Phil of Relig
Kirchner, Landon, MA, Asst Prof, Phil of Sci

WEST VIRGINIA COLLEGE OF GRADUATE STUDIES
Institute, West Virginia 25112 (N; st; coed; sem; II; 3590) NP

WEST VIRGINIA INSTITUTE OF TECHNOLOGY
Montgomery, West Virginia 25136 (N; st; coed; sem; II; 2441) Courses with no degree specialization, --, 304-442-3071

WEST VIRGINIA NORTHERN COMMUNITY COLLEGE AT WEIRTON
Weirton, West Virginia 26063 (N; st; coed; sem; I; 399) Courses with no degree specialization, Div of Human, 304-233-5900

WEST VIRGINIA NORTHERN COMMUNITY COLLEGE AT WHEELING
Wheeling, West Virginia 26003 (N; st; coed; sem; I; 650) Courses with no degree specialization, Div of Human, 304-233-5900 Ext 33

WEST VIRGINIA STATE COLLEGE
Institute, West Virginia 25112 (N; st; coed; sem; II; 3590) BA major, Dept of Phil, 304-766-3237

Allinson, Robert E, PhD, Asst Prof, Chm, Epistem, Hist of Phil, Kant, East Phil, Soc and Polit Phil, Aes
Oltman, John M, BA, Instr

WEST VIRGINIA UNIVERSITY
Morgantown, West Virginia 26506 (N; st; coed; sem; IV; 17,941) BA major, --, 304-293-3641

Clark, Ralph W, PhD, Asst Prof, Anc and Med Phil, Ethics, Aes
D'Amour, Gene A, PhD, Asst Prof, Logic, Phil of Sci, Anal Phil
Drange, Theodore M, PhD, Assoc Prof, Metaph, Epistem, Phil of Lang, Phil of Mind
Haymond, William S, PhD, Prof, Mod Phil, Exist, Soc and Polit Phil
Long, Patricia S, MA, Instr, Introductory Logic

Cresswell, John R, PhD, Prof Emer

WEST VIRGINIA WESLEYAN COLLEGE
Buckhannon, West Virginia 26201 (N; U Meth; coed; sem; II; 1675) BA major, Dept of Phil, 304-473-8439

Mow, Joseph B, PhD, Prof, Chm, Ethics
Hill, David, MA, Instr, Phil of Mind

Franquiz, Jose, PhD, Prof Emer, Phil of Relig

WHEELING COLLEGE
Wheeling, West Virginia 26003 (N; RC; coed; sem; II; 683) BA major, Dept of Phil, 304-243-2000

Jenemann, Albert H, PhD, Assoc Prof, Chm, Ethics, Exist, J S Mill
Gannon, Edward, PhD, Visit Prof, Phil of Art, Exist, A Malraux
O'Brien, James A, MA, Asst Prof, Phil of Relig, John Dewey
Sendaydiego, Henry B, PhL. Assoc Prof, Phenomen, Heidegger

McFadden, Daniel, PhD, Prof Emer, Ethics, Anc Phil

WISCONSIN

ALVERNO COLLEGE
  Milwaukee, Wisconsin 53215 (N; p; wo; sem; II; 1101) BA major, Dept of Phil, 414-671-5400

  Egan, William T, PhD, Asst Prof, Chm, Value Phil, Amer Phil, Phil of Relig
  Hammond, John, MA, Lect, Metaph Theories, East Phil
  Simec, Mary, PhD, Prof, Amer Phil, Hist of Phil
  Trimberger, Christine, MA, Assoc Prof, Metaph Theories
  Walsh, John J, MA, Lect, Greek Phil

BELOIT COLLEGE
  Beloit, Wisconsin 53511 (N; p; coed; tri; III; 1783) BA major, Dept of Phil, 608-365-3391 Ext 320

  Crom, Scott E, PhD, Prof, Chm
  Cook, Gary A, PhD, Assoc Prof, Deputy Chm
  Fendrich, Roger P, PhD, Asst Prof
  Morden, Michael, PhD, Instr

BLACKHAWK TECHNICAL INSTITUTE
  Janesville, Wisconsin 53545 (--; st and local; coed; sem; I; 5179) NR

CARDINAL STRITCH COLLEGE
  Milwaukee, Wisconsin 53217 (N; RC; coed; sem; III; 869) BA minor, Dept of Mod Foreign Lang, 414-352-5400

CARROLL COLLEGE
  Waukesha, Wisconsin 53186 (N; U Preb; coed; 4-1-4; II; 1259) BA major, Dept of Phil, 414-547-1211 Ext 324

  Williams, Thomas R, PhD, Assoc Prof, Chm

  Van Tuinen, Jacob, PhD, Prof Emer

CARTHAGE COLLEGE
  Kenosha, Wisconsin 53140 (N; Luth; coed; 4-1-4; II; 1678) BA major, Dept of Phil, 414-551-8501 Ext 233

  Boyer, Merle William, PhD, Prof, Chm
  Jurkoric, Kathryn, MA, Lect

CONCORDIA COLLEGE
  Milwaukee, Wisconsin 53208 (N; Luth Mo Synod; coed; 4-1-4; I; 346) NP

DISTRICT ONE TECHNICAL INSTITUTE
  Eau Claire, Wisconsin 54701 (--; local; coed; sem; I; 1533) NP

DOMINICAN COLLEGE AT RACINE
  Racine, Wisconsin 53402 (N; p; coed; sem; II; 614) Courses with no degree specialization, --, 414-639-7100

EDGEWOOD COLLEGE
    Madison, Wisconsin 53711 (N; RC; coed; 4-1-4; II; 430) BA minor, Dept of Phil,
    608-257-4861 Ext 230

    Cordon, Catherine, MA, Assoc Prof, Chm, Soc Phil
    Guilfoil, Daniel J, PhD, Prof, Ethics, Theory of Knowl

FOX VALLEY TECHNICAL INSTITUTE
    Appleton, Wisconsin 54911 (--; st and local; coed; sem; I; 3232) NP

GATEWAY TECHNICAL INSTITUTE AT KENOSHA
    Kenosha, Wisconsin 53140 (N; local; coed; sem; I; 3238) NP

GATEWAY TECHNICAL INSTITUTE AT RACINE
    Racine, Wisconsin 53403 (--; st and local; coed; sem; I; 1987) NP

HOLY FAMILY COLLEGE
    Manitowoc, Wisconsin 54220 (N; RC; coed; sem; II; 606) --, Dept of Phil and Relig
    Stud, 414-684-6691

    Golden, Thomas, Lic, Instr
    Hoffmann, Mary de Sales, MA, Instr, Phil of Man
    Morneau, Robert, MA, Instr Part-time, Phil of Man
    Scheu, Marina, PhD, Prof, Metaph

HOLY REDEEMER COLLEGE
    Waterford, Wisconsin 53185 (--; RC; men; tri; II; 70) BA major, Div of Phil and
    Theol, 414-534-3191

    Dinan, Stephen, PhD, Ethics, Contemp Phil, Anal Phil, Phenomen-Logical Phil
    Fenili, J Robert, MA, Academic Dean, Anc Phil, Class Phil, Mod Phil
    Majchrzak, Colman, PhD, Metaph, Med Phil

THE INSTITUTE OF PAPER CHEMISTRY
    Appleton, Wisconsin 54911 (N; p; coed; qr; IV; 68) NP

LAKELAND COLLEGE
    Sheboygan, Wisconsin 53081 (N; U Ch of Christ; coed; 4-1-4; II; 524) BA major, Dept
    of Phil and Relig, 414-565-1274, 414-565-1284

    Ulrich, Reinhard, STD, Prof, Chm, Phil of Relig, Ethics
    Leach, Richard D, ThD, Asst Prof, Hist of Phil

LAKESHORE TECHNICAL INSTITUTE
    Manitowoc, Wisconsin 54220 (--; local; coed; sem; I; 1800) NR

LAWRENCE UNIVERSITY
    Appleton, Wisconsin 54911 (N; p; coed; --; II; 1470) BA major, Dept of Phil, 414-
    739-3681

    Boardman, William S, PhD, Asst Prof, Chm, Metaph, Phil of Mind, Human Action,
        Theory of Knowl, Ethics, Phil of Law
    Dreher, John P, PhD, Assoc Prof, Hist of Anc Phil, Mod Phil, Prag, Phil of Soc Sci
    Marchal, Joseph, PhD, Asst Prof, Logic, Phil of Sci, Phil of Soc Sci, Phil of Lang

WISCONSIN

LAYTON SCHOOL OF ART AND DESIGN
  Milwaukee, Wisconsin 53212 (Art; p; coed; sem; II; 234) NP

MADISON AREA TECHNICAL COLLEGE
  Madison, Wisconsin 53703 (N; st and local; coed; sem; I; 5369) --, Dept of Soc Sci,
  608-257-6711

MADISON BUSINESS COLLEGE
  Madison, Wisconsin 53703 (JRCB; p; coed; tri; II; 486) NP

MARIAN COLLEGE OF FOND DU LAC
  Fond du Lac, Wisconsin 54935 (N; RC; coed; sem; II; 450) BA major, Dept of Humanistic
  Stud, 414-921-3900

  Brotz, Edith, PhD, Prof, Chm
  Bertram, Maryanne, PhD, Asst Prof, Contemp Phil
  Jansch, Ronald, MA, Instr
  Paulus, Agnes Louise, MA, Asst Prof

MARQUETTE UNIVERSITY
  Milwaukee, Wisconsin 53233 (N; RC; coed; sem; IV; 10,235) PhD major, Dept of Phil,
  414-224-6857

  Byrne, Paul M, PhD, Assoc Prof, Chm, Augustine, Platonism
  O'Malley, Joseph J, PhD, Assoc Prof, Asst Chm, Marx, Ethics, Soc Phil, Polit Phil
  Algozin, Keith W, PhD, Asst Prof, German Phil, Phil of Hist
  Anderson, Thomas C, PhD, Assoc Prof, Exist, Phil Anthrop
  Ashmore, Robert B, PhD, Asst Prof, Ethical Theory, Natur, Utilitarianism
  Beach, John D, PhD, Prof, Aristotle, Metaph, Ethics
  Carter, Curtis, PhD, Asst Prof, Aes, Phil of Lang, Continen Ethics
  Coffey, Patrick J, PhD, Asst Prof, Ethics, Amer Phil, Bergson, Whitehead
  Collingwood, Francis J, PhD, Prof, Phil of Relig, Phil of Sci
  Davis, Richard, MA, Instr
  Davitt, Thomas E, PhD, Prof, Phil of Law, Phil Anthrop
  Dooley, William E, STL, Assoc Prof, Plato, Plotinus, Neoplatonism
  Etzwiler, James P, PhD, Asst Prof, Aquinas, Aristotle
  Griesbach, Marc F, PhD, Prof, Epistem, Ethics, Anal Phil
  Kainz, Howard P, PhD, Assoc Prof, Exist, German Phil, Polit Phil
  Kendzierski, Lottie H, PhD, Prof, Aristotle, Aquinas, Bonaventure
  Maloney, William, PhD, Assoc Prof
  Mattea, James, PhD, Asst Prof
  Naus, John E, PhD, Asst Prof
  Prendergast, Thomas, PhD, Asst Prof, Wittgenstein, Descartes, Phil of Mind
  Rice, Lee C, PhD, Assoc Prof, Spinoza, British Empir, Math Logic
  Robb, James H, PhD, Prof, Med Phil, Contemp French Phil, Metaph of Love
  Rousseau, Edward L, PhD, Assoc Prof, Anselm, Aquinas, Phil of Hist
  Savage, Denis D, PhD, Assoc Prof, Kant, Phenomen, Theory of Perception
  Simmons, Edward D, PhD, Prof, Aristotelian Logic, Epistem, Neo-Thomism
  Stohrer, Walter, PhD, Asst Prof
  Tallon, Andrew, PhD, Asst Prof, Phil of Person, Phenomen, Exist, Soc Phil
  Vater, Michael, PhD, Asst Prof, Contemp Metaph, German Idealism
  Wade, Francis C, STL, Prof, Cartesianism, Metaph, Ethics
  Zedler, Beatrice H, PhD, Prof, Med Arab Phil, Amer Phil

  Smith, Gerard, Prof Emer

  Colapietro, Vincent, BA, Res Asst   Keyes, Thomas, MA, Teach Asst
  Conlon, James, BA, Teach Asst   Plecnik, John, MA, Teach Asst
  Doyle, Patrick, BA, Teach Asst   Rasmussen, Douglas, BA, Teach Asst

Hansen, Linda, BA, Teach Asst
Hassler, Christine, BA, Res Asst
Hogans, Donna, BA, Res Asst

Rudoff, John, MA, Teach Asst
Thomas, A J, BA, Res Asst
St Pierre, Paul, MA, Teach Asst

MEDICAL COLLEGE OF WISCONSIN
Milwaukee, Wisconsin 53233 (N; p; coed; --; IV; 471) NR

MILTON COLLEGE
Milton, Wisconsin 53563 (N; p; coed; 4-1-4; II; 827) BA minor, Dept of Phil and Relig, 608-868-2912

Pautz, Zane E W, PhD, Prof

MILWAUKEE AREA TECHNICAL COLLEGE
Milwaukee, Wisconsin 53203 (N; local; coed; sem; I; 15,032) NP

MILWAUKEE SCHOOL OF ENGINEERING
Milwaukee, Wisconsin 53201 (N; p; coed; qr; III; 2281) NP

MORAINE PARK TECHNICAL INSTITUTE
Fond du Lac, Wisconsin 54935 (--; local; coed; sem; I; 795) NR

MOUNT MARY COLLEGE
Milwaukee, Wisconsin 53222 (N; RC; wo; sem; II; 791) BA major, Dept of Phil, 414-258-4810

Overfield, Mary Brian, MPhil, Asst Prof, Chm, Ethics, Aes, Metaph
Carmichael, John, Assoc Prof, Logic, Anc Phil, Ethics
McMullen, George, Assoc Prof, Polit Phil, Amer Phil, Ethics

MOUNT SENARIO COLLEGE
Ladysmith, Wisconsin 54848 (--; p; coed; sem; II; 228) BA joint or combined major, Dept of Phil, 715-532-5511 Ext 232

MacDonald, Ronald, MA, Asst Prof, Chm

NASHOTAH HOUSE SEMINARY
Nashotah, Wisconsin 53058 (Theol; PE; coed; sem; III; 80) MA joint or combined major, Dept of Phil and Syst Theol, 414-646-3371 Ext 38

Griffiss, James E, PhD, Prof, Chm, Phil of Relig
Cooper, Robert M, D Div, Assoc Prof, Ethics, Moral Theol

NICOLET COLLEGE
Rhinelander, Wisconsin 54501 (--; st; coed; sem; I; 793) AA major, Dept of Arts and Phil, 715-369-4418

Feiereisen, Jack, Instr, Ethics

NORTH CENTRAL TECHNICAL INSTITUTE
Wausau, Wisconsin 54401 (N; local; coed; sem; I; 1447) NP

NORTHEAST WISCONSIN TECHNICAL INSTITUTE
    Green Bay, Wisconsin 54303 (--; local; coed; sem; I; 2057) NP

NORTHLAND COLLEGE
    Ashland, Wisconsin 54806 (N; p; coed; 4-1-4; II; 632) BA major, Dept of Phil and
    Relig, 715-682-4531 Ext 250, 218

    Bennett, John B, PhD, Assoc Prof, Process Phil, Phil of Relig
    Williams, Robert, ThD, Assoc Prof, Phenomen, Phil of Relig

RIPON COLLEGE
    Ripon, Wisconsin 54971 (N; p; coed; sem; II; 1024) BA major, Dept of Phil, 414-748-
    8131

    Hannaford, Robert, PhD, Prof, Chm, Ethics
    Doss, Seale R, PhD, Assoc Prof, Logic
    Kasten, Vamce R, PhD, Asst Prof, Polit Theory
    Tyree, William E, PhD, Prof, Phil of Hist

SAINT FRANCIS DE SALES COLLEGE
    Milwaukee, Wisconsin 53207 (N; RC; men; sem; II; 125) BA major, Dept of Phil, 414-
    744-7139

    Puechner, William E, MA, Assoc Prof, Chm, Logic
    Breitbach, Richard C, MA, Assoc Prof, Polit Phil
    Michalski, Melvin E, PhL, Instr, Med Phil
    Twomey, John E, PhD, Prof, Metaph

SAINT FRANCIS SCHOOL OF PASTORAL MINISTRY
    Milwaukee, Wisconsin 53207 (N; RC; coed; sem; III; 166) NP

SAINT NORBERT COLLEGE
    De Pere, Wisconsin 54115 (N; RC; coed; sem; II; 1659) BA major, Div of Human and
    Fine Arts, 414-336-3181 Ext 332

    Colavechio, X G, Chm
    Conway, Vincent, PhD, Asst Prof, Logic, Epistem
    Giguere, John, PhD, Asst Prof, British Anal
    O'Callaghan, William, PhD, Prof, Med Phil
    Phelan, Thomas, MA, Prof, Metaph
    Regan, James T, MA, Prof, Ethics, East Phil
    Vanden Burgt, Robert, PhD, Assoc Prof, Contemp Phil

SILVER LAKE COLLEGE OF THE HOLY FAMILY
    Manitowoc, Wisconsin 54220 (N; RC; coed; sem; II; 606) BA minor, Dept of Phil and
    Relig Stud, 414-684-6691

    Hoffmann, Mary de Sales, MA, Asst Prof, Chm, Phil of Man
    Morneau, Robert, MA, Part-time Lect, Phil of Morality
    Scheu, Marina, PhD, Prof, Metaph

SOUTHWEST WISCONSIN VOCATIONAL TECHNICAL SCHOOL
    Fennimore, Wisconsin 53805 (--; local; coed; sem; I; 1204) NP

UNIVERSITY OF WISCONSIN
Madison, Wisconsin (N; st; coed; sem; IV; 34,003) PhD major, Dept of Phil, 608-263-3700

Crawford, Donald W, PhD, Assoc Prof, Chm
Moulton, John R, Lect, Asst to Chm
Aamodt, Gary J N, MA, Lect
Ammerman, Robert R, PhD, Prof
Byrd, Michael E, PhD, Asst Prof
Card, Claudia F, PhD, Assoc Prof
Cole, H Brock, PhD, Asst Prof
Daly, Jr, Richard T, PhD, Asst Prof
Dretske, Frederick I, PhD, Prof
Enc, Berent, DPhil, Asst Prof
Fain, Haskell, PhD, Prof
Hambourger, Robert, BA, Instr
Hay, William H, PhD, Prof
Holmstrom, Nancy, PhD, Asst Prof
Huntley, Martin A, PhD, Asst Prof
MacCallum, Jr, Gerald C, PhD, Prof
Moline, Jon N, PhD, Prof
Parks, R Zane, MA, Instr
Penner, Terrence M I, BPhil, Assoc Prof
Schrag, Francis K, DEd, Asst Prof
Singer, Marcus G, PhD, Prof
Soll, A Ivan, PhD, Prof
Stampe, Dennis W, DPhil, Prof
Yandell, Keith E, PhD, Assoc Prof
Young, Gary, PhD, Asst Prof

Bögholt, Carl M, PhD, Prof Emer
Ramsperger, Albert G, PhD, Prof Emer

Amundson, Ronald A, BA, Teach Asst
Bertolet, Rodney J, BA, Ford Fel Sem I, Teach Asst Sem II
Beyer, Landon E, BA, Bradish Scholar Sem I, Ford Fel Sem II
Bryce, Charles Geoffrey, BA, Univ Fel
Burke, Michael B, BA, Teach Asst
Clark, Maudemarie A, MA, Teach Asst Sem I
Code, Alan D, BA, Teach Asst
Eggan, Lloyd A, BA, Univ Fel
Feagin, Susan L, BA, Teach Asst
Good, Robert C, AB, Ford Fel
Gutenstein, Lenore L, BA, Ford Fel Sem I, Teach Asst Sem II
Henry, Dennis R, BS, Ford Fel
Iannone, Abel P, MA, Teach Asst
Jakovina, John A, BA, Teach Asst Sem I
Jones, Bryce J, BA, Ford Fel Sem I, Teach Asst Sem II
Kaufman, Stanley B, BA, Teach Asst
Kline, Alton D, MA, Teach Asst
Lovell, David G, BA, Teach Asst Sem I
Luebke, Stephen W, MA, Teach Asst
Oppenheim, David, BA, Ford Fel
Pallin, Jeffrey J, BA, Teach Asst
Pavlat, John R, BA, Teach Asst Sem I, Ford Fel Sem II
Popovich, Thomas E, BS, Teach Asst
Smith, Terry L, BA, Ford Fel
Starr, William C, MA, Teach Asst
Sweeney, Kevin W, BA, Teach Asst
Tharp, Lynn H, BA, Ford Fel Sem I, Teach Asst Sem II
Tobin, Richard J, MA, Teach Asst
Weis, Richard F, MA, Teach Asst
West, Jai, BA, NDEA IV
Wright, Michael B, BA, Teach Asst

UNIVERSITY OF WISCONSIN AT EAU CLAIRE
Eau Claire, Wisconsin 54701 (n; st; coed; sem; III; 8686) BA major, --, 715-836-0123

Griffin, Phillip, PhD, Prof, Chm
Behling, Richard, MA, Instr
Bettenhausen, Elizabeth, PhD, Asst Prof
Brummer, James, MA, Instr

Gertner, Willis, PhD, Assoc Prof
Koshoshek, Ronald, MA, Asst Prof
Rice, Daniel, PhD, Assoc Prof
Rocco, Thomas, PhD, Asst Prof
Shigefuji, Shenie, PhD, Asst Prof
Jannusch, Bruce, PhD, Assoc Prof

UNIVERSITY OF WISCONSIN AT GREEN BAY
Green Bay, Wisconsin 54302 (N; st; coed; 4-1-4; II; 3531) BA joint or combined
major, Phil Option, 414-465-2348

Kersten, Fred, PhD, Prof, Chm, Phenomen, Hist of Phil
Clark, Orville, PhD, Asst Prof, Aes
Greif, Gary, PhD, Asst Prof, Phil Psych, Soc Phil
Yake, J Stanley, PhD, Asst Prof, Ethics, Polit Phil

UNIVERSITY OF WISCONSIN AT LA CROSSE
La Crosse, Wisconsin 54601 (N; st; coed; sem; III; 7180) BA major, Dept of Phil,
608-784-6050 Ext 324

Felch, William E, PhD, Prof, Chm, Phil of Mind, Value Theory
Brodrick, Daniel L, MA, Instr, Modal Logic, Phil of Sci
Campbell, William E, MA, Instr, Ling Phil, Wittgenstein
Glass, Ronald J, PhD, Asst Prof, Leibniz, Theory of Knowl
Miller, David L, PhD, Asst Prof, Whitehead, Amer Phil
Rasmussen, Paul E, PhD, Assoc Prof, Exist, Descartes

UNIVERSITY OF WISCONSIN AT MILWAUKEE
Milwaukee, Wisconsin 53201 (N; st; coed; sem; IV; 22,227) MA major, Dept of Phil,
414-228-4719

Peltz, Richard W, PhD, Prof, Chm, Hist of Mod Phil, Aes
Casper, Dennis J, PhD, Asst Prof, Anc Phil
Coleman, Ellen R, MA, Instr, Phil of Mind, Phil of Law
Coleman, Jules, PhD, Asst Prof, Phil of Law
Hawi, Sami S, PhD, Asst Prof, Islamic Phil, Phenomen
Hedman, Carl G, PhD, Asst Prof, Phil of Mind
Hull, David L, PhD, Prof, Phil of Biology
Keim, Robert G, PhD, Asst Prof, Modal Logic
Khatchadourian, Haig, PhD, Prof, Aes, Phil of Lang
Koethe, John L, PhD, Asst Prof, Epistem
Luce, David R, PhD, Assoc Prof, Phil of Sci, Soc Phil
Norman, John E, PhD, Asst Prof, Metaph
Perloff, Michael N, MA, Instr, Phil of Soc Sci, Logic
Shevach, David R, PhD, Asst Prof, Phil Psych
Wainwright, William J, PhD, Assoc Prof, Phil of Relig
Weiss, Raymond L, PhD, Assoc Prof, Med Phil

Riddle, Glenn K, PhD, Prof Emer

Gould, Charles, Grad Teach Asst	Rajani, Karl, Grad Teach Asst
Katzfey, Mark, Grad Teach Asst	Simons, Joseph, Grad Teach Asst

UNIVERSITY OF WISCONSIN AT OSHKOSH
Oshkosh, Wisconsin 54901 (N; st; coed; sem; III; 12,323) BA major, Dept of Phil,
414-424-1366

Burr, John R, PhD, Prof, Chm, Hist of Phil, Aes, Phil of India
Austin, Stephen S, BA, Instr, Kant, Hume, Metaph
Cordero, Ronald A, PhD, Asst Prof, Ethics, Phil of Lang, Exist, Soc Phil

Goldinger, Milton, PhD, Assoc Prof, Ethics, Contemp Phil, Metaph
Kates, Lawrence R, PhD, Asst Prof, Phil of Mind, Phil of Sci, Epistem
Missner, Marshall, PhD, Asst Prof, Phil of Lang, Phil of Sci, Epistem
Wu, Kuang-ming, PhD, Assoc Prof, Phenomen, Phil of Relig, Metaph

UNIVERSITY OF WISCONSIN AT PLATTEVILLE
Platteville, Wisconsin 53818 (N; st; coed; sem; III; 4710) BA major, Dept of Phil,
608-342-1828

Moore, Stanley R, PhD, Prof, Chm, Soc Phil, Phil of Educ
Hood, C Ellsworth, PhD, Prof, Ontology, Kant
Parsons, Barbara, PhD, Assoc Prof, Whitehead

UNIVERSITY OF WISCONSIN AT RIVER FALLS
River Falls, Wisconsin 54022 (N; st; coed; qr; III; 4468) BA minor, --, 715-425-6701

Maier, Eugene, PhD, Prof, Ethics, Phil of Relig
Stockton, C N, PhD, Assoc Prof, Phil of Hist

UNIVERSITY OF WISCONSIN AT STEVENS POINT
Stevens Point, Wisconsin 54481 (N; st; coed; sem; III; 9744) --, Dept of Phil, 715-
346-5638

Zawadsky, John P, PhD, Prof, Chm, Russian Phil
Bailiff, John D, PhD, Assoc Prof, Exist
Billings, John R, PhD, Assoc Prof, British Phil
Callicott, John B, PhD, Asst Prof, Environ Stud
Cassidy, Robert, PhD, Asst Prof
Feldman, Richard J, PhD, Asst Prof, Phil of Law
Hein, Karl, PhD, Asst Prof, Phenomen
Herman, Arthur, PhD, Assoc Prof, Indian Phil
Kalke, William, PhD, Asst Prof, Logic
Schuler, Joseph L, MS, Assoc Prof, Phil of Educ
Vollrath, John, PhD, Asst Prof, Phil of Sci
Wenz, Peter, PhD, Asst Prof, British Empir

UNIVERSITY OF WISCONSIN AT SUPERIOR
Superior, Wisconsin 54880 (N; st; coed; sem; III; 3004) BA minor, Dept of Hist and
Phil, 715-392-8101

Wenninger, William A, MA, Lect, Hist of Phil

UNIVERSITY OF WISCONSIN AT WHITEWATER
Whitewater, Wisconsin 53190 (N; st; coed; sem; III; 9355) BA minor, Dept of Phil,
414-473-1456

Shibles, Warren A, MA, Asst Prof, Chm, Phil Psych, Ordinary Lang
Spiegel, Richard, PhD, Asst Prof, Ethics, Soc Phil, Hume

UNIVERSITY OF WISCONSIN, BARRON COUNTY CENTER
Rice Lake, Wisconsin 54868 (N; st; coed; sem; I; --) Courses with no degree
specialization, Dept of Comm Sci, 715-234-8176 Ext 21

Fitz, Thomas R, STM, Asst Prof

UNIVERSITY OF WISCONSIN, CENTER SYSTEM
Madison, Wisconsin 53706 (N; st; coed; sem; I; 4412) Courses with no degree
specialization, Dept of Eng, Lit, and Phil, 608-263-3770

Allen, Duane, BA, Instr, Epistem, Aes
Cooley, Kenneth W, MA, Asst Prof
Hosler, Douglas, PhD, Asst Prof, Ethics, Phil of Mind
Knight, John H, Asst Prof
McClain, Edward F, PhD, Assoc Prof, Polit and Legal Phil
Rigterink, Roger J, PhD, Asst Prof
Sweet, Donald G, MA, Instr, Soc and Polit Phil, R G Collingwood, Chinese Phil

UNIVERSITY OF WISCONSIN, MEDFORD CENTER
Medford, Wisconsin 54451 (N; st; coed; sem; I; 144) Courses with no degree
specialization, --, 715-748-3600

Dennis, Donald D, MA, Instr

UNIVERSITY OF WISCONSIN, PARKSIDE CAMPUS
Kenosha, Wisconsin 53140 (N; st; coed; sem; II; 4343) BA major, Div of Human Stud,
414-553-2331

Johnson, Mary, PhD, Asst Prof, Phil of Sci, Logic
Johnson, Wayne G, PhD, Assoc Prof, Phil of Relig, Ethics
McMahon, Deanna, PhD, Visit Asst Prof, Hist of Phil, Phil of Relig, Aes
McMahon, M Brian, PhD, Asst Prof, Metaph, Polit Phil
Schrader, Robert W, PhD, Asst Prof, Phil of Relig, Hist of Phil
Snyder, Aaron, PhD, Assoc Prof, Metaph, Epistem

UNIVERSITY OF WISCONSIN, RICHLAND CENTER
Richland Center, Wisconsin 53581 (N; st; coed; sem; I; --) AA major, Dept of Phil
and Politics, 608-647-3384

Malik, PhD, Assoc Prof, Chm

UNIVERSITY OF WISCONSIN, STOUT CAMPUS
Menomonie, Wisconsin 54751 (N; st; coed; sem; III; 5231) --, Dept of Eng, 715-232-
0123

Barlow, Raoul M, MA, Asst Prof

VITERBO COLLEGE
La Crosse, Wisconsin 54601 (N; p; coed; sem; II; 484) BA minor, Dept of Phil, 608-
785-3450

Chiu, Alec K F, PhD, Assoc Prof, Chm, Ethics, Orient Phil
Heagle, John, MA, Asst Prof, Phil of Man, Aes, Exist
Schulte, Lyle, MA, Asst Prof, Polit and Soc Phil, Phil of Relig

WAUKESHA COUNTY TECHNICAL INSTITUTE
Pewaukee, Wisconsin 53072 (--; st and local; coed; sem; I; 2389) NP

WESTERN WISCONSIN TECHNICAL INSTITUTE
La Crosse, Wisconsin 54601 (N; st and local; coed; qr; I; 1838) NP

WISCONSIN COLLEGE CONSERVATORY
    Milwaukee, Wisconsin 53202 (Mus; p; coed; sem; III; 82) NP

WYOMING

CASPER COLLEGE
    Casper, Wyoming 82601 (N; local; coed; sem; I; 2821) NP

CENTRAL WYOMING COLLEGE
    Riverton, Wyoming 82501 (--; local; coed; sem; I; 688) NP

EASTERN WYOMING COLLEGE
    Torrington, Wyoming 82240 (--; local; coed; sem; I; 341) NP

LARAMIE COUNTY COMMUNITY COLLEGE
    Cheyenne, Wyoming 82001 (--; st and local; coed; sem; I; 1383) Courses with no
    degree specialization, --, 307-634-5853

NORTHWEST COMMUNITY COLLEGE
    Powell, Wyoming 82435 (N; local; coed; sem; I; 946) NP

SHERIDAN COLLEGE
    Sheridan, Wyoming 82801 (N; local; coed; sem; I; 441) Courses with no degree
    specialization, Div of Human, 307-674-4421

    Aro, John H, MA, Instr
    Harkins, Cynthia, MA, Asst Prof

UNIVERSITY OF WYOMING
    Laramie, Wyoming 82071 (N; st; coed; sem; IV; 11,924) MA major, Dept of Phil, 307-
    766-3203

    Howey, Richard, PhD, Assoc Prof, Head, Exist, Phenomen, Nietzsche, Heidegger
    Blatz, Charles, PhD, Asst Prof, Ling Anal, Ethics, Epistem
    Dudeck, Caroline, PhD, Asst Prof, Hegel, Kant, Soc and Polit Phil
    Forrester, James, PhD, Asst Prof, Greek Phil, Med Phil, 18th Cent Phil, Metaph
    Martin, James, PhD, Asst Prof, Logic, Epistem, Phil of Sci

    Bradsher, Donald, BA, Teach Asst   Dellai, Debby, BA, Teach Asst
    Cartwright, David, BA, Teach Asst

WESTERN WYOMING COMMUNITY COLLEGE
    Rock Springs, Wyoming 82901 (--; st and local; coed; sem; I; 447) NP

ASSISTANTSHIPS

UNITED STATES

UNIVERSITIES OFFERING A DOCTORATE IN PHILOSOPHY

American University: 5 F varies+TW; 4 TF $2500+TW
Andover Newton Theological School: None
Boston College: 1 F $3300+TW; 21 TF $3000+TW; 10 A $2000+TW; 2 OA TW
Boston University: 7 TF $1500+TW; 24 TA $1500+TW; 4 OA TW
Brandeis University: 8F $1562
Brown University: 12 F $1000-$2500+TW; 8 TA $2600+TW; 3 OA TW
Bryn Mawr College: 1 F $1500+TW; 2 A $1300+TW; 2 OA $1200+TW
Case Western Reserve University: F varies+TW
Catholic University of America: 25 F $1200-$4000; 3 TF $2400+TW
Claremont Graduate School: 9 F $1500+TW
Columbia University: F stipend varies+TW; 16 TF $1000-$4000+TW
Columbia University Teachers College: None. "Scholarships and Fellowships are awarded
    mainly on a College-wide basis, and philosophy of education students compete for
    these along with others"
Cornell University: 3 F $2000+TW; 1 TF TW; 9 TA $2700+TW
DePaul University: 4 F $2000-$2400+TW; 14 TA $2000-$3000+TW
Duke University: 12 F $1800-$3800; OA TW
Duquesne University: 2 TF $2200+TW; 8 A $1700+TW
Emory University: 12 A $1080-$1814+TW
Florida State University: 6 F $3000; 6 TA $3000; 1 A $3000
Fordham University: 6 TF $2400+TW; 8 A $1700+TW
Garrett Theological Seminary*: None
Georgetown University: 9 F $2500+TW; 2 TA $3000-$5000
Graduate School, CUNY: Data unavailable
Harvard University: Data unavailable
Iliff School of Theology: 1 F $600; 1 A $600
Indiana University (Dept of Phil): 1 F $3000; 18 TA $2700+TW
Indiana University (Dept of Hist and Phil of Sci): 3 F $1000; 8 A $1500+ TW
Johns Hopkins University: 20 F varies up to $1800 and $400 for summer +TW
Loyola University of Chicago: 3 TA $2120+TW; 6 A $2120+TW; 1 OA $1000
Marquette University: 7 TA $2600-$3000+TW; 4 A $2400-$2800+TW
Massachusetts Institute of Technology: 10 F varies+TW; 2 TA $3000+TW
Michigan State University: 12 A $2800-$3200
New School for Social Research: Data unavailable
New York University: 7 F $1000+TW; OA(NDEA) $3000+TW
Northwestern University: 9 F $2300+TW; 10 TA $2400+TW; 9 OA TW
Ohio State University: 3 F $2400+TW; 5 TF $2835+TW; 29 TA $2610-$5004+TW
Oklahoma State University*: 2 TA $2070; 1 A $1035; OA varies
Pennsylvania State University: 5 F $2400-$3500+TW; 17 TA $2646-$3024+TW; 5 A $2466+TW
Princeton Theological Seminary: Data unavailable
Princeton University: Data unavailable
Purdue University: 10 TA $3000+TW
Rice University: 7 F $2300+TW; 3 OA TW
Rockefeller University: 8 F $4000+TW
Rutgers, the State University: 6 TA $3500+TW
Saint Louis University: 4 F $2400+TW; 8 TA $2500+TW; OA TW
Smith College: Data unavailable
Southern Illinois University at Carbondale: TA TW
Stanford University: 4 TF $1300+TW
State University at Binghamton, SUNY: 10 TA $2300-$3000+TW; 9 A up to $3000+TW; 1 OA(NDEA)
    $2600+TW
State University at Buffalo, SUNY; 3 F $3000+TW; 26 TA $2800-$3000+TW
State University at Stony Brook, SUNY: 4 F $3000+TW; 17 TA $2800-$3000+TW; 3 OA $4000
Syracuse University: 2 F $3000-$4000+TW; 12 TA $2400+TW

Temple University: Data unavailable
Tulane University: 6 F $1000-$4800+TW; 1 TF $8000+TW; 8 TA $1000-$2400+TW; 2 A $200-$400
Union Theological Seminary: None
University of Arizona: 15 TA $3000+TW
University of Arkansas: 3 TA $2400-$3600+TW
University of California at Berkeley: 8 F varies; 10 TA $3789
University of California at Davis: F varies; 4 TA $3789
University of California at Irvine: 12 TA $4000
University of California at Los Angeles: 2 F $2521 & $2400; 20 TA $3789
University of California at Riverside: 5 TA $1895
University of California at San Diego: 2 F $2400+TW; 16 TA $4010; 2 A $3600
University of California at Santa Barbara: 3 F $3333; 10 TA $3789
University of California at Santa Cruz: Data unavailable
University of Chicago: 8 F $900-$2550+TW; F (Ford Found) 12 $2400+TW and 4 TW
University of Cincinnati: 1-3 TF $2700-$3000+TW; 15 TA $2700-$3000+TW; 1-5 OA TW
University of Colorado at Boulder: 10-14 TF $850 per 3/hr course+TW; 2-3 TA $700+TW
University of Connecticut: F varies; TF varies; TA varies
University of Dallas*: Data unavailable
University of Florida: 2 F $1050-$1200; TA $880; A $880
University of Georgia: 9 TA $2725-$2925+TW; 9 A $2725-$2925+TW
University of Hawaii: 1 F(HEA) $2400-$2800+TW; 4 TA $3700-$4308+TW; 7 OA TW
University of Illinois at Chicago Circle: F $2000+TW; TA $3200+TW; A $3200+TW; OA TW
University of Illinois at Urbana-Champaign: 2 F $2000-TW; 33 TA $3130+TW
University of Iowa: 3 F $3000; 14 TA $3825
University of Kansas: 1 F $2800; 2 TF $2900; 17 TA $2900; 2 OA $800
University of Maryland: 1 F $2500+TW; 14 TA $2900-$3800+TW
University of Massachusetts at Amherst: 4 F $2500-$2800+TW; 17 TA $625-$3800+TW;
    1 A $3400+TW; 4-6 OA $200-$750
University of Miami: 2 F $2000-$2800+TW; 8 TA $2400+TW; 4 A $2150+TW
University of Michigan: 14 F $2400-$2800+TW; 33 TF $3450-$5266
University of Minnesota: 1 F $1800; 12 TA $3600
University of Missouri at Columbia: 2 F $2000; 16 TA $3000
University of Nebraska-Lincoln: 1 F $2400; 12 TA $3233; 2 OA (work study)
University of New Mexico: 6 TA $2500-$2900+TW
University of North Carolina: 3 F $2800+TW; 28 TA $1800-$2500
University of Notre Dame: 5 F $1800-$2000+TW; 17 TA $2400+TW; 12 OA TW; 2 OA(NDEA);
    1 OA (NSF)
University of Oklahoma: 1 F $2400-$2600+TW; 3 TF $3000+TW; 10 TA $2400-$2600
University of Oregon: 5 TF $2695-$3228
University of Pennsylvania: 10 TF $3000+TW; 6 A $300+TW
University of Pittsburgh: 6 F $3000+TW; 28 TA $2700+TW; 4 OA $500
University of Rochester: 1 F $2800+TW; 14 TA $2300-$2600+TW; 8 OA TW
University of Southern California: 2 F $3000+TW; 9 TA $3000-$3400+TW
University of Tennessee: 8 TA $1400+TW; 4 A $1200+TW
University of Texas at Austin: 2 F $2000-$2500; 50 TA $2000-$2500
University of Utah: 2 F $2500; 9 TA $2650+TW
University of Virginia: 6 F $500-$3000; 12 TA $1800-$2250; 6 A $1500-$1800
University of Washington: 21 TA $3969
University of Wisconsin: 17 F $1188-$3438+TW; 23 TA $2889-$4491+TW
Vanderbilt University: 10 TF $2600-$4000; 7 TA $500-$2300
Washington University: 4 F $2100+TW; 7 TA $2000+TW; 64 TA $1000-$2000+TW; 7 OA TW
Wayne State University: 6 F $3000+TW; 10 TA $3000+TW
Yale University: 40 F $1700-$5200; 21 TA $900/term

* Combined major only

UNIVERSITIES OFFERING A MASTER'S DEGREE IN PHILOSOPHY

OR A DOCTORAL MINOR IN PHILOSOPHY

Aquinas Institute of Theology: None
Arizona State University: TA varies
Arkansas State University: None
Athenaeum of Ohio: Data unavailable
Ball State University: None
Baylor University: 5-7 F $1000-$2500+TW
Brigham Young University: None
Brooklyn College, CUNY: None
Bowling Green State University: 9 TA $2205+TW
Bucknell University: None
Butler University: None
California State University at Long Beach: 2 A $2480
California State University at Los Angeles: 4 TA $1000
California State University at Northridge: A $620 per semester
California State University at San Diego: None
California State University at San Francisco: 5 A $1400
California State University at San Jose: None
City College, CUNY: 1 F ; 1 A
Cleveland State University: TA $900-$2700; A $900-$2700; OA varies
Colgate University: None
College at Brockport, SUNY: 2 A $2500+TW
Colorado State University: 3 TA $2340-$2475+TW
Connecticut College: TF varies
East Tennessee State University: 1 TA $2500+TW; 3 A $700+TW
George Washington University: None
Georgia State University: 0-3 A $1800
Gonzaga University: 1 TA $500 per course+TW; 1 OA TW
Howard University: TA $3433
Hunter College, CUNY: None
Indiana State University: 2 A $1800+TW
Kansas State University: None
Kent State University: 12 TA $2500+TW
Louisiana State University: 4 A $2000+TW
Lone Mountain College: Data unavailable
Memphis State University: TA $2500+TW; A $2500+TW
Miami University: 2 A $2610+TW
Mississippi State University: None
Murray State University*: None
Nashotah House Seminary*: None
Niagara University: A $2000+TW; OA 2 TW
North Dakota State University*: None
North Texas State University: None
Northern Illinois University: 13 TA $1500+TW
Oberlin College: None
Ohio University: 2 TA $2600+TW; 3 A $2600+TW; 2½ OA TW
Oregon State University: None
Pacific Lutheran University*: None
Pacific University: None
Purdue University at Fort Wayne: TA $600 per course
Rensselaer Polytechnical Institute: 3 TA $2500+TW; 3 OA varies
Roosevelt University: 1 F $2000+TW
Queens College, CUNY: None
Saint Albert's College: None
Saint John's College: Data unavailable
Seattle University: None
Southern Illinois University at Edwardsville: 4 TA $2700+TW
Southern Methodist University: 2 F $1800; 2 A $500
Swarthmore College: None

Texas A & M University: None
Texas Christian University: 3 A TW
Texas Tech University: None
Trinity College (Hartford): None
Trinity University: None
Tufts University: 4 F TW; 6 TA $625
Universidad de Puerto Rico: Data unavailable
University of Akron: 1 TA $2400+TW; 2 A $2600+TW
University of Alabama: 2 A $2500
University of Dayton: 16 TA $2400+TW
University of Delaware: 2 F $2800+TW; 4 TA $3050+TW
University of Denver: TA $2500+TW
University of Detroit: A TW
University of Houston: 4 TF $2700
University of Idaho: 1 TA $2380-$3180+TW
University of Kentucky: 2 F $2600+TW; 8 TA $2500-$3000+TW
University of Louisville: None
University of Mississippi: 1 F varies; 2 OA varies
University of Montana: 6 TA $2100
University of Nevada: 1 F $2500+TW; 1 TA $3050+TW
University of North Dakota: None
University of Rhode Island: 5 TA $2800+TW; 4 A $2800+TW
University of Toledo: 1 F TW; 9 TA $2700+TW; 1 OA $200
University of South Carolina: 10 A $2400
University of South Florida: 3 TA $2400
University of Vermont: None
University of Wisconsin at Milwaukee: 5 TA $4230-$4392
University of Wyoming: 2 TA $1449+TW
Villanova University: 5 TA $2400+TW
Virginia Polytechnic Institute and State University: None
Washington State University: 4 TA $2000
Wellesley College*: None
West Chester State College: 2 TA $2705+TW
Western Kentucky University: 1 TA $2400+TW; 2 A $1800+TW
Wichita State University: 6 TA $2100
Xavier University: None

* Combined major only

SOCIETIES

UNITED STATES

ALABAMA PHILOSOPHICAL SOCIETY 1963 (55)
P O Box 6289, University, Alabama 35486

Purpose: To promote inter-departmental discussion of philosophy among teachers
of philosophy in the state of Alabama
Activities: Annual meeting featuring papers by faculty and students. Encouragement
of student papers by recognizing one each year with a prize
Meetings: Annual meeting in Fall of year
Pres: J B McMinn, University of Alabama
Sec: Norvin Richards, University of Alabama
Mem reqt: Approval by a majority of members present at annual meeting
Dues: $2, Students $1

AMERICAN ACADEMY OF RELIGION 1909 (3915)
Department of Religion, Florida State University, Tallahassee, Florida 32306

Purpose: To stimulate scholarship, foster research in the complex of disciplines
that together constitute religion as an area of learning
Activities: Annual, national and regional meetings. Sponsorship of a variety of
learned publications in the field of religion. Improving the quality of teaching
about religion especially in higher education.
Meetings: Annual meeting
Pres: Charles Long, University of Chicago
Sec: Jill Raitt (1972-1975), Duke Divinity School, Duke University
Publ: Journal of the American Academy of Religion, Bulletin of the Council on the
Study of Religion, and the series "AAR Monograph Series," "AAR Dissertation
Series," and "AAR and SBL Religion in Art Series"
Mem reqt: Teaching and research in the field of religion
Dues: $15, Students $7.50

AMERICAN CATHOLIC PHILOSOPHICAL ASSOCIATION 1926 (1600)
The Catholic University of America, Washington, DC 20017

Purpose: To promote philosophical scholarship, to improve the teaching of philosophy,
and to communicate with other individuals and groups of like interest
Activities: Placement service, awards for advanced and junior service to the profession,
Committees on: Research publication, international congresses, the teaching of
philosophy, the development of philosophical resource
Meetings: Annual National Convention; quarterly regional meetings
Pres: Thomas D Langan, University of Toronto
Sec: George F McLean, School of Philosophy, Catholic University
Publ: The New Scholasticism, Proceedings of the ACPA
Other Inf: Member of Federation Internationale des Societes de Philosophie (FISP)

DETROIT-WINDSOR CONFERENCE, ACPA 1958 (50)
Detroit Institute of Technology, Detroit, Michigan 48201

Purpose: To promote philosophical scholarship, to improve the teaching of
philosophy, and to communicate with other individuals and groups of like
interest in the Detroit-Windsor area
Activities: Semi-annual meetings in which papers are read and discussed
Meetings: October and April, rotating among the colleges and universities in
the Detroit-Windsor area

THE FLORIDA CHAPTER, ACPA 1965 (33)
11300 N E Second Avenue, Miami Shores, Florida 33161

Purpose: To promote philosophical scholarship, to improve the teaching of
philosophy, and to communicate with other individuals and groups of the
like interest
Meetings: Twice a year
Pres: Agnes Cecile Prendergast (1973-74), Barry College
Sec: Charles J Cassini (1973-74), Barry College
Mem reqt: All who accept the objectives of the organization are eligible for
membership. Election to membership is made by the Executive Council.
Nomination to membership may be made to the Executive Council by any member
of the organization
Dues: $2

NEW ENGLAND REGIONAL CONFERENCE, ACPA (200)
Catholic University of America, Washington, DC 20017

Purpose: To promote philosophical scholarship, to improve the teaching of
philosophy and to communicate with groups and individuals of like interest
Meetings: Two a year
Pres: George L Concordia, Providence College
Sec: Elise Tougas, 173-4-11 London Road, Concord, New Hampshire 03301
Mem reqt: Membership in ACPA
Dues: $2

NORTHEASTERN PENNSYLVANIA BRANCH, ACPA 1958 (30)
University of Scranton, Scranton, Pennsylvania 18510

Purpose: Lectures, meetings, discussions in philosophy
Meetings: Two or three times a year
Pres: Edward Capestany, University of Scranton
Mem reqt: Professional interest in philosophy

NORTHWEST REGIONAL CONFERENCE, ACPA 1924 (35)
Mount Angel Seminary, Saint Benedict, Oregon 97373

Purpose: To relate the gospel to issues in contemporary philosophy
Activities: Papers, discussions, panels
Meetings: Irregular
Pres: Louis R Geiselman, Mount Angel Seminary

AMERICAN PHILOSOPHICAL ASSOCIATION 1900 (5000)
Hamilton College, Clinton, New York 13323

Purpose: To promote the exchange of ideas among philosophers, to encourage creative
and scholarly activity in philosophy, and to facilitate the professional work of
teachers of philosophy
Activities: The Association publishes annually, in the Proceedings and Addresses of
the American Philosophical Association, its proceedings and those of its three
divisions (Eastern, Western, Pacific), together with addresses of the presidents of
the divisions and a list of members. It also publishes the APA Bulletin and Jobs
in Philosophy and Grants and Fellowships of Interest to Philosophers. With the
exception of the Grants and Fellowships booklet, APA publications are mailed
five or six times a year. The three regular annual meetings of the Associations,
are the responsibility of the executive committee of the Association. The Board
of Officers is comprised of a chairman, an executive secretary, officers and
representatives of the three divisions, and the chairman of the four standing

committees. There is a committee on lectures, publications, and research, a
committee on international cooperation, on placement and on the status and
future of the profession. Among the subcommittees of the last-named committee
is the subcommittee on the participation of blacks in philosophy. The Board
of Officers also established special committees, the committee on the defense
of professional rights of philosophers, the committee on the teaching of philosophy,
the committee on philosophy in two year colleges, and the committee on the status
of women in the profession.
Meetings: Three annual meetings; one on the East Coast in December, one on the West
    Coast in March, and one in the Midwest in April
Chm: Maurice Mandelbaum (1971-74), The John Hopkins University
Sec: Norman E Bowie, Hamilton College, Clinton, New York 13323
Chm of the Standing Committees
    Lectures, Publications, and Research: Alan Ross Anderson (1970-75) University
    of Pittsburgh
    International Cooperation: John D Goheen (1969-74), Stanford University
    Placement: Ruth Barcan Marcus (1972-77), Northwestern University
    Status and Future of the Profession: Gerald MacCallum (1973-78), University of
    Wisconsin
Presidents of the Divisions
    Eastern Division: Donald Davidson (1973-74), The Rockefeller University
    Western Division: Alan Gewirth (1973-74), The University of Chicago
    Pacific Division: Alonzo Church (1973-74), University of California
Secretaries of the Divisions
    Eastern Division: John J Compton (1971-74), Vanderbilt University
    Western Division: Kenneth R Pahel (1972-75), Knox College
    Pacific Division: Oliver A Johnson (1973-76), University of California, Riverside
Representatives of the Divisions
    Eastern Division: Gregory Vlastos (1971-74), Princeton University
    Western Division: Alan Donagan (1973-76), University of Chicago
    Pacific Division: A I Melden (1972-75), University of California at Irvine
Publ: Proceedings and Addresses of the American Philosophical Association, Jobs in
    Philosophy, APA Bulletin, Grants and Fellowships of Interest to Philosophers
Mem reqt: The Constitution of the American Philosophical Association limits regular
    membership to:
    a. Persons whose training in philosophy has been advanced and systematic enough
        to make them competent to teach the subject at the college or university
        level
    b. Persons whose interests or achievements in philosophy are regarded by the
        Board of Officers of the Association as warranting their affiliation with
        the Association
    International association: qualifications for membership, and residence outside
    the US and Canada. For student association: active engagement in graduate study
    of philosophy, but not gainfully full-time employment of any kind
Other Inf: Member of Fédération Internationale des Sociétés de Philosophie (FISP)
Dues: Full members $16 (if salary is $11,000 or less); $23 (if salary is between
    $11,000 and $17,000); $30 (if salary is $17,000 or more); Student associates $6
    International associates $7.50

AMERICAN SECTION OF INTERNATIONAL ASSOCIATION FOR PHILOSOPHY OF LAW AND SOCIAL PHILOSOPHY
    1963 (166)
    Gray L Dorsey, AMINTAPHIL, School of Law, Washington University, Saint Louis,
    Missouri 63130

Purpose: To study philosophy of law and social philosophy and to discuss various
    aspects of this field in conferences
Meetings: AMINTAPHIL Plenary Conferences, Biennially; AMINTAPHIL will host the
    next World Congress on Philosophy of Law and Social Philosophy in St Louis,
    Missouri, August 25-29, 1975
Pres: Gray L Dorsey (1973-75), Graduate Center, The City University of New York
Sec: James F Doyle, Dept of Phil, University of Missouri, St Louis

Publ: Periodic volumes of proceedings beginning with Human Rights: AMINTAPHIL I 1971
Mem req: Serious interest and scholarly qualifications in philosophy of law and
    social philosophy and the approval of two members of the Executive Committee
Dues: $5

THE AMERICAN SOCIETY FOR AESTHETICS 1942 (800)
    The Cleveland Museum of Art, 11150 East Blvd, Cleveland, Ohio 44106

    Purpose: To promote the study, research, discussion, and publication in aesthetics
        and related fields
    Meetings: Annual meeting and some local chapters have meetings
    Pres: Melvin Rader (through 1974), Dept of Philosophy, University of Washington,
        Seattle
    Sec: James R Johnson (through 1975), Dean, School of Fine Arts, University of
        Connecticut
    Publ: The Journal of Aesthetics & Art Criticism
    Other Inf: Member of Fédération Internationale des Sociétés de Philosophie (FISP)
    Dues: $15

THE AMERICAN SOCIETY FOR POLITICAL AND LEGAL PHILOSOPHY 1955 (475)
    c/o Professor Martin P Golding, John Jay College of Criminal Justice, 444 W 56th
        Street, New York, New York 10019

    Purpose: To encourage interdisciplinary exploration, treatment and discussion of
        those issues of political and legal philosophy that are of common interest to
        the fields of law, philosophy, and the social sciences
    Activities: An annual meeting devoted to the discussion of one particular topic
        in political and legal philosophy. The publication of a yearbook, Nomos,
        following three professional organizations, in rotation: The American
        Philosophical Association, The American Political Science Association, and
        the Association of American Law Schools
    Pres: Graham Hughes, New York University Law School
    Sec: Martin P Golding, 25 Claremont Avenue, New York, New York 10027
    Mem reqt: A member is one who is making or has made a contribution to the field of
        political or legal philosophy and who is elected by a favorable vote of the
        Membership Committee
    Other inf: Member of Fédération Internationale des Sociétés de Philosophie (FISP)
    Dues: $10

AMERICAN SOCIETY FOR VALUE INQUIRY 1970 (85)
    SUNY College at Geneseo, Geneseo, New York 14454

    Purpose: The advancement of the study of values
    Meetings: Annual meeting with Western Division of the APA
    Pres: James B Wilbur, Department of Philosophy, SUNY College at Geneseo
    Sec: William Blackstone, Department of Philosophy, University of Georgia
    Dues: $5

ASSOCIATION FOR PHILOSOPHY OF THE UNCONSCIOUS 1972 (100)
    Department of Philosophy, Georgetown University, Washington, D C 20007

    Purpose: To promote the opportunity to reflect philosophically about the claims
        and the information provided by psychoanalysis
    Activities: Yearly meeting in conjunction with APA Meeting (Eastern Division);
        Newsletter
    Meeting: Yearly meeting in conjunction with APA Meeting (Eastern Division)
    Pres: Wilfried ver Eecke, Department of Philosophy, Georgetown University
    Dues: $1

ASSOCIATION FOR SYMBOLIC LOGIC 1936 (1900)
    P O Box 6248, Providence, Rhode Island 02904

    Purpose: Promotion of work in symbolic logic
    Activities: Meetings; Publication of Journal of Symbolic Logic
    Meetings: Annual December or January with APA Eastern Division or American Mathematical
        Society in the spring; summer (Europe)
    Pres: Joseph R Shoenfield, Department of Mathematics, Duke University
    Sec: Charles D Parsons (through 1974), Department of Philosophy, Columbia University
    Publ: Journal of Symbolic Logic
    Dues: $15, Students $5

ASSOCIATION OF PHILOSOPHY JOURNAL EDITORS 1971 (55)
    Department of Philosophy, Clark University, Worcester, Massachusetts 01610

    Purpose: To bring the editors of philosophy journals together so that they may
        discuss and take action which is to their mutual benefit
    Meetings: The annual meeting is held in conjunction with the Eastern Division
        meeting of the American Philosophical Association. In addition, meetings are
        frequently held in connection with the Western Division meetings of the American
        Philosophical Association
    Pres: Robert N Beck, Department of Philosophy, Clark University
    Sec: Richard H Lineback, Department of Philosophy, Bowling Green State University
    Mem reqt: Membership is limited to the editors of philosophy journals
    Dues: $5

ASSOCIATION OF PHILOSOPHY TEACHERS 1970 (18)
    Department of Philosophy, Skagit Valley College, Mt Vernon, Washington 98273

    Purpose: To promote philosophical instruction in the two-year colleges of Washington
        and contiguous states
    Activities: Workshops and seminars
    Meetings: Semi-annually
    Chm: Walter A Coole, Department of Philosophy, Skagit Valley College
    Mem reqt: Full-time instructors in philosophy at a two-year college in Washington,
        British Columbia, Oregon or Idaho

THE COLLOQUIUM FOR SOCIAL PHILOSOPHY 1972 (36)
    The Pennsylvania State University, Delaware County Campus, Media, Pennsylvania 19063

    Purpose: To facilitate philosophic activity in the greater Philadelphia region in
        the examination of issues troubling men and society
    Activities: The work of the Colloquium is multidisciplinary and inter-institutional
        in nature and brings together scholars with the general citizenry. An annual
        conference is held. Visiting philosophers, workshops, essay projects, and a
        documentation file are supported
    Meetings: Annual conferences in the Spring
    Dir: Robert Ginsberg, The Pennsylvania State University, Delaware County Campus
    Mem reqt: Membership is strictly by invitation. At present no more than one member
        has been designated at any particular institution. Members may serve as
        coordinators of Colloquium activities at their own campuses. Distinguished
        social thinkers who are not within the Colloquium's region may be invited to
        Associate Membership. They are consulted in the programs and development of
        the Colloquium.

CREIGHTON CLUB-NEW YORK STATE PHILOSOPHICAL ASSOCIATION 1924 (80)
Department of Philosophy, Vassar College, Poughkeepsie, New York 12601

Purpose: To provide a forum for philosophical exchange among the philosophers of
the state of New York
Activities: Meetings for the presentation of papers and philosophical discussions
Meetings: Semi-annual, Fall and Spring
Pres: Richard E Creel, Department of Philosophy, Ithaca College
Sec: Jesse Kalin, Department of Philosophy, Vassar College
Publ: Proceedings of the Creighton Club
Mem reqt: Professional interest in philosophy and New York state residence
Dues: $4, Departments $13

DIVISIONS OF PHILOSOPHICAL PSYCHOLOGY 1892 (510)
1200 17th Street, N W, Washington, D C 20036

Purpose: To encourage and to facilitate the active and informed exploration and
discussion of the relationships of psychology and psychological theory to the
problems of philosophy; the philosophical issues that arise as psychology develops
as a science and a profession; and the particular contribution of philosophy to
psychology as a means of promoting human welfare
Activities: Programs of symposia, panels, invited papers, submitted papers, and
other activities in conjunction with the annual convention of the American
Psychological Association; publication of an occasional newsletter; dissemination
of information concerning philosophical psychology
Meetings: Annually; in conjunction with the convention of the American Psychological
Association
Pres: Magda B Arnold (1973-74), Department of Psychology, Spring Hill College
Sec: Michael Wertheimer (1972-75), Department of Psychology, Spring Hill College
Publ: Occasional newsletter, from one to four issues per year
Other inf: The Division wishes to make contact with philosophers interested in
philosophical psychology and to explore possible activities of mutual interest
Mem reqt: Membership is open to persons who are actively interested in the
philosophical bases and implications of psychology as a science or as a profession.
There are three classes of members: fellows, members, and affiliates. The first
two classes are restricted to fellows and members of the American Psychological
Association, but "...affiliates shall be primarily philosophers, theologians, other
behavioral scientists or others appropriately concerned with the relationship
of psychology to philosophy." Inquiries about affiliate membership should be
directed to Dr. Wilse B Webb, Department of Psychology, University of Florida,
Gainsville, Florida 32601
Dues: Annual Divisional dues $2, the Division has also voted an annual additional
assessment of $3

FAR WESTERN PHILOSOPHY OF EDUCATION SOCIETY 1952 (128)
California State College, Fullerton, California 92631

Purpose: To bring the component disciplines of philosophy to bear on education
issues of the day, and to encourage exploration of the many educational alternatives
for the future
Activities: The society holds an annual three day meeting during the first week in
December, and publishes papers and responses given at those meetings in an annual
journal, Proceedings
Meetings: Annual meetings for three days during the first week in December
Pres: James J Jelinek, Arizona State University, Tempe
Sec: Robert B McLaren, California State College, Fullerton
Publ: Proceedings

Mem reqt: Members must be engaged in teaching at least one course yearly in philosophy
    of education, or in a comparable course
Dues: $7.50

FELLOWSHIP OF RELIGIOUS HUMANISTS 1967 (1100)
    106 W North College Street, Yellow Springs, Ohio 45387

    Purpose: The Fellowship of Religious Humanists is principally concerned with the
        practice and philosophy of humanism as a religion by promoting and encouraging
        the religious, ethical and philosophical thought and life of its members
    Activities: Arranges lectures, encourages writing, publishes a quarterly, Religious
        Humanism, holds discussion seminars, and hosts an annual meeting in different
        locations
    Meetings: Annual
    Pres: Paul H Beattie, 5805 E 56th Street, Indianapolis, Indiana 46226
    Sec: Edgar Metzger, 8 Crag Knob, St Louis, Missouri 63120
    Publ: Religious Humanism
    Mem reqt: Membership requirements are not spelled out upon entrance to the
        organization. Any one who wishes to become a member may do so upon application
    Dues: $10

FLORIDA PHILOSOPHICAL ASSOCIATION 1955 (139)
    University of North Florida, P O Box 17074, Jacksonville, Florida 32216

    Purpose: To promote philosophy in Florida by facilitating the exchange of ideas
        among those engaged in this field of inquiry
    Activities: Forum for papers by members. Junior Award competition recognizes the
        best undergraduate paper and the best graduate paper submitted
    Meetings: Annual meeting in November, rotating among the colleges and universities
        in the state
    Pres: W H Werkmeister
    Sec: Robert Loftin
    Dues: $2, Graduate students $1

FULLERTON CLUB
    Bryn Mawr, Pennsylvania

    Meetings: Monthly, on the first Saturday of each month
    Pres: Paul Desjardins, Haverford College
    Sec-Treas: Ronald Duska, Rosemont College
    Mem reqt: Any philosopher is eligible for membership
    Dues: $4

GEORGIA PHILOSOPHICAL SOCIETY 1950 (100)
    Department of Philosophy, Oglethorpe College, Atlanta, Georgia 30319

    Purpose: To promote philosophical activity
    Activities: Hearing papers by visiting scholars and by members of the Society
    Meetings: Two or three per year
    Pres: J D Nordenhaug, Mercer University
    Sec: Ken Nishimura, Oglethorpe College
    Dues: $1

HEGEL SOCIETY OF AMERICA 1969 (260)
Department of Philosophy, Marquette University, Milwaukee, Wisconsin 53233

Purpose: To promote the study of the philosophy of Hegel, its place in the history
of thought, its relation to social, political, and cultural movements since his
time and its relevance to contemporary issues and fields of knowledge and to
promote the furtherance of original philosophic thought which has its basis in
the philosophy of Hegel or which treats issues in the style, manner, or method
of Hegel
Activities: Conducts symposia and publishes their proceedings
Meetings: Biennially
Pres: Louis Dupré, Georgetown University
Sec: Joseph O'Malley, Marquette University
Publ: The Owl of Minerva
Other inf: Next meeting to be held at Georgetown University in fall of 1974, double
theme: Hegel's Logic/Hegel's Aesthetics
Dues: $5

THE ILLINOIS PHILOSOPHY CONFERENCE 1957 (146)
c/o Prescott Johnson, Pres, Department of Philosophy, Monmouth College, Monmouth,
Illinois 61462

Purpose: A statewide association of philosophers
Activities: Yearly meeting for two days for the purpose of reading and discussing
original papers in various selected areas of philosophy
Meetings: November
Pres: J Prescott Johnson, Department of Philosophy, Monmouth College
Sec: John Oastler (1972-74), College of DuPage
Other inf: Inquiries about the association are welcome
Mem reqt: Members are generally from the state of Illinois or surrounding areas
Dues: $2

INTERNATIONAL PHENOMENOLOGICAL SOCIETY 1939
State University of New York at Buffalo, Buffalo, New York 14226

Pres: Marvin Farber, SUNY at Buffalo
Sec-Treas: V J McGill, San Francisco State College
Publ: Philosophy and Phenomenological Research

INTERNATIONAL SOCIETY FOR THE HISTORY OF IDEAS 1960 (60)
Department of Philosophy, Temple University, Philadelphia, Pennsylvania 19122

Purpose: To bring together scholars at work in the history of ideas in philosophy,
literature, science, and religion
Activities: Arranging conferences on topics in the history of ideas
Pres: Philip P Wiener, Department of Philosophy, Temple University
Sec: John Fisher, Department of Philosophy, Temple University
Publ: Journal of the History of Ideas
Mem reqt: By invitation
Dues: Registration fee at conferences

JOHN DEWEY SOCIETY FOR THE STUDY OF EDUCATION AND CULTURE
One Dupont Circle, Suite 610, Washington, D C 20036

Purpose: To encourage and sponsor in the spirit of John Dewey the study of educational
and cultural problems of special concern to the teaching profession
Activities: Sponsors yearbooks and presents a yearly John Dewey lecture
Meetings: Holds annual meetings in Chicago as part of the annual meeting of the

419

American Association of Colleges for Teacher Education
Pres: Donald Arnstine, Department of Education, University of California at Davis
Sec: Peter A Baldino, School of Education, Youngstown State University
Publ: Education Theory, Studies in Educational Theory, and the annual John Dewey
    lecture
Mem reqt: The Society is open to all who wish to further its purpose and participate
    in its increasingly important work
Dues: Institutional members $15, Sustaining fel $25, Patrons $100, Student and
    Retired fel $5, Fel $15

KENTUCKY PHILOSOPHICAL ASSOCIATION 1960 (120)
    Spalding College, Louisville, Kentucky 40203

Purpose: To promote philosophical activity in Kentucky
Activities: Regular meetings for discussion of topics presented in papers by members
    or by invited speakers from outside the state; annual undergraduate essay contests
Meetings: Spring and Autumn each year
Pres: James Eberenz (1973-74), Spalding College
Sec: Jesse DeBoer (1972-74), Department of Philosophy, University of Kentucky
Mem reqt: Active service in the profession, and/or interest in promotion of
    philosophical activity
Dues: $2

LONG ISLAND PHILOSOPHICAL SOCIETY 1964 (85)
    Department of Philosophy, State University of New York, Stony Brook, New York 11790

Purpose: To encourage philosophy on Long Island
Meetings: Fall and Spring
Pres: David W Benfield (1972-74), Department of Philosophy, SUNY at Stony Brook
Sec: James Friel (1972-74), Department of Philosophy, SUNY at Farmingdale
Publ: The Society publishes a detailed copy of the program of its meetings complete
    with abstracts of the papers
Mem reqt: A person is eligible for membership provided he or she has an interest
    in philosophy. In effect there are no requirements; however, most members are
    either teachers or graduate students of philosophy
Dues: $2

MAINE PHILOSOPHICAL INSTITUTE 1943 (40)
    Department of Philosophy, Bates College, Lewiston, Maine 04240

Purpose: To discuss philosophy and the teaching of philosophy
Activities: The Institute meets the Saturday nearest May 1
Meetings: Annually
Sec: Edward W James, Department of Philosophy, Bates College
Mem reqt: Faculty status in philosophy or religion at one of the colleges in Maine

METAPHYSICAL SOCIETY OF AMERICA 1950 (700)
    Department of Philosophy, Marquette University, Milwaukee, Wisconsin 53233

Purpose: To study reality
Activities: Annual meeting for presentation and discussion of papers on philosophical
    issues
Meetings: In March
Pres: Ernan McMullin (1973-74), Notre Dame University
Sec-Treas: Marc F Griesbach (1971-74), Marquette University
Mem reqt: Recommendation of two members and approval by executive council and
    members present at business session of annual meeting

Other inf: Member of Fédération Internationale des Sociétés de Philosophie (FISP)
Dues: $5

MIDDLE ATLANTIC STATES PHILOSOPHY OF EDUCATION SOCIETY 1956 (200)
Department of Foundations of Education, Hofstra University, Hempstead, New York 11550

Purpose: To promote the fundamental philosophical treatment of the problems of
education, to promote the clarification of agreements and disagreements
between the several philosophies of education through the opportunities for
discussion afforded by annual meetings, to advance and improve teaching in
philosophy of education, both in schools for the education of teachers and in
other educational institutions, to cultivate fruitful relationships between
workers in general philosophy and workers in philosophy of education and to
encourage promising young students in the field of philosophy of education
Meetings: Fall and Spring meetings
Pres: Timothy H Smith, Hofstra University
Sec: James H M Afshar, Bloomsburg State College
Mem reqt: Fellow of National Philosophy of Education Society
Dues: $5, Students $2

MINNESOTA PHILOSOPHICAL SOCIETY 1957 (60)
Saint Cloud State College, Saint Cloud, Minnesota 56301

Purpose: To promote study, research, discussion, and publication in the field of
philosophy
Activities: To discuss papers written by philosophers in Minnesota
Meetings: Annually, generally a Saturday in October
Pres: George E Yoos, St Cloud State College
Sec: Richard Berquist, College of St Thomas
Mem reqt: Membership shall be open to residents of Minnesota who are interested in
furthering the purposes of the Society. Persons who by teaching philosophy in
the colleges and universities of the state or by research and publication have
shown an interest in the aims of the Society shall qualify for membership
automatically. Others shall qualify by action of the officers
Dues: $1

MISSISSIPPI PHILOSOPHY ASSOCIATION 1948 (32)
University of Southern Mississippi, Hattiesburg, Mississippi 39401

Purpose: To increase the understanding and appreciation of philosophy, to encourage
research and advance the standards and ideals of the teaching of philosophy and
to cultivate an interest in the study of philosophy in the Mississippi institutions
of higher learning through the exchange of ideas and the discussion of common
problems
Meetings: Annually in Jackson
Pres: W Hal Furr, University of Mississippi
Sec: Michael H Mitias, Millsaps College
Mem reqt: Professional interest in philosophy
Dues: $2

MOUNTAIN-PLAINS PHILOSOPHICAL CONFERENCE 1947 (50)
Department of Philosophy, University of Colorado, Boulder, Colorado 80382

Meetings: Yearly meetings in Mountain-Plains area in October
Chm of Bd: Richard Cole, University of Kansas
Other inf: Member of Fédération Internationale des Sociétés de Philosophie (FISP)
Dues: $1

NEW MEXICO AND WEST TEXAS PHILOSOPHICAL SOCIETY 1949 (35)
c/o H G Alexander, Department of Philosophy, University of New Mexico, Albuquerque,
New Mexico 87131

Purpose: To present papers on philosophical topics and further the interests in
philosophy in the region
Activities: Annual meeting in mid-April. Sponsorship of an essay contest on
philosophical topics among high school seniors in the state of New Mexico.
Winner receives a one-year tuition scholarship at one of several participating
universities in the state of New Mexico
Meetings: Yearly for presentation of papers
Pres: Peter Robinson, Department of Philosophy, University of Texas at El Paso
Sec: Hubert G Alexander, Department of Philosophy, University of New Mexico
Publ: Proceedings of the New Mexico and West Texas Philosophical Society
Other inf: Member of Fédération Internationale des Societés de Philosophie (FISP)
Mem reqt: Interest in philosophy and payment of dues
Dues: $2

NORTH CAROLINA PHILOSOPHICAL SOCIETY (189)
Department of Philosophy, Wake Forest University, Winston-Salem, North Carolina 28036

Purpose: To encourage the study of philosophy among North Carolina philosophers
Activities: Annual meetings to read and listen to philosophical papers
Meetings: Annually, first Saturday in May
Pres: Earl R MacCormac (1973-75), Department of Philosophy, Davidson College
Sec: Robert H Vorsteg (1973-75), Department of Philosophy, Wake Forest University
Dues: $1

NORTH CENTRAL PHILOSOPHY OF EDUCATION SOCIETY (75)
139-B Burton Hall, University of Minnesota 55455

Purpose: To promote fundamental philosophic treatment of the problems of education,
to promote the clarification of agreements and differences between the several
philosophies of education through the opportunities for discussion afforded by
annual meetings, to advance and improve teaching in the philosophy of education
both in schools for the education of teachers and in other educational institutions,
to cultivate fruitful relationships between workers in general philosophy and workers
in philosophy of education, and to encourage promising young students in the field of
philosophy of education
Meetings: Annually
Pres: Robert H Beck, 139-B Burton Hall, University of Minnesota
Sec: Stanley D Anderson, Bethel College
Publ: Newsletter
Mem reqt: Membership is open to all who are interested
Dues: $3.50

NORTHERN ILLINOIS PHILOSOPHICAL SOCIETY 1960 (105)
Department of Philosophy, Loyola University, 820 N Michigan Avenue, Chicago,
Illinois 60611

Purpose: To encourage philosophic discussion and dialogue
Activities: Reading papers and informal discussions
Meetings: Spring and Fall of every year
Pres: A R Gini, Loyola University, Chicago
Sec: A R Gini, Loyola University, Chicago
Mem reqt: Open to any college or university teacher of philosophy in Northern
Illinois and vicinity. Also open to graduate students.

THE OHIO PHILOSOPHICAL ASSOCIATION 1930 (300)
    P O Box 105, New Concord, Ohio 43762

    Purpose: To encourage research in philosophy and the interchange of ideas among
        teachers in philosophy in colleges and universities of Ohio
    Activities: Continuing activity through committees
    Meeting: Annually
    Pres: Ramona Cormier (1973-76), Bowling Green State University
    Sec: Stephen Taylor (1972-75), University of Toledo
    Publ: Proceedings of the Ohio Philosophical Association
    Mem reqt: The members of any department of philosophy or any department which
        combines philosophy with some other area, in an institution which holds
        membership in the Ohio College Association, or any person teaching in such an
        institution who has a PhD in philosophy
    Dues: $4

THE OHIO VALLEY PHILOSOPHY OF EDUCATION SOCIETY 1948 (161)
    c/o Frederick M Schultz, Secretary-Treasurer, Ohio Valley Philosophy of Education
        Society, Department of Education Foundations, College of Education, The University
        of Akron, Akron, Ohio 44325

    Purpose: To foster and to engage in philosophical studies in philosophy and education
    Activities: An annual meeting, usually held in the Cincinnati, Ohio metropolitan area,
        at which philosophical papers are read and discussed; the Proceedings of this
        meeting are published annually. The Society has, in recent years, also made a
        small annual contribution to the journal Studies in Philosophy and Education
    Meeting: Annual meetings are held
    Pres: Richard Pratte, 145 Ramseyer Hall, The Ohio State University
    Sec-Treas: Frederick M Schultz, College of Education, The University of Akron
    Publ: Proceedings of the Ohio Valley Philosophy of Education Society (published annually)
    Other inf: This society is composed of philosophers dedicated to the study of
        philosophy of education in terms of critical analysis of the moral and
        epistemological foundations of education as well as to the achievement of
        social-philosophical insight into the problems of education and the human
        dilemmas in educational contexts
    Mem reqt: A member must be a scholar in philosophy or philosophy of education who
        demonstrates primary interest, or at least significant interest, in philosophical
        studies as they relate to education where education is defined in its broadest
        cultural terms and not merely limited to schooling
    Dues: $5, Grad students $2

PERSONALISTIC DISCUSSION GROUP 1938
    Boston University, Boston, Massachusetts 02215

    Purpose: To discuss philosophical issues related (without special restriction) to
        the philosophy of personalism
    Meetings: Annually in connection with the Eastern Division of the APA
    Executive Committee: Peter Bertocci, Boston University; Robert Beck, Clark University;
        John H Lavely, Boston University
    Other inf: Papers are mimeographed, distributed to a list of members and others, then
        discussed at each open meeting after a critic comments on the paper
    Mem reqt: Interest in the programs
    Voluntary dues: $1

WESTERN DIVISION, PERSONALIST DISCUSSION GROUP 1950 (50)
    Xavier University, Cincinnati, Ohio 45207

    Purpose: To discuss philosophical issues in context of American Personalism
    Activities: Basic activities limited to annual meeting held as a special group
        in conjunction with the annual meeting of the American Philosophical

Association, Western Division
Meetings: Annual
Pres: Bernard A Gendreau, Department of Philosophy, Xavier University
Sec: Arthur W Munk, Department of Philosophy, Albion College
Mem reqt: Interest in American Personalism as a philosophical perspective and as
a basis for open dialogue developed in comparative studies of Western and
Oriental philosophical styles

PHI SIGMA TAU 1955 (11,000)
National Headquarters, Department of Philosophy, Marquette University, Milwaukee,
Wisconsin 53233

Purpose: To promote ties nationally between philosophy departments and students in
philosophy, and to honor academic excellence in philosophy
Activities: Meetings organized by each of sixty-five local chapters. National
convention. Essay competition in philosophy
Pres: John Kozy, Jr, Department of Philosophy, East Carolina University
Sec: Lee C Rice, Department of Philosophy, Marquette University
Publ: Dialogue (three issues per year), Newsletter (two issues per year)
Mem reqt: Students and teachers of philosophy who qualify
Dues: $10 National initiation fee, plus regional dues

PHILOSOPHIC SOCIETY FOR THE STUDY OF SPORT 1972 (105)
Brockport College, SUNY, Brockport, New York 14420

Purpose: To promote scholarly interest in sport
Activities: Meetings
Meetings: Yearly
Pres: Paul Weiss, Catholic University of America
Sec: Francis Keenan, Brockport College, SUNY
Mem reqt: Interest by qualified students of sports
Dues: $10

THE PHILOSOPHY OF EDUCATION SOCIETY 1941 (750)
School of Education, University of Missouri-Kansas City, Kansas City, Missouri 64110
(attn to Young Pai, Sec-Treas)

Purpose: To promote the philosophic treatment of the problems of education, to promote
the clarification of agreements and differences among the several philosophies of
education, to advance and improve teaching in the philosophy of education, and to
cultivate fruitful relationships between workers in general philosophy and
workers in philosophy of education
Activities: Publishes the Proceedings of the Annual Meeting and a co-sponsor with
the University of Illinois in publishing Educational Theory. Grants given to
such journals as Studies in Philosophy and Education and the Journal of Aesthetic
Education
Meetings: Annually, the week before Easter
Pres: Kingsley Price (1973-74), Department of Philosophy, Johns Hopkins University
Sec-Treas: Young Pai (1972-74), School of Education, University of Missouri, Kansas City
Publ: The Proceedings of Annual Meeting; Educational Theory
Mem reqt: There are three classes of membership: Fellows, Associates and Emeriti
Dues: Fellows $20, Student associates $12, Others $15, Emiritus none

PHILOSOPHY OF SCIENCE ASSOCIATION 1934 (100)
Department of Philosophy, 18 Morrill Hall, Michigan State University, East Lansing,
Michigan 48823

Purpose: To further studies and free discussion from diverse standpoints in
the field of philosophy of science, publishing, and job placement service
Meetings: Biennial meetings; Fourth Biennial Meeting will be held in Notre Dame,
Indiana, October 25-27, 1974
Pres: Israel Scheffler (1973-74), Emerson Hall, Harvard University
Sec: Peter D Asquith (1973-74), Department of Philosophy, Michigan State University
Publ: Philosophy of Science, and Association Newsletter
Mem reqt: Full member: doctorate in any philosophical or scientific field; Associate
member: sympathy with the objectives of the Association; Student member: full
time student in any discipline
Dues: Full or Associate members $10, Student members $6

SOCIETY FOR ANCIENT GREEK PHILOSOPHY 1953
Department of Philosophy, Emory University, Atlanta, Georgia 30322

Purpose: To encourage research in and discussion of ancient Greek philosophy
Meetings: Annual meetings with the American Philological Association, and with the
Eastern Division of the American Philosophical Association
Pres: Rosamond Kent Sprague, Department of Philosophy, University of South Carolina
Sec: John P Anton, Department of Philosophy, Emory University
Mem reqt: Interest in ancient Greek philosophy
Dues: $2, Canada $2.50

SOCIETY FOR ASIAN AND COMPARATIVE PHILOSOPHY 1967 (217)
1993 East-West Road, Honolulu, Hawaii 96822

Purpose: To serve the professional interests and needs of scholars who are involved
in Asian and comparative philosophy, to encourage the development of those
disciplines in the academic world through the holding of annual meetings, to
sponsor workshops, to support publications, and in various other suitable ways
to bring Asian and Western philosophers together for the exchange of ideas
Meetings: Annually
Pres: Kenneth K Inada, Department of Philosophy, SUNY at Buffalo
Sec: Eliot Deutsch, 1993 East-West Road, Honolulu, Hawaii 96822
Publ: Sponsors monograph series
Mem reqt: Open to established scholars and graduate students in Asian and comparative
philosophy
Dues: $12 (Includes special discount subscription to the Philosophy East and West)

THE SOCIETY FOR COMPARATIVE PHILOSOPHY 1962 (600)
P O Box 857, Sausalito, California 94965

Purpose: To assist Alan Watts and others in their research, writing and lectures
on the fruitful interchange of ideas and experiences between the philosophies
of Asia and the West
Activities: Lectures, seminars, and workshops
Pres: Alan Watts, Society for Comparative Philosophy
Sec: Hisayo Saijo, Society for Comparative Philosophy
Publ: Bulletin, The Alan Watts Journal
Dues: $20

SOCIETY FOR PHENOMENOLOGY AND EXISTENTIAL PHILOSOPHY 1962 (850)
c/o Don Ihde, Department of Philosophy, State University of New York, Stony Brook,
New York 11790

Purpose: To further research and inquiry in the area of phenomenology and existentialism
Activities: Annual meeting
Meetings: October every year

Co-Sec: Don Ihde, SUNY at Stony Brook
      Richard M Zaner, Southern Methodist University
Publ: Selected papers from the Society for Phenomenology and Existential Philosophy
Dues: $5, Student $3

SOCIETY FOR PHILOSOPHY AND PUBLIC AFFAIRS 1969 (400)
    c/o Hugo Bedan, Department of Philosophy, Tufts University, Medford, Massachusetts 02155

Purpose: To promote discussion and action by philosophers on matters of general
    concern
Meetings: Annual business meeting at the APA Eastern Division meeting. Symposia at
    the meetings of other APA Divisions. Regular local group meetings.
Pres: Hugo Bedan, Tufts University
Vice-Pres: Beverly Woodward, Center for International Studies, Princeton University
Publ: Occasional newsletter
Mem reqt: Teacher or graduate student of philosophy, others with approval of
    Executive Committee
Dues: $5, Students $2

SOCIETY FOR PHILOSOPHY OF CREATIVITY 1957
    303 South Tower Road, Carbondale, Illinois 62901

Purpose: To contribute to the development of a Philosophy of Creativity
Activities: Research and publication of philosophy of creativity
Meetings: With the Eastern Division of the APA in December, with the Western Division
    of the APA in May, and with the Pacific Division of the APA in March
Dir: William S Minor, 303 South Tower Road, Carbondale, Illinois 62901
Publ: Philosophy of Creativity Monograph Series
Mem reqt: Similar to those of the APA
Dues: $5

THE SOCIETY FOR PHILOSOPHY OF RELIGION 1938 (100)
    c/o Frank R Harrison, III, Department of Philosophy, University of Georgia, Athens,
    Georgia 30602

Purpose: The clarification and advancement of issues in religious philosophy through
    investigation and discussion
Meetings: Annual
Pres: Bowman L Clarke, Department of Philosophy and Religion, University of Georgia
Sec-Treas: Frank R Harrison, III, Department of Philosophy and Religion, University
    of Georgia
Publ: The International Journal for Philosophy of Religion
Mem reqt: By nomination and election
Dues: $5

SOCIETY FOR THE ADVANCEMENT OF AMERICAN PHILOSOPHY 1972 (235)
    Fairfield University, Fairfield, Connecticut 06430

Purpose: To promote research on the history of American philosphy, to promote
    original creative works in American philosophy, and to provide in general a
    forum for the exchange of information on American philosophy
Meetings: A spring meeting, March 1 and 2, 1974, will be held at Vanderbilt
    University. The topic for the two-day meeting will be "Human Rights and the
    American Tradition."
Executive Circle: John P Anton, Emory; Joseph G Grassi, Secretary, Fairfield;
    Lewis E Hahn, Southern Illinois; John Lachs, Vanderbilt; John J McDermott,
    Queens; Richard Robin, Mount Holyoke; Beth Singer, Brooklyn College

Sec: Joseph G Grassi, Fairfield University
Mem reqt: An interest in American philosophy
Dues: $5, Retired professors and grad students: No dues

THE SOCIETY FOR THE HISTORY OF TECHNOLOGY 1958 (1750)
    Department of Social Sciences, Georgia Institute of Technology, Atlanta, Georgia
        30332

    Purpose: To encourage the study of the development of technology and its relations
        with society and culture
    Activities: Holds annual meetings with scholarly programs; publishes a quarterly
        journal, Technology and Culture; publishes on an irregular basis, in conjunction
        with MIT Press, a monograph series on the history of technology
    Meetings: Held annually at the end of December with American Historical Association.
        Also meets occasionally with American Association for the Advancement of Science,
        and co-sponsors meetings with other professional organizations.
    Pres: John B Rae (1973-74), Department of Humanities and Social Sciences, Harvey
        Mudd College
    Sec: Melvin Kranzberg (1973-74), Department of Social Sciences, Georgia Institute of
        Technology
    Publ: Technology and Culture (international quarterly); Monograph series in the
        history of technology, published in conjunction with MIT Press
    Other inf: The April 1973 issue of Technology and Culture had a 205-page supplement:
        Bibliography of the Philosophy of Technology, compiled by Carl Mitcham and
        Robert Mackey. It is a fully annotated bibliography. This supplement is
        available as a separate hardbound book from the University of Chicago Press
    Mem reqt: Payment of dues; an interest in the history of technology. SHOT is a
        multi-disciplinary organization, members include historians, philosophers,
        sociologists, economists, engineers, etc
    Dues: $12, Institutions $15

SOCIETY FOR THE PHILOSOPHICAL STUDY OF DIALECTICAL MATERIALISM (100)
    c/o John Somerville, 1426 Merritt Drive, El Cajon, California 92020

    Purpose: To provide interested philosophers of all viewpoints with opportunities
        to clarify issues and discuss problems pertaining to Marxism
    Activities: Symposium also open to all APA members and guests; conferences, seminars,
        research groups, workshops
    Meetings: SPSDM has three regional divisions, corresponding to the divisions of the
        APA: Eastern, Western and Pacific, each of which has been meeting annually in
        conjunction with the respective APA meeting; also local meetings
    Pres: John Somerville, 1426 Merritt Drive, El Cajon, California 92020
    Eastern Div: Chm: Dale Riepe, SUNY at Buffalo
                 Sec: George Hampsch, College of the Holy Cross
    Western Div: Chm: K T Fann, Atkinson College, York University
                 Sec: Frank Cunningham, University of Toronto
    Pacific Div: Chm: Walter Koppelman, California State University at San Diego
                 Sec: Bernd Magnus, University of California at Riverside
    Publ: SPSDM Newsletter; Dialogues on the Philosophy of Marxism; Marxism Revolution
        and Peace
    Other inf: Member of Fédération Internationale des Sociétés de Philosophie (FISP)
    Dues: $2

SOCIETY FOR THE SCIENTIFIC STUDY OF RELIGION 1949 (1520)
    Box U68A, University of Connecticut, Storrs, Connecticut 06268

    Purpose: To stimulate and communicate significant scientific research on religious
        institutions and religious experience
    Meetings: Annually, last week of October

427

Pres: James E Dittes, Yale Divinity School
Sec: Phillip E Hammond, Department of Sociology, University of Arizona
Publ: Journal for the Scientific Study of Religion
Mem reqt: Open to students and scholars interested in the application of the
    scientific method to the study of religion
Dues: $15, Students $8

SOCIETY FOR THE STUDY OF PROCESS PHILOSOPHIES 1965 (350)
    Dickinson College, Carlisle, Pennsylvania 17013

    Purpose: To encourage the study of the philosophies of process and the development of
        original work in process philosophy
    Meetings: In conjunction with the Eastern Division of the APA, and the morning before
        the Metaphysical Society of America meetings
    Cord: George Allan, Dickinson College
        Robert Neville, Department of Philosophy, SUNY at Purchase
    Other inf: SSPP cooperates closely with the journal Process Studies, since they
        share a similar purpose, but the two organizations are independent of one another
    Mem reqt: No requirements; request membership by writing to one of the coordinators
    Dues: Voluntary contributions only

SOCIETY FOR WOMEN IN PHILOSOPHY
    Department of Philosophy, Western Illinois University, Macomb, Illinois 61455

    Activities: The Society plans to hold sessions at each of the regional meetings
        of the APA, as well as independently organized programs. Theses will be
        devoted to papers by women on philosophical issues related to the problems of
        women.
    Sec: Hannah Hardgrave, Department of Philosophy, Western Illinois University

SOUTH CAROLINA SOCIETY FOR PHILOSOPHY 1953 (55)
    c/o James Stiver, Department of Philosophy, University of South Carolina, Columbia,
        South Carolina 29208

    Purpose: To foster the study and discussion of philosophy in the state of South
        Carolina
    Activities: At the annual meeting a student essay contest and scholarly papers are
        presented, and innovative teaching methods are discussed
    Pres: James Stiver, Department of Philosophy, University of South Carolina
    Sec: Ted Peters, Department of Religion and Philosophy, Newberry College
    Dues: $3

SOUTHEAST PHILOSOPHY OF EDUCATION SOCIETY 1948 (200)
    College of Education, Florida State University, Tallahassee, Florida 32306

  ⌐ Purpose: To promote scholarly research in philosophy of education and to encourage
        instruction in philosophy of education in Southeastern colleges and universities
    Meetings: Annually, in early February
    Pres: C J B Macmillan, Florida State University, Tallahassee
    Sec: Daniel DeNicola, Rollins College
    Mem reqt: An active interest in philosophy of education and residence in the Southeast
    Dues: $2

SOUTHERN SOCIETY FOR PHILOSOPHY AND PSYCHOLOGY 1904 (700)
    Department of Psychology, University of Louisville, Louisville, Kentucky 40208

    Purpose: To promote philosophy and psychology in the Southern section of the United
        States by facilitating the exchange of ideas among those engaged in these fields

of inquiry, by encouraging investigation, by fostering the educational function
of philosophy and psychology, and by improving the academic status of these
subjects
Meetings: Annual meetings. Annual meeting in 1974 to be held in Tampa, Florida
Pres: Lelon J Peacock (1973-74), University of Georgia
Sec: Michel Loeb (1972-75), Department of Psychology, University of Louisville
Publ: Newsletter and copies of the program for the annual meeting
Mem reqt: Candidates shall be engaged professionally in either philosophy or psychology
    or shall give evidence of a substantially equivalent interest and competence
Dues: Full member $5, Associate member $3

SOUTHWESTERN PHILOSOPHICAL SOCIETY   1935   (220)
    Department of Philosophy, University of Oklahoma, 455 W Lindsey Street, Rm 605,
    Norman, Oklahoma 73069

    Purpose: To promote philosophical dialogue and inquiry, to facilitate intercourse
        among philosophers in the Southwest, to stimulate interest and improve the
        quality of the teaching of philosophy at colleges and universities in the Southwest
    Meetings: Annually in November
    Pres: Elmer Duncan, Baylor University
    Sec: A Y Gunter, North Texas State University
    Publ: Newsletter
    Other inf: The proceedings of the annual meeting are published in the Southwestern
        Journal of Philosophy
    Mem reqt: Regular membership, PhD with a major in philosophy and a teaching assignment
        in the field of philosophy, or "...significant contributions to philosophy through
        research or writing..."; Associate membership otherwise available
    Dues: $6

SOUTHWESTERN PHILOSOPHY OF EDUCATION SOCIETY   1950   (40-60)
    1905 Hardy Drive, Edmond, Oklahoma 73034

    Purpose: Professional forum
    Activities: Yearly meeting to present and discuss papers
    Meetings: First weekend in November
    Pres: Donna Lee Yonker, 1905 Hardy Drive, Edmond, Oklahoma 73034
    Sec: Clinton Allison, College of Education, University of Tennessee, Knoxville
    Publ: Proceedings of the Southwestern Philosophy of Education Society
    Mem reqt: Open to anyone interested in education
    Dues: $1

SWEDENBORG SCIENTIFIC ASSOCIATION   1898   (350)
    Bryn Athyn, Pennsylvania 19009

    Purpose: The preservation, translation, publication, and distribution of the
        scientific and philosophical works of Emanuel Swedenborg; the promotion
        of the principles taught in these works, having in view likewise their
        relation to the science and philosophy of the present day
    Meetings: Annually, in early May
    Pres: Edward F Allen, Bryn Athyn, Pennsylvania 19009
    Sec: Morna Hyatt, Bryn Athyn, Pennsylvania 19009
    Publ: The New Philosophy (quarterly), $4 subscription fee
    Dues: $5 (includes subscription)

TRI-STATE PHILOSOPHICAL ASSOCIATION   1967   (130)
    State University College, Fredonia, New York 14063

    Purpose: To promote philosophical dialogue by the presentation and discussion of
        papers

Activities: Occasional newsletters
Meetings: Semi-annually, Fall and Spring
Mem reqt: Staff of philosophy departments in this region
Dues: $10 Institutional

VIRGINIA PHILOSOPHICAL ASSOCIATION 1939 (150)
Department of Philosophy, Longwood College, Farmville, Virginia 23901

Purpose: To present and discuss papers in philosophy and to promote fellowship
    among philosophers in Virginia
Meetings: Second weekend in October
Pres: Allan Carlson, Virginia Military Institute
Sec: Lewis A Foster, College of William and Mary
Mem reqt: To be a philosophy teacher in some of the Virginia colleges or universities
    or to have proof that one is interested and competent in the discipline of
    philosophy

WASHINGTON PHILOSOPHY CLUB 1956 (95)
4307 38th Street, NW, Washington, DC 20016

Purpose: To arrange for professional-level philosophical discussions in the
    Washington, DC, area
Meetings: Three fall meetings; three spring meetings, one of which is an all-day
    meeting with a banquet in the evening
Pres: Stephen F Barker (1973-74), Department of Philosophy, Johns Hopkins University
Sec: William Gerber (1973-74), 4307 38th Street, N W, Washington, DC 20016
Publ: Newsletter issued during the summer
Mem reqt: Serious interest in philosophy
Dues: $3.25

WEST VIRGINIA PHILOSOPHICAL SOCIETY 1947 (100)
c/o John Goodwin, Marshall University, Huntington, West Virginia 25701

Purpose: The advancement of creative work in philosophy
Activities: Two annual meetings, publication of a journal
Meetings: Fall and Spring
Pres: John Goodwin, (1973-74), Marshall University
Sec: Gene D'Amour, West Virginia University
Publ: Journal of the West Virginia Philosophical Society
Mem reqt: Professional members, those who teach philosophy or in related areas, or
    do philosophic research; Lay members, those interested in philosophy; Student
    members, those studying philosophy

WESTERN CONFERENCE ON THE TEACHING OF PHILOSOPHY 1951
Department of History and Philosophy of Education, College of Education, University
    of Illinois, Urbana, Illinois 61801

Purpose: To promote and encourage excellence in the teaching of philosophy
Activities: Conducts colloquies of papers, discussions, and projects devoted to the
    improvement of the teaching of philosophy
Meetings: One meeting each year, in conjunction with the Western Division of the
    American Philosophical Association
Pres: Hugh G Petrie (1973-74), 503 S Chicago Avenue, Champaign, Illinois
Mem reqt: Consists of interested parties attending the yearly colloquies

CENTERS AND INSTITUTES

UNITED STATES

THE CENTER FOR INTEGRATIVE EDUCATION 1947 (300)
   12 Church Street, New Rochelle, New York 10805

   Purpose: To encourage philosophical, historical and comparative culture studies;
      we are interested in culture studies which explore the unity of the process of
      knowing, in the contributions of the natural sciences toward a unified world
      picture, and in the insights of the cultural and humanistic disciplines which
      provide a more profound understanding of man and his communities
   Activities: Summer institutes and workshops with the cooperation of colleges and
      universities interested in exploring the foundations of integrative liberal
      education and in possible applications to their own curricula.
   Meetings: Symposia undertaken with the support of cooperating institutions and
      invited scholars to explore fundamental themes in epistemology (theory of
      knowledge) and the philosophical foundations of the natural and social sciences,
      arts and literature
   Pres: Henry Margenau, 12 Church Street, New Rochelle, New York 10805
   Sec: Robert Drew-Bear, 12 Church Street, New Rochelle, New York 10805
   Publ: Main Currents in Modern Thought
   Other inf: Members of the Council are available by arrangement for special lectures
      on integrative studies
   Mem reqt: Interest in the work of the Center
   Dues: Associates $10, Friends $20, Sustaining members $100

CENTER FOR PROCESS STUDIES 1973
   1325 N College, Claremont, California 91711

   Purpose: To explore the relevance of process thought, especially that of Alfred
      North Whitehead, as a perspective with which to seek an integrative world view,
      integrative of Eastern and Western visions as well as integrative of the various
      Western disciplines
   Dir: John B Cobb, Jr, 1325 N College, Claremont, California 91711
   Executive Dir: David R Griffin, 1325 N College, Claremont, California 91711

THE COUNCIL FOR PHILOSOPHICAL STUDIES 1965 (15)
   University of Connecticut, Storrs, Connecticut 06268

   Purpose: To sponsor projects for the advancement of teaching and research in
      philosophy
   Activities: Summer institutes for teachers of philosophy, working conferences and
      a visiting philosopher program
   Meetings: Twice a year
   Pres: Roderick M Chisholm, Brown University
   Sec: Samuel Gorovitz, University of Maryland

INSTITUTE FOR PHILOSOPHICAL RESEARCH AND DEVELOPMENT
   1915 Las Lomas Road, N E, Albuquerque, New Mexico 87106

   Dir: Archie J Bahm, 1915 Las Lomas Road, N E, Albuquerque, New Mexico 87106

THE NATIONAL COUNCIL FOR CRITICAL ANALYSIS 1968 (300)
   Jersey City State College, 2039 Kennedy Boulevard, Jersey City, New Jersey 07503

   Purpose: To introduce philosophy to the pre-college level; to publish the Journal

of Critical Analysis; and to encourage dialogue among the various academic
disciplines
Pres: P S Schievella, Jersey City State College
Publ: The Journal of Critical Analysis
Mem reqt: An interest in philosophy
Dues: $10. Dues includes a subscription to The Journal of Critical Analysis

PHILOSOPHY DOCUMENTATION CENTER 1966
Bowling Green State University, Bowling Green, Ohio 43403

Purpose: To serve philosophers by providing them with bibliographic and other types
of information
Dir: Richard H Lineback, Bowling Green State University
Bus Mgr: Gerald E Slivka, Bowling Green State University
Publ: The Philosopher's Index, Directory of American Philosophers, International
Directory of Philosophy and Philosophers
Other inf: The Center serves as the Editorial Center, U.S.A., for Bibliography of
Philosophy. The Center also operates the Philosopher's Information Retrieval
System, which prepares custom bibliographies upon request in the area of
philosophy. In addition, a series of "Bibliographies of Philosophers" is
published by the Center.   •

TRANSLATION CENTER 1967
Southern Illinois University, Edwardsville, Illinois 62025

Purpose: Gathering of information on philosophical translations in progress
Activities: Quarterly publication of "Translations in Progress" in The Philosopher's
Index
Dir: Fritz Marti, Southern Illinois University

JOURNALS

UNITED STATES

AGORA 1970
Ed: Martin A Bertman, State University at Potsdam, SUNY, Potsdam, New York 13676

Purpose: To publish technical philosophy and, also, theoretical and methodological
studies in the humanities and social sciences
Semi-ann; Circ: 1400; 6 or more phil articles per yr; Bk Rev
$2.50, Institutions $4

AMERICAN PHILOSOPHICAL QUARTERLY 1964
Ed: Nicholas Rescher, Dept of Phil, University of Pittsburgh, Pittsburgh, Pennsylvania
15260

Purpose: To publish technical papers
Q; Circ: 1800; About 36 phil articles per yr
Publ: Basil Blackwell, 49 Broad Street, Oxford, England
$8, Institutions $18

ANNALS OF MATHEMATICAL LOGIC 1970
Eds: C C Chang, Dept of Math, University of California, Los Angeles, California 90024,
A Mostowski, Institute of Mathematics, University of Warsaw, Poland, M O Rabin,
Institute of Mathematics, Hebrew University, Jerusalem, Israel, H Rogers, Jr, Dept
of Math, Massachusetts Institute Of Technology, Cambridge, Massachusetts 02139

Purpose: To publish brief monographs in mathematical logic and the foundations of
mathematics
Q
Publ: North-Holland Publishing Co, Journal Division, 335 Jan van Galenstraat, P O Box
211, Amsterdam, The Netherlands
$37

THE ANTIOCH REVIEW
Ed: Lawrence Grauman, Jr, Yellow Springs, Ohio 45387

Q; Bk Rev
Publ: The Antioch Press
$6, Pan-American $6.50, Foreign $7

BEHAVIORISM: A Forum for Critical Discussion
Ed: Willard F Day, Dept of Psych, University of Nevada, Reno, Nevada 89507

Purpose: To serve as an outlet for philosophical and psychological papers dealing
with conceptual issues related to behaviorism
Semi-ann; Circ: 1200; 15 phil articles per yr
Publ: University of Nevada, Reno
$10, Institutions $15

CHINESE STUDIES IN PHILOSOPHY 1969
Ed: Chung-ying Cheng, University of Hawaii, Honolulu, Hawaii 96822

Purpose: To present unabridged translations of the most important philosophical articles
from Chinese sources

433

Q; Circ: 400; About 12 phil articles per yr
Publ: International Arts and Sciences Press, Inc
$15, Institutions $60

CLIO: An Interdisciplinary Journal of Literature, History, and the Philosophy of History
1971
Ed: Robert H Canary and Henry Kozicki, The University of Wisconsin at Parkside, Kenosha,
    Wisconsin 53140

Purpose: To bring together material on the interplay of literary criticism, histor-
    iography, and the philosophy of history
3 issues per yr; Circ: 300; 2-3 phil articles per yr; Bk Rev
Publ: CLIO Association, University of Wisconsin at Parkside
$4.50, Institutions $12

CULTURAL HERMENEUTICS 1973
Ed: David M Rasmussen, Dept of Phil, Boston College, Chestnut Hill, Massachusetts
    02167

Purpose: To provide a forum for critical cultural theory
Q; Circ: 400; 12-20 phil articles per yr; Bk Rev
Publ: D Reidel Publishing Co, P O Box 17, Dordrecht, The Netherlands
$26.78

DIALOGOS 1963
Ed: Roberto Torretti, P O Box 21572-UPR Sta, Rio Piedras, Puerto Rico 00931

Purpose: Dialogos is the journal of the Department of Philosophy of the University
    of Puerto Rico. Articles are published in Spanish and English.
Semi-ann; Circ: 1300; 12-16 articles per yr; Bk Rev
Publ: Oficina de Publicaciones, Facultad de Humanidades, Universidad de Puerto Rico,
    Rio Piedras
$4

DIALOGUE 1956
Ed: Sherman M Stanage, Dept of Phil, Northern Illinois University, DeKalb, Illinois
    60115

Purpose: To publish articles in philosophy by persons who have not received a terminal
    degree
Sponsor: Phi Sigma Tau
3 issues per yr; Circ: 1000; Bk Rev
Publ: Lee C Rice, Dept of Phil, Marquette University, Milwaukee, Wisconsin 53233
$3, Foreign $3.50

EDUCATIONAL THEORY 1951
Ed: Joe R Burnett, College of Education, University of Illinois, Urbana, Illinois
    61801

Purpose: To foster the continuing development of educational theory and to encourage
    wide and effective discussion of theoretical problems within the educational profes-
    sion
Q; Circ: 2200; About 60-70% phil articles; Bk Rev
Publ: Educational Theory, Education Building, University of Illinois, Urbana
$8, Foreign $6

ETHICS: An International Journal of Social, Political, and Legal Philosophy 1890
    Eds: Charles Wegener and Warner Wick, Cobb Hall, University of Chicago, 5811 Ellis
      Avenue, Chicago, Illinois 60637

    Purpose: To publish articles in ethical theory, social science, and jurisprudence,
      contributing to the understanding of the basic structure of civilization and
      society
    Q; Circ: 2400; About 30 phil articles per yr; Bk Rev
    Publ: University of Chicago Press
    $10, Foreign $11, Student $7

FRANCISCAN STUDIES 1941
    Ed: Conrad L Harkins, Saint Bonaventure University, Saint Bonaventure, New York 14778

    Purpose: To publish articles and texts concerned with the Franciscan contribution to
      theological, philosophical, and scientific thought, and with the historical evol-
      ution of the Franciscan movement, principally in the medieval period. Articles
      are accepted for publication in English and other major languages of western Europe.
    Ann; Circ: 700; About 4 phil articles per yr
    Publ: The Franciscan Institute, Saint Bonaventure University
    $7

HISTORY AND THEORY: Studies in the Philosophy of History 1960
    Eds: George H Nadel and Richard T Vann, Wesleyan Station, Middletown, Connecticut
      06457

    Purpose: To publish essays, reviews, notes, and bibliographies in theories of history,
      historiography, methods of history, and in the relationship of problems in historical
      method and theory to those of economics, psychology, and other social sciences
    Q; Circ: 2600; About 8 phil articles per yr; Bk Rev
    Publ: Wesleyan University Press
    $7.50, Institutions $10

THE HUMANIST 1941
    Ed: Paul Kurtz, Dept of Phil, State University of New York at Buffalo, SUNY, 4244 Ridge
      Lea Road, Amherst, New York 14226

    Purpose: To publish a journal of normative ethics that attempts to relate theoretical
      philosophy to practical moral and social issues
    Sponsors: American Humanist Association and American Ethical Union
    Bi-mo; Circ: 28,000; About 15 phil articles per yr; Bk Rev
    Publ: American Humanist Association and American Ethical Union
    $7

HUMANITAS: Journal of the Institute of Man 1965
    Ed: Adrian van Kaam, Center for the Study of Human Development, Institute of Man,
      Duquesne University, Pittsburgh, Pennsylvania 15219

    Purpose: To provide an interdisciplinary approach to man
    Sponsor: Center for the Study of Human Development
    3 issues per yr; Circ: 3000; About 6 phil articles per yr
    Publ: Institute of Man
    $7.50, Foreign $8

IDEALISTIC STUDIES 1971
    Ed: Robert N Beck, Dept of Phil, Clark University, Worcester, Massachusetts, 01610

    Purpose: To publish studies of idealistic themes

435

Three issues per yr; Circ: 550
Publ: Clark University Press
$7, Institutions $10

INTERNATIONAL JOURNAL FOR PHILOSOPHY OF RELIGION 1970
    Ed: Frank R Harrison III, Dept of Phil and Relig, University of Georgia, Athens,
        Georgia 30601

    Purpose: To publish important philosophical insights and theories relevant to religion
    Sponsor: The Society for Philosophy of Religion
    Q; Circ: 1000; 20-25 phil articles per yr; Bk Rev
    Publ: Martinus Nijhoff, P O Box 269, The Hague, The Netherlands
    28.8 guilders, Institutions 36 guilders

INTERNATIONAL PHILOSOPHICAL QUARTERLY 1961
    Ed: Norris Clarke, Fordham University, Bronx, New York 10458

    Purpose: To provide an international forum in English for the interchange of basic
        philosophical ideas
    Q; Circ: 1900; 28 phil articles per yr; Bk Rev
    Publ: Foundation for International Philosophical Exchange, Fordham University
    $8, Institutions $10

INTERPRETATION: A Journal of Political Philosophy 1969
    Eds: Seth Benardete, Hilail Gildin and Howard White, Jefferson Hall 305, Queens College,
        Flushing, New York 11367

    Purpose: To provide an organ for scholarly writings on political philosophy
    Three times per yr; 12-14 phil articles per yr; Bk Rev
    Publ: Martinus Nijhoff, Lange-Voorhout 9-11, P O Box 269, The Hague, The Netherlands
    28.80 guilders, Institutions 36 guilders

JOURNAL FOR THE SCIENTIFIC STUDY OF RELIGION 1962
    Ed: Benton Johnson, Dept of Soc, University of Oregon, Eugene, Oregon 97403

    Purpose: To publish reports of social scientific research and analysis pertaining
        to religion
    Sponsor: The Society for the Scientific Study of Religion
    Q; Circ: 2500; 1-2 phil articles per yr; Bk Rev
    Publ: University of Montana Printing Dept
    $15, Student $8

JOURNAL FOR THE THEORY OF SOCIAL BEHAVIOR 1971
    Eds: Paul F Secord, Dept of Urban Studies, Queens College, CUNY, Flushing, New York
        11367 and Theodore Mischel, Dept of Phil, SUNY, Binghamton, New York 13901

    Purpose: To encourage critical discussion of theory and methods used in the study
        of social behavior, using philosophy and the behavioral sciences
    Semi-ann; Circ: 1000; 2-3 phil articles per yr
    Publ: Basil Blackwell, 108 Cowley Road, Oxford, ox4 1jf, England
    $6.50

JOURNAL OF AESTHETIC EDUCATION 1966
    Ed: Ralph A Smith, 228 B Education, College of Education, University of Illinois at
        Urbana, Champaign, Illinois 61801

    Purpose: To provide an educational response to perennial challenges to improve the

436

quality and style of our civilization
Q; Circ: 1350; About 50% phil articles; Bk Rev
Publ: University of Illinois Press
$7.50, Foreign $8

THE JOURNAL OF AESTHETICS AND ART CRITICISM 1941
Ed: John Fisher, Dept of Phil, Temple University, Philadelphia, Pennsylvania 19122

Purpose: To promote the study of the problems of aesthetics in the widest sense
Sponsor: The American Society for Aesthetics
Q; Circ: 2600; 30 phil articles per yr; Bk Rev
Publ: Waverly Press
$15, Foreign $16

JOURNAL OF CHINESE PHILOSOPHY 1973
Ed: Chung-Ying Cheng, Dept of Phil, University of Hawaii, Honolulu, Hawaii 96800

Purpose: To promote and cultivate the study of various phases of Chinese philosophy
and Chinese thought
Q; 25-30 phil articles per yr; Bk Rev
Publ: D Reidel Publishing Co, Dordrecht, The Netherlands
$19.65, Institutions $35.70

THE JOURNAL OF CRITICAL ANALYSIS 1969
Ed: P S Schievella, Jersey City State College, 2039 Kennedy Blvd, Jersey City,
New Jersey, 07305

Purpose: To publish papers on philosophical issues and to introduce philosophy to
pre-college education
Sponsor: The National Council for Critical Analysis
Q; Circ: 500; About 30 phil articles per yr; Bk Rev
Publ: The National Council for Critical Analysis
$10

JOURNAL OF PHILOSOPHY 1904
Ed: John H Randall, Bernard Berofsky, Arthur C Danto, Sidney Morgenbesser, Charles
D Parsons and James J Walsh, Managing Ed: Leigh S Cauman, 720 Philosophy Hall,
Columbia University, New York, New York 10027

Purpose: To publish philosophical articles of current interest
22 issues per yr; Circ: 4750; 75 phil articles per yr; Bk Rev
Publ: Journal of Philosophy, Inc, Columbia University
$10, Institutions $12, Students $7

JOURNAL OF SOCIAL PHILOSOPHY 1970
Ed: Richard Ray, John Knox Press, P O Box 1176, Richmond, Virginia 23209

Purpose: To facilitate communication among philosophers on important social issues
Sponsor: Society for Social Philosophy
3 times per yr; Circ: 500; 18 phil articles per yr
Publ: McGowen Press
$2, Institutions $3

JOURNAL OF SYMBOLIC LOGIC 1936
Ed: Alfons Borgers, P O Box 6248, Providence, Rhode Island 02904

Purpose: To promote research and critical studies in the field of mathematical logic

437

and immediately related fields
Sponsor: Association for Symbolic Logic
Q; Circ: 3300; Bk Rev
Publ: Association for Symbolic Logic
$35

JOURNAL OF THE AMERICAN ACADEMY OF RELIGION 1933
Ed: Ray L Hart, University of Montana, Missoula, Montana 59801

Purpose: To publish scholarly articles in the field of academic religious studies
Sponsor: American Academy of Religion
Q; Circ: 4800; About 8 phil articles per yr; Bk Rev
Publ: American Academy of Religion, University of Montana
$20

JOURNAL OF THE HISTORY OF IDEAS 1940
Ed: Philip P Wiener, Dept of Phil, Temple University, Philadelphia, Pennsylvania
19122

Purpose: To publish interdisciplinary studies
Q; Circ: 36,000; 40 phil articles per yr; Bk Rev
Publ: Science Press, Inc, 300 West Chestnut Street, Ephrata, Pennsylvania 17522
$8, Institutions $10, Foreign $7.50

JOURNAL OF THE HISTORY OF PHILOSOPHY 1963
Ed: Richard H Popkin, Dept of Phil, Washington University, St Louis, Missouri 63130

Purpose: To advance the history of philosophy
Q; Circ: 1600; 20-25 phil articles per yr; Bk Rev
Publ: Journal of the History of Philosophy Inc
$8, Institutions $15, Students $4

JOURNAL OF THE WEST VIRGINIA PHILOSOPHICAL SOCIETY 1970
Ed: Landon C Kirchner, West Liberty State College, West Liberty, West Virginia 26074

Purpose: To facilitate communication between members of the Society
Sponsor: West Virginia Philosophical Society
Bi-ann; Circ: 150; 12 phil articles per yr
Publ: West Liberty State College
$1.50, Institutions $3

JOURNAL OF THOUGHT 1966
Ed: James J Van Patten, 434 Hawthorn Street, Fayetteville, Arkansas 72701

Purpose: To publish an interdisciplinary journal devoted to humanities, philosophy
and philosophy of education
Q; Circ: 500; About 90% phil articles; Bk Rev
J Publ: Higginbotham Inc
$4

THE JOURNAL OF VALUE INQUIRY 1967
Eds: Ervin Laszlo, Executive Ed: James B Wilbur, and Bk Rev Ed: Gary Cox, Dept of
Phil, College at Geneseo, SUNY, Geneseo, New York 14454

Purpose: An international philosophical quarterly devoted to the stimulation and
communication of current research in axiology, value studies and related areas
Q; Circ: About 800; Bk Rev
Publ: Martinus Nijhoff, 9-11 Lange Voorhout, P O Box 269, The Hague, The Netherlands
$9, Institutions $13

KINESIS: Graduate Journal in Philosophy 1968
   Ed: Gerald J Carruba, Dept of Phil, Southern Illinois University, Carbondale, Illinois
      62901

   Purpose: To offer a forum for graduate students in all fields to express their phil-
      osophical views in a critical yet open-ended context
   Semi-ann; 10-12 phil articles per yr; Bk Rev
   Publ: Dept of Phil, Southern Illinois University
   $2.50, Institutions $5

MAIN CURRENTS IN MODERN THOUGHT 1940
   Eds: Emily B Sellon and Henry Margenau, 12 Church Street, New Rochelle, New York 10805

   Purpose: To call attention to significant contributions currently being made in a
      variety of fields, relating these to each other and to Western and Eastern thought,
      both classical and contemporary
   Sponsor: Center for Integrative Education, 12 Church Street, New Rochelle, New York
      10805
   5 issues per yr; Circ: 2800; About 6 phil articles per yr; Bk Rev
   Publ: Julius Stulman, 777 United Nations Plaza, New York, New York 10017
   $6.50, Institutions $14.50

MAN AND WORLD 1967
   Eds: John M Anderson and Joseph Kockelmans, Pennsylvania State University, University
      Park, Pennsylvania 16802, and Calvin O Schrag, Purdue University, Lafayette, Indiana
      47907

   Purpose: To provide a multi-lingual scholarly publication in philosophy
   Q; Circ: About 500; 20-25 phil articles per yr; Bk Rev
   Publ: Martinus Nijhoff Publishing Co, P O Box 269, The Hague, The Netherlands
   34.2 guilders, Institutions 54 guilders

METAPHILOSOPHY 1968
   Ed: Terrell Ward Bynum, Dept of Phil, State University at Albany, SUNY, 1400 Washington
      Avenue, Albany, New York 12222

   Purpose: To publish articles stressing considerations about philosophy as a whole or
      about some particular school, method or field of philosophy
   Sponsor: Metaphilosophy Foundation, State University at Albany, SUNY
   Q; Circ: 750; 25 phil articles per yr; Bk Rev
   Publ: Basil Blackwell, 5 Alfred Street, Oxford, ox4 1hb, England
   $10, Institutions $15

MINERVA'S OWL: Philosophical Journal for Undergraduates 1970
   Ed: C E Schuetzinger, Mercy College of Detroit, 8200 West Outer Drive, Detroit,
      Michigan 48219

   Purpose: Stimulation and exchange of philosophical ideas, and problems between students
      and instructors of philosophy
   6 issues per yr; Circ: 500; 75% phil articles; Bk Rev
   Publ: Mercy College of Detroit, Printing Office
   $3

THE MODERN SCHOOLMAN 1925
   Ed: William J Weiler, 3700 West Pine Blvd, St Louis, Missouri 63108

   Purpose: To publish scholarly articles, notes, and discussions in philosophy
   Q; Circ: 880; 12 phil articles per yr; Bk Rev

439

Publ: Dept of Phil, St Louis University
$6

THE MONIST 1888
    Ed: Eugene Freeman, Dept of Phil, California State University, San Jose, California
        95192

    Purpose: To publish an international quarterly journal of general philosophical
        inquiry devoted to problems arising in any area of philosophy and to interdis-
        ciplinary problems arising out of the philosophical issues considered in related
        disciplines
    Q; Circ: 1900; 30-40 phil articles per yr; Bk Rev
    Publ: Open Court Publishing Co
    $6, Institutions $8

NEW LITERARY HISTORY 1969
    Ed: Ralph Cohen, Wilson Hall, University of Virginia, Charlottesville, Virginia 22903

    Purpose: To explore the relation between literary problems and those shared by related
        disciplines
    3 issues per yr; Circ: 1450; 3-6 phil articles per yr
    Publ: New Literary History
    $8

THE NEW PHILOSOPHY 1898
    Ed: Lennart O Alfelt, Bryn Athyn, Pennsylvania 19009

    Purpose: To expose and promote philosophic principles contained in works of Emanuel
        Swedenborg
    Sponsor: Swedenborg Scientific Association, Bryn Athyn, Pennsylvania 19009
    Q; Circ: 370; 7-10 phil articles per yr; Bk Rev
    Publ: Swedenborg Scientific Association
    $4

THE NEW SCHOLASTICISM 1926
    Ed: John A Oesterle, University of Notre Dame, Notre Dame, Indiana 46556

    Purpose: To promote philosophical scholarship
    Sponsor: American Catholic Philosophical Association, The Catholic University of
        America
    Q; Circ: 2550; 35-40 phil articles per yr; Bk Rev
    Publ: American Catholic Philosophical Association
    $8

NOTRE DAME JOURNAL OF FORMAL LOGIC 1960
    Ed: Bolesaw Sobociński, P O Box 28, Notre Dame, Indiana 46556

    Purpose: The Journal is devoted primarily to logic and the foundations of
        mathematics, i.e., algebraic logic, classical logical systems, constructive
        mathematics, methodology of deductive systems, model theory, non-classical formal
        systems, proof theory, recursion theory, and set theory
    Q; Circ: About 850; 25% phil articles
    Publ: University of Notre Dame
    $10, Institutions $16

NOUS 1967
    Ed: Hector-Neri Castaneda, Dept of Phil, Sycamore Hall 027, Indiana University,

Bloomington, Indiana 47401

Purpose: To publish original research essays and brief discussions on philosophical
    problems
Q; Circ: 900; 30 phil articles per yr
Publ: Indiana University
$8, Institutions $12, Student $6

OPINION 1959
    Ed: James E Kurtz, P O Box 688, Evanston, Illinois 60204

    Purpose: To stimulate independent thought on various sociological, philosophical
        and theological subjects, as well as to promote depth of thought combined with logic
    M; Circ: 10,000; About 35 phil articles per yr; Bk Rev
    Publ: Opinion Publications

THE OWL OF MINERVA 1969
    Ed: Frederick G Weiss, Dept of Phil, University of Virginia, Charlottesville, Virginia
        22901

    Purpose: To further scholarship in Hegel and related areas
    Sponsor: Hegel Society of America
    Q; About 550; 100% phil articles; Bk Rev
    Publ: Hegel Society of America
    $5, Institutions $3, Students $3

PRS JOURNAL 1958
    Ed: Manly P Hall, 3910 Los Feliz Blvd, Los Angeles, California 90027

    Purpose: To present articles dealing with the nature of man and based upon the
        disciplines of philosophy, comparative religion, and psychology
    Sponsor: The Philosophical Research Society, Inc
    Q; Circ: 3000; 33% phil articles
    Publ: The Philosophical Research Society, Inc
    $4, Foreign $5

THE PERSONALIST 1920
    Ed: John Hospers, School of Phil, University of Southern California, University Park,
        Los Angeles, California 90007

    Purpose: An international journal of philosophy of primary interest to philosophers and
        scholars
    Q; 100% phil articles; Bk Rev
    Publ: University of Southern California
    $6

THE PHILOSOPHER'S INDEX: An International Index to Philosophical Periodicals 1967
    Ed: Richard H Lineback, Dept of Phil, Bowling Green University, Bowling Green, Ohio
        43403

    Purpose: To provide an up-to-date subject and author index of articles in more than
        250 major philosophy journals. Abstracts of articles are included, as well as a
        book review index. In addition, there is a section on Translations in Progress.
    Q; Circ: 1650
    Publ: Philosophy Documentation Center, Bowling Green University, Bowling Green, Ohio
        43403
    $12, Institutions $24

PHILOSOPHIA MATHEMATICA 1964
  Ed: J Fang, Paideia Press, Hauppauge, New York 11787

  Purpose: To study the philosophy of modern mathematics
  Semi-ann; Circ: 600; 10-15 phil articles per yr; Bk Rev
  Publ: Paideia Press
  $8, Institutions $12

PHILOSOPHIC EXCHANGE 1970
  Ed: Howard E Kiefer, College at Brockport, SUNY, Brockport, New York 14420

  Purpose: To publish annual proceedings of the Center for Philosophic Exchange
  Ann; Circ: 1000; 6 phil articles per yr
  Publ: Center for Philosophic Exchange

THE PHILOSOPHICAL FORUM 1943
  Ed: Marx W Wartofsky, 232 Bay State Road, Boston, Massachusetts 02215

  Purpose: Open-minded discussion which aims not so much at agreement as at lively
    response
  Q; 100% phil articles; Bk Rev
  Publ: Dept of Phil, Boston University
  $10, Institutions $15, Students $6

THE PHILOSOPHICAL REVIEW 1892
  Eds: The Faculty of The Sage School of Philosophy, Cornell University, Ithaca, New York
    14850

  Purpose: Publication of original research in philosophy
  Q; Circ: About 4000; About 25 phil articles per yr; Bk Rev
  Publ: The Philosophical Review, 218 Goldwin Smith Hall, Cornell University, Ithaca
    New York 14850
  $5, Institutions $8

PHILOSOPHICAL STUDIES: An International Journal for Philosophy in the Analytic
    Tradition 1949
  Ed: Wilfrid Sellars, 353 Cathedral of Learning, University of Pittsburgh, Pittsburgh,
    Pennsylvania 15213

  Purpose: To present a disciplined application of methods of analysis and clarification
    of meaning
  6 times per yr; Circ: 1500
  Publ: D Reidel Publishing Co, P O Box 17, Dordrecht, The Netherlands
  $19.64, Institutions $33.92

PHILOSOPHY AND PHENOMENOLOGICAL RESEARCH 1940
  Ed: Marvin Farber, State University at Buffalo, SUNY, Buffalo, New York 14226

  Purpose: To publish materials on phenomenology and articles representing the most
    important philosophical trends
  Sponsor: International Phenomenological Society
  Q; Bk Rev

Publ: University of Buffalo Foundation, State University at Buffalo, SUNY
$7.50, Institutions $9

PHILOSOPHY AND PUBLIC AFFAIRS 1971
   Ed: Marshall Cohen, Graduate Center, CUNY, 33 West 42nd Street, New York, New York
      10036

   Purpose: To serve those concerned with the philosophical exploration of public issues
   Q; Circ: 2000; 100% phil articles
   Publ: Princeton University Press
   $7.50, Institutions $10

PHILOSOPHY AND RHETORIC 1968
   Ed: Henry W Johnstone, Jr, 246 Sparks Building, Pennsylvania State University,
      University Park, Pennsylvania 16802

   Purpose: To publish articles on rhetoric as a philosophical concept
   Q; Circ: 800; 15 phil articles per yr; Bk Rev
   Publ: The Pennsylvania State University Press
   $10, Foreign $13, Canada $11

PHILOSOPHY EAST AND WEST 1951
   Ed: Eliot Deutsch, 1993 East-West Road, Honolulu, Hawaii 96822

   Purpose: To publish specialized articles in Asian philosophy and articles which seek
      to illuminate, in a comparative manner, the distinctive characteristics of the
      various philosophical traditions in the East and West
   Sponsor: Society for Asian and Comparative Philosophy
   Q; Circ: 1500; 28 phil articles per yr; Bk Rev
   Publ: University Press of Hawaii
   $8

THE PHILOSOPHY FORUM 1962
   Ed: Ervin Laszlo, Dept of Phil, College at Geneseo, SUNY, Geneseo, New York 14454

   Purpose: To deal with philosophic issues of wide human concern, promoting
      interdisciplinary dialogue and the integration of knowledge
   Q; Circ: About 600; 12-20 phil articles per yr; Bk Rev
   Publ: Gordon and Breach Science Publishers, Inc
   $7.50, Institutions $14.50

PHILOSOPHY IN CONTEXT 1972
   Ed: Leslie Armour, Cleveland State University, Cleveland, Ohio 44115

   Publ: Dept of Phil, Cleveland State University
   $2

PHILOSOPHY OF EDUCATION SOCIETY: Proceedings
   Ed: Mary Anne Raywid, School of Education, Hofstra University, Hempstead, New York
      11550

Sponsor: The Philosophy of Education Society
Publ: Studies in Philosophy of Education, Southern Illinois University

PHILOSOPHY OF SCIENCE 1933
Ed: Richard S Rudner, Dept of Phil, Washington University, St Louis, Missouri 63130

Purpose: To publish articles of merit or significant interest in the field of
    philosophy of science broadly construed
Sponsor: Philosophy of Science Association
Q; Circ: 2800; 40-60 phil articles per yr; Bk Rev
Publ: Philosophy of Science Association
$10, Institutions $15

PHILOSOPHY TODAY 1957
Ed: Robert F Lechner, Carthagena Station, Celina, Ohio 45822

Purpose: A presentation of the problems and issues in contemporary philosophy
Q; Circ: 1375; 30 phil articles per yr
Publ: Messenger Press
$7, Foreign $7.50

PHRONESIS 1955
Ed: G B Kerferd, School of Class Stud, University of Manchester, England, Assoc Ed:
    D J Furley, Dept of Class, Princeton University, Princeton, New Jersey 08540

Purpose: To publish articles on Greek Philosophy
Three issues per yr; About 25 phil articles per yr
Publ: Royal Van Gorcum Ltd, Assen, The Netherlands
$12

PROCEEDINGS AND ADDRESSES OF THE AMERICAN PHILOSOPHICAL ASSOCIATION 1928
Ed: Norman E Bowie, Hamilton College, Clinton, New York 13323

Sponsor: The American Philosophical Association
Ann; Circ: 5000; 3 phil articles per yr
Publ: The American Philosophical Association
$5

PROCEEDINGS OF THE AMERICAN CATHOLIC PHILOSOPHICAL ASSOCIATION 1926
Ed: George F McLean, American Catholic Philosophical Association, Catholic University,
    Washington, DC 20017

Purpose: To promote philosophical scholarship
Sponsor: American Catholic Philosophical Association
Ann; Circ: 1960; 21 phil articles per yr
Publ: American Catholic Philosophical Association
$5

PROCEEDINGS OF THE NEW MEXICO-WEST TEXAS PHILOSOPHICAL SOCIETY 1965
Ed: Ivan L Little, Texas Technical University, Lubbock, Texas 79409

Purpose: To reproduce papers of the annual meeting
Sponsor: The New Mexico-West Texas Philosophical Society
Ann; 12-15 phil articles per yr
Publ: Technical Press, Texas Technical University
$3

PROCEEDINGS OF THE SOUTHWESTERN PHILOSOPHY OF EDUCATION SOCIETY   1950
    Ed: Chipman G Stuart, College of Education 204, University of Oklahoma, Norman,
      Oklahoma 73069

    Purpose: To publish the papers presented at the yearly meeting of the Southwestern
      Philosophy of Education Society
    Sponsor: Southwestern Philosophy of Education Society
    Ann; Circ: 100; 10-20 phil articles per yr
    Publ: The College of Education, The University of Oklahoma
    $2

PROCESS STUDIES 1971
    Eds: Lewis S Ford, 111 Spring Hill Lane, State College, Pennsylvania 16801 and
      John B Cobb, Jr, School of Theology at Claremont, 1325 North College Avenue,
      Claremont, California 91711

    Purpose: To explore the philosophical and theological implications of the thought
      of Alfred North Whitehead and other process thinkers
    Q; Circ: 780; 18 phil articles per yr; Bk Rev
    Publ: Process Studies
    $6, Institutions $7

RELIGIOUS HUMANISM 1967
    Ed: Robert S Hoagland, 218 N Blackhawk Avenue, Madison, Wisconsin 53705

    Purpose: To advance naturalistic humanism with a religious accent
    Sponsor: Fellowship of Religious Humanists, 105 West North College Street, Yellow
      Springs, Ohio 45387
    Q; Circ: 1500; About 25% phil articles; Bk Rev
    Publ: Fellowship of Religious Humanists
    $5

THE REVIEW OF METAPHYSICS 1947
    Ed: Jude P Dougherty, Catholic University of America, Washington, DC 20017

    Purpose: To promote technically competent and definite contributions to philosophical
      knowledge
    Q; Circ: 3500; 25 phil articles per yr; Bk Rev
    Publ: Philosophy of Education Society, Inc
    $8, Institutions $15, Students $5

SOCIAL THEORY AND PRACTICE 1970
    Ed: E F Kaelin, Dept of Phil, Florida State University, Tallahassee, Florida 32306

    Purpose: To provide a forum for the expression of controversial social and political
      issues
    Semi-ann; Circ: 450; 20 phil articles per yr; Bk Rev
    Publ: Dept of Phil, Florida State University
    $10, Institutions $21

THE SOUTHERN JOURNAL OF PHILOSOPHY 1963
    Ed: Carroll R Bowman, Dept of Phil, Memphis State University, Memphis, Tennessee
      38152

    Purpose: To serve as a forum for the expression of philosophical ideas
    Q; Circ: 800; 100% phil articles; Bk Rev
    Publ: Dept of Phil, Memphis State University
    $8, Institutions $12, Students $4

445

SOUTHWESTERN JOURNAL OF PHILOSOPHY 1970
  Ed: Robert W Shahan, 455 W Lindsey Street, Room 605, Norman, Oklahoma 73069

  Purpose: To publish technical philosophy and articles on philosophical problems
    which arise in conjunction with the analysis of the content and methods of other
    disciplines
  Sponsor: Southwestern Philosophical Society
  Three times per yr; Circ: 550; 40 phil articles per year; Bk Rev
  Publ: University of Oklahoma Press, Inc
  $8, Institutions $12

SOVIET STUDIES IN PHILOSOPHY 1962
  Ed: John Somerville, 1426 Merritt Drive, El Cajon, California 92020

  Purpose: To publish translations of current articles in Soviet philosophy
  Q; About 25 phil articles per yr; Bk Rev
  Publ: International Arts and Sciences Press
  $15, Institutions $60

STUDIES IN HISTORY AND PHILOSOPHY OF SCIENCE 1969
  Eds: Gerd Buchdahl, Dept of Hist and Phil of Sci, University of Cambridge, England,
    and L L Laudan, University of Pittsburgh, Pittsburgh, Pennsylvania 15213

  Q; 6-10 phil articles per yr; Bk Rev
  Publ: Macmillan Journals Limited
  $15

STUDIES IN PHILOSOPHY AND EDUCATION 1960
  Ed: Francis T Villemain, Southern Illinois University, Edwardsville, Illinois 62025

  Purpose: To publish philosophic analysis and criticism of educational thought and
    practice
  Sponsor: Studies in Philosophy and Education Society, Southern Illinois University
  Irr; Circ: 1500; Bk Rev
  $8, Institutions $9, Foreign $8.50

STUDIES IN PHILOSOPHY AND THE HISTORY OF PHILOSOPHY 1960
  Ed: John K Ryan, Catholic University of America, Washington, DC 20017

  Purpose: To publish solid, scholarly articles on special problems in logic,
    epistemology, ethics, metaphysics, and the other divisions of philosophy,
    and the history of philosophy
  Every two yrs; Circ: 1200; 10 phil articles per yr
  Publ: Catholic University of America Press

STUDIES IN SOVIET THOUGHT
  Eds: Joseph M Bochenski, 1 Rue de l'Hôspital, 1700 Fribourg, Switzerland and Thomas
    J Blakeley, Dept of Phil, Boston College, Chestnut Hill, Massachusetts 02167

  Purpose: To publish research papers, short notes, critical reviews and other
    writings about contemporary Soviet philosophy
  Q; Circ: 750; Bk Rev
  Publ: D Reidel Publishing Co, P O Box 17, Dordrecht, The Netherlands
  $14

TECHNOLOGY AND CULTURE 1959
    Ed: Melvin Kranzberg, Dept of Soc Sci, Georgia Institute of Technology, Atlanta,
      Georgia 30332

    Purpose: To study the development of technology and its relations with society and
      culture
    Sponsor: The Society for the History of Technology, Dept of Soc Sci, Georgia Institute
      of Technology
    Q; Circ: 1900; About 6 phil articles per yr; Bk Rev
    Publ: University of Chicago Press
    $12, Institutions $15

TELOS 1968
    Ed: Paul Piccone, Dept of Soc, Washington University, St Louis, Missouri 63130

    Purpose: To publish an interdisciplinary quarterly of radical theory having as main
      focus the works of leading European scholars
    Q; Circ: 3000, 33% phil articles; Bk Rev
    Publ: Dept of Soc, Washington University
    $6, Institutions $8

THEORY AND DECISION: An International Journal for Philosophy and Methodology of the
    Social Sciences 1970
    Ed: W Leinfellner, Dept of Phil, University of Nebraska, Lincoln, Nebraska 68508

    Purpose: To publish an international journal for philosophy and methodology of the
      social sciences
    Q; Circ: 680; 40 phil articles per yr; Bk Rev
    Publ: D Reidel Publishing Co, P O Box 17, Dordrecht, The Netherlands
    70.40 Fl

THE THOMIST 1939
    Ed: Nicholas Halligan, 487 Michigan Avenue, NW, Washington, DC 20017

    Purpose: To publish speculative reviews of philosophy and theology
    Q; Circ: 1100; 12-20 phil articles per yr; Bk Rev
    Publ: Dominican Fathers, 869 Lexington Ave, New York, New York 10021
    $7, Foreign $7.50

THOUGHT 1926
    Ed: Joseph E O'Neill, Fordham University, Bronx, New York 10458

    Purpose: To review the world of culture and ideas in a scholarly fashion from a
      humanistic, cosmopolitan and Christian point of view
    Q; Circ: 1750; About 4 phil articles per yr; Bk Rev
    Publ: Fordham University Press
    $10

TRADITIO: Studies in Ancient and Medieval History, Thought, and Religion 1943
    Ed: Edwin A Quain, Charles H Lohr, Bernard M Peebles and Richard E Doyle, Fordham
      University, Bronx, New York 10458

    Ann; Circ: 1000; 2-3 phil articles per yr
    Publ: Fordham University Press
    $13.50

TRANSACTIONS OF THE CHARLES S PIERCE SOCIETY
    Ed: Richard S Robin, Dept of Phil, Mount Holyoke College, South Hadley, Massachusetts,
       01075

    Sponsor: Charles S Pierce Society
    Q
    Publ: The Greater Buffalo Press
    $10

TULANE STUDIES IN PHILOSOPHY 1952
    Ed: Robert C Whittemore, Dept of Phil, Tulane University, New Orleans, Louisiana 70118

    Purpose: To publish original contributions to philosophy and philosophical scholarships
       by members of the Tulane University Department of Philosophy and by PhD graduates
       in philosophy from Tulane University
    Ann; Circ: 1000; 100% phil articles
    Publ: Dept of Phil, Tulane University
    $5

UNDERGRADUATE JOURNAL OF PHILOSOPHY 1969
    Ed: Undergraduate philosophy students, Oberlin College, Oberlin, Ohio 44074

    Purpose: To publish philosophical works of undergraduate philosophy students
    Semi-ann; Circ: 250; 10-12 phil articles per yr; Bk Rev
    Publ: Oberlin College
    $1.50, Institutions $2, Students $1

ZYGON: Journal of Religion and Science 1966
    Ed: Ralph Wendell Burhoe, 5711 Woodlawn Avenue, Chicago, Illinois 60637

    Purpose: To reunite values with facts and religion with science
    Sponsors: Institute of Religion in an Age of Science and Center for the Study of
       Religion and Science, 5711 Woodlawn Avenue, Chicago, Illinois 60637
    Q; Circ: 1500; About 20% phil articles; Bk Rev
    Publ: University of Chicago Press
    $9, Institutions $12, Students $6

PUBLISHERS

UNITED STATES

ABINGDON PRESS 1789
201 Eighth Avenue S, Nashville, Tennessee 37203

ADDISON-WESLEY PUBLISHING CO, INC* 1942
Reading, Massachusetts 01867

AHM PUBLISHING CORPORATION 1972
1500 Skokie Boulevard, Northbrook, Illinois 60062

ALBA HOUSE 1960
2187 Victory Blvd, Staten Island, New York 10314

ALDINE PUBLISHING COMPANY 1961
529 S Wabash Avenue, Chicago 60605

Ser Publ: "Islamic Surveys," a series of introductory works on special subjects
showing the present state of scholarship in the field of Islamic studies,
ed by W Montgomery Watt

ALLYN AND BACON, INC 1869
470 Atlantic Avenue, Boston, Massachusetts 02210

AMERICAN ACADEMY OF RELIGION 1923
c/o Dept of Religion, Florida State University, Tallahassee, Florida 32306

Jour Publ: Journal of the American Academy of Religion; Journal of Religious Ethics
Ser Publ: "American Academy of Religion Studies in Religion" a collection that
publishes monographs in the general field of religion, ed by Stephen Crites

AMERICAN CONTINENTAL PUBLISHING COMPANY, INC 1969
P O Box 13265, Fort Worth, Texas 76118

THE ANTIOCH PRESS
Yellow Springs, Ohio 45387

Jour Publ: The Antioch Review

APPLETON-CENTURY-CROFTS 1825
440 Park Avenue South, New York, New York 10016

Ser Publ: "The Century Philosophy Series," a collection of texts and reference
works; "Appleton-Century Philosophy Source Books," original sources, ed by
Sterling P Lamprecht; "Contemporary Problems in Philosophy," a collection that
deals with philosophical problems analyzed by specialists who present possible
solutions, ed by George F McLean

449

ARNO PRESS 1966
330 Madison Avenue, New York, New York 10017

Ser Publ: "The Atheist Viewpoint," books, booklets, leaflets, broadsides and
memoirs critical of theism, edited by Madalyn Murray O'Hair; "The Philosophy
of Plato and Aristotle," a collection of works on Plato and Aristotle, and a
wide-ranging study of myths and imagery which influenced Greek philosophers,
ed by Gregory Vlastos; "Religion in America," a reprint collection, ed by
Edwin S Gaustad; "The Right Wing Individualist Tradition in America," a
collection that attempts to restore a proper balance to the right wing
individualist tradition in America, ed by Murray N Rothbard and Jerome Tuccille

AUGSBURG PUBLISHING HOUSE*
426 South Fifth Street, Minneapolis, Minnesota 55415

BARNES & NOBLE* 1873
105 Fifth Avenue, New York, New York 10003

BARRON'S EDUCATIONAL SERIES, INC*
113 Crossways Park Drive, Woodbury, New York 11797

Ser Publ: "The Philosophy and Literature of Existentialism," ed by Wesley Barnes

BASIC BOOKS, INC 1951
10 East 53rd Street, New York, New York 10022

William L BAUHAN, INC 1929
Dublin, New Hampshire 03444

BEACON PRESS 1902
25 Beacon Street, Boston, Massachusetts 02108

THE BETHANY PRESS 1953
Box 179, Saint Louis, Missouri 63166

Ser Publ: "The Library of Contemporary Theology," a series that intends to help
open doors to nonprofessional theologians of many callings, ed by Walter S Sikes

BIBLO & TANNEN BOOKSELLERS AND PUBLISHERS, INC* 1928
63 Fourth Avenue, New York, New York 10003

The BOBBS-MERRILL COMPANY, INC* 1928
4300 West 62nd Street, Indianapolis, Indiana 46206

Ser Publ: "The Text and Commentary Series," an authoritative text of philosophical
classics together with contemporary critical essays, ed by Harold Weisberg;
"The Library of Liberal Arts," texts of important works which represent the
highest standards of scholarship; "The Bobbs-Merrill Reprint Series in
Philosophy," a collection that provides facsimile reproductions of scholarly
articles from leading journals, ed by William Alston, Monroe Beardsley, Richard
Brandt, Ernest Nagel, Rolf Sartorius, and Gregory Vlastos; "Pegasus Traditions
in Philosophy Series," an introduction to a major field in philosophy, ed by
Nicholas Capaldi

BOOKS FOR LIBRARIES PRESS, INC   1963
   One Dupont Street, Plainview, New York 11803

   Ser Publ: "Essay Index Reprint Series," reprints of scholarly works;   "BCL/Select
      Bibliographies Reprint Series," reprints of scholarly works

George BRAZILLER, INC   1954
   One Park Avenue, New York, New York 10016

   Ser Publ: "International Library of Systems Theory and Philosophy," a collection
      which offers critical and creative examination of philosophical perspectives
      of systems theory, and offers a forum for international work, ed by Ervin Laszlo

BROWN UNIVERSITY PRESS   1932
   129 Waterman Street, Providence, Rhode Island 02912

BUCKNELL UNIVERSITY PRESS   1969
   Lewisburg, Pennsylvania 17837

CAMBRIDGE UNIVERSITY PRESS   1521
   32 East 57th Street, New York, New York 10022

   Jour Publ: The British Journal of the Philosophy of Science

CHELSEA PUBLISHING COMPANY   1944
   159 East Tremont Avenue, The Bronx, New York 10453

The CHRISTOPHER PUBLISHING HOUSE   1910
   53 Billings Road, North Quincy, Massachusetts 02171

CLARK UNIVERSITY PRESS   1927
   Worcester, Massachusetts 01610

   Jour Publ: Idealistic Studies

CLIFFS NOTES, INC   1957
   Box 80728, Lincoln, Nebraska 68501

   Ser Publ: "Cliffs Notes Series," ed by Harry Kaste;   "Course Outline Series," ed
      by Harry Kaste

COLUMBIA UNIVERSITY PRESS   1893
   562 West 113 Street, New York, New York 10025

   Ser Publ: "John Dewey Lectures"

CONSORTIUM PRESS
   821 Fifteenth Street NW, Washington, DC 20005

   Ser Publ: "Studies in Philosophy and the History of Philosophy," ed by John K Ryan

451

CORNELL UNIVERSITY PRESS 1869
124 Roberts Place, Ithaca, New York 14850

Ser Publ: "Contemporary Philosophy Series," book-length essays in the analytic
tradition dealing with a single problem or a set of related problems, ed by
Max Black

Thomas Y CROWELL COMPANY (College Dept) 1834
666 Fifth Avenue, 8th Floor, New York, New York 10019

DEFINITION PRESS 1954
39 Grove Street, New York 10014

Jour Publ: Definition: A Journal of Events and Aesthetic Realism; The Right of
Aesthetic Realism to be Known

DICKENSON PUBLISHING COMPANY, INC 1964
16561 Ventura Boulevard, Encino, California 91316

Ser Publ: "Dickenson Series in Philosophy," basic textbooks and text-anthologies
for use in college philosophy courses, ed by Joel Feinberg

DORRANCE AND COMPANY, INC 1920
1617 J F Kennedy Boulevard, Suite 324, Philadelphia, Pennsylvania 19103

DOUBLEDAY & COMPANY, INC (Anchor Books) 1899
245 Park Avenue, New York, New York 10017

Ser Publ: "Modern Studies in Philosophy," a series that presents contemporary
interpretations of the works of major philosophers, ed by Amelie Oksenberg Rorty;
"New Introductions to Philosophy," a collection that introduces students to
the major subdivisions of philosophy, ed by D J O'Connor; "Problems in Philosophy,"
a series that presents individual problems basic to all philosophical thought, ed
by D J O'Connor

DOUBLEDAY & COMPANY, INC (Image Books Division) 1954
277 Park Avenue, New York, New York 10017

Ser Publ: "A History of Philosophy," a comprehensive history of philosophy from
Greece and Rome to early 20th Century, ed by Frederick C Copleston

DOVER PUBLICATIONS, INC 1943
180 Varick Street, New York, New York 10014

DUKE UNIVERSITY PRESS 1925
Box 6697 College Station, Durham, North Carolina 27708

DUQUESNE UNIVERSITY PRESS 1927
University Hall, Pittsburgh, Pennsylvania 15219

Jour Publ: Research in Phenomenology
Ser Publ: "Duquesne Studies: Philosophical Series," works in contemporary philosophy
with an emphasis on the phenomenological approach, ed by Henry J Koren and André
Schuwer

452

E P DUTTON AND COMPANY, INC 1852
    201 Park Avenue South, New York, New York 10003

William B EERDMANS PUBLISHING COMPANY 1910
    255 Jefferson SE, Grand Rapids, Michigan 49502

FAWCETT PUBLICATIONS, INC 1950*
    1 Astor Plaza, New York, New York 10036

FORDHAM UNIVERSITY PRESS 1907
    Box L, Fordham University, Bronx, New York 10458

    Jour Publ: Traditio: Studies in Ancient and Medieval History, Thought, and
        Religion; Thought: A Review of Culture and Idea
    Ser Publ: "The Orestes Brownson Series on Contemporary Thought and Affairs,"
        individual studies of the influence of philosophers of more recent generations
        on contemporary thought

FORTRESS PRESS 1855
    2900 Queen Lane, Philadelphia, Pennsylvania 19129

Burt FRANKLIN* 1943
    235 E 44th Street, New York, New York 10017

THE FREE PRESS 1947
    866 Third Avenue, New York, New York 10022

W H FREEMAN AND COMPANY 1946
    660 Market Street, San Francisco, California 94104

GARLAND PUBLISHING COMPANY, INC 1971
    10 East 44th Street, New York, New York 10017

    Ser Publ: "The Garland Library of War and Peace," a collection of reference material
        which reflects the growing concern over the causes of war and the necessity for
        peace, ed by Blanche W Cook, Sandi E Cooper, and Charles Chatfield

GORDON AND BREACH SCIENCE PUBLISHERS, INC 1961
    One Park Avenue, New York, New York 10016

    Jour Publ: The Philosophy Forum; International Journal of General Systems
    Ser Publ: "General Systems," works in the area of Systems Theory, ed by George J
        Klir; "Current Topics of Contemporary Thought," a wide range of books on areas
        of interest to students of contemporary philosophy, ed by Rubin Gotesky

The GREATER BUFFALO PRESS*
    302 Grote Street, Buffalo, New York 14207

    Jour Publ: Transactions of the Charles S Pierce Society

Warren H GREEN, INC   1966
   10 South Brentwood Boulevard, St Louis, Missouri 63105

    Ser Publ: "Modern Concepts of Philosophy," works on current scholarly thinking in
      philosophy, ed by Marvin Farber

GREENWOOD PRESS   1967
   51 Riverside Avenue, Westport, Connecticut 06880

    Ser Publ: "Contributions in Philosophy," original scholarly contributions in the
      field of philosophy

HAFNER PRESS   1946
   866 Third Avenue, New York, New York 10022

    Ser Publ: "Hafner Library of Classics"

HARCOURT BRACE JOVANOVICH, INC*
   757 Third Avenue, New York, New York 10017

HARPER & ROW, PUBLISHERS   1817
   10 East 53rd Street, New York, New York 10022

    Ser Publ: "World Perspectives," a collection concerned with basic new trends in
      modern civilization, ed by Ruth Nanda Anshen

HARVARD UNIVERSITY PRESS   1913
   79 Garden Street, Cambridge, Massachusetts 02138

HASKELL HOUSE PUBLISHERS, LIMITED   1964
   280 Lafayette Street, New York, New York 10012

    Ser Publ: "Studies in Philosophy," Series #40, ed by H Roseman

HELICON PRESS, INC*   1957
   1120 N Calvert Street, Baltimore, Maryland 21202

HERDER AND HERDER, INC*   1957
   232 Madison Avenue, New York, New York 10016

B HERDER BOOK COMPANY*   1873
   818 Olive Street, Rm 840, St Louis, Missouri 63101

HIGGINBOTHAM, INC   1944
   1108 Moore Avenue, Anniston, Alabama 36201

   Jour Publ: <u>Journal</u> <u>of</u> <u>Thought</u>

HOLT, RINEHART AND WINSTON, INC
   383 Madison Avenue, New York, New York 10017

454

HORIZON PRESS 1952
   156 Fifth Avenue, New York, New York 10010

HOUGHTON MIFFLIN COMPANY 1864
   Educational Division, 110 Tremont Street, Boston, Massachusetts 02107

HUMANITIES PRESS, INC 1950
   450 Park Avenue South, New York, New York 10016

   Jour Publ: Journal of Phenomenological Psychology; Research in Phenomenology
   Ser Publ: "International Library of Philosophy and Scientific Method," ed by Ted
     Hondrich; "International Library of Psychology, Philosophy and Scientific
     Method," ed by C K Ogden; "Muirhead Library of Philosophy," a contribution to
     the history of modern philosophy under the heads of different schools of thought-
     sensationalist, realist, idealist, intuitivist--and on different subjects--
     psychology, ethics, aesthetics, political philosophy and theology, ed by
     H D Lewis, "New Studies in Practical Philosophy," designed to provide understanding
     of contemporary analytical philosophy, particularly in the logic of moral discourse,
     and the practical problems of morality, ed by W D Hudson

INDIANA UNIVERSITY PRESS 1950
   10th & Morton Streets, Bloomington, Indiana 47401

INTERNATIONAL ARTS AND SCIENCES PRESS, INC 1958
   901 North Broadway, White Plains, New York 10603

   Jour Publ: Chinese Studies in Philosophy; Soviet Studies in Philosophy

IOWA STATE UNIVERSITY PRESS 1924
   South State Avenue, Ames, Iowa 50010

The JOHNS HOPKINS UNIVERSITY PRESS 1878
   Baltimore, Maryland 21218

   Ser Publ: "Seminars in the History of Ideas," a new series relating the history
     of ideas to many of the problems and issues facing the modern world, ed by
     George E Owen; "The Thalheimer Lectures," a publication of lectures on a single
     topic given by one or several distinguished philosophers invited to the Johns
     Hopkins University, ed by Maurice Mandelbaum

JUDSON PRESS 1824
   Valley Forge, Pennsylvania 19481

   Ser Publ: "Makers of Modern Thought," a series in paperback on the principal teachings
     of various famous seminal thinkers of today, ed by A D Galloway

JOHNSON REPRINT CORPORATION* 1945
   111 Fifth Avenue, New York, New York 10003

   Ser Publ: "Texts in Early Modern Philosophy," a series presenting reprints of
     important and interesting works in philosophy and theology originally published
     from the Renaissance to the Enlightenment, ed by Richard H Popkin

William KAUFMANN, INC 1972
   One First Street, Los Altos, California 94022

KENNIKAT PRESS, INC 1962
   90 South Bayles Avenue, Port Washington, New York 11050

The KENT STATE UNIVERSITY PRESS 1965
   Kent, Ohio 44242

KRAUS-THOMSON ORGANIZATION LIMITED 1957
   FL - 9491 Nendeln, Liechtenstein

   Ser Publ: "Philosophische Dokumentation," classified general indexes to Philosophy
      Journals, ed by Alwin Diemer and Norbert Henrichs

KREIGER PUBLISHING COMPANY, INC
   P O Box 542, Huntington, New York 11743

The LANGUAGE PRESS 1970
   Box 342, Whitewater, Wisconsin 53190

   Ser Publ: "Metaphor," a series that clarifies the concept and promotes research into
      it, ed by Warren Shibles; "Philosophical Psychology," a series that gives a
      conceptual analysis of basic terms on death and emotions, ed by Warren Shibles

LENOX HILL PUBLISHING & DISTRIBUTING CORPORATION 1953
   235 E 44th Street, New York, New York 10017

J B LIPPINCOTT COMPANY 1792
   East Washington Square, Philadelphia, Pennsylvania 19105

   Ser Publ: "Portraits," a series that consists of intellectual biographies of figures
      who have changed the world we live in, ed by Edward Burlingame

LITTLE, BROWN AND COMPANY*
   45 Beacon Street, Boston, Massachusetts 02106

LOUISIANA STATE UNIVERSITY PRESS 1935
   Hill Memorial Building, Baton Rouge, Louisiana 70803

LOYOLA UNIVERSITY PRESS 1912
   3441 N Ashland, Chicago, Illinois 60657

The M I T PRESS 1933
   28 Carleton Street, Cambridge, Massachusetts 02142

MACMILLAN PUBLISHING COMPANY 1875
   866 Third Avenue, New York, New York 10022

Ser Publ: "Sources in Philosophy," 10 volumes for use in combinations that suit instructors in introduction to philosophy courses, ed by Louis White Beck; "Readings in the History of Philosophy," emphasizes the significance of philosophic contributions of each period and the interrelationships of important philosophers, ed by Paul Edwards and Richard Popkin

MCGRAW-HILL BOOK COMPANY 1906
1221 Avenue of the Americas, New York, New York 10020

David MCKAY COMPANY, INC 1882
750 Third Avenue, New York, New York 10017

MAGI BOOKS, INC 1964
33 Buckingham Drive, Albany, New York 12208

Ser Publ: "Overview Studies," monographs on contemporary issues and problems in philosophy and religion

MEMPHIS STATE UNIVERSITY PRESS 1968
Meeman 318, Memphis, Tennessee 38152

Jour Publ: The Southern Journal of Philosophy

Charles E MERRILL PUBLISHING COMPANY
1300 Alum Creek Drive, Columbus, Ohio 43216

MESSENGER PRESS 1894
Carthagena Station, Celina, Ohio 45822

Jour Publ: Philosophy Today

C V MOSBY COMPANY 1933
11830 Westline Industrial Drive, St Louis, Missouri 63141

NASH PUBLISHING CORPORATION 1969
9255 Sunset Boulevard, Los Angeles, California 90069

NEW AMERICAN LIBRARY, INC* 1948
1301 Avenue of the Americas, New York, New York 10019

Ser Publ: "Mentor Philosophers," ed by Robert Paul Wolff; "Perspectives in Humanism," ed by Ruth Nanda Anshen

NEW VIEWPOINTS, A Division of Franklin Watts, Inc 1942
730 Fifth Avenue, New York, New York 10019

NORTHWESTERN UNIVERSITY PRESS 1957
1735 Benson Avenue, Evanston, Illinois 60201

Ser Publ: "Studies in Phenomenology and Existential Philosophy," translations of the important works of phenomenology and existential philosophy from Europe, as well as original works in these fields, ed by James M Edie; "Northwestern University Publications in Analytical Philosophy," a series emphasizing studies in the history of philosophy as well as studies in contemporary issues and figures, ed by Moltke S Gram

W W NORTON & COMPANY, INC 1924
   500 Fifth Avenue, New York, New York 10036

The ODYSSEY PRESS*
   4300 West 62nd Street, Indianapolis, Indiana 46268

OHIO STATE UNIVERSITY PRESS 1957
   2070 Neil Avenue, Columbus, Ohio 43210

OHIO UNIVERSITY PRESS 1964
   Administrative Annex, Athens, Ohio 45701

OPEN COURT PUBLISHING COMPANY 1887
   Box 599, La Salle, Illinois 61301

   Jour Publ: The Monist, ed by Eugene Freeman
   Ser Publ: "Paul Carus Lecture Series," publication of lectures on free and original
      philosophical inquiry; "The Library of Living Philosophers," a series in which
      leading philosophers submit their ideas to the most thorough examination by
      their critics, and in turn reply to them, ed by Paul A Schilpp

OPINION PUBLICATIONS 1959
   P O Box 688, Evanston, Illinois 60204

   Jour publ: Opinion, Jim's Journal

OXFORD UNIVERSITY PRESS 1484
   200 Madison Avenue, New York, New York 10016

   Ser Publ: "Clarendon Aristotle Series," ed by J L Ackrill; "Library of Logic and
      Philosophy," a series that aims at encouraging new research of a professional
      standard into problems that are of current or perennial interest, ed by L
      Jonathan Cohen; "Oxford Readings in Philosophy," ed by G J Warnock

PAIDEIA PRESS* 1969
   26 Ranich Road, Hauppauge, New York 11787

   Jour Publ: Philosophia Mathematica

PATHFINDER PRESS, INC 1970
   410 West Street, New York, New York 10014

PEGASUS*
   4300 West 62nd Street, Indianapolis, Indiana 46268

   Ser Publ: "Pegasus Traditions in Philosophy Series," ed by Nicholas Capaldi

The PENNSYLVANIA STATE UNIVERSITY PRESS
215 Wagner Building, University Park, Pennsylvania 16802

Jour Publ: Philosophy and Rhetoric

PHILOSOPHICAL LIBRARY, INC 1942
15 East 40th Street, New York, New York 10016

PHILOSOPHY DOCUMENTATION CENTER 1966
Bowling Green University, Bowling Green, Ohio 43403

Jour Publ: The Philosopher's Index
Ser Publ: "Bibliographies of Philosophers," a series of bibliographies of important
philosophers, ed by Richard H Lineback
Other: Directory of American Philosophers, ed by Archie J Bahm and International
Directory of Philosophy and Philosophers

PLENUM PUBLISHING CORPORATION 1946
227 West 17th Street, New York, New York 10011

Jour Publ: Algebra and Logic, Foundations of Physics; International Journal of
Theoretical Physics; General Relativity and Gravitation
Ser Publ: "Symposia on Theoretical Physics and Mathematics," a series of proceedings
of symposia held at the Institute of Mathematical Sciences, Madras, ed by Alladi
Ramakrishnan

PRAEGER PUBLISHERS, INC 1950
111 Fourth Avenue, New York, New York 10003

PRENTICE-HALL, INC 1913
Route 9W, Englewood Cliffs, New Jersey 07632

Ser Publ: "The Foundation of Philosophy Series," a series that presents the integral
field of philosophy in separate volumes, each written by an expert in his field,
ed by Elizabeth Beardsley and Monroe Beardsley; "Central Issues in Philosophy
Series," a series of anthologies designed to introduce the reader to major
problems in philosophy, including an introduction, an analytical index and a
short bibliography, ed by Baruch Brody; "The Prentice-Hall Context of Thought
Series," a series that deals with the history of the different fields in
philosophy, ed by Harry Frankfurt

The PRESS OF CASE WESTERN RESERVE UNIVERSITY 1938
Frank Adgate Quail Building, Case Western Reserve University, Cleveland, Ohio 44106

Ser Publ: "Oberlin Philosophy Colloquia"

PRINCETON UNIVERSITY PRESS 1910
41 William Street, Princeton, New Jersey 08540

Jour Publ: Philosophy & Public Affairs
Ser Publ: "Papers from the Eranos Yearbooks," ed by Joseph Campbell; "Plato," ed
by Paul Friedländer; "Jewish Symbols in the Greco-Roman Period," ed by E R
Goodenough; "Archetypal Images in Greek Religion," ed by C Kerenyi

459

QUADRANGLE BOOKS, INC* 1959
    12 East Delaware Place, Chicago, Illinois 60611

    Ser Publ: "Great Philosophers," short intellectual biographies of the major Western
        philosophers since Aristotle, ed by James M Edie

RANDOM HOUSE, INC 1925
    201 East 50th Street, New York, New York 10022

Fred B ROTHMAN & CO* 1946
    57 Leuning Street, South Hackensack, New Jersey 07606

RUSSELL & RUSSELL, PUBLISHERS 1953
    122 East 42nd Street, New York, New York 10017

SCARECROW PRESS, INC 1950
    52 Liberty Street, Metuchen, New Jersey 08840

SCHENKMAN PUBLISHING COMPANY, INC 1961
    3 Mt Auburn Place, Cambridge, Massachusetts 02138

    Ser Publ: "Contemporary Ethics Series," ed by Peter French; "Philosophers in
        Perspective," ed by A D Woozley

SCHOCKEN BOOKS, INC 1946
    200 Madison Avenue, New York, New York 10016

    Ser Publ: "Studies in Ethics and the Philosophy of Religion," ed by D Z Phillips

SCHOLARS' FACSIMILES & REPRINTS 1936
    P O Box 344, Delmar, New York 12054

    Ser Publ: "History of Psychology Series," ed by Robert I Watson

SCOTT, FORESMAN AND COMPANY 1896
    1900 East Lake Avenue, Glenview, Illinois 60025

Charles SCRIBNER'S SONS 1846
    597 Fifth Avenue, New York, New York 10017

    Ser Publ: "Lyceum Editions, Philosophy Series, Scribner Library," selections of
        writings of famous philophers, ed by W D Ross and Mary Wilton Calkins

SEVEN BRIDGES PUBLISHING COMPANY*
    8 South Michigan Avenue, Chicago, Illinois 60603

    Jour Publ: <u>Existential Psychiatry</u>

SHAMBHALA PUBLICATIONS, INC 1969
  1409 Fifth Street, Berkeley, California 94710

  Jour Publ: Maitreya

SHEED & WARD, INC* 1927
  64 University Place, New York, New York 10003

The SHOE STRING PRESS, INC 1952
  995 Sherman Avenue, Hamden, Connecticut 06514

SIMON AND SCHUSTER 1924
  630 Fifth Avenue, New York, New York 10020

  Ser Publ: "The Credo Perspectives," a series that explores the ways in which man,
    in a world increasingly materialistic, conformist, and abstract, searches for
    meaning and inspiration, ed by Ruth Nanda Anshen

Peter SMITH PUBLISHER, INC 1929
  6 Lexington Avenue, Magnolia, Massachusetts 01930

SOUTHERN ILLINOIS UNIVERSITY PRESS 1953
  P O Box 3697, Carbondale, Illinois 62901

  Ser Publ: "Philosophical Explorations," ed by George K Plochmann

SPRINGER-VERLAG 1924
  175 Fifth Avenue, New York, New York 10010

  Ser Publ: "LEP Library of Exact Philosophy," a series that keeps alive the spirit
    of the Vienna Circle, demanding the clear statement of problems, their careful
    handling with the relevant logical or mathematical tools, and a critical
    analysis of the assumptions and results, ed by Mario Bunge

STATE UNIVERSITY OF NEW YORK PRESS 1966
  99 Washington Avenue, Albany, New York 12210

  Jour Publ: Philosophy and Phenomenological Research
  Ser Publ: "Contemporary Philosophic Thought," a collection of papers presented at
    the International Philosophy Year Conferences at Brockport, New York, ed by
    Howard E Kiefer and Milton K Munitz

SWEDENBORG FOUNDATIONS, INC 1849
  139 East 23rd Street, New York, New York 10010

  Jour Publ: The New Philosophy

SYRACUSE UNIVERSITY PRESS 1943
  Box 8, University Station, Syracuse, New York 13210

THEOSOPHICAL PUBLISHING HOUSE*
  Box 270, Wheaton, Illinois 60187

TEACHERS COLLEGE PRESS 1904
  1234 Amsterdam Avenue, New York, New York 10027

  Ser Publ: "Problems in Education," a series concerned with the problems and needs
    of education in a philosophical context, ed by Jonathan C Messerli and Jonas
    F Soltis

Charles C THOMAS, PUBLISHER 1925
  301-327 East Lawrence Avenue, Springfield, Illinois 62703

  Ser Publ: "American Lectures in Philosophy," ed by Marvin Farber; "Modern Concepts
    of Philosophy," ed by Marvin Farber

Charles E TUTTLE COMPANY, INC 1832
  28 South Main Street, Rutland, Vermont 05701

Frederick UNGAR PUBLISHING COMPANY 1941
  250 Park Avenue South, New York, New York 10003

The UNIVERSITY OF ALABAMA PRESS 1947
  Drawer 2877, University, Alabama 35486

  Ser Publ: "Studies in the Humanities," monographs on literature, philosophy, art
    and music, ed by James Travis

The UNIVERSITY OF ARIZONA PRESS 1959
  Box 3398, Tucson, Arizona 85722

UNIVERSITY OF CALIFORNIA PRESS 1893
  2223 Fulton Street, Berkeley, California 94720

  Ser Publ: "New Titles in Practical Philosophy," a series of studies on aspects of
    moral philosophy, giving particular attention to the logic of moral discourse
    and the practical problems of morality, ed by W D Hudson

UNIVERSITY OF CHICAGO PRESS 1891
  5801 S Ellis Avenue, Chicago, Illinois 60637

  Jour Publ: Ethics

UNIVERSITY OF GEORGIA PRESS 1939
  Waddel Hall, University of Georgia, Athens, Georgia 30602

UNIVERSITY OF ILLINOIS PRESS 1919
  Urbana, Illinois 61801

The UNIVERSITY OF MASSACHUSETTS PRESS 1964
  505 East Pleasant Street, Amherst, Massachusetts 01002

UNIVERSITY OF MIAMI PRESS 1947
  Drawer 9088, Coral Gables, Florida 33124

The UNIVERSITY OF MICHIGAN PRESS 1930
    615 East University, Ann Arbor, Michigan 48106

UNIVERSITY OF MINNESOTA PRESS 1925
    2037 University of Avenue SE, Minneapolis, Minnesota 55455

    Ser Publ: "Minnesota Studies in the Philosophy of Science," publications on research
        sponsored by the Minnesota Center for the Philosophy of Science, ed by Herbert
        Feigl and Grover Maxwell

UNIVERSITY OF MISSOURI PRESS 1959
    107 Swallow Hall, Columbia, Missouri 65201

    Ser Publ: "Brick Lectures Series," commentaries on the "Science of Ethics"

UNIVERSITY OF MONTANA PRESS
    Missoula, Montana 59801

UNIVERSITY OF NEBRASKA PRESS 1941
    901 North 17th Street, Lincoln, Nebraska 68508

The UNIVERSITY OF NORTH CAROLINA PRESS 1922
    Box 2288, Chapel Hill, North Carolina 27514

UNIVERSITY OF NOTRE DAME PRESS 1949
    Notre Dame, Indiana 46556

UNIVERSITY OF OKLAHOMA PRESS 1928
    Norman, Oklahoma 73069

    Jour Publ: The Southwestern Journal of Philosophy

The UNIVERSITY OF PENNSYLVANIA PRESS, INC 1889
    3933 Walnut Street, Philadelphia, Pennsylvania 19104

    Ser Publ: "Works in Continental Philosophy," translations of the complete works
        of continental philosophers from Kant to the present, ed by John Silber

UNIVERSITY OF PITTSBURGH PRESS 1937
    127 N Bellefield, Pittsburgh, Pennsylvania 15260

    Ser Publ: "The Philosophy of Science Series," ed by Robert Colodny

UNIVERSITY OF SOUTH CAROLINA PRESS 1948
    Columbia, South Carolina 29208

The UNIVERSITY OF TENNESSEE PRESS 1940
    293 Communications Building, Knoxville, Tennessee 37916

UNIVERSITY OF TEXAS PRESS   1951
   Box 7819, Austin, Texas 78712

   Ser Publ: "Contemporary Political and Social Philosophy," translations of selected
      major European works in political and social philosophy, ed by Joseph J Bien

UNIVERSITY OF WASHINGTON PRESS   1940
   Seattle, Washington 98195

The UNIVERSITY OF WISCONSIN PRESS   1937
   Box 1379, Madison, Wisconsin 53701

The UNIVERSITY PRESS OF HAWAII   1947
   535 Ward Avenue, Honolulu, Hawaii 96814

   Jour Publ: Philosophy East and West

The UNIVERSITY PRESS OF KANSAS   1946
   366 Watson Library, Lawrence, Kansas 66044

The UNIVERSITY PRESS OF KENTUCKY   1969
   Lexington, Kentucky 40506

UNIVERSITY PRESS OF VIRGINIA   1963
   Box 3608 University Station, Charlottesville, Virginia 22903

D VAN NOSTRAND COMPANY   1848
   450 West 33rd Street, New York, New York 10001

VANDERBILT UNIVERSITY PRESS   1940
   Nashville, Tennessee 37235

The VIKING PRESS, INC   1925
   625 Madison Avenue, New York, New York 10022

   Ser Publ: "Modern Masters," critiques of the most important thinkers of our time,
      ed by Frank Kermode; "The B'nai B'rith Jewish Heritage Classics," a self-
      contained and fundamental library of Jewish classics from Biblical times to
      the present, ed by David Patterson and Lily Edelman

WADSWORTH PUBLISHING COMPANY, INC*   1956
   10 Davis Drive, Belmont, California 94002

The WAVERLY PRESS*
   Mount Royal and Guilford Avenues, Baltimore, Maryland 21202

   Jour Publ: Journal of Aesthetics and Art Criticism

WAYNE STATE UNIVERSITY PRESS 1941
   5980 Cass Avenue, Detroit, Michigan 48202

   Jour Publ: <u>American Imago</u>

WESLEYAN UNIVERSITY PRESS 1957
   356 Washington Street, Middletown, Connecticut 06457

   Jour Publ: <u>History and Theory: Studies in the Philosophy of History</u>

WESTMINSTER PRESS 1838
   Witherspoon Building, Philadelphia, Pennsylvania 19107

John WILEY & SONS, INC
   One Wiley Drive, Somerset, New Jersey 08873

WORLD PUBLISHING 1905
   2080 West 117 Street, Cleveland, Ohio 44111

XEROX COLLEGE PUBLISHING 1970
   191 Spring Street, Lexington, Massachusetts 02173

   Ser Publ: "Monuments of Western Thought," a series that includes the writings of
      major contributors of the development of Western thought, ed by Norman Cantor

YALE UNIVERSITY PRESS 1908
   Box 92A Yale Station, New Haven, Connecticut 06520

PART II

CANADA

UNIVERSITIES

ALBERTA

BANFF SCHOOL OF FINE ARTS, Constituent of the University of Calgary
Banff, Alberta (--) NR

CAMROSE LUTHERAN COLLEGE
Camrose, Alberta (u 261) Courses with no degree specialization, --, 403-672-3381

Eriksson, Vincent E, MA, Assoc Prof, Kierkegaard

CANADIAN UNION COLLEGE
College Heights, Alberta (u 82) NP

COLLEGE SAINT JEAN
Edmonton, Alberta (u 109) NR

COLLEGE UNIVERSITAIRE SAINT JEAN, Faculty of the University of Alberta, Edmonton
Edmonton, Alberta T6C 4G9 (u 109) Courses with no degree specialization, Div des
Langues et Humanités 403-466-2196

Bilodeau, Thomas, LPh, Assoc Prof, Dir, Phil of Relig
Godbout, Laurent A, LPh, Asst Prof, Hist of Phil, Ethics

CONCORDIA COLLEGE
Edmonton, Alberta (u 67) NP

FAIRVIEW COLLEGE
Fairview, Alberta (--) NP

GRANDE PRAIRIE REGIONAL COLLEGE
Grande Prairie, Alberta (u 122) Courses with no degree specialization, Dept of Libr
Educ, 403-532-3855

McLean, Murdith, DPhil, Sess Lect, Phil of Relig, Phil of Mind

HILLCREST CHRISTIAN COLLEGE
Medicine Hat, Alberta (--) NP

LETHBRIDGE COMMUNITY COLLEGE
Lethbridge, Alberta (u 1409) NR

MEDICINE HAT COLLEGE
Medicine Hat, Alberta (u 200) AA major, Div of Human and Soc Sci, 403-527-7141
Ext 211

Thiessen, Elmer J, MA, Phil of Relig

MOUNT ROYAL COLLEGE, Affiliate of the University of Calgary
    Calgary, Alberta (u 800) NP

NORTHERN ALBERTA INSTITUTE OF TECHNOLOGY
    Edmonton, Alberta (--) NP

RED DEER COLLEGE, Affiliate of the University of Alberta
    Red Deer, Alberta (u 554) NR

SAINT JOSEPH'S COLLEGE, Federated with the University of Alberta
    Edmonton, 61, Alberta (--) MA joint or combined major, Dept of Phil, 403-439-7311

    Daley, J E, MA, Asst Prof
    Dore, J W, PhD, Prof, Psych of Man
    Eshpeter, A, MA, Assoc Prof
    Firth, J J F, PhD, Asst Prof, Hist of Phil

SAINT STEPHEN'S COLLEGE, Affiliate of the University of Alberta
    Edmonton, Alberta (u 2) NP

SOUTHERN ALBERTA INSTITUTE OF TECHNOLOGY
    Calgary, Alberta (--) NP

UNIVERSITY OF ALBERTA
    Edmonton, Alberta (u 15,890; g 2353) PhD major, Dept of Phil, 403-432-3307

    Schouls, P A, PhD, Assoc Prof, Chm, Epistem, Hist of Phil
    Shiner, R A, PhD, Assoc Prof, Act Chm, Greek Phil, Ethics, Phil of Relig, Wittgenstein
    Bosley, R N, PhD, Assoc Prof, Aristotelian Logic, Anc Phil, Med Phil
    Carlson, A A, PhD, Asst Prof, Aes
    Christensen, F M, PhD, Asst Prof, Phil of Sci
    Cooper, W E, BA, Asst Prof, Phil of Mind, Action Theory, Ethics, Wittgenstein
    Eastman, W, PhD, Assoc Prof, Theory of Knowl
    Haynes, P, PhD, Visit Asst Prof, Phil of Mind
    Hicks, D C, PhD, Assoc Prof, Ethics, Phil of Relig
    King-Farlow, J, PhD, Prof, Phil of Relig, Phil of Lang
    McGilp, I, MA, Asst Prof, Polit Phil, Soc Phil
    MacKenzie, J C, MLitt, Asst Prof, Ethics
    McLean, M, PhD, Visit Asst Prof, Phil of Relig
    Mardiros, A M, MLitt, Prof, Aes, Ethics, Soc and Polit Phil
    Morgan, C G, PhD, Assoc Prof, Phil of Sci, Math
    Pelletier, F J, PhD, Asst Prof, Phil of Lang, Phil of Logic, Anc Greek Phil
    Sharp, W D, BA, Asst Prof, Phil of Sci
    Tennessen, H, Mag, PhL, Prof, Phil of Lang, Logic, Exist
    van de Pitte, F P, PhD, Assoc Prof, Kant, Continen Phil, Phil Anthrop
    Whitling, D, BA, Asst Prof, Med Phil, Logic, Metaph

    Aberant, M, Grad Asst   Lawton, E, Grad Asst
    Bichenback, J, Scholarship   Leighton, S, Grad Asst
    Borcoman, K D, Grad Asst   Leonard, R, Grad Asst
    Carlson, J, Grad Asst   Mix, L, Canada Council
    Coles, M, Grad Asst   Pelletier, A, Grad Asst
    Dalon, R, Grad Asst   Ross, M, Grad Asst
    Davis, J, Grad Asst   Schafer, H, Grad Asst
    Donahoe, I M, Grad Asst   Sharp, G, Grad Asst
    Elugardo, R, Fel   Smith, D, Grad Asst
    Haley, S, Canada Council   Spangler, A, Fel
    Jacobsen, R, Grad Asst   Tokerud, B, Grad Asst

Jones, P, Grad Asst
Lahey, L, Grad Asst

Wehrell, R, Canada Council

UNIVERSITY OF CALGARY
Calgary 44, Alberta T2N 1N4 (u 8344; g 829) PhD major, Dept of Phil, 403-284-5539

Baker, Brenda, BLitt, Asst Prof
Baker, John A, DPhil, Assoc Prof
Dyson, Verena, PhD, Visit Asst Prof
Grant, Brian, PhD, Asst Prof
Greig, Gordon M, MA, Prof
Hanen, Marsha P, PhD, Assoc Prof
Jewell, Robert D, PhD, Asst Prof
MacIntosh, J J, MA, Prof
Mamo, P S, PhD, Assoc Prof
Martin, C B, PhD, Prof
Nielsen, Kai, PhD, Prof
Penelhum, T M, BPhil, Prof
Stewart, W F M, PhD, Prof
Travis, Charles, PhD, Asst Prof
Von Morstein, Petra, Asst Prof
Ware, Robert X, DPhil, Asst Prof

Bean, William, Grad Teach Asst
Boetzkes, Elizabeth, Grad Teach Asst
Cromwell, William, Grad Teach Asst
Davison, John, Grad Teach Asst
De Wit, Sonja, Grad Teach Asst
Eberle, James, Grad Teach Asst

Kornfein, Roger, Grad Teach Asst
Mercer, David, Grad Teach Asst
Scheinberg, Patricia, Grad Teach Asst
Strand, David, Grad Teach Asst
Troth, Peter, Grad Teach Asst
Whittaker, Gareth, Grad Teach Asst

UNIVERSITY OF LETHBRIDGE
Lethbridge, Alberta (u 1218) BA major, Dept of Phil, 403-329-2500

Preuss, P S, PhD, Assoc Prof, Chm, 19th Cent Phil
Butterfield, P, MA, Assoc Prof, Phil of Relig, Aes
Hall, R A, MA, Assoc Prof, Phil of Man
Kubara, M P, MA, Asst Prof, Plato
Patten, S C, MA, Asst Prof, Kant
Yoshida, R M, PhD, Asst Prof, Logic, Phil of Sci

VERMILION COLLEGE
Vermilion, Alberta TOB 4MO (--) NP

BRITISH COLUMBIA

ANGLICAN THEOLOGICAL COLLEGE OF BRITISH COLUMBIA, Affiliate of the University of
British Columbia
Vancouver, British Columbia (u 19) NR

BRITISH COLUMBIA INSTITUTE OF TECHNOLOGY
Burnaby 2, British Columbia (--) NP

CAPILANO COLLEGE
North Vancouver, British Columbia (u 422) Courses with no degree specialization,
Div of Human, 604-926-4367

CARIBOO COLLEGE
Kamloops, British Columbia (u 247) NP

COLLEGE OF NEW CALEDONIA
Prince George, British Columbia (u 179) Courses with no degree specialization,
Div of Arts and Sci, 604-562-2131

Ingalls, Gordon, BA, Moral Phil, Polit Phil

DOUGLAS COLLEGE
New Westminster, British Columbia (u 1124) Courses with no degree specialization,
Dept of Libr Arts, 604-521-4851

Christensen, W N, MA, Chm, Ethics, Phenomen, Exist
Davies, J, ThD, Logic, Polit Phil
DeJonge, J, MPhil, Ethics, Phenomen, Metaph
Jones, E D, ThM, Ethics, Metaph, Phil of Relig

KING EDWARD CENTRE
Vancouver, British Columbia (--) NR

MALASPINA COLLEGE
Nanaimo, British Columbia (u 421) Courses with no degree specialization, Area of
Human, 604-753-1211

Lane, Robert D, MA, Chm, Aes
Smith, Patricia, MA, Part-time, Comp Relig

NOTRE DAME UNIVERSITY OF NELSON
Nelson, British Columbia (u 510) BA major, Dept of Phil, 604-352-2241, Local 59

Micallef, P J, PhD, Asst Prof, Chm, Ethics, Polit Phil, Logic
Bonney R, MA, Asst Prof, Hist of Phil, Mod Phil
Brown, M L, MA, Assoc Prof, Metaph, Phil Psych
Laurie, W J, PhL, Instr, Contemp Phil

OKANAGA REGIONAL COLLEGE
Kelowna, British Columbia (u 432) NR

ROYAL ROADS MILITARY COLLEGE, Affiliate of the Royal Military College of Canada
Victoria, British Columbia (u 206) --, --, --

La Bossière, C R, MA, Lect, Aristotelian Logic
Morgan, G M, PhD, Prof, Aristotelian Logic

SAINT ANDREW'S HALL, Affiliate of the University of British Columbia
Vancouver, British Columbia (--) NR

SAINT MARK'S COLLEGE, Affiliate of the University of British Columbia
  Vancouver, British Columbia (--) NR

SELKIRK COLLEGE
  Castlegar, British Columbia (u 417) NP

SEMINARY OF CHRIST THE KING
  Mission City, British Columbia (u 2) NR

SIMON FRASER UNIVERSITY
  Burnaby 2, British Columbia (u 3364; g 759) MA major, Dept of Phil, 604-291-3343

  Resnick, L, PhD, Prof, Chm, Epistem, Ethics
  Angelo, A A, MA, Asst Prof
  Bradley, R D, PhD, Prof, Hist of Mod Phil, Metaph, Phil of Logic
  Davis, S, PhD, Assoc Prof, Logic, Phil of Lang
  Finn, D R, PhD, Asst Prof, Phil Psych, Moral Phil
  Herbst, P, MA, Prof, Metaph, Ethics, Polit Phil
  Jennings, R J, PhD, Asst Prof, Phil of Logic, Phil of Mind
  Swartz, N M, PhD, Assoc Prof, Phil of Sci
  Tietz, J H, PhD, Asst Prof, Ethics, Hist of Mod Phil, Phil of Mind
  Todd, D D, PhD, Assoc Prof, Hist of Mod Phil, Epistem
  Wheatley, J, PhD, Prof, Contemp Anal Phil

TRINITY WESTERN COLLEGE
  Langley, British Columbia (u 338) Courses with no degree specialization, Div of
  Human in Arts College, 604-534-5381

  Mattson, Enoch E, ThD, Prof, Plato
  Thompson, Robert N, BS, Spec Lect, Polit Theory

UNION COLLEGE OF BRITISH COLUMBIA, Affiliate of the University of British Columbia
  Vancouver, British Columbia (--) NR

UNIVERSITY OF BRITISH COLUMBIA
  Vancouver 8, British Columbia (u 16,185; g 2808) PhD major, Dept of Phil, 604-228-
  3292

  Remnant, Peter, PhD, Prof, Head, Hist of Phil, Metaph, Polit Phil
  Rowan, Robert J, PhD, Prof, Act Head, Anc Phil, Polit Phil
  Bennett, Jonathan F, BPhil, Prof, Hist of Mod Phil, Phil of Lang
  Brown, Donald G, DPhil, Prof, Ethics, Polit Phil
  Brown, Elizabeth, MA, Visit Asst Prof, Aes, Epistem, Phil of Lang, Metaph
  Coval, Samuel C, DPhil, Prof, Phil of Lang, Phil of Mind
  Dybikowski, James C, PhD, Assoc Prof, Aes, Anc Phil
  Jackson, Howard O, PhD, Asst Prof, Phil of Lang, Logic
  Levine, Andrew, PhD, Visit Asst Prof, Hist of Phil, Polit Phil
  Levy, Edwin, PhD, Asst Prof, Phil of Sci
  Mullins, Warren J, PhD, Assoc Prof, Aes, Phil of Soc Sci
  Patton, Thomas E, PhD, Prof, Phil of Lang
  Rand, Elbridge N, BA, Sr Instr, Ethics, Polit Phil
  Robertson, John E, BA, Visit Asst Prof, Anc Phil, Phil of Man, Phil of Sci
  Robinson, Richard E, PhD, Assoc Prof, Logic, Phil of Math
  Savitt, Steven, PhD, Asst Prof, Logic, Phil of Sci
  Sikora, Richard I, PhD, Asst Prof, Ethics, Phil of Mind
  Stewart, John P, MS, Asst Prof, Epistem, Phil of Math, Metaph
  Wedeking, Gary A, PhD, Asst Prof, Epistem, Ethics, Metaph, Polit Phil

Winkler, Earl R, PhD, Asst Prof, Polit Phil, Soc Phil
Zimmerman, David P, MA, Visit Asst Prof, Polit Phil, Soc Phil

Savery, Barnett, PhD, Prof Emer

UNIVERSITY OF VICTORIA
Victoria, British Columbia (u 4623; g 177) MA major, Dept of Phil, 604-477-6911
Ext 619

Rankin, K W, PhD, Prof, Chm, Phil of Tht and Action, Phil of Time
Beehler, R G, PhD, Asst Prof, Polit Phil, Phil of Law
Butkus, R G, BA, Visit Lect, Exist, Phenomen
Daniels, C B, PhD, Assoc Prof, Phil of Mind, Ethics
Drengson, A R, MA, Asst Prof, Hist of Phil
Horsburgh, H J N, BLitt, Prof, Ethics, Phil of Relig
Kluge, E W, PhD, Assoc Prof, Frege, Med Phil
Michelsen, J M, PhD, Asst Prof, Contemp Euro Phil
Woods, J H, PhD, Prof, Phil of Logic

VANCOUVER CITY COLLEGE, LANGARA CAMPUS
Vancouver, British Columbia (u 1876) AA major, Dept of Phil, Soc and Anthrop, 604-324-5237

Kunin, Jack, MA, Instr, Cord, Epistem
Burbidge, Don, MA, Instr, Polit Phil
Dunik, Peter, MA, Instr, Logic
Pagee, Sam, MA, Instr, Phil of Educ
Postma, John, MA, Instr, Ethics
Smith, George, MA, Instr, Soc Phil

VANCOUVER CITY COLLEGE, VANCOUVER VOCATIONAL INSTITUTE
Vancouver 3, British Columbia (--) NP

VANCOUVER SCHOOL OF ART
Vancouver, British Columbia (--) NR

VANCOUVER SCHOOL OF THEOLOGY
Vancouver 8, British Columbia (u 35) MA major, Div of Hist of Theol, 604-228-9031

Wilson, R A, PhD, Prof, Chm, Theol
Crockett, W R A, PhD, Assoc Prof, Syst Theol
Taylor, W S, PhD, Sess Lect, Phil of Relig

MANITOBA

ASSINIBOINE COMMUNITY COLLEGE
Brandon, Manitoba (--) NR

BRANDON UNIVERSITY
Brandon, Manitoba (u 1220) BA major, Dept of Phil, 204-727-5401 Ext 340

Gosselin, Philip, MPhil, Asst Prof, Hist of Phil
Hanly, Ken, PhD, Asst Prof, Polit Phil, Ling Phil
Yoh, May, MA, Asst Prof, Phil of Sci

Simmons, R Murray, STM, Prof Emer

CANADIAN MENNONITE BIBLE COLLEGE
Winnipeg, Manitoba (--) Courses with no degree specialization, --, 204-888-6781

Huebner, Harry, Instr, Epistem
Schroeder, David, PhD, Prof, Ethics

COLLEGE DE SAINT-BONIFACE, Affiliate of the University of Manitoba
Saint-Boniface, Manitoba (--) NR

KEEWATIN COMMUNITY COLLEGE
The Pas, Manitoba (--) NP

MENNONITE BRETHREN COLLEGE OF ARTS, Affiliate of Waterloo Lutheran University
Winnipeg, Manitoba R2L 1L1 (u 79) Courses with no degree specialization, Dept of
Phil, 204-667-9560

Ratzlaff, Vernon, MA, Asst Prof, Polit Phil

RED RIVER COMMUNITY COLLEGE
Winnipeg 23, Manitoba (--) NP

SAINT ANDREW'S COLLEGE IN WINNIPEG, Associated with the University of Manitoba
Winnipeg, Manitoba R3T 2M7 (u 15) Courses with no degree specialization, --, --

SAINT JOHN'S COLLEGE, Affiliate of the University of Manitoba
Winnipeg, Manitoba (--) --, --, 204-269-3550

SAINT PAUL'S COLLEGE, Affiliate of the University of Manitoba
Winnipeg, Manitoba (--) NR

UNIVERSITY OF MANITOBA
Winnipeg 19, Manitoba (u 11,992; g 1410) MA major, Dept of Phil, 204-474-9571

Vincent, R H, MA, Assoc Prof, Head
Bailey, J A, PhD, Asst Prof
Basham, R R, BTh, Lect
Churchland, P M, PhD, Asst Prof
Churchland, P S, MPhil, Asst Prof

Conner, O, PhD, Asst Prof
Cosby, G, MA, Asst Prof
Feld, M, PhD, Asst Prof
Fleming, E, MA, Lect
Gerwin, M, MA, Asst Prof
Glassen, P, MA, Prof
McCarthy, D J, PhD, Prof
Nielsen, W H, MA, Asst Prof
Schafer, A M, BPhil, Asst Prof
Sibley, W M, PhD, Prof
Stack, M, PhD, Asst Prof
Warmbrod, K, PhD, Asst Prof
Yarvin, H, PhD, Asst Prof

UNIVERSITY OF WINNIPEG
Winnipeg, Manitoba R3B 2E9 (u 2375; g 3) BA major, Dept of Phil, 304-786-7811

Stearns, J Brenton, PhD, Assoc Prof, Chm, Phil of Relig
Burns, William D, MA, Asst Prof, Wittgenstein
Keenan, Brian M, MA, Lect, Phil of Soc Sci
Levine, Elliott M, MA, Asst Prof, Exist, Aes
Miller, W Peter, PhD, Assoc Prof, Metaph, Space and Time, Value Theory
Pfeiffer, W M, PhD, Asst Prof, Greek Phil, Anc Phil
Shimizu, Victor Y, MA, Assoc Prof, Ethics
Walton, Douglas N, PhD, Asst Prof, Phil of Logic, Phil of Action
Wright, Philip B, PhD, Assoc Prof

Owen, David, DD, Prof Emer, Hist of Phil

NEW BRUNSWICK

COLLEGE DE BATHURST, Affilié à l'Université de Moncton
Bathurst, Nouveau Brunswick (--) BA minor, Dépt de Phil, 506-546-9851 Ext 37

Chiasson, Euclide P, MPhil, Prof Agége, Dir, Phil of Educ
Doiron, Narcisse, LPh, Prof Titulaire

COLLEGE SAINT-JOSEPH, Affilié à l'Université de Moncton
Moncton, Nouveau Brunswick (--) NR

COLLEGE SAINT-LOUIS, Affilié à l'Université de Moncton
Edmundston, Nouveau Brunswick (--) BA minor, Dépt de Phil, 506-735-8804

Belanger, Marion, DPh, Exist
Lachance, J G, LPh, Ethics
Samson, André, DPh, Thomism
Wang, C S, DPh, Ethics

MOUNT ALLISON UNIVERSITY
  Sackville, New Brunswick (u 1337; g 1) BA major, Dept of Phil, 506-536-2040
  Ext 440

  Stanway, R A, PhD, Assoc Prof, Chm, British Idealism
  Bogaard, P A, PhD, Asst Prof, Phil of Sci
  Poole, C F, PhD, Prof, Kant
  Treash, G S, PhD, Assoc Prof, Whitehead
  Welch, C, PhD, Assoc Prof, Exist, Phenomen

NEW BRUNSWICK INSTITUTE OF TECHNOLOGY
  Moncton, New Brunswick (--) NR

SAINT JOHN INSTITUTE OF TECHNOLOGY
  Saint John, New Brunswick (--) NR

SAINT THOMAS UNIVERSITY, Affiliate of the University of New Brunswick
  Fredericton, New Brunswick (u 1095) BA major, Dept of Phil, 506-455-3337

  Waugh, R O'Brien, MA, Prof, Chm, Phil Psych
  Alexander, Hafeez, MA, Asst Prof, Polit Phil
  Asher, James, MA, Lect, Ethics
  Cronin, Francis R, PhD, Asst Prof, Exist
  Ferrari, Leo, PhD, Prof, St Augustine
  Kinsella, Noel A, PhD, Lect
  Renshaw, Richard W, MA, Lect, Phil of Relig
  Rigby, Harry W, BA, Lect
  Smith, Marc E, MA, Lect, Med Phil

UNIVERSITE DE MONCTON
  Moncton, Nouveau Brunswick (u 3191; g 146) BA major, Dépt de Phil, 506-858-4000
  Ext 4020

  Morin, Serge, MA, Chm, Phenomen, Polit Phil
  Daigle, Louis-Marcel, LPh, Prof, Aristotle, Aquinas
  François, Georges, LPh, Asst Prof, Logique, Phil des Sci
  Gallant, Corinne, DPh, Prof, Personalism, Greek Phil
  Hennuy, Gustave, DPh, Prof, Phil of Educ, Kant
  LeBlanc, Valmond, Lect, Hegel, Phil of Soc Sci
  Rainville, Maurice, MA, Asst Prof, Phenomen, Exist, Structuralism
  Richard, Arsène, LPh, Asst Prof, Phil of Relig, Anc Phil

UNIVERSITY OF NEW BRUNSWICK
  Fredericton, New Brunswick (u 4678; g 504) MA major, Dept of Phil, 506-455-9471
  Local 275

  MacGill, N W, MA, Assoc Prof, Chm, Ethics
  Cupples, B W, PhD, Asst Prof, Phil of Sci
  Demopoulos, W G, BA, Lect, Phil of Sci
  Elderkin, W R M, MA, Asst Prof, Exist
  Iwanicki, J A, MA, Asst Prof, Kant
  MacDonald, R C, MA, Asst Prof, C I Lewis
  Robinson, P R, PhD, Prof, Phil of Relig

  Bishop, S J, BA   Ray, R K, MA
  Hallam, R F D, BA   Soucoup, D G, BA

UNIVERSITY OF NEW BRUNSWICK IN SAINT JOHN
    Saint John, New Brunswick (u 146) --, --, --

    Langham, P, MA, Lect, Phil of Hist
    Robertson, J C, PhD, Asst Prof, Scottish Phil

NEWFOUNDLAND

COLLEGE OF TRADES AND TECHNOLOGY
    St John's, Newfoundland (--) NP

COUGHLAN COLLEGE, Affiliate of Memorial University
    St John's, Newfoundland (--) NP

MEMORIAL UNIVERSITY OF NEWFOUNDLAND
    St John's, Newfoundland (u 6725; g 352) --, Dept of Phil, 709-753-1200

    Dawson, J G, MA, Prof, Head
    Andrews, F Elizabeth, MA, Assoc Prof
    Jackson, F L, MA, Assoc Prof
    Jackson, M J B, PhD, Asst Prof
    Lai, T L, MS, Asst Prof
    Langford, M J, PhD, Assoc Prof
    Lochhead, D M, PhD, Asst Prof
    Maxwell, D V, MA, Asst Prof
    Mulholland, L A, MA, Asst Prof
    Thompson, D L, MA, Asst Prof

NEWFOUNDLAND COLLEGE OF TRADES AND TECHNOLOGY
    Saint John's, Newfoundland (--) NR

QUEEN'S COLLEGE, Affiliate of Memorial University
    Saint John's, Newfoundland (--) NP

SAINT BRIDE'S COLLEGE, Affiliate of Memorial University
    Littledale, Newfoundland (--) NP

SAINT JOHN'S COLLEGE, Affiliate of Memorial University
    Saint John's, Newfoundland (--) NP

NOVA SCOTIA

ACADIA UNIVERSITY
 Wolfville, Nova Scotia (u 2303; g 66) BA major, Dept of Phil, 902-542-2201
 Local 279

 Lewis, Herbert, PhD, Prof, Head, Aristotle, Ortega y Gasset, Hist of Phil
 Kampe, Cornelius, MA, Lect, Ethics, Phil of Sci
 Smale, Peter G W, PhD, Asst Prof, Exist, Phenomen

ACADIA DIVINITY COLLEGE, Affiliate of Acadia University
 Wolfville, Nova Scotia (--) BA major, --, --

ATLANTIC SCHOOL OF THEOLOGY
 Halifax, Nova Scotia (--) NR

COLLEGE SAINTE ANNE
 Church Point, Nova Scotia (u 65) Courses with no degree specialization, Dept of
 Human, 902-769-2115

 Desjardins, Urbain, MA

DALHOUSIE UNIVERSITY
 Halifax, Nova Scotia (u 5150; g 953) MA major, Dept of Phil, 902-424-6570

 Puccetti, Roland, D de l'U, Prof, Chm, Phil of Mind, Phil of Relig
 Armstrong, A Hilary, MA, Prof, Anc and Med Phil
 Braybrooke, David, PhD, Prof, Soc and Polit Phil, Ethics, Phil of Soc Sci
 Burns, Steven A M, PhD, Asst Prof, Metaph, Anc Phil
 Campbell, Richmond M, PhD, Asst Prof, Ethics, Phil of Mind
 Hare, William F, PhD, Asst Prof, Phil of Educ, Phil of Mind
 Martin, Robert M, PhD, Asst Prof, Phil in Lit, Phil of Lang
 MacLennan, Ian A, MA, Assoc Prof, Logic, Exist
 Page, F Hilton, DD, Prof, Phil of Relig
 Rosenberg, Alexander, PhD, Asst Prof, Epistem, Phil of Sci
 Schotch, Peter K, PhD, Asst Prof, Logic, Epistem
 Vingoe, Robert H, PhD, Assoc Prof, Hist of Phil

 Grennan, Wayne, MA, Pre-Doct Fel, Phil of Relig

MARITIME SCHOOL OF SOCIAL WORK, Affiliate of Dalhousie University
 Halifax, Nova Scotia (--) NR

MOUNT SAINT BERNARD COLLEGE, Affiliate of Saint Francis Xavier University
 Antigonish, Nova Scotia (--) NR

MOUNT SAINT VINCENT UNIVERSITY
 Halifax, Nova Scotia (u 942) BA minor, Dept of Phil, 902-453-4450 Ext 197

 Foy, J, MA, Instr
 Payer, P, PhD, Assoc Prof, Med Phil

MOUNT SAINT VINCENT UNIVERSITY, Associated with Dalhousie University
 Rockingham, Nova Scotia (u 998) NR

NOVA SCOTIA AGRICULTURAL COLLEGE
 Truro, Nova Scotia (u 194) NR

NOVA SCOTIA COLLEGE OF ART AND DESIGN
Halifax, Nova Scotia (u 342) NR

NOVA SCOTIA EASTERN INSTITUTE OF TECHNOLOGY
Sydney, Nova Scotia (--) NP

NOVA SCOTIA TECHNICAL COLLEGE, Associated with Dalhousie University
Halifax, Nova Scotia (u 433; g 57) NP

PINE HILL DIVINITY HALL
Halifax, Nova Scotia (u 37) MA major, --, 902-423-6939

Chalmers, R C, ThD, Prof

SAINT FRANCIS XAVIER UNIVERSITY
Antigonish, Nova Scotia (u 2940; g 20) BA joint or combined major, Dept of Phil,
902-867-2204

Bryson, Kenneth, PhD, Instr
Cary, Edward A, MA, Asst Prof
Gatto, Edo, PhD, Assoc Prof
MacDonald, C R, PhD, Prof
MacDonald, C W, PhD, Assoc Prof
MacLeod, Gregory, PhD, Asst Prof
Sanderson, George, PhL, Asst Prof
Shea, Howard, PhD, Assoc Prof
Soucy, Armand, PhL, Asst Prof

SAINT FRANCIS XAVIER UNIVERSITY, SYDNEY CAMPUS
Sydney, Nova Scotia (u 2940; g 20) BA major, Dept of Phil, 902-539-5520

Bryson, K A, PhD, Asst Prof, Chm, Metaph
Bishop J, PhD, Part-time Lect
MacLeod, G, PhD, Asst Prof, Polit Phil
MacManus, O, PhD, Part-time Lect, Ethics

SAINT MARTHA'S HOSPITAL SCHOOL OF NURSING, Affiliate of Saint Francis Xavier University
Antigonish, Nova Scotia (--) NR

SAINT MARY'S UNIVERSITY
Halifax, Nova Scotia (u 2531; g 17) MA major, Dept of Phil, 902-422-7331

Beis, Richard H, PhD, Assoc Prof, Chm, Ethics
Ansell, Robert N, PhD, Asst Prof, Logic, Phil of Logic
Kindred, Sheila, MA, Lect, Aes
Lackner, Henry, BA, Asst Prof, Phil of Sci, Soc Phil
Lowry, James, MA, Lect, Greek Phil
Marshall, Rowland C, PhD, Assoc Prof, Phenomen, Hegel
Monahan, Arthur P, PhD, Prof, Med Phil
Stewart, William A, PhL, Prof, Epistem

UNIVERSITY OF KING'S COLLEGE, Associated with Dalhousie University
Halifax, Nova Scotia (u 251; g 3) BA major, Dept of Phil, 902-423-6695

Page, F Hilton, MA, Prof, Phil of Relig

ONTARIO

ALGOMA COLLEGE, Affiliate of Laurentian University of Sudbury
Sault Sainte Marie, Ontario P6A 2G4 (u 329) BA major, Dept of Phil, 705-949-2301

Bannerman, Lloyd, PhD, Assoc Prof, Chinese Phil
Guth, Francis, LPh, Asst Prof, Contemp Continen Phil

ALGONQUIN COLLEGE OF APPLIED ARTS AND TECHNOLOGY
Ottawa, Ontario K2G 1V8 (--) Courses with no degree specialization, Dept of Soc Sci, 613-725-7233

Tanner, PhD, Instr

ALTHOUSE COLLEGE, Constituent of University of Western Ontario
London, Ontario (u 759) MA minor, Althouse College of Education, 519-679-3182

Burke, D R, PhD, Assoc Prof, Exist
Houston, B, MA, Lect, Ethics
Howard, V A, PhD, Assoc Prof, Aes
Koutsouvilis, PhD, Asst Prof, Greek Phil, Soc Phil
McPeck, PhD, Asst Prof, Phil of Sci
O'Leary, PhD, Asst Prof, Phil of Hist

ASSUMPTION UNIVERSITY, Federated with the University of Windsor
Windsor, Ontario (--) NP

ATKINSON COLLEGE
Downsview, Ontario (--) BA major, Dept of Phil, 416-667-3661

Mallin, S B, MA, Asst Prof, Chm, Epistem, Metaph, Mod Euro Phil
Adelman, H, PhD, Assoc Prof, Soc Phil, Phil of Hist
Bassford, H, PhD, Asst Prof, Phil of Mind, Ethics
Carter, W B, PhD, Prof, 17th and 18th Cent Ration and Empir, Phil of Mind
Fann, K T, PhD, Prof, Anal Phil, Phil of Lang, Soc Phil

BRESCIA COLLEGE, Affiliate of the University of Western Ontario
London, Ontario (u 277) BA major, Dept of Phil, 519-432-8353

Ryan, M T, PhD, Prof, Chm, Contemp Phil
Cavanagh, P E, PhD, Assoc Prof, Ethics
Guinan, St Michael, PhD, Prof, Aes

BROCK UNIVERSITY
St Catharines, Ontario (u 2336; g 34) MA major, Dept of Phil, 416-684-7201

Adamczewski, Zygmunt, PhD, Prof, Chm, Ontology, Exist Phil
Goicoechea, David L, PhD, Asst Prof, Phil of Relig
Halbfass, Wilhelm, PhD, Assoc Prof, Indian Phil, Comp Phil
Hansen, James E, PhD, Asst Prof, Phenomen, Soc Phil
Husain, Martha, PhD, Asst Prof, Anc Phil
Malone, Robert W, PhD, Asst Prof, Phil of Sci, Metaph
Mayer, John R A, PhD, Prof, Logic, Phenomen
Nathan, George J, PhD, Asst Prof, Epistem, Phil of Relig
Nota, John H, PhD, Prof, Med Phil, Phil of Hist
Sprung, G Mervyn C, PhD, Prof, Indian Phil, Comp Phil

CAMBRIAN COLLEGE OF APPLIED ARTS AND TECHNOLOGY
    Sault Sainte Marie, Ontario (--) --, Div of Applied Arts, 705-949-2050

    Bulger, David, MA, Asst Master

CAMBRIAN COLLEGE, NORTH BAY CAMPUS
    North Bay, Ontario (--) NR

CAMBRIAN COLLEGE, SAULT SAINTE MARIE CAMPUS
    Sault Sainte Marie, Ontario (--) NR

CAMBRIAN COLLEGE, SUDBURY CAMPUS
    Sudbury, Ontario (--) Courses with no degree specialization, Dept of Libr Stud and
    Communic, 705-566-8101

    Harper, David, MA, Asst Prof, Cord, Mod Phil, Orient Phil
    Heggie, Henry, MA, Asst Prof, Logic

CANTERBURY COLLEGE, Affiliate of the University of Windsor
    Windsor, Ontario (--) NP

CARLETON UNIVERSITY
    Ottawa, Ontario K1S 5B6 (u 7743; g 711) MA major, Dept of Phil, 613-231-3868

    Leyden, J W, BA, Asst Prof, Chm, Logic
    Bordo, S R, BA, Sess Lect, Ethics
    Brook, J A, DPhil, Asst Prof, Phil of Mind
    Clarke, S G, PhD, Asst Prof, Epistem
    Dubrule, D E, PhD, Asst Prof, Med Phil
    Egyed, B I, PhD, Asst Prof, Phil of Sci
    Glass, M, MA, Asst Prof, Ethics
    Jeffrey, A, MA, Assoc Prof, Anc Phil
    Marlin, R R A, MA, Asst Prof, Phil of Law
    O'Manique, J T, DPh, Assoc Prof, Phil of Sci
    Talmage, S, MA, Assoc Prof, Phil of Mind
    Thompson, J M, MA, Assoc Prof, Aes
    Wand, B, PhD, Prof, Polit Phil
    Wernham, J C S, STM, Prof, Mod Phil
    Wolfe, J, BA, Asst Prof, Phil of Relig

CATHARINE PARR TRAILL COLLEGE, Constituent of Trent University
    Peterborough, Ontario (--) NR

CENTENNIAL COLLEGE OF APPLIED ARTS AND TECHNOLOGY
    Scarborough, Ontario (--) Courses with no degree specialization, Dept of Human,
    416-694-3241 Ext 341

    Kuehn, B A, MA, Master, Chm
    Hartley, T J A, MA, Assoc Master
    McDonough, J T, MA, Master

CHAMPLAIN COLLEGE, Constituent of Trent University
    Peterborough, Ontario (--) NR

CHRISTIAN BROTHERS COLLEGE
    Orangeville, Ontario (--) NP

COLLEGE DE HEARST, Affiliate of Laurentian University of Sudbury
    Hearst, Ontario (u 38) AA major, Art Faculty, 705-362-4841

    Gosselin, Gilles, MA
    Tremblay, André, MA

COLLEGE DOMINICAIN DE PHILOSOPHIE ET DE THEOLOGIE
    Ottawa, Ontario K1R 7G2 (u 180; g 63) MA major, --, --

    Pierre, S, DPhil, Prof, Dir
    Bernier, R, BPhil, Lect
    Comtois, R, MA, Assoc Prof
    Dion, D, BPhil, Lect
    Lacroix, B, MA, Visit Prof
    Lavoie, J, PhL, Prof
    Mailloux, N, DPhil, Visit Prof
    Métivier, P, DPhil, Assoc Prof
    Raymond, G, MA, Prof
    Régis, L, DPhil, Prof

CONESTOGA COLLEGE OF APPLIED ARTS AND TECHNOLOGY
    Kitchener, Ontario (--) NR

CONFEDERATION COLLEGE OF APPLIED ARTS AND TECHNOLOGY
    Thunder Bay "F", Ontario (--) Courses with no degree specialization, Div of Applied
    Arts, 807-577-5751 Ext 306

    Stuhr, Christian A, MA, College Master

CONRAD GREBEL COLLEGE, Affiliate of the University of Waterloo
    Waterloo, Ontario (--) NR

DURHAM COLLEGE OF APPLIED ARTS AND TECHNOLOGY
    Ontario, Ontario L1H 7L7 (--) NP

EMMANUEL COLLEGE, Constituent of Victoria University
    Toronto 5, Ontario (--) NP

FANSHANE COLLEGE OF APPLIED ARTS AND TECHNOLOGY
    London, Ontario (--) --, Div of Soc Sci and Human, 519-451-7270

    Traynor, W T, PhD, Chm, Soc Phil
    Milne, Eric, MA, Master, Hist of Phil

THE GEORGE BROWN COLLEGE OF APPLIED ARTS AND TECHNOLOGY
    Toronto, Ontario M5T 2T9 (--) NP

GEORGIAN COLLEGE OF APPLIED ARTS AND TECHNOLOGY
    Barrie, Ontario (--) NR

GLENDON COLLEGE
    Toronto, Canada M4N 3M6 (--) BA major, --, --

    Tursman, Richard A, PhD, Assoc Prof, Chm, Logic, Phil of Sci
    Goldenberg, Sydney, LLB, Lect, Phil of Law, Soc Phil
    Gonda, Joseph P, MA, Lect, Anc Phil
    Harris, H S, PhD, Prof, Anc Phil, German Idealism, Soc Phil, Hegel
    MacKenzie, Ann Wilbur, PhD, Asst Prof, Phil of Psych, Phil of Mind, Hist of Mod Phil
    MacKenzie, Nollaig, PhD, Asst Prof, Anal Phil, Ethics
    Olin, Doris, PhD, Asst Prof, Anal Phil, Epistem
    Tweyman, Stanley, PhD, Asst Prof, Ethics, Early Mod Phil

HEARST COLLEGE, Affiliate of Laurentian University of Sudbury
    Hearst, Ontario (u 42) NR

HOLY REDEEMER COLLEGE
    Windsor, Ontario N9G 1V8 (--) NP

HUMBER COLLEGE OF APPLIED ARTS AND TECHNOLOGY
    Rexdale, Ontario M9W 5L7 (--) Courses with no degree specialization, --, --

HUNTINGTON UNIVERSITY, Federated with Laurentian University
    Sudbury, Ontario (--) NR

HURON COLLEGE, Affiliate of the University of Western Ontario
    London, Ontario (u 525) NR

IGNATIOUS COLLEGE, Affiliate of Saint Mary's University
    Guelph, Ontario (--) NP

IONA COLLEGE, Affiliate of the University of Windsor
    Windsor, Ontario (--) NP

KEMPTVILLE COLLEGE OF AGRICULTURAL TECHNOLOGY
    Kemptville, Ontario K0G 1J0 (--) NP

KING'S COLLEGE, Affiliated with the University of Western Ontario
    London, Ontario (u 814) BA major, Dept of Phil and Relig Stud, 519-433-3491 Ext 66

    Snyder, John J, PhD, Assoc Prof, Chm, Phil of Relig, Exist
    Cavanagh, Patrick, PhD, Assoc Prof
    Graveline, Robert, PhL, Assoc Prof, Ethics
    Ring, William, PhL, Prof Part-time, Logic, Polit Phil
    Ryan, Michael, PhD, Assoc Prof, Soc Ethics

KNOX COLLEGE, Federated with the University of Toronto
    Toronto 181, Ontario (u 51; g 9) PhD major, Dept of Hist and Phil of Relig, and Christ
    Ethics, 416-928-7795

    Farris, W S J, PhD, Prof, Phil of Relig

LADY EATON COLLEGE, Constituent of Trent University
Peterborough, Ontario (--) NR

LAKEHEAD UNIVERSITY
Thunder Bay P, Ontario, P7B 5E1 (u 2776; g 94) BA major, Dept of Phil, 807-345-2121
Ext 334, 346

Morris, William Sparkes, PhD, Prof, Chm, Phil of Relig, Ethics, Early Mod Phil, Anc Phil
Doan, Frank Meldor, PhD, Prof, Metaph, Aes, Contemp Phil
Rabb, James Douglas, PhD, Phil of Mind, Empir, Ling and Phenomen Anal
Ripley, Robert Charles R, PhD, Asst Prof, Logic, Epistem, Phil Psych, Phil of Sci

LAMBTON COLLEGE OF APPLIED ARTS AND TECHNOLOGY
Sarnia, Ontario (--) NR

LAURENTIAN UNIVERSITY OF SUDBURY
Sudbury, Ontario (u 2042; g 20) BA major, Joint Dept of Phil, 705-675-1151 Ext 297

Paterson, G M, PhD, Asst Prof, Chm, Phil of Relig, Phil of Mind
Albert, H, DPh, Assoc Prof, Hist of Phil
Beauchamp, D, MA, Part-time Lect, Hist of Phil
Berens, V, LPh, Assoc Prof, 19th Cent German Phil, Phil of Culture
Clarke, G I, BD, Asst Prof, Greek Phil, Polit Phil
Cragg, A W, BPhil, Asst Prof, Ethics, Hist of Phil
Di Norcia, V J, PhD, Asst Prof, Phil of Educ, Phil of Soc Sci
Ford, J A, PhD, Asst Prof, Logic, Phil of Mind
Fortier, N, LPh, Part-time Lect, Philosophie et littérature
Gaboury, P, PhD, Asst Prof, Aes, Phil of Lit
Misgeld, D, DPhil, Asst Prof, Exist, Polit Phil
Monahan, E J, LMS, Prof, Phil of Educ
Nash, R L, MA, Asst Prof, Phil and Psych
Pion, D, LTh, Part-time Lect, Philosophie et littérature
Warenda, C J, DPh, Asst Prof, Phil of Culture, Med Phil

LOYALIST COLLEGE OF APPLIED ARTS AND TECHNOLOGY
Belleville, Ontario (--) NP

MASSEY COLLEGE, Federated with the University of Toronto
Toronto 5, Ontario (--) NP

MCMASTER DIVINITY COLLEGE, Affiliate of McMaster University
Hamilton, Ontario (--) NR

MCMASTER UNIVERSITY
Hamilton, Ontario L8S 4K1 (u 7023; g 1405) PhD major, Dept of Phil, 416-522-4971
Ext 275, 312, 419

Najm, Sami, PhD, Assoc Prof, Chm, Metaph, Theory of Knowl, Value Theory, Phil of
Relig
Ajzenstat, Samuel, MA, Asst Prof, Logic, Phil of Sci, Soc and Polit Phil
Bristol, John, PhD, Asst Prof, 18th Cent British Phil, Value Theory
Dulmage, Horace, PhD, Prof, Whitehead, Philosophy of Relig, Metaph
Georgiadis, Constantine, PhD, Assoc Prof, Greek Phil, Metaph
Gadamer, Hans-Georg, Anc Phil, Plato
Hitchcock, David, BA, Lect, Greek Phil, Sym Logic
Madison, G B, DPh, Asst Prof, Phenomen, Exist, Prag, Metaph
Noxon, James, PhD, Prof, British Empir, Value Theory, Phil of Mind

Radner, Michael, PhD, Asst Prof, Logic and Phil of Math, Phil of Phys
Shalom, Albert, D en Lettres, Prof, Concep Anal, Phil of Mind, Metaph
Simpson, J E, PhD, Assoc Prof, Ling Phil, Soc Phil
Thomas, John E, PhD, Prof, Greek Phil, Phil of Relig, Metaph
Wilson, Neil, PhD, Prof, Ling Phil, Metaph, Formal Anal, Seman

Waters, F W, PhD, Prof Emer

MOHAWK COLLEGE
Hamilton, Ontario, L8N 3T2 (--) Courses with no degree specialization, Dept of
Soc Sci, 416-389-4461 Ext 418

Evans, Les, PhD, Master

NIAGARA COLLEGE OF APPLIED ARTS AND TECHNOLOGY
Welland, Ontario (--) Courses with no degree specialization, School of Applied Arts
and Health Sci, 416-735-2211 Ext 273

Habermehl, F, MA, Chm

NIPISSING COLLEGE, Affiliate of Laurentian University
North Bay, Ontario (u 84) NR

NORTHERN COLLEGE OF APPLIED ARTS AND TECHNOLOGY
Timmins, Ontario P4N 7J1 (--) NP

ONTARIO COLLEGE OF ART
Toronto 130, Ontario (--) NP

ONTARIO INSTITUTE FOR STUDIES IN EDUCATION
Toronto, Ontario M5S 1V6 (--) PhD major, Dept of Hist and Phil of Educ, 416-923-6641
Ext 501, 510

Wigney, T J, EdM, Chm, Hist of Tht
Beck, C M, PhD, Prof, Phil of Value, Phil of Practical Inquiry, Moral Educ,
    Theory of Educ Inquiry
Eisenberg, J A, AM, Asst Prof, Phil of Hist, Phil of Soc Sci
Olsen, E C, PhD, Asst Prof, Phil of Mind, Theory of Knowl, Theory of Human Action,
    Concept of a Person
Wellmer, A, DPhil, Assoc Prof, Phil Anthrop, Phil of Sci, Soc Phil, Phil of Soc Sci
Winchester, I, BPhil, Asst Prof, Phil of Sci, Historiography, Phil of Traditions
    Hist and Phil of 17th Cent Sci

Biener, E, MA, Res Assoc, Aes   Nabbe, H, MA, Res Asst, Aes
Harris, M, MA, Res Asst   Pagliuso, S M, MA, Res Asst, Moral Educ
Joy, M, EdD, Project Dir, Moral Educ   Palmer, L, BA, Res Asst

PETER ROBINSON COLLEGE, Constituent of Trent University
Peterborough, Ontario (--) NR

QUEEN'S THEOLOGICAL COLLEGE
Kingston, Ontario (u 38) Courses with no degree specialization, --, 613-547-2788

Andrews, Elias, PhD, Prof, Phil of Relig
Schumaker, Millard, PhD, Asst Prof, Moral Phil
Zion, William Potts, PhD, Asst Prof, Moral Phil

QUEEN'S UNIVERSITY AT KINGSTON
Kingston, Ontario (u 7493; g 997) PhD major, Dept of Phil, 613-547-6233

Duncan, A R C, MA, Prof, Head, Ethics, Kant, Plato, Metaph
Árdal, Páll S, PhD, Prof, Ethics, Hume, Phil of Mind, Phil of Action
Bond, E J, PhD, Prof, Ethics, Aes, Epistem, Metaph
Brown, Norman J, MA, Prof, Phil of Lang, Ethics, Phil of Relig, Thomas Aquinas
De Lucca, John, PhD, Prof, Epistem, Metaph, Hist of Phil, Phil of Sci
Fell, Albert P, PhD, Prof, Phil of Hist, Phil of Art
Fox, M A, PhD, Asst Prof, 19th Cent Phil, Continen Ration, Phil of Mind, Metaph
Laycock, Henry, BA, Asst Prof, Phil of Lang, Ontology, Marxism and Ideology
Maclachlan, D L C, PhD, Assoc Prof, Phil of Perception, Phil Logic
Macleod, A M, PhD, Prof, Ethics, Soc and Polit Phil, Phil of Mind
Prado, C G, PhD, Asst Prof, Phil of Relig, Phil of Mind, Epistem
Robinson, Thomas H, MA, Assoc Prof, Greek Phil, Ethics, Epistem
Russell, Joseph, MA, Prof, Phil of Sci, Phil of Mind, Logic, Kant

Estall, H M, PhD, Prof Emer, Exist, Phenomen

Backhaus, W K, MA, Grad Asst
Baker, L F, MA, R Samuel McLaughlin
  Fel
Brown, P, MA, D W Stewart Fel and
  Asst
Bryan, R S, MA, Queen's Grad Fel and
  Asst
Corbett, S M, MA, Queen's Grad Fel
Cracknell, R J F, BA, R Samuel
  McLauglin Scholar and Asst
Davis, J H, BA, James Macbeth
  Milligan Fel and Asst
Gadd, C D, MA, Canada Council Fel

Handy, T E D, BA, Ontario Grad Fel
Hart, D S, BA, Ontario Grad Fel
Jellicoe, Andrea, MA, Ontario Grad Fel
Mallov, J A, BA, Asst
Mazurski, A A, BA, Asst
McFarlane, L, MA, R Samuel McLaughlin
  Fel
Melakopides, C J, MA, R Samuel McLaughlin
  Fel
Savage, R R, MA, Ontario Grad Fel and
  Asst
Sayers, B W, MA, Canada Council Fel

REGIS COLLEGE, Affiliate of Saint Mary's University
Willowdale, Ontario M2M 3S5 (u 80; g 15) NP

RENISON COLLEGE, Affiliate of the University of Waterloo
Waterloo, Ontario (--) NR

ROYAL MILITARY COLLEGE OF CANADA
Kingston, Ontario (u 493; g 17) Courses with no degree specialization, Dept of
Eng and Phil, 613-545-7253, 7335

Binnie, D J, MA, Lect, Concept of Existence

RYERSON POLYTECHNICAL UNIVERSITY
Toronto, Ontario (u 156) Courses with no degree specialization, Dept of Soc Sci, 416-
595-5221

Aspevig, K, MA, Lect, Ethics
Bilek, G, PhD, Prof, Kant
Kehoe, E, MA, Lect, Ethics
Murray, R, MA, Prof, Phil of Soc Sci
Paulin, M, MA, Prof
Sleep, R, PhD, Prof, Epistem
Stratton, J, PhD, Lect, Wittgenstein

SAINT AUGUSTINE'S SEMINARY, Affiliate of Saint Paul University
Scarborough, Ontario (u 56; g 2) Courses with no degree specialization, Dept of

Phil, 416-261-7207

Moss, J E, MA, Prof, Chm
Will, R D, MA, Prof

SAINT CLAIRE COLLEGE OF APPLIED ARTS AND TECHNOLOGY
Windsor, Ontario (--) NP

SAINT LAWRENCE COLLEGE OF APPLIED ARTS AND TECHNOLOGY
Kingston, Ontario (--) NP

SAINT PAUL UNIVERSITY, Federated with Ottawa University
Ottawa, Ontario (u 259; g 136) NP

SAINT PAUL'S UNITED COLLEGE, Affiliate of the University of Waterloo
Waterloo, Ontario (--) NR

SAULT-SAINTE-MARIE COLLEGE
Sault-Sainte-Marie, Ontario (--) NP

SENECA COLLEGE OF APPLIED ARTS AND TECHNOLOGY
Willowdale, Ontario (--) --, Div of Libr Stud, 416-491-5050 Ext 335

Legate, John J, BA, Subject Cord of Phil, Exist, Phenomen
Glazbrook, Jack, MA, Phil of Sci, Phil of Educ
Ohan, Farid, MA, Ethics
Phillips, J David, MA, Polit Phil
Pickup, Ian, MA, Epistem, Phil of Mind

SHERIDAN COLLEGE
Oakville, Ontario (--) BA minor, Dept of Phil, 416-845-9430 Ext 259

Reynolds, H, MA, Cord of Phil
Mowat, H, MA, Master, Hist of Phil
Wilson, F, PhD, Master, Contemp Phil

SHERIDAN COLLEGE OF APPLIED ARTS AND TECHNOLOGY
Oakville, Ontario (--) Courses with no degree specialization, School of Applied and Libr Arts, 416-362-5861

Wilson, R Frances, MPhil, Teach Master, Logic, Phil of Sci

SIR SANDFORD FLEMING COLLEGE OF APPLIED ARTS AND TECHNOLOGY
Peterborough, Ontario K9J 7B1 (--) Courses with no degree specialization, --, --,

McCreary, John, PhD, Master

THORNELOE COLLEGE
Sudbury, Ontario P3E 2C6 (--) NP

TRENT UNIVERSITY
    Peterborough, Ontario (u 1764; g 12) BA major, Dept of Phil, 705-748-1409

    Gallop, David, MA, Prof, Chm, Greek Phil, Contemp British Phil
    Boundas, Constantine V, PhD, Asst Prof, Phenomen, Greek Phil
    Burbidge, John W, PhD, Assoc Prof, Hegel, Phil of Relig
    Carter, Robert E, PhD, Assoc Prof, Ethics
    Dray, William H, DPh, Prof, Phil of Hist
    Fry, Marion G, BLitt, Assoc Prof, Greek Phil, Med Phil
    Govier, Trudy R, PhD, Asst Prof, 17th and 18th Cent Phil
    MacAdam, James I, PhD, Prof, Polit Phil, Ethics
    McMullen, W A, PhD, Assoc Prof, Epistem
    Orenstein, Alan, MA, Asst Prof, Phil of Mind, Aes
    Rautenkranz, K R, MA, Asst Prof, Phil of Sci, Logic
    Rubinoff, M L, PhD, Prof, Phenomen, Phil of Soc Sci

UNIVERSITY OF GUELPH
    Guelph, Ontario (u 6535; g 527) PhD major, Dept of Phil, 519-824-4120

    Todd, G F, PhD, Assoc Prof, Chm
    Amstutz, J, PhD, Prof
    Brett, N, MA, Visit Lect
    Bruce, J A, PhD, Prof
    Calvert, B, BLitt, Assoc Prof
    Chapman, T, DPhil, Assoc Prof
    Dorter, K N, PhD, Assoc Prof
    Godlovitch, S, MA, Visit Lect
    Hems, J M, PhD, Prof
    Hughes, W H, PhD, Assoc Prof
    Hunter, K, PhD, Visit Asst Prof
    Lehman, H S, PhD, Assoc Prof
    Leslie, J, BLitt, Asst Prof
    McMurtry, J, MA, Lect
    Michalos, A C, PhD, Prof
    Montague, K, MA, Lect
    Newman, J, PhD, Asst Prof
    Odegard, D, PhD, Prof
    Panagiotou, S, MA, Visit Lect
    Reeves, C, MA, Lect
    Robinson, H J, PhD, Assoc Prof
    Ruse, M E, PhD, Assoc Prof
    Settle, T W, PhD, Assoc Prof
    Smook, R, PhD, Asst Prof
    Stewart, C, PhD, Asst Prof
    Stewart, D B, PhD, Asst Prof
    Williams, T C, MA, Assoc Prof

UNIVERSITY OF OTTAWA
    Ottawa, Ontario K1N 6N5 (u 6857; g 1305) PhD major, Faculty of Phil, 613-231-2294

    Laberge, Pierre, PhD, Assoc Prof, Dean of the Faculty, German Phil, Kant, Logic
    Allard, Jean-Louis, PhD, Prof, Mod Phil, Descartes, Phil of Educ
    Arnold, Keith, PhD, Asst Prof, Logic and Formal Ling
    Bordeleau, Léo-Paul, PhD, Asst Prof, Contemp French Phil
    Bouchard, Roch, PhD, Asst Prof, Contemp French Phil
    Carignan, Maurice, PhD, Assoc Prof, Metaph
    Cazabon, Gilles, PhD, Assoc Prof, Phenomen
    Charette, Léon, PhD, Assoc Prof, Polit Phil, Phil of Educ
    Charron, Ghyslain, PhD, Assoc Prof, Contemp French Phil, Epistem, Exist Psych
    Croteau, Jacques, PhD, Prof, Epistem, Exist Psych
    Ducharme, Léonard, PhD, Prof, Metaph, Med Phil
    Duchesneau, François, PhD, Assoc Prof, Ration, British Empir, Phil of Biological Sci

Gallagher, Donald, PhD, Non-Resident Visit Prof, Contemp Continen Phil
Gallagher, Idella, PhD, Non-Resident Visit Prof, Contemp Continen Phil
Garceau, Benoît, PhD, Prof, Med Phil, German Phil
Geraets, Théodore, PhD, Assoc Prof, German Phil, Contem French Phil
Healey, Joseph, MA, Lect, Contemp Continen Phil
Kelloway, William, MA, Lect, Phil Psych
Lafrance, Guy, PhD, Assoc Prof, Soc and Polit Phil, French Phil
LaPlante, Robert, LPh, Asst Prof, Phil of Sci, Aquinas
Marchand, Jean-Paul, MA, Asst Prof, Phil of Time, Whitehead
McCormick, Peter, PhD, Asst Prof, German Phil, Heidegger, Phenomen
Mendenhall, Vance, PhD, Asst Prof, Phil of Art, Value Theory
Moran, Lawrence, MA, Lect, Personalism, Metaph, Ethics, Soc Phil
Morrisey, Brian, MA, Lect, Phil of Right, Kant
Paquet, Léonce, PhD, Assoc Prof, Greek Phil
Pearson, Léon, MA, Asst Prof, French Value Theory
Petraroja, Serge, PhD, Assoc Prof, Ethics, Greek Phil
Russell, Anthony, MA, Asst Prof, Phil of Hist, British Idealism
Scully, Edward, PhD, Prof, Med Phil, Ethics, Soc Phil, Marxism
Stroick, Clemens, PhD, Prof, Med Phil
Theau, Jean, PhD, Prof, French Phil, Bergson
Waters, Raphael, PhD, Asst Prof, Epistem, Medical Ethics
Wojciechowski, Jerzy, PhD, Prof, Phil of Sci, Phil of Cutlture

Saint-Denis, Henry, PhD, Prof Emer

Dunne, R, PhD, Asst	Grant, L R, MA, Asst
Iannoni, J E, PhD, Asst	Hurst, D R, MA, Asst
Minhinnick, J, PhD, Asst	Perera, P E H, MA, Asst
Nabakwe, W, PhD, Asst	Phakathi, C, MA, Asst
Pollock, A, PhD, Asst	Ruane, T J, MA, Asst
Prystanski, A H, PhD, Asst	Tsai, L S C, MA, Asst
Rashid, A, PhD, Asst	Vaillant, D, MA, Asst
Richard, A, PhD, Asst	Vennes, A R, MA, Asst
Fournier, S, MA, Asst	

UNIVERSITY OF SAINT JEROME'S COLLEGE, Federated with the University of Waterloo
Waterloo, Ontario (u 450) BA major, Dept of Phil, 519-884-8110

Centore, F F, PhD, Assoc Prof, Chm, Metaph, Phil of Sci
Brown, E E, AB, Lect Part-time
DeMarco, D T, PhD, Asst Prof, Aes, Ethics
Dobos, A, PhD, Asst Prof, Phil of Sci, Soc Phil

UNIVERSITY OF SAINT MICHAEL'S COLLEGE, Federated with the University of Toronto
Toronto 181, Ontario (g 144) PhD major, --, 416-921-3151

Lynch, L E M, PhD, Prof, Head
Brown, B F, PhD, Assoc Prof
Cameron, J M, Visit Prof
Dunphy, W B, PhD, Prof
Gilson, E, DLitt, Prof
Hartley, J, PhD, Asst Prof
Kelly, J M, PhD, Prof
Kremer, E J, PhD, Assoc Prof
Lang, T J F, MA, Prof
Maurer, A A, PhD, Prof
Owens, J, MSD, Prof
Pegis, A C, PhD, Prof
Synan, E A, PhD, Prof

Tully, R, DPh, Asst Prof
Weisheipl, J A, DPhil, Visit Prof
Wingell, A E, PhD, Assoc Prof

UNIVERSITY OF SUDBURY, Federated with Laurentian University of Sudbury
    Sudbury, Ontario (--) BA major, Dept of Phil, 705-673-5661

    Berens, Vladimir, MA, Assoc Prof, Chm, German Phil, Ration, 17th and 18th Cent
        German Idealism, Phil Anthrop
    Albert, Hughes, DPh, Assoc Prof, Phenomen, Hist of Phil
    Champagne, Réné, DPh, Asst Prof, Marx and Marxism, Descartes
    DiNorcia, Vincent, PhD, Asst Prof, Amer Phil, Soc and Polit Phil
    Gaboury, Placide, DPh, Assoc Prof, Ethics
    Misgeld, Dieter, DPh, Asst Prof, Exist, Critical Theory, Phenomen, Marx and Marxism
    Warenda, Chester, DPh, Asst Prof, Ethics

UNIVERSITY OF TORONTO
    Toronto, Ontario M5S 1A1 (u 21,244; g 4879) PhD major, Dept of Phil, --

    Slater, J G, PhD, Assoc Prof, Chm
    Allen, R E, PhD, Prof
    Canfield, J W, PhD, Assoc Prof
    Cassin, C, PhD, Asst Prof
    Chastain, C H, MA, Asst Prof
    Clark, L M G, BPhil, Asst Prof
    Cunningham, F A, PhD, Asst Prof
    de Sousa, R B, PhD, Assoc Prof
    Dryer, D P, AM, Prof
    Ehrcke, W F, MA, Visit Lect
    Evans, D D, DPh, Prof
    Fackenheim, E L, PhD, Prof
    Forguson, L W, PhD, Assoc Prof
    Gauthier, D P, DPh, Prof
    Gilbert, M, BA, Visit Lect
    Goldstick, D, DPh, Assoc Prof
    Gombe, A, BPhil, Visit Assoc Prof
    Gooch, P W, PhD, Assoc Prof
    Goudge, T A, PhD, Prof
    Graham, W C, PhD, Asst Prof
    Hanly, C M T, PhD, Assoc Prof
    Herzberger, H G, PhD, Assoc Prof
    Huggett, W J, PhD, Prof
    Hunter, J F M, PhD, Assoc Prof
    Imlay, R A, PhD, Assoc Prof
    Langan, T D, PhD, Prof
    Morrison, J C, PhD, Assoc Prof
    Mosher, D L, PhD, Asst Prof
    McRae, R F, PhD, Prof
    Nagel, G, MA, Visit Lect
    Nicholson, G A, PhD, Asst Prof
    Payzant, G B, PhD, Assoc Prof
    Robinson, T M, BLitt, Assoc Prof
    Rosenthal, A, PhD, Asst Prof
    Savan, D, AM, Prof
    Sobel, J H, PhD, Assoc Prof
    Stevenson, J T, MA, Assoc Prof
    Sumner, L W, PhD, Assoc Prof
    Urquhart, A I F, MA, Lect
    van Fraassen, B C, PhD, Prof
    Webb, C W, PhD, Assoc Prof
    Wheatley, J M C, PhD, Assoc Prof
    Wilson, F F, PhD, Assoc Prof

Alperson, P, Asst
Artibello, J, Asst
Benglian, V, Asst
Bergmann, M, Asst
Beyer, C, Asst
Bucher, S, Asst
Charlwood, G W, Asst
Djuth, M, Asst
Donougho, M, Asst
Ely, P, Asst
Flippen, D, Asst
Gill, J, Asst
Ghanotakis, G, Asst
Gutman, A, Asst
Hartwig, H, Asst
Hubbs, G, Asst
Johnson, D, Asst
Johnson, P, Asst
Jursheveski, S, Asst
Kalinski, W, Asst
Knases, J, Asst
Leland, K, Asst

Lennox, J, Asst
Maroosis, J, Asst
Mohr, R, Asst
Morelli, M, Asst
Morelli, E, Asst
Moritz, K, Asst
Morreall, J, Asst
Nageotte, G, Asst
Peterson, S, Asst
Rajnovich, J, Asst
Rinehart, B, Asst
Rubinstein, R, Asst
Scarlett, B, Asst
Schwankl, P R, Asst
Stroud-Drinkwater, C G, Asst
Tischer, D H, Asst
Treen, D, Asst
Vandevelde, R, Asst
Vieyra, S B, Asst
Wachtel, R, Asst
Walsh, P K J, Asst

UNIVERSITY OF TRINITY COLLEGE, Federated with the University of Toronto
Toronto 181, Ontario (u 32; g 4) --, --, 416-928-2522

Edison, G, PhD, Chm
Hardy, H, PhD, Assoc Prof
Neelands, D, MA, Lect
Schmitz, K, PhD, Prof
Elliston, F, Teach Asst

UNIVERSITY OF WATERLOO
Waterloo, Ontario (u 11,115; g 1169) PhD major, Dept of Phil, 519-885-1211 Ext 2245

Horne, James R, PhD, Assoc Prof, Chm
Abbott, William R, PhD, Assoc Prof
Ashworth, E Jennifer, PhD, Assoc Prof
Centore, Floyd, PhD, Asst Prof
DeMarco, Donald T, PhD, Asst Prof
Dobos, A, PhD, Asst Prof
George, Rolf A, PhD, Prof
Haworth, Lawrence L, PhD, Prof
Hendley, Brian P, PhD, Assoc Prof
Huertas-Jourda, Jose, PhD, Assoc Prof
Holmes, Richard H, PhD, Asst Prof
McDonald, Michael F, PhD, Asst Prof
Minas, Anne C, PhD, Assoc Prof
Minas, J Sayer, PhD, Prof
Narveson, Jan F, PhD, Prof
Penelhum, Terence M, MA, Visit Prof
Roberts, Don D, PhD, Assoc Prof
Seligman, Paul, PhD, Prof
Suits, Bernard H, PhD, Prof
Tucker, John W, PhD, Prof
Van Evra, James W, PhD, Assoc Prof
Wubnig, Judith, PhD, Asst Prof

Angus, Ian
Arnold, Robert
Barthelemy, William

Lewis, George
Long, Robert
MacDonald, Eric

Beattie, Lorraine	MacIntyre, Jane
Bilinski, Michael	Merriman, Kate
Bourgeois, Eugene	Morazain, Andre
Butkus, Linda	Munro, Brad
Crombie, E James	Pagliuso, Saverio
Czarny, Peter	Pernu, David
Davies, James	Reeder, Harry
Gilbert, Michael	Sachs, Sandra
Gilbert, Ruth	Schochet, Immanuel
Goeller, Richard	Spadoni, Carl
Gough, James E	Suits, David
Hart, James	Thiessen, Elmer
Heiges, Ken	Thode, Richard
Hoisveen, Tom	Thomsett, Derek
Husain, Martha	Tien, Shen
Hymmen, James	Wallace, Jean
Jones, Steven	Weber, Gary
Jordak, Frank	Westwood, John
Kent, Beverley	White, Margaret
Lee, Arthur	Zuch, Tim

UNIVERSITY OF WESTERN ONTARIO

London, Ontario N6A 3K7 (u 10,949; g 1611) PhD major, Dept of Phil, 519-679-3453

Binkley, Robert W, PhD, Prof, Chm, Phil of Mind
Beaman, Edward, BA, Asst Prof, Phil of Sci
Block, Irving L, PhD, Assoc Prof, Anc Phil
Bronaugh, Richard N, PhD, Assoc Prof, Ethics
Bub, Jeffrey, PhD, Assoc Prof, Phil of Phys Sci
Butts, Robert E, PhD, Prof, Hist of Mod Phil
Davis, John W, PhD, Prof, Hist of Mod Phil
Demopoulos, William G, BA, Visit Asst Prof, Phil of Sci
Freed, R Bruce, PhD, Assoc Prof, Phil of Lang
Harper, William L, MA, Asst Prof, Phil of Logic
Henry, W Cameron, PhD, Assoc Prof, Ethics
Hockney, Donald J, PhD, Assoc Prof, Phil of Lang
Hooker, Clifford A, PhD, Prof, Phil of Phys Sci
Johnson, Allison H, PhD, Senior Prof, Ethics, Metaph
Johnson, Harold J, PhD, Prof, Med Phil
Leach, James J, PhD, Prof, Phil of Soc Sci
Lennon, Thomas M, PhD, Assoc Prof, Hist of Mod Phil
Marras, Ausonio, PhD, Assoc Prof, Phil of Mind
Maynard, Patrick L, PhD, Assoc Prof, Aes
Muehlmann, Robert G, PhD, Asst Prof, Contemp Anglo Amer Phil
Nicholas, John M, MS, Asst Prof, Hist of Sci
Pearce, Glenn A, BA, Assoc Prof, Logic
Rudinow, Joel, BA, Visit Asst Prof, Aes
Shorten, Sarah J, MA, Asst Prof, Anc Phil
Williams, Martha E, PhD, Assoc Prof, 19th Cent Phil

Bejerring, Andrew, MA, Grad Asst	Korte, Herbert, MA, Grad Asst
Bowers, Thomas, BA, Grad Asst	Kulathungam, L Christopher, MA, Grad Asst
Brown, David, BA, Grad Asst	Lenhardt, Wayne, A J, MA, Grad Asst
Buijs, Joseph, MA, Grad Asst	Lithown, Robert, MA, Grad Asst
Cardarelli, John, MA, Grad Asst	Little, Blaine, BA, Grad Asst
Clemence, Patrick, BA, Grad Asst	McArdle, John, MA, Grad Asst
Coleman, Robert A, PhD, Grad Asst	McCrimmon, Mitchell, MA, Grad Asst
Covil, James, BA, Grad Asst	McEneany, George, BA, Grad Asst
Curtis, Ronald C, MS, Grad Asst	Melokopides, Constantine J, MA, Grad Asst
Davey, Elizabeth, BA, Grad Asst	Ormiston, Gayle L, MA, Grad Asst
DiFilippo, Joseph P, BA, Grad Asst	Parkinson, Michael, BA, Grad Asst
Evans, R Cameron, BA, Grad Asst	Purdy, Robert D, MA, Grad Asst

Fargen, Bruce, MA, Grad Asst
Feder, Henry, BS, Grad Asst
Foss, Jeffrey, MA, Grad Asst
Galinaitis, John, BA, Grad Asst
Garlough, Louanna, MA, Grad Asst
Godfrey, Ian, MA, Grad Asst
Gooding, Wayne, MA, Grad Asst
Griener, Glenn, BA, Grad Asst
Hanna, Allan A, MEng, Grad Asst
Hitchon, Roger, BA, Grad Asst
Holdsworth, David G, MS, Grad Asst
Horban, Peter, MA, Grad Asst
Jewison, Lynda M, MA, Grad Asst

Reed, Ronald, MA, Grad Asst
Rice, Donald C, BA, Grad Asst
Rivett, David, MA, Grad Asst
Slack, Ransom, MA, Grad Asst
Spurrell, Lloyd A C, BA, Grad Asst
Stairs, Allen E, BA, Grad Asst
Steinberg, Danny, MA, Grad Asst
Tallon, James, BA, Grad Asst
Tempest, Albert E, MA, Grad Asst
Thorpe, Derrick G S, BA, Grad Asst
Walker, Foster, BA, Grad Asst
Zaslow, Jon, BA, Grad Asst

UNIVERSITY OF WINDSOR
Windsor, Ontario N9B 3P4 (u 5351; g 487) MA major, Dept of Phil, 519-253-4232 Ext 240

Wilkinson, Peter F, MA, Assoc Prof, Head, Ethics
Blair, John A, BA, Asst Prof, Ethics
Brown, Jerome V, PhD, Assoc Prof, Metaph
Cunningham, Stanley B, PhD, Prof, Ethics, Epistem
Deck, John N, PhD, Prof, Metaph
Flood, Patrick F, PhD, Prof, Metaph
Johnson, Ralph H, PhD, Assoc Prof, Logic
Kennedy, Leonard A, PhD, Prof, Ethics
Kingston, F Temple, PhD, Prof, Ethics
Lewis, John U, PhD, Assoc Prof, Ethics
Nielsen, Harry A, PhD, Prof, Ethics, Metaph
Pinto, Robert C, MA, Asst Prof, Epistem, Metaph
Stokes, Thomas J, PhD, Asst Prof, Logic

VICTORIA COLLEGE, Constituent of Victoria University
Toronto 5, Ontario (u 56; g 12) --, Dept of Phil, Victoria College, 416-928-3925

Graff, James A, PhD, Assoc Prof, Chm, Ethics, Metaph
Harvey, W R C, PhD, Asst Prof, Ethics
Hess, P H, PhD, Asst Prof, Epistem
Pietersma, H, PhD, Assoc Prof, Phenomen, Metaph
Thornton, M T, PhD, Asst Prof, Phil of Mind
Sparshott, F E, MA, Prof, Ethics, Aes

Donner, Wendi, MA, Teach Asst

VICTORIA UNIVERSITY, Federated with the University of Toronto
Toronto 181, Ontario (u 5; g 68) --, --, 416-928-3801

Choptiany, L R, MA, Lect
Harvey, W R C, PhD, Asst Prof
Hess, P, PhD, Asst Prof
Pietersma, H, PhD, Assoc Prof
Sparshott, R, MA, Prof
Thornton, M T, PhD, Asst Prof

WATERLOO LUTHERAN UNIVERSITY, Constituent of the University of Waterloo
Waterloo, Ontario (u 2574; g 218) BA major, Dept of Phil, 519-884-1970 Ext 327

Little, J Frederick, PhD, Prof, Chm, Phil of Relig
Alexander, Robert, PhD, Asst Prof, Ling Anal, Epistem
Langen, Robert, MA, Assoc Prof, Aes, Exist

Lewis, Chester, MA, Asst Prof, Hist of Phil
Thiry, Léon, PhD, Prof, Moral and Soc Phil, Peace Res

WYCLIFFE COLLEGE, Federated with the University of Toronto
    Toronto 181, Ontario (u 12; g 32) PhD major, Dept of Phil of Relig, 416-923-7307

YORK UNIVERSITY
    Downsview, Ontario M3J 1P3 (u 10,076; g 946) PhD major, Dept of Phil, 416-667-2206

    Cowley, G Fraser, PhD, Prof, Chm, Epistem, Metaph, Exist
    Bakan, Mildred B, PhD, Assoc Prof, Phenomen, Exist, Phil Psych
    Clements, Gerald G, MA, Asst Prof, Contemp Phil, Soc Phil
    Cobb, R Allan, BA, Lect, Greek Phil, Phenomen
    Creery, Walter E, PhD, Assoc Prof, Med Phil, Phil of Relig, Logic
    Danielson, Peter A, MA, Lect, Soc Phil, Polit Phil
    Hattiangadi, Jagdish N, PhD, Assoc Prof, Phil of Sci, Hist of Sci
    Jack, Percival J H, MA, Assoc Prof, Logic, Seman, Phil of Lang
    Jarvie, Ian C, PhD, Prof, Phil of Sci, Phil of Soc Sci
    Johnson, David M, PhD, Assoc Prof, Phil of Mind, Epistem
    MacNiven, C Donald, DPhil, Assoc Prof, Ethics, 19th Cent Phil, Phil Psych
    McFarland, John D, DPhil, Assoc Prof, Kant, Contemp Phil, Wittgenstein
    Minkus, Peter A, PhD, Assoc Prof, Wittgenstein, Phil of Lang, Rhetoric
    Normore, Calvin G, MA, Sess Lect, Logic, Phil Logic, Med Phil
    Nowell-Smith, Patrick H, MA, Prof, Dir of Grad Program, Phil of Hist
    Simpson, Robert E, BA, Asst Prof, Aes, Hist of Mod Phil, Epistem
    Wisdom, J O, PhD, Univ Prof, Phil of Soc Sci, Phil Psych
    Yolton, John W, DPhil, Prof, Act Pres, Metaph, Epistem, 17th Cent Phil

PRINCE EDWARD ISLAND

HOLLAND COLLEGE
    Charlottetown, Prince Edward Island (--) NP

UNIVERSITY OF PRINCE EDWARD ISLAND
    Charlottetown, Prince Edward Island (u 1771) BA major, Dept of Phil, 902-892-4121

    Smithenan, V, MPhil, Assoc Prof, Chm, Phil of Educ, Sartre
    Butler, K, MA, Instr, Phil of Sci, Chardin
    Holmes, C, PhD, Asst Prof, Lewis, Ethics
    Koch, P, PhD, Asst Prof, Logic, Soc and Polit Phil
    Naylor, J, MA, Instr, Fichte, Marxism, Transcendent Phil

QUEBEC

ABBAYE SAINT BENOIT
St Benoît-du-Lac (Brome) Québec (--) Courses with no degree specialization, --, 819-843-4080

Cyr, Jean Marie, Lic Phil

BISHOP'S UNIVERSITY
Lennoxville, Quebec (u 516; g 10) BA major, Dept of Phil, 819-569-9551

Englebretsen, G F, PhD, Asst Prof, Chm, Logic, Anal Phil
McCargar, D, MA, Asst Prof, Anc Phil
Shearson, W A, PhD, Assoc Prof, Mod Euro Phil

BOURGET COLLEGE
Rigaud, Quebec (--) NP

LE CENTRE D'ETUDES UNIVERSITAIRES DE RIMOUSKI, Centre constituant de l'Université due Québec
Rimouski, Québec (--) NR

CENTRE DE FORMATION DES MAITRES
Cap-Rouge, Québec (--) BA minor, Dépt de Phil, 418-656-6713

Letendre, Roger, DPh
Morales, Washington, DPh
Neron, Roméo, MPh

CENTRE DE GRANBY, Extension Centre of the University of Sherbrook
Granby, Quebec (--) NR

COLLEGE ANDRE-GRASSET
Montréal, Québec (--) Courses with no degree specialization, --, --

Bedard, Serge, MPh
Belanger, Martin, PhD
Caron, Charles, DPh
Chbat, Joseph, MPh
Remy, Thérèse, MPh

COLLEGE BOIS-DE-BOULOGNE, COLLEGE D'ENSEIGNEMENT GENERAL ET PROFESSIONNEL
Montréal, Québec (--) --, Dépt de Phil, 514-332-3000 poste 272

Beaudry, Pierre, Maîtrise
Beaulieu, Yves-Michel, Maîtrise
Belanger, Roland, Maîtrise
Bourgie, Aurèle, Maîtrise
Charbonneau, Paul, PhD
Delorme, Andrée, Maîtrise
Dorion, Madeleine, Maîtrise
Filion, Gérard, Maîtrise
George, Fernando, Maîtrise
Laliberté, François, Maîtrise
Larsen, André, Maîtrise
Peloquin, Claude, Maîtrise

Richer, Ronald, Maîtrise
St-Antoine, Jude, Maîtrise
Trahan, Louise, Maîtrise

COLLEGE BOURGET, Affiliate of the University of Montréal
Rigaud, Québec (--) NP

COLLEGE D'AHUNTSIC, COLLEGE D'ENSEIGNEMENT GENERAL ET PROFESSIONNEL
Montréal, Québec (--) --, --, 514-389-5921 poste 224, 285

Dandonneau, Antoni, Maîtrise, Chef, Phil Ancienne
Beaudry, Denise, Maîtrise
Benhaime, Guila, Maîtrise
Boulianne, Jacques, Maîtrise
Brisson, Marcelle, Dr, Phil de la Relig
Charbonneau, François, Maîtrise
Da Silva, Maurice, Maîtrise, Phil Méd
De Croot, Marie-Josée, Maîtrise, Logique
Drisdelle, Gérard, Maîtrise
Dufresne, Jacques, Dr
Fournier, Jean-Louis, Dr, Phil de la Relig
Fournier, Marylise, Dr
Fredette, Raymond, Dr, Phil des Sci
Lapalme, André, Maîtrise
Martin, Jean-Claude, Lic
Martineau, Jean-François, Lic
Leblond, Bernard, Lic
Leflaguais, Robert, Maîtrise
Mongeau, Yves, Maîtrise, Phil Française Contemp
Proulx, Bernard, Dr
Proulx, Jean, Lic
Savignac, François, Maîtrise
Vacher, Michel, Maîtrise

COLLEGE DE CHICOUTIMI, COLLEGE D'ENSEIGNEMENT GENERAL ET PROFESSIONNEL
Chicoutimi, Québec (--) NR

COLLEGE DE HAUTERIVE, COLLEGE D'ENSEIGNEMENT GENERAL ET PROFESSIONNEL
Hauterive, Québec (--) Courses with no degree specialization, --, --

Dumont, Roger, MPh, Dir
Bourassa, Michel, BPh
Gendron, Clémence, MPh
Mercure, Guy, BPh

COLLEGE DE HULL, COLLEGE D'ENSEIGNEMENT GENERAL ET PROFESSIONNEL
Hull, Québec (--) BA joint or combined major, Dépt de Phil, 819-771-6231

Frappier, B, Lic Phil, Ethics, Epistem

COLLEGE DE JOLIETTE, CENTRE D'ENSEIGNEMENT GENERAL ET PROFESSIONNEL
Joliette, Québec (--) --, --, 514-753-7466

COLLEGE DE JONQUIERE, COLLEGE D'ENSEIGNEMENT GENERAL ET PROFESSIONNEL
Jonquière, Québec (--) NR

COLLEGE DE L'ASSOMPTION
    L'Assomption, Québec (--) --, Dépt de Phil, 514-589-5621

    Goulet, Richard, MPh, Ethics
    Corriveau, Gaston, Lic Theol
    Smiard, Louis, BPh

COLLEGE DE LA GASPESIE, COLLEGE D'ENSEIGNEMENT GENERAL ET PROFESSIONNEL
    Gaspé, Québec (--) --, Dépt de Phil, 418-368-2201 Ext 178

COLLEGE DE LA POCATIERE, COLLEGE D'ENSEIGNEMENT GENERAL ET PROFESSIONNEL
    La Pocatière, Québec (--) Courses with no degree specialization, Dépt de Phil, 418-856-1525

    Laberge, Jacques, Lic, Chef
    Allaire, Georges, Dr
    Begin, Anne-Marie, Lic
    Besner, Pierre-Paul, Lic
    Gaumond, André, Lic
    Jeffrey, Jean-René, Lic
    Michaud, Régis, Dr
    Theberge, Guy

COLLEGE DE LEVIS
    Lévis, Québec (--) NR

COLLEGE DE LEVIS-LAUZON, COLLEGE D'ENSEIGNEMENT GENERAL ET PROFESSIONNEL
    Lauzon, Québec (--) Courses with no degree specialization, --, 418-837-0253 Loc 29

    Beaudet, Joël, Maîtrise, Chm
    Boursiquot, Joseph, Maîtrise
    Bouffard, Germain, Maîtrise
    Jeanmart, Pierre, Maîtrise
    Lapegna, Nicola, Dr
    Louro, Manuel, Maîtrise
    Pelletier, J Jacques, Maîtrise

COLLEGE DE LIMOILOU, COLLEGE D'ENSEIGNEMENT GENERAL ET PROFESSIONNEL
    Québec, Québec (--) NR

COLLEGE DE MAISONNEUVE, COLLEGE DE'ENSEIGNEMENT GENERAL ET PROFESSIONNEL
    Montréal, Québec (--) --, Dépt de Phil, 514-254-7131 poste 235

    Perrois, Charles, Dir
    Berlus, Monique, Lic Phil
    Bertraud, Claude, MA
    Bernten, Marc, Lic Phil
    Boucher, Geneviève, MA
    Brouillet, Guy, Lic Phil
    Brouillet, Raymond, DPh
    Charlebois, Denis, BPh
    Chénier, Jean-Marc, Lic Phil
    Cupault, J P, MA
    Daoust, Jean-Guy, Lic
    Gareau, Suzanne, BPh
    Gour, Gilles, Lic Phil
    Gravel, Pierre, DPh

Koux, Yvon, Lic Phil
LeBel, Marcelle, Lic Phil
Lepage, Daniel, Lic Phil
Morin, Y, DPh
Renaud, Laurent, DPh
Soucy, Marcel, Lic Phil
Talbot, François, MA
Turcotte, Pierre, Lic

COLLEGE DE MATANE
   Matana, Québec (--) NR

COLLEGE DE RIMOUSKI, COLLEGE D'ENSEIGNEMENT GENERAL ET PROFESSIONNEL
   Rimouski, Québec (--) NR

COLLEGE DE RIVIERE-DU-LOUP, COLLEGE D'ENSEIGNEMENT GENERAL ET PROFESSIONNEL
   Rivière-du-Loup, Québec 65R 1R1 (--) AA major, Dépt de Phil, 418-862-6903

   Délanger, Marcel, MA, Phil de la Nature, Phil des Sci, Phil du Lang, Logique
   Brière, Michel, Lic, Phil de la Nature, Phil de l'home
   Duguay, Michel, BPh, Logique, Ethique
   Franck, Thomas, MA, Logique, Ethique
   Pelletier, Yves, BPh, Phénomén, Phil de l'homme
   Roy, Jacques, Lic, Phil de l'homme, Phil de la Nature
   Ruest, Paul, BPh, Logique, Ethique

COLLEGE DE ROSEMONT, COLLEGE D'ENSEIGNEMENT GENERAL ET PROFESSIONNEL
   Montréal, Québec (--) NR

COLLEGE DE ROUYN, Affilié à l'Université de Montréal
   Rouyn, Québec (--) NR

COLLEGE DE ROUYN-NORANDA, COLLEGE D'ENSEIGNEMENT GENERAL ET PROFESSIONNEL
   Rouyn, Québec (--) --, Dépt de Phil, 819-762-0931 Ext 248

   Aubert, Fernand, MPh
   Bastien, Ovide, MPh
   Dumas, Céline, MPh
   Gagnon, Renald, MPh
   Larouche, Robert, MPh
   L'Heureux, Jacques, Lic
   Robert, Roland, Lic

COLLEGE DE SAINT-HYACINTHE, COLLEGE D'ENSEIGNEMENT GENERAL ET PROFESSIONNEL
   Saint-Hyacinthe, Québec (--) NR

COLLEGE DE SAINT-LAURENT, COLLEGE D'ENSEIGNEMENT GENERAL ET PROFESSIONNEL
   Montréal, Québec (--) NR

COLLEGE DE SAINTE-FOY, COLLEGE D'ENSEIGNEMENT GENERAL ET PROFESSIONNEL
   Sainte-Foy, Québec (--) NR

COLLEGE DE SALABERRY-DE-VALLEYFIELD, COLLEGE D'ENSEIGNEMENT GENERAL ET PROFESSIONNEL
   Salaberry-de-Valleyfield, Québec (--) NR

COLLEGE DE SHAWINIGA, COLLEGE D'ENSEIGNEMENT GENERAL ET PROFESSIONNEL
 Shawinigan, Québec (--) NR

COLLEGE DE SHERBROOKE, COLLEGE D'ENSEIGNEMENT GENERAL ET PROFESSIONNEL
 Sherbrooke, Québec (--) Courses with no degree specialization, Dépt de Phil, 819-
 563-3150 Ext 128

    Boisvert, François, MA, Head
    Allard, Jean-René, MA
    Beaudry, Pierre, PhD
    Berthold, Daniel, MA
    Caza, Gérald, MA
    Cloutier, Yvan, MA
    Daigle, Yvon, MA
    Daniel, Hélène, MA
    Erkoreka, Yon, MA
    Garon, Jean-Denis, MA
    Lafleur, Jacques, MA
    Lapriss, Jean-Paul, MA
    Lopez, Pascual, PhD
    Marquis, Jean-Yves, MA
    Nadon, Benoît, MA
    Pelletier, Jacques, MA
    Pelletier, René, MA
    Poulin, Louis, MA

COLLEGE DE THETFORD MINES, COLLEGE D'ENSEIGNEMENT GENERAL ET PROFESSIONNEL
 Megantie, Québec (--) --, Dépt de Phil, 419-338-8591

    Massieotte, Guy-Paul, Maîtrise, Chef
    Gagne, Claude, Maîtrise
    Gagnon, Claude, Maîtrise
    Houle, Roland, Maîtrise
    Patoine, Yvon, Dr
    Rainville, Frederic, Maîtrise
    Tardif, Germain, Dr

COLLEGE DE TROIS-RIVIERES, COLLEGE D'ENSEIGNEMENT GENERAL ET PROFESSIONNEL
 Trois-Rivières, Québec (u 1591; g 106) --, Dépt de Phil, 819-378-9171

    Bergeron, Gustave, Lic Phil
    Boutet, Marcelle, MPh
    Cardin, Mario
    Chapdelaine, Gilles, MPh
    Chicoyne, Pierre, MPh
    Clément, Marie-Rose, DPh
    Debays, Jean-Marie, Lic Phil
    Forget, Mario, Lic Phil
    Gagnon, Donat, MPh
    Gagnon, Luc
    Gaudet, Marcel, DPh
    Gibeault, Marcel, MA
    Lallier, Alain, MA
    Leclair, Jean-Claude, Lic Phil
    Lessard, Adèle, MPh
    Levesque, Gyslain
    Ouellet, Alain, Lic Phil
    Paille, Yvon
    Patry, Jacques, MA
    Rebello, Alfred, Lic Phil
    Rezende, Antonio, DPh

Roy, Yves
Thibault, Serge
Vincent, Robert, Lic Phil

COLLEGE DE VALLEYFIELD
Valleyfield, Québec (--) Courses with no degree specialization, Dépt de Phil, 373-9441

Legault, Alton, MA, Chef
Collette, Richard, MPh, Reg Fac
Fleury, Guy, MPh, Reg Fac
Jalbert, Gilles, MPh, Reg Fac
Larocque, Guy, MPh, Reg Fac
Lavigne, Jacques, PhD, Reg Fac
Lecompte, Michel, MPh, Reg Fac
Proulx, Carole, MPh, Reg Fac
Vrarasik, Boydan, MPh, Reg Fac

COLLEGE DE VICTORIAVILLE, COLLEGE D'ENSEIGNEMENT GENERAL ET PROFESSIONNEL
Victoriaville, Québec (--) Courses with no degree specialization, Dépt de Phil, --

Batani, Gabriel, Maîtrise
Boucher, Yvan, Maîtrise
de Callières, Yves C, Lic
Desfossés, Pierre, Maîtrise
Mercier, Suzanne, Maîtrise, Phil Soc
Sabri, Jean, Maîtrise, Anthrop Phil
Saulnier, Thérèse, Maîtrise, Phil Soc

COLLEGE DES JESUITES
St-Cyrille, Québec (--) NP

COLLEGE DU MONT SAINTE ANN, Affilié à l'Université de Sherbrooke
Sherbrooke, Québec (--) NR

COLLEGE DU VIEUX-MONTREAL, COLLEGE D'ENSEIGNEMENT GENERAL ET PROFESSIONNEL
Montréal, Québec (--) AA major, Dépt de Phil, 514-842-7161 Ext 257

Allaire, Réjean, Temps Plein
Ayoub, Josiane, Temps Plein
Batista, Filipe, Temps Plein
Beauchemin, Lucille, Temps Plein
Boyer, Roland, Temps Plein
Chaput, Paul, Temps Plein
Collin, Claude, Temps Plein
Comtois, Raoul, Temps Plein
Coté, Michel, Temps Plein
Dagenais, André, Temps Plein
Dastous, Emile, Temps Plein
Décarie, Claude, Temps Plein
Despres, Pierre, Temps Plein
De Mestral, Charles, Temps Plein
Filion, Maurice, Temps Plein
Finn, Danielle Julien, Temps Plein
Forget, Gilles, Temps Plein
Gelinas, Gérard, Temps Plein
Grenier, Monique, Temps Plein
Haddad, Jamil, Temps Plein
Hellyer, Lorne, Temps Plein

Kemp, William, Temps Plein
Labrousse, Bernard, Temps Plein
Lamoureux, Philippe, Temps Plein
Lanctôt-Bélanger, Marie Claire, Temps Plein
Lafrance, Germain, Temps Plein
Landry, Cécile, Temps Plein
Lapointe, Jocelyne, Temps Plein
Lefebvre, Guy, Temps Plein
Normandeau, G Yannick, Temps Plein
Olivier, Nicole, Temps Plein
Osana, Zdencko A, Temps Plein
Otis, Mario, Temps Plein
Poirier, Jean-Guy, Temps Plein
Ranger, Philippe, Temps Plein
Sheitoyan, Victor, Temps Plein
Simard, Yvon, Temps Plein
St-Jean, Robert, Temps Plein
Tanguay, Jean-Charles, Temps Plein
Tourangeau, Bernard, Temps Plein
Valdenaire, Jean, Temps Plein
Wattelle, Chislaine, Temps Plein
Zambo, Louis, Temps Plein

COLLEGE EDOUARD-MONTPETIT, COLLEGE D'ENSEIGNEMENT GENERAL ET PROFESSIONNEL
Longueuil, Québec (--) BA minor, --, 514-679-2630

Giasson, Claude, DPh, Dir du Dépt
Labelle, Geneviève, MA, Sec du Dépt
Boutin, Jean-Pierre, Lic Phil
Brès, Jean-Claude, Lic Phil
Brochu, Jacques, Lic Phil
Chancy, Max, DPh
Duhaime, Micheline, MA
Gagnon, Claude, MA
Girovard, Claude, MA
Lemieux, Raymond, MA
Morin, Michel, MA
Patar, Benoît, Lic Phil
Robert, Serge, MA
Rodrigue, Réal, Lic Phil
Sénécal, France, Lic Phil
Tremblay, Jacques, MA
Tremblay, Normand, MA
Van Schendel, Céline, Lic Phil

COLLEGE FRANCOIS-XAVIER-GARNEAU, COLLEGE D'ENSEIGNEMENT GENERAL ET PROFESSIONNEL
Québec City, Québec (--) Courses with no degree specialization, Dept of Phil, 418-681-6284

Bailly, Maurice, Dr, Chm
Ayotte, Jacques, Lic, Ethics
Banville, Paul, Dr, Ethics
Bez, Gabriel, Lic, Phil of Art
Boucher, Remi, Dr, Ethics
Claude, Paul, MA, Ethics
Eurard, Paule, MA
Freire, Antonio, Dr, Phil of Relig
Guerette, Jean-Paul, Dr, Logic
Morel, Raymond, Lic, Soc Phil
Poinlane, Evelyne, Dr, Ethics

COLLEGE JEAN-DE-BREBEUF, Affilié à l'Université de Montréal
  Montréal, Québec (u 230) NR

COLLEGE JESUS-MARIE DE SILLERY
  Sillery, Québec (--) NR

COLLEGE LIONEL-GROULX
  Ste-Thérèse-de-Blainville, Québec (--) Courses with no degree specialization, Dépt
  de Phil, 514-430-3120

  Presseault, Jacques, PhD, Chm
  Chénard, Rosaire, MA
  Cherentant, Gérald, MA
  Demers, Guy, MA, Marxism
  Dumouchel, Thérèse, MA, Marxism
  Gendron, Jocelyn, MA
  Giroux, Jean-Paul, MA, Med Phil
  Labarre, Françoise, MA, Med Phil
  Latraverse, François, MA
  Lespérance, Suzanne, MA
  Marsan, Germain, MA, Aes
  Métayer, Michel, MA, Phil of Nature
  Poisson, Louise, MA, Phil of Nature
  Saucier, Jean, MA, Morals
  Saulnier, Denyse, MA, Phil of Nature

COLLEGE MARGUERITE-BOURGEOYS
  Montréal, Québec (--) Courses with no degree specialization, --, --

  Bouchard, Lise, PhD, Chm, Metaph
  Bouchard, Marie, Lic Phil, Prof, Phil of Art
  Laurent, Guy, BPh, Prof
  Martel, Jean-Paul, PhD, Prof, Ethics
  Turcotte, Lucie, MA, Prof
  Venne, Louis, MA, Prof

COLLEGE MILITAIRE ROYAL DE SAINT-JEAN, Affiliate of the Royal Military College of Canada
  Saint-Jean, Québec (u 396) Courses with no degree specialization, --, --

  Arnold, Winston, PhD, Asst Prof, Med Phil

COLLEGE NOTRE-DAME-DE-BELLEVUE
  Québec, Québec (--) NR

COLLEGE NOTRE-DAME-DES SERVITES, Affilié à l'Université de Sherbrooke
  Ayer's Cliff, Québec (--) NR

COLLEGE RIGAUD DE VAUDREUIL
  Rigaud, Québec (--) NR

COLLEGE SAINT-JEAN VIANNEY
  Montréal 479, Québec (--) AA major, --, --

  Blondin, Félix, PhD
  Daoust, Aurèle, PhD

503

    Gagné, Jeanne d'Arc, MA
    Gervais, Bernadette, MA

COLLEGE SAINT-JEAN-SUR-RICHELIEU, COLLEGE D'ENSEIGNEMENT GENERAL ET PROFESSIONNEL
    Saint-Jean, Québec (--) NR

COLLEGE STANISLAS, Affilié à l'Université de Montréal
    Montréal, Québec (--) NR

DAWSON COLLEGE, COLLEGE D'ENSEIGNEMENT GENERAL ET PROFESSIONNEL
    Montréal, Québec (--) Courses with no degree specialization, Dept of Phil, 514-931-8731 Local 246

    Spencer, John, PhD, Chm, Hist of Logic
    DeWolfe, May, MA, Instr, Metaph
    Milkman, Kenneth, MA, Instr, Ethics

ECOLE DE MUSIQUE VINCENT D'INDY, Affilié á l'Université de Sherbrook
    Montréal, Québec (--) NR

L'ECOLE NATIONALE D'ADMINISTRATION PUBLIQUE, Ecole Constituante de l'Université due Québec
    Québec, Québec (g 51) NR

GRAND SEMINAIRE DE NICOLET, Affilié à l'Université de Sherbrooke
    Nicolet, Québec (--) NR

GRAND SEMINAIRE DE SHERBROOKE, Affilié à l'Université de Sherbrooke
    Sherbrooke, Québec (--) NR

JOHN ABBOTT COLLEGE
    Ste Anne de Bellevue, Québec (--) Courses with no degree specialization, Dept of Human, Phil and Relig, 457-6610 Loc 322

LOYOLA COLLEGE, Affiliate of the University of Montréal
    Montréal, Québec (u 2075) BA major, Dept of Phil, 514-482-0320 Ext 413

    Morgan, John, PhD, Assoc Prof, Chm, Natur Law Ethics
    Cavanaugh, Brendan, PhD, Asst Prof
    Crotty, Gerard, MA, Lect, Phil of Lit
    Doyle, John, MA, Assoc Prof, Thomistic Phil
    Egan, Edmund, PhD, Asst Prof, Ethics, Aes
    Gray, Christopher, PhD, Asst Prof, Phil of Law
    Hinners, Richard, PhD, Prof, Soc Phil, Metaph
    Joos, Ernest, PhD, Assoc Prof, Med Phil
    Kawczak, Andrew, PhD, Prof, Phil Anthrop
    Lau, Herman, MA, Asst Prof, Phil of Educ
    McGraw, John, PhD, Assoc Prof, Phil of Relig
    McNamara, Vincent, PhD, Assoc Prof, Soc Phil
    O'Connor, Dennis, PhD, Asst Prof, Phil of Soc Sci
    O'Hanley, Leonard, MA, Asst Prof, Metaph, Epistem
    Park, Desiree, PhD, Assoc Prof, British Empir
    Reidy, Martin, PhD, Assoc Prof, Anc Phil
    Roy, Eugene, MA, Asst Prof, Ethics

MACDONALD COLLEGE, Constitutent of McGill University
   Sainte-Anne de Bellevue, Québec (--) NR

MARIANOPOLIS COLLEGE, Affiliate of the University of Montréal
   Montréal, Québec (u 114) NR

MCGILL UNIVERSITY
   Montréal, Québec (u 7717; g 3060) PhD major, Dept of Phil, 514-392-5170

   Robinson, Jonathan, PhD, Chm, German Idealism
   Beatty, Harry, PhD, Logic
   Bracken, Harry M, PhD, Early Mod Phil
   Bunge, Mario, PhD, Phil of Sci
   DiGiovanni, George, PhD, German Idealism, Phenomen
   Harvey, Warren, PhD, Med Phil, Jewish Phil
   McGilvray, James, PhD, Phil of Lang
   McKinnon, Alastair, PhD, Kierkegaard, Phil of Relig
   Montefiore, Alan, Part-time, MA, Moral Phil
   Popkin, Richard H, PhD, Part-time, Hist of Mod Phil
   Schleifer, Michael, PhD, Phil Psych
   Shea, William, PhD, Hist and Phil of Sci
   Taylor, Charles, DPhil, Moral Phil
   Tretman, John A, PhD, Med Phil
   Walker, Jeremy, MA, Moral Phil

Arthur, R W T, Teach Asst	King, William, Teach Asst
Baer, Thomas, Teach Asst	Marcil, Louise, Fel
Beliveau, Guy, Fel	Morel, Denise, Fel
Bender, Barbara, Teach Asst	Morin, Denis, Fel
Bimson, Norman	Offenbach, Elizabeth
Crosby, R A, Fel	O'Malley-Keyes, Anthony
Désautels, Guy, Fel	Raphael, Leyla, Teach Asst
Gendron, Marc, Fel	Sharkey, Robert, Fel
Hungerford, Thomas, Teach Asst	Smith, J, Teach Asst
Keel, Othmar, Fel	Smith, P J, Teach Asst

MONT NOTRE-DAME Affilié à l'Université de Sherbrooke
   Sherbrooke, Québec (--) NR

MONTREAL DIOCESAN THEOLOGICAL COLLEGE, Affiliate of McGill University
   Montréal, Québec (u 2) NR

PETIT SEMINAIRE DE QUEBEC
   Québec, Québec (--) NR

LE PETIT SEMINAIRE DE SAINT-GEORGES DE BEAUSE
   Ville-Saint-Georges, Québec (--) Courses with no degree specialization, Dépt de
   Phil, 418-228-8896

   Poulin, Louis-Philippe, DPh, Chm
   Bourque, Jean-Marie, DPh
   Nadeau, Jean, Lic Phil
   Rodrigue, Marcel, Lic Phil

POLYTECHNIC SCHOOL, Affiliate of the University of Montréal
   Montréal 26, Québec (--) NR

PRESBYTERIAN COLLEGE OF MONTREAL, Affiliate of McGill University
   Montréal, Québec (u 4) NR

ROYAL VICTORIA COLLEGE' Constituent of McGill University
   Montréal, Québec (--) NR

SCHOLASTICAT DE L'ABBAYE SAINT-BENOIT-DU-LAC, Affilié à l'Université de Sherbrooke
   Québec, Québec (--) NR

SEMINAIRE DE QUEBEC
   Québec, Québec (--) Courses with no degree specialization, --, 418-529-9931

   Lemieux, Jacques, DPh, Chm, Moral Phil, Metaph
   Bernier, Pierre, Lic, Logic, Phil of Nature
   Gariepy, Benoît, DPh, Moral Phil, Metaph
   Labrie, Robert, DPh, Vice Chm, Phil of Nature, Moral Phil, Metaph
   Pelletier, Jacques, Lic, Logic, Phil of Nature

SEMINAIRE DE SAINT-JEAN, Affilié à l'Université de Montréal
   Saint-Jean, Québec (--) NR

SEMINAIRE DE SAINTE-THERESE, Affilié à l'Université de Montréal
   Sainte-Thérèse-de-Blainville, Québec (--) NR

SEMINAIRE DE SHERBROOKE
   Sherbrooke, Québec (--) Courses with no degree specialization, Dépt de Phil, 819-562-3050

   Labrecque, Claude, Dr, Résponsable du Dépt
   Cambron, Antoine, Lic
   Chauve, Maryvonne, Dipl 3° Cycle
   Larose, Jean-François, Lic

SEMINAIRE DES SAINTS-APOTRES, Affilié à l'Université de Montréal
   Montréal, Québec (--) NR

SIR GEORGE WILLIAMS UNIVERSITY
   Montréal 107, Québec (u 3189; g 198) --, Dept of Phil, 514-879-7262

   Zeman, Vladimir, PhD, Assoc Prof, Chm
   Angel, Roger B, PhD, Assoc Prof
   Ahmad, M Mobin, PhD, Assoc Prof
   Bauer, Frances, BA, Part-time Lect
   Beatty, Harry, MA, Part-time Lect
   Drtina, Richard, PhD, Part-time Lect
   French, Stanley G, PhD, Prof
   Egan, Edmund
   Garside, Christine, PhD, Asst Prof
   Germain, Paul, PhD, Prof
   Goldberg, Barbara, MA, Part-time Lect
   Hartt, Joel, MA, Part-time Lect
   Laskey, Dallas, PhD, Prof
   Lavalley, Gerald, BA, Part-time Lect
   Mullett, Sheila, PhD, Collegial Instr
   Ornstein, Jack, PhD, Asst Prof

Ahmad, Ingrid, BA   Stall, Rosanna, BA
Nordell, Veronica, BA

UNITED THEOLOGICAL COLLEGE OF MONTREAL, Affiliate of McGill University
    Montréal, Québec (u 3) NR

UNIVERSITE DE MONTREAL
    Montréal, Québec (u 12,007; g 2601) PhD major, Dépt de Phil, 514-343-6464

    Cauchy, Venant, DPh, Dir, Tit, Phil de la Relig, Phil Grecque
    Allard, Guy-H, DPh, Ch de C, Agr, Phil Méd
    Audet, Jean-Paul, DTh, Tit, Phil de la Culture et des Institutions
    Bernier, Réjane, BS, Agr, Phil de Sci Biologiques
    Blanchard, Yvon, DPh, Tit, Phil Econ, Phil Sco
    Boglioni, Pietro, LPh, Ch de C, Prof Adj, Phil Méd
    Cromp, Germaine, DPh, Tit, Hist de la Phénomén et Phil de l'Exist
    Décarie, Vianney, DPh, Tit, Hist de la Phil Grecque, Phil de la Relig
    D'Hondt, Jacques, Dr ès Lettres, Invité, Phil Contemp
    Gauthier, Yvon, PhD, Agr, Logique, Phil de Sci, Phil des Math
    Granel, Gérard, Dr ès Lettres, Invité, Phil Contemp
    Gravel, Pierre, DPh, Ch de C, Phil Mod, Esthétique
    Hélal, Georges, PhD, Agr, Epistém, Phil de la Nature, Phil des Sci
    Houde, Roland, DPh, Agr, Logique, Méth
    Klimov, Alexis, Lic Phil, Ch de C, Phil Orient, Phil Russe, Esth
    Kortian, Garbis, PhD, Prof Adj, Hist de la Phil Allemande
    Lagadec, Claude, DPh, Prof, Adj, Epistém, Phil Marxist
    Lagueux, Maurice, DPh, Agr, Phil de l'Hist, Phil Econ
    Lévesque, Claude, DPh, Agr, Anthropol Phil
    Liu, Joseph, Dr, Ch de C, Phil Chinoise
    Murin, Charles, DPh, Agr, Ethique, Hist de la Phil Mod
    Pépin, Jean, PhD, Invité, Phil Grecque
    Potvin, Gérard, Lic Phil, Ch de C, Enseign de la Phil
    Poulain, Jacques, DPh, Prof Adj, Phil Anal, Phil du Lang
    Reboul, Olivier, Dr ès Lettres, Tit, Phil Mod et Contemp, Phil de l'Educ
    Rioux, Bertrand, Dr, Tit, Ontologie
    Roy, Jean, DPh, Prof Adj, Ethique, Phil Polit

    Régis, Louis-Marie, DPh, Prof Emer

UNIVERSITE DE SHERBROOKE
    Sherbrooke, Québec (u 3544; g 915) MA major, Dépt de Phil, 819-565-4661

    Dandenault, Germain, DTh, Agr, Métaph, Phil Contemp
    Gagnon, Maurice, DPh, Agr, Logique, Phil des Sci
    Goulet, Jean, DPh, Agr, Phil Grecque, Métaph
    Granger, G-G, DPh, Prof Invité, Epistém Comp
    Luc, Laurent-Paul, Lic Phil, Ch d'Enseign, Phil de l'Hist, Phil Mod
    McDonald, Patrick, Lic Phil, Ch d'Enseign, Phil de l'Educ, Phil Contemp
    Plamondon, Jacques, DPh, Logique, Phil du Lang
    Pruche, Benoît, DPh, Agr, Epistém, Esth
    Tchao, Joseph Ho-Jou, DPh, Agr, Phénomén, Phil Contemp
    Valcke, Louis, DPh, Tit, Epistém, Phil Mod

UNIVERSITE DU QUEBEC A CHICOUTIMI, Université constituante de l'Université du Québec
    Chicoutimi, Québec (u 1102; g 1) BA joint or combined major, Dépt des Sci Humaines,
    418-549-4354

UNIVERSITE DU QUEBEC A MONTREAL, Université constituante de l'Université du Québec
    Montréal, Québec (u 4311; g 101) MA major, Dépt de Phil, 514-876-5611

    Lacharite, Normand, DPh, Chm, Prof
    Brodeur, Jean-Paul, MA, Prof
    Carnois, Bernard, DPh, Prof
    Couturier, Fernand, DPh, Prof
    Dionne, Gilbert, DPh, Prof
    Lambert, Roger, DPh, Prof
    LeClerc, Michel, MA, Prof
    LeRoux, Georges, MA, Prof
    Malouin, Harel, DPh, Prof
    Meunier, Jean-Guy, DPh, Prof
    Monette, Lise, MA, Prof
    Nadeau, Robert, DPh, Prof
    Paradis, André, DPh, Prof
    Pichette, Michel, MA, Prof
    Saint-Pierre, Gaétan, MA, Prof
    Vidricaire, André, MA, Prof

UNIVERSITE DU QUEBEC A RIMOUSKI
    Rimouski, Québec (u 467) NP

UNIVERSITE DU QUEBEC A TROIS-RIVIERES
    Trois-Rivieres, Québec (u 1772; g 78) PhD major, Dépt de Phil, 819-376-5639

    Savary, Claude, PhD, Prof, Dir, Epistém, Phil of Culture
    Gagne, Paul, Lic Phil, Prof, Phil Polit
    Giroux, Laurent, PhD, Prof, German and Continen Phil
    Klimov, Alexis, L és L, Prof Part-time, Anc and East Phil
    Lane, Gilles, DLitt, Prof, Phil of Sci
    Naud, Julien, PhD, Prof, Epistém
    Renault, Marc, PhD, Prof, Metaph
    Rose, Robert, MA, Prof, Logic
    Therrien, Vincent, DLitt, Prof, Part-time, Aes

UNIVERSITE LAVAL
    Cité Universitaire, Québec G1K 7P4 (u 8795; g 954) PhD major, Faculté de Phil, --

    Trépanier, Emmanuel, DPh, Doyen, Prof Tit, Phil Contemp
    Babin, Eugène, DPh, Prof Tit, Ethique
    Blais, Martin, DPh, Prof Agr, Phil Méd
    Blanchet, Louis-Emile, DPh, Prof Tit, Phil Math
    Bouchard, Guy, DPh, Prof Adj, Phil de l'Art
    Boulay, Jasmin, DTh, Prof Tit, Phil de l'Art
    Brouillet, Raymond, DPh, Prof Adj, Phil Mod
    Champagne, René, DPh, Ch D'Enseign, Hegel
    Côté, André, DPh, Prof Tit, Logique
    Cunningham, Henri-Paul, DPh, Prof Adj, Phil de la Nature
    Danek, Jaromir, DPh, Prof Agr, Logique
    DeKoninck, Thomas, DPh, Prof Agr, Phil de la Nature
    De Monléon, Jacques, DPh, Prof Agr, Phil Mod
    Dionne, Maurice, Lic Phil, Prof Tit, Logique
    Dumont, Fernand, DSoc, Prof Invité, Idéologie
    Ebacher, Roger, DPh, Prof Invité, Bergson
    Gallup, John R, DPh, Prof Agr, Phil du Lang
    Gariépy, Benoit, DPh, Ch d'Enseign, Ethique
    Godin, Guy, DPh, Prof Tit, Metaph
    Hamel, Albert F, DPh, Prof Invité, Phil Mod
    Murray, Warren J, Lic Phil, Prof Adj, Phil Sci

Plante, Robert, DPh, Prof Tit
Ponton, Lionel, DPh, Prof Agr, Phil de la Nature
Saint-Jacques, Alphonse, Lic Phil, Prof Agr, Phil Mod
Valois, Raynald, DPh, Prof Adj, Logique

SASKATCHEWAN

CAMPION COLLEGE' Federated with the University of Saskatchewan, Regina
  Regina, Saskatchewan (u 427) BA major, --, --

  McGovern, Kenneth C, PhD, Asst Prof, Chm, Contemp Phil
  Grisez, Germain, PhD, Prof, Ethics
  Marshall, George J, BA, Asst Prof, Contemp Phil
  Nash, P W, PhD, Prof, Med Phil

COLLEGE OF EMMANUEL AND SAINT CHAD' Affiliate of the University of Saskatchewan, Saskatoon
  Saskatoon, Saskatchewan (u 22) NR

COLLEGE SAINT THOMAS, Affilié à l'Université de Saint-Paul
  North Battleford, Saskatchewan (--) NR

LUTHER COLLEGE' Federated with the University of Saskatchewan, Regina
  Regina, Saskatchewan (u 30) BA major, Dept of Phil, 306-584-0255

  Krentz, Arthur A, PhD, Asst Prof, Greek Phil, Contemp Phil, Phil of Relig

LUTHERAN THEOLOGICAL SEMINARY' Affiliate of the University of Saskatchewan
  Saskatoon, Saskatchewan (u 4; g 39) NP

NOTRE DAME OF CANADA COLLEGE, Affiliate of the University of Ottawa
  Wilcox, Saskatchewan SOG 5EO (u 57) Courses with no degree specialization, Dean of
  Arts, Dean of Stud, 306-732-2123

  Mansbridge, Christopher, PhD, Asst Prof, Metaph
  Murray, J Athol, BA, Lect, Ethics

SAINT ANDREW'S COLLEGE, Affiliate of the University of Saskatchewan, Saskatoon
  Saskatoon, Saskatchewan, S7N 0W3 (u 14; g 1) Courses with no degree specialization,
  --, --

SAINT CHARLES SCHOLASTICATE, Affiliate of the University of Ottawa
  Battleford, Saskatchewan (u 14) NP

SAINT JOSEPH'S COLLEGE, Affiliate of the University of Saskatchewan, Saskatoon
  Yorkton, Saskatchewan (u 15) Courses with no degree specialization, Dept of Phil,

783-3638

Irvine, Lance, MA

SAINT PETER'S JUNIOR COLLEGE, Affiliate of the University of Saskatchewan, Saskatoon
   Muenster, Saskatchewan SOK 2UO (u 31) Courses with no degree specialization, Dept of
   Phil, 306-682-3373

   Pomedli, Michael M, PhD, Prof, Chm, Phenomen, Exist

SAINT THOMAS MORE COLLEGE, Federated with the University of Saskatchewan
   Saskatoon, Saskatchewan (u 749) BA major, Dept of Phil, 306-343-4561

   McCullough, E J, PhD, Asst Prof, Chm, Ethics, Med Phil
   Bisztyo, J, STD, Assoc Prof, Phil of Relig, Ethics
   McRiavy, J, MA, Asst Prof, Logic, Hist of Phil
   Penna, J, PhD, Asst Prof, 19th Cent Phil, Med Phil, Contemp Euro Phil
   Pomedli, M, PhD, Sess Lect, Continen Phil, Ethics, Hist of Phil
   Swan, P, PhD, Prof, Ethics, Med Phil

SASKATCHEWAN INSTITUTE OF APPLIED ARTS AND SCIENCES
   Saskatoon, Saskatchewan (--) NR

UNIVERSITY OF SASKATCHEWAN, REGINA
   Regina, Saskatchewan (u 3065; g 133) BA major, Dept of Phil and Class, 306-584-4336

   Berriman, W, MA, Asst Prof, Chm, Phil of Lang, Phil of Mind
   Archer, R, PhD, Lect, Hist of Phil
   Givner, D, PhD, Assoc Prof, Problem of Perception
   Jack, H, PhD, Prof, Ethics
   Kekes, J, PhD, Prof, Metaph, Phil of Mind
   Purton, A C, MA, Instr, Phil of Sci

UNIVERSITY OF SASKATCHEWAN, SASKATOON
   Saskatoon, Saskatchewan (u 9373; g 571) MA major, Dept of Phil, 306-343-4304

   Miller, L G, PhD, Prof, Chm, Ethics, 20th Cent Anglo Amer Phil, 17th and 18th Cent
      Phil, Metaph
   Crossley, D J, PhD, Assoc Prof, Aes, Greek Phil, Phil of Mind, 19th Cent Phil,
      Contemp Phil
   Dayton, E B, MA, Asst Prof
   Henderson, T Y, PhD, Assoc Prof, Phil of Relig, Ethics, Anal Phil
   Krutzen, R W, PhD, Assoc Prof, Epistem, Phil of Sci, Phil of Hist, Phil of Relig
   Loptson, P J, PhD, Asst Prof, Epistem, Metaph, Logic, 20th Cent Anglo Amer Phil
   Mackenzie, P T, MLitt, Assoc Prof, Ethics, Wittgenstein, 20th Cent British Phil
   Thompson, III, H E, AB, Asst Prof, Phil of Sci

ASSISTANTSHIPS

CANADA

UNIVERSITIES OFFERING A DOCTORATE IN PHILOSOPHY

Knox College, University of Toronto: OA
McGill University: 8-10 F $2500-$4000+TW; 10 TA $3500-$4000
McMaster University: 26 TA $1800-$4500
Ontario Institute for Studies in Education: 2 F $1500; 9 A $900-$2400
Queen's University: 1 F $800; 8 TA $1000-$1920
Université de Montréal: None
Université du Québec à Trois-Rivières: None
Université Laval: None
University of Alberta: 5 F $4500; 21 TA $3300+TW
University of British Columbia: 6 TA $2650
University of Guelph: 4 TF $3600-$4000; 13 A $2400
University of Calgary: 17 TA $3000-$3600+TW; 2 A $2400
University of Ottawa: 22 F $800-$1000; 4 TA $1800
University of Toronto: 20 TA $1800; 30 A $1800
University of Waterloo: 10 F $2240; 30 TF $2400
University of Western Ontario: 18 TA totaling $35,500; 30 A totaling $50,191; 13 OA
    (Ontario Graduate Fellowships) totaling $20,250; 7 OA (Canada Council) totaling
    $28,500
Wycliffe College, University of Toronto: Data unavailable
York University: 10 TA $1800; A $1800; OA $1000-$1500

UNIVERSITIES OFFERING A MASTER'S DEGREE IN PHILOSOPHY

Brock University: 2 TF $3450; 4 TA $2900
Carleton University: 4 TA $2400
Collège Dominicain de Philosophie: Data unavailable
Dalhousie University: 7 TF $3550; 1 TA $1425; 2 A $525
Saint Mary's University: Data unavailable
Simon Fraser University: 8 TA $1425 per trimester; 6 OA $1000 per trimester
Sir George Williams University: 4 TA $2400+TW
Université de Sherbrooke: None
University of Manitoba: 15 A totaling $20,000
University of New Brunswick: TA $2000
University of Saskatchewan, Saskatoon: 1 TA $2500
University of Victoria: 1 F $2500, TA $1400
University of Windsor: 3 F $1000-$1500; 2-3 TA $1200-$1500; 4-6 A $650
Vancouver School of Theology: Data unavailable

SOCIETIES

CANADA

THE CANADIAN PHILOSOPHICAL ASSOCIATION, L'ASSOCIATION CANADIENNE DE PHILOSOPHIE (800)
    Department of Philosophy, York University, Downsview, Ontario

    Purpose: To promote philosophical scholarship and education in Canada by discussion,
        research and the dissemination of information
    Meetings: Annually in June
    Pres: John W Yolton, Department of Philosophy, York University
    Sec: Claude Savary, Department of Philosophy, University of Québec, Trois Rivières
    Publ: <u>Dialogue</u>
    Other inf: Member of Fédération Internationale des Sociétés de Philosophie (FISP)
    Mem reqt: Teacher of philosophy at an institution of higher learning on the
        recommendation of a member
    Dues: $12

CANADIAN SOCIETY FOR HISTORY AND PHILOSOPHY OF SCIENCE, SOCIETE CANADIENNE D'HISTOIRE
    ET DE PHILOSOPHIE DES SCIENCES 1956 (230)
    6220 Godfrey Avenue, Montreal 261, Québec

    Purpose: To promote throughout Canada discussion, research, teaching and publication
        in the History and the Philosophy of Science and of Technology
    Activities: Periodical lectures in its branches (Montreal, Toronto), and a yearly
        conference usually at the time and place of the Conference of Learned Societies.
        Encourages exchanges among scholars of similar interests through its yearly
        Directory listing members and their fields of research.
    Pres: John W Abrams, Institute for History and Philosophy of Science and Technology,
        University of Toronto
    Sec: Michel Paradis, 6220 Godfrey Avenue, Montreal 261, Québec
    Other inf: Member of Fédération Internationale des Sociétés de Philosophie (FISP)
    Mem reqt: Nomination by two regular members, election by Council
    Dues: Determined by the annual general meeting (1973-1974: $5)

JOURNALS

CANADA

CANADIAN JOURNAL OF PHILOSOPHY 1971
　　Eds: J King-Farlow and W Rozeboom, Department of Philosophy, University of Alberta,
　　　　Edmonton, Alberta T6G 2E1, K Nielsen and T Penelhum, Department of Philosophy,
　　　　University of Calgary, Calgary, Alberta

　　Purpose: To publish in English or French, works in any field of philosophy
　　Q; Circ: About 530; 100% phil
　　Publ: Canadian Association for Publishing in Philosophy, Department of Philosophy,
　　　　University of Guelph
　　$10, Institutions $12, Students $5

DIALOGUE: Canadian Philosophical Review--Revue Canadienne de Philosophie 1962
　　Eds: H M Estall, Department of Philosophy, Queen's University, and Venant Cauchy,
　　　　Department de Philosophie, Université de Montréal

　　Purpose: To publish scholarly articles, notes, discussions and book reviews in
　　　　philosophy in French or English
　　Sponsor: Canadian Philosophical Association--L'Association Canadienne de Philosophie
　　Q; Circ: 1500; About 25 phil articles per yr; Bk Rev
　　Publ: Canadian Philosophical Association
　　$12 Can

HUMANIST IN CANADA 1967
　　Ed: J Lloyd Brereton, 1337 Fairfield Road, Victoria, British Columbia

　　Purpose: To explain and discuss the Humanist philosophy
　　Q; Circ: About 1400; 25-35 phil articles per yr; Bk Rev
　　Publ: Pacific Northwest Humanist Publication, P O Box 157, Victoria, British Columbia
　　$2

JOURNAL OF INDIAN PHILOSOPHY 1970
　　Ed: B K Matilal, Department of Sanskrit and Indian Studies, University of Toronto,
　　　　Toronto, Ontario

　　Q; Circ: 1000; Bk Rev
　　Publ: D Reidel Publishing Company, P O Box 17, Dordrecht, The Netherlands
　　Dfl 110

JOURNAL OF PHILOSOPHICAL LOGIC 1971
　　Ed: Bas C van Fraassen, Department of Philosophy, University of Toronto, Toronto
　　　　M5S 1A1, Ontario

　　Purpose: To provide a forum for work which is at the same time of definite philosophical
　　　　interest and yet is technical in nature
　　Q;
　　Publ: D Reidel Publishing Company, P O Box 17, Dordrecht, The Netherlands
　　Dfl 60, Institutions Dfl 100

LAVAL THEOLOGIQUE ET PHILOSOPHIQUE 1945
　　Eds: Emmanuel Trépanier, Paul-Emile Langevin, Michel Gervais, Michel Roberge, sr,
　　　　Martin Blais, Thomas De Koninck, Faculté de philosophie, Université Laval, Québec
　　　　G1K 7P4

Three times per yr; Cir: 1000; 10 phil articles per yr; Book Rev
Publ: Les Presses de l'Université Laval, C P 2447, Québec G1K 7R4
$7, Foreign $8

MEDIAEVAL STUDIES 1939
    Ed: J Reginald O Donnell, Pontifical Institute of Mediaeval Studies, 59 Queen^s Pk
        Cres E, Toronto, Ontario M5S 2C4

    Purpose: To publish research on the Middle Ages
    Sponsor: Pontifical Institute of Mediaeval Studies
    Circ: 1100-1200; 5-6 phil articles per yr
    Publ: Pontifical Institute of Mediaeval Studies
    $12

MILL NEWS LETTER 1965
    Eds: John M Robson and Michael Laine, Victoria College, University of Toronto,
        Toronto M5S 1K7, Ontario

    Purpose: To publish scholarly articles, reports, bibliography, and news about John
        Stuart Mill and his contemporaries
    Semi-annual; Circ: 500; 2 phil articles per yr; Bk Rev
    Publ: University of Toronto Press, University of Toronto

PHILOSOPHY OF THE SOCIAL SCIENCES 1971
    Eds: Harold Kaplan, John O'Neill, J O Wisdom, I C Jarvie, Department of Philosophy,
        York University, Downsview, Ontario

    Purpose: To publish scholarly papers in the area of the philosophy of the Social
        Sciences
    Q; Circ: 400; 20 phil articles per yr; Bk Rev
    Publ: The Aberdeen University Press, Farmer's Hall, Aberden, Scotland AB9 2XT
    $8

REVUE DE L'UNIVERSITE D'OTTAWA 1931
    Ed: Gaston Carrière, c/o The University of Ottawa Press, Ottawa, Ontario K1N 6N5

    Purpose: To publish the result of research by university professors
    Q; Circ: 850; 4-5 phil articles per yr; Bk Rev
    Publ: The University of Ottawa Press, 65 Hastey Avenue, Ottawa, Ontario K1N 6N5
    $7.50

RUSSELL: THE JOURNAL OF THE BERTRAND RUSSELL ARCHIVES 1971
    Ed: Kenneth Blackwell, Bertrand Russell Archives, McMaster University Library,
        Hamilton, Ontario L8S 4L6

    Purpose: To publish a bulletin providing scholars in Russell with current
        bibliographical and biographical information; news concerning the Archives;
        brief articles arising from current research projects and details about others
    Q; Cir: 375; 10 phil articles per yr; Bk Rev
    Publ: McMaster University Library Press
    $2

SOCIAL PRAXIS 1973
    Ed: K T Fann, Dept of Phil, Atkinson College, Constituent of York University,
        Downsview 463, Ontario

    Purpose: To publish an international and interdisciplinary journal of social thought
    Q; Circ: 6000; 25 phil articles per yr; Bk Rev
    Publ: Mouton, P O Box 482, The Hague 2076, The Netherlands

PUBLISHERS

CANADA

THE COPP CLARK PUBLISHING COMPANY
517 Wellington Street, W Toronto 135, Ontario

EDITIONS DE L'UNIVERSITE D'OTTAWA 1931
65 Hastey Avenue, Ottawa, Ontario K1N 6N5

Ser Publ: "Collection Philosophica," a publication of works by the University of Ottawa professors, ed by Jean-Louis Allard

EDITIONS FIDES 1937
245 est, boul, Dorchester, Montréal 129, Québec

Ser Publ: Philosophie et problèmes contemporain

MCGILL-QUEEN'S UNIVERSITY PRESS 1960
3458 Redpath Street, Montreal, Québec

MCMASTER UNIVERSITY LIBRARY*
Hamilton, Ontario

Jour Publ: Russell

PACIFIC NORTHWEST HUMANIST PUBLICATIONS*
Box 157, Victoria, British Columbia

Jour Publ: Humanist in Canada

Les PRESSES DE L'UNIVERSITE DE MONTREAL 1962
Case postale 6128, Montréal 101, Québec

Les PRESSES DE L'UNIVERSITE LAVAL
C P 2447, Québec, Québec G1K 7R4

UNIVERSITY OF TORONTO PRESS 1965
University of Toronto, Toronto, 5, Ontario

Jour Publ: Mill News Letter

PART III

LATE REPORTS

LATE REPORTS (UNIVERSITIES)

INDIANA UNIVERSITY AT BLOOMINGTON
  Bloomington, Indiana 47401 (N; st; coed; sem; IV; 30,744) PhD major, Dept of Hist
  and Phil of Sci, 812-337-3622

  Grant, Edward, PhD, Prof, Chm
  Buck, Roger C, BPhil, Prof, Phil of Soc Sci
  Coffa, J Alberto, PhD, Asst Prof, Induc Explanation, Formal Methods
  Giere, Ronald N, PhD, Assoc Prof, Sci Method, Induc Reasoning, Found of Statistics
  Koertge, Noretta, PhD, Assoc Prof, Hist Devel of Phil of Sci
  Williams, Mary B, PhD, Visit Asst Prof, Phil of Biology
  Winnie, John A, PhD, Assoc Prof, Space, Time and Relativity, Phil of Psych

NORTH AMERICAN BIBLE COLLEGE
  Dodge City, Kansas 67801 (--) --, --, 316-225-5032

  Kurtz, James E, PhD, Academic Dean

RUSSELL COLLEGE
  Burlingame, California 94010 (W; RC; wo; sem; II; 42) Courses with no degree
  specialization, Dept of Phil, 415-342-8346

  Rouleau, M Celeste, PhD, Prof, Syst Phil, Phil of Man

SEABURY WESTERN THEOLOGICAL SEMINARY
  Evanston, Illinois 60201 (Theol; Prot Epis; coed; qr; II; 61) Courses with no degree
  specialization, Dept of Phil Theol, 312-328-9300

  Casserley, J V Langmead, DLitt, Chm, 20th Cent Phil of Relig
  Elmen, Paul, PhD, Ethics

UNIVERSITY OF CONNECTICUT HEALTH CENTER (SCHOOL OF MEDICINE)
  Farmington, Connecticut 06032 (Med; st; coed; --; IV; 186) --, --, 203-677-4011

  Spicker, Stuart F, PhD, Assoc Prof

LATE REPORTS (JOURNALS)

MIDWESTERN JOURNAL OF PHILOSOPHY 1972
     Ed: Wayne Sheeks, Dept of Phil, Murray State University, Murray, Kentucky 42071

     Purpose: To provide a conduit for essays by little-known authors. With several of
          the main journals publishing in one field or publishing mostly the work of
          well-known authors, there seemed to be a dearth of channels for the "not-well-
          known-non-analyst" who was creative. Our solution to this problem is the
          Midwestern Journal of Philosophy
     Bi-ann; Circ: 75; 10 phil articles per yr
     Publ: Dept of Phil, Murray State University
     $2, Institutions $4, Students $1

REVOLUTIONARY WORLD 1973
     Ed: David H DeGrood, University of Bridgeport, Bridgeport, Connecticut 06602

     Purpose: To serve as an organ for philosophers to go to the roots of our revolutionary
          world
     5 issues per yr; 80% phil articles; Bk Rev
     Publ: B R Grüner Publishing Co, P O Box 70020, Nieuwe Herengracht 31, Amsterdam,
          The Netherlands
     $25, Institutions $40, Single volumes $10

PART IV

STATISTICS

STATISTICS

UNITED STATES

SIZE OF DEPARTMENTS

	No Phil	Unknown	1	2-4	5-9	10-14	15+	No Response
Alabama	16	5	8	10	5	0	0	6
Alaska	2	1	2	2	0	0	0	0
Arizona	3	1	3	5	4	1	1	1
Arkansas	5	1	7	8	2	0	0	2
California	22	17	35	72	26	15	13	26
Canal Zone	0	0	1	0	0	0	0	0
Colorado	3	1	10	10	6	1	2	6
Connecticut	10	3	13	8	7	3	3	6
Delaware	2	2	1	1	0	1	0	1
Dist of Columbia	4	0	2	4	1	2	2	5
Florida	3	6	16	30	6	1	2	1
Georgia	11	6	17	19	2	3	0	5
Guam	0	0	0	1	0	0	0	0
Hawaii	2	1	3	6	0	0	1	1
Idaho	1	1	3	4	0	0	0	0
Illinois	20	16	23	57	9	2	9	10
Indiana	12	4	6	23	10	1	3	5
Iowa	12	2	15	23	4	1	0	7
Kansas	10	5	14	17	4	0	1	2
Kentucky	8	3	12	17	4	3	0	2
Louisiana	6	1	12	5	4	2	0	2
Maine	5	1	5	7	3	0	0	1
Maryland	7	1	13	15	4	4	1	6
Massachusetts	16	13	20	28	18	3	4	19
Michigan	12	6	25	32	10	2	2	4
Minnesota	12	6	13	15	10	1	1	4
Mississippi	12	5	12	10	0	0	0	5
Missouri	10	2	20	28	7	3	2	5
Montana	2	0	4	4	1	0	1	0
Nebraska	6	4	8	7	1	1	1	0
Nevada	1	1	2	0	2	0	0	0
New Hampshire	0	1	6	8	4	0	0	0
New Jersey	2	0	13	23	15	3	2	8
New Mexico	3	1	3	3	2	1	0	4
New York	19	13	35	67	30	14	14	48
North Carolina	27	6	21	26	5	3	1	25
North Dakota	4	2	4	3	1	0	0	0
Ohio	13	11	22	34	17	3	3	18
Oklahoma	10	4	12	12	1	1	0	3
Oregon	8	1	12	11	4	0	1	6
Pennsylvania	17	6	40	62	24	3	7	15
Puerto Rico	4	0	2	4	1	2	1	8
Rhode Island	1	3	1	4	1	2	1	0
Samoa	0	0	0	0	0	0	0	1
South Carolina	17	6	10	14	0	0	1	9
South Dakota	3	0	3	10	0	0	0	1
Tennessee	10	1	21	18	5	1	1	9
Texas	36	8	27	31	15	1	1	20
Utah	5	1	2	3	0	1	2	1
Vermont	1	1	5	6	2	1	0	3
Virgin Islands	0	0	0	1	0	0	0	1
Virginia	11	5	16	29	5	2	0	5
Washington	0	2	13	15	4	1	2	4
West Virginia	2	5	5	13	2	0	0	1
Wisconsin	15	3	8	20	6	2	3	6
Wyoming	5	1	0	1	1	0	0	0
TOTALS	448	196	606	886	295	91	89	328

STATISTICS
UNITED STATES

	HIGHEST DEGREE OFFERED IN PHILOSOPHY						NUMBER OF PHILOSOPHERS		
	None	<BA*	BA	MA	PHD	Unknown	Faculty	Assts	Total
Alabama	12	5	10	1	0	0	64	6	70
Alaska	4	0	1	0	0	0	7	0	7
Arizona	7	3	3	1	1	0	63	13	76
Arkansas	5	3	6	2	1	1	39	3	42
California	62	36	41	9	14	18	836	72	908
Canal Zone	1	0	0	0	0	1	1	0	1
Colorado	13	4	8	2	2	1	135	5	140
Connecticut	7	7	13	3	2	5	188	0	188
Delaware	3	1	0	1	0	0	14	11	25
Dist of Columbia	1	1	2	2	3	2	78	27	105
Florida	24	6	16	1	3	11	170	39	209
Georgia	20	6	15	1	2	3	112	30	142
Guam	0	1	0	0	0	0	2	0	2
Hawaii	3	3	3	0	1	1	36	12	48
Idaho	3	1	3	1	0	0	16	0	16
Illinois	36	12	40	5	8	16	444	139	583
Indiana	10	5	22	4	4	3	216	43	259
Iowa	15	5	22	1	1	1	114	15	129
Kansas	15	4	15	2	1	4	96	18	114
Kentucky	13	0	12	5	2	7	116	13	129
Louisiana	5	4	10	1	1	3	76	9	85
Maine	6	2	6	0	0	2	41	0	41
Maryland	17	3	10	1	2	6	146	10	156
Massachusetts	30	8	27	3	9	9	337	104	441
Michigan	32	6	30	1	3	10	242	73	315
Minnesota	18	3	23	0	1	1	152	15	167
Mississippi	11	2	8	2	0	4	37	0	37
Missouri	20	9	27	0	3	3	215	53	268
Montana	2	1	4	1	0	2	34	6	40
Nebraska	11	2	8	0	1	0	58	13	71
Nevada	3	0	1	1	0	0	14	2	16
New Hampshire	1	1	7	0	0	1	56	0	56
New Jersey	15	10	23	0	3	6	248	8	256
New Mexico	5	1	2	1	1	0	38	6	44
New York	60	13	64	8	16	12	972	176	1148
North Carolina	25	5	22	0	2	6	166	35	201
North Dakota	7	0	1	2	0	0	16	0	16
Ohio	26	7	37	11	3	9	387	108	495
Oklahoma	13	2	7	0	2	5	65	18	83
Oregon	10	4	12	2	1	0	83	7	90
Pennsylvania	44	8	69	5	7	9	549	47	596
Puerto Rico	3	2	3	1	0	1	78	0	78
Rhode Island	3	1	5	1	1	1	54	23	77
Samoa	0	0	0	0	0	0	0	0	0
South Carolina	13	2	11	1	0	4	63	10	73
South Dakota	4	1	6	0	1	0	26	0	26
Tennessee	19	7	14	2	1	3	124	18	142
Texas	31	17	17	7	4	7	249	19	268
Utah	2	1	2	1	1	1	43	9	52
Vermont	6	0	8	1	0	0	45	0	45
Virgin Islands	0	0	1	0	0	0	2	0	2
Virginia	22	5	24	1	1	5	169	12	181
Washington	10	8	8	4	1	6	131	0	131
West Virginia	10	4	10	0	0	1	48	0	48
Wisconsin	5	10	21	1	2	3	201	43	244
Wyoming	2	0	0	1	0	0	7	0	7
TOTALS	745	252	760	100	112	194	7928	1270	9189

*Less than BA

STATISTICS
CANADA

SIZE OF DEPARTMENTS

	No Phil	Unknown	1	2-4	5-9	10-14	15+	No Response
Alberta	9	0	3	2	1	0	2	4
British Columbia	4	1	1	6	2	1	1	8
Manitoba	2	2	0	3	0	1	1	3
New Brunswick	1	0	0	3	4	0	0	2
Newfoundland	5	0	0	0	0	1	0	1
Nova Scotia	1	1	1	5	2	1	0	7
Ontario	20	2	9	11	12	5	10	17
Prince Edward Is	1	0	0	0	1	0	0	0
Quebec	4	4	3	8	11	2	13	39
Saskatchewan	2	1	3	2	3	0	0	3
TOTALS	49	11	70	40	36	11	27	84

	HIGHEST DEGREE OFFERED IN PHILOSOPHY						NUMBER OF PHILOSOPHERS		
	None	<BA*	BA	MA	PHD	Unknown	Faculty	Assts	Total
Alberta	3	1	1	1	2	0	51	36	87
British Columbia	5	1	1	3	1	1	66	0	66
Manitoba	3	0	2	1	0	1	35	0	35
New Brunswick	0	2	3	1	0	1	37	4	41
Newfoundland	0	0	0	0	0	1	10	0	10
Nova Scotia	1	0	6	3	0	0	42	0	42
Ontario	13	2	12	4	11	6	399	155	554
Prince Edward Is	0	0	1	0	0	0	5	0	5
Quebec	17	5	5	2	4	10	424	20	444
Saskatchewan	4	0	4	1	0	0	29	0	29
TOTALS	46	11	35	16	18	20	1098	215	1313

*Less than BA

PART V

INDICES

INDEX OF UNIVERSITIES

BERKLEE COLLEGE OF MUSIC 157
BERKSHIRE CHRISTIAN COLLEGE 157
BERKSHIRE COMMUNITY COLLEGE 157
BERNARD BARUCH COLLEGE, CUNY 234
BERRY COLLEGE 78
BETH JACOB HEBREW TEACHERS COLLEGE
    235
BETH MEDRASH GOVOHA 220
BETHANY BIBLE COLLEGE 16
BETHANY COLLEGE, KANSAS 128
BETHANY COLLEGE, WEST VIRGINIA 394
BETHANY LUTHERAN COLLEGE 186
BETHANY NAZARENE COLLEGE 302
BETHANY THEOLOGICAL SEMINARY 90
BETHEL COLLEGE, INDIANA 111
BETHEL COLLEGE, KANSAS 129
BETHEL COLLEGE, MINNESOTA 186
BETHEL COLLEGE, TENNESSEE 350
BETHEL THEOLOGICAL SEMINARY 186
BETHUNE-COOKMAN COLLEGE 68
BIG BEND COMMUNITY COLLEGE 388
BIOLA COLLEGE 16
BIRDWOOD JUNIOR COLLEGE 78
BIRMINGHAM-SOUTHERN COLLEGE 4
BISCAYNE COLLEGE 68
BISHOP COLLEGE 359
BISHOP STATE JUNIOR COLLEGE 4
BISHOP'S UNIVERSITY 496
BISMARCK JUNIOR COLLEGE 282
BLACK HAWK COLLEGE 90
BLACK HAWK COLLEGE, EAST CAMPUS 90
BLACK HILLS STATE COLLEGE 348
BLACKBURN COLLEGE 90
BLACKHAWK TECHNICAL INSTITUTE 398
BLADEN TECHNICAL INSTITUTE 270
BLINN COLLEGE 359
BLISS COLLEGE 284
BLOOMFIELD COLLEGE 220
BLOOMSBURG STATE COLLEGE 313
BLUE MOUNTAIN COLLEGE 194
BLUE MOUNTAIN COMMUNITY COLLEGE
    306
BLUE RIDGE COMMUNITY COLLEGE 379
BLUE RIDGE TECHNICAL INSTITUTE 270
BLUEFIELD COLLEGE 379
BLUEFIELD STATE COLLEGE 395
BLUFFTON COLLEGE 284
BOB JONES UNIVERSITY 342
BOBOVER YESH BNEI ZION 235
BOISE STATE COLLEGE 88
BOROUGH OF MANHATTAN COMMUNITY
    COLLEGE, CUNY 235
BORROMEO SEMINARY OF OHIO 285
BOSTON COLLEGE 157, 408
BOSTON CONSERVATORY OF MUSIC 158
BOSTON STATE COLLEGE 158
BOSTON UNIVERSITY 159, 408
BOURGET COLLEGE 496
BOWDOIN COLLEGE 146
BOWIE STATE COLLEGE 149
BOWLING GREEN STATE UNIVERSITY
    285, 410
BOWLING GREEN STATE UNIVERSITY,
    FIRELANDS BRANCH 285

BRADFORD COLLEGE 159
BRADLEY UNIVERSITY 90
BRAINERD STATE JUNIOR COLLEGE 186
BRANDEIS UNIVERSITY 159, 408
BRANDON UNIVERSITY 475
BRANDYWINE COLLEGE 63
BRAZOSPORT COLLEGE 359
BRENAU COLLEGE 78
BRESCIA COLLEGE, KENTUCKY 136
BRESCIA COLLEGE, ONTARIO 481
BREVARD COLLEGE 271
BREVARD COMMUNITY COLLEGE 68
BREWTON-PARKER COLLEGE 78
BRIAR CLIFF COLLEGE 120
BRIARCLIFF COLLEGE 235
BRIDGEPORT ENGINEERING INSTITUTE
    56
BRIDGEWATER COLLEGE 379
BRIDGEWATER STATE COLLEGE 160
BRIGHAM YOUNG UNIVERSITY 374, 410
BRISTOL COMMUNITY COLLEGE 160
BRITISH COLUMBIA INSTITUTE OF
    TECHNOLOGY 472
BROCK UNIVERSITY 481, 511
BRONX COMMUNITY COLLEGE, CUNY 235
BROOKDALE COMMUNITY COLLEGE 221
BROOKLYN COLLEGE, CUNY 235, 410
BROOKLYN LAW SCHOOL 236
BROOKS INSTITUTE, SANTA BARBARA 16
BROOME COMMUNITY COLLEGE, SUNY 236
BROWARD COMMUNITY COLLEGE 68
BROWN UNIVERSITY 339, 408
BRUNSWICK JUNIOR COLLEGE 78
BRYAN COLLEGE 350
BRYANT COLLEGE OF BUSINESS
    ADMINISTRATION 340
BRYANT-STRATTON COMMERCIAL SCHOOL
    160
BRYN MAWR COLLEGE 313, 408
BUCKNELL UNIVERSITY 313, 410
BUCKS COUNTY COMMUNITY COLLEGE 313
BUENA VISTA COLLEGE 120
BURDETT COLLEGE 160
BURLINGTON COUNTY COLLEGE 221
BUTLER COUNTY COMMUNITY COLLEGE
    313
BUTLER COUNTY COMMUNITY JUNIOR
    COLLEGE 129
BUTLER UNIVERSITY 111, 410
BUTTE COLLEGE 16
CABRILLO COLLEGE 16
CABRINI COLLEGE 313
CAL BAPTIST COLLEGE 16
CAL COLLEGE OF ARTS AND CRAFTS 16
CAL INSTITUTE OF ARTS 16
CAL INSTITUTE OF TECHNOLOGY 17
CAL LUTHERAN COLLEGE 17
CAL MARITIME ACADEMY 17
CAL POLYTECHNIC STATE UNIV AT SAN
    LUIS OBISPO 17
CAL SCHOOL OF PROFESSIONAL PSYCH,
    LOS ANGELES 17
CAL SCHOOL OF PROFESSIONAL PSYCH,
    SAN FRANCISCO 17

CAL STATE COLLEGE AT BAKERSFIELD
17
CAL STATE COLLEGE AT DOMINGUEZ
HILLS 17
CAL STATE COLLEGE AT SAN
BERNARDINO 18
CAL STATE COLLEGE AT SONOMA 18
CAL STATE COLLEGE AT STANISLAUS 18
CAL STATE POLYTECHNIC UNIV AT
POMONA 18
CAL STATE UNIV AT FULLERTON 19
CAL STATE UNIV AT HAYWARD 19
CAL STATE UNIVERSITY AT CHICO 18
CAL STATE UNIVERSITY AT FRESNO 19
CAL STATE UNIVERSITY AT HUMBOLDT
20
CAL STATE UNIVERSITY AT LONG BEACH
20, 410
CAL STATE UNIVERSITY AT LOS
ANGELES 20, 410
CAL STATE UNIVERSITY AT NORTHRIDGE
21, 410
CAL STATE UNIVERSITY AT SACRAMENTO
21
CAL STATE UNIVERSITY AT SAN DIEGO
21, 410
CAL STATE UNIVERSITY AT SAN
FRANCISCO 22, 410
CAL STATE UNIVERSITY AT SAN JOSE
22, 410
CALDWELL COLLEGE 221
CALDWELL COMMUNITY COLLEGE AND
TECHNICAL INSTITUTE 271
CALIFORNIA STATE COLLEGE 314
CALVARY BIBLE COLLEGE 198
CALVIN COLLEGE 173
CALVIN THEOLOGICAL SEMINARY 173
CAMBRIAN COLLEGE OF APPLIED ARTS
AND TECHNOLOGY 482
CAMBRIAN COLLEGE, NORTH BAY CAMPUS
482
CAMBRIAN COLLEGE, SAULT SAINTE
MARIE CAMPUS 482
CAMBRIAN COLLEGE, SUDBURY CAMPUS
482
CAMBRIDGE JUNIOR COLLEGE 160
CAMDEN COUNTY COLLEGE 221
CAMERON COLLEGE 302
CAMPBELL COLLEGE 271
CAMPBELLSVILLE COLLEGE 136
CAMPION COLLEGE' 509
CAMROSE LUTHERAN COLLEGE 469
CANAAN COLLEGE 217
CANADA COLLEGE 22
CANADIAN MENNONITE BIBLE COLLEGE
475
CANADIAN UNION COLLEGE 469
CANAL ZONE COLLEGE 49
CANISIUS COLLEGE 236
CANTERBURY COLLEGE 482
CAPE COD COMMUNITY COLLEGE 160
CAPE FEAR TECHNICAL INSTITUTE 271
CAPILANO COLLEGE 472

CAPITAL UNIVERSITY 285
CAPITOL INSTITUTE OF TECHNOLOGY
149
CARDINAL GLENNON COLLEGE 198
CARDINAL STRITCH COLLEGE 398
CARIBBEAN CENTER FOR ADVANCED
STUDIES, PSYCH INST OF P R 336
CARIBOO COLLEGE 472
CARL ALBERT JUNIOR COLLEGE 302
CARL SANDBURG COLLEGE 90
CARLETON COLLEGE 186
CARLETON UNIVERSITY 482, 511
CARLOW COLLEGE 314
CARNEGIE-MELLON UNIVERSITY 314
CARROLL COLLEGE 210
CARROLL COLLEGE 398
CARSON-NEWMAN COLLEGE 350
CARTERET TECHNICAL INSTITUTE 271
CASE WESTERN RESERVE UNIVERSITY
285, 408
CASPER COLLEGE 407
CASTLETON STATE COLLEGE 376
CATAWBA COLLEGE 271
CATAWBA VALLEY TECHNICAL INSTITUTE
271
CATHARINE PARR TRAILL COLLEGE 482
CATHEDRAL COLLEGE OF THE
IMMACULATE CONCEPTION 236
CATHOLIC THEOLOGICAL UNION AT
CHICAGO 90
CATHOLIC UNIVERSITY OF AMERICA
65, 408
CATHOLIC UNIVERSITY OF PUERTO RICO
337
CATONSVILLE COMMUNITY COLLEGE 149
CAZENOVIA COLLEGE 237
CECIL COMMUNITY COLLEGE 149
CEDAR CREST COLLEGE 314
CEDARVILLE COLLEGE 286
CEN YESH TOM TMIMIM LUBVZ 237
CENTENARY COLLEGE FOR WOMEN 221
CENTENARY COLLEGE OF LOUISIANA 142
CENTENNIAL COLLEGE OF APPLIED ARTS
AND TECHNOLOGY 482
CENTRAL ARIZONA COLLEGE 9
CENTRAL BAPTIST THEOLOGICAL
SEMINARY 129
CENTRAL BIBLE COLLEGE 198
CENTRAL CAROLINA TECHNICAL
INSTITUTE 271
CENTRAL COLLEGE 129
CENTRAL CONNECTICUT STATE COLLEGE
56
CENTRAL FLORIDA COMMUNITY COLLEGE
68
CENTRAL INSTITUTE OF TECHNOLOGY
198
CENTRAL METHODIST COLLEGE 199
CENTRAL MICHIGAN UNIVERSITY 173
CENTRAL MISSOURI STATE UNIVERSITY
199
CENTRAL NEBRASKA TECHNICAL COLLEGE
212

CENTRAL OREGON COMMUNITY COLLEGE
306
CENTRAL PIEDMONT COMMUNITY COLLEGE
271
CENTRAL STATE UNIVERSITY, OHIO 286
CENTRAL STATE UNIVERSITY, OKLAHOMA
302
CENTRAL TEXAS COLLEGE 359
CENTRAL UNIVERSITY OF IOWA 121
CENTRAL VIRGINIA COMMUNITY COLLEGE
379
CENTRAL WASHINGTON STATE COLLEGE
388
CENTRAL WESLEYAN COLLEGE 342
CENTRAL WYOMING COLLEGE 407
CENTRAL YMCA COMMUNITY COLLEGE 91
CENTRALIA COLLEGE 388
CENTRE COLLEGE OF KENTUCKY 136
CENTRE DE FORMATION DES MAITRES
496
CENTRE DE GRANBY 496
CERRITOS COLLEGE 23
CHABOT COLLEGE 23
CHADRON STATE COLLEGE 212
CHAFFEY COLLEGE 23
CHAMBERLAYNE JUNIOR COLLEGE 160
CHAMINADE COLLEGE OF HONOLULU 86
CHAMPLAIN COLLEGE, ONTARIO 482
CHAMPLAIN COLLEGE, VERMONT 376
CHAPMAN COLLEGE 23
CHARLES COUNTY COMMUNITY COLLEGE
149
CHARLES STEWART MOTT COMMUNITY
COLLEGE 174
CHARTHAGE COLLEGE 398
CHATFIELD COLLEGE 286
CHATHAM COLLEGE 314
CHATTANOOGA STATE TECHNICAL
COMMUNITY COLLEGE 350
CHEMEKETA COMMUNITY COLLEGE 307
CHESAPEAKE COLLEGE 149
CHESTERFIELD-MARLBORO TECHNICAL
EDUCATION CENTER 343
CHESTNUT HILL COLLEGE 314
CHEYNEY STATE COLLEGE 314
CHICAGO ACADEMY OF FINE ARTS 91
CHICAGO COLLEGE OF OSTEOPATHIC
MEDICINE 91
CHICAGO CONSERVATORY COLLEGE 91
CHICAGO STATE UNIVERSITY 91
CHICAGO TECHNICAL COLLEGE 91
CHICAGO THEOLOGICAL SEMINARY 91
CHIPOLA JUNIOR COLLEGE 68
CHOWAN COLLEGE 271
CHRISTIAN BROTHERS COLLEGE,
ONTARIO 483
CHRISTIAN BROTHERS COLLEGE,
TENNESSEE 351
CHRISTIAN THEOLOGICAL SEMINARY 111
CHRISTOPHER NEWPORT COLLEGE 379
CHURCH COLLEGE OF HAWAII 86
CHURCH DIVINITY SCHOOL OF THE
PACIFIC 23

CINCINNATI BIBLE SEMINARY 286
CINCINNATI TECHNICAL INSTITUTE 286
CISCO JUNIOR COLLEGE 359
CITADEL MILITARY COLLEGE OF SOUTH
CAROLINA 343
CITRUS COLLEGE 23
CITY COLLEGE OF SAN FRANCISCO 23
CITY COLLEGE, CUNY 237, 410
CLACKAMAS COMMUNITY COLLEGE 307
CLAFLIN UNIVERSITY 343
CLAREMONT GRADUATE SCHOOL 24, 408
CLAREMONT MEN'S COLLEGE 24
CLAREMORE JUNIOR COLLEGE 302
CLARENDON COLLEGE 359
CLARION STATE COLLEGE 314
CLARION STATE COLLEGE, VENANGO
CAMPUS 315
CLARK COLLEGE, GEORGIA 78
CLARK COLLEGE, WASHINGTON 388
CLARK COUNTY COMMUNITY COLLEGE 216
CLARK TECHNICAL COLLEGE 286
CLARK UNIVERSITY 160
CLARKE COLLEGE, IOWA 121
CLARKE COLLEGE, MISSISSIPPI 194
CLARKSON COLLEGE OF TECHNOLOGY 237
CLATSOP COMMUNITY COLLEGE 307
CLAYTON JUNIOR COLLEGE 79
CLEARY COLLEGE 174
CLEMSON UNIVERSITY 343
CLEMSON UNIVERSITY, GREENVILLE
BRANCH 343
CLEMSON UNIVERSITY, SUMTER BRANCH
343
CLEVELAND COUNTY TECHNICAL
INSTITUTE 271
CLEVELAND INSTITUTE OF ART 286
CLEVELAND INSTITUTE OF MUSIC 286
CLEVELAND STATE COMMUNITY COLLEGE
351
CLEVELAND STATE UNIVERSITY 286,
410
CLINCH VALLEY COLLEGE, UNIVERSITY
OF VIRGINIA 379
CLINTON COMMUNITY COLLEGE 121
CLINTON COMMUNITY COLLEGE, SUNY
237
CLOUD COUNTY COMMUNITY JUNIOR
COLLEGE 129
COAHOMA JUNIOR COLLEGE 194
COASTAL CAROLINA COMMUNITY COLLEGE
271
COCHISE COLLEGE 9
COE COLLEGE 121
COFFEYVILLE COMMUNITY JUNIOR
COLLEGE 129
COGSWELL POLYTECHNIC COLLEGE 24
COKER COLLEGE 343
COL ANDRE-GRASSET 496
COL AT BROCKPORT, SUNY 238, 410
COL AT BUFFALO, SUNY 238
COL AT CORTLAND, SUNY 239
COL AT FREDONIA, SUNY 239
COL AT GENESEO, SUNY 239

COL AT HERKMER-ROME-UTICA, SUNY 239
COL AT NEW PALTZ, SUNY 239
COL AT OLD WESTBURY, SUNY 239
COL AT ONEONTA, SUNY 240
COL AT OSWEGO, SUNY 240
COL AT PLATTSBURGH, SUNY 240
COL AT POTSDAM, SUNY 240
COL AT PURCHASE, SUNY 240
COL BOIS-DE-BOULOGNE, CEGP 496
COL BOURGET 497
COL D'AHUNTSIC, CEGP 497
COL DE BATHURST 476
COL DE CHICOUTIMI, CEGP 497
COL DE HAUTERIVE, CEGP 497
COL DE HEARST 483
COL DE HULL, CEGP 497
COL DE JESUITES 501
COL DE JOLIETTE, CEGP 497
COL DE JONQUIERE, CEGP 497
COL DE L'ASSOMPTION 498
COL DE LA GASPESIE, CEGP 498
COL DE LA POCATIERE, CEGP 498
COL DE LA TIERRA 24
COL DE LEVIS 498
COL DE LEVIS-LAUZON, CEGP 498
COL DE LIMOILOU, CEGP 498
COL DE MAISONNEUVE, CEGP 498
COL DE MATANE 499
COL DE RIMOUSKI, CEGP 499
COL DE RIVIERE-DU-LOUP, CEGP 499
COL DE ROSEMONT, CEGP 499
COL DE ROUYN 499
COL DE ROUYN-NORANDA, CEGP 499
COL DE SAINT-BONIFACE 475
COL DE SAINT-HYACINTHE, CEGP 499
COL DE SAINT-LAURENT, CEGP 499
COL DE SAINTE-FOY, CEGPN 499
COL DE SALABERRY-DE-VALLEYFIELD, CEGP 499
COL DE SHAWINIGA, CEGP 500
COL DE SHERBROOKE, CEGP 500
COL DE THETFORD MINES, CEGP 500
COL DE TROIS-RIVIERES, CEGP 500
COL DE VALLEYFIELD 501
COL DE VICTORIAVILLE, CEGP 501
COL DOMINICAIN DE PHILOSOPHIE ET DE THEOLOGIE 483, 511
COL DU MONT SAINTE ANN 501
COL DU VIEUX-MONTREAL, CEGP 501
COL EDOUARD-MONTPETIT, CEGP 502
COL FOR HUMAN SERVICES 240
COL FRANCOIS-XAVIER-GARNEAU, CEGP 502
COL JEAN-DE-BREBEUF 503
COL JESUS-MARIE DE SILLERY 503
COL LIONEL-GROULX 503
COL MARGUERITE-BOURGEOYS 503
COL MILITAIRE ROYAL DE SAINT-JEAN 503
COL MISERCORDIA 315
COL NOTRE-DAME-DE-BELLEVUE 503
COL NOTRE-DAME-DES SERVITES 503

COL OF ALAMEDA 24
COL OF CHARLESTON 343
COL OF DUPAGE 91
COL OF EASTERN UTAH 374
COL OF EMMANUEL AND SAINT CHAD' 509
COL OF EMPORIA 129
COL OF GANADO 9
COL OF GREAT FALLS 210
COL OF IDAHO 88
COL OF INSURANCE 241
COL OF LAKE COUNTY 91
COL OF MARIN 24
COL OF MOUNT SAINT JOSEPH 287
COL OF MOUNT SAINT VINCENT 241
COL OF NEW CALEDONIA 472
COL OF NEW ROCHELLE 241
COL OF NOTRE DAME 24
COL OF NOTRE DAME OF MARYLAND 150
COL OF OSTEOPATHIC MEDICINE AND SURGERY 121
COL OF OUR LADY OF ELMS 161
COL OF SAINT BENEDICT 186
COL OF SAINT CATHERINE 187
COL OF SAINT ELIZABETH 221
COL OF SAINT FRANCIS 91
COL OF SAINT JOSEPH THE PROVIDER 376
COL OF SAINT MARY 212
COL OF SAINT ROSE 241
COL OF SAINT SCHOLASTICA 187
COL OF SAINT TERESA 187
COL OF SAINT THOMAS 187
COL OF SAN MATEO 25
COL OF SANTA FE 230
COL OF SOUTHERN IDAHO 88
COL OF STEUBENVILLE 287
COL OF THE ALBEMARLE 272
COL OF THE CANYONS 25
COL OF THE DESERT 25
COL OF THE HOLY CROSS 161
COL OF THE HOLY NAMES 25
COL OF THE MAINLAND 359
COL OF THE OZARKS 12
COL OF THE POTOMAC 65
COL OF THE REDWOODS 25
COL OF THE SACRED HEART 337
COL OF THE SEQUOIAS 25
COL OF THE SISKIYOUS 25
COL OF THE VIRGIN ISLAND 378
COL OF THE VIRGIN ISLANDS, SAINT CROIX CAMPUS 379
COL OF TRADES AND TECHNOLOGY 478
COL OF WHITE PLAINS 241
COL OF WILLIAM AND MARY 380
COL OF WOOSTER 287
COL RIGAUD DE VAUDREUIL 503
COL SAINT JEAN 469
COL SAINT THOMAS 509
COL SAINT-JEAN VIANNEY 503
COL SAINT-JEAN-SUR-RICHELIEU, CEGP 504
COL SAINT-JOSEPH 476

LAWRENCE UNIVERSITY 399
LAYTON SCHOOL OF ART AND DESIGN
  400
LE CENTRE D'ETUDES UNIVERSITAIRES
  DE RIMOUSKI 496
LE MOYNE COLLEGE 250
LE MOYNE-OWEN COLLEGE 353
LE PETIT SEMINAIRE DE
  SAINT-GEORGES DE BEAUSE 505
LEBANON VALLEY COLLEGE 322
LEE COLLEGE, TENNESSEE 353
LEE COLLEGE, TEXAS 362
LEES JUNIOR COLLEGE 137
LEES-MCRAE COLLEGE 275
LEEWARD COMMUNITY COLLEGE, UNIV OF
  HAWAII 87
LEHIGH COUNTY COMMUNITY COLLEGE
  322
LEHIGH UNIVERSITY 322
LEHMAN COLLEGE, CUNY 250
LEICESTER JUNIOR COLLEGE 164
LENOIR COMMUNITY COLLEGE 275
LENOIR-RHYNE COLLEGE 275
LESLEY COLLEGE 164
LETHBRIDGE COMMUNITY COLLEGE 469
LETOURNEAU COLLEGE 362
LEWIS AND CLARK COLLEGE 307
LEWIS AND CLARK COMMUNITY COLLEGE
  97
LEWIS AND CLARK STATE COLLEGE 88
LEWIS COLLEGE 97
LEXINGTON TECHNOLOGICAL INSTITUTE,
  UNIVERSITY OF KENTUCKY 137
LEXINGTON THEOLOGICAL SEMINARY 137
LIMA TECHNICAL COLLEGE 291
LIMESTONE COLLEGE 344
LINCOLN CHRISTIAN COLLEGE 97
LINCOLN COLLEGE 97
LINCOLN LAND COMMUNITY COLLEGE 97
LINCOLN MEMORIAL UNIVERSITY 353
LINCOLN TRAIL COLLEGE 98
LINCOLN UNIVERSITY, CALIFORNIA 30
LINCOLN UNIVERSITY, MISSOURI 201
LINCOLN UNIVERSITY, PENNSYLVANIA
  322
LINCOLNLAND TECH INST, INDIANA
  VOCATIONAL TECH COLLEGE 115
LINDENWOOD COLLEGES 201
LINDSEY WILSON COLLEGE 137
LINFIELD COLLEGE 308
LINN-BENTON COMMUNITY COLLEGE 308
LIVINGSTON UNIVERSITY 5
LIVINGSTONE COLLEGE 275
LOCK HAVEN STATE COLLEGE 322
LOMA LINDA UNIVERSITY 30
LON MORRIS COLLEGE 362
LONE MOUNTAIN COLLEGE 31, 410
LONG BEACH CITY COLLEGE 30
LONG ISLAND UNIVERSITY, BROOKLYN
  CENTER 251
LONG ISLAND UNIVERSITY, BROOKLYN
  COLLEGE OF PHARMACY 251
LONG ISLAND UNIVERSITY, C W POST
  COLLEGE 251

LONG ISLAND UNIVERSITY,
  SOUTHAMPTON COLLEGE 251
LONGVIEW COMMUNITY COLLEGE 201
LONGWOOD COLLEGE 381
LOOP COLLEGE, CITY COLLEGE OF
  CHICAGO 98
LORAIN COUNTY COMMUNITY COLLEGE
  291
LORAS COLLEGE 124
LORD FAIRFAX COMMUNITY COLLEGE 382
LORETTO HEIGHTS COLLEGE 52
LOS ANGELES BAPTIST
  COLLEGE-THEOLOGICAL SEMINARY 31
LOS ANGELES CITY COLLEGE 31
LOS ANGELES COLLEGE OF OPTOMETRY
  31
LOS ANGELES HARBOR COLLEGE 31
LOS ANGELES PIERCE COLLEGE 31
LOS ANGELES SOUTHWEST COLLEGE 32
LOS ANGELES TRADE-TECHNICAL
  COLLEGE 32
LOS ANGELES VALLEY COLLEGE 32
LOUISBURG COLLEGE 275
LOUISIANA COLLEGE 142
LOUISIANA STATE UNIVERSITY 142,
  410
LOUISIANA STATE UNIVERSITY AT
  ALEXANDRIA 142
LOUISIANA STATE UNIVERSITY AT
  EUNICE 142
LOUISIANA STATE UNIVERSITY AT NEW
  ORLEANS 143
LOUISIANA STATE UNIVERSITY AT
  SHREVEPORT 143
LOUISIANA STATE UNIVERSITY MEDICAL
  CTR AT NEW ORLEANS 143
LOUISIANA STATE UNIVERSITY MEDICAL
  CTR AT SHREVEPORT 143
LOUISIANA TECHNOLOGICAL UNIVERSITY
  143
LOUISVILLE PRESBYTERIAN
  THEOLOGICAL SEMINARY 137
LOURDES COLLEGE 291
LOWELL STATE COLLEGE 164
LOWELL TECHNOLOGICAL INSTITUTE 164
LOWER COLUMBIA COLLEGE 390
LOYALIST COLLEGE OF APPLIED ARTS
  AND TECHNOLOGY 485
LOYOLA CITY COLLEGE, LOYOLA
  UNIVERSITY 143
LOYOLA COLLEGE, MARYLAND 152
LOYOLA COLLEGE, QUEBEC 504
LOYOLA UNIVERSITY OF LOS ANGELES
  32
LOYOLA UNIVERSITY, ILLINOIS 98,
  408
LOYOLA UNIVERSITY, LOUISIANA 143
LUBBOCK CHRISTIAN COLLEGE 363
LURLEEN B WALLACE STATE JUNIOR
  COLLEGE 5
LUTHER COLLEGE, IOWA 124
LUTHER COLLEGE, NEW JERSEY 224
LUTHER COLLEGE', SASKATCHEWAN 509

MCNEESE STATE UNIVERSITY 143
MCPHERSON COLLEGE 132
MEADVILLE-LOMBARD THEOLOGICAL
  SCHOOL 99
MEDAILLE COLLEGE 253
MEDGAR EVERS COLLEGE, CUNY 253
MEDICAL COLLEGE OF GEORGIA 81
MEDICAL COLLEGE OF OHIO 292
MEDICAL COLLEGE OF PENNSYLVANIA
  323
MEDICAL COLLEGE OF WISCONSIN 401
MEDICAL UNIVERSITY OF SOUTH
  CAROLINA 345
MEDICINE HAT COLLEGE 469
MEHARRY MEDICAL COLLEGE 353
MEMORIAL UNIVERSITY OF
  NEWFOUNDLAND 478
MEMPHIS ACADEMY OF ARTS 353
MEMPHIS STATE UNIVERSITY 353, 410
MEMPHIS THEOLOGICAL SEMINARY 353
MENLO COLLEGE 32
MENNONITE BIBLICAL SEMINARY 116
MENNONITE BRETHREN BIBLICAL
  SEMINARY 33
MENNONITE BRETHREN COLLEGE OF ARTS
  475
MERAMEC COMMUNITY COLLEGE 202
MERCED COLLEGE 33
MERCER COUNTY COMMUNITY COLLEGE
  224
MERCER UNIVERSITY 82
MERCER UNIVERSITY SOUTHERN SCHOOL
  OF PHARMACY 82
MERCY COLLEGE 253
MERCY COLLEGE OF DETROIT 178
MERCYHURST COLLEGE 323
MEREDITH COLLEGE 275
MERIDIAN JUNIOR COLLEGE 195
MERRILL-PALMER INSTITUTE 178
MERRIMACK COLLEGE 165
MERRITT COLLEGE 33
MESA COLLEGE 52
MESA COMMUNITY COLLEGE 10
MESABI COMMUNITY COLLEGE 189
MESIVTA EASTERN PARKWAY RABBINICAL
  SEMINARY 253
MESIVTHA TIFERETH JER AMR 254
MESSIAH COLLEGE 324
METHODIST COLLEGE 276
METHODIST THEOLOGICAL SCHOOL IN
  OHIO 292
METROPOLITAN STATE COLLEGE 52
METROPOLITAN STATE JUNIOR COLLEGE
  189
MIAMI UNIVERSITY 292, 410
MIAMI UNIVERSITY, HAMILTON BRANCH
  292
MIAMI UNIVERSITY, MIDDLETOWN
  BRANCH 292
MIAMI-DADE JUNIOR COLLEGE 72
MIAMI-JACOBS JUNIOR COLLEGE OF
  BUSINESS 292
MICHAEL J OWENS TECHNICAL COLLEGE
  292

MICHIGAN CHRISTIAN JUNIOR COLLEGE
  179
MICHIGAN STATE UNIVERSITY 179, 408
MICHIGAN TECHNOLOGICAL UNIVERSITY
  179
MID-AMERICAN NAZARENE COLLEGE 132
MID-MICHIGAN COMMUNITY COLLEGE 179
MID-SOUTH BIBLE COLLEGE 354
MIDDLE GEORGIA COLLEGE 82
MIDDLE TENNESSEE STATE UNIVERSITY
  354
MIDDLEBURY COLLEGE 377
MIDDLESEX COMMUNITY COLLEGE,
  CONNECTICUT 58
MIDDLESEX COMMUNITY COLLEGE,
  MASSACHUSETTS 165
MIDDLESEX COUNTY COLLEGE 224
MIDLAND LUTHERAN COLLEGE 213
MIDLANDS TECHNICAL EDUCATION
  CENTER 345
MIDWAY COLLEGE 138
MIDWEST COLLEGE OF ENGINEERING 99
MIDWESTERN BAPTIST THEOLOGICAL
  SEMINARY 202
MIDWESTERN UNIVERSITY 363
MILES COLLEGE 5
MILES COMMUNITY COLLEGE 210
MILLERSVILLE STATE COLLEGE 324
MILLIGAN COLLEGE 354
MILLIKIN UNIVERSITY 100
MILLS COLLEGE 33
MILLS COLLEGE OF EDUCATION 254
MILLSAPS COLLEGE 195
MILTON COLLEGE 401
MILWAUKEE AREA TECHNICAL COLLEGE
  401
MILWAUKEE SCHOOL OF ENGINEERING
  401
MINERAL AREA COLLEGE 202
MINNEAPOLIS COLLEGE OF ART DESIGN
  189
MINNESOTA BIBLE COLLEGE 189
MINNESOTA METROPOLITAN STATE
  COLLEGE 189
MINOT STATE COLLEGE 282
MIRA COSTA COLLEGE 33
MIRRER YESHIVA CENTRAL INSTITUTE
  254
MISSISSIPPI COLLEGE 195
MISSISSIPPI DELTA JUNIOR COLLEGE
  195
MISSISSIPPI GULF COAST JR COL,
  JACKSON COUNTY CAMPUS 195
MISSISSIPPI GULF COAST JR COL,
  JEFFERSON DAVIS CAMPUS 195
MISSISSIPPI GULF COAST JR COL,
  PERKINSTON CAMPUS 196
MISSISSIPPI INDUSTRIAL COLLEGE 196
MISSISSIPPI STATE COLLEGE FOR
  WOMEN 196
MISSISSIPPI STATE UNIVERSITY 196,
  410
MISSISSIPPI VALLEY STATE COLLEGE
  196

NATCHEZ JUNIOR COLLEGE 196
NATHANIEL HAWTHORNE COLLEGE 218
NATIONAL BUSINESS COLLEGE 383
NATIONAL COLLEGE OF BUSINESS 348
NATIONAL COLLEGE OF CHIROPRACTIC
100
NATIONAL COLLEGE OF EDUCATION,
MAIN CAMPUS 100
NATIONAL COLLEGE OF EDUCATION,
URBAN CAMPUS 100
NAVAJO COMMUNITY COLLEGE 10
NAVARRO JUNIOR COLLEGE 363
NAZARENE THEOLOGICAL SEMINARY 203
NAZARETH COLLEGE 180
NAZARETH COLLEGE OF ROCHESTER 255
NEBRASKA SOUTHERN COMMUNITY
COLLEGE 213
NEBRASKA WESLEYAN UNIVERSITY 214
NEBRASKA WESTERN COLLEGE 214
NEOSHO COUNTY COMMUNITY JUNIOR
COLLEGE 132
NER ISRAEL RAB COLLEGE 153
NES TORAH VODAATH SEMINARY 253
NEW BRUNSWICK INSTITUTE OF
TECHNOLOGY 477
NEW BRUNSWICK THEOLOGICAL SEMINARY
225
NEW COLLEGE 72
NEW COLLEGE OF CALIFORNIA 34
NEW ENGLAND AERONAUTICAL INSTITUTE
218
NEW ENGLAND COLLEGE 218
NEW ENGLAND CONSERVATORY OF MUSIC
166
NEW ENGLAND INST OF ANATOMY,
SANITARY SCI AND EMBALMING 166
NEW ENGLAND INSTITUTE 58
NEW ENGLAND SCHOOL OF LAW 166
NEW HAMPSHIRE COLLEGE 218
NEW HAMPSHIRE TECHNICAL INSTITUTE
AT CONCORD 218
NEW MEXICO HIGHLANDS UNIVERSITY
231
NEW MEXICO INSTITUTE OF MINING AND
TECHNOLOGY 231
NEW MEXICO JUNIOR COLLEGE 231
NEW MEXICO MILITARY INSTITUTE 231
NEW MEXICO STATE UNIVERSITY 231
NEW MEXICO STATE UNIVERSITY AT
ALAMOGORDO 231
NEW MEXICO STATE UNIVERSITY AT
CARLSBAD 231
NEW MEXICO STATE UNIVERSITY AT
GRANTS 231
NEW MEXICO STATE UNIVERSITY AT SAN
JUAN 231
NEW ORLEANS BAPTIST THEOLOGICAL
SEMINARY 144
NEW RIVER COMMUNITY COLLEGE 383
NEW SCHOOL FOR SOCIAL RESEARCH
255, 408
NEW YORK CITY COMMUNITY COLLEGE,
CUNY 255

NEW YORK COLLEGE OF PODIATRIC
MEDICINE 255
NEW YORK INSTITUTE OF TECHNOLOGY,
NEW YORK CAMPUS 255
NEW YORK INSTITUTE OF TECHNOLOGY,
OLD WESTBURY CAMPUS 255
NEW YORK LAW SCHOOL 255
NEW YORK MEDICAL COLLEGE 256
NEW YORK STATE COL OF AGR AND LIFE
SCI AT CORNELL UNIV 256
NEW YORK STATE COL OF CERAMICS AT
ALFRED UNIV 256
NEW YORK STATE COL OF HUMAN
ECOLOGY AT CORNELL UNIV 256
NEW YORK THEOLOGICAL SEMINARY 256
NEW YORK UNIVERSITY 256, 408
NEWARK COLLEGE OF ENGINEERING 225
NEWARK STATE COLLEGE 225
NEWBERRY COLLEGE 345
NEWBURY JUNIOR COLLEGE 166
NEWFOUNDLAND COLLEGE OF TRADES AND
TECHNOLOGY 478
NEWTON COLLEGE OF THE SACRED HEART
166
NEWTON JUNIOR COLLEGE 166
NIAGARA COLLEGE OF APPLIED ARTS
AND TECHNOLOGY 486
NIAGARA COUNTY COMMUNITY COLLEGE,
SUNY 256
NIAGARA UNIVERSITY 256, 410
NICHOLLS STATE COLLEGE 144
NICHOLS COLLEGE 166
NICOLET COLLEGE 401
NIPISSING COLLEGE 486
NORFOLK STATE COLLEGE 383
NORMANDALE STATE JUNIOR COLLEGE
190
NORTH ADAMS STATE COLLEGE 166
NORTH AMERICAN BAPTIST SEMINARY
348
NORTH AMERICAN BIBLE COLLEGE 519
NORTH CAROLINA AGRICULTURAL AND
TECHNICAL STATE UNIV 276
NORTH CAROLINA CENTRAL UNIVERSITY
276
NORTH CAROLINA SCHOOL OF THE ARTS
276
NORTH CAROLINA STATE UNIVERSITY
276
NORTH CAROLINA WESLEYAN COLLEGE
277
NORTH CENTRAL BIBLE COLLEGE 190
NORTH CENTRAL COLLEGE 101
NORTH CENTRAL MICHIGAN COLLEGE 180
NORTH CENTRAL TECH INST, INDIANA
VOCATIONAL TECH COLLEGE 116
NORTH CENTRAL TECHNICAL COLLEGE
293
NORTH CENTRAL TECHNICAL INSTITUTE
401
NORTH COUNTRY COMMUNITY COLLEGE,
SUNY 257
NORTH DAKOTA STATE SCHOOL OF
SCIENCE 283

PRESBYTERIAN COLLEGE 345
PRESBYTERIAN COLLEGE OF MONTREAL 506
PRESBYTERIAN SCHOOL OF CHRISTIAN EDUCATION 384
PRESCOTT COLLEGE 11
PRESENTATION COLLEGE 349
PRESTONSBURG COMMUNITY COLLEGE, UNIVERSITY OF KENTUCKY 138
PRINCE GEORGE'S COMMUNITY COLLEGE 153
PRINCETON THEOLOGICAL SEMINARY 225, 408
PRINCETON UNIVERSITY 226, 408
PRINCIPIA COLLEGE 103
PROTESTANT EPISCOPALIAN THEOLOGICAL SEM IN VIR 384
PROVIDENCE COLLEGE 340
PUERTO RICO JUNIOR COLLEGE 338
PURDUE UNIVERSITY 116, 408
PURDUE UNIVERSITY, CALUMET CAMPUS 117
PURDUE UNIVERSITY, FORT WAYNE CAMPUS 117, 410
PURDUE UNIVERSITY, NORTH CENTRAL CAMPUS 117
QUEEN'S COLLEGE 478
QUEEN'S THEOLOGICAL COLLEGE 486
QUEEN'S UNIVERSITY AT KINGSTON 487
QUEENS COLLEGE 277
QUEENS COLLEGE, CUNY 258, 410
QUEENSBOROUGH COMMUNITY COLLEGE, SUNY 259
QUINCY COLLEGE 103
QUINCY JUNIOR COLLEGE 167
QUINEBAUG VALLEY COMMUNITY COLLEGE 58
QUINNIPIAC COLLEGE 59
QUINSIGAMOND COMMUNITY COLLEGE 167
RABBI JACOB JOSEPH RABBINICAL COLLEGE AT NEW YORK 259
RABBINICAL ACADEMY, MESIVTA RABBI CHAIM BERLIN 259
RABBINICAL COLLEGE AT LONG ISLAND 259
RABBINICAL COLLEGE OF C CH'SAN SOFER AT NEW YORK 259
RABBINICAL COLLEGE OF KAMENITZ YESHIVA 259
RABBINICAL COLLEGE OF TELSHE 296
RABBINICAL SEMINARY NETZACH ISR RAM 259
RABBINICAL SEMINARY OF AMERICA 259
RADCLIFFE COLLEGE 167
RADFORD COLLEGE 384
RAINY RIVER STATE JUNIOR COLLEGE 190
RAMPAO COLLEGE 226
RAND GRADUATE INSTITUTE OF POLITICAL STUDIES 37
RANDOLPH TECHNICAL INSTITUTE 277
RANDOLPH-MACON COLLEGE 384
RANDOLPH-MACON WOMAN'S COLLEGE 384

RANGELY COLLEGE 53
RANGER JUNIOR COLLEGE 364
RAPPAHANNOCK COMMUNITY COLLEGE 384
RAYMOND COLLEGE, UNIV OF THE PACIFIC 37
RCA INSTITUTES 259
READING AREA COMMUNITY COLLEGE 329
RED DEER COLLEGE 470
RED RIVER COMMUNITY COLLEGE 475
REED COLLEGE 310
REEDLEY COLLEGE 37
REFORMED BIBLE COLLEGE 181
REFORMED PRESBYTERIAN THEOLOGICAL SEMINARY 329
REFORMED THEOLOGICAL SEMINARY 196
REGIS COLLEGE, COLORADO 53
REGIS COLLEGE, MASSACHUSETTS 168
REGIS COLLEGE, ONTARIO 487
REINHARDT COLLEGE 83
REND LAKE COLLEGE 104
RENISON COLLEGE 487
RENSSELAER POLYTECHNIC INSTITUTE, CONNECTICUT 59
RENSSELAER POLYTECHNICAL INSTITUTE 259, 410
RHODE ISLAND COLLEGE 340
RHODE ISLAND JUNIOR COLLEGE 340
RHODE ISLAND SCHOOL OF DESIGN 341
RICE UNIVERSITY 364, 408
RICHARD BLAND COLLEGE OF WILLIAM AND MARY 384
RICHLAND COLLEGE 365
RICHMOND COLLEGE, CUNY 260
RICHMOND TECHNICAL INSTITUTE 277
RICKER COLLEGE 147
RICKS COLLEGE 88
RIDER COLLEGE 226
RIO GRANDE COLLEGE 297
RIO HONDO JUNIOR COLLEGE 37
RIPON COLLEGE 402
RIVERSIDE CITY COLLEGE 37
RIVIER COLLEGE 219
ROANE STATE COMMUNITY COLLEGE 354
ROANOKE COLLEGE 384
ROANOKE-CHOWAN TECHNICAL INSTITUTE 278
ROBERT MORRIS COLLEGE, ILLINOIS 104
ROBERT MORRIS COLLEGE, PENNSYLVANIA 329
ROBERTS WESLEYAN COLLEGE 260
ROBESON TECHNICAL INSTITUTE 278
ROCHESTER INSTITUTE OF TECHNOLOGY 260
ROCHESTER STATE JUNIOR COLLEGE 190
ROCK VALLEY COLLEGE 104
ROCKFELLER UNIVERSITY 260, 408
ROCKFORD COLLEGE 104
ROCKHURST COLLEGE 204
ROCKINGHAM COMMUNITY COLLEGE 278
ROCKLAND COMMUNITY COLLEGE, SUNY 260
ROCKMONT COLLEGE 53

STATE UNIVERSITY AT STONY BROOK,
  SUNY 265, 408
STATEN ISLAND COMMUNITY COLLEGE,
  SUNY 265
STEED COLLEGE 355
STEPHEN F AUSTIN STATE UNIVERSITY
  367
STEPHENS COLLEGE 206
STERLING COLLEGE 133
STETSON UNIVERSITY 75
STEVENS HENAGER COLLEGE 374
STEVENS HENAGER COLLEGE AT OGDEN
  375
STEVENS INSTITUTE OF TECHNOLOGY
  229
STILLMAN COLLEGE 6
STOCKTON STATE COLLEGE 229
STONEHILL COLLEGE 169
STRATFORD COLLEGE 385
STRAYER COLLEGE 67
SUE BENNETT COLLEGE 139
SUFFOLK COUNTY COMMUNITY COLLEGE,
  SUNY 266
SUFFOLK UNIVERSITY 169
SUL ROSS STATE UNIVERSITY 367
SULLINS COLLEGE 385
SULLIVAN COUNTY COMMUNITY COLLEGE,
  SUNY 266
SULPICIAN SEMINARY OF THE
  NORTHWEST 392
SUMTER AREA TECHNICAL EDUCATION
  CENTER 346
SUOMI COLLEGE 182
SURRY COMMUNITY COLLEGE 279
SUSQUEHANNA UNIVERSITY 331
SWAIN SCHOOL OF DESIGN 169
SWARTHMORE COLLEGE 331, 410
SWEET BRIAR COLLEGE 385
SYRACUSE UNIVERSITY 266, 408
TABOR COLLEGE 133
TACOMA COMMUNITY COLLEGE 392
TAFT COLLEGE 42
TALLADEGA COLLEGE 6
TALLAHASSEE COMMUNITY COLLEGE 75
TARKIO COLLEGE 206
TARLETON STATE UNIVERSITY 367
TARRANT COUNTY JUNIOR COLLEGE,
  NORTHEAST CAMPUS 368
TARRANT COUNTY JUNIOR COLLEGE,
  SOUTH CAMPUS 368
TAYLOR UNIVERSITY 118
TECHNICAL INSTITUTE OF ALAMANCE
  279
TEMPLE JUNIOR COLLEGE 368
TEMPLE UNIVERSITY 331, 409
TEMPLE UNIVERSITY, AMBLER CAMPUS
  332
TENNESSEE STATE UNIVERSITY 355
TENNESSEE TECHNOLOGICAL UNIVERSITY
  355
TENNESSEE TEMPLE COLLEGE 355
TENNESSEE WESLEYAN COLLEGE 355
TEXARKANA COLLEGE 368

TEXAS A & M MARITIME ACADEMY 368
TEXAS A & M UNIVERSITY 368, 411
TEXAS AGRICULTURAL AND INDUSTRIAL
  UNIVERSITY 368
TEXAS CHRISTIAN UNIVERSITY 368,
  411
TEXAS COLLEGE 369
TEXAS COLLEGE OF OSTEOPATHIC
  MEDICINE 369
TEXAS LUTHERAN COLLEGE 369
TEXAS SOUTHERN UNIVERSITY 369
TEXAS SOUTHMOST COLLEGE 369
TEXAS STATE TECHNICAL INSTITUTE,
  JAMES CONNALLY CAMPUS 369
TEXAS STATE TECHNICAL INSTITUTE,
  MID-CONTINENT CAMPUS 369
TEXAS STATE TECHNICAL INSTITUTE,
  RIO GRANDE CAMPUS 369
TEXAS TECH UNIVERSITY 369, 411
TEXAS WESLEYAN COLLEGE 369
TEXAS WOMAN'S UNIVERSITY 370
THAMES VALLEY STATE TECHNICAL
  COLLEGE 60
THE WRIGHT INSTITUTE, GRADUATE DIV
  49
THEODORE A LAWSON STATE JUNIOR
  COLLEGE 6
THEOLOGICAL SEMINARY OF THE
  REFORMED EPISCOPAL CHURCH 332
THIEL COLLEGE 332
THOMAS COLLEGE 147
THOMAS JEFFERSON UNIVERSITY 332
THOMAS MORE COLLEGE 140
THOMAS NELSON COMMUNITY COLLEGE
  385
THORNELOE COLLEGE 488
THORNTON COMMUNITY COLLEGE 107
THREE RIVERS COMMUNITY COLLEGE 206
THUNDERBIRD GRADUATE SCHOOL 11
TIFFIN UNIVERSITY 297
TIFT COLLEGE 83
TOCCOA FALLS INSTITUTE 83
TOMBROCK COLLEGE 229
TOMPKINS-CORTLAND COMMUNITY
  COLLEGE, SUNY 266
TOUGALOO COLLEGE 197
TOURO COLLEGE 266
TOWSON STATE COLLEGE 154
TRANSYLVANIA UNIVERSITY 140
TREASURE VALLEY COMMUNITY COLLEGE
  310
TRENT UNIVERSITY 489
TRENTON JUNIOR COLLEGE 206
TRENTON STATE COLLEGE 229
TREVECCA NAZARENE COLLEGE 355
TRI-COUNTY TECHNICAL EDUCATION
  CENTER 346
TRI-COUNTY TECHNICAL INSTITUTE 279
TRI-STATE COLLEGE 119
TRINIDAD STATE JUNIOR COLLEGE 53
TRINITY CHRISTIAN COLLEGE 107
TRINITY COLLEGE, CONNECTICUT 60,
  411

WESLEY COLLEGE 64
WESLEY THEOLOGICAL SEMINARY 67
WESLEYAN COLLEGE 84
WESLEYAN UNIVERSITY 62
WEST CHESTER STATE COLLEGE 335,
411
WEST COAST BIBLE COLLEGE 48
WEST COAST UNIVERSITY 48
WEST COAST UNIVERSITY, ORANGE
COUNTY CTR 48
WEST GEORGIA COLLEGE 84
WEST HILLS COLLEGE. 48
WEST LIBERTY STATE COLLEGE 396
WEST LOS ANGELES COLLEGE 48
WEST SHORE COMMUNITY COLLEGE 185
WEST TEXAS STATE UNIVERSITY 373
WEST VALLEY COLLEGE 48
WEST VIRGINIA COLLEGE OF GRADUATE
STUDIES 396
WEST VIRGINIA INSTITUTE OF
TECHNOLOGY 396
WEST VIRGINIA NORTHERN COMMUNITY
COLLEGE AT WEIRTON 397
WEST VIRGINIA NORTHERN COMMUNITY
COLLEGE AT WHEELING 397
WEST VIRGINIA STATE COLLEGE 397
WEST VIRGINIA UNIVERSITY 397
WEST VIRGINIA WESLEYAN COLLEGE 397
WESTARK COMMUNITY COLLEGE 14
WESTBROOK JUNIOR COLLEGE 148
WESTCHESTER COMMUNITY COLLEGE,
SUNY 269
WESTERN BAPTIST BIBLE COLLEGE 311
WESTERN CAROLINA UNIVERSITY 281
WESTERN COLLEGE 300
WESTERN CONNECTICUT STATE COLLEGE
62
WESTERN CONSERVATIVE BAPTIST
THEOLOGICAL SEMINARY 311
WESTERN ILLINOIS UNIVERSITY 110
WESTERN KENTUCKY UNIVERSITY 141,
411
WESTERN MARYLAND COLLEGE 155
WESTERN MICHIGAN UNIVERSITY 185
WESTERN MONTANA COLLEGE 211
WESTERN NEVADA COMMUNITY COLLEGE
216
WESTERN NEW ENGLAND COLLEGE 171
WESTERN NEW MEXICO UNIVERSITY 232
WESTERN PIEDMONT COMMUNITY COLLEGE
281
WESTERN STATE COLLEGE OF COLORADO
55
WESTERN STATES COLLEGE OF
ENGINEERING 48
WESTERN TEXAS COLLEGE 373
WESTERN THEOLOGICAL SEMINARY 185
WESTERN WASHINGTON STATE COLLEGE
393
WESTERN WISCONSIN TECHNICAL
INSTITUTE 406
WESTERN WYOMING COMMUNITY COLLEGE
407

WESTFIELD STATE COLLEGE 171
WESTMAR COLLEGE 127
WESTMINSTER CHOIR COLLEGE 230
WESTMINSTER COLLEGE, MISSOURI 209
WESTMINSTER COLLEGE, PENNSYLVANIA
335
WESTMINSTER COLLEGE, UTAH 376
WESTMINSTER THEOLOGICAL SEMINARY
335
WESTMONT COLLEGE 48
WESTMORELAND COUNTY COMMUNITY
COLLEGE 335
WHARTON COUNTY JUNIOR COLLEGE 373
WHATCOM COMMUNITY COLLEGE 393
WHEATON COLLEGE, ILLINOIS 110
WHEATON COLLEGE, MASSACHUSETTS 171
WHEELING COLLEGE 397
WHEELOCK COLLEGE 171
WHITE PINES COLLEGE 219
WHITE RIVER VALLEY TECH INST,
INDIANA VOCATIONAL COLLEGE 120
WHITMAN COLLEGE 394
WHITTIER COLLEGE 48
WHITWORTH COLLEGE, MISSISSIPPI 197
WHITWORTH COLLEGE, WASHINGTON 394
WICHITA STATE UNIVERSITY 134, 411
WIDENER COLLEGE 336
WILBERFORCE UNIVERSITY 300
WILEY COLLEGE 373
WILKES COLLEGE 336
WILKES COMMUNITY COLLEGE 281
WILLIAM CAREY COLLEGE 198
WILLIAM JEWELL COLLEGE 209
WILLIAM MITCHELL COLLEGE OF LAW
193
WILLIAM PATERSON COLLEGE OF NEW
JERSEY 230
WILLIAM PENN COLLEGE 128
WILLIAM RAINEY HARPER COLLEGE 110
WILLIAM WOODS COLLEGE 209
WILLIAMETTE UNIVERSITY 311
WILLIAMS COLLEGE 171
WILLIAMSPORT AREA COMMUNITY
COLLEGE 336
WILLMAR STATE JUNIOR COLLEGE 193
WILMINGTON COLLEGE, DELAWARE 64
WILMINGTON COLLEGE, OHIO 300
WILSON COLLEGE 336
WILSON COUNTY TECHNICAL INSTITUTE
281
WINDHAM COLLEGE 378
WINGATE COLLEGE 281
WINONA STATE COLLEGE 193
WINSTON-SALEM STATE UNIVERSITY 282
WINTHROP COLLEGE 347
WISCONSIN COLLEGE CONSERVATORY 407
WITTENBERG UNIVERSITY 300
WOFFORD COLLEGE 347
WOOD JUNIOR COLLEGE 198
WOODBURY COLLEGE 48
WOODSTOCK COLLEGE 269
WORCESTER JUNIOR COLLEGE 172
WORCESTER POLYTECHNIC INSTITUTE
172

INDEX OF SOCIETIES

SOCIETIES

INDEX OF CENTERS AND INSTITUTES

INDEX OF JOURNALS

JOURNALS

NAMES AND ADDRESSES OF PHILOSOPHERS

AAMODT, GARY J N, PHILOSOPHY DEPT, UNIV OF WISCONSIN, MADISON WI 53706
ABBARNO, JOHN, PHIL DEPT, S ILLINOIS UNIV, CARBONDALE IL 62901
ABBATE, NANCY, PHIL DEPT, DEPAUL UNIVERSITY, CHICAGO IL 60604
ABBOTT, JAMES, PHILOSOPHY DEPT, COL OF CHARLESTON, CHARLESTON SC 29401
ABBOTT, WILLIAM R, PHILOSOPHY DEPT, UNIV OF WATERLOO, WATERLOO ONT   CAN
ABEGG, EDMUND, PHILOSOPHY DEPT, EDINBORO ST COL, EDINBORO PA 16412
ABEL, DONALD, PHILOSOPHY DEPT, GONZAGA UNIV, SPOKANE WA 99202
ABEL, JOHN W, GEN EDUC DEPT, SOUTHWESTERN ST COL, WEATHERFORD OK 73096
ABEL, REUBEN, PHIL DEPT, NW SCH FOR SOC RES, NEW YORK NY 10003
ABELSON, RAZIEL, PHIL DEPT, NEW YORK UNIVERSITY, NEW YORK NY 10003
ABERANT, M, PHILOSOPHY DEPT, UNIV OF ALBERTA, EDMONTON ALB   CAN
ABERNETHY, GEORGE L, PHILOSOPHY DEPT, DAVIDSON COLLEGE, DAVIDSON NC 28036
ABOULAFIA, MITCHELL S, PHIL DEPT, BOSTON COLLEGE, CHESTNUT HILL MA 02167
ABRAHAM, WILLIAM E, PHILOSOPHY DEPT, MACALESTER COLLEGE, ST PAUL MN 55101
ABU SHANAB, ROBERT E, PHIL DEPT, FLORIDA STATE UNIV, TALLAHASSEE FL 32306
ACCURSIA, MARY, ALVERNIA COLLEGE, READING, PA 19607
ACHINSTEIN, PETER, PHIL DEPT, JOHNS HOPKINS UNIV, BALTIMORE MD 21218
ACKERMAN, TERRENCE, PHIL DEPT, UNIV OF ROCHESTER, ROCHESTER NY 14627
ACKERMANN, DAVID, PHIL DEPT, COLUMBIA UNIVERSITY, NEW YORK NY 10027
ACKERMANN, ROBERT, PHILOSOPHY DEPT, UNIV OF MASS, AMHERST MA 01002
ACKERT, PAUL, RELIG & PHIL DEPT, OTTERBEIN COL, WESTERVILLE OH 43081
ACKLEY, CHARLES W, SOC SCI DEPT, CAL ST POLYTECH UNIV, POMONA CA 91768
ACKLEY, SHELDON, PHIL DEPT, ST UNIV OF NY, STONY BROOK NY 11790
ACRI, MICHAEL, PHILOSOPHY DEPT, GANNON COLLEGE, ERIE PA 16501
ACUNA, JUNA J, ASHLAND COLLEGE, ASHLAND, OH 44805
ADAMCZEWSKI, ZYGMUNT, PHIL DEPT, BROCK UNIVERSITY, ST CATHARINES ONT   CAN
ADAMI, RICHARD R, PHIL DEPT, PORTLAND ST UNIV, PORTLAND OR 97207
ADAMS, ANNE DONCHIN, COMP HIST, COL AT OLD WESTBURY, OLD WESTBURY NY 11568
ADAMS, CHARLES T R, HUMAN DEPT, CEN FLORIDA COM COL, OCALA FL 32670
ADAMS, E M, PHIL DEPT, UNIV OF N CAROLINA, CHAPEL HILL NC 27514
ADAMS, ERNEST W, PHIL DEPT, UNIV OF CALIFORNIA, BERKELEY CA 94720
ADAMS, FREDERICK R, PHIL STUD DEPT, S ILLINOIS UNIV, EDWARDSVILLE IL 62025
ADAMS, JOHN STOKES, PHIL DEPT, LAKE ERIE COLLEGE, PAINESVILLE OH 44077
ADAMS, MARILYN, PHIL DEPT, UNIV OF CALIFORNIA, LOS ANGELES CA 90024
ADAMS, PEDRO, PHIL DEPT, COL OF MT ST JOSEPH, MT ST JOSEPH OH 45051
ADAMS, RICHARD C, PHIL DEPT, QUINNIPIAC COLLEGE, HAMDEN CT 06518
ADAMS, ROBERT, PHIL DEPT, UNIV OF CALIFORNIA, LOS ANGELES CA 90024
ADDIS, LAIRD, PHIL DEPT, UNIVERSITY OF IOWA, IOWA CITY IA 52240
ADELL, ARVID W, PHILOSOPHY DEPT, MILLIKIN UNIVERSITY, DECATUR IL 62522
ADELMAN, BERNARD H, PHIL DEPT, BENTLEY COLLEGE, WALTHAM MA 02154
ADELMAN, FREDERICK J, PHIL DEPT, BOSTON COLLEGE, CHESTNUT HILL MA 02167
ADELMAN, H, PHILOSOPHY DEPT, ATKINSON COLLEGE, DOWNSVIEW ONT   CAN
ADLER, HANS, PHIL & RELIG DEPT, NATIONAL COL OF EDUC, EVANSTON IL 60201
ADNOU, ETEL, PHILOSOPHY DEPT, DOMINICAN COLLEGE, SAN RAFAEL CA 94901
AFFLECK, BERT, PHILOSOPHY DEPT, MCMURRAY COLLEGE, ABILENE TX 79605
AFSHAR, JAMES H M, PHIL DEPT, BLOOMSBURG ST COL, BLOOMSBURG PA 17815
AGASSI, JOSEPH, PHIL DEPT, BOSTON UNIVERSITY, BOSTON MA 02215
AGER, TRYG, PHIL DEPT, ST UNIV OF NY, BINGHAMTON NY 13901
AGONITO, ROSEMARY, PHIL & RELIG DEPT, COLGATE UNIVERSITY, HAMILTON NY 13346
AGUS, JACOB, REL & PHIL DEPT, DROPSIE UNIVERSITY, PHILADELPHIA PA 19131
AHEARN, JOHN, SOCIAL SCI DIV, ARIZONA WESTERN COL, YUMA AZ 85364
AHERN, ALVIN A, PHILOSOPHY DEPT, ROBERTS WESLEYAN COL, ROCHESTER NY 14624
AHERN, DENNIS, PHIL DEPT, YALE UNIVERSITY, NEW HAVEN CT 06520
AHLERS, ROLF, PHILOSOPHY DEPT, RUSSELL SAGE COL, TROY NY 12180
AHLSTROM, J MILLARD, HUMAN DEPT, LAKEWOOD ST JR COL, WHITE BEAR LK MN 55110
AHLUALIA, BRIJ, PHIL DEPT, PRINCE GEORGE'S COM, LARGO MD 20870
AHMAD, INGRID, PHIL DEPT, GEORGE WILLIAMS UNIV, MONTREAL 107 QUE   CAN
AHMAD, M MOBIN, PHIL DEPT, GEORGE WILLIAMS UNIV, MONTREAL 107 QUE   CAN
AHRENS, JOHN, PHIL DEPT, UNIVERSITY OF IOWA, IOWA CITY IA 52240
AHUJA, YOGA, PHIL DEPT, METROPOLITAN ST COL, DENVER CO 80204

AICHELE, RONALD G, PHIL DEPT, S COLORADO ST COL, PUEBLO CO 81001
AIKEN, HENRY D, PHIL DEPT, BRANDEIS UNIVERSITY, WALTHAM MA 02154
AIKEN, LILLIAN W, HUMAN DIV, NASSON COLLEGE, SPRINGVALE ME 04083
AIKEN, WILLIAM H, PHILOSOPHY DEPT, VANDERBILT UNIV, NASHVILLE TN 37235
AJZENSTAT, SAMUEL, PHILOSOPHY DEPT, MCMASTER UNIVERSITY, HAMILTON ONT CAN
AKE, CHRISTOPHER, PHIL DEPT, TULANE UNIVERSITY, NEW ORLEANS LA 70118
AKERS, LAWRENCE KEITH, PHILOSOPHY DEPT, UNIV OF TEXAS, AUSTIN TX 78712
AKERS, SAMUEL, REL & PHIL DEPT, WESLEYAN COLLEGE, MACON GA 31201
ALAMSHAH, WILLIAM H, PHIL DEPT, CALIFORNIA ST UNIV, FULLERTON CA 92634
ALBAUGH, STEVE, PHIL DEPT, S ILLINOIS UNIV, CARBONDALE IL 62901
ALBERT, H, PHILOSOPHY DEPT, LAURENTIAN UNIV, SUDBURY ONT CAN
ALBERT, SIDNEY, PHIL DEPT, CALIFORNIA ST UNIV, LOS ANGELES CA 90032
ALBERTS, KELLY, PHIL DEPT, UNIV OF CALIFORNIA, LOS ANGELES CA 90024
ALBRIGHT, GARY L, PHIL DEPT, CALIFORNIA ST UNIV, SAN JOSE CA 95114
ALDANA, MANUEL, PHIL & RELIG, WESTMAR COLLEGE, LEMARS IA 51031
ALDER, GEORGE, GEN EDUC DEPT, SAN JOSE BIBLE COL, SAN JOSE CA 95108
ALDERMAN, HAROLD, PHIL DEPT, CAL ST COL AT SONOMA, ROHNERT PARK CA 94928
ALDRICH, VIRGIL C, PHILOSOPHY DEPT, UNIV OF UTAH, SALT LAKE CTY UT 84112
ALDRIDGE, WILSON A, PHIL DEPT, UNIV OF SN FRANCISCO, SAN FRANCISCO CA 94117
ALESSIA, RAFFAELE, PHIL DEPT, LEWIS COLLEGE, LOCKPORT IL 60441
ALEXANDER, BRUCE, PHIL DEPT, LOWELL STATE COLLEGE, LOWELL MA 01854
ALEXANDER, DAVID, HUMAN DIV, SOUTHERN OREGON COL, ASHLAND OR 97520
ALEXANDER, HAFEEZ, PHIL DEPT, SAINT THOMAS UNIV, FREDERICTON N B CAN
ALEXANDER, HENRY A, PHILOSOPHY DEPT, UNIV OF OREGON, EUGENE OR 97403
ALEXANDER, HUBERT G, PHIL DEPT, UNIV OF NEW MEXICO, ALBUQUERQUE NM 87106
ALEXANDER, J DAVIDSON, PHIL DEPT, IOWA STATE UNIV, AMES IA 50010
ALEXANDER, JOHN, HUMAN DIV, SOUTHERN OREGON COL, ASHLAND OR 97520
ALEXANDER, R, PHILOSOPHY DEPT, WARTBURG COLLEGE, WAVERLY IA 50677
ALEXANDER, ROBERT, PHILOSOPHY DEPT, WATERLOO LUTH UNIV, WATERLOO ONT CAN
ALEXANDER, WILLIAM M, REL & PHIL, ST ANDREWS PRESB COL, LAURINBURG NC 28352
ALFARO, BONITA, PHIL DEPT, UNIV OF CALIFORNIA, LOS ANGELES CA 90024
ALFORD, BEN ROBERT, RELIG DEPT, MARTIN COLLEGE, PULASKI TN 38478
ALGOZIN, KEITH W, PHILOSOPHY DEPT, MARQUETTE UNIV, MILWAUKEE WI 53233
ALKSNIS, GUNNAR, PHILOSOPHY DEPT, WASHBURN UNIVERSITY, TOPEKA KS 66621
ALLAIRE, EDWIN B, PHILOSOPHY DEPT, UNIV OF TEXAS, AUSTIN TX 78712
ALLAIRE, GEORGES, PHIL DEPT, COL DE LA POCATIERE, LA POCATIERE QUE CAN
ALLAIRE, REJEAN, PHIL DEPT, COL VIEUX-MONTREAL, MONTREAL QUE CAN
ALLAN, D MAURICE, PHIL DEPT, HAMPDEN-SYDNEY COL, HAMPDEN-SYDNY VA 23943
ALLAN, GEORGE, PHILOSOPHY DEPT, DICKINSON COLLEGE, CARLISLE PA 17013
ALLARD, GUY-H, PHILOSOPHY DEPT, UNIV DE MONTREAL, MONTREAL QUE CAN
ALLARD, JEAN-LOUIS, PHIL FACULTY, UNIV OF OTTAWA, OTTAWA ONT CAN
ALLARD, JEAN-RENE, PHIL DEPT, COL DE SHERBROOKE, SHERBROOKE QUE CAN
ALLCHIN, KEITH, PHIL DEPT, BOSTON UNIVERSITY, BOSTON MA 02215
ALLEMAND, L EDWARD, PHIL DEPT, DEPAUL UNIVERSITY, CHICAGO IL 60604
ALLEN, BERNARD L, SOC SCI DIV, PARKERSBURG COM COL, PARKERSBURG WV 26101
ALLEN, CARL J, PHIL DEPT, LA SALLE COLLEGE, PHILADELPHIA PA 19141
ALLEN, DIOGENES, THEOL DEPT, PRINCETON THEOL SEM, PRINCETON NJ 08540
ALLEN, DOUGLAS M, PHIL DEPT, CENTRAL CONN ST COL, NEW BRITAIN CT 06050
ALLEN, DUANE, ENGLISH LIT & PHIL, UNIV OF WISCONSIN, MADISON WI 53706
ALLEN, EDWARD F, ACADEMY OF NW CHURCH, BRYN ATHYN, PA 19009
ALLEN, GLEN O, PHIL DEPT, IDAHO STATE UNIV, POCATELLO ID 83201
ALLEN, HAROLD J, PHIL DEPT, ADELPHI UNIVERSITY, GARDEN CITY NY 11530
ALLEN, JEFFNER, PHILOSOPHY DEPT, DUQUESNE UNIV, PITTSBURGH PA 15219
ALLEN, JOSEPH, PHIL & RELIG DEPT, UPSALA COL, EAST ORANGE NJ 07019
ALLEN, MICHAEL, PHIL DEPT, BOSTON UNIVERSITY, BOSTON MA 02215
ALLEN, PAUL, PHIL DEPT, E STROUDSBURG ST COL, E STROUDSBURG PA 18301
ALLEN, R E, PHILOSOPHY DEPT, UNIV OF TORONTO, TORONTO ONT CAN
ALLEN, THOMAS, PHIL & REL DEPT, UNIV OF GEORGIA, ATHENS GA 30602
ALLEN, TIMOTHY W, PHIL DEPT, UNIV OF KENTUCKY, LEXINGTON KY 40506
ALLINSON, ROBERT E, PHIL DEPT, WEST VIRGINIA ST COL, INSTITUTE WV 25112
ALLISON, CLINTON, EDUC COLLEGE, UNIV OF TENNESSEE, KNOXVILLE TN 37916
ALLISON, DAVID, PHIL DEPT, ST UNIV OF NY, STONY BROOK NY 11790
ALLISON, HENRY, PHIL DEPT, U OF CAL -SAN DIEGO, LA JOLLA CA 92037
ALLMAKER, ALI M, PHIL DEPT, NORTH ADAMS ST COL, NORTH ADAMS MA 01247

ALMEDER, ROBERT F, PHIL DEPT, GEORGIA ST UNIV, ATLANTA GA   30303
ALMGUIST, CALVIN B, PHIL DEPT, S METHODIST UNIV, DALLAS TX   75222
ALPERSON, P, PHILOSOPHY DEPT, UNIV OF TORONTO, TORONTO ONT   CAN
ALSMEYER JR, H L, PHIL & HUM DEPT, TEXAS A & M UNIV, COL STATION TX   77843
ALSTON, WILLIAM P, PHILOSOPHY DEPT, RUTGERS UNIV, NEW BRUNSWICK NJ   08903
ALTMAN, IRA, PHIL DEPT, BROOKLYN COLLEGE, BROOKLYN NY   11210
ALVES, MARY J, PHIL DEPT, BOSTON COLLEGE, CHESTNUT HILL MA   02167
ALVEY, LEONARD, BRESCIA COLLEGE, OWENSBORO, KY   42301
ALVY, RALPH, PHIL DEPT, UNIV OF CALIFORNIA, LOS ANGELES CA   90024
ALWILL, JOHN, PHIL DEPT, NORTHWESTERN UNIV, EVANSTON IL   60201
AMAN, KENNETH, PHIL & RELIG DEPT, MCNTCLAIR ST COL, UPR MONTCLAIR NJ   07043
AMBERG, JOHN V, ST PETER'S COLLEGE, JERSEY CITY, NJ   07306
AMBROSE, JAMES, PHILOSOPHY DEPT, UNIV OF ARIZONA, TUCSON AZ   85721
AMBROSIO, FRANCIS J, PHIL DEPT, FORDHAM UNIVERSITY, BRONX NY   10458
AMERIKS, KARL, PHIL DEPT, UNIV OF NOTRE DAME, NOTRE DAME IN   46556
AMES, VAN METER, PHIL DEPT, UNIV OF CINCINNATI, CINCINNATI OH   45221
AMMERMAN, ROBERT R, PHILOSOPHY DEPT, UNIV OF WISCONSIN, MADISON WI   53706
AMSTUTZ, J, PHILOSOPHY DEPT, UNIV OF GUELPH, GUELPH ONT   CAN
AMUNDSON, RONALD A, PHILOSOPHY DEPT, UNIV OF WISCONSIN, MADISON WI   53706
AMY, WILLIAM, RELIG & PHIL DEPT, OTTERBEIN COL, WESTERVILLE OH   43081
ANAGNOSTIS, MARY W, PHILOSOPHY DEPT, EL CAMINO COLLEGE, TORRENCE CA   90506
ANAGNOSTOPOULOS, G, PHIL DEPT, U OF CAL -SAN DIEGO, LA JOLLA CA   92037
ANDELSON, R V, PHILOSOPHY DEPT, AUBURN UNIVERSITY, AUBURN AL   36830
ANDERBERG, CLIFFORD, PHIL & REL DEPT, UNIV OF NEBRASKA, OMAHA NE   68132
ANDERSON, ALAN ROSS, PHIL DEPT, UNIV OF PITTSBURGH, PITTSBURGH PA   15260
ANDERSON, ALBERT A, PHIL DEPT, CLARK UNIVERSITY, WORCESTER MA   01610
ANDERSON, ALBERT B, PHIL DEPT, CONCORDIA COLLEGE, MOORHEAD MN   56560
ANDERSON, ANTHONY, PHIL DEPT, CALIFORNIA ST UNIV, LOS ANGELES CA   90032
ANDERSON, C ALAN, HUMAN DIV, CURRY COLLEGE, MILTON MA   02186
ANDERSON, CLARENCE, PHIL & RELIG, PATRICK HENRY COL, MARTINSVILLE VA   24112
ANDERSON, CLIFFORD, PHIL DEPT, CALIFORNIA ST UNIV, SACRAMENTO CA   95819
ANDERSON, DANIEL, PHIL DEPT, OHIO WESLEYAN UNIV, DELAWARE OH   43105
ANDERSON, DAVID A, PHIL DEPT, UNIV CF MARYLAND, COLLEGE PARK MD   20742
ANDERSON, FREDERICK, HIST & PHIL DEPT, E MICHIGAN UNIV, YPSILANTI MI   48197
ANDERSON, GERALD, PHILOSOPHY DEPT, UNIV OF VERMONT, BURLINGTON VT   05401
ANDERSON, GRAHAM, SOC STUD DEPT, SIMON'S ROCK, GR BARRINGTON MA   01230
ANDERSON, JAMES, PHIL DEPT, SYRACUSE UNIVERSITY, SYRACUSE NY   13210
ANDERSON, JAMES, RELIG & PHIL DEPT, PAUL QUINN COLLEGE, WACO TX   76703
ANDERSON, JOHN M, PHILOSOPHY DEPT, PENN STATE UNIV, UNIV PARK PA   16802
ANDERSON, JOHN, SETON HALL UNIV, SOUTH ORANGE, NJ   07079
ANDERSON, JOHN, BIBL STUD & PHIL DIV, BRYAN COLLEGE, DAYTON TN   37321
ANDERSON, MYRON, PHIL DEPT, ST CLOUD ST COL, ST CLOUD MN   56301
ANDERSON, PAUL B L, SOC SCI DEPT, SEATTLE CEN COM COL, SEATTLE WA   98122
ANDERSON, ROBERT F, PHIL DEPT, UNIV OF NEBRASKA, LINCOLN NE   68502
ANDERSON, ROBERT M, SOC SCI DEPT, NE OKLAHOMA A & M COL, MIAMI OK   74354
ANDERSON, STANLEY, PHIL DEPT, BETHEL COLLEGE, ST PAUL MN   55112
ANDERSON, THOMAS C, PHILOSOPHY DEPT, MARQUETTE UNIV, MILWAUKEE WI   53233
ANDERSON, TYSON, PHIL & THEOL DEPT, SAINT LEO COLLEGE, SAINT LEO FL   33574
ANDERSON, WALLACE, PHILOSOPHY DEPT, OHIO STATE UNIV, COLUMBUS OH   43210
ANDERSON, WILLIAM D, JOHN F KENNEDY COL, WAHOO, NE   68066
ANDERSON, WILLIAM R, PHILOSOPHY DEPT, PENN STATE UNIV, UNIV PARK PA   16802
ANDIC, MARTIN, PHILOSOPHY DEPT, UNIV OF MASS, BOSTON MA   02116
ANDRADE, LOUIS E, PHILOSOPHY DEPT, ILLINOIS ST UNIV, NORMAL IL   61761
ANDRE, JUDITH, PHIL DEPT, MICHIGAN STATE UNIV, EAST LANSING MI   48823
ANDRE, SHANE, PHIL DEPT, CALIFORNIA ST UNIV, LONG BEACH CA   90840
ANDREWS, ALLAN, BIOLOGY & PHIL DEPT, RAPPAHANNOCK COM COL, GLENNS VA   23149
ANDREWS, ELIAS, QUEEN'S THEOL COL, KINGSTON, ONT   CAN
ANDREWS, F ELIZABETH, PHILOSOPHY DEPT, MEMORIAL UNIV, ST JOHN'S N F   CAN
ANDREWS, FRANK EDWIN, PHILOSOPHY DEPT, UNIV OF TEXAS, AUSTIN TX   78712
ANDREWS, JOHN T, PHIL DEPT, MIDDLEBURY COLLEGE, MIDDLEBURY VT   05753
ANDREWS, STEPHEN T, PHILOSOPHY DEPT, CEN YMCA COM COL, CHICAGO IL   60606
ANDREWS, THOMAS, PHIL DEPT, NORTHWESTERN UNIV, EVANSTON IL   60201
ANDRIOPOULOS, DIMITRI, PHIL DEPT, UNIV OF MISSOURI, KANSAS CITY MO   64110
ANDRUS, CHARLES E, SOC SCI DEPT, CAMERON COLLEGE, LAWTON OK   73501

ANDRUS, MICHAEL P, SOC SCI DEPT, CALVARY BIBLE COL, KANSAS CITY MO 64111
ANDRY, CARL, PHIL DEPT, BALL ST UNIVERSITY, MUNCIE IN 47306
ANDRYCHOWICZ, STANLEY, HUMAN DEPT, HONOLULU COM COL, HONOLULU HI 96817
ANGEL, GARY L, PHIL STUD DEPT, S ILLINOIS UNIV, EDWARDSVILLE IL 62025
ANGEL, ROGER B, PHIL DEPT, GEORGE WILLIAMS UNIV, MONTREAL 107 QUE CAN
ANGELELLI, IGNAZIO, PHILOSOPHY DEPT, UNIV OF TEXAS, AUSTIN TX 78712
ANGELES, PETER, PHIL DEPT, SN BARBARA CY COL, SANTA BARBARA CA 93105
ANGELL, CHARLES E, HUMANITIES DIV, COL OF THE OZARKS, CLARKSVILLE AR 72830
ANGELL, RICHARD B, PHIL DEPT, WAYNE STATE UNIV, DETROIT MI 48202
ANGELO, A A, PHILOSOPHY DEPT, SIMON FRASER UNIV, BURNABY 2 B C CAN
ANGENE, LYLE, PHILOSOPHY DEPT, RICE UNIVERSITY, HOUSTON TX 77001
ANGUS, IAN, PHILOSOPHY DEPT, UNIV OF WATERLOO, WATERLOO ONT CAN
ANGUS, ROBERT J, PHIL & REL STUD, CAL STATE COL, BAKERSFIELD CA 93309
ANKER, WILLO G, SOC SCI DEPT, NORTHWOOD INSTITUTE, MIDLAND MI 48640
ANKNER, WILLIAM, HUM DEVEL DIV, SAINT MARY'S COL, ST MARY'S CY MD 20686
ANNESE, THOMAS, PHIL DEPT, CALIFORNIA ST UNIV, LOS ANGELES CA 90032
ANNIS, DAVID, PHIL DEPT, BALL ST UNIVERSITY, MUNCIE IN 47306
ANSBRO, JOHN J, PHIL DEPT, MANHATTAN COLLEGE, RIVERDALE NY 10471
ANSCOMBE, G E M, PHILOSOPHY DEPT, UNIV OF PENN, PHILADELPHIA PA 19174
ANSELL, ROBERT N, PHIL DEPT, ST MARY'S UNIVERSITY, HALIFAX N S CAN
ANSLOW, THOMAS C, ST JOHN'S COLLEGE, CAMARILLO, CA 93010
ANTHONY, CLIFFORD H, HUMAN DIV, NEW ENGLAND COLLEGE, HENNIKER NH 03242
ANTON, ANATOLE, PHIL DEPT, UNIV OF COLORADO, BOULDER CO 80302
ANTON, JOHN P, PHIL DEPT, EMORY UNIVERSITY, ATLANTA GA 30322
ANTON, PETER, PHIL DEPT, OREGON STATE UNIV, CORVALLIS OR 97331
AOKI, HIDEO, HUMANITIES DIV, UNIVERSITY OF HAWAII, HILO HI 96720
APETZ, E, PHIL DEPT, W CONNECTICUT ST COL, DANBURY CT 06810
APOSTOL, ROBERT Z, PHIL DEPT, CREIGHTON UNIV, OMAHA NE 68178
APPLEBY, PETER C, PHILOSOPHY DEPT, UNIV OF UTAH, SALT LAKE CTY UT 84112
APSLER, ALFRED, PHILOSOPHY DEPT, CLARK COLLEGE, VANCOUVER WA 98663
AQUILA, RICHARD, PHILOSOPHY DEPT, DUKE UNIVERSITY, DURHAM NC 27706
ARATO, ANDREW, HUMAN DEPT, COOPER UNION, COOPER SQUARE NY 10003
ARBAUGH, GEORGE B, PHIL DEPT, AUGUSTANA COLLEGE, ROCK ISLAND IL 61201
ARBAUGH, GEORGE E, PHILOSOPHY DEPT, PACIFIC LUTH UNIV, TACOMA WA 98447
ARBINI, RONALD A, PHIL DEPT, UNIV OF CALIFORNIA, DAVIS CA 95616
ARCARIO, PETER, PHIL DEPT, SUFFOLK CO COM COL, SELDEN NY 11784
ARCHER, R, PHIL & CLASS DEPT, UNIV OF SASKATCHEWAN, REGINA SAS CAN
ARCHIE, LEE, PHIL DEPT, UNIV OF ARKANSAS, FAYETTEVILLE AR 72701
ARDAL, PALL S, PHILOSOPHY DEPT, QUEEN'S UNIVERSITY, KINGSTON ONT CAN
ARDIS, JULE, SOC SCI DEPT, RIVERSIDE CITY COL, RIVERSIDE CA 92506
ARENDALE, M, BASIC STUD DIV, CHATTANOOGA ST TECH, CHATTANOOGA TN 37406
ARENDT, HANNAH, PHIL DEPT, NW SCH FOR SOC RES, NEW YORK NY 10003
ARENTZ, DONALD, PHIL & RELIG DEPT, COLGATE UNIVERSITY, HAMILTON NY 13346
ARIAS, RICARDO, PHIL & REL DEPT, FLORIDA INTNL UNIV, MIAMI FL 33144
ARIEUX, MARIANNE, PHIL DEPT, UNIV OF CALIFORNIA, IRVINE CA 92664
ARIEW, ROGER, PHIL DEPT, UNIV OF ILLINOIS, URBANA IL 61801
ARJUNE, HARRY, PHIL DEPT, UNIV OF ILLINOIS, URBANA IL 61801
ARKIN, MARC, PHIL DEPT, UNIV OF N CAROLINA, CHAPEL HILL NC 27514
ARMANTAGE, W W, PHILOSOPHY DEPT, CERRITOS COLLEGE, NORWALK CA 90605
ARMOUR, LESLIE, PHILOSOPHY DEPT, CLEVELAND ST UNIV, CLEVELAND OH 44115
ARMSTRONG, A HILARY, PHIL DEPT, DALHOUSIE UNIVERSITY, HALIFAX N S CAN
ARMSTRONG, BENJAMIN F, PHILOSOPHY DEPT, UNIV OF DELAWARE, NEWARK DE 19711
ARMSTRONG, ROBERT L, PHIL & REL STUD, UNIV OF W FLORIDA, PENSACOLA FL 32504
ARMSTRONG, SUSAN B, PHIL DEPT, CAL ST UNIV -HUMBOLDT, ARCATA CA 95521
ARNAUD, RICHARD, PHIL DEPT, UNIV OF MINNESOTA, MINNEAPOLIS MN 55455
ARNER, DOUGLAS G, PHILOSOPHY DEPT, ARIZONA STATE UNIV, TEMPE AZ 85281
ARNESON, RICHARD, PHIL DEPT, U OF CAL -SAN DIEGO, LA JOLLA CA 92037
ARNETT, WILLARD E, PHIL & RELIG, CHATHAM COLLEGE, PITTSBURGH PA 15232
ARNETT, WILLIAM M, THEOL & PHIL DIV, ASBURY THEOL SEM, WILMORE KY 40390
ARNOLD, JOHN J, PHILOSOPHY DEPT, OHIO UNIVERSITY, ZANESVILLE OH 43701
ARNOLD, KEITH, PHIL FACULTY, UNIV OF OTTAWA, OTTAWA ONT CAN
ARNOLD, MAGDA B, PSYCH DEPT, SPRING HILL COLLEGE, MOBILE AL 36608
ARNOLD, ROBERT, PHILOSOPHY DEPT, UNIV OF WATERLOO, WATERLOO ONT CAN
ARNOLD, WINSTON, COL MILITAIRE ROYAL, SAINT-JEAN, QUE CAN

ARO, JOHN, HUMANITIES DIV, SHERIDAN COLLEGE, SHERIDAN WY 82801
ARONOVITCH, H, PHIL & RELIG DEPT, COLGATE UNIVERSITY, HAMILTON NY 13346
ARONSON, JERROLD L, PHIL DEPT, ST UNIV OF NY, BINGHAMTON NY 13901
ARRAS, JOHN, PHIL DEPT, UNIV OF REDLANDS, REDLANDS CA 92373
ARRINGTON, ROBERT L, PHIL DEPT, GEORGIA ST UNIV, ATLANTA GA 30303
ARSENAULT, ALFRED, PHILOSOPHY DEPT, UNIV OF MASS, AMHERST MA 01002
ARTHUR, ALCOTT S, PHIL DEPT, HOWARD UNIVERSITY, WASHINGTON DC 20001
ARTHUR, R W T, PHILOSOPHY DEPT, MCGILL UNIVERSITY, MONTREAL QUE   CAN
ARTHURS, MARIE, NW STATE COLLEGE, ALVA, OK 73717
ARTIBELLO, J, PHILOSOPHY DEPT, UNIV OF TORONTO, TORONTO ONT   CAN
ASADOURIAN, VAZKEN N, PHIL DEPT, TULANE UNIVERSITY, NEW ORLEANS LA 70118
ASCHENBRENNER, KARL, PHIL DEPT, UNIV OF CALIFORNIA, BERKELEY CA 94720
ASHBY, WARREN, PHIL DEPT, UNIV OF N CAROLINA, GREENSBORO NC 27412
ASHENFELDER, JOHN, HUMAN & SOC SCI, TIDEWATER COM COL, PORTSMOUTH VA 23703
ASHER, JAMES, PHIL DEPT, SAINT THOMAS UNIV, FREDERICTON N B   CAN
ASHER, PATRICK, ENG DEPT, JOLIET JR COLLEGE, JOLIET IL 60436
ASHLEY, BENEDICT, PHILOSOPHY DEPT, AQUINAS INST THEOL, DUBUQUE IA 52001
ASHLEY, LAWRENCE, PHIL DEPT, COL AT CORTLAND, CORTLAND NY 13045
ASHMORE, ROBERT B, PHILOSOPHY DEPT, MARQUETTE UNIV, MILWAUKEE WI 53233
ASHWORTH, E JENNIFER, PHILOSOPHY DEPT, UNIV OF WATERLOO, WATERLOO ONT   CAN
ASKREN, ROBERT, HUM DEPT, SOUTH FLORIDA JR COL, AVON PARK FL 33825
ASP, WALDO, PHIL DEPT, NORMANDALE ST JR COL, BLOOMINGTON MN 55431
ASPEVIG, K, SOC SCI DEPT, RYERSON POLYTECH U, TORONTO ONT   CAN
ASQUITH, PETER D, PHIL DEPT, MICHIGAN STATE UNIV, EAST LANSING MI 48823
ASSALI, ROBIN N, PHIL DEPT, UNIVERSITY OF HAWAII, HONOLULU HI 96822
ATHAY, MICHAEL, REED COLLEGE, PORTLAND, OR 97202
ATHERTON, MARGARET, PHIL DEPT, NEW YORK UNIVERSITY, NEW YORK NY 10003
ATKIN, EUGENE L, HUMAN DIV, OTTUMWA HTS COLLEGE, OTTUMWA IA 52501
ATKINS, ROBERT A, PHIL & RELIG DEPT, ANTIOCH COL, YELLOW SPGS OH 45387
ATKINSON, BARRY W, HUMAN DIV, RICKER COLLEGE, HOULTON ME 04730
ATKINSON, FRANKLIN, E TEXAS BAPT COL, MARSHALL, TX 75670
ATKINSON, GARY, PHIL DEPT, WILLIAM WOODS COL, FULTON MO 65251
ATLAS, JAY, PHILOSOPHY DEPT, POMONA COLLEGE, CLAREMONT CA 91711
ATTIG, THOMAS, PHIL DEPT, BOWLING GREEN UNIV, BOWLING GREEN OH 43403
ATWELL, JOHN, PHIL DEPT, TEMPLE UNIVERSITY, PHILADELPHIA PA 19122
AUBERT, FERNAND, PHILOSOPHY DEPT, CCL DE ROUYN-NORANDA, ROUYN QUE   CAN
AUBLE, JOEL, PHIL DEPT, WEST GEORGIA COLLEGE, CARROLLTON GA 30117
AUDET, JEAN-PAUL, PHILOSOPHY DEPT, UNIV DE MONTREAL, MONTREAL QUE   CAN
AUDI, MICHAEL N, PHIL DEPT, S ILLINCIS UNIV, CARBONDALE IL 62901
AUDI, ROBERT N, PHIL DEPT, UNIV OF NEBRASKA, LINCOLN NE 68502
AUGROS, ROBERT, PHIL DEPT, ST ANSELM'S COLLEGE, MANCHESTER NH 03102
AUGSBURGER, DANIEL, RELIG DEPT, ANDREWS UNIVERSITY, BERRIEN SPGS MI 49104
AUGUR, SHERWOOD, PHIL DEPT, CENTRAL CONN ST COL, NEW BRITAIN CT 06050
AUNE, BRUCE, PHILOSOPHY DEPT, UNIV CF MASS, AMHERST MA 01002
AUSTIN, HAROLD J, PHIL DEPT, COL OF ST THOMAS, ST PAUL MN 55105
AUSTIN, HOLCOMBE MC, PHIL DEPT, WHEATON COLLEGE, NORTON MA 02766
AUSTIN, JAMES, PHILOSOPHY DEPT, MEMPHIS ST UNIV, MEMPHIS TN 38152
AUSTIN, PAGE I, PHILOSOPHY DEPT, UNIV OF HOUSTON, HOUSTON TX 77004
AUSTIN, STEPHEN S, PHILOSOPHY DEPT, UNIV OF WISONSIN, OSH KOSH WI 54901
AUTH, KURT, PHILOSOPHY DEPT, CHAPMAN COLLEGE, ORANGE CA 92666
AUXTER, THOMAS P, PHIL DEPT, UNIV OF FLORIDA, GAINESVILLE FL 32611
AVERILL, EDWARD, PHIL DEPT, UNIV OF CALIFORNIA, SANTA BARBARA CA 93106
AVLICK, LYNN, PHILOSOPHY DEPT, CEDAR CREST COLLEGE, ALLENTOWN PA 18104
AWALT, HOUSTON M, RELIG & PHIL DEPT, BELMONT COLLEGE, NASHVILLE TN 37203
AWBREY, DAVID, HUMAN DEPT, SOUTHEASTERN COM COL, W BURLINGTON IA 52655
AWERKAMP, DONALD T, PHIL DEPT, VALDOSTA ST COL, VALDOSTA GA 31601
AXEL, LARRY, PHIL DEPT, PURDUE UNIVERSITY, LAFAYETTE IN 47907
AXELSEN, DIANA E, PHIL & RELIG DEPT, SPELMAN COLLEGE, ATLANTA GA 30314
AXER, ENGELBERT, PHILOSOPHY DEPT, SEATTLE UNIVERSITY, SEATTLE WA 98122
AXINN, SIDNEY, PHIL DEPT, TEMPLE UNIVERSITY, PHILADELPHIA PA 19122
AXTELLE, GEORGE, PHIL DEPT, S ILLINCIS UNIV, CARBONDALE IL 62901
AYERS, ROBERT H, PHIL & REL DEPT, UNIV OF GEORGIA, ATHENS GA 30602
AYLWARD, WILLIAM, PHIL DEPT, LA SALLE COLLEGE, PHILADELPHIA PA 19141
AYOTTE, JACQUES, PHIL DEPT, COL FRANCOIS-X-GARN, GUEBEC CITY QUE   CAN

AYOUB, JOSIANE, PHIL DEPT, COL VIEUX-MONTREAL, MONTREAL QUE   CAN
AZAR, LAWRENCE, PHIL DEPT, IONA COLLEGE, NEW ROCHELLE NY   10801
BABAD, JOSEPH, PHIL & REL DEPT, HEBREW THEOL COL, SKOKIE IL   60076
BABIN, EUGENE, PHIL FACULTE, UNIVERSITE LAVAL, CITE UNIV QUE   CAN
BACH, KENT, PHIL DEPT, CALIFORNIA ST UNIV, SAN FRANCISCO CA   94132
BACHMAN, JAMES, LAKE CITY COM COL, LAKE CITY, FL   32055
BACHRACH, JAY E, PHIL DEPT, CEN WASH STATE COL, ELLENSBURG WA   98926
BACKHAUS, W K, PHILOSOPHY DEPT, QUEEN'S UNIVERSITY, KINGSTON ONT   CAN
BACON, JOHN, PHIL DEPT, FORDHAM UNIVERSITY, BRONX NY   10458
BACON, WILLIAM, PHIL DEPT, WAYNE STATE UNIV, DETROIT MI   48202
BADC, WALTER J, PHILOSOPHY DEPT, XAVIER UNIVERSITY, CINCINNATI OH   45207
BADRA, ROBERT, HUMAN DEPT, KALAMAZOO VLY COL, KALAMAZOO MI   49001
BAER, CAMPION, PHIL DEPT, ST JOSEPH'S COLLEGE, EAST CHICAGO IN   46312
BAER, EUGENE S, PHIL DEPT, HOBART & WM SMITH, GENEVA NY   14456
BAER, RICHARD, PHIL DEPT, WAYNE STATE UNIV, DETROIT MI   48202
BAER, THOMAS, PHILOSOPHY DEPT, MCGILL UNIVERSITY, MONTREAL QUE   CAN
BAGEN, JOHN J, PHIL DEPT, ST MARY'S SEM COL, PERRYVILLE MO   63775
BAHDE, JOHN, PHIL DEPT, ST CLOUD ST COL, ST CLOUD MN   56301
BAHM, ARCHIE, PHIL DEPT, UNIV OF NEW MEXICO, ALBUQUERQUE NM   87106
BAID, JOHN M, CHURCH & MINISTRY, PITTS THEOL SEM, PITTSBURGH PA   15206
BAIER, ANNETTE, PHIL DEPT, UNIV OF PITTSBURGH, PITTSBURGH PA   15260
BAIER, KURT E, PHIL DEPT, UNIV OF PITTSBURGH, PITTSBURGH PA   15260
BAILEY, CHARLES, COM COL OF BALTIMORE, BALTIMORE, MD   21215
BAILEY, DAVID L, REL & PHIL DEPT, BLUE RIDGE COM COL, WEYERS CAVE VA   24486
BAILEY, GEORGE W, PHIL DEPT, UNIVERSITY OF MIAMI, CORAL GABLES FL   33124
BAILEY, J A, PHIL DEPT, UNIV OF MANITOBA, WINNIPEG 19 MAN   CAN
BAILEY, JOAN, HUMAN DIV, NEW ENGLAND COLLEGE, HENNIKER NH   03242
BAILEY, ROBERT E, PHIL & REL DEPT, PARK COLLEGE, KANSAS CITY MO   64152
BAILEY, ROBERT Q, PHIL & REL DEPT, CENTRAL COLLEGE, MCPHERSON KS   67460
BAILEY, THOMAS, PHILOSOPHY DEPT, NYACK COLLEGE, NYACK NY   10931
BAILIFF, JOHN D, PHIL DEPT, UNIV OF WISCONSIN, STEVENS POINT WI   54481
BAILLIE, HAROLD W, PHIL DEPT, BOSTON COLLEGE, CHESTNUT HILL MA   02167
BAILLY, MAURICE, PHIL DEPT, COL FRANCOIS-X-GARN, QUEBEC CITY QUE   CAN
BAIRD, ROBERT M, PHILOSOPHY DEPT, BAYLOR UNIVERSITY, WACO TX   76703
BAKAN, MILDRED B, PHILOSOPHY DEPT, YORK UNIVERSITY, DOWNSVIEW ONT   CAN
BAKER, BRENDA, PHILOSOPHY DEPT, UNIV OF CALGARY, CALGARY 44 ALB   CAN
BAKER, BRUCE, PHIL DEPT, UNIV OF MISSOURI, KANSAS CITY MO   64110
BAKER, IRWIN, PHIL DEPT, INDIANA UNIVERSITY, BLOOMINGTON IN   47401
BAKER, J, PHIL DEPT, LOUISIANA ST UNIV, BATON ROUGE LA   70803
BAKER, JEFFREY E, PHIL DEPT, UNIV OF ILLINOIS, URBANA IL   61801
BAKER, JOHN A, PHILOSOPHY DEPT, UNIV OF CALGARY, CALGARY 44 ALB   CAN
BAKER, L F, PHILOSOPHY DEPT, QUEEN'S UNIVERSITY, KINGSTON ONT   CAN
BAKER, LYNNE R, RELIG & PHIL DEPT, MARY BALDWIN COL, STAUNTON VA   24401
BAKER, PETER H, PHIL DEPT, MARYMOUNT MANHATTAN, NEW YORK NY   10021
BAKER, RAY, HUMAN DEPT, SOUTHWEST COLLEGE, CHICAGO IL   60652
BAKER, RICHARD R, PHIL DEPT, UNIVERSITY OF DAYTON, DAYTON OH   45469
BAKER, ROBERT B, PHIL DEPT, UNION OCLLEGE, SCHENECTADY NY   12308
BAKER, ROBERT, CULT ARTS DEPT, N SHORE COM COL, BEVERLY MA   01915
BALAS, DAVID, PHIL DEPT, UNIVERSITY OF DALLAS, IRVING TX   75062
BALDINO, PETER A, EDUCATION SCHOOL, YOUNGSTOWN ST UNIV, YOUNGSTOWN OH   44503
BALDUF, EMERY W, PHIL DEPT, ROOSEVELT UNIVERSITY, CHICAGO IL   60605
BALCUSTY, RICHARD, SOC SCI DEPT, SPOKANE FLS COM COL, SPOKANE WA   99202
BALCWIN, DONALD, BIBL STUD & PHIL, EVANGEL COLLEGE, SPRINGFIELD MO   65802
BALDWIN, HAROLD W, PHILOSOPHY DEPT, UNIV OF S ALABAMA, MOBILE AL   36688
BALCWIN, ROBERT C, PHIL DEPT, AMERICAN INTERNAT COL, SPRINGFIELD MA   01109
BALES, EUGENE, PHIL DEPT, UNIV OF MISSOURI, COLUMBIA MO   65201
BALES, ROYAL EUGENE, HUMANITIES DEPT, MENLO COLLEGE, MENLO PARK CA   94025
BALESTRA, DOMINIC J, PHIL DEPT, ST LOUIS UNIVERSITY, ST LOUIS MO   63103
BALEY, JAMES M, PHIL DEPT, UNIV OF N CAROLINA, CHAPEL HILL NC   27514
BALINSKY, MARGARET, PHIL DEPT, TULANE UNIVERSITY, NEW ORLEANS LA   70118
BALL, DAVID, HUMAN DEPT, HONOLULU COM COL, HONOLULU HI   96817
BALL, M TARCISIA, RELIG STUD, MARIA REGINA COL, SYRACUSE NY   13208
BALL, PATRICIA G, PHIL DEPT, UNIV OF N CAROLINA, CHAPEL HILL NC   27514
BALL, STEVE, PHIL DEPT, UNIV OF MICHIGAN, ANN ARBOR MI   48104

BALLARD, BROOK B, REL & PHIL DEPT, PRINCIPIA COLLEGE, ELSAH IL 62028
BALLARD, EDWARD G, PHIL DEPT, TULANE UNIVERSITY, NEW ORLEANS LA 70118
BALLISTY, ALOYSIUS, PHIL DEPT, LA SALLE COLLEGE, PHILADELPHIA PA 19141
BALMER, JAMES, PHILOSOPHY DEPT, UNIV OF MASS, AMHERST MA 01002
BALMUTH, JEROME, PHIL & RELIG DEPT, COLGATE UNIVERSITY, HAMILTON NY 13346
BALOWITZ, VICTOR H, PHIL DEPT, COL AT BUFFALO, BUFFALO NY 14222
BALSLEV, ANINDITA, PHILOSOPHY DEPT, CAL STATE COL, DOMINGUEZ HLS CA 90747
BALTAZAR, EULALIO R, HIST & PHIL DEPT, FEDERAL CY COL, WASHINGTON DC 20001
BALTO, DAVID ALAN, PHILOSOPHY DEPT, UNIV OF TEXAS, AUSTIN TX 78712
BANCMAN, BERTRAM, PHIL DEPT, LONG ISLAND UNIV, BROOKLYN NY 11201
BANGS, JUDITH, PHILOSOPHY DEPT, UNIV OF NW HAMPSHIRE, DURHAM NH 03824
BANJA, JOHN, PHIL DEPT, FORDHAM UNIVERSITY, BRONX NY 10458
BANKS, JERRY E, PHIL DEPT, TEXAS CHRISTIAN UNIV, FORT WORTH TX 76129
BANNAN, JOHN F, PHIL DEPT, LOYOLA UNIVERSITY, CHICAGO IL 60626
BANNER, WILLIAM A, PHIL DEPT, HOWARD UNIVERSITY, WASHINGTON DC 20001
BANNERMAN, LLOYD, PHILOSOPHY DEPT, ALGOMA COLLEGE, SALT ST MARIE ONT   CAN
BANNING, CYRUS, PHILOSOPHY DEPT, KENYON COLLEGE, GAMBIER OH 43022
BANU, BEATRICE, PHIL DEPT, HUNTER COLLEGE, NEW YORK NY 10021
BANVILLE, PAUL, PHIL DEPT, COL FRANCOIS-X-GARN, QUEBEC CITY QUE   CAN
BANYACSKI, PAUL, PHIL DEPT, WEST CHESTER ST COL, WEST CHESTER PA 19380
BARAC, VLADIMIR, COL OF VIRGIN ISLAND, SAINT THOMAS, VI 00801
BARAN, GARY, PHIL DEPT, CALIFORNIA ST UNIV, NORTHRIDGE CA 91324
BARBER, KENNETH F, PHIL DEPT, ST UNIV OF NY, AMHERST NY 14226
BARBER, MICHAEL, PHIL DEPT, ROCKHURST COLLEGE, KANSAS CITY MO 64110
BARBER, RICHARD, PHIL DEPT, UNIV OF LOUISVILLE, LOUISVILLE KY 40208
BAREOUR, IAN, PHIL DEPT, PURDUE UNIVERSITY, LAFAYETTE IN 47907
BARFORD, ROBERT, PHILOSOPHY DEPT, E ILLINOIS UNIV, CHARLESTON IL 61920
BARGER, BILL D, PHILOSOPHY DEPT, EL CAMINO COLLEGE, TORRENCE CA 90506
BARKER JR, ORUS C, PHIL & RELIG AREA, SHAW UNIVERSITY, RALEIGH NC 27602
BARKER, DONALD R, PHIL DEPT, UNIV OF SW LOUISIANA, LAFAYETTE LA 70501
BARKER, EVELYN, PHIL DEPT, UNIV OF MARYLAND, BALTIMORE MD 21228
BARKER, GEORGE, PHIL DEPT, BALL ST UNIVERSITY, MUNCIE IN 47306
BARKER, JOHN A, PHIL STUD DEPT, S ILLINOIS UNIV, EDWARDSVILLE IL 62025
BARKER, LINCOLN, PHIL & RELIG DEPT, YANKTON COLLEGE, YANKTON SD 57078
BARKER, PETER, PHIL DEPT, ST UNIV OF NY, AMHERST NY 14226
BARKER, STEPHEN, PHIL DEPT, JOHNS HOPKINS UNIV, BALTIMORE MD 21218
BARKER, WARREN J, HUMAN DIV, SOUTHEASTERN UNIV, WASHINGTON DC 20024
BARLOW, DANIEL L, SOC SCI DEPT, SW VIRGINIA COM COL, RICHLANDS VA 24641
BARLOW, RAOUL M, ENGLISH DEPT, UNIV OF WISCONSIN, MENOMONIE WI 54751
BARMRIN, BERNARD, PHIL DEPT, LEHMAN COLLEGE, BRONX NY 10468
BARNES, ANNETTE, PHIL DEPT, UNIV OF MARYLAND, BALTIMORE MD 21228
BARNES, GERALD, PHIL & RELIG DEPT, TRENTON STATE COL, TRENTON NJ 08625
BARNES, HAZEL, PHIL DEPT, UNIV OF COLORADO, BOULDER CO 80302
BARNES, JOHN, FINE & APPL ARTS, PIMA COLLEGE, TUCSON AZ 85721
BARNES, MAHLON W, PHIL DEPT, UNIV OF HARTFORD, WEST HARTFORD CT 06117
BARNES, R T, PHIL DEPT, METROPOLITAN ST COL, DENVER CO 80204
BARNES, ROBERT F, PHIL DEPT, LEHIGH UNIVERSITY, BETHLEHEM PA 18015
BARNETT, ROBERT A, HUMAN DIV, EISENHOWER COLLEGE, SENECA FALLS NY 13148
BARNETT, SAMUEL, HIST & PHIL DIV, TUSCULUM COLLEGE, GREENEVILLE TN 37743
BARNETTE, RONALD L, PHIL DEPT, VALDOSTA ST COL, VALDOSTA GA 31601
BARNHART, J E, PHILOSOPHY DEPT, N TEXAS STATE UNIV, DENTON TX 76203
BARON, BAT-AMI, PHILOSOPHY DEPT, OHIO STATE UNIV, COLUMBUS OH 43210
BARON, HAROLD, HUMAN DIV, DOWLING COLLEGE, LONG ISLAND NY 11769
BARR, WILLIAM R, LEXINGTON THEOL SEM, LEXINGTON, KY 40508
BARR, WILLIAM, PHIL DEPT, COL AT CORTLAND, CORTLAND NY 13045
BARRAL, MARY ROSE, SETON HALL UNIV, SOUTH ORANGE, NJ 07079
BARRANDA, NATIVIDAD, WILBERFORCE UNIV, WILBERFORCE, OH 45384
BARRAS, ABRAHAM D, PHIL & REL STUD, WILKES COLLEGE, WILKES BARRE PA 18703
BARRETT, J EDWARD, PHIL & RELIG, MUSKINGUM COLLEGE, NEW CONCORD OH 43762
BARRETT, JOSEPH L, PHIL DEPT, BOSTON COLLEGE, CHESTNUT HILL MA 02167
BARRETT, ROBERT B, PHIL DEPT, WASHINGTON UNIV, ST LOUIS MO 63130
BARRETT, WILLIAM, PHIL DEPT, NEW YORK UNIVERSITY, NEW YORK NY 10003
BARRON, WILLIAM, PHIL DEPT, NORTHWESTERN UNIV, EVANSTON IL 60201
BARRY, JOHN A, PHILOSOPHY DEPT, BAPTIST COLLEGE, CHARLESTON SC 29411

BARRY, ROBERT M, PHIL DEPT, LOYOLA UNIVERSITY, CHICAGO IL 60626
BARRY, VINCENT, PHIL DEPT, BAKERSFIELD COLLEGE, BAKERSFIELD CA 93305
BARTH, EUGENE, PHILOSOPHY DEPT, ALBRIGHT COLLEGE, READING PA 19604
BARTH, LOUIS A, PHIL DEPT, ST LOUIS UNIVERSITY, ST LOUIS MO 63103
BARTHEL, PAULA, COMMUNIC & HUMAN, OAKLAND COM COLLEGE, AUBURN HTS MI 48057
BARTHELEMY, WILLIAM, PHILOSOPHY DEPT, UNIV OF WATERLOO, WATERLOO ONT CAN
BARTKUS, GYTIS, PHIL DEPT, UNIV OF MICHIGAN, ANN ARBOR MI 48104
BARTKY, SANDRA L, PHIL DEPT, UNIV OF ILLINOIS, CHICAGO IL 60680
BARTLETT, EDWART T, PHILOSOPHY DEPT, CLEVELAND ST UNIV, CLEVELAND OH 44115
BARTLETT, JAMES, HUMANITIES DIV, S W VA COM COL, LOGAN WV 25601
BARTLETT, STEVEN, PHIL DEPT, UNIV OF HARTFORD, WEST HARTFORD CT 06117
BARTLEY III, W W, PHIL DEPT, UNIV OF PITTSBURGH, PITTSBURGH PA 15260
BARTLEY, WILLIAM W, PHILOSOPHY DEPT, CALIFORNIA ST UNIV, HAYWARD CA 94542
BARTON, CHARLES J, PHILOSOPHY DEPT, MEMPHIS ST UNIV, MEMPHIS TN 38152
BARTON, GEORGE E, PHIL DEPT, TULANE UNIVERSITY, NEW ORLEANS LA 70118
BARTON, WILLIAM B, PHILOSOPHY DEPT, MEMPHIS ST UNIV, MEMPHIS TN 38152
BASEHART, MARY C, PHIL DEPT, SPALDING COLLEGE, LOUISVILLE KY 40203
BASHAM, R R, PHIL DEPT, UNIV OF MANITOBA, WINNIPEG 19 MAN CAN
BASHOR, PHILIP S, PHIL DEPT, UNIV OF ARKANSAS, FAYETTEVILLE AR 72701
BASINGER, DAVID, PHIL DEPT, UNIV OF NEBRASKA, LINCOLN NE 68502
BASS, DAVID, PHIL & POLIT SCI, FORT LEWIS COLLEGE, DURANGO CO 81301
BASS, WALTER A, PHIL DEPT, INDIANA ST UNIV, TERRE HAUTE IN 47809
BASS, WILLIAM, PHILOSOPHY DEPT, BIOLA COLLEGE, LA MIRADA CA 90638
BASSEN, PAUL C, PHILOSOPHY DEPT, CALIFORNIA ST UNIV, HAYWARD CA 94542
BASSETT, FREDERICK, RELIG & PHIL DEPT, LIMESTONE COLLEGE, GAFFNEY SC 29340
BASSFORD, H, PHILOSOPHY DEPT, ATKINSON COLLEGE, DOWNSVIEW ONT CAN
BASTIEN, OVIDE, PHILOSOPHY DEPT, COL DE ROUYN-NORANDA, ROUYN QUE CAN
BATANI, GABRIEL, PHIL DEPT, COL DE VICTORIAVILLE, VICTORIAVILLE QUE CAN
BATES, LESLIE, REL & PHIL DEPT, STEPHENS COLLEGE, COLUMBIA MO 65201
BATES, STANLEY, PHIL DEPT, MIDDLEBURY COLLEGE, MIDDLEBURY VT 05753
BATISTA, FILIPE, PHIL DEPT, COL VIEUX-MONTREAL, MONTREAL QUE CAN
BATRAWI, SALAH A, BAY PATH JR COLLEGE, LONGMEADOW, MA 01106
BATTIN, PEGGY, PHIL DEPT, UNIV OF CALIFORNIA, IRVINE CA 92664
BATTLE, JOHN, PHIL DEPT, DEPAUL UNIVERSITY, CHICAGO IL 60604
BAUER, FRANCES, PHIL DEPT, GEORGE WILLIAMS UNIV, MONTREAL 107 QUE CAN
BAUER, FREDERICK, PHIL DEPT, ASSUMPTION COLLEGE, WORCESTER MA 01609
BAUM, MAURICE, PHILOSOPHY DEPT, KENT STATE UNIV, KENT OH 44242
BAUM, ROBERT J, PHIL DEPT, RENSSELAER POLYTECH, TROY NY 12181
BAUMAN, CLARENCE, HIST & THEOL, GOSHEN BIB SEM, ELKHART IN 46514
BAUMER, WILLIAM H, PHIL DEPT, ST UNIV OF NY, AMHERST NY 14226
BAUMGARTEN, JOSEPH, PHIL & REL DEPT, TOWSON STATE COL, BALTIMORE MD 21204
BAUMGARTNER, JORG, PHIL DEPT, MICHIGAN STATE UNIV, EAST LANSING MI 48823
BAUMLI, FRANCIS, PHIL DEPT, UNIV OF MISSOURI, COLUMBIA MO 65201
BAUMRIN, BERNARD H, PHIL PROGRAM, GRADUATE SCH -CUNY, NEW YORK NY 10036
BAUR, FRANCIS, SYST & PHIL, GRADUATE THEOL UNION, BERKELEY CA 94709
BAXLEY, THOMAS F, PHIL DEPT, FLORIDA ATLANTIC U, BOCA RATON FL 33432
BAYLES, MICHAEL D, PHIL DEPT, UNIV OF KENTUCKY, LEXINGTON KY 40506
BAYLEY, JAMES E, PHIL DEPT, CITY COLLEGE, NEW YORK NY 10031
BAYSDEN, RICHARD, PHIL DEPT, DEPAUL UNIVERSITY, CHICAGO IL 60604
BAZEMORE, WALLACE D, PHIL DEPT, CAL ST UNIV -HUMBOLDT, ARCATA CA 95521
BEACH, EDWARD, PHIL DEPT, NORTHWESTERN UNIV, EVANSTON IL 60201
BEACH, JANE ADELE, PHIL DEPT, INDIANA UNIVERSITY, BLOOMINGTON IN 47401
BEACH, JOHN D, PHILOSOPHY DEPT, MARQUETTE UNIV, MILWAUKEE WI 53233
BEAIRD, CHARLES T, PHIL DEPT, CENTENARY COL OF LA, SHREVEPORT LA 71104
BEAL, MELVIN W, PHIL DEPT, UNIV OF CALIFORNIA, DAVIS CA 95616
BEALS, DUANE, GEN STUD DIV, FT WAYNE BIBLE COL, FORT WAYNE IN 46807
BEALS, LAWRENCE, PHIL DEPT, WILLIAMS COLLEGE, WILLIAMSTOWN MA 01267
BEAMAN, EDWARD, PHIL DEPT, UNIV OF WEST ONTARIO, LONDON ONT CAN
BEAN, EDWARD H F, PHILOSOPHY DEPT, MERCED COLLEGE, MERCED CA 95340
BEAN, WILLIAM, PHILOSOPHY DEPT, UNIV OF CALGARY, CALGARY 44 ALB CAN
BEANBLOSSOM, RONALD E, PHIL DEPT, N ILLINOIS UNIV, DEKALB IL 60115
BEARD, ROBERT W, PHIL DEPT, FLORIDA STATE UNIV, TALLAHASSEE FL 32306
BEARDSLEY, ELIZABETH, PHIL DEPT, TEMPLE UNIVERSITY, PHILADELPHIA PA 19122
BEARDSLEY, HARRY, PHIL & REL, DRAKE UNIVERSITY, DES MOINES IA 50311

BEARDSLEY, MONROE, PHIL DEPT, TEMPLE UNIVERSITY, PHILADELPHIA PA   19122
BEARY, THOMAS, PHILOSOPHY DEPT, TRINITY COLLEGE, BURLINGTON VT   05401
BEATIE, WILLIAM, ST MARY'S COL OF CAL, MORAGA, CA   94575
BEATTIE, LORRAINE, PHILOSOPHY DEPT, UNIV OF WATERLOO, WATERLOO ONT   CAN
BEATTY, HARRY, PHILOSOPHY DEPT, MCGILL UNIVERSITY, MONTREAL QUE   CAN
BEATTY, HARRY, PHIL DEPT, GEORGE WILLIAMS UNIV, MONTREAL 107 QUE   CAN
BEATTY, JOSEPH W, PHIL DEPT, WILLIAMS COLLEGE, WILLIAMSTOWN MA   01267
BEATTY, MICHAEL, LIBR ARTS FAC, ATHENAEUM OF OHIO, CINCINNATI OH   45230
BEAUCHAMP, D, PHILOSOPHY DEPT, LAURENTIAN UNIV, SUDBURY ONT   CAN
BEAUCHAMP, EMMETTE W, PHILOSOPHY DEPT, UNIV OF TEXAS, AUSTIN TX   78712
BEAUCHAMP, TOM L, PHIL DEPT, GEORGETOWN UNIV, WASHINGTON DC   20007
BEAUCHEMIN, LUCILLE, PHIL DEPT, COL VIEUX-MONTREAL, MONTREAL QUE   CAN
BEAUCHESNE, RICHARD, PHIL DEPT, OBLATE COLLEGE & SEM, NATICK MA   01760
BEAUDET, JOEL, COL DE LEVIS-LAUZON, LAUZON, QUE   CAN
BEAUDRY, DENISE, COLLEGE D'AHUNTSIC, MONTREAL, QUE   CAN
BEAUDRY, PIERRE, PHIL DEPT, COL DE SHERBROOKE, SHERBROOKE QUE   CAN
BEAULIEU, RICHARD J, PHIL DEPT, ST LOUIS UNIVERSITY, ST LOUIS MO   63103
BEAULIEU, YVES-MICHEL, PHIL DEPT, CCL BOIS-DE-BOULOGNE, MONTREAL QUE   CAN
BEAUREGARD-BEZOU, M J, LIBR ARTS, DETROIT COL BUSINESS, DEARBORN MI   48126
BEAUREGARD, LAURENT, REED COLLEGE, PORTLAND, OR   97202
BEAVERS, TEDD D, PHIL & HIST DEPT, EL RENO JUNIOR COL, EL RENO OK   73036
BECK, C M, PHIL OF EDUC & HIST, ONTARIO INSTITUTE, TORONTO ONT   CAN
BECK, FLORENCE, THEOL & PHIL DEPT, AVILA COLLEGE, KANSAS CITY MO   64145
BECK, LEWIS W, PHIL DEPT, UNIV OF ROCHESTER, ROCHESTER NY   14627
BECK, ROBERT H, 139-B BURTON HALL, UNIV OF MINNESOTA, MINNEAPOLIS MN   55455
BECK, ROBERT N, PHIL DEPT, CLARK UNIVERSITY, WORCESTER MA   01610
BECKA, RICHARD, PHIL & HUM DEPT, TEXAS A & M UNIV, COL STATION TX   77843
BECKER, CARL B, PHIL DEPT, UNIVERSITY OF HAWAII, HONOLULU HI   96822
BECKER, EDWARD F, PHIL DEPT, UNIV OF NEBRASKA, LINCOLN NE   68502
BECKER, JAMES B, REL & PHIL DEPT, PRINCIPIA COLLEGE, ELSAH IL   62028
BECKER, LAWRENCE, PHIL & RELIG DEPT, HOLLINS COLLEGE, HOLLINS COL VA   24020
BECKETT, WILLIAM, PHILOSOPHY DEPT, UNIV OF VERMONT, BURLINGTON VT   05401
BECKMAN, TAD A, HUMAN & SOC SCI DEPT, HARVEY MUDD COL, CLAREMONT CA   91711
BECKNER, MORTON, PHILOSOPHY DEPT, POMONA COLLEGE, CLAREMONT CA   91711
BECNEL, EDWIN R, PHILOSOPHY DEPT, UNIV OF HOUSTON, HOUSTON TX   77004
BEDARD, SERGE, COL ANDRE-GRASSET, MONTREAL, QUE   CAN
BEDAU, HUGO ADAM, PHIL DEPT, TUFTS UNIVERSITY, MEDFORD MA   02155
BEDELL, GARY, PHIL DEPT, ROCKHURST COLLEGE, KANSAS CITY MO   64110
BEDFORD, MITCHELL, HARTNELL COLLEGE, SALINAS, CA   93901
BEEBE, WILLIAM, PHIL & THEOL DEPT, FELICIAN COLLEGE, LODI NJ   07644
BEEHLER, R G, PHILOSOPHY DEPT, UNIV OF VICTORIA, VICTORIA B C   CAN
BEELICK, DONALD J, PHILOSOPHY DEPT, WRIGHT STATE UNIV, DAYTON OH   45431
BEERMAN, LEONARD, IMMACULATE HEART COL, LOS ANGELES, CA   90027
BEGIN, ANNE-MARIE, PHIL DEPT, COL DE LA POCATIERE, LA POCATIERE QUE   CAN
BEGUS, OTTO R, PHILOSOPHY DEPT, MORGAN STATE UNIV, BALTIMORE MD   21239
BEHANNON, W, RELIG & PHIL DEPT, SOUTH BAPTIST COL, WALNUT RIDGE AR   72476
BEHLING, RICHARD, PHIL DEPT, UNIV OF WISCONSIN, EAU CLAIRE WI   54701
BEHR, STANLEY M, HUMAN DEPT, WESTCHESTER COM COL, VALHALLA NY   10595
BEICLER, WILLIAM, PHILOSOPHY DEPT, GUILFORD COLLEGE, GREENSBORO NC   27410
BEIS, RICHARD H, PHIL DEPT, ST MARY'S UNIVERSITY, HALIFAX N S   CAN
BEISWANGER, GEORGE, PHIL DEPT, GEORGIA ST UNIV, ATLANTA GA   30303
BEJERRING, ANDREW, PHIL DEPT, UNIV OF WEST ONTARIO, LONDON ONT   CAN
BEKEART, DANA, LIBR ARTS & SOC SCI, KAUAI COM COL, LIHUE HI   96766
BELAIEF, GAIL A, PHILOSOPHY DEPT, RUTGERS UNIV, NEW BRUNSWICK NJ   08903
BELAIEF, LYNNE, PHIL DEPT, STATEN IS COM COL, STATEN ISLAND NY   10301
BELANGER, MARCEL, PHIL DEPT, COL RIVIERE DU LOUP, RIVIERE LOUP QUE   CAN
BELANGER, MARION, PHIL DEPT, COLLEGE SAINT-LOUIS, EDMUNDSTON N B   CAN
BELANGER, MARTIN, COL ANDRE-GRASSET, MONTREAL, QUE   CAN
BELANGER, ROLAND, PHIL DEPT, COL BOIS-DE-BOULOGNE, MONTREAL QUE   CAN
BELCHER, JOHN C, PHIL DEPT, S ILLINOIS UNIV, CARBONDALE IL   62901
BELFORD, CHARLES E, PHIL DEPT, KING'S COLLEGE, WILKES BARRE PA   18711
BELFORD, JULES, LIBR ARTS DIV, MARYMOUNT COLLEGE, BOCA RATON FL   33432
BELIVEAU, GUY, PHILOSOPHY DEPT, MCGILL UNIVERSITY, MONTREAL QUE   CAN
BELK, LEOTIS, COLGATE DIV SCHOOL, ROCHESTER, NY   14620

BELL, JAMES, PHILOSOPHY DEPT, BLOOMFIELD COLLEGE, BLOOMFIELD NJ 07003
BELL, LINDA A, PHIL DEPT, GEORGIA ST UNIV, ATLANTA GA 30303
BELL, ROGER, PHIL DEPT, ST UNIV OF NY, STONY BROOK NY 11790
BELLEVILLE, RICHARD, PHIL DEPT, ANNA MARIA COLLEGE, PAXTON MA 01612
BELNAP JR, NUEL D, PHIL DEPT, UNIV OF PITTSBURGH, PITTSBURGH PA 15260
BELOW, WILLIAM A, PHIL DEPT, UNIV OF CALIFORNIA, SANTA BARBARA CA 93106
BELSAN, RICHARD C, PHIL & REL STUD, YOUNGSTOWN ST UNIV, YOUNGSTOWN OH 44503
BELZER, PAUL, UNDERGRAD DEPT, ST JOHN VIANNEY SEM, E AURORA NY 14052
BEN-HORIN, MEIR, DROPSIE UNIVERSITY, PHILADELPHIA, PA 19132
BENACERRAF, PAUL, PHIL DEPT, PRINCETON UNIVERSITY, PRINCETON NJ 08540
BENANDER, DONALD, HUMAN DEPT, GREENFIELD COM COL, GREENFIELD MA 01301
BENARDETE, JOSE, PHIL DEPT, SYRACUSE UNIVERSITY, SYRACUSE NY 13210
BENARDETE, SETH, PHIL DEPT, NW SCH FOR SOC RES, NEW YORK NY 10003
BENAVIDES, MANUEL, PHIL DEPT, CATHOLIC UNIVERSITY, PONCE PR 00731
BENDALL, L KENT, PHILOSOPHY DEPT, WESLEYAN UNIV, MIDDLETOWN CT 06457
BENDER, BARBARA, PHILOSOPHY DEPT, MCGILL UNIVERSITY, MONTREAL QUE CAN
BENDER, FRED A, PHIL DEPT, SAN ANTONIO COL, SAN ANTONIO TX 78284
BENDER, FREDERIC L, PHIL DEPT, UNIVERSITY OF HAWAII, HONOLULU HI 96822
BENDER, GERALD E, GEN EDUC DEPT, CLEARY COLLEGE, YPSILANTI MI 48197
BENDER, THORWALD W, THEOL DEPT, E BAPT THEOL SEM, PHILADELPHIA PA 19151
BENDITT, THEODORE, PHILOSOPHY DEPT, DUKE UNIVERSITY, DURHAM NC 27706
BENEDICT, JAMES, HUMAN DEPT, LINCOLN TRAIL COL, ROBINSON IL 62454
BENFIELD, D, PHIL & RELIG DEPT, MONTCLAIR ST COL, UPR MONTCLAIR NJ 07043
BENGLIAN, V, PHILOSOPHY DEPT, UNIV OF TORONTO, TORONTO ONT CAN
BENHAIME, GUILA, COLLEGE D'AHUNTSIC, MONTREAL, QUE CAN
BENIN, ITALO, PHIL DEPT, MARIST COLLEGE, POUGHKEEPSIE NY 12601
BENJAMIN, MARTIN, PHIL DEPT, MICHIGAN STATE UNIV, EAST LANSING MI 48823
BENNETT, DANIEL, PHIL DEPT, SWARTHMORE COLLEGE, SWARTHMORE PA 19081
BENNETT, DAVID W, PHILOSOPHY DEPT, UNIV OF UTAH, SALT LAKE CITY UT 84112
BENNETT, HENRY G, HUMAN DIV, CORNING COM COL, CORNING NY 14830
BENNETT, HOWARD, PHIL DEPT, MIAMI-DADE JUN COL, MIAMI FL 33156
BENNETT, JAMES D, PHILOSOPHY DEPT, RUTGERS UNIV, NEW BRUNSWICK NJ 08903
BENNETT, JAMES O, PHIL DEPT, UNIV OF TENNESSEE, KNOXVILLE TN 37916
BENNETT, JOHN B, PHIL & RELIG DEPT, NORTHLAND COLLEGE, ASHLAND WI 54806
BENNETT, JOHN B, RELIG & PHIL DEPT, W CAROLINA UNIV, CULLOWHEE NC 28723
BENNETT, JONATHAN F, PHIL DEPT, UNIV BRIT COLUMBIA, VANCOUVER 8 B C CAN
BENNETT, LEWIS F, PHIL DEPT, NIAGARA UNIVERSITY, NIAGARA UNIV NY 14109
BENNETT, OWEN, PHIL DEPT, ST HYACINTH COLLEGE, GRANBY MA 01033
BENNETT, PHILIP, PHIL DEPT, COL AT CORTLAND, CORTLAND NY 13045
BENNETT, ROBERT C, SOC SCI DIV, EL CENTRO COL, DALLAS TX 75202
BENNETT, STEPHAN, PHIL DEPT, SACRED HEART UNIV, BRIDGEPORT CT 06604
BENNETT, THOMAS E, SOC SCI DEPT, NORTHWOOD INSTITUTE, MIDLAND MI 48640
BENNETT, WILLIAM, PHIL DEPT, BOSTON UNIVERSITY, BOSTON MA 02215
BENNEWITZ, DONALD, PHIL DEPT, COL OF SAINT TERESA, WINONA MN 55987
BENSKY, JEROLD M, PHIL DEPT, UNIVERSITY OF MIAMI, CORAL GABLES FL 33124
BENSON, ARTHUR, PHIL DEPT, CALIFORNIA ST UNIV, LOS ANGELES CA 90032
BENSON, JOHN, PHIL DEPT, AUGSBURG COLLEGE, MINNEAPOLIS MN 55404
BENSON, JOHN, PHIL & REL DEPT, TOCCOA FALLS INST, TOCCOA FALLS GA 30577
BENSON, P JANN, PHIL DEPT, COLORADO ST UNIV, FORT COLLINS CO 80521
BENSON, RICHARD, PHILOSOPHY DEPT, UNIV OF MASS, AMHERST MA 01002
BENSON, ROBERT, PHIL DEPT, WAGNER COLLEGE, STATEN ISLAND NY 10301
BENSON, RONALD E, PHIL & RELIG DEPT, OHIO NORTHERN UNIV, ADA OH 45810
BENSON, THOMAS, PHIL DEPT, UNIV OF MARYLAND, BALTIMORE MD 21228
BENT, R S, PHIL & RELIG DEPT, ROANOKE COLLEGE, SALEM VA 24153
BERENDA, CARLTON W, PHILOSOPHY DEPT, UNIV OF OKLAHOMA, NORMAN OK 73069
BERENS, V, PHILOSOPHY DEPT, LAURENTIAN UNIV, SUDBURY ONT CAN
BERG, DONALD J, ARTS & SCI DEPT, IOWA WEST COM COL, COUNCIL BLFS IA 51501
BERG, PAUL C, PHIL DIV, SACRED HEART SEM, DETROIT MI 48206
BERG, RICHARD, PHIL DEPT, INDIANA-PURDUE UNIV, INDIANAPOLIS IN 46202
BERGEL, ALICE ROSE, PSYCH DEPT, EAST LOS ANGELES COL, LOS ANGELES CA 90022
BERGEN, JOHN D, ENG DEPT, U S MILITARY ACAD, WEST POINT NY 10996
BERGER, ALAN, PHIL DEPT, ROCKEFELLER UNIV, NEW YORK NY 10021
BERGER, CAROL A, PHIL DEPT, ST LOUIS UNIVERSITY, ST LOUIS MO 63103
BERGER, DANIEL P, PHIL DEPT, UNIV OF ILLINOIS, CHICAGO IL 60680

BERGER, FRED R, PHIL DEPT, UNIV OF CALIFORNIA, DAVIS CA 95616
BERGER, JEFFREY, HIST & PHIL, COM COL PHILADELPHIA, PHILADELPHIA PA 19107
BERGERON, GUSTAVE, PHIL DEPT, COL TROIS-RIVIERES, 3 RIVIERES QUE   CAN
BERGGREN, DOUGLAS C, PHILOSOPHY DEPT, NEW COLLEGE, SARASOTA FL 33578
BERGHEL, HAROLD L, PHIL DEPT, UNIV CF NEBRASKA, LINCOLN NE 68502
BERGMANN, FRITHJOF, PHIL DEPT, UNIV OF MICHIGAN, ANN ARBOR MI 48104
BERGMANN, GUSTAV, PHIL DEPT, UNIVERSITY OF IOWA, IOWA CITY IA 52240
BERGMANN, M, PHILOSOPHY DEPT, UNIV OF TORONTO, TORONTO ONT   CAN
BERGMARK, ROBERT E, PHIL DEPT, MILLSAPS COLLEGE, JACKSON MS 39210
BERGOFFEN, DEBRA B, HUMAN DEPT, GEORGE MASON UNIV, FAIRFAX VA 22030
BERKOVITS, ELIEZER, PHIL & REL DEPT, HEBREW THEOL COL, SKOKIE IL 60076
BERKSON, WILLIAM, PHIL DEPT, BRIDGEWATER ST COL, BRIDGEWATER MA 02324
BERLEANT, ARNOLD, PHIL DEPT, LONG ISLAND UNIV, GREENVALE NY 11548
BERLINSKI, DAVID, PHILOSOPHY DEPT, RUTGERS UNIV, NEWARK NJ 07102
BERLUS, MONIQUE, PHILOSOPHY DEPT, CCL DE MAISONNEUVE, MONTREAL QUE   CAN
BERMAN, MYRON, PHIL & RELIG, VA COMMONWEALTH UNIV, RICHMOND VA 23220
BERNAL, JUAN, PHIL DEPT, UNIV OF CALIFORNIA, IRVINE CA 92664
BERNDTSON, ARTHUR, PHIL DEPT, UNIV CF MISSOURI, COLUMBIA MO 65201
BERNHARDT, WILLIAM H, REL PHIL DEPT, ILIFF SCH OF THEOL, DENVER CO 80210
BERNIER, PIERRE, SEMINAIRE DE QUEBEC, QUEBEC, QUE   CAN
BERNIER, R, COL DOM PHIL & THEOL, OTTAWA, ONT   CAN
BERNIER, REJANE, PHILOSOPHY DEPT, UNIV DE MONTREAL, MONTREAL QUE   CAN
BERNOFF, MAXON A, COSUMNES RIVER COL, SACRAMENTO, CA 95823
BERNSTEIN, RICHARD J, PHIL DEPT, HAVERFORD COLLEGE, HAVERFORD PA 19041
BERNTEN, MARC, PHILOSOPHY DEPT, COL DE MAISONNEUVE, MONTREAL QUE   CAN
BEROFSKY, BERNARD, PHIL DEPT, COLUMBIA UNIVERSITY, NEW YORK NY 10027
BERGUIST, DUANE H, PHIL DEPT, ASSUMPTION COLLEGE, WORCESTER MA 01609
BERGUIST, RICHARD, PHIL DEPT, COL OF ST THOMAS, ST PAUL MN 55105
BERRECKMAN, CARLETON, PHILOSOPHY DEPT, DUQUESNE UNIV, PITTSBURGH PA 15219
BERRIMAN, W, PHIL & CLASS DEPT, UNIV OF SASKATCHEWAN, REGINA SAS   CAN
BERRY, CORNELIUS, SYST & PHIL, GRADUATE THEOL UNION, BERKELEY CA 94709
BERRY, DONALD L, PHIL & RELIG DEPT, COLGATE UNIVERSITY, HAMILTON NY 13346
BERRY, GEORGE, PHIL DEPT, BOSTON UNIVERSITY, BOSTON MA 02215
BERRY, JOHN, PHIL DEPT, XAVIER UNIVERSITY, NEW ORLEANS LA 70125
BERRYMAN, JAMES, PHIL DEPT, OUACHITA BAPTIST U, ARKADELPHIA AR 71923
BERSTEIN, MICHAEL, HUMAN DEPT, LONG ISLAND UNIV, BROOKLYN NY 11216
BERTHOLD, DANIEL, PHIL DEPT, COL DE SHERBROOKE, SHERBROOKE QUE   CAN
BERTLING, MARTIN, PHIL DEPT, LEWIS COLLEGE, LOCKPORT IL 60441
BERTMAN, MARTIN, PHIL DEPT, COL AT POTSDAM, POTSDAM NY 13676
BERTOCCI, PETER A, PHIL DEPT, BOSTON UNIVERSITY, BOSTON MA 02215
BERTOLET, RODNEY J, PHILOSOPHY DEPT, UNIV OF WISCONSIN, MADISON WI 53706
BERTRAM, MARYANNE, HUMAN STUD DEPT, MARIAN COLLEGE, FOND DU LAC WI 54935
BERTRAM, ROBERT W, SYST THEOL DEPT, CONCORDIA SEMINARY, ST LOUIS MO 63105
BERTRAUD, CLAUDE, PHILOSOPHY DEPT, COL DE MAISONNEUVE, MONTREAL QUE   CAN
BERTSCH, JACK H, SOC SCI DEPT, CLARION STATE COL, CLARION PA 16214
BERUBE, EDWARD, PHILOSOPHY DEPT, DUQUESNE UNIV, PITTSBURGH PA 15219
BESANCON, RICHARD, PHIL & REL DIV, JUDSON COLLEGE, ELGIN IL 60120
BESNER, PIERRE-PAUL, PHIL DEPT, COL DE LA POCATIERE, LA POCATIERE QUE   CAN
BETHEL, ARTHUR C W, PHIL DEPT, CAL POLYTECH ST U, SAN LUIS OBIS CA 93407
BETTENHAUSEN, E, PHIL DEPT, UNIV OF WISCONSIN, EAU CLAIRE WI 54701
BETTY, L STAFFORD, PHIL & REL STUD, CAL STATE COL, BAKERSFIELD CA 93309
BETZ, JOSEPH M, PHILOSOPHY DEPT, VILLANOVA UNIV, VILLANOVA PA 19085
BEUKEMA, CAL C, APPALACHIAN BIB INST, BRADLEY, WV 25818
BEUTTENMULLER, PAUL, PHIL & THEOL DEPT, MARILLAC COLLEGE, ST LOUIS MO 63121
BEVERSLUIS, ERIC, PHILOSOPHY DEPT, CAPITAL UNIV, COLUMBUS OH 43209
BEVERSLUIS, JOHN, PHIL DEPT, BUTLER UNIVERSITY, INDIANAPOLIS IN 46205
BEVIER, WILLIAM A, DETROIT BIB COLLEGE, DETROIT, MI 48235
BEYER, C, PHILOSOPHY DEPT, UNIV OF TORONTO, TORONTO ONT   CAN
BEYER, E, PHILOSOPHY DEPT, PFEIFFER COLLEGE, MISENHEIMER NC 28109
BEYER, LANDON E, PHILOSOPHY DEPT, UNIV OF WISCONSIN, MADISON WI 53706
BEYERS, JOHN M, LANG & PHIL DEPT, UTAH STATE UNIV, LOGAN UT 84322
BEZ, GABRIEL, PHIL DEPT, COL FRANCOIS-X-GARN, QUEBEC CITY QUE   CAN
BIAYS, PAUL M, PHIL DEPT, BARTON CO COM JR COL, GREAT BEND KS 67530
BICHL, WILLIAM M, PHIL DEPT, JOHN CARROLL UNIV, UNIVERSITY HT OH 44118

BICKHAM, STEPHEN, PHIL DEPT, MANSFIELD ST COLLEGE, MANSFIELD PA 16933
BICKLEY, THEODORE, PHILOSOPHY DEPT, KENT STATE UNIV, KENT OH 44242
BIEDERMAN, CHARLES, PHILOSOPHY DEPT, RUTGERS UNIV, NEWARK NJ 07102
BIEFELD, REBECCA, PHIL DEPT, DEPAUL UNIVERSITY, CHICAGO IL 60604
BIEN, JOSEPH, PHIL DEPT, UNIV OF MISSOURI, COLUMBIA MO 65201
BIENER, E, PHIL OF EDUC & HIST, ONTARIO INSTITUTE, TORONTO ONT   CAN
BIERMAN, ARTHUR K, PHIL DEPT, CALIFORNIA ST UNIV, SAN FRANCISCO CA 94132
BIFFLE, JAMES, PHIL DEPT, SN BERNARDINO VALLEY, SN BERNARDINO CA 92403
BIGELOW, LESLIE COLE, PHIL DEPT, MIDDLEBURY COLLEGE, MIDDLEBURY VT 05753
BIGGER, C, PHIL DEPT, LOUISIANA ST UNIV, BATON ROUGE LA 70803
BIGGS, THEODORE, SOC SCI DIV, SOLANO COLLEGE, SUISUN CITY CA 94585
BIGHAM, KYLE, LANG DIV, GENESEE COM COL, FLINT MI 47503
BILBIJA, ZARKO, PHIL DEPT, FLORIDA STATE UNIV, TALLAHASSEE FL 32306
BILEK, G, SOC SCI DEPT, RYERSON POLYTECH U, TORONTO ONT   CAN
BILIK, LAURIE, LIBR ARTS DIV, COL OF INSURANCE, NEW YORK NY 10038
BILINSKI, MICHAEL, PHILOSOPHY DEPT, UNIV OF WATERLOO, WATERLOO ONT   CAN
BILL, THOMAS L, PHILOSOPHY DEPT, UNIV OF PORTLAND, PORTLAND OR 97203
BILLER, MARY ANN, PHIL DEPT, ST THOS AQUINAS COL, SPARKILL NY 10976
BILLING, MARTIN, HUMAN DEPT, SOUTHWEST COLLEGE, CHICAGO IL 60652
BILLINGS, JOHN R, PHIL DEPT, UNIV OF WISCONSIN, STEVENS POINT WI 54481
BILODEAU, THOMAS, LANG & HUMAN DIV, COL UNIV ST JEAN, EDMONTON ALB   CAN
BILSKY, MANUEL, HIST & PHIL DEPT, E MICHIGAN UNIV, YPSILANTI MI 48197
BIMSON, NORMAN, PHILOSOPHY DEPT, MCGILL UNIVERSITY, MONTREAL QUE   CAN
BINGHAM, WILLIAM, FLORIDA KEYS COM COL, KEY WEST, FL 33040
BINKLEY, LUTHER J, PHIL DEPT, FRANKLIN & MARSHALL, LANCASTER PA 17604
BINKLEY, ROBERT W, PHIL DEPT, UNIV OF WEST ONTARIO, LONDON ONT   CAN
BINNIE, D J, ENG & PHIL DEPT, ROYAL MILITARY COL, KINGSTON ONT   CAN
BINSWANGER, HARRY, PHIL DEPT, HUNTER COLLEGE, NEW YORK NY 10021
BIRCH, THOMAS, PHIL DEPT, UNIV OF MONTANA, MISSOULA MT 59801
BIRCHENBACK, J, PHILOSOPHY DEPT, UNIV OF ALBERTA, EDMONTON ALB   CAN
BIRD, DENNIS, PHIL DEPT, MICHIGAN STATE UNIV, EAST LANSING MI 48823
BIRD, OTTO, PHIL DEPT, NORTHWESTERN UNIV, EVANSTON IL 60201
BIRMINGHAM, FRANK, PHILOSOPHY DEPT, UNIV OF NW HAMPSHIRE, DURHAM NH 03824
BIRMINGHAM, JOHN T, PHILOSOPHY DEPT, CALIFORNIA ST UNIV, HAYWARD CA 94542
BIRNEY, GEORGE H, PHIL & REL DEPT, NORWICH UNIVERSITY, NORTHFIELD VT 05663
BISHOP, CLAYTON K, HUM & SOC SCI, LAKE-SUMTER COM COL, LEESBURG FL 32748
BISHOP, DONALD H, PHILOSOPHY DEPT, WASHINGTON ST UNIV, PULLMAN WA 99163
BISHOP, J, PHILOSOPHY DEPT, ST FRAN XAVIER UNIV, SYDNEY N S   CAN
BISHOP, S J, PHIL DEPT, UNIV OF NW BRUNSWICK, FREDERICTON N B   CAN
BISZTYO, J, PHILOSOPHY DEPT, ST THOMAS MORE COL, SASKATOON SAS   CAN
BJELLAND, ANDREW, PHILOSOPHY DEPT, GONZAGA UNIV, SPOKANE WA 99202
BJORNSTAD, JAMES, PHILOSOPHY DEPT, NE COL BIBLE INST, ESSEX FELLS NJ 07021
BJURLOFF, THOMAS A, PHIL DEPT, UNIV OF N CAROLINA, CHAPEL HILL NC 27514
BLACHOWICZ, JAMES, PHIL DEPT, LOYOLA UNIVERSITY, CHICAGO IL 60626
BLACK, BRYAN T, PHIL DEPT, UNIV OF MONTANA, MISSOULA MT 59801
BLACK, CAROLYN C, PHIL DEPT, CALIFORNIA ST UNIV, SAN JOSE CA 95114
BLACK, EDWARD J, PHIL DEPT, CALIFORNIA ST UNIV, SAN JOSE CA 95114
BLACK, MAX, SAGE SCHOOL, CORNELL UNIVERSITY, ITHACA NY 14850
BLACK, MILTON, SOC SCI DEPT, SHASTA COLLEGE, REDDING CA 96001
BLACKBURN, ROBERT J, PHILOSOPHY AREA, ROGER WILLIAMS COL, BRISTOL RI 02809
BLACKMAN, LARRY, PHIL DEPT, COL AT GENESEO, GENESEO NY 14454
BLACKSTONE, WILLIAM T, PHIL & REL DEPT, UNIV OF GEORGIA, ATHENS GA 30602
BLACKWELL, RICHARD J, PHIL DEPT, ST LOUIS UNIVERSITY, ST LOUIS MO 63103
BLACKWOOD, RUSSELL T, PHIL DEPT, HAMILTON COLLEGE, CLINTON NY 13323
BLAIN, LIONEL A, PHILOSOPHY DEPT, SEM OF LADY OF PROV, WARWICK RI 02889
BLAIR, ALEXANDER, NEW MEXICO ST UNIV, ALAMOGORDO, NM 88310
BLAIR, ELENA, PHILOSOPHY DEPT, XAVIER UNIVERSITY, CINCINNATI OH 45207
BLAIR, GEORGE A, PHIL DEPT, THOMAS MORE COLLEGE, COVINGTON KY 41017
BLAIR, JOHN A, PHILOSOPHY DEPT, UNIV OF WINDSOR, WINDSOR ONT   CAN
BLAIR, KATHRYN, SOC SCI DEPT, NE MISSOURI ST UNIV, KIRKSVILLE MO 63501
BLAIS, MARTIN, PHIL FACULTE, UNIVERSITE LAVAL, CITE UNIV QUE   CAN
BLAKE, ARTHUR J, ST PETER'S COLLEGE, JERSEY CITY, NJ 07306
BLAKE, BETSY A, PHILOSOPHY DEPT, OHIO STATE UNIV, COLUMBUS OH 43210
BLAKELEY, THOMAS J, PHIL DEPT, BOSTON COLLEGE, CHESTNUT HILL MA 02167

BLANCHARD, ERIC, PHIL DEPT, WASHINGTON UNIV, ST LOUIS MO 63130
BLANCHARD, JOHN P, PHIL DEPT, UNIV OF N CAROLINA, CHAPEL HILL NC 27514
BLANCHARD, YVON, PHILOSOPHY DEPT, UNIV DE MONTREAL, MONTREAL QUE CAN
BLANCHET, LOUIS-EMILE, PHIL FACULTE, UNIVERSITE LAVAL, CITE UNIV QUE CAN
BLANCHETTE, OLIVIA, PHIL DEPT, BOSTON COLLEGE, CHESTNUT HILL MA 02167
BLANCO, ENRIQUE, HIST GOV & PHIL, ADAMS STATE COL, ALAMOSA CO 81101
BLANDFORD, JAMES C, PHILOSOPHY DEPT, UNIV OF DELAWARE, NEWARK DE 19711
BLANK, JOHN S, PHIL DEPT, PORTLAND ST UNIV, PORTLAND OR 97207
BLANK, LEONARD B, PHIL DEPT, HOWARD UNIVERSITY, WASHINGTON DC 20001
BLANKENSHIP, J DAVID, PHIL DEPT, COL AT NEW PLATZ, NEW PLATZ NY 12561
BLASEN, CHARLES, PHIL DEPT, ST MARY'S UNIVERSITY, SAN ANTONIO TX 78228
BLASIUS, RON, PHILOSOPHY DEPT, REGIS COLLEGE, DENVER CO 80221
BLATZ, CHARLES, PHILOSOPHY DEPT, UNIV OF WYOMING, LARAMIE WY 82071
BLECHER, MARLENE, PHIL DEPT, PRINCE GEORGE'S COM, LARGO MD 20870
BLEE, MICHAEL, PHIL DEPT, ST JOSEPH'S COL, PHILADELPHIA PA 19131
BLEICH, HAROLD, PHIL DEPT, MONTGOMERY COLLEGE, TAKOMA PARK MD 20012
BLESER, ROBERT, PHIL DEPT, UNIV OF CALIFORNIA, SANTA BARBARA CA 93106
BLEYER, JOHN FRANCIS, PHILOSOPHY DEPT, SETON HILL COL, GREENSBURG PA 15601
BLICKLE, THOMAS, PHILOSOPHY DEPT, OHIO STATE UNIV, COLUMBUS OH 43210
BLIZEK, WILLIAM, PHIL & REL DEPT, UNIV OF NEBRASKA, OMAHA NE 68132
BLOCK, IRVING L, PHIL DEPT, UNIV OF WEST ONTARIO, LONDON ONT CAN
BLOCK, NED J, PHIL DEPT, MASS INST TECH, CAMBRIDGE MA 02139
BLOCKER, H GENE, PHILOSOPHY DEPT, OHIO UNIVERSITY, ATHENS OH 45701
BLOM, JOHN, PHIL DEPT, HUNTER COLLEGE, NEW YORK NY 10021
BLOMGREN, FRED J, ENG & HUM DEPT, MCNROE COM COL, ROCHESTER NY 14623
BLONDIN, FELIX, COL ST-JEAN VIANNEY, MONTREAL, QUE CAN
BLOCM, WALTER S, FINE ARTS DEPT, YUBA COLLEGE, MARYSVILLE CA 95901
BLOOMFIELD, E H, PHILOSOPHY DEPT, CERRITOS COLLEGE, NORWALK CA 90605
BLOSE, BARRY L, PHIL DEPT, THE AMERICAN UNIV, WASHINGTON DC 20016
BLOUSTEIN, EDWARD J, PHILOSOPHY DEPT, RUTGERS UNIV, NEW BRUNSWICK NJ 08903
BLOW, WILLIAM O, SOC SCI DEPT, PATRICK HENRY JR COL, MONROEVILLE AL 36460
BLUE, CRAIG, PHIL DEPT, UNIV OF CALIFORNIA, IRVINE CA 92664
BLUHM, DAVID, PHIL & RELIG, UNIV OF NORTH IOWA, CEDAR FALLS IA 50613
BLUM, GARY, PHIL & REL DEPT, UNIV OF NEBRASKA, OMAHA NE 68132
BLUM, LAWRENCE, PHILOSOPHY DEPT, UNIV OF MASS, BOSTON MA 02116
BLUM, ROLAND P, PHIL & RELIG DEPT, COLGATE UNIVERSITY, HAMILTON NY 13346
BLUMBERG, ALBERT E, PHILOSOPHY DEPT, RUTGERS UNIV, NEW BRUNSWICK NJ 08903
BLUMBERG, DAVID, HUMAN DEPT, NEW YORK CY COM COL, BROOKLYN NY 11201
BLUMENFELD, DAVID, PHIL DEPT, UNIV OF ILLINOIS, CHICAGO IL 60680
BLUMENFELD, JEAN, PHILOSOPHY DEPT, UNIV OF TEXAS, AUSTIN TX 78712
BLYSTONE, JASPER, LOYOLA UNIVERSITY, LOS ANGELES, CA 90045
BOARDMAN, WILLIAM S, PHILOSOPHY DEPT, LAWRENCE UNIV, APPLETON WI 54911
BOAS, GEORGE, PHIL DEPT, JOHNS HOPKINS UNIV, BALTIMORE MD 21218
BOATRIGHT, JOHN R, PHIL DEPT, JOHN CARROLL UNIV, UNIVERSITY HT OH 44118
BOATRIGHT, L, PHILOSOPHY DEPT, UNIV OF RHODE ISLAND, KINGSTON RI 02881
BOBIK, JOSEPH, PHIL DEPT, UNIV OF NOTRE DAME, NOTRE DAME IN 46556
BOBINSKI, JOHN, PHILOSOPHY DEPT, KENT STATE UNIV, KENT OH 44242
BODANSZKY, EVA, PHILOSOPHY DEPT, UNIV OF MASS, AMHERST MA 01002
BODE, HUGH H, PHIL DEPT, BORROMEO SEM OF OHIO, WICKLIFFE OH 44092
BODE, ROY R, PHIL SCH, CATH UNIV OF AMER, WASHINGTON DC 20017
BODINE, PAUL E, GEN HUM DIV, DES MOINES COM COL, BOONE IA 50036
BOEKELHEIDE, CAROL J, PHIL DEPT, UNIV OF CALIFORNIA, SANTA BARBARA CA 93106
BOELEN, BERNARD J, PHIL DEPT, DEPAUL UNIVERSITY, CHICAGO IL 60604
BOER, STEVEN E, PHILOSOPHY DEPT, OHIO STATE UNIV, COLUMBUS OH 43210
BOERSCH, ALFRED H, PHIL DEPT, COLORADO ST UNIV, FORT COLLINS CO 80521
BOETZKES, ELIZABETH, PHILOSOPHY DEPT, UNIV OF CALGARY, CALGARY 44 ALB CAN
BOGAARD, P A, PHILOSOPHY DEPT, MT ALLISON UNIV, SACKVILLE N B CAN
BOGEN, JAMES, PHIL DEPT, PITZER COLLEGE, CLAREMONT CA 91750
BOGER, GEORGE, PHIL DEPT, ST UNIV OF NY, AMHERST NY 14226
BOGGS, CHARLES, PHILOSOPHY DEPT, WASH & LEE UNIV, LEXINGTON VA 24450
BOGHOLT, CARL M, PHILOSOPHY DEPT, UNIV OF WISCONSIN, MADISON WI 53706
BOGLIONI, PIETRO, PHILOSOPHY DEPT, UNIV DE MONTREAL, MONTREAL QUE CAN
BOH, IVAN, PHILOSOPHY DEPT, OHIO STATE UNIV, COLUMBUS OH 43210
BOHL JR, F ROBERT, PHIL DEPT, COL WILLIAM & MARY, WILLIAMSBURG VA 23185

BOHN, RALPH P, PHIL & RELIG DEPT, JOHNSON C SMITH UNIV, CHARLOTTE NC 28216
BOHNERT, HERBERT G, PHIL DEPT, MICHIGAN STATE UNIV, EAST LANSING MI 48823
BOILEAU, DAVID, PHIL DEPT, LOYOLA UNIVERSITY, NEW ORLEANS LA 70118
BOISVERT, FRANCOIS, PHIL DEPT, COL DE SHERBROOKE, SHERBROOKE QUE   CAN
BOK, SISSELA, PHILOSOPHY DEPT, SIMMONS COLLEGE, BOSTON MA 02115
BOLE, T J, PHILOSOPHY DEPT, AUBURN UNIVERSITY, AUBURN AL 36830
BOLER, JOHN F, PHILOSOPHY DEPT, UNIV OF WASHINGTON, SEATTLE WA 98195
BOLES, JOE R, RELIG & PHIL DIV, DALLAS BAPT COL, DALLAS TX 75211
BOLLWEG, JOHN, COMMUNIC ARTS DIV, WASHTENAW COM COL, ANN ARBOR MI 48107
BOLTON, MARTHA, PHILOSOPHY DEPT, RUTGERS UNIV, NEW BRUNSWICK NJ 08903
BOLTON, ROBERT, PHILOSOPHY DEPT, RUTGERS UNIV, NEW BRUNSWICK NJ 08903
BONANSEA, BERNARDINO M, PHIL SCH, CATH UNIV OF AMER, WASHINGTON DC 20017
BOND, E J, PHILOSOPHY DEPT, QUEEN'S UNIVERSITY, KINGSTON ONT   CAN
BOND, RICHARD, AMER STUD SCHOOL, RAMAPO COLLEGE, MAHWAH NJ 07430
BOND, STEVE, PHILOSOPHY DEPT, VANDERBILT UNIV, NASHVILLE TN 37235
BONDESON, WILLIAM, PHIL DEPT, UNIV OF MISSOURI, COLUMBIA MO 65201
BONIFAZI, CONRAD, SYST & PHIL, GRADUATE THEOL UNION, BERKELEY CA 94709
BONIS, WILLIAM D, PHIL DEPT, CALIFORNIA ST UNIV, LONG BEACH CA 90840
BONJOUR, LAURENCE, PHILOSOPHY DEPT, UNIV OF TEXAS, AUSTIN TX 78712
BONNET, CHRISTIAN, PHILOSOPHY DEPT, REGIS COLLEGE, DENVER CO 80221
BONNETTE, DENNIS, PHIL DEPT, NIAGARA UNIVERSITY, NIAGARA UNIV NY 14109
BONNEY, R, PHILOSOPHY DEPT, NOTRE DAME UNIV, NELSON B C   CAN
BONVILLAIN, R H, PHILOSOPHY DEPT, XAVIER UNIVERSITY, CINCINNATI OH 45207
BONYHARD, JANET F, PHIL DEPT, MARY WASHINGTON COL, FREDERICKSBG VA 22401
BOOLOS, GEORGE S, PHIL DEPT, MASS INST TECH, CAMBRIDGE MA 02139
BOON, KEVIN, PHILOSOPHY DEPT, BROWN UNIVERSITY, PROVIDENCE RI 02912
BOONE, DANIEL, PHIL DEPT, INDIANA UNIV OF PENN, INDIANA PA 15701
BOONE, ROBERT L, PHIL & HUM DEPT, TEXAS A & M UNIV, COL STATION TX 77843
BOONIN, LEONARD, PHIL DEPT, UNIV OF COLORADO, BOULDER CO 80302
BOORSE, CHRISTOPHER L, PHILOSOPHY DEPT, UNIV OF DELAWARE, NEWARK DE 19711
BOOSINGER, JOHN W, NW CHRISTIAN COLLEGE, EUGENE, OR 97401
BOOTHE, STEPHEN, PHIL DEPT, UNIV OF CALIFORNIA, IRVINE CA 92664
BOPP, C JOHN, PHIL DEPT, WAYNE STATE UNIV, DETROIT MI 48202
BORCHERT, DONALD M, PHILOSOPHY DEPT, OHIO UNIVERSITY, ATHENS OH 45701
BORCHERT, G, HERITAGE & THT DIV, N AMERICAN BAPT SEM, SIOUX FALLS SD 57105
BORCOMAN, K D, PHILOSOPHY DEPT, UNIV OF ALBERTA, EDMONTON ALB   CAN
BORDEAU, EDWARD, PHIL DEPT, SACRED HEART UNIV, BRIDGEPORT CT 06604
BORDELEAU, LEO-PAUL, PHIL FACULTY, UNIV OF OTTAWA, OTTAWA ONT   CAN
BORDENKIRCHER, ROBERT, PHILOSOPHY DEPT, PRESENTATION COL, ABERDEEN SD 57401
BORDO, S R, PHILOSOPHY DEPT, CARLETON UNIVERSITY, OTTAWA ONT   CAN
BORDOLI, JAMES, SOCIAL SCIENCE DIV, BUTTE COLLEGE, DURHAM CA 95938
BORGMANN, ALBERT, PHIL DEPT, UNIV OF MONTANA, MISSOULA MT 59801
BORJA, FRANCISCO, PHILOSOPHY DEPT, MARYWOOD COLLEGE, SCRANTON PA 18509
BORNSTEIN, ALFRED, PHIL DEPT, LOS ANGELES CY COL, LOS ANGELES CA 90029
BORTZFIELD, ERIC R, PHIL & REL DEPT, ENDICOTT JR COL, BEVERLY MA 01915
BOSCHI, LORRAINE, DIV OF HUMAN, MESA COL, GRAND JCT CO 81501
BOSLEY, PAUL, PHILOSOPHY DEPT, UNIV OF MASS, AMHERST MA 01002
BOSLEY, R N, PHILOSOPHY DEPT, UNIV OF ALBERTA, EDMONTON ALB   CAN
BOSSART, WILLIAM H, PHIL DEPT, UNIV OF CALIFORNIA, DAVIS CA 95616
BOSTON, JAMES, REL & PHIL DEPT, HOOD COLLEGE, FREDERICK MD 21701
BOSTWICK, JAMES, SOC SCI DEPT, ALLAN HANCOCK COL, SANTA MARIA CA 93454
BOSWORTH, JOHN R, PHIL DEPT, OKLAHOMA STATE UNIV, STILLWATER OK 74074
BOTKIN, ROBERT, PHIL DEPT, E TENNESSEE ST UNIV, JOHNSON CITY TN 37601
BOUCHARD, GUY, PHIL FACULTE, UNIVERSITE LAVAL, CITE UNIV QUE   CAN
BOUCHARD, LISE, COL MARGUERITE-BOURG, MONTREAL, QUE   CAN
BOUCHARD, MARIE, COL MARGUERITE-BOURG, MONTREAL, QUE   CAN
BOUCHARD, ROCH, PHIL FACULTY, UNIV OF OTTAWA, OTTAWA ONT   CAN
BOUCHER, GENEVIEVE, PHILOSOPHY DEPT, COL DE MAISONNEUVE, MONTREAL QUE   CAN
BOUCHER, REMI, PHIL DEPT, COL FRANCOIS-X-GARN, QUEBEC CITY QUE   CAN
BOUCHER, YVAN, PHIL DEPT, COL DE VICTORIAVILLE, VICTORIAVILLE QUE   CAN
BOUCK, WARREN L, ENG & HUMAN DEPT, AGR & TECH COL, ALFRED NY 14802
BOUDREAUX, JACK, PHIL SCH, CATH UNIV OF AMER, WASHINGTON DC 20017
BOUFFARD, GERMAIN, COL DE LEVIS-LAUZON, LAUZON, QUE   CAN
BOULAY, JASMIN, PHIL FACULTE, UNIVERSITE LAVAL, CITE UNIV QUE   CAN

BOULIANNE, JACQUES, COLLEGE D'AHUNTSIC, MONTREAL, QUE   CAN
BOUNDAS, C V, PHIL DEPT, TRENT UNIVERSITY, PETERBOROUGH ONT   CAN
BOURASSA, MICHEL, COL DE HAUTERIVE, HAUTERIVE, QUE   CAN
BOURGEOIS, EUGENE, PHILOSOPHY DEPT, UNIV OF WATERLOO, WATERLOO ONT   CAN
BOURGEOIS, PATRICK, PHIL DEPT, LOYOLA UNIVERSITY, NEW ORLEANS LA   70118
BOURGEOIS, WARREN, PHIL DEPT, UNIV OF CALIFORNIA, IRVINE CA   92664
BOURGIE, AURELE, PHIL DEPT, COL BOIS-DE-BOULOGNE, MONTREAL QUE   CAN
BOURKE, VERNON J, PHIL DEPT, ST LOUIS UNIVERSITY, ST LOUIS MO   63103
BOURQUE, JEAN-MARIE, PHIL DEPT, LE SEM ST GEORGES, VL-ST-GEORGES QUE   CAN
BOURSIQUOT, JOSEPH, COL DE LEVIS-LAUZON, LAUZON, QUE   CAN
BOUTET, MARCELLE, PHIL DEPT, COL TROIS-RIVIERES, 3 RIVIERES QUE   CAN
BOUTIN, JEAN-PIERRE, COL EDOUARD-MONTPETIT, LONGUEUIL, QUE   CAN
BOUWSMA, O K, PHILOSOPHY DEPT, UNIV OF TEXAS, AUSTIN TX   78712
BOWDEN, LARRY R, PHIL DEPT, SIOUX FALLS COLLEGE, SIOUX FALLS SD   57101
BOWELL, JAMES, PHIL & RELIG, WEST KENTUCKY UNIV, BOWLING GREEN KY   42101
BOWEN, NORAN K, PHILOSOPHY DEPT, UNIV OF S CAROLINA, BEAUFORT SC   29902
BOWER, K, PHILOSOPHY DEPT, UNIV OF RHODE ISLAND, KINGSTON RI   02881
BOWERS, DAVID W, PHIL DEPT, BOSTON COLLEGE, CHESTNUT HILL MA   02167
BOWERS, THOMAS, PHIL DEPT, UNIV OF WEST ONTARIO, LONDON ONT   CAN
BOWIE, G LEE, PHIL DEPT, UNIV OF MICHIGAN, ANN ARBOR MI   48104
BOWIE, NORMAN E, PHIL DEPT, HAMILTON COLLEGE, CLINTON NY   13323
BOWLDEN, LARRY S, PHIL DEPT, PORTLAND ST UNIV, PORTLAND OR   97207
BOWLER, T DOWNING, PHIL & REL DEPT, BRADFORD COLLEGE, BRADFORD MA   01830
BOWLES, GEORGE, PHILOSOPHY DEPT, AUGUSTANA COLLEGE, SIOUX FALLS SD   57102
BOWLING, A C, CHRIST EDUC & PHIL, JOHN BROWN UNIV, SILOAM SPGS AR   72761
BOWMAN, ALLEN, REL & PHIL DEPT, WILLIAM PENN COLLEGE, OSKALOOSA IA   52577
BOWMAN, CARROLL R, PHILOSOPHY DEPT, MEMPHIS ST UNIV, MEMPHIS TN   38152
BOWMAN, HOWARD, HUMAN DIV, RICKER COLLEGE, HOULTON ME   04730
BOWMAN, PETER A, PHIL DEPT, UNIV OF TENNESSEE, KNOXVILLE TN   37916
BOWNE, DALE R, PHIL & RELIG, GROVE CITY COLLEGE, GROVE CITY PA   16127
BOX, ROBERT, PHIL & REL STUD DEPT, U S INTNL UNIV, SAN DIEGO CA   92131
BOXILL, BERNARD R, PHIL DEPT, UNIV OF CALIFORNIA, LOS ANGELES CA   90024
BOXILL, JEANETTE, PHIL DEPT, UNIV OF CALIFORNIA, LOS ANGELES CA   90024
BOYACK, ALICE, PHIL & RELIG, WESTMINSTER COL, SALT LAKE CTY UT   84105
BOYACK, JAMES D, PHIL & RELIG, WESTMINSTER COL, SALT LAKE CTY UT   84105
BOYD, JAMES W, PHIL DEPT, COLORADO ST UNIV, FORT COLLINS CO   80521
BOYD, RICHARD, SAGE SCHOOL, CORNELL UNIVERSITY, ITHACA NY   14850
BOYD, TOM W, PHILOSOPHY DEPT, UNIV OF OKLAHOMA, NORMAN OK   73069
BOYDEN, JAMES E, HUMAN DEPT, BROOME COM COL, BINGHAMTON NY   13902
BOYER, DAVID, PHIL DEPT, BOSTON UNIVERSITY, BOSTON MA   02215
BOYER, LYNN, HIST & PHIL DEPT, BRIARCLIFF COL, BRIARCLF MNR NY   10510
BOYER, MERLE WILLIAM, PHILOSOPHY DEPT, CARTHAGE COLLEGE, KENOSHA WI   53140
BOYER, ROLAND, PHIL DEPT, COL VIEUX-MONTREAL, MONTREAL QUE   CAN
BOYLE JR, JOSEPH, PHIL DEPT, AQUINAS COLLEGE, GRAND RAPIDS MI   49506
BOYLE, JEROME, PHIL DEPT, UNIV OF NOTRE DAME, NOTRE DAME IN   46556
BOYLE, JOSEPH P, HUMAN DEPT, HILLSBOROUGH JUN COL, TAMPA FL   33622
BOZICK, LAWRENCE M, PHILOSOPHY DEPT, KENT STATE UNIV, KENT OH   44242
BRABY, ROBERT D, ASHLAND COLLEGE, ASHLAND, OH   44805
BRACKEN, HARRY M, PHILOSOPHY DEPT, MCGILL UNIVERSITY, MONTREAL QUE   CAN
BRACKEN, A W, DIV OF HUM, UNIV OF ALABAMA, HUNTSVILLE AL   35807
BRADFORD, DENNIS, PHIL DEPT, UNIVERSITY OF IOWA, IOWA CITY IA   52240
BRADFORD, JAMES, PHIL DEPT, UNIV OF CINCINNATI, CINCINNATI OH   45221
BRADFORD, M GERALD, PHILOSOPHY DEPT, BRIGHAM YOUNG UNIV, PROVO UT   84601
BRACIE, MICHAEL, PHIL DEPT, BOWLING GREEN UNIV, BOWLING GREEN OH   43403
BRADLEY, DENIS J M, PHIL DEPT, GEORGETOWN UNIV, WASHINGTON DC   20007
BRADLEY, JOHN, PHIL DEPT, IONA COLLEGE, NEW ROCHELLE NY   10801
BRADLEY, R D, PHILOSOPHY DEPT, SIMON FRASER UNIV, BURNABY 2 B C   CAN
BRADLEY, RAYMOND, ST FRANCIS COL, LORETTO, PA   15940
BRADSHER, DONALD, PHILOSOPHY DEPT, UNIV OF WYOMING, LARAMIE WY   82071
BRADT, RAYMOND K, HUMAN & ARTS SCH, HAMPSHIRE COLLEGE, AMHERST MA   01002
BRADY, DOMINIC, ST EDWARD'S UNIV, AUSTIN, TX   78704
BRADY, FEURMAN NEIL, PHILOSOPHY DEPT, UNIV OF TEXAS, AUSTIN TX   78712
BRADY, JAMES B, PHIL DEPT, ST UNIV OF NY, AMHERST NY   14226
BRADY, JULES M, PHIL DEPT, ROCKHURST COLLEGE, KANSAS CITY MO   64110

BRADY, MARY L, PHILOSOPHY DEPT, COL OF MT ST VINCENT, RIVERDALE NY 10471
BRADY, ROBBY RAY, PHILOSOPHY DEPT, STETSON UNIVERSITY, DELAND FL 32720
BRADY, RONALD, AMER STUD SCHOOL, RAMAPO COLLEGE, MAHWAH NJ 07430
BRAHINSKY, DAVID, HUMANITIES DIV, KEYSTONE JR COL, LA PLUME PA 18440
BRAMANN, JOHN K, PHIL DEPT, FROSTBURG STATE COL, FROSTBURG MD 21532
BRAND, MYLES, PHIL DEPT, UNIV OF ILLINOIS, CHICAGO IL 60680
BRANDON, MELVIN, PHIL DEPT, SPRING HILL COLLEGE, MOBILE AL 36608
BRANDT, CARL, PHIL DEPT, UNIV OF MINNESOTA, MINNEAPOLIS MN 55455
BRANDT, RICHARD B, PHIL DEPT, UNIV OF MICHIGAN, ANN ARBOR MI 48104
BRANHAM, BARRY H, PHIL DEPT, UNIV OF N CAROLINA, CHAPEL HILL NC 27514
BRANICK, VINCENT, PHIL DEPT, CHAMINADE COLLEGE, HONOLULU HI 96816
BRANNAN, PATRICK, PHILOSOPHY DEPT, CARDINAL GLENNON COL, ST LOUIS MO 63119
BRANSHARD, BRAND, PHIL DEPT, YALE UNIVERSITY, NEW HAVEN CT 06520
BRANSON, ROY, RELIG DEPT, ANDREWS UNIVERSITY, BERRIEN SPGS MI 49104
BRANTL, GEORGE, PHIL & RELIG DEPT, MONTCLAIR ST COL, UPR MONTCLAIR NJ 07043
BRATMAN, MICHAEL, PHIL DEPT, ROCKEFELLER UNIV, NEW YORK NY 10021
BRATTON, MORRIS H, MOUNT VERNON COLLEGE, WASHINGTON, DC 20017
BRAUDE, STEPHEN, PHIL DEPT, UNIV OF MARYLAND, BALTIMORE MD 21228
BRAUN, FRANCIS R, PHIL DEPT, CANISIUS COLLEGE, BUFFALO NY 14208
BRAUNINGER, R KENT, HUMAN DIV, PENINSULA COLLEGE, PORT ANGELES WA 98362
BRALTIGAM, HERMAN, PHIL & RELIG DEPT, COLGATE UNIVERSITY, HAMILTON NY 13346
BRAYBROOKE, DAVID, PHIL DEPT, DALHOUSIE UNIVERSITY, HALIFAX N S CAN
BREAULT, CHARLES, PHIL DEPT, OBLATE COLLEGE & SEM, NATICK MA 01760
BREAZEALE, J DANIEL, PHIL DEPT, UNIV OF KENTUCKY, LEXINGTON KY 40506
BRECHBILL, TIMOTHY, PHILOSOPHY DEPT, OHIO STATE UNIV, COLUMBUS OH 43210
BRECKENRIDGE, JAMES, SOC SCI DEPT, CAL ST POLYTECH UNIV, POMONA CA 91768
BRECKENRIDGE, JAMES, BIB & THEOL DEPT, NORTHWEST BIBLE COL, MINOT ND 58701
BREDENBERG, PAUL A, PHIL & REL DEPT, N CAROLINA ST UNIV, RALEIGH NC 27607
BREEN, JOSEPH S, PHIL DEPT, NIAGARA UNIVERSITY, NIAGARA UNIV NY 14109
BREIDENBACH, FRANCIS J, PHIL & RELIG, LADYCLIFF COL, HIGHLAND FLS NY 10928
BREITBACH, RICHARD C, PHIL DEPT, ST FRANCIS DE SALES, MILWUAKEE WI 53207
BREMER, PAUL, PHIL & RELIG, GROVE CITY COLLEGE, GROVE CITY PA 16127
BRENKERT, GEORGE G, PHIL DEPT, UNIV OF TENNESSEE, KNOXVILLE TN 37916
BRENNAN, BERNARD P, SOC SCI DEPT, PACE COLLEGE, NEW YORK NY 10038
BRENNAN, MARY A, PHILOSOPHY DEPT, CCL OF MT ST VINCENT, RIVERDALE NY 10471
BRENNAN, SHEILAH, PHIL DEPT, UNIV OF NOTRE DAME, NOTRE DAME IN 46556
BRENNER, WILLIAM H, PHILOSOPHY DEPT, OLD DOMINION UNIV, NORFOLK VA 23508
BRENTLINGER, JOHN, PHILOSOPHY DEPT, UNIV OF MASS, AMHERST MA 01002
BRES, JEAN-CLAUDE, COL EDOUARD-MONTPETIT, LONGUEUIL, QUE CAN
BRESLAUER, DANIEL, PHIL & RELIG DEPT, COLGATE UNIVERSITY, HAMILTON NY 13346
BRESLIN, CHARLES F, PHIL DEPT, UNIV OF LOUISVILLE, LOUISVILLE KY 40208
BRESTER, LEONARD E, HUMANITIES DEPT, PENN STATE UNIV, MIDDLETOWN PA 17057
BRETALL, ROBERT W, PHILOSOPHY DEPT, UNIV OF ARIZONA, TUCSON AZ 85721
BRETT, N, PHILOSOPHY DEPT, UNIV OF GUELPH, GUELPH ONT CAN
BREWER JR, HOMER, KENTUCKY STATE UNIV, FRANKFORT, KY 40601
BREWER, MARTHA, PHIL & REL DEPT, UNIV OF GEORGIA, ATHENS GA 30602
BREWER, PAUL D, PHIL DEPT, CARSON-NEWMAN COL, JEFFERSON CY TN 37760
BREZIK, VICTOR B, PHILOSOPHY DEPT, UNIV OF ST THOMAS, HOUSTON TX 77006
BREZNA, GEORGE, PHIL DEPT, UNIVERSITY OF DAYTON, DAYTON OH 45469
BRICKE, JOHN, PHIL DEPT, UNIVERSITY OF KANSAS, LAWRENCE KS 66044
BRICKHOUSE, THOMAS, PHIL & RELIG DEPT, MADISON COL, HARRISONBURG VA 22801
BRIDGES, GEOFFREY, PHIL DEPT, UNIV CF SN FRANCISCO, SAN FRANCISCO CA 94117
BRIDGES, RUTH, SOC SCI DIV, KANSAS CY COM COL, KANSAS CITY KS 66112
BRIDGES, T, PHIL & RELIG DEPT, MONTCLAIR ST COL, UPR MONTCLAIR NJ 07043
BRIDGEWATER, BRADLEY S, PHIL DEPT, WASHINGTON UNIV, ST LOUIS MO 63130
BRIDSTON, DEITH, SYST & PHIL, GRADUATE THEOL UNION, BERKELEY CA 94709
BRIEF, JEAN-CLAUDE, PHIL STUD BOARD, U OF CALIFORNIA, SANTA CRUZ CA 95060
BRIER, ROBERT, PHIL DEPT, LONG ISLAND UNIV, GREENVALE NY 11548
BRIERE, MICHEL, PHIL DEPT, COL RIVIERE DU LOUP, RIVIERE LOUP QUE CAN
BRIMMER, HARVEY H, PHILOSOPHY DEPT, CLEVELAND ST UNIV, CLEVELAND OH 44115
BRINDLEY, DONALD, PHIL DEPT, ST JOSEPH'S COLLEGE, RENNSSELAER IN 47978
BRINKMAN, PAUL, PHIL DEPT, COL OF ST BENEDICT, ST JOSEPH MN 56374
BRINTON, ALAN, PHIL DEPT, UNIV OF MINNESOTA, MINNEAPOLIS MN 55455
BRICNES, ERNESTO, PHILOSOPHY DEPT, UNIV OF TEXAS, EL PASO TX 79968

BRISSON, MARCELLE, COLLEGE D·AHUNTSIC, MONTREAL, QUE   CAN
BRISTOL, JOHN, PHILOSOPHY DEPT, MCMASTER UNIVERSITY, HAMILTON ONT   CAN
BRITTAN, GORDON, HIST & PHIL, MONTANA ST UNIV, BOZEMAN MT 59715
BRKIC, JOVAN, PHILOSOPHY DEPT, N DAKOTA ST UNIV, FARGO ND 58102
BROADHURST, FRANCES N, PHIL & REL, COLLEGE OF EMPORIA, EMPORIA KS 66801
BROCHU, JACQUES, COL EDOUARD-MONTPETIT, LONGUEUIL, QUE   CAN
BROCK, DAN W, PHILOSOPHY DEPT, BROWN UNIVERSITY, PROVIDENCE RI 02912
BROCK, JARRETT E, PHIL DEPT, CALIFORNIA ST UNIV, SAN JOSE CA 95114
BROCKELMAN, PAUL, PHILOSOPHY DEPT, UNIV OF NW HAMPSHIRE, DURHAM NH 03824
BROCKHAUS, RICHARD, PHIL DEPT, BUCKNELL UNIVERSITY, LEWISBURG PA 17837
BROCKWAY, GEORGE, PHILOSOPHY DEPT, UNIV OF RICHMOND, RICHMOND VA 23173
BROCBECK, MAY, PHIL DEPT, UNIV OF MINNESOTA, MINNEAPOLIS MN 55455
BROCEUR, JEAN-PAUL, PHILOSOPHY DEPT, UNIV DU QUEBEC, MONTREAL QUE   CAN
BROCRICK, DANIEL L, PHIL DEPT, UNIV OF WISCONSIN, LA CROSSE WI 54601
BRODSKY, G M, PHIL DEPT, UNIV OF CONNECTICUT, STORRS CT 06268
BRODY, ALAN, PHIL DEPT, BROOKLYN COLLEGE, BROOKLYN NY 11210
BRODY, BORCH A, PHIL DEPT, MASS INST TECH, CAMBRIDGE MA 02139
BRODY, LEON, PHIL DEPT, MICHIGAN STATE UNIV, EAST LANSING MI 48823
BROERING, JOSEPH H, PHIL DEPT, SEM OF ST PIUS X, ERLANGER KY 41018
BROGAN, A P, PHILOSOPHY DEPT, UNIV OF TEXAS, AUSTIN TX 78712
BROGAN, HAROLD, PHIL DEPT, LORAS COLLEGE, DUBUQUE IA 52001
BROGAN, WALTER, PHILOSOPHY DEPT, DUQUESNE UNIV, PITTSBURGH PA 15219
BROIDO, J, HUMANITIES DEPT, POINT PARK COL, PITTSBURGH PA 15222
BROMBERGER, SYLVAIN, PHIL DEPT, MASS INST TECH, CAMBRIDGE MA 02139
BRONAUGH, RICHARD N, PHIL DEPT, UNIV OF WEST ONTARIO, LONDON ONT   CAN
BROCK, J A, PHILOSOPHY DEPT, CARLETON UNIVERSITY, OTTAWA ONT   CAN
BROCK, RICHARD J, PHIL DEPT, BLOOMSBURG ST COL, BLOOMSBURG PA 17815
BROCKE, MARGARET G, PHIL DEPT, UNIV OF ALABAMA, UNIVERSITY AL 35486
BROCKS, JAMES, PHIL DEPT, UNIV OF CINCINNATI, CINCINNATI OH 45221
BROOKO, RICHARD W, PHIL DEPT, OAKLAND UNIVERSITY, ROCHESTER MI 48063
BROSS, JAMES B, CENTRAL WESLEYAN COL, CENTRAL, SC 29630
BROTZ, EDITH, HUMAN STUD DEPT, MARIAN COLLEGE, FOND DU LAC WI 54935
BROUGH, JOHN B, PHIL DEPT, GEORGETOWN UNIV, WASHINGTON DC 20007
BROUILLET, GUY, PHILOSOPHY DEPT, CQL DE MAISONNEUVE, MONTREAL QUE   CAN
BROUILLET, RAYMOND, PHILOSOPHY DEPT, COL DE MAISONNEUVE, MONTREAL QUE   CAN
BROUSSARD, JOSEPH D, PHIL DEPT, MT SAINT MARY'S COL, EMMITSBURG MD 21727
BROUWER, FRED, PHIL DEPT, COL AT POTSDAM, POTSDAM NY 13676
BROWDER, JIMMIE, PHIL DEPT, NORTHWESTERN UNIV, EVANSTON IL 60201
BROWN, ARTHUR A, PHIL DEPT, BENTLEY COLLEGE, WALTHAM MA 02154
BROWN, B F, UNIV OF ST MICHAEL'S, TORONTO 181, ONT   CAN
BROWN, C D, PHILOSOPHY DEPT, AUBURN UNIVERSITY, AUBURN AL 36830
BROWN, COLEMAN, PHIL & RELIG DEPT, COLGATE UNIVERSITY, HAMILTON NY 13346
BROWN, DAVID, PHIL DEPT, UNIV OF WEST ONTARIO, LONDON ONT   CAN
BROWN, DELWIN, PHIL DEPT, ANDERSON COLLEGE, ANDERSON IN 46011
BROWN, DION K, LANG ARTS DEPT, POLK COM COLLEGE, WINTER HAVEN FL 33880
BROWN, DONALD G, PHIL DEPT, UNIV BRIT COLUMBIA, VANCOUVER 8 B C   CAN
BROWN, E E, PHILOSOPHY DEPT, UNIV ST JEROME'S COL, WATERLOO ONT   CAN
BROWN, EDWARD, HUMANITIES DIV, KEYSTONE JR COL, LA PLUME PA 18440
BROWN, ELIZABETH, PHIL DEPT, UNIV BRIT COLUMBIA, VANCOUVER 8 B C   CAN
BROWN, GEOFFREY W, PHIL DEPT, WHITMAN COLLEGE, WALLA WALLA WA 99362
BROWN, HAROLD I, PHIL DEPT, N ILLINOIS UNIV, DEKALB IL 60115
BROWN, HAROLD, SOC SCI DEPT, PACE COLLEGE, NEW YORK NY 10038
BROWN, HARVEY, HUMANITIES DEPT, CUMBERLAND COLLEGE, LEBANON TN 37087
BROWN, HELEN C, PHIL DEPT, ST UNIV OF NY, BINGHAMTON NY 13901
BROWN, J DANIEL, REL & PHIL DEPT, CATAWBA COLLEGE, SALISBURY NC 28144
BROWN, JAMES W, PHIL & FINE ARTS, N ESSEX COM COL, HAVERHILL MA 01830
BROWN, JAMES, PHIL DEPT, UNIV OF MICHIGAN, ANN ARBOR MI 48104
BROWN, JAMES, PHIL & RELIG, JERSEY CITY ST COL, JERSEY CITY NJ 07305
BROWN, JEROME V, PHILOSOPHY DEPT, UNIV OF WINDSOR, WINDSOR ONT   CAN
BROWN, JOHN H, PHIL DEPT, UNIV OF MARYLAND, COLLEGE PARK MD 20742
BROWN, KENNETH, REL & PHIL, MANCHESTER COLLEGE, N MANCHESTER IN 46962
BROWN, LEE, PHIL DEPT, UNIV OF MICHIGAN, ANN ARBOR MI 48104
BROWN, LUDLOW, PHIL DEPT, ST UNIV OF NY, AMHERST NY 14226
BROWN, M L, PHILOSOPHY DEPT, NOTRE DAME UNIV, NELSON B C   CAN

BROWN, MALCOLM, PHIL DEPT, BROOKLYN COLLEGE, BROOKLYN NY   11210
BROWN, MARGARET, HUMAN DEPT, NORWALK COM COL, NORWALK CT   06854
BROWN, MARK, PHIL DEPT, SYRACUSE UNIVERSITY, SYRACUSE NY   13210
BROWN, MARY A, PHIL DEPT, ST BONAVENTURE UNIV, ST BONVENTURE NY   14778
BROWN, NORMAN J, PHILOSOPHY DEPT, QUEEN'S UNIVERSITY, KINGSTON ONT   CAN
BROWN, P, PHILOSOPHY DEPT, QUEEN'S UNIVERSITY, KINGSTON ONT   CAN
BROWN, PAUL L, PHILOSOPHY DEPT, UNIVERSITY OF TULSA, TULSA OK   74104
BROWN, PAUL, ENGLISH DEPT, GEORGIA SOUTHERN COL, STATESBORO GA   30458
BROWN, PETER C, PHILOSOPHY DEPT, MERCER UNIVERSITY, MACON GA   31207
BROWN, PETER I, PHIL DEPT, WELLS COLLEGE, AURORA NY   13026
BROWN, ROBERT A, PHIL DEPT, BRANDEIS UNIVERSITY, WALTHAM MA   02154
BROWN, ROBERT F, PHILOSOPHY DEPT, UNIV OF DELAWARE, NEWARK DE   19711
BROWN, STEPHEN, PHILOSOPHY DEPT, BLOOMFIELD COLLEGE, BLOOMFIELD NJ   07003
BROWN, W MILLER, PHIL DEPT, TRINITY COLLEGE, HARTFORD CT   06106
BROWN, WALTER E, REL & PHIL DEPT, WESLEYAN COLLEGE, MACON GA   31201
BROWN, WILLIAM G, PHIL DEPT, SEM OF ST PIUS X, ERLANGER KY   41018
BROWN, WILLIAM R, POLIT SCI & PHIL, SW MISSOURI ST U, SPRINGFIELD MO   65802
BROWNE, GWENNETH L, PHIL DEPT, UNIV OF THE PACIFIC, STOCKTON CA   95204
BROWNE, HELEN C, PHIL DEPT, WASHINGTON UNIV, ST LOUIS MO   63130
BROWNE, ROBERT, HIST & RELATED AREAS, E CONN ST COL, WILLIMANTIC CT   06226
BROWNE, SAMUEL S S, PHIL DEPT, UNIV OF CINCINNATI, CINCINNATI OH   45221
BROWNING, DOUGLAS, PHILOSOPHY DEPT, UNIV OF TEXAS, AUSTIN TX   78712
BROWNING, LORIN, PHILOSOPHY DEPT, CCL OF CHARLESTON, CHARLESTON SC   29401
BROWNING, ROBERT W, PHIL DEPT, NORTHWESTERN UNIV, EVANSTON IL   60201
BROWNS, RALPH E, PHIL DEPT, ILL WESLEYAN UNIV, BLOOMINGTON IL   61701
BROWNSTEIN, DONALD, PHIL DEPT, UNIVERSITY OF KANSAS, LAWRENCE KS   66044
BROYER, JOHN A, PHIL STUD DEPT, S ILLINOIS UNIV, EDWARDSVILLE IL   62025
BROYLES, JAMES E, PHILOSOPHY DEPT, WASHINGTON ST UNIV, PULLMAN WA   99163
BRUCE, CHARLES, PHIL DEPT, MICHIGAN STATE UNIV, EAST LANSING MI   48823
BRUCE, J A, PHILOSOPHY DEPT, UNIV OF GUELPH, GUELPH ONT   CAN
BRUCER, KENNETH J, PHILOSOPHY DEPT, CALIFORNIA ST UNIV, CHICO CA   95926
BRUEHL, ELIZABETH, PHIL DEPT, NW SCH FOR SOC RES, NEW YORK NY   10003
BRUENING, WILLIAM, PHIL DEPT, PURDUE UNIVERSITY, FORT WAYNE IN   46805
BRUMBAUGH, ROBERT, PHIL DEPT, YALE UNIVERSITY, NEW HAVEN CT   06520
BRUMFIELD, DONALD R, PHILOSOPHY DEPT, GULF COAST BIB COL, HOUSTON TX   77008
BRUMMER, JAMES, PHIL DEPT, UNIV OF WISCONSIN, EAU CLAIRE WI   54701
BRUMMET, ROBERT, PHILOSOPHY DEPT, OHIO STATE UNIV, COLUMBUS OH   43210
BRUNIUS, TEDDY, PHIL DEPT, ST UNIV CF NY, ALBANY NY   12203
BRUNK, CONRAD, PHIL DEPT, NORTHWESTERN UNIV, EVANSTON IL   60201
BRUSH, FRANCIS W, PHIL DEPT, UNIV OF DENVER, DENVER CO   80210
BRUSHABER, GEORGE, PHILOSOPHY DEPT, GORDON COLLEGE, WENHAM MA   01984
BRUSHER, EDWARD W, PHIL DEPT, UNIV CF SN FRANCISCO, SAN FRANCISCO CA   94117
BRUZELIUS, C, PHIL DEPT, W CONNECTICUT ST COL, DANBURY CT   06810
BRUZINA, RONALD, PHIL DEPT, UNIV OF KENTUCKY, LEXINGTON KY   40506
BRYAN, LAWRENCE, SOC SCI DIV, MCKENDREE COL, LEBANON IL   62254
BRYAN, R S, PHILOSOPHY DEPT, QUEEN'S UNIVERSITY, KINGSTON ONT   CAN
BRYAN, ROBERT S, PHIL & REL DEPT, N CAROLINA ST UNIV, RALEIGH NC   27607
BRYANT, DAVID C, PHIL DEPT, COL AT FREDONIA, FREDONIA NY   14063
BRYANT, PAUL, GEN EDUC DEPT, SCHENECTADY CO COL, SCHENECTADY NY   12305
BRYAR, WILLIAM, PHIL DEPT, HUNTER COLLEGE, NEW YORK NY   10021
BRYDE, GEORGE, THEOL & PHIL DEPT, AVILA COLLEGE, KANSAS CITY MO   64145
BRYSON, KENNETH, PHILOSOPHY DEPT, ST FRAN XAVIER UNIV, ANTIGONISH N S   CAN
BUB, JEFFREY, PHIL DEPT, UNIV OF WEST ONTARIO, LONDON ONT   CAN
BUBACZ, BRUCE, PHIL DEPT, UNIV OF MISSOURI, KANSAS CITY MO   64110
BUCCHINO, ANGELO A, PHIL DEPT, FROSTBURG STATE COL, FROSTBURG MD   21532
BUCHANAN, ALLEN, PHIL DEPT, UNIV OF N CAROLINA, CHAPEL HILL NC   27514
BUCHANAN, EMERSON, HIST & PHIL DEPT, FAIRLEIGH DICKINSON, MADISON NJ   07940
BUCHANAN, JAMES H, PHILOSOPHY DEPT, UNIV OF AKRON, AKRON OH   44325
BUCHANAN, MARY L, SOC STUD DEPT, SANTA MONICA COL, SANTA MONICA CA   90405
BUCHANAN, RUPERT A, PHIL DEPT, PORTLAND ST UNIV, PORTLAND OR   97207
BUCHER, RAYMOND, SYST & PHIL, GRADUATE THEOL UNION, BERKELEY CA   94709
BUCHER, S, PHILOSOPHY DEPT, UNIV OF TORONTO, TORONTO ONT   CAN
BUCHER, VITUS, PHIL DEPT, SAINT JOHN'S UNIV, COLLEGEVILLE MN   56321
BUCHLER, JUSTUS, PHIL DEPT, ST UNIV OF NY, STONY BROOK NY   11790

BUCHWALTER, ANDREW, PHIL DEPT, BOSTON UNIVERSITY, BOSTON MA 02215
BUCK, ROGER C, HIST & PHIL SCI, INDIANA UNIV, BLOOMINGTON IN 47401
BUCKALEW, CHARLES, PHIL DEPT, UNIV CF VIRGINIA, CHARLOTTESVL VA 22903
BUCKEY, DONALD R, RELIG & PHIL DEPT, MOUNT UNION COLLEGE, ALLIANCE OH 44601
BUCKHOUT, GERARD, GEN EDUC DEPT, SCHENECTADY CO COL, SCHENECTADY NY 12305
BUCKLEY, EUGENE C, PHILOSOPHY DEPT, MARYCREST COLLEGE, DAVENPORT IA 52804
BUCKLEY, JOHN J, PHILOSOPHY DEPT, UNIV OF S ALABAMA, MOBILE AL 36688
BUCKLEY, JOSEPH A, PHIL DEPT, JOHN CARROLL UNIV, UNIVERSITY HT OH 44118
BUCKLEY, MICHAEL, SYST & PHIL, GRADUATE THEOL UNION, BERKELEY CA 94709
BUDER, NORMAN, PHILOSOPHY DEPT, CALIFORNIA ST UNIV, HAYWARD CA 94542
BUDESHEIM, THOMAS L, THEOL DEPT, CEN BAPTIST THEO SEM, KANSAS CITY KS 66102
BUDLONG, THEODORE W, PHIL DEPT, PURCUE UNIVERSITY, LAFAYETTE IN 47907
BUEHNER, THOMAS, PHILOSOPHY DEPT, DUQUESNE UNIV, PITTSBURGH PA 15219
BUESCHER, JEROME, PHIL DEPT, DUNS SCOTUS COL, SOUTHFIELD MI 48075
BUFFORD, SAMUEL, HIST & PHIL DEPT, E MICHIGAN UNIV, YPSILANTI MI 48197
BUFORD, THOMAS, PHILOSOPHY DEPT, FURMAN UNIVERSITY, GREENVILLE SC 29613
BUGBEE, HENRY G, PHIL DEPT, UNIV OF MONTANA, MISSOULA MT 59801
BUGG, EUGENE, PHILOSOPHY DEPT, VANDERBILT UNIV, NASHVILLE TN 37235
BUHR, MARJORIE, PHIL DEPT, MIAMI-DACE JUN COL, MIAMI FL 33156
BUHRER, RICHARD, PHILOSOPHY DEPT, GONZAGA UNIV, SPOKANE WA 99202
BUIJS, JOSEPH, PHIL DEPT, UNIV OF WEST ONTARIO, LONDON ONT CAN
BUKALA, CASIMIR R, PHIL DEPT, JOHN CARROLL UNIV, UNIVERSITY HT OH 44118
BULGER, DAVID, APPL ARTS DIV, CAMBRIAN COL OF ARTS, SALT ST MARIE ONT CAN
BUNCH, ROBERT, PHIL DEPT, ST UNIV OF NY, STONY BROOK NY 11790
BUNGE, MARIO, PHILOSOPHY DEPT, MCGILL UNIVERSITY, MONTREAL QUE CAN
BUONOCORE, GLORIA, PHIL DEPT, UNIV CF CONNECTICUT, WATERBURY CT 06710
BURBIDGE, DON, PHIL & SOC DEPT, VANCOUVER CITY COL, VANCOUVER B C CAN
BURBIDGE, JOHN W, PHIL DEPT, TRENT UNIVERSITY, PETERBOROUGH ONT CAN
BURCH, GEORGE BOSWORTH, PHIL DEPT, TUFTS UNIVERSITY, MEDFORD MA 02155
BURCH, R W, PHILOSOPHY DEPT, RICE UNIVERSITY, HOUSTON TX 77001
BURDICK, HOWARD, PHIL DEPT, ROCKEFELLER UNIV, NEW YORK NY 10021
BURDICK, JOHN M, PHIL DEPT, UNIV OF MARYLAND, COLLEGE PARK MD 20742
BURES, CHARLES E, HUM & SOC SCI DIV, CAL INST OF TECH, PASADENA CA 91101
BURGE, C TYLER, PHIL DEPT, UNIV OF CALIFORNIA, LOS ANGELES CA 90024
BURGESS, HAROLD, REL & PHIL DIV, BETHEL COLLEGE, MISHAWAKA IN 46544
BURGESS, JOSEPH C, PHIL DEPT, UNIV OF SANTA CLARA, SANTA CLARA CA 95053
BURHENN, HERBERT W, PHIL & RELIG, UNIV OF TENNESSEE, CHATTANOOGA TN 37401
BURIAN, RICHARD, PHIL DEPT, BRANDEIS UNIVERSITY, WALTHAM MA 02154
BURKE, D R, EDUCATION COLLEGE, ALTHOUSE COLLEGE, LONDON ONT CAN
BURKE, JAMES P, ST FRANCIS COL, LORETTO, PA 15940
BURKE, JOHN P, PHILOSOPHY DEPT, UNIV OF WASHINGTON, SEATTLE WA 98195
BURKE, JOHN PATRICK, PHILOSOPHY DEPT, SEATTLE UNIVERSITY, SEATTLE WA 98122
BURKE, MICHAEL B, PHILOSOPHY DEPT, UNIV OF WISCONSIN, MADISON WI 53706
BURKE, RICHARD J, PHIL DEPT, OAKLAND UNIVERSITY, ROCHESTER MI 48063
BURKE, SEAN, PHIL DEPT, INCARNATE WORD COL, SAN ANTONIO TX 78209
BURKETT, JOHN, PHIL DEPT, BOSTON UNIVERSITY, BOSTON MA 02215
BURKHOLDER, PETER M, PHIL DEPT, CEN WASH STATE COL, ELLENSBURG WA 98926
BURKS, ARTHUR W, PHIL DEPT, UNIV OF MICHIGAN, ANN ARBOR MI 48104
BURKS, STEVEN V, PHIL DEPT, INDIANA UNIVERSITY, BLOOMINGTON IN 47401
BURKS, THOMPSON, PHIL DEPT, UNIV OF CINCINNATI, CINCINNATI OH 45221
BURLAGE, CARL J, PHIL DEPT, LOYOLA UNIVERSITY, CHICAGO IL 60626
BURLINGAME, CHARLES E, PHILOSOPHY DEPT, KENT STATE UNIV, KENT OH 44242
BURNEY, THOMAS, SOCIO-HUMAN STUD, TRI-STATE COLLEGE, ANGOLA IN 46703
BURNS, JOHN V, PHIL DEPT, NIAGARA UNIVERSITY, NIAGARA UNIV NY 14109
BURNS, JOHN, RELIG DEPT, MISSOURI BAPT COL, HANNIBAL MO 63401
BURNS, JOSEPHINE, PHIL & THEOL DEPT, MARILLAC COLLEGE, ST LOUIS MO 63121
BURNS, ROBERT W, DIV OF HUM, UNIV OF ALABAMA, HUNTSVILLE AL 35807
BURNS, STEVEN A M, PHIL DEPT, DALHOUSIE UNIVERSITY, HALIFAX N S CAN
BURNS, WILLIAM D, PHILOSOPHY DEPT, UNIV OF WINNIPEG, WINNIPEG MAN CAN
BURNSIDE, RONALD L, HUMANITIES DEPT, SINCLAIR COM COL, DAYTON OH 45402
BURCKER, BARBARA JILL, PHIL DEPT, UNIV OF CALIFORNIA, IRVINE CA 92664
BURR, JOHN R, PHILOSOPHY DEPT, UNIV OF WISONSIN, OSH KOSH WI 54901
BURRELL, DAVID, PHIL DEPT, UNIV OF NOTRE DAME, NOTRE DAME IN 46556
BURRILL, DONALD, PHIL DEPT, CALIFORNIA ST UNIV, LOS ANGELES CA 90032

BURRINGTON, DALE E, PHIL & RELIG DEPT, HARTWICK COLLEGE, ONEONTA NY 13820
BURSTEIN, HARVEY, PHILOSOPHY DEPT, QUEENS COLLEGE, FLUSHING NY 11367
BURT, DONALD, HUMAN DIV, BISCAYNE COLLEGE, MIAMI FL 33054
BURTON, ROBERT G, PHIL & REL DEPT, UNIV OF GEORGIA, ATHENS GA 30602
BURTT, EDWIN A, SAGE SCHOOL, CORNELL UNIVERSITY, ITHACA NY 14850
BURTT, GEORGE T, PHIL DEPT, NEWARK STATE COL, UNION NJ 07083
BURUNAT, JULIO, PHIL DEPT, ST THOS AQUINAS COL, SPARKILL NY 10976
BUSCH, THOMAS W, PHILOSOPHY DEPT, VILLANOVA UNIV, VILLANOVA PA 19085
BUSCHMAN, HAROLD, PHIL DEPT, UNIV OF MISSOURI, KANSAS CITY MO 64110
BUSCHMANN, WALTER, SYST THEOL DEPT, NW LUTH THEOL SEM, ST PAUL MN 55108
BUSE, ROBERT O, PHILOSOPHY DEPT, EDGECLIFF COLLEGE, CINCINNATI OH 45206
BUSH, RICHARD C, PHIL DEPT, OKLAHOMA STATE UNIV, STILLWATER OK 74074
BUSHMAN, RITA MARIE, PHIL DEPT, ST LOUIS UNIVERSITY, ST LOUIS MO 63103
BUSSY, J GERARD, PHILOSOPHY DEPT, SEATTLE UNIVERSITY, SEATTLE WA 98122
BUTCHVAROV, PANAYOT, PHIL DEPT, UNIVERSITY OF IOWA, IOWA CITY IA 52240
BUTKUS, LINDA, PHILOSOPHY DEPT, UNIV OF WATERLOO, WATERLOO ONT   CAN
BUTKUS, R G, PHILOSOPHY DEPT, UNIV OF VICTORIA, VICTORIA B C   CAN
BUTLER, CLARK, PHIL DEPT, PURDUE UNIVERSITY, FORT WAYNE IN 46805
BUTLER, K, PHILOSOPHY DEPT, UNIV PR EDWARD IS, CHARLOTTETOWN PEI   CAN
BUTLER, KATHERINE, ENG DEPT, WAYNE STATE COL, WAYNE NE 68787
BUTLER, WILLIAM W, DEVEL STUD CTR, COLUMBIA COLLEGE, CHICAGO IL 60611
BUTLER, WILLIAM W, HUM RELATIONS DEPT, COLUMBIA COLLEGE, COLUMBIA SC 29203
BUTRICK, RICHARD P, PHILOSOPHY DEPT, OHIO UNIVERSITY, ATHENS OH 45701
BUTTERFIELD, P, PHILOSOPHY DEPT, UNIV OF LETHBRIDGE, LETHBRIDGE ALB   CAN
BUTTS, ROBERT E, PHIL DEPT, UNIV OF WEST ONTARIO, LONDON ONT   CAN
BUTTS, WILLIAM H, HIST & GEOGRAPHY, NORFOLK ST COL, NORFOLK VA 23504
BUXO, ARTURO M, PHIL DEPT, CATHOLIC UNIVERSITY, PONCE PR 00731
BUXTON, JAMES H, PHILOSOPHY DEPT, OLD DOMINION UNIV, NORFOLK VA 23508
BUYS, EDKAL, SOC & BEHAV SCI DEPT, CENTRAL ARIZONA COL, COOLIDGE AZ 85228
BYASSEE, WILLIAM, PHIL DEPT, UNIV OF KENTUCKY, LEXINGTON KY 40506
BYER, INEZ, PHIL & RELIG DEPT, COTTEY COLLEGE, NEVADA MO 64772
BYERLY, HENRY C, PHILOSOPHY DEPT, UNIV OF ARIZONA, TUCSON AZ 85721
BYNUM, TERRELL, PHIL DEPT, ST UNIV OF NY, ALBANY NY 12203
BYRCE, CHARLES G, PHILOSOPHY DEPT, UNIV OF WISCONSIN, MADISON WI 53706
BYRD, MICHAEL E, PHILOSOPHY DEPT, UNIV OF WISCONSIN, MADISON WI 53706
BYRNE, EDMUND F, PHIL DEPT, INDIANA-PURDUE UNIV, INDIANAPOLIS IN 46202
BYRNE, PATRICK, PHIL DEPT, ST UNIV OF NY, STONY BROOK NY 11790
BYRNE, PAUL M, PHILOSOPHY DEPT, MARQUETTE UNIV, MILWAUKEE WI 53233
BYRNE, RODNEY P, PHIL DEPT, COL AT OSWEGO, OSWEGO NY 13126
BYRTUS, PAUL HUNTER, PHILOSOPHY DEPT, UNIV OF TEXAS, AUSTIN TX 78712
BYWATER, WILLIAM, PHIL & REL DEPT, ALLEGHENY COLLEGE, MEADVILLE PA 16335
CABCTAJE, FELISBERTO, RELIG & PHIL, BETHUNE-COOKMAN COL, DAYTONA FL 32015
CABRAL, SUSAN C, PHIL DEPT, ST UNIV OF NY, BINGHAMTON NY 13901
CACACE, MAXINE, HARTNELL COLLEGE, SALINAS, CA 93901
CADBURY, WARDER H, PHIL DEPT, ST UNIV OF NY, ALBANY NY 12203
CADENHEAD, I EDWARD, PHIL DEPT, FLORIDA STATE UNIV, TALLAHASSEE FL 32306
CADIEUX, J ANDRE, PHILOSOPHY DEPT, ILLINOIS ST UNIV, NORMAL IL 61761
CADWALLADER, EVA, REL & PHIL DEPT, WESTMINSTER COL, NW WILMINGTON PA 16142
CADY, DUANE, PHIL DEPT, GUSTAVUS ADOLPHUS COL, ST PETER MN 56082
CADY, LYMAN V, RELIG & PHIL DEPT, FISK UNIVERSITY, NASHVILLE TN 37203
CAFAGNA, ALBERT C, PHIL DEPT, MICHIGAN STATE UNIV, EAST LANSING MI 48823
CAFFENTZIS, C GEORGE, PHIL DEPT, BROOKLYN COLLEGE, BROOKLYN NY 11210
CAHALAN, JOHN C, PHIL DEPT, MERRIMACK COLLEGE, NORTH ANDOVER MA 01845
CAHALAN, WILLIAM, PHIL DEPT, THOMAS MORE COLLEGE, COVINGTON KY 41017
CAHILL, CHRISTOPHER, PHIL DEPT, SYRACUSE UNIVERSITY, SYRACUSE NY 13210
CAHILL, M CAMILLA, PHIL DEPT, THOMAS MORE COLLEGE, COVINGTON KY 41017
CAHN, STEVEN, PHILOSOPHY DEPT, UNIV OF VERMONT, BURLINGTON VT 05401
CAIAZZA, JOHN, MATH & PHYS DEPT, ALLIANCE COLLEGE, CAMBRG SPGS PA 16403
CAIN, GERVASE, ST FRANCIS COL, LORETTO, PA 15940
CAIN, GLEN T, CHRIST & PHIL DEPT, HOUSTON BAPT COL, HOUSTON TX 77036
CAIN, THOMAS, PHIL DEPT, UNIVERSITY OF DALLAS, IRVING TX 75062
CAIRNS, JOHN B, HUMAN STUD DIV, ALFRED UNIVERSITY, ALFRED NY 14802
CALDWELL, HUGH H, PHILOSOPHY DEPT, UNIV OF THE SOUTH, SEWANEE TN 37375
CALDWELL, ROBERT L, PHILOSOPHY DEPT, UNIV OF ARIZONA, TUCSON AZ 85721

CALDWELL, WAYNE E, REL & PHIL DIV, MARION COLLEGE, MARION IN 46952
CALIGIURI, ANGELO, UNDERGRAD DEPT, ST JOHN VIANNEY SEM, E AURORA NY 14052
CALLAGHAN, WILLIAM J, PHIL DEPT, MICHIGAN STATE UNIV, EAST LANSING MI 48823
CALLAHAN, FRANCIS F, PHIL DEPT, COL OF HOLY CROSS, WORCESTER MA 01610
CALLAHAN, J E, SOC SCI DEPT, CHESAPEAKE COL, WYE MILLS MD 21679
CALLAHAN, JOHN F, PHIL DEPT, GEORGETOWN UNIV, WASHINGTON DC 20007
CALLAHAN, THOMAS, PHIL DEPT, MICHIGAN STATE UNIV, EAST LANSING MI 48823
CALLAHAN, WILLIAM, PHIL & RELIG DEPT, MADISON COL, HARRISONBURG VA 22801
CALLEN, DONALD, PHIL DEPT, COLLEGE AT BROCKPORT, BROCKPORT NY 14420
CALLICOTT, JOHN B, PHIL DEPT, UNIV OF WISCONSIN, STEVENS POINT WI 54481
CALVERT, B, PHILOSOPHY DEPT, UNIV OF GUELPH, GUELPH ONT CAN
CALVERT, ROBERT M, PHILOSOPHY DEPT, UNIV OF OKLAHOMA, NORMAN OK 73069
CAMBRON, ANTOINE, PHIL DEPT, SEM DE SHERBROOKE, SHERBROOKE QUE CAN
CAMELE, ANTHONY M, INTEGRATED STUD, SACRED HEART COLLEGE, BELMONT NC 28012
CAMERON, J M, UNIV OF ST MICHAEL'S, TORONTO 181, ONT CAN
CAMINITI, FRANCIS, SETON HALL UNIV, SOUTH ORANGE, NJ 07079
CAMP JR, JOSEPH, PHIL DEPT, UNIV OF PITTSBURGH, PITTSBURGH PA 15260
CAMPANA, JAMES, PHIL DEPT, MICHIGAN STATE UNIV, EAST LANSING MI 48823
CAMPBELL, CHARLES, REL & PHIL DIV, SPRING ARBOR COL, SPRING ARBOR MI 49283
CAMPBELL, DANIEL, PHIL DEPT, LE MOYNE COLLEGE, SYRACUSE NY 13214
CAMPBELL, GERALD LEE, PHIL & RELIG DEPT, MARYMOUNT COL, ARLINGTON VA 22207
CAMPBELL, GERALD P, PHYS SCI & MATH, SOMERSET COM COL, SOMERSET KY 42501
CAMPBELL, JAMES I, HUMAN DIV, EISENHOWER COLLEGE, SENECA FALLS NY 13148
CAMPBELL, MALCOLM, BIBL STUD & PHIL, EVANGEL COLLEGE, SPRINGFIELD MO 65802
CAMPBELL, R ALAN, HUMAN & PHIL DEPT, GROSSMONT COL, EL CAJON CA 92020
CAMPBELL, RICHARD, PHILOSOPHY DEPT, PENN STATE UNIV, HAZLETON PA 18201
CAMPBELL, RICHMOND M, PHIL DEPT, DALHOUSIE UNIVERSITY, HALIFAX N S CAN
CAMPBELL, THOMAS, PHIL DEPT, SYRACUSE UNIVERSITY, SYRACUSE NY 13210
CAMPBELL, WILLIAM E, PHIL DEPT, UNIV OF WISCONSIN, LA CROSSE WI 54601
CANEVI, PINAR, PHIL DEPT, EMORY UNIVERSITY, ATLANTA GA 30322
CANFIELD, J W, PHILOSOPHY DEPT, UNIV OF TORONTO, TORONTO ONT CAN
CANGEMI, DOMINIC, SOC SCI DEPT, ALCORN A & M COLLEGE, LORMAN MS 39096
CANNAVO, SALVATOR, PHIL DEPT, BROOKLYN COLLEGE, BROOKLYN NY 11210
CANNING, JERRY, PHILOSOPHY DEPT, WILLIAMETTE UNIV, SALEM OR 97301
CANNON, THOMAS, PHILOSOPHY DEPT, DUQUESNE UNIV, PITTSBURGH PA 15219
CANTIN, EILEEN, PHIL DEPT, INDIANA-PURDUE UNIV, INDIANAPOLIS IN 46202
CANTY, JOHN T, PHIL DEPT, CALIFORNIA ST UNIV, SAN JOSE CA 95114
CANZONERI, JOSEPH, PHIL DEPT, EMORY UNIVERSITY, ATLANTA GA 30322
CAPALDI, NICHOLAS, PHILOSOPHY DEPT, QUEENS COLLEGE, FLUSHING NY 11367
CAPEK, MILIC, PHIL DEPT, BOSTON UNIVERSITY, BOSTON MA 02215
CAPESTANY, EDWARD, PHILOSOPHY DEPT, UNIV OF SCRANTON, SCRANTON PA 18510
CAPLAN, ARTHUR, PHIL DEPT, COLUMBIA UNIVERSITY, NEW YORK NY 10027
CAPONIGRI, ROBERT A, PHIL DEPT, UNIV OF NOTRE DAME, NOTRE DAME IN 46556
CAPPELLUCCI, GABRIEL, HUMAN DEPT, BROOME COM COL, BINGHAMTON NY 13902
CAPUTO, JOHN D, PHILOSOPHY DEPT, VILLANOVA UNIV, VILLANOVA PA 19085
CARBONARA, JOHN C, PHIL DEPT, COL AT BUFFALO, BUFFALO NY 14222
CARD, CLAUDIA F, PHILOSOPHY DEPT, UNIV OF WISCONSIN, MADISON WI 53706
CARCARELLI, JOHN, PHIL DEPT, UNIV OF WEST ONTARIO, LONDON ONT CAN
CARCIN, MARIO, PHIL DEPT, COL TROIS-RIVIERES, 3 RIVIERES QUE CAN
CARCONI, ALBERT, PHIL DEPT, FAIRFIELD UNIVERSITY, FAIRFIELD CT 06430
CARDWELL, CHARLES E, PHIL & RELIG, VA POLYTECH INST, BLACKSBURG VA 24061
CARE, NORMAN S, PHILOSOPHY DEPT, OBERLIN COLLEGE, OBERLIN OH 44074
CARELLA, MICHAEL J, PHIL DEPT, CALIFORNIA ST UNIV, SAN DIEGO CA 92115
CAREW, GEORGE M, PHIL DEPT, HOWARD UNIVERSITY, WASHINGTON DC 20001
CAREY JR, ARCHIBALD, REL & PHIL DEPT, PRINCIPIA COLLEGE, ELSAH IL 62028
CAREY, STEVE, SOC SCI DEPT, PORTLAND COM COLLEGE, PORTLAND OR 97219
CARGILE, JAMES T, PHIL DEPT, UNIV OF VIRGINIA, CHARLOTTESVL VA 22903
CARIGNAN, MAURICE, PHIL FACULTY, UNIV OF OTTAWA, OTTAWA ONT CAN
CARLIN, THOMAS J, ARTS & SCI COL, UNIV OF SAN DIEGO, SAN DIEGO CA 92110
CARLOUGH, WILLIAM L, PHIL DEPT, BLOOMSBURG ST COL, BLOOMSBURG PA 17815
CARLOYE, JACK C, PHILOSOPHY DEPT, WASHINGTON ST UNIV, PULLMAN WA 99163
CARLSON, A A, PHILOSOPHY DEPT, UNIV OF ALBERTA, EDMONTON ALB CAN
CARLSON, ALLAN, VA MILITARY INST, LEXINGTON, VA 24450
CARLSON, J, PHILOSOPHY DEPT, UNIV OF ALBERTA, EDMONTON ALB CAN

CARLSON, JOHN W, PHIL DEPT, ST LOUIS UNIVERSITY, ST LOUIS MO 63103
CARLSSON, P ALLAN, PHIL & RELIG DEPT, VIRGINIA MIL INST, LEXINGTON VA 24450
CARMICHAEL, DOUGLAS, PHIL DEPT, ST LAWRENCE UNIV, CANTON NY 13617
CARMICHAEL, JOHN, PHILOSOPHY DEPT, MOUNT MARY COL, MILWAUKEE WI 53222
CARNES, JOHN, PHIL DEPT, UNIV OF COLORADO, BOULDER CO 80302
CARNES, RALPH, PHIL DEPT, ROOSEVELT UNIVERSITY, CHICAGO IL 60605
CARNES, ROBERT D, PHIL DEPT, COL AT OSWEGO, OSWEGO NY 13126
CARNEY, EDWARD J, PHIL DEPT, IMMACULATA COLLEGE, WASHINGTON DC 20016
CARNEY, FRANCIS W, ST JOHN COLLEGE, CLEVELAND, OH 44114
CARNEY, JAMES D, PHILOSOPHY DEPT, ARIZONA STATE UNIV, TEMPE AZ 85281
CARNEY, THOMAS LEE, HUMANITIES DIV, ROSEMONT COLLEGE, ROSEMONT PA 19010
CARNEY, WILLIAM, PHILOSOPHY DEPT, GONZAGA UNIV, SPOKANE WA 99202
CARNOIS, BERNARD, PHILOSOPHY DEPT, UNIV DU QUEBEC, MONTREAL QUE CAN
CARON, CHARLES, COL ANDRE-GRASSET, MONTREAL, QUE CAN
CARPENTER, ELIZABETH, PHIL DEPT, UNIV OF NEBRASKA, LINCOLN NE 68502
CARPENTER, GARRETT R, DIV OF SOC SCI, COM COL OF DENVER, DENVER CO 80216
CARPENTER, STANLEY, PHIL & HUM DEPT, TEXAS A & M UNIV, COL STATION TX 77843
CARPENTER, TOM, LANG & LIT DEPT, UNIV OF ARKANSAS, MONTICELLO AR 71655
CARPENTIER, E, REL STUD & PHIL, SPRINGFIELD COL, SPRINGFIELD IL 62702
CARR, CHARLES, PHILOSOPHY DEPT, UNIV OF ARIZONA, TUCSON AZ 85721
CARR, DAVID, PHIL DEPT, YALE UNIVERSITY, NEW HAVEN CT 06520
CARR, JAMES E, PHIL DEPT, UNIV OF ROCHESTER, ROCHESTER NY 14627
CARR, WILLIAM, PHIL DEPT, FAIRFIELD UNIVERSITY, FAIRFIELD CT 06430
CARRICK, PAUL, COMMUNIC & ARTS, HARRISBURG COM COL, HARRISBURG PA 17110
CARRIER, DAVID, PHIL DEPT, CARNEGIE-MELLON UNIV, PITTSBURGH PA 15213
CARRIER, LEONARD S, PHIL DEPT, UNIVERSITY OF MIAMI, CORAL GABLES FL 33124
CARRINGTON, WILLIAM, PHIL DEPT, ST JOHN FISHER COL, ROCHESTER NY 14618
CARROLL, MICHAEL, PHIL DEPT, UNIVERSITY OF IOWA, IOWA CITY IA 52240
CARROLL, OWEN, ST MARY'S COL OF CAL, MORAGA, CA 94575
CARRUBA, JERRY, PHIL DEPT, S ILLINOIS UNIV, CARBONDALE IL 62901
CARSON, HARRY A, PHIL DIV, SACRED HEART SEM, DETROIT MI 48206
CARSON, THOMAS, PHILOSOPHY DEPT, BROWN UNIVERSITY, PROVIDENCE RI 02912
CARTAGENOVA, GONZALO, PHIL DEPT, UNIVERSITY OF DAYTON, DAYTON OH 45469
CARTER, CHARLES, REL & PHIL DIV, MARION COLLEGE, MARION IN 46952
CARTER, CURTIS, PHILOSOPHY DEPT, MARQUETTE UNIV, MILWAUKEE WI 53233
CARTER, DAVID K, PHILOSOPHY DEPT, CALIFORNIA ST UNIV, CHICO CA 95926
CARTER, JOHN, PHIL & RELIG DEPT, COLGATE UNIVERSITY, HAMILTON NY 13346
CARTER, K CODELL, PHILOSOPHY DEPT, BRIGHAM YOUNG UNIV, PROVO UT 84601
CARTER, RICHARD, PHILOSOPHY DEPT, WINDHAM COLLEGE, PUTNEY VT 05346
CARTER, ROBERT E, PHIL DEPT, TRENT UNIVERSITY, PETERBOROUGH ONT CAN
CARTER, W B, PHILOSOPHY DEPT, ATKINSON COLLEGE, DOWNSVIEW ONT CAN
CARTER, W R, PHIL & REL DEPT, N CAROLINA ST UNIV, RALEIGH NC 27607
CARTLIDGE, DAVID R, PHIL & RELIG DEPT, MARYVILLE COL, MARYVILLE TN 37801
CARTWRIGHT, DAVID, PHILOSOPHY DEPT, UNIV OF WYOMING, LARAMIE WY 82071
CARTWRIGHT, HELEN, PHIL DEPT, TUFTS UNIVERSITY, MEDFORD MA 02155
CARTWRIGHT, JOHN H, PHIL OF RELIG, GARRETT THEOL SEM, EVANSTON IL 60201
CARTWRIGHT, NANCY, PHIL DEPT, STANFORD UNIVERSITY, STANFORD CA 94305
CARTWRIGHT, RICHARD L, PHIL DEPT, MASS INST TECH, CAMBRIDGE MA 02139
CARVER, EVERETT I, PHILOSOPHY DEPT, GULF COAST BIB COL, HOUSTON TX 77008
CARY, EDWARD A, PHILOSOPHY DEPT, ST FRAN XAVIER UNIV, ANTIGONISH N S CAN
CASALIS, MATTHIEU, PHIL DEPT, UNIV OF NEW MEXICO, ALBUQUERQUE NM 87106
CASARES, ANGEL J, PHIL DEPT, UNIV OF PUERTO RICO, RIO PIEDRAS PR 00931
CASASSA, CHARLES S, PHIL DEPT, MARYMOUNT COLLEGE, LOS ANGELES CA 90045
CASE, JAMES J, PHIL DEPT, ST MICHAEL'S COLLEGE, WINOOSKI VT 05404
CASEBIER, ALLAN, PHIL SCH, UNIV OF S CALIFORNIA, LOS ANGELES CA 90007
CASEY, DONALD P, PHIL DEPT, CATH COL IMM CONCEPT, DOUGLASTON NY 11362
CASEY, EDWARD, PHIL DEPT, YALE UNIVERSITY, NEW HAVEN CT 06520
CASEY, JOHN, PHIL DEPT, ILL WESLEYAN UNIV, BLOOMINGTON IL 61701
CASEY, JOHN, PHILOSOPHY DEPT, CERRITOS COLLEGE, NORWALK CA 90605
CASEY, JOHN, PHILOSOPHY DEPT, BELKNAP COLLEGE, CENTER HARBOR NH 03226
CASEY, JOSEPH H, PHIL DEPT, BOSTON COLLEGE, CHESTNUT HILL MA 02167
CASEY, MICHAEL M, SOC SCI DIV, MT HOOD COM COLLEGE, GRESHAM OR 97030
CASEY, SUSAN, PHILOSOPHY DEPT, BELKNAP COLLEGE, CENTER HARBOR NH 03226
CASEY, THOMAS, PHIL DEPT, MARIST COLLEGE, POUGHKEEPSIE NY 12601

CASPAR, RUTH, PHILOSOPHY DEPT, OHIO DOMINICAN COL, COLUMBUS OH   43219
CASPER, DENNIS J, PHIL DEPT, UNIV OF WISCONSIN, MILWAUKEE WI   53201
CASPER, JAMES T, HUMAN DIV, BRAINERD ST JR COL, BRAINERD MN   56401
CASSEL, CARL, HUMANITIES DEPT, PINEBROOK JR COL, E STROUDSBURG PA   18301
CASSEL, HERBERT, PHIL & REL DEPT, INDIANA CTR COL, INDIANAPOLIS IN   46227
CASSELL, WALTER E, HUMAN DIV, KANSAS WESLEYAN UNIV, SALINA KS   67401
CASSERLEY, J V, PHIL THEOL DEPT, SEABURY W THEOL SEM, EVANSTON IN   60201
CASSIDY, JOHN H, PHIL DEPT, UNIV OF ROCHESTER, ROCHESTER NY   14627
CASSIDY, JOHN ROBERT, AMER STUD SCHOOL, RAMAPO COLLEGE, MAHWAH NJ   07430
CASSIDY, LAURENCE L, ST PETER'S COLLEGE, JERSEY CITY, NJ   07306
CASSIDY, ROBERT, PHIL DEPT, UNIV OF WISCONSIN, STEVENS POINT WI   54481
CASSIN, C, PHILOSOPHY DEPT, UNIV OF TORONTO, TORONTO ONT   CAN
CASSINI, CHARLES J, PHIL DEPT, BARRY COLLEGE, MIAMI SHORES FL   33153
CASTANEDA, HECTOR, PHIL DEPT, INDIANA UNIVERSITY, BLOOMINGTON IN   47401
CASTELLANETA, NICHOLAS, PHIL DEPT, EMORY UNIVERSITY, ATLANTA GA   30322
CASTILLA-LAZARO, R, PHIL DEPT, UNIV OF PUERTO RICO, RIO PIEDRAS PR   00931
CASTLETON, TOBY, PHIL DEPT, UNIV OF ILLINOIS, URBANA IL   61801
CASTUERA, IGNACIO, S CAL SCH OF THEOL, CLAREMONT, CA   91711
CASULLO, ALBERT, PHIL DEPT, UNIVERSITY OF IOWA, IOWA CITY IA   52240
CATALANO, JOSEPH S, PHIL DEPT, NEWARK STATE COL, UNION NJ   07083
CATAN, JOHN, PHIL DEPT, COLLEGE AT BROCKPORT, BROCKPORT NY   14420
CATANIA, FRANCIS J, PHIL DEPT, LOYOLA UNIVERSITY, CHICAGO IL   60626
CATANZARO, JAMES L, PHIL DEPT, CALIFORNIA ST UNIV, FULLERTON CA   92634
CATER, ROBERT M, PHILOSOPHY DEPT, PENN STATE UNIV, UNIV PARK PA   16802
CATON, CHARLES E, PHIL DEPT, UNIV OF ILLINOIS, URBANA IL   61801
CAUCHY, VENANT, PHILOSOPHY DEPT, UNIV DE MONTREAL, MONTREAL QUE   CAN
CAUGHRAN, JACKIE R, PHIL DEPT, UNIV OF ILLINOIS, URBANA IL   61801
CAULFIELD, JOSEPH R, ST PETER'S COLLEGE, JERSEY CITY, NJ   07306
CAUMAN, LEIGH S, PHIL DEPT, COLUMBIA UNIVERSITY, NEW YORK NY   10027
CAUSEY, ROBERT L, PHILOSOPHY DEPT, UNIV OF TEXAS, AUSTIN TX   78712
CAUTHEN, KENNETH, COLGATE DIV SCHOOL, ROCHESTER, NY   14620
CAUVEL, JANE, PHIL DEPT, COLORADO COLLEGE, COLORADO SPGS CO   80903
CAVANAGH, PATRICK, PHIL & RELIG STUD, KING'S COLLEGE, LONDON ONT   CAN
CAVANAUGH, BRENDAN, PHILOSOPHY DEPT, LOYOLA COLLEGE, MONTREAL QUE   CAN
CAVE JR, GEORGE H, HUMAN & PHIL DIV, UNIVERSITY OF TAMPA, TAMPA FL   33606
CAVELL, MARCIA, PHIL BOARD STUD, COL AT PURCHASE, PURCHASE NY   10577
CAVELL, STANLEY L, PHIL DEPT, HARVARD UNIVERSITY, CAMBRIDGE MA   02138
CAWS, PETER, PHIL DEPT, HUNTER COLLEGE, NEW YORK NY   10021
CAYARD, W WALLACE, PHIL & REL DEPT, W LIBERTY ST COL, WEST LIBERTY WV   26074
CAZA, GERALD, PHIL DEPT, COL DE SHERBROOKE, SHERBROOKE QUE   CAN
CAZABON, GILLES, PHIL FACULTY, UNIV OF OTTAWA, OTTAWA ONT   CAN
CEBIK, LEROY B, PHIL DEPT, UNIV OF TENNESSEE, KNOXVILLE TN   37916
CELARIER, JAMES L, PHIL DEPT, UNIV OF MARYLAND, COLLEGE PARK MD   20742
CELESTIAN, GEORGE, ST EDWARD'S UNIV, AUSTIN, TX   78704
CELL, HOWARD R, PHIL & RELIG DEPT, GLASSBORO ST COL, GLASSBORO NJ   08028
CELMS, THEODORE, PHIL DEPT, AUGUSTANA COLLEGE, ROCK ISLAND IL   61201
CENTORE, F F, PHILOSOPHY DEPT, UNIV ST JEROME'S COL, WATERLOO ONT   CAN
CERF, WALTER, PHIL DEPT, BROOKLYN COLLEGE, BROOKLYN NY   11210
CERNIC, DAVID, PHILOSOPHY DEPT, HOFSTRA UNIVERSITY, HEMPSTEAD NY   11550
CERULLO, MARGARET, PHIL DEPT, BOSTON UNIVERSITY, BOSTON MA   02215
CHACON, ROGER, NE ILLINOIS ST UNIV, CHICAGO, IL   60625
CHAFFIN, BILL M, RELIG & PHIL DEPT, SOUTHERN STATE COL, MAGNOLIA AR   71753
CHAKRABARTI, CHANDANA, PHIL DEPT, ST UNIV OF NY, AMHERST NY   14226
CHAKRABARTI, KISOR, PHIL DEPT, ST UNIV OF NY, AMHERST NY   14226
CHAKRAVARTI, SITANSU, PHIL DEPT, SYRACUSE UNIVERSITY, SYRACUSE NY   13210
CHAKRAVARTY, AMIYA, PHIL DEPT, COL AT NEW PLATZ, NEW PLATZ NY   12561
CHALKER, WILLIAM, REL & PHIL DEPT, THE COLLEGE OF IDAHO, CALDWELL ID   83605
CHALMERS, A BURNS, PHILOSOPHY DEPT, BELKNAP COLLEGE, CENTER HARBOR NH   03226
CHALMERS, R C, PINE HILL DIV HALL, HALIFAX, N S   CAN
CHAMBERS, ALMA C, SOUTH MISSIONARY COL, COLLEGEDALE, TN   37315
CHAMBERS, JEFFREY J, PHILOSOPHY DEPT, UNIV OF HOUSTON, HOUSTON TX   77004
CHAMBERS, MARJORIE, RELIG & PHIL DEPT, MARY BALDWIN COL, STAUNTON VA   24401
CHAMBERS, PAUL A, HUMAN DEPT, BROOME COM COL, BINGHAMTON NY   13902
CHAMPAGNE, RENE, PHIL FACULTE, UNIVERSITE LAVAL, CITE UNIV QUE   CAN

CHAMPAWAT, NARAYAN, PHIL DEPT, CALIFORNIA ST UNIV, NORTHRIDGE CA 91324
CHAN, BENJAMIN, PHIL DEPT, INDIANA UNIV OF PENN, INDIANA PA 15701
CHAN, WING-MING, HUMAN DIV, EISENHOWER COLLEGE, SENECA FALLS NY 13148
CHAN, WING-TSIT, PHIL & RELIG, CHATHAM COLLEGE, PITTSBURGH PA 15232
CHANCE, JERRY M, PHIL & REL, FLORIDA A & M UNIV, TALLAHASSEE FL 32307
CHANCY, MAX, COL EDOUARD-MONTPETIT, LONGUEUIL, QUE   CAN
CHANDLER, DAVID, PHIL DEPT, S ILLINOIS UNIV, CARBONDALE IL 62901
CHANDLER, GEORGE P, HUM RELATIONS DEPT, COLUMBIA COLLEGE, COLUMBIA SC 29203
CHANDLER, HUGH S, PHIL DEPT, UNIV OF ILLINOIS, URBANA IL 61801
CHANDLER, KENNETH, PHIL DEPT, UNIV OF MISSOURI, COLUMBIA MO 65201
CHANDLER, MARTHE DE R, PHILOSOPHY DEPT, CEN YMCA COM COL, CHICAGO IL 60606
CHANEY, NORMAN, RELIG & PHIL DEPT, OTTERBEIN COL, WESTERVILLE OH 43081
CHANG, CHING-MEI, PHIL DEPT, S ILLINOIS UNIV, CARBONDALE IL 62901
CHANG, CHUNG-YUAN, PHIL DEPT, UNIVERSITY OF HAWAII, HONOLULU HI 96822
CHANG, KEE SOO, PHIL DEPT, WICHITA ST UNIV, WICHITA KS 67208
CHANG, KEY H, HUMANITIES DIV, FERRUM COLLEGE, FERRUM VA 24088
CHANG, MATTHEW, PHILOSOPHY DEPT, GONZAGA UNIV, SPOKANE WA 99202
CHANG, PETER, THEOL PROGRAM, MARYKNOLL SEM, MARYKNOLL NY 10545
CHANNELL, CRAIG, PHIL DEPT, THE AMERICAN UNIV, WASHINGTON DC 20016
CHAPDELAINE, GILLES, PHIL DEPT, COL TROIS-RIVIERES, 3 RIVIERES QUE   CAN
CHAPMAN, HARLEY, PHIL DEPT, WM RAINEY HARPER COL, PALATINE IL 60067
CHAPMAN, JAMES P, HUMAN DIV, MADISONVILLE COM COL, MADISONVILLE KY 42431
CHAPMAN, MARILYN, PHIL DEPT, UNIV OF CALIFORNIA, LOS ANGELES CA 90024
CHAPMAN, SAMUEL C, PHIL DEPT, S ILLINOIS UNIV, CARBONDALE IL 62901
CHAPMAN, SIDNEY, HUMANITIES DIV, RICHLAND COLLEGE, DALLAS TX 75202
CHAPMAN, T, PHILOSOPHY DEPT, UNIV OF GUELPH, GUELPH ONT   CAN
CHAPPELL, JAMES, PHIL DEPT, LORAS COLLEGE, DUBUQUE IA 52001
CHAPPELL, VERE, PHILOSOPHY DEPT, UNIV OF MASS, AMHERST MA 01002
CHAPUT, PAUL, PHIL DEPT, COL VIEUX-MONTREAL, MONTREAL QUE   CAN
CHARBONNEAU, FRANCOIS, COLLEGE D'AHUNTSIC, MONTREAL, QUE   CAN
CHARBONNEAU, PAUL, PHIL DEPT, COL BOIS-DE-BOULOGNE, MONTREAL QUE   CAN
CHARETTE, LEON, PHIL FACULTY, UNIV OF OTTAWA, OTTAWA ONT   CAN
CHARLEBOIS, DENIS, PHILOSOPHY DEPT, COL DE MAISONNEUVE, MONTREAL QUE   CAN
CHARLESWORTH, ARTHUR R, RELIG & PHIL, BETHUNE-COOKMAN COL, DAYTONA FL 32015
CHARLSON, PRICE, PHIL DEPT, COL AT NEW PLATZ, NEW PLATZ NY 12561
CHARLTON, TERRENCE, PHILOSOPHY DEPT, XAVIER UNIVERSITY, CINCINNATI OH 45207
CHARLWOOD, G W, PHILOSOPHY DEPT, UNIV OF TORONTO, TORONTO ONT   CAN
CHARRON, GHYSLAIN, PHIL FACULTY, UNIV OF OTTAWA, OTTAWA ONT   CAN
CHARRON, WILLIAM C, PHIL DEPT, ST LOUIS UNIVERSITY, ST LOUIS MO 63103
CHASE, ALSTON S, PHILOSOPHY DEPT, MACALESTER COLLEGE, ST PAUL MN 55101
CHASTAIN, C H, PHILOSOPHY DEPT, UNIV OF TORONTO, TORONTO ONT   CAN
CHATALIAN, GEORGE, PHIL & RELIG DEPT, FRANKLIN PIERCE COL, RINDGE NH 03461
CHATEAUBRIAND, OSWALDO, SAGE SCHOOL, CORNELL UNIVERSITY, ITHACA NY 14850
CHAUVE, MARYVONNE, PHIL DEPT, SEM DE SHERBROOKE, SHERBROOKE QUE   CAN
CHBAT, JOSEPH, COL ANDRE-GRASSET, MONTREAL, QUE   CAN
CHECKER, JUDITH A, PHIL DEPT, UNIV OF ILLINOIS, URBANA IL 61801
CHEEMOOKE, ROBERT, PHILOSOPHY DEPT, MORGAN STATE UNIV, BALTIMORE MD 21239
CHEKOLA, MARK, PHIL DEPT, MOORHEAD STATE COL, MOORHEAD MN 56560
CHELLAS, BRIAN, PHILOSOPHY DEPT, UNIV OF PENN, PHILADELPHIA PA 19174
CHEN, CHUNG-HWAN, PHIL DEPT, UNIV OF S FLORIDA, TAMPA FL 33620
CHENARD, ROSAIRE, PHIL DEPT, COL LIONEL-GROULX, STE-THERESE QUE   CAN
CHENEY, DAVID R, PHIL DEPT, BRIDGEWATER ST COL, BRIDGEWATER MA 02324
CHENEY, DAVID, PHIL DEPT, UNIV OF CALIFORNIA, SANTA BARBARA CA 93106
CHENG, CHUNG-YING, PHIL DEPT, UNIVERSITY OF HAWAII, HONOLULU HI 96822
CHENG, HSUEH-LI, PHILOSOPHY DEPT, OHIO UNIVERSITY, ATHENS OH 45701
CHENIER, JEAN-MARC, PHILOSOPHY DEPT, COL DE MAISONNEUVE, MONTREAL QUE   CAN
CHERENTANT, GERALD, PHIL DEPT, COL LIONEL-GROULX, STE-THERESE QUE   CAN
CHERVIN, RONDA, LOYOLA UNIVERSITY, LOS ANGELES, CA 90045
CHESTER, JOSEPH, PHIL DEPT, INDIANA UNIVERSITY, BLOOMINGTON IN 47401
CHETHIMATTAM, JOHN B, PHIL DEPT, FORDHAM UNIVERSITY, BRONX NY 10458
CHIARIELLO, M V, PHIL DEPT, ST BONAVENTURE UNIV, ST BONVENTURE NY 14778
CHIASSON, EUCLIDE P, PHIL DEPT, COLLEGE DE BATHURST, BATHURST N B   CAN
CHICHESTER JR, HELON L, SOC SCI DIV, COLLEGE OF ALAMEDA, ALAMEDA CA 94501
CHICOYNE, PIERRE, PHIL DEPT, COL TROIS-RIVIERES, 3 RIVIERES QUE   CAN

CHIESA, ERNESTO, PHIL DEPT, UNIV OF PUERTO RICO, RIO PIEDRAS PR 00931
CHIHARA, CHARLES S, PHIL DEPT, UNIV OF CALIFORNIA, BERKELEY CA 94720
CHILD, ARTHUR, PHIL DEPT, UNIV OF CALIFORNIA, DAVIS CA 95616
CHILDERS, GINGER H, PHILOSOPHY DEPT, MEMPHIS ST UNIV, MEMPHIS TN 38152
CHILDRESS, MARIANNE, PHIL DEPT, ST LOUIS UNIVERSITY, ST LOUIS MO 63103
CHILDS, JOHN, PHIL & SOC SCI, TEACHERS COLLEGE, NEW YORK NY 10027
CHINN, EWING, PHIL DEPT, TRINITY UNIVERSITY, SAN ANTONIO TX 78284
CHINNI, ANGELO, PHIL DEPT, SCHOOLCRAFT COLLEGE, LIVONIA MI 48151
CHISHOLM, RODERICK, PHILOSOPHY DEPT, BROWN UNIVERSITY, PROVIDENCE RI 02912
CHIU, ALEC K F, PHILOSOPHY DEPT, VITERBO COLLEGE, LA CROSSE WI 54601
CHO, KAH-KYUNG, PHIL DEPT, ST UNIV OF NY, AMHERST NY 14226
CHOATE JR, J E, DAVID LIPSCOMB COL, NASHVILLE, TN 37203
CHOBOT, NEAL L, PHIL DEPT, UNIVERSITY OF HAWAII, HONOLULU HI 96822
CHOI, CHANG-HAN, PHIL DEPT, ST UNIV OF NY, AMHERST NY 14226
CHOI, SUNG, PHILOSOPHY DEPT, PATERSON COL OF NJ, WAYNE NJ 07470
CHOPTIANY, L R, PHILOSOPHY DEPT, VICTORIA UNIV, TORONTO 181 ONT CAN
CHRISTENSEN, F M, PHILOSOPHY DEPT, UNIV OF ALBERTA, EDMONTON ALB CAN
CHRISTENSEN, L, PHIL DEPT, PURDUE UNIVERSITY, LAFAYETTE IN 47907
CHRISTENSEN, W N, LIBR ARTS DEPT, DOUGLAS COLLEGE, NW WESTMINSTR B C CAN
CHRISTENSON, THOMAS, PHIL DEPT, CONCORDIA COLLEGE, MOORHEAD MN 56560
CHRISTIE, FRANCIS, PHILOSOPHY DEPT, HENDRIX COLLEGE, CONWAY AR 72032
CHRISTIE, JOSEPH C, PHIL DEPT, FLORIDA STATE UNIV, TALLAHASSEE FL 32306
CHRISTMAS, DONALD, HUMAN DEPT, OKALOOSA-WALTON JR C, NICEVILLE FL 32578
CHRISTOPHER, DENNIS, PHIL DEPT, UNIV OF N CAROLINA, CHAPEL HILL NC 27514
CHRISTOPHER, JOHN F, SOC SCI DEPT, PASADENA CY COLLEGE, PASADENA CA 91106
CHRISTOPHERSON, R, PHILOSOPHY DEPT, PENN STATE UNIV, UNIV PARK PA 16802
CHUNG, BONG, PHIL DEPT, UNIV OF NEW MEXICO, ALBUQUERQUE NM 87106
CHURCH, ALONZO, PHIL DEPT, UNIV OF CALIFORNIA, LOS ANGELES CA 90024
CHURCHILL, JAMES, PHIL DEPT, PURDUE UNIVERSITY, FORT WAYNE IN 46805
CHURCHLAND, P S, PHIL DEPT, UNIV OF MANITOBA, WINNIPEG 19 MAN CAN
CICANTELLI, PATRICIA, PHIL DEPT, UNIVERSITY OF DAYTON, DAYTON OH 45469
CIPOLLONE, ANTHONY, PHIL DEPT, DEPAUL UNIVERSITY, CHICAGO IL 60604
CISEK, ROBERT, PHILOSOPHY DEPT, MERCYHURST COLLEGE, ERIE PA 16501
CISNEROS, MARCELINO, HUMAN DEPT, UNIV OF PUERTO RICO, MAYAGUEZ PR 00708
CLACK, R JEROLD, LATIN & PHIL DEPT, NC CENTRAL UNIV, DURHAM NC 27707
CLAGHORN, GEORGE S, PHIL DEPT, WEST CHESTER ST COL, WEST CHESTER PA 19380
CLAIBORNE, J H, ENG PHIL & LANG DIV, ARKANSAS ST U, ST UNIVERSITY AR 72467
CLANCY, JOHN P, SOC SCI DEPT, SADDLEBACK COLLEGE, MISSION VIEJO CA 92675
CLARK, ANN K, PHIL DEPT, INDIANA UNIVERSITY, SOUTH BEND IN 46615
CLARK, CHERYL, PHIL DEPT, CALIFORNIA ST UNIV, LONG BEACH CA 90840
CLARK, DAVID K, PHIL DEPT, PURDUE UNIVERSITY, LAFAYETTE IN 47907
CLARK, DEVIN M, PHILOSOPHY DEPT, UNIV OF S CAROLINA, COLUMBIA SC 29208
CLARK, GEORGE A, PHILOSOPHY DEPT, LAFAYETTE COLLEGE, EASTON PA 18042
CLARK, JAMES W, PHIL DEPT, UNIV OF ALABAMA, UNIVERSITY AL 35486
CLARK, JOHN A, PHIL & REL DEPT, COLBY COLLEGE, WATERVILLE ME 04901
CLARK, JOHN, LOYOLA CY COLLEGE, NEW ORLEANS, LA 70118
CLARK, JOSEPH T, PHIL DEPT, CANISIUS COLLEGE, BUFFALO NY 14208
CLARK, KEN, SOC SCI DIV, KANSAS CY COM COL, KANSAS CITY KS 66112
CLARK, L M G, PHILOSOPHY DEPT, UNIV OF TORONTO, TORONTO ONT CAN
CLARK, LEONARD, PHIL DEPT, EARLHAM COLLEGE, RICHMOND IN 47374
CLARK, M E, PHILOSOPHY DEPT, LOYOLA COLLEGE, BALTIMORE MD 21210
CLARK, M, PHIL DEPT, W CONNECTICUT ST COL, DANBURY CT 06810
CLARK, MARY T, PHIL DEPT, MANHATTANVILLE COL, PURCHASE NY 10577
CLARK, MAUDEMARIE A, PHILOSOPHY DEPT, UNIV OF WISCONSIN, MADISON WI 53706
CLARK, ORVILLE, PHIL OPTION, UNIV OF WISCONSIN, GREEN BAY WI 54302
CLARK, RALPH W, PHIL DEPT, WEST VIRGINIA UNIV, MORGANTOWN WV 26506
CLARK, ROMANE L, PHIL DEPT, INDIANA UNIVERSITY, BLOOMINGTON IN 47401
CLARK, THEODORE R, BEHAVIOR SCI, PAN AMERICAN UNIV, EDINBURG TX 78539
CLARK, WILLIAM, PHIL DEPT, LEWIS COLLEGE, LOCKPORT IL 60441
CLARKE, BOWMAN L, PHIL & REL DEPT, UNIV OF GEORGIA, ATHENS GA 30602
CLARKE, DAVID S, PHIL DEPT, S ILLINOIS UNIV, CARBONDALE IL 62901
CLARKE, DESMOND, PHIL DEPT, ALBION COLLEGE, ALBION MI 49224
CLARKE, G I, PHILOSOPHY DEPT, LAURENTIAN UNIV, SUDBURY ONT CAN
CLARKE, NORRIS W, PHIL DEPT, FORDHAM UNIVERSITY, BRONX NY 10458

CLARKE, RICHARD, PHIL DEPT, UNIV OF MINNESOTA, MINNEAPOLIS MN 55455
CLARKE, ROBERT E, PHIL DEPT, OKLA BAPT UNIV, SHAWNEE OK 74801
CLARKE, S G, PHILOSOPHY DEPT, CARLETON UNIVERSITY, OTTAWA ONT CAN
CLARKE, SHELTON, PHILOSOPHY DEPT, VOORHEES COLLEGE, DENMARK SC 29042
CLARKE, THOMPSON M, PHIL DEPT, UNIV OF CALIFORNIA, BERKELEY CA 94720
CLASEMAN, FRANCIS A, PHIL DEPT, PARKS COL AERO TECH, VIA CAHOKIA MO 62206
CLATTERBAUGH, KEN C, PHILOSOPHY DEPT, UNIV OF WASHINGTON, SEATTLE WA 98195
CLAUDE, PAUL, PHIL DEPT, COL FRANCOIS-X-GARN, QUEBEC CITY QUE CAN
CLAY, CHRISTOPHER C, PHIL DEPT, FORDHAM UNIVERSITY, BRONX NY 10458
CLAY, MARJORIE A, PHILOSOPHY DEPT, UNIV OF OKLAHOMA, NORMAN OK 73069
CLAYTON, MARUS, HUMAN DIV, PAINE COLLEGE, AUGUSTA GA 30901
CLEGG, JERRY STEPHEN, PHIL DEPT, MILLS COLLEGE, OAKLAND CA 94613
CLEMENCE, PATRICK, PHIL DEPT, UNIV OF WEST ONTARIO, LONDON ONT CAN
CLEMENS, EUGENE P, RELIG & PHIL, ELIZABETHTOWN COL, ELIZABETHTOWN PA 17022
CLEMENT, MARIE-ROSE, PHIL DEPT, COL TROIS-RIVIERES, 3 RIVIERES QUE CAN
CLEMENTS, GERALD G, PHILOSOPHY DEPT, YORK UNIVERSITY, DOWNSVIEW ONT CAN
CLEMENTS, TAD, PHIL DEPT, COLLEGE AT BROCKPORT, BROCKPORT NY 14420
CLEWELL, R, LANG ARTS DEPT, LEHIGH CO COM COL, SCHNECKSVILLE PA 18078
CLIFFORD, JOHN E, PHIL DEPT, UNIV OF MISSOURI, ST LOUIS MO 63121
CLINTON, STEVE, BIB & PHIL DEPT, TABOR COLLEGE, HILLSBORO KS 67063
CLITHEROE, ERIC L, PHIL DEPT, PURDUE UNIVERSITY, LAFAYETTE IN 47907
CLIVE, GEOFFREY, PHILOSOPHY DEPT, UNIV OF MASS, BOSTON MA 02116
CLODIUS, ALBERT, SOC SCI DEPT, VENTURA COLLEGE, VENTURA CA 93003
CLOEREN, HERMANN-JOSEF, PHIL DEPT, COL OF HOLY CROSS, WORCESTER MA 01610
CLOUSER, K DANNER, HUMANITIES DEPT, PENN STATE UNIV, HERSHEY PA 17033
CLOUSER, ROY, PHIL & RELIG DEPT, TRENTON STATE COL, TRENTON NJ 08625
CLOUTIER, RONALD, PHIL DEPT, ANNA MARIA COLLEGE, PAXTON MA 01612
CLOUTIER, YVAN, PHIL DEPT, COL DE SHERBROOKE, SHERBROOKE QUE CAN
COATS, JAMES B, ENG & PHIL, THREE RIVERS COM COL, POPLAR BLUFF MO 63901
COBB JR, WILLIAM S, PHIL DEPT, COL WILLIAM & MARY, WILLIAMSBURG VA 23185
COBB, JOHN B, 1325 N COLLEGE, CLAREMONT, CA 91711
COBB, R ALLAN, PHILOSOPHY DEPT, YORK UNIVERSITY, DOWNSVIEW ONT CAN
COBB, W H, PHIL DEPT, UNIV OF CONNECTICUT, STORRS CT 06268
COBB, WILLIAM DANIEL, PHILOSOPHY DEPT, EUREKA COLLEGE, EUREKA IL 61530
COBITZ, JOSEPH, SOC SCI DEPT, PRATT INSTITUTE, BROOKLYN NY 11205
COBURN, ROBERT C, PHILOSOPHY DEPT, UNIV OF WASHINGTON, SEATTLE WA 98195
COCCHIARELLA, N B, PHIL DEPT, INDIANA UNIVERSITY, BLOOMINGTON IN 47401
COCHRAN, DAN W, PHIL DEPT, SW BAPT COL, BOLIVAR MO 65613
COCKING, HERBERT, DETROIT BIB COLLEGE, DETROIT, MI 48235
CODE, ALAN D, PHILOSOPHY DEPT, UNIV OF WISCONSIN, MADISON WI 53706
CODER, DAVID, PHILOSOPHY DEPT, DUKE UNIVERSITY, DURHAM NC 27706
CODY, ARTHUR B, PHIL DEPT, CALIFORNIA ST UNIV, SAN JOSE CA 95114
COE, WILLIAM, PHIL & POLIT SCI, FORT LEWIS COLLEGE, DURANGO CO 81301
COERVER, ROBERT, PHIL & THEOL DEPT, MARILLAC COLLEGE, ST LOUIS MO 63121
COFFA, J ALBERTO, HIST & PHIL SCI, INDIANA UNIV, BLOOMINGTON IN 47401
COFFEY, PATRICK J, PHILOSOPHY DEPT, MARQUETTE UNIV, MILWAUKEE WI 53233
COFFIN, MARY S, PHIL DEPT, UNIVERSITY OF TOLEDO, TOLEDO OH 43606
COFFIN, PETER, PHILOSOPHY DEPT, CEDAR CREST COLLEGE, ALLENTOWN PA 18104
COFFMAN, FREDERICK, PHIL DEPT, UNIV OF CINCINNATI, CINCINNATI OH 45221
COGAN, ROBERT, PHILOSOPHY DEPT, EDINBORO ST COL, EDINBORO PA 16412
COGELL, WAYNE, HUMAN DEPT, UNIV OF MISSOURI, ROLLA MO 65401
COGGIN, WALTER A, PHIL DEPT, BELMONT ABBEY COL, BELMONT NC 28012
COHEN, BARRY F, PHIL & REL STUD, YOUNGSTOWN ST UNIV, YOUNGSTOWN OH 44503
COHEN, CARL, PHIL DEPT, UNIV OF MICHIGAN, ANN ARBOR MI 48104
COHEN, CYNTHIA B, PHIL DEPT, UNIV OF DENVER, DENVER CO 80210
COHEN, ELI, PHIL DEPT, BROOKLYN COLLEGE, BROOKLYN NY 11210
COHEN, HOWARD, PHILOSOPHY DEPT, UNIV OF MASS, BOSTON MA 02116
COHEN, MARK, PHIL DEPT, HUNTER COLLEGE, NEW YORK NY 10021
COHEN, MARSHALL, HUMAN DIV, RICHMOND COLLEGE, STATEN ISLAND NY 10301
COHEN, MAURICE, PHIL DEPT, CITY COLLEGE, NEW YORK NY 10031
COHEN, MENDEL F, PHILOSOPHY DEPT, UNIV OF UTAH, SALT LAKE CTY UT 84112
COHEN, RICHARD, PHIL DEPT, ST UNIV OF NY, STONY BROOK NY 11790
COHEN, ROBERT S, PHIL DEPT, BOSTON UNIVERSITY, BOSTON MA 02215
COHEN, S MARC, PHILOSOPHY DEPT, UNIV OF WASHINGTON, SEATTLE WA 98195

COHEN, SHELDON M, PHIL DEPT, UNIV OF TENNESSEE, KNOXVILLE TN 37916
COHEN, TED, PHIL DEPT, UNIV OF CHICAGO, CHICAGO IL 60637
COIN, DIANNE, PHIL DEPT, MICHIGAN STATE UNIV, EAST LANSING MI 48823
COKER, H E, BIB & REL EDUC, CAMPBELLSVILLE COL, CAMPBELLSVL KY 42718
COLAPIETRO, VINCENT, PHILOSOPHY DEPT, MARQUETTE UNIV, MILWAUKEE WI 53233
COLAVECHIO, X G, HUM & FINE ARTS DEPT, ST NORBERT COL, DE PERE WI 54115
COLAVITA, LAWRENCE J, PHIL DEPT, WASHINGTON UNIV, ST LOUIS MO 63130
COLBERT, JAMES G, PHIL DEPT, BOSTON STATE COL, BOSTON MA 02115
COLBURN, BROOKS, PHIL DEPT, MANHATTANVILLE COL, PURCHASE NY 10577
COLBURN, SUSAN, PHIL DEPT, UNIV OF CONNECTICUT, STAMFORD CT 06903
COLE, CHARLES, ACADEMY OF NW CHURCH, BRYN ATHYN, PA 19009
COLE, H BROCK, PHILOSOPHY DEPT, UNIV OF WISCONSIN, MADISON WI 53706
COLE, RICHARD, PHIL DEPT, UNIVERSITY OF KANSAS, LAWRENCE KS 66044
COLE, ROBERT, PHIL DEPT, JEFFERSON COM COL, LOUISVILLE KY 40205
COLEMAN, A W, PHIL & HIST DEPT, EL RENO JUNIOR COL, EL RENO OK 73036
COLEMAN, DONALD A, PHIL DEPT, FAIRFIELD UNIVERSITY, FAIRFIELD CT 06430
COLEMAN, EARLE J, PHIL & RELIG, VA COMMONWEALTH UNIV, RICHMOND VA 23220
COLEMAN, ELLEN R, PHIL DEPT, UNIV OF WISCONSIN, MILWAUKEE WI 53201
COLEMAN, FRANCIS J, PHIL DEPT, BOSTON UNIVERSITY, BOSTON MA 02215
COLEMAN, JULES, PHIL DEPT, UNIV OF WISCONSIN, MILWAUKEE WI 53201
COLEMAN, ROBERT A, PHIL DEPT, UNIV OF WEST ONTARIO, LONDON ONT CAN
COLEMAN, W R, PHIL & RELIG DEPT, JOHNSON C SMITH UNIV, CHARLOTTE NC 28216
COLES, M, PHILOSOPHY DEPT, UNIV OF ALBERTA, EDMONTON ALB CAN
COLGAN, QUENTIN, PHIL DIV, ST MEINRAD COLLEGE, SAINT MEINRAD IN 47577
COLLAMATI, ERNEST J, HUMAN DIV, ST MARY WOODS COL, ST MARY WOODS IN 47876
COLLETTE, RICHARD, PHIL DEPT, COL DE VALLEYFIELD, VALLEYFIELD QUE CAN
COLLIER, JOHN, PHIL DEPT, UNIV OF CALIFORNIA, LOS ANGELES CA 90024
COLLIER, KENNETH W, PHIL STUD DEPT, S ILLINOIS UNIV, EDWARDSVILLE IL 62025
COLLIN, CLAUDE, PHIL DEPT, COL VIEUX-MONTREAL, MONTREAL QUE CAN
COLLINGWOOD, FRANCIS J, PHILOSOPHY DEPT, MARQUETTE UNIV, MILWAUKEE WI 53233
COLLINS, ARDIS B, PHIL DEPT, LOYOLA UNIVERSITY, CHICAGO IL 60626
COLLINS, ARTHUR W, PHIL DEPT, CITY COLLEGE, NEW YORK NY 10031
COLLINS, GEORGE, PHIL DEPT, ST ANSELM'S COLLEGE, MANCHESTER NH 03102
COLLINS, JAMES D, PHIL DEPT, ST LOUIS UNIVERSITY, ST LOUIS MO 63103
COLLINS, MAURICE, PHILOSOPHY DEPT, DUQUESNE UNIV, PITTSBURGH PA 15219
COLLINS, PAUL W, PHIL DEPT, COL AT ONEONTA, ONEONTA NY 13820
COLLINS, ROBERT, PHIL DEPT, COL OF SAINT TERESA, WINONA MN 55987
COLLINSON, JOHN, PHIL DEPT, UNIV OF NEW HAVEN, WEST HAVEN CT 06516
COLLORD, PAUL, PHILOSOPHY DEPT, NYACK COLLEGE, NYACK NY 10931
COLOVOS, POLYGNOTOS H, PHIL DEPT, RENSSELAER POLYTECH, TROY NY 12181
COLTER, L W, PHIL DEPT, ILL WESLEYAN UNIV, BLOOMINGTON IL 61701
COLUCCI, ROBERT, PENN STATE UNIV, MCKEESPORT, PA 15132
COLVER, A WAYNE, PHILOSOPHY DEPT, CALIFORNIA ST UNIV, FRESNO CA 93740
COME, ARNOLD, SYST & PHIL, GRADUATE THEOL UNION, BERKELEY CA 94709
COMMENATOR, GEORGE E, HUMAN DEPT, NEW HAMPSHIRE CCL, MANCHESTER NH 03104
COMMEREE, NOEL, HUMANITIES DEPT, COLUMBIA BASIN COL, PASCO WA 99301
COMPTON, JOHN J, PHILOSOPHY DEPT, VANDERBILT UNIV, NASHVILLE TN 37235
COMPTON, RUSSELL J, PHIL & REL, DEPAUW UNIVERSITY, GREENCASTLE IN 46135
COMPTON, STAFFORD, SOC SCI DEPT, SW VIRGINIA COM COL, RICHLANDS VA 24641
COMTOIS, R, COL DOM PHIL & THEOL, OTTAWA, ONT CAN
COMTOIS, RAOUL, PHIL DEPT, COL VIEUX-MONTREAL, MONTREAL QUE CAN
CONCORDIA, GEORGE L, PHIL DEPT, PROVIDENCE COLLEGE, PROVIDENCE RI 02919
CONGDON, HOWARD K, ENG & PHIL DEPT, LOCK HAVEN ST COL, LOCK HAVEN PA 17745
CONGDON, WILLIAM, FRANCONIA COLLEGE, FRANCONIA, NH 03580
CONGLETON, ANN, PHIL DPET, WELLESLEY COLLEGE, WELLESLEY MA 02181
CONKLING, MARK L, PHILOSOPHY DEPT, NM HIGHLANDS UNIV, LAS VEGAS NM 87701
CONLON, JAMES, PHILOSOPHY DEPT, MARQUETTE UNIV, MILWAUKEE WI 53233
CONLON, MICHAEL J, PHIL DEPT, FITCHBURG STATE COL, FITCHBURG MA 01420
CONN, JOANN, REL & PHIL DEPT, STEPHENS COLLEGE, COLUMBIA MO 65201
CONNALLY, JOHN, PHIL DEPT, SMITH COLLEGE, NORTHAMPTON MA 01060
CONNELL, RICHARD J, PHIL DEPT, COL OF ST THOMAS, ST PAUL MN 55105
CONNELLY, FRANK, HIST & RELATED AREAS, E CONN ST COL, WILLIMANTIC CT 06226
CONNELLY, GEORGE, PHIL DEPT, LOYOLA UNIVERSITY, CHICAGO IL 60626
CONNELLY, ROBERT J, PHILOSOPHY DEPT, FONTBONNE COLLEGE, ST LOUIS MO 63105

CONNICK, C MILO, PHIL DEPT, WHITTIER COLLEGE, WHITTIER CA 90608
CONNOLLY, JOHN, COMMUNIC ARTS, NORTH IDAHO COLLEGE, COEUR D'ALENE ID 83814
CONNOLLY, WILLIAM, REL & PHIL, UNIV OF EVANSVILLE, EVANSVILLE IN 47701
CONNOR, JOHN W, PHIL DEPT, ST VIN DE PAUL SEM, BOYNTON FL 33435
CONNOR, JOHN, PHIL DEPT, S ILLINOIS UNIV, CARBONDALE IL 62901
CONNOR, O, PHIL DEPT, UNIV OF MANITOBA, WINNIPEG 19 MAN   CAN
CONNOR, WILLIAM, REL & PHIL DEPT, PHILLIPS UNIVERSITY, ENID OK 73701
CONOVER, C EUGENE, PHIL & RELIG, LINDENWOOD COLLEGES, ST CHARLES MO 63301
CONRADI, J CHRISTIAN, PHIL DEPT, WASHINGTON UNIV, ST LOUIS MO 63130
CONRATH, RICHARD, HUMANITIES DEPT, LAKELAND COM COL, MENTOR OH 44060
CONROY, BERNARD, HUMAN DEPT, LOOP COLLEGE, CHICAGO IL 60601
CONROY, GRAHAM P, PHIL DEPT, PORTLAND ST UNIV, PORTLAND OR 97207
CONSENTINO, DANTE, PHIL DEPT, UNIV OF CALIFORNIA, SANTA BARBARA CA 93106
CONSTANTIKES, JOHN J, PHILOSOPHY DEPT, UNIV OF OKLAHOMA, NORMAN OK 73069
CONWAY, DAVID A, PHIL DEPT, UNIV OF MISSOURI, ST LOUIS MO 63121
CONWAY, GERTRUDE, PHIL DEPT, FORDHAM UNIVERSITY, BRONX NY 10458
CONWAY, VINCENT, HUM & FINE ARTS DEPT, ST NORBERT COL, DE PERE WI 54115
COOK, GARY A, PHILOSOPHY DEPT, BELOIT COLLEGE, BELOIT WI 53511
COOK, JAMES, PHIL DEPT, UNIVERSITY OF KANSAS, LAWRENCE KS 66044
COOK, JEFFREY S, PHILOSOPHY DEPT, UNIV OF UTAH, SALT LAKE CTY UT 84112
COOK, JOHN W, PHILOSOPHY DEPT, UNIV OF OREGON, EUGENE OR 97403
COOK, JOYCE MITCHELL, PHIL DEPT, HOWARD UNIVERSITY, WASHINGTON DC 20001
COOK, KATHLEEN, PHIL DPET, WELLESLEY COLLEGE, WELLESLEY MA 02181
COOK, MONTE L, PHILOSOPHY DEPT, UNIV OF OKLAHOMA, NORMAN OK 73069
COOK, THOMAS, PHIL DEPT, UNIV OF N CAROLINA, CHARLOTTE NC 28213
COOKE, LEE, PHIL DEPT, UNIV OF VIRGINIA, CHARLOTTESVL VA 22903
COOKE, VINCENT M, PHIL DEPT, FORDHAM UNIVERSITY, BRONX NY 10458
COOLE, WALTER A, PHIL DEPT, SKAGIT VALLEY COL, MOUNT VERNON WA 98273
COOLEY, KENNETH W, ENGLISH LIT & PHIL, UNIV OF WISCONSIN, MADISON WI 53706
COOMBER, DAVID A, HUMANITIES DEPT, SHELBY ST COM COL, MEMPHIS TN 38111
COONEY, BRIAN, PHILOSOPHY DEPT, UNIV OF TEXAS, AUSTIN TX 78712
COONEY, NEILL L, PHILOSOPHY DEPT, CYPRESS COLLEGE, CYPRESS CA 90630
COOPER, BARON, COLLEGE OF SAN MATEO, SAN MATEO, CA 94402
COOPER, DAVID E, PHIL DEPT, N MICHIGAN UNIV, MARQUETTE MI 49855
COOPER, JAMES G, SOC SCI DEPT, SOUTH PLAINS COL, LEVELLAND TX 79336
COOPER, JOE M, PHIL DEPT, MISSISSIPPI COLLEGE, CLINTON MS 39058
COOPER, JOHN M, PHIL DEPT, UNIV OF PITTSBURGH, PITTSBURGH PA 15260
COOPER, ROBERT M, PHIL & SYST THEOL, NASHOTAH HOUSE SEM, NASHOTA WI 53058
COOPER, TED L, EDUCATION DEPT, CENTRAL WASH ST COL, ELLENSBURG WA 98926
COOPER, W E, PHILOSOPHY DEPT, UNIV OF ALBERTA, EDMONTON ALB   CAN
COOPER, WILLIAM F, PHILOSOPHY DEPT, BAYLOR UNIVERSITY, WACO TX 76703
COOPERSTEIN, PAUL, PHIL DEPT, UNIV OF NEW MEXICO, ALBUQUERQUE NM 87106
COPELAND, JOHN W, PHILOSOPHY DEPT, CREW UNIVERSITY, MADISON NJ 07940
COPI, IRVING M, PHIL DEPT, UNIVERSITY OF HAWAII, HONOLULU HI 96822
COPPENGER, RAYMOND, PHIL DEPT, QUACHITA BAPTIST U, ARKADELPHIA AR 71923
COPPS, HENRY L, LANG ARTS DEPT, POLK COM COLLEGE, WINTER HAVEN FL 33880
CORBETT, ROBERT, PHIL DEPT, WEBSTER COLLEGE, ST LOUIS MO 63119
CORBETT, S M, PHILOSOPHY DEPT, QUEEN'S UNIVERSITY, KINGSTON ONT   CAN
CORBITT, J H, RELIG & PHIL DEPT, PHILANDER SMITH COL, LITTLE ROCK AR 72203
CORCORAN, ALBERT C, PHIL DEPT, UNIV OF SN FRANCISCO, SAN FRANCISCO CA 94117
CORCORAN, JAMES, PHILOSOPHY DEPT, UNIV OF VERMONT, BURLINGTON VT 05401
CORCORAN, JOHN P, PHIL DEPT, ST UNIV OF NY, AMHERST NY 14226
CORDERO, RONALD A, PHILOSOPHY DEPT, UNIV OF WISONSIN, OSH KOSH WI 54901
CORDING, RICHARD, PHIL DEPT, SAM HOUSTON ST UNIV, HUNTSVILLE TX 77340
CORDING, ROCHARD, PHIL DEPT, SAM HOUSTON ST UNIV, HUNTSVILLE TX 77340
CORCON, CATHERINE, PHILOSOPHY DEPT, EDGEWOOD COLLEGE, MADISON WI 53711
CORDUA DE TORRETTI, C, PHIL DEPT, UNIV OF PUERTO RICO, RIO PIEDRAS PR 00931
CORISH, DENIS J, BOWDOIN COLLEGE, BRUNSWICK, ME 04011
CORKERY, JOSEPH, PHIL DEPT, BRIDGEWATER ST COL, BRIDGEWATER MA 02324
CORKEY, W B H, PHIL DEPT, UNIV OF N CAROLINA, CHARLOTTE NC 28213
CORLISS, RICHARD, PHIL DEPT, ST CLOUD ST COL, ST CLOUD MN 56301
CORMAN, JAMES W, PHILOSOPHY DEPT, UNIV OF PENN, PHILADELPHIA PA 19174
CORMIER, RAMONA, PHIL DEPT, BOWLING GREEN UNIV, BOWLING GREEN OH 43403
CORNAY, D, PHIL DEPT, LOUISIANA ST UNIV, BATON ROUGE LA 70803

CORNETT, LINDA B, PHIL DEPT, AGNES SCOTT COLLEGE, DECATUR GA 30030
CORNETT, ROBERT, PHIL DEPT, RANDOLPH-MACON COL, LYNCHBURG VA 24504
CORNWELL, SANDRA G, PHILOSOPHY DEPT, UNIV OF HOUSTON, HOUSTON TX 77004
CORR, CHARLES A, PHIL STUD DEPT, S ILLINOIS UNIV, EDWARDSVILLE IL 62025
CORRADO, MICHAEL, PHILOSOPHY DEPT, OHIO UNIVERSITY, ATHENS OH 45701
CORRIVEAU, GASTON, PHIL DEPT, COL DE L'ASSOMPTION, L'ASSOMPTION QUE   CAN
CORSI, JEROME, FRANCONIA COLLEGE, FRANCONIA, NH 03580
CORSON, LAWRENCE, PHIL DEPT, ST UNIV OF NY, AMHERST NY 14226
CORTES, ALBERTO, PHILOSOPHY DEPT, TEXAS TECH UNIV, LUBBOCK TX 79409
CORWELL, GEORGE, PHILOSOPHY DEPT, VILLANOVA UNIV, VILLANOVA PA 19085
COSBY, G, PHIL DEPT, UNIV OF MANITOBA, WINNIPEG 19 MAN   CAN
COSGROVE, MATTHEW R, PHIL SCH, CATH UNIV OF AMER, WASHINGTON DC 20017
COSS, THURMAN, PHIL & REL STUD DEPT, U S INTNL UNIV, SAN DIEGO CA 92131
COSTELLO, EDWARD B, PHIL DEPT, UNIV OF MISSOURI, ST LOUIS MO 63121
COTE, ANDRE, PHIL FACULTE, UNIVERSITE LAVAL, CITE UNIV QUE   CAN
COTE, MAXINE, PHIL DEPT, UNIV OF MARYLAND, BALTIMORE MD 21228
COTE, MICHEL, PHIL DEPT, COL VIEUX-MONTREAL, MONTREAL QUE   CAN
COTE, RICHARD, PHIL DEPT, ST UNIV OF NY, STONY BROOK NY 11790
COTTEE, WILLIAM L, HUMANITIES DEPT, WIDENER COLLEGE, CHESTER PA 19013
COTTLE, RONALD E, SOC SCI DEPT, PASADENA CY COLLEGE, PASADENA CA 91106
COTTON, DAVID A H, PHIL DEPT, CALIFORNIA ST UNIV, LOS ANGELES CA 90032
COTTON, J HARRY, PHIL DEPT, WABASH COLLEGE, CRAWFORDSVL IN 47933
COUCH, BONITA H, PHILOSOPHY DEPT, KENT STATE UNIV, KENT OH 44242
COULTER, CHAN, PHIL DEPT, GETTYSBURG COLLEGE, GETTYSBURG PA 17325
COUNTESS, ROBERT H, SPEECH & DRAMA, TENN STATE UNIV, NASHVILLE TN 37203
COUNTS, HERMAN, PHIL & RELIG DEPT, JOHNSON C SMITH UNIV, CHARLOTTE NC 28216
COURTNEY, CHARLES, PHILOSOPHY DEPT, DREW UNIVERSITY, MADISON NJ 07940
COUSINEAU, ROBERT H, ST PETER'S COLLEGE, JERSEY CITY, NJ 07306
COUTURIER, FERNAND, PHILOSOPHY DEPT, UNIV DU QUEBEC, MONTREAL QUE   CAN
COVAL, SAMUEL C, PHIL DEPT, UNIV BRIT COLUMBIA, VANCOUVER 8 B C   CAN
COVEY, JUDITH, PHILOSOPHY DEPT, BROWN UNIVERSITY, PROVIDENCE RI 02912
COVEY, PRESTON, PHIL DEPT, CARNEGIE-MELLON UNIV, PITTSBURGH PA 15213
COVIL, JAMES, PHIL DEPT, UNIV OF WEST ONTARIO, LONDON ONT   CAN
COWAN, DENIS, HUMAN AREA, SHIMER COLLEGE, MOUNT CARROLL IL 61053
COWAN, JOSEPH L, PHILOSOPHY DEPT, UNIV OF ARIZONA, TUCSON AZ 85721
COWLEY, BARBARA, PHIL DEPT, SYRACUSE UNIVERSITY, SYRACUSE NY 13210
COWLEY, FRASER, PHIL DEPT, NEW YORK UNIVERSITY, NEW YORK NY 10003
COWLEY, G FRASER, PHILOSOPHY DEPT, YORK UNIVERSITY, DOWNSVIEW ONT   CAN
COX, DAVID, PHILOSOPHY DEPT, UNIV OF AKRON, AKRON OH 44325
COX, GARY, PHIL DEPT, COL AT GENESEO, GENESEO NY 14454
COX, JAMES WILLIAM, PHIL DEPT, WEST GEORGIA COLLEGE, CARROLLTON GA 30117
COX, JOHN F, PHILOSOPHY DEPT, SEM OF LADY OF PROV, WARWICK RI 02889
COX, KENDALL, PHIL DEPT, UNIV OF MICHIGAN, FLINT MI 48503
COX, L HUGHES, PHIL DEPT, CENTENARY COL OF LA, SHREVEPORT LA 71104
COX, ROBERT, PHILOSOPHY DEPT, PENN STATE UNIV, MEDIA PA 19063
COX, RONALD, PHIL & REL DEPT, COE COLLEGE, CEDAR RAPIDS IA 52402
COX, WILLIAM, HUMAN DIV, MACOMB CO COM COL, WARREN MI 48093
COYNE, ANTHONY M, PHIL DEPT, UNIV OF N CAROLINA, CHAPEL HILL NC 27514
COYNE, MARGARET, PHIL DEPT, NORTHWESTERN UNIV, EVANSTON IL 60201
CRACKNELL, R J F, PHILOSOPHY DEPT, QUEEN'S UNIVERSITY, KINGSTON ONT   CAN
CRAFT, JIMMY, PHILOSOPHY DEPT, UNIV OF TEXAS, AUSTIN TX 78712
CRAGG, A W, PHILOSOPHY DEPT, LAURENTIAN UNIV, SUDBURY ONT   CAN
CRAIG, DANIEL B, PHIL & REL DEPT, UNIV OF BALTIMORE, BALTIMORE MD 21201
CRAIG, ROBERT H, PHIL DEPT, UNIV OF MAINE, ORONO ME 04773
CRAIG, ROBERT, PHILOSOPHY DEPT, MADONNA COLLEGE, LIVONIA MI 48150
CRAIG, WILLIAM, PHIL DEPT, UNIV OF CALIFORNIA, BERKELEY CA 94720
CRAIGHEAD, HOUSTON, PHIL & RELIG DEPT, WINTHROP COLLEGE, ROCKHILL SC 29730
CRALLE, HARRY T, PHIL DEPT, DEPAUL UNIVERSITY, CHICAGO IL 60604
CRANDON-GRAEF, DAVID, PHIL DEPT, CALIFORNIA ST UNIV, NORTHRIDGE CA 91324
CRANE, JOHN D, HUMAN DEPT, CUYAHOGA COM COL, PARMA HEIGHTS OH 44130
CRANOR, CARL F, PHIL DEPT, UNIV OF CALIFORNIA, RIVERSIDE CA 92502
CRATER, WARREN H, HUMAN DEPT, NEWARK COL OF ENG, NEWARK NJ 07102
CRAWFORD JR, EDWIN E, HUMAN DEPT, LINN-BENTON COM COL, ALBANY OR 97321
CRAWFORD, A BERRY, LANG & PHIL DEPT, UTAH STATE UNIV, LOGAN UT 84322

CRAWFORD, DAVID, PHIL DEPT, UNIV OF DETROIT, DETROIT MI 48221
CRAWFORD, DONALD W, PHILOSOPHY DEPT, UNIV OF WISCONSIN, MADISON WI 53706
CRAWFORD, JOHN E, PHIL DEPT, NOTRE DAME COLLEGE, SOUTH EUCLID OH 44121
CRAWFORD, PATRICIA A, PHIL DEPT, CALIFORNIA ST UNIV, SAN DIEGO CA 92115
CREAGER, ALFRED LEON, PHIL & RELIG, URSINUS COLLEGE, COLLEGEVILLE PA 19426
CREAN, JOHN J, PHIL DEPT, ST XAVIER COLLEGE, CHICAGO IL 60655
CREARY, LEWIS, PHILOSOPHY DEPT, CASE WESTERN RESERVE, CLEVELAND OH 44106
CREEGAN, ROBERT F, PHIL DEPT, ST UNIV OF NY, ALBANY NY 12203
CREEL, RICHARD, PHIL & REL DEPT, ITHACA COLLEGE, ITHACA NY 14850
CREER, LELAND M, PHIL DEPT, CENTRAL CONN ST COL, NEW BRITAIN CT 06050
CREERY, WALTER E, PHILOSOPHY DEPT, YORK UNIVERSITY, DOWNSVIEW ONT CAN
CREM, THERESA, PHIL DEPT, UNIV OF SN FRANCISCO, SAN FRANCISCO CA 94117
CREMER, PETER, PHIL DEPT, UNIV OF MISSOURI, COLUMBIA MO 65201
CRENSHAW, FLOYD D, RELIG & PHIL DEPT, NEWBERRY COLLEGE, NEWBERRY SC 29108
CRENSHAW, MARY L, PHIL & RELIG, LINDENWOOD COLLEGES, ST CHARLES MO 63301
CRESS, DONALD A, PHIL DEPT, N ILLINOIS UNIV, DEKALB IL 60115
CRESSWELL, JOHN R, PHIL DEPT, WEST VIRGINIA UNIV, MORGANTOWN WV 26506
CRILLIE, HENA, PHIL DEPT, SOUTH UNIV A & M COL, BATON ROUGE LA 70813
CRIM, KEITH R, PHIL & RELIG, VA COMMONWEALTH UNIV, RICHMOND VA 23220
CRIMMEL, HENRY H, PHIL DEPT, ST LAWRENCE UNIV, CANTON NY 13617
CRISPO, ALPHONSE, PHILOSOPHY DEPT, GANNON COLLEGE, ERIE PA 16501
CRITELLI, MICHAEL, PHIL DEPT, LOS ANGELES CY COL, LOS ANGELES CA 90029
CRITTENDEN, CHARLES, PHIL DEPT, CALIFORNIA ST UNIV, NORTHRIDGE CA 91324
CROAKE, LAWRENCE, PHIL DEPT, PENN STATE UNIV, NW KENSINGTON PA 15068
CROCKER, DAVID A, PHIL DEPT, COLORADO ST UNIV, FORT COLLINS CO 80521
CROCKER, J LAWRENCE, PHILOSOPHY DEPT, UNIV OF WASHINGTON, SEATTLE WA 98195
CROCKER, SYLVIA, PHILOSOPHY DEPT, CAL STATE COL, SN BERNARDINO CA 92407
CROCKETT, CAMPBELL, PHIL DEPT, UNIV OF CINCINNATI, CINCINNATI OH 45221
CROCKETT, W R, HIST OF THEOL DIV, VANCOUVER SCH THEOL, VANCOUVER 8 B C CAN
CRODDY, W STEPHEN, PHIL DEPT, WEST CHESTER ST COL, WEST CHESTER PA 19380
CROLL, CHARLES, HUMAN DEPT, BROOME COM COL, BINGHAMTON NY 13902
CROM, SCOTT E, PHILOSOPHY DEPT, BELOIT COLLEGE, BELOIT WI 53511
CROMBIE, E JAMES, PHILOSOPHY DEPT, UNIV OF WATERLOO, WATERLOO ONT CAN
CROMP, GERMAINE, PHILOSOPHY DEPT, UNIV DE MONTREAL, MONTREAL QUE CAN
CROMWELL, WILLIAM E, PHILOSOPHY DEPT, UNIV OF OKLAHOMA, NORMAN OK 73069
CROMWELL, WILLIAM, PHILOSOPHY DEPT, UNIV OF CALGARY, CALGARY 44 ALB CAN
CRONE, AGNES, PHIL DEPT, SPALDING COLLEGE, LOUISVILLE KY 40203
CRONIN, FRANCIS R, PHIL DEPT, SAINT THOMAS UNIV, FREDERICTON N B CAN
CRONK, GEORGE F, SOC SCI DEPT, BERGEN COM COL, PARAMUS NJ 07652
CRONQUIST, JOHN, PHIL DEPT, CALIFORNIA ST UNIV, FULLERTON CA 92634
CROSBY, DONALD A, PHIL DEPT, COLORADO ST UNIV, FORT COLLINS CO 80521
CROSBY, H LAMAR, PHIL & RELIG DEPT, HOLLINS COLLEGE, HOLLINS COL VA 24020
CROSBY, ISAAC, REL & PHIL DEPT, STEPHENS COLLEGE, COLUMBIA MO 65201
CROSBY, JOHN, PHIL DEPT, UNIVERSITY OF DALLAS, IRVING TX 75062
CROSBY, R A, PHILOSOPHY DEPT, MCGILL UNIVERSITY, MONTREAL QUE CAN
CROSSLEY, D J, PHILOSOPHY DEPT, UNIV OF SASKATCHEWAN, SASKATOON SAS CAN
CROSSLEY, RONALD C, REL & PHIL, ST ANDREWS PRESB COL, LAURINBURG NC 28352
CROSSON, FREDERICK, PHIL DEPT, UNIV OF NOTRE DAME, NOTRE DAME IN 46556
CROSTHWAITE, JANE, PHILOSOPHY DEPT, QUEENS COLLEGE, CHARLOTTE NC 28207
CROTEAU, JACQUES, PHIL FACULTY, UNIV OF OTTAWA, OTTAWA ONT CAN
CROTTY, GERARD, PHILOSOPHY DEPT, LOYOLA COLLEGE, MONTREAL QUE CAN
CROUSE, W THOMAS, PHIL DEPT, UNIV OF MARYLAND, COLLEGE PARK MD 20742
CROW, EARL, REL & PHIL DEPT, HIGH POINT COLLEGE, HIGH POINT NC 27262
CROWE, LAWSON, PHIL DEPT, UNIV OF COLORADO, BOULDER CO 80302
CROWLEY, CALE, PHIL DEPT, ST PATRICK'S COLLEGE, MOUNTAIN VIEW CA 94040
CROWLEY, JAMES, SOC SCI AREA, COLUMBIA JUNIOR COL, COLUMBIA CA 95310
CROWLEY, MARGARET, PHIL DEPT, ST JOSEPH COLLEGE, WEST HARTFORD CT 06117
CROWNFIELD, DAVID, PHIL & RELIG, UNIV OF NORTH IOWA, CEDAR FALLS IA 50613
CROY, MARVIN, PHIL DEPT, FLORIDA STATE UNIV, TALLAHASSEE FL 32306
CRUM, TERRELLE B, PHIL DEPT, BARRINGTON COLLEGE, BARRINGTON RI 22806
CRUMBINE, NANCY JAY, PHIL & RELIG, CHATHAM COLLEGE, PITTSBURGH PA 15232
CRUNKLETON, MARTHA, PHIL DEPT, UNIV OF KENTUCKY, LEXINGTON KY 40506
CRUZ, FEODOR F, PHIL DEPT, ST LOUIS UNIVERSITY, ST LOUIS MO 63103
CUA, ANTONIO S, PHIL SCH, CATH UNIV OF AMER, WASHINGTON DC 20017

CUBIE, DAVID L, RELIG & PHIL, MT VERNON NAZ COL, MOUNT VERNON OH 43050
CUDAHY, BRIAN J, PHIL DEPT, BOSTON COLLEGE, CHESTNUT HILL MA 02167
CUDMORE, ANNE K, HUMANE STUD, NEW CCL OF CAL, SAUSALITO CA 94965
CULBERTSON, JAMES T, PHIL DEPT, CAL POLYTECH ST U, SAN LUIS OBIS CA 93407
CULBRETH, JOHN MAXWELL, PHILOSOPHY DEPT, UNIV OF TEXAS, AUSTIN TX 78712
CULLEN, JOHN, PHIL DEPT, S CONNECTICUT ST COL, NEW HAVEN CT 06515
CULMBACK, BARRETT, PHIL DEPT, SN BARBARA CY COL, SANTA BARBARA CA 93105
CULMER, CHARLES W, PHIL DEPT, BRANDEIS UNIVERSITY, WALTHAM MA 02154
CULP, JOHN, REL & PHIL DIV, BETHEL COLLEGE, MISHAWAKA IN 46544
CUMBEE, JACK, PHIL DEPT, OAKLAND UNIVERSITY, ROCHESTER MI 48063
CUMMING, ROBERT D, PHIL DEPT, COLUMBIA UNIVERSITY, NEW YORK NY 10027
CUMMINGS, NANCY PEKIN, HUMANITIES DIV, EL PASO COM COL, EL PASO TX 79904
CUMMINGS, PHILIP, PHIL & RELIG DEPT, TRENTON STATE COL, TRENTON NJ 08625
CUMMINS, PHILLIP, PHIL DEPT, UNIVERSITY OF IOWA, IOWA CITY IA 52240
CUMMINS, ROBERT, PHIL DEPT, JOHNS HOPKINS UNIV, BALTIMORE MD 21218
CUNEEN, CHARLES, PHIL DEPT, FLORIDA STATE UNIV, TALLAHASSEE FL 32306
CUNEO, JOHN, PHILOSOPHY DEPT, PENN STATE UNIV, UNIV PARK PA 16802
CUNNINGHAM, ALAN, HUMAN DIV, JOHNSON CO COM COL, OVERLAND PARK KS 66210
CUNNINGHAM, BRUCE, SOC SCI DIV, FLATHEAD VLY COM COL, KALISPELL MT 59901
CUNNINGHAM, F A, PHILOSOPHY DEPT, UNIV OF TORONTO, TORONTO ONT   CAN
CUNNINGHAM, F J, PHILOSOPHY DEPT, LOYOLA COLLEGE, BALTIMORE MD 21210
CUNNINGHAM, HENRI-PAUL, PHIL FACULTE, UNIVERSITE LAVAL, CITE UNIV QUE   CAN
CUNNINGHAM, JOHN F, PHIL DEPT, PROVIDENCE COLLEGE, PROVIDENCE RI 02919
CUNNINGHAM, R L, PHIL DEPT, UNIV OF SN FRANCISCO, SAN FRANCISCO CA 94117
CUNNINGHAM, RICHARD, GOLDEN GATE BAPT SEM, MILL VALLEY, CA 94941
CUNNINGHAM, RONALD, SOC SCI DIV, LANE COLLEGE, JACKSON TN 38301
CUNNINGHAM, STANLEY, PHILOSOPHY DEPT, UNIV OF WINDSOR, WINDSOR ONT   CAN
CUNNINGHAM, SUZANNE, PHIL DEPT, LOYOLA UNIVERSITY, CHICAGO IL 60606
CUNNINGHAM, THOMAS J, PHIL DEPT, GRAND VALLEY ST COL, ALLENDALE MI 49401
CUPAULT, J P, PHILOSOPHY DEPT, COL DE MAISONNEUVE, MONTREAL QUE   CAN
CUPPLES, B W, PHIL DEPT, UNIV OF NW BRUNSWICK, FREDERICTON N B   CAN
CURELLO, ANTHONY, PHIL DEPT, ADELPHI UNIVERSITY, GARDEN CITY NY 11530
CURLEY, THOMAS V, PHIL DEPT, LE MOYNE COLLEGE, SYRACUSE NY 13214
CURRAN, GEORGE A, PHILOSOPHY DEPT, XAVIER UNIVERSITY, CINCINNATI OH 45207
CURRAN, WILLIAM S, PHILOSOPHY DEPT, UNIV OF TEXAS, AUSTIN TX 78712
CURREY, E KILIAN, PHIL DEPT, IONA COLLEGE, NEW ROCHELLE NY 10801
CURRY JR, MELVIN D, PHIL DIV, FLORIDA COLLEGE, TEMPLE TER FL 33617
CURTIN, BRENDAN, LIBR ARTS DIV, JEFFERSON COM COL, WATERTOWN NY 13601
CURTIN, J CLAUDE, PHIL DEPT, NAZARETH COLLEGE, ROCHESTER NY 14610
CURTIS, BARRY A, PHIL DEPT, UNIV OF MARYLAND, COLLEGE PARK MD 20742
CURTIS, OLIVER B, PHIL & REL, GEORGIA COLLEGE, MILLEDGEVILLE GA 31061
CURTIS, RONALD C, PHIL DEPT, UNIV OF WEST ONTARIO, LONDON ONT   CAN
CURTLER, HUGH, SW MINNESOTA ST COL, MARSHALL, MN 56258
CUSMARIU, ARNOLD, PHILOSOPHY DEPT, BROWN UNIVERSITY, PROVIDENCE RI 02912
CYR, JEAN MARIE, ABBAYE ST BENOIT, ST BENOIT, QUE   CAN
CYRAN, WILLIAM T, SOC SCI DEPT, SAN DIEGO MESA COL, SAN DIEGO CA 92111
CZARNY, PETER, PHILOSOPHY DEPT, UNIV OF WATERLOO, WATERLOO ONT   CAN
CZERWIONKA, FELICIA, PHIL DEPT, SIENA HEIGHTS COL, ADRIAN MI 49221
D'ABBRACCI, ANTHONY, HUMAN & PHIL, SANTA ROSA JR COL, SANTA ROSA CA 95401
D'ALFONSO, JOSEPH, PHIL & REL DEPT, BATES COLLEGE, LEWISTON ME 04240
D'AMORE, MICHAEL, PHILOSOPHY DEPT, OHIO STATE UNIV, COLUMBUS OH 43210
D'AMOUR, GENE A, PHIL DEPT, WEST VIRGINIA UNIV, MORGANTOWN WV 26506
D'ANGELO, EDWARD, PHIL DEPT, UNIV OF BRIDGEPORT, BRIDGEPORT CT 06602
D'HONDT, JACQUES, PHILOSOPHY DEPT, UNIV DE MONTREAL, MONTREAL QUE   CAN
D'ONOFRIO, JOHN, PHIL DEPT, HAMLINE UNIVERSITY, ST PAUL MN 55104
D'SOUZA, ANTHONY, PHIL DEPT, PRINCE GEORGE'S COM, LARGO MD 20870
DA SILVA, MAURICE, COLLEGE D'AHUNTSIC, MONTREAL, QUE   CAN
DABOUB, ANTHONY, PHIL DEPT, UNIVERSITY OF DALLAS, IRVING TX 75062
DAGENAIS, ANDRE, PHIL DEPT, COL VIEUX-MONTREAL, MONTREAL QUE   CAN
DAGLEY, HANSA, HUMAN DIV, NIAGARA CC COM COL, NIAGARA FALLS NY 14303
DAHER, ADEL H, PHIL DEPT, MANHATTAN COLLEGE, RIVERDALE NY 10471
DAHL, NORMAN O, PHIL DEPT, UNIV OF MINNESOTA, MINNEAPOLIS MN 55455
DAHLSTROM, DANIEL O, PHIL DEPT, ST LOUIS UNIVERSITY, ST LOUIS MO 63103
DAI, DAVID, PHIL DEPT, OLIVET NAZARENE COL, KANKAKEE IL 60901

DAIB, WALTER, RELIG & PHIL DEPT, LUTHER COLLEGE, TEANECK NJ 07666
DAIGLE, LOUIS-MARCEL, PHILOSOPHY DEPT, UNIV DE MONCTON, MONCTON N B   CAN
DAIGLE, YVON, PHIL DEPT, COL DE SHERBROOKE, SHERBROOKE QUE   CAN
DAISE, BENJAMIN, PHIL DEPT, HOBART & WM SMITH, GENEVA NY 14456
DAKIN, MARION, PHIL DEPT, UNIV OF MONTANA, MISSOULA MT 59801
DAKO, MARTIN, SHIPPENSBURG ST COL, SHIPPENSBURG, PA 17257
DALCOURT, GERARD, SETON HALL UNIV, SOUTH ORANGE, NJ 07079
DALE, ROBERT D, PHIL DEPT, OREGON STATE UNIV, CORVALLIS OR 97331
DALEY, J E, PHILOSOPHY DEPT, ST JOSEPH'S COLLEGE, EDMONTON 61 ALB   CAN
DALEY, JAMES, PHIL DEPT, UNIVERSITY OF TOLEDO, TOLEDO OH 43606
DALEY, LEO C, PHIL & RELIG, JERSEY CITY ST COL, JERSEY CITY NJ 07305
DALLERY, ARLEEN, PHIL DEPT, ST UNIV OF NY, STONY BROOK NY 11790
DALLERY, CARLETON, PHIL DEPT, ST UNIV OF NY, STONY BROOK NY 11790
DALON, R, PHILOSOPHY DEPT, UNIV OF ALBERTA, EDMONTON ALB   CAN
DALRYMPLE, HOUGHTON B, HIST & PHIL DEPT, UNIV OF TEXAS, ARLINGTON TX 76010
DALRYMPLE, STUART, PHILOSOPHY DEPT, RUTGERS UNIV, NEWARK NJ 07102
DALTON, PETER C, PHIL DEPT, FLORIDA STATE UNIV, TALLAHASSEE FL 32306
DALTON, ROBERT O, DIXIE COLLEGE, ST GEORGE, UT 84770
DALY JR, RICHARD T, PHILOSOPHY DEPT, UNIV OF WISCONSIN, MADISON WI 53706
DALY, PAUL, PHIL DEPT, MERRIMACK COLLEGE, NORTH ANDOVER MA 01845
DAMASIA, MARY, HUMAN DEPT, FELICIAN COLLEGE, CHICAGO IL 60659
DAMER, T EDWARD, RELIG & PHIL DEPT, EMORY & HENRY COL, EMORY VA 24327
DANA, J C, REL & PHIL DEPT, BLACKBURN COLLEGE, CARLINVILLE IL 62626
DANCY, RUSSELL, SAGE SCHOOL, CORNELL UNIVERSITY, ITHACA NY 14850
DANDENAULT, GERMAIN, PHIL DEPT, UNIV DE SHERBROOKE, SHERBROOKE QUE   CAN
DANDONNEAU, ANTONI, COLLEGE D'AHUNTSIC, MONTREAL, QUE   CAN
DANEK, JAROMIR, PHIL FACULTE, UNIVERSITE LAVAL, CITE UNIV QUE   CAN
DANIEL, HELENE, PHIL DEPT, COL DE SHERBROOKE, SHERBROOKE QUE   CAN
DANIEL, JAMES, PHILOSOPHY DEPT, DUQUESNE UNIV, PITTSBURGH PA 15219
DANIEL, MARY, PHIL & REL DEPT, UNIV OF GEORGIA, ATHENS GA 30602
DANIEL, STEPHEN H, PHIL DEPT, ST LOUIS UNIVERSITY, ST LOUIS MO 63103
DANIEL, WILLIAM W, PHIL & RELIG DEPT, WINTHROP COLLEGE, ROCKHILL SC 29730
DANIELS, C B, PHILOSOPHY DEPT, UNIV OF VICTORIA, VICTORIA B C   CAN
DANIELS, NORMAN, PHIL DEPT, TUFTS UNIVERSITY, MEDFORD MA 02155
DANIELS, RICHARD, PHIL DEPT, UNIV OF KENTUCKY, LEXINGTON KY 40506
DANIELSON, PETER A, PHILOSOPHY DEPT, YORK UNIVERSITY, DOWNSVIEW ONT   CAN
DANILOWICZ, RICHARD D, PHIL DEPT, PROVIDENCE COLLEGE, PROVIDENCE RI 02919
DANKEL, S, PHIL DEPT, UNIV OF N CAROLINA, WILMINGTON NC 28401
DANNER, DAN, HUMAN DIV, COLUMBIAN CHRIST COL, PORTLAND OR 97220
DANNER, ROBERT P, PHIL DEPT, EMORY LNIVERSITY, ATLANTA GA 30322
DANNER, ROBERT, PHIL DEPT, UNIV OF MISSOURI, COLUMBIA MO 65201
DANTO, ARTHUR C, PHIL DEPT, COLUMBIA UNIVERSITY, NEW YORK NY 10027
DAOUST, AURELE, COL ST-JEAN VIANNEY, MONTREAL, QUE   CAN
DAOUST, JEAN-GUY, PHILOSOPHY DEPT, COL DE MAISONNEUVE, MONTREAL QUE   CAN
DARMSTADTER, HOWARD, PHILOSOPHY DEPT, UNIV OF MASS, BOSTON MA 02116
DARNOI, DENNIS, PSYCH & PHIL, MONMOUTH COLLEGE, W LONG BRANCH NJ 07764
DARRAH, T S, REL & PHIL DEPT, ROLLINS COLLEGE, WINTER PARK FL 32789
DARWALL, STEPHEN L, PHIL DEPT, UNIV OF N CAROLINA, CHAPEL HILL NC 27514
DASTOUS, EMILE, PHIL DEPT, COL VIEUX-MONTREAL, MONTREAL QUE   CAN
DATES, RALPH O, ST PETER'S COLLEGE, JERSEY CITY, NJ 07306
DATKO, JAMES L, PHIL DEPT, CREIGHTON UNIV, OMAHA NE 68178
DAUBNER, EDITH, ENG & PHIL DEPT, LONGWOOD COLLEGE, FARMVILLE VA 23901
DAUENHAUER, BERNARD P, PHIL & REL DEPT, UNIV OF GEORGIA, ATHENS GA 30602
DAUER, FRANCIS, PHIL DEPT, UNIV OF CALIFORNIA, SANTA BARBARA CA 93106
DAUES, VINCENT, PHIL DEPT, ROCKHURST COLLEGE, KANSAS CITY MO 64110
DAUGERT, STANLEY, PHIL DEPT, W WASHINGTON ST COL, BELLINGHAM WA 98225
DAUGHERTY, JERRY W, PHIL DEPT, U S AIR FORCE ACAD, COLORADO SPGS CO 80840
DAUGHERTY, MARY L, REL & PHIL DEPT, MORRIS HARVEY COL, CHARLESTON WV 25304
DAVENPORT, M M, PHIL & HUM DEPT, TEXAS A & M UNIV, COL STATION TX 77843
DAVEY, ELIZABETH, PHIL DEPT, UNIV OF WEST ONTARIO, LONDON ONT   CAN
DAVID, KEITH R, PHIL DEPT, WILLIAM JEWELL COL, LIBERTY MO 64068
DAVIDOFF, ALLEN, PHIL DEPT, UNIV OF CINCINNATI, CINCINNATI OH 45221
DAVIDSON, DONALD, PHIL DEPT, ROCKEFELLER UNIV, NEW YORK NY 10021
DAVIDSON, ROBERT B, PHIL DEPT, TEX AGR & INDUST UNIV, KINGSVILLE TX 78363

DAVIE, WILLIAM E, PHILOSOPHY DEPT, UNIV OF OREGON, EUGENE OR 97403
DAVIES, J, LIBR ARTS DEPT, DOUGLAS COLLEGE, NW WESTMINSTR B C   CAN
DAVIES, JAMES, PHILOSOPHY DEPT, UNIV OF WATERLOO, WATERLOO ONT   CAN
DAVIES, JULIAN A, PHIL DEPT, SIENA COLLEGE, LOUDONVILLE NY 12211
DAVIS, AVROHOM, JEWISH PHIL DEPT, RABBINICAL ACADEMY, BROOKLYN NY 11230
DAVIS, E VANCE, REL & PHIL DEPT, HIGH POINT COLLEGE, HIGH POINT NC 27262
DAVIS, FOREST K, EMPIRE ST COL, SARATOGA SPGS, NY 12866
DAVIS, GARY, HUMAN & PHIL DEPT, NE MISSOURI ST UNIV, MARYVILLE MO 64468
DAVIS, GREGORY, PHIL DEPT, INDIANA ST UNIV, TERRE HAUTE IN 47809
DAVIS, J H, PHILOSOPHY DEPT, QUEEN'S UNIVERSITY, KINGSTON ONT   CAN
DAVIS, JAMES ARLIS, PHIL DEPT, CALIFORNIA ST UNIV, LONG BEACH CA 90840
DAVIS, JOHN B, PHIL DEPT, UNIV OF ILLINOIS, URBANA IL 61801
DAVIS, JOHN W, PHIL DEPT, UNIV OF WEST ONTARIO, LONDON ONT   CAN
DAVIS, JOHN W, PHIL DEPT, UNIV OF TENNESSEE, KNOXVILLE TN 37916
DAVIS, LAWRENCE, PHIL DEPT, JOHNS HOPKINS UNIV, BALTIMORE MD 21218
DAVIS, LEWIS A, PHIL DEPT, GEORGETOWN UNIV, WASHINGTON DC 20007
DAVIS, LEWIS, PHIL DEPT, MONTGOMERY COLLEGE, TAKOMA PARK MD 20012
DAVIS, MERRILL C, PHIL & RELIG, WESTMAR COLLEGE, LEMARS IA 51031
DAVIS, MICHAEL, PHILOSOPHY DEPT, PENN STATE UNIV, UNIV PARK PA 16802
DAVIS, OREN, PHILOSOPHY DEPT, TRINITY COLLEGE, BURLINGTON VT 05401
DAVIS, PHILIP E, PHIL DEPT, CALIFORNIA ST UNIV, SAN JOSE CA 95114
DAVIS, R I, PHIL DEPT, UNIV OF FLORIDA, GAINESVILLE FL 32611
DAVIS, RALPH, PHIL DEPT, ALBION COLLEGE, ALBION MI 49224
DAVIS, RICHARD S, PHIL DEPT, UNIV OF TENNESSEE, KNOXVILLE TN 37916
DAVIS, RICHARD, PHILOSOPHY DEPT, MARQUETTE UNIV, MILWAUKEE WI 53233
DAVIS, ROBERT B, HUMAN DIV, MATER DEI COLLEGE, OGDENSBURG NY 13669
DAVIS, S, PHILOSOPHY DEPT, SIMON FRASER UNIV, BURNABY 2 B C   CAN
DAVIS, STEVEN, PHILOSOPHY DEPT, DUQUESNE UNIV, PITTSBURGH PA 15219
DAVIS, THOMAS, PHIL DEPT, UNIV OF REDLANDS, REDLANDS CA 92373
DAVIS, W H, PHILOSOPHY DEPT, AUBURN UNIVERSITY, AUBURN AL 36830
DAVIS, WILLIAM ALBERT, DIV OF SOC SCI, COM COL OF DENVER, DENVER CO 80216
DAVISON, DANIEL, PHILOSOPHY DEPT, UNIV OF TEXAS, AUSTIN TX 78712
DAVISON, JOHN, PHILOSOPHY DEPT, UNIV OF CALGARY, CALGARY 44 ALB   CAN
DAVISON, ROY J, SOC SCI EDUC DEPT, JACKSON STATE COL, JACKSON MS 39217
DAVISON, VERNON G, DIV OF REL & PHIL, SAMFORD UNIV, BIRMINGHAM AL 35209
DAVITT, THOMAS E, PHILOSOPHY DEPT, MARQUETTE UNIV, MILWAUKEE WI 53233
DAWE, DONALD G, THEOL DEPT, UNION THEOL SEM, RICHMOND VA 23227
DAWSON JR, WILLIAM J, HUMANITIES DEPT, NEW RIVER COM COL, DUBLIN VA 24084
DAWSON, GEORGE, PHILOSOPHY DEPT, UNIV OF ARIZONA, TUCSON AZ 85721
DAWSON, J G, PHILOSOPHY DEPT, MEMORIAL UNIV, ST JOHN'S N F   CAN
DAWSON, LAWRENCE, HUMANITIES DIV, CCL OF THE REDWOODS, EUREKA CA 95501
DAWSON, WILLIAM, PHIL DEPT, ST AMBROSE COLLEGE, DAVENPORT IA 52803
DAY, JAMES, PHIL & REL DEPT, ALLEGHENY COLLEGE, MEADVILLE PA 16335
DAY, MICHAEL A, PHIL DEPT, UNIV OF NEBRASKA, LINCOLN NE 68502
DAYANANDA, JAMES Y, ENG & PHIL DEPT, LOCK HAVEN ST COL, LOCK HAVEN PA 17745
DAYE, DOUGLAS, PHIL DEPT, BOWLING GREEN UNIV, BOWLING GREEN OH 43403
DAYRON, NORMAN, HUMANE STUD, NEW COL OF CAL, SAUSALITO CA 94965
DAYTON, E B, PHILOSOPHY DEPT, UNIV CF SASKATCHEWAN, SASKATOON SAS   CAN
DE ANGELIS, ROGER, PHIL DEPT, FORDHAM UNIVERSITY, BRONX NY 10458
DE ARMAS, ALEXIO, PHIL DEPT, CATHOLIC UNIVERSITY, PONCE PR 00731
DE CALLIERES, YVES, PHIL DEPT, COL DE VICTORIAVILLE, VICTORIAVILLE QUE   CAN
DE CARLO, RALPH, PHIL DEPT, FORDHAM UNIVERSITY, BRONX NY 10458
DE COURSEY, MARY EDWIN, SAINT MARY COLLEGE, LEAVENWORTH, KS 66048
DE FALCO, JOSEPH, ENG DEPT, AGR & TECH COLLEGE, FARMINGDALE NY 11735
DE GROOT, MARIE J, COLLEGE D'AHUNTSIC, MONTREAL, QUE   CAN
DE LA COVA, ALICE, PHIL DEPT, UNIV CF MINNESOTA, MINNEAPOLIS MN 55455
DE LA TORRE, ARMANDO, PHIL & RELIG DEPT, HAMPTON INST, HAMPTON VA 23368
DE LA TORRE, TEODORO, PHIL & THEOL, DOMINICAN COLLEGE, HOUSTON TX 77021
DE LAGUNA, GRACE A, BRYN MAWR COLLEGE, BRYN MAWR, PA 19010
DE LUCCA, JOHN, PHILOSOPHY DEPT, QUEEN'S UNIVERSITY, KINGSTON ONT   CAN
DE MAN, PETER, SYST & PHIL, GRADUATE THEOL UNION, BERKELEY CA 94709
DE MESTRAL, CHARLES, PHIL DEPT, COL VIEUX-MONTREAL, MONTREAL QUE   CAN
DE MONLEON, JACQUES, PHIL FACULTE, UNIVERSITE LAVAL, CITE UNIV QUE   CAN
DE NYS, MARTIN J, PHIL SCH, CATH UNIV OF AMER, WASHINGTON DC 20017

DE PRIMO, BERNARD, GRAND RAPIDS JR COL, GRAND RAPIDS, MI 49502
DE SIMONE, ROBERT, PHIL DEPT, HUNTER COLLEGE, NEW YORK NY 10021
DE SOUSA, R B, PHILOSOPHY DEPT, UNIV OF TORONTO, TORONTO ONT CAN
DE VINCK, JOSE M, PHILOSOPHY DEPT, TOMBROCK COLLEGE, WEST PATERSON NJ 07424
DE WIT, SONJA, PHILOSOPHY DEPT, UNIV OF CALGARY, CALGARY 44 ALB CAN
DEAN, DAVID A, GEN ARTS DIV, BERKSHIRE CHRIST COL, LENOX MA 01240
DEAN, ERIC, PHIL DEPT, WABASH COLLEGE, CRAWFORDSVL IN 47933
DEAN, LLOYD, SOC SCI DEPT, RHODE ISLAND JR COL, PROVIDENCE RI 02908
DEANE, BRIAN C, PHIL & RELIG, VA COMMONWEALTH UNIV, RICHMOND VA 23220
DEANE, FRANK, BERKSHIRE COM COL, PITTSFIELD, MA 01201
DEANGELIS, WILLIAM J, PHIL & REL DEPT, NORTHEASTERN UNIV, BOSTON MA 02115
DEARBORN, STEPHEN C, REL & PHIL DIV, GRACE COLLEGE, WINONA LAKE IN 46590
DEBAYS, JEAN-MARIE, PHIL DEPT, COL TROIS-RIVIERES, 3 RIVIERES QUE CAN
DEBBINS, WILLIAM, PHIL DEPT, CORNELL COLLEGE, MOUNT VERNON IA 52314
DEBOER, JESSE, PHIL DEPT, UNIV OF KENTUCKY, LEXINGTON KY 40506
DEBRABANDER, RENE F, PHIL & REL DEPT, TOWSON STATE COL, BALTIMORE MD 21204
DEBROCK, GUY, PHIL DEPT, RIVIER COLLEGE, NASHUA NH 03060
DECARIE, CLAUDE, PHIL DEPT, COL VIEUX-MONTREAL, MONTREAL QUE CAN
DECARIE, VIANNEY, PHILOSOPHY DEPT, UNIV DE MONTREAL, MONTREAL QUE CAN
DECAROLIS, ARNOLD, PHIL DEPT, BOWLING GREEN UNIV, BOWLING GREEN OH 43403
DECESARE, RICHARD A, PHIL DEPT, FITCHBURG STATE COL, FITCHBURG MA 01420
DECK, JOHN N, PHILOSOPHY DEPT, UNIV OF WINDSOR, WINDSOR ONT CAN
DECKERT, MARION, PHIL DEPT, BETHEL COLLEGE, NORTH NEWTON KS 67117
DEGENNARD, ANGELO, LOYOLA UNIVERSITY, LOS ANGELES, CA 90045
DEGEORGE, RICHARD, PHIL DEPT, UNIVERSITY OF KANSAS, LAWRENCE KS 66044
DEGROOD, DAVID, PHIL DEPT, UNIV OF BRIDGEPORT, BRIDGEPORT CT 06602
DEHLER, WILLIAM, PHIL DEPT, LOYOLA UNIVERSITY, CHICAGO IL 60626
DEHNERT, EDMUND, HUMAN DEPT, AMUNDSEN-MAYFAIR COL, CHICAGO IL 60630
DEIGH, JOHN, PHIL DEPT, UNIV OF CALIFORNIA, LOS ANGELES CA 90024
DEININGER, WHITAKER T, PHIL DEPT, CALIFORNIA ST UNIV, SAN JOSE CA 95114
DEITSCH, MARTIN, PHIL DEPT, ST UNIV OF NY, ALBANY NY 12203
DEJNOZKA, JAN, PHIL DEPT, UNIVERSITY OF IOWA, IOWA CITY IA 52240
DEJONGE, J, LIBR ARTS DEPT, DOUGLAS COLLEGE, NW WESTMINSTR B C CAN
DEKONINCK, THOMAS, PHIL FACULTE, UNIVERSITE LAVAL, CITE UNIV QUE CAN
DEL CARRIL, MARIO F, PHIL DEPT, GEORGETOWN UNIV, WASHINGTON DC 20007
DELACRE, GEORGES, PHIL DEPT, UNIV OF PUERTO RICO, RIO PIEDRAS PR 00931
DELAMOTTE, ROY, HUMAN DIV, PAINE COLLEGE, AUGUSTA GA 30901
DELAND, PETER, ENG DEPT, AGR & TECH COLLEGE, FARMINGDALE NY 11735
DELANEY, CORNELIUS, PHIL DEPT, UNIV OF NOTRE DAME, NOTRE DAME IN 46556
DELANEY, HOWARD, LOYOLA UNIVERSITY, LOS ANGELES, CA 90045
DELANGE, DAVID L, PHIL DEPT, ADELPHI UNIVERSITY, GARDEN CITY NY 11530
DELATTRE, EDWIN, PHIL DEPT, UNIVERSITY OF TOLEDO, TOLEDO OH 43606
DELAURENTIS, M, PHILOSOPHY DEPT, BROWN UNIVERSITY, PROVIDENCE RI 02912
DELFINI, ALEXANDER, ENG DEPT, ROCKLAND COM COL, SUFFERN NY 10901
DELL, ROBERT, REL & PHIL, MANCHESTER COLLEGE, N MANCHESTER IN 46962
DELLA PENTA, J, PHIL DEPT, DEPAUL UNIVERSITY, CHICAGO IL 60604
DELLAI, DEBBY, PHILOSOPHY DEPT, UNIV OF WYOMING, LARAMIE WY 82071
DELONG, HOWARD, PHIL DEPT, TRINITY COLLEGE, HARTFORD CT 06106
DELORME, ANDREE, PHIL DEPT, COL BOIS-DE-BOULOGNE, MONTREAL QUE CAN
DELP, PAUL, PHILOSOPHY DEPT, CHAPMAN COLLEGE, ORANGE CA 92666
DELUCA, EMERIC, COMMUNIC & ARTS, HARRISBURG COM COL, HARRISBURG PA 17110
DEMARCO, DONALD T, PHILOSOPHY DEPT, UNIV OF WATERLOO, WATERLOO ONT CAN
DEMARCO, ELAINE CHOATE, PHILOSOPHY DEPT, BUCKS CO COM COL, NEWTOWN PA 18940
DEMARCO, JOSEPH P, PHILOSOPHY DEPT, CLEVELAND ST UNIV, CLEVELAND OH 44115
DEMATTEIS, PHILIP, PHILOSOPHY DEPT, UNIV OF S CAROLINA, COLUMBIA SC 29208
DEMAY, WILLIAM, PHIL DEPT, UNIV OF NEW MEXICO, ALBUQUERQUE NM 87106
DEMERCHANT, BLANCHARD, PHIL DEPT, WAYNE STATE UNIV, DETROIT MI 48202
DEMERS, GUY, PHIL DEPT, COL LIONEL-GROULX, STE-THERESE QUE CAN
DEMOPOULOS, W G, PHIL DEPT, UNIV OF NW BRUNSWICK, FREDERICTON N B CAN
DEMPSTER, MURRAY W, REL & PHIL DIV, S CALIFORNIA COL, COSTA MESA CA 92626
DENICOLA, D R, REL & PHIL DEPT, ROLLINS COLLEGE, WINTER PARK FL 32789
DENICOLAS, ANTONIO, PHIL DEPT, ST UNIV OF NY, STONY BROOK NY 11790
DENISE, T C, PHIL DEPT, SYRACUSE UNIVERSITY, SYRACUSE NY 13210
DENMAN, ALVIN L, PHIL & RELIG DEPT, ANTIOCH COL, YELLOW SPGS OH 45387

DENNES, WILLIAM R, PHIL DEPT, UNIV OF CALIFORNIA, BERKELEY CA 94720
DENNETT, DANIEL C, PHIL DEPT, TUFTS UNIVERSITY, MEDFORD MA 02155
DENNEY, ROBERT, PHIL DEPT, UNIV OF CALIFORNIA, LOS ANGELES CA 90024
DENNING, LAVERNE J, SOC SCI DEPT, MAPLE WOODS COM COL, KANSAS CITY MO 64156
DENNIS, DONALD D, UNIV OF WISCONSIN, MEDFORD, WI 54451
DENOUDEN, BERNARD, PHIL DEPT, UNIV OF HARTFORD, WEST HARTFORD CT 06117
DEPLOIS, BARBAR C, PHILOSOPHY DEPT, UNIV OF OKLAHOMA, NORMAN OK 73069
DERDEN, JAMES K, PHIL DEPT, CAL ST UNIV -HUMBOLDT, ARCATA CA 95521
DERONNE, WILLIAM, PHIL DEPT, DEPAUL UNIVERSITY, CHICAGO IL 60604
DESAN, WILFRID, PHIL DEPT, GEORGETOWN UNIV, WASHINGTON DC 20007
DESANI, G V, PHILOSOPHY DEPT, UNIV OF TEXAS, AUSTIN TX 78712
DESAULNIERS, LAWRENCE, UNIV OF ALBUQUERQUE, ALBUQUERQUE, NM 87120
DESAUTELS, GUY, PHILOSOPHY DEPT, MCGILL UNIVERSITY, MONTREAL QUE   CAN
DESCH, PAUL T, PHIL DEPT, DUNS SCOTUS COL, SOUTHFIELD MI 48075
DESFOSSES, PIERRE, PHIL DEPT, COL DE VICTORIAVILLE, VICTORIAVILLE QUE   CAN
DESHARNAIS, RICHARD, PHIL DEPT, KING'S COLLEGE, WILKES BARRE PA 18711
DESILETS, DONALD A, PHIL DEPT, COL OUR LADY OF ELMS, CHICOPEE MA 01013
DESJARDINS JR, PAUL, PHIL DEPT, HAVERFORD COLLEGE, HAVERFORD PA 19041
DESJARDINS, URBAIN, HUMAN DEPT, COLLEGE SAINTE ANNE, CHURCH POINT N S   CAN
DESPRES, PIERRE, PHIL DEPT, COL VIEUX-MONTREAL, MONTREAL QUE   CAN
DEUTSCH, ELIOT, PHIL DEPT, UNIVERSITY OF HAWAII, HONOLULU HI 96822
DEUTSCH, HARRY, PHIL DEPT, INDIANA UNIVERSITY, BLOOMINGTON IN 47401
DEVEREUX, DANIEL T, PHIL DEPT, UNIV OF VIRGINIA, CHARLOTTESVL VA 22903
DEVETTERE, RAYMOND, PHIL DEPT, EMMANUEL COLLEGE, BOSTON MA 02115
DEVINE, MICHAEL, PHIL DEPT, WAYNE STATE UNIV, DETROIT MI 48202
DEVINE, PHILIP E, PHIL DEPT, NORTH ADAMS ST COL, NORTH ADAMS MA 01247
DEVINE, ROBERT V, PHIL DEPT, PROVIDENCE COLLEGE, PROVIDENCE RI 02919
DEVLIN, WILLIAM, PHILOSOPHY DEPT, UNIV OF SCRANTON, SCRANTON PA 18510
DEVOS, PETER, PHIL DEPT, CALVIN COLLEGE, GRAND RAPIDS MI 49506
DEVREES, BERNARD, PHIL & THEOL DEPT, MARILLAC COLLEGE, ST LOUIS MO 63121
DEWEY, ERNEST W, PHIL DEPT, UNIVERSITY OF TOLEDO, TOLEDO OH 43606
DEWEY, ROBERT E, PHIL DEPT, UNIV OF NEBRASKA, LINCOLN NE 68502
DEWOLFE, MAY, PHILOSOPHY DEPT, DAWSON COLLEGE, MONTREAL QUE   CAN
DEXTER, ROGER, PHIL DEPT, PORTLAND ST UNIV, PORTLAND OR 97207
DHILLON, S S, HUMANITIES DEPT, COLLEGE OF MARIN, KENTFIELD CA 94904
DI LASCIA, ALFRED, PHIL DEPT, HUNTER COLLEGE, NEW YORK NY 10021
DI NORCIA, V J, PHILOSOPHY DEPT, LAURENTIAN UNIV, SUDBURY ONT   CAN
DI PASQUALE, RALPH, PHILOSOPHY DEPT, IMMAC CONCEPTION SEM, TROY NY 12180
DI PIAZZA, JOSEPH, PHIL DEPT, S CONNECTICUT ST COL, NEW HAVEN CT 06515
DIAMANDOPOULOS, PETER, PHIL DEPT, BRANDEIS UNIVERSITY, WALTHAM MA 02154
DIAMOND JR, JOHN C, THEOL & PHIL, INTERDENOM THEOL CTR, ATLANTA GA 30314
DIAMOND, CORA, PHIL DEPT, UNIV OF VIRGINIA, CHARLOTTESVL VA 22903
DIANDA, JAMES J, PHIL DEPT, UNIVERSITY OF TOLEDO, TOLEDO OH 43606
DIAZ, MANUEL RICHARD, PHILOSOPHY DEPT, UNIV OF TEXAS, AUSTIN TX 78712
DICKER, GEORGES, PHIL DEPT, COLLEGE AT BROCKPORT, BROCKPORT NY 14420
DICKERSON, C, SOC SCI DEPT, INDIAN HILLS COM COL, CENTERVILLE IA 52544
DICKERSON, DWAYNE, PHIL DEPT, S ILLINOIS UNIV, CARBONDALE IL 62901
DICKIE, GEORGE T, PHIL DEPT, UNIV OF ILLINOIS, CHICAGO IL 60680
DICKOFF, JAMES W, PHILOSOPHY DEPT, KENT STATE UNIV, KENT OH 44242
DICKS, CLAUDE, MUS & HUM DEPT, PENSACOLA JUN COL, PENSACOLA FL 32504
DIDOHA, MICHAEL, PHIL & RELIG DEPT, MARYMOUNT COL, ARLINGTON VA 22207
DIEFENBECK, JAMES A, PHIL DEPT, S ILLINOIS UNIV, CARBONDALE IL 62901
DIEHL, JOHN, HUMAN DIV, UNIV OF MINNESOTA, MORRIS MN 56267
DIEMER, RICHARD, SOC & PHIL DEPT, TENN TECH UNIV, COOKEVILLE TN 38501
DIENHART, JOHN, PHIL DEPT, UNIV OF ILLINOIS, URBANA IL 61801
DIESING, PAUL R, PHIL DEPT, ST UNIV OF NY, AMHERST NY 14226
DIESKA, JOSEPH L, PHIL DEPT, UNIVERSITY OF DAYTON, DAYTON OH 45469
DIETERLE, RICHARD, PHIL DEPT, UNIV OF MINNESOTA, MINNEAPOLIS MN 55455
DIETRICH, GARY J, PHILOSOPHY DEPT, KENT STATE UNIV, KENT OH 44242
DIETRICHSON, PAUL, PHILOSOPHY DEPT, UNIV OF WASHINGTON, SEATTLE WA 98195
DIETZ, CONRAD R, PHIL DEPT, CATH COL IMM CONCEPT, DOUGLASTON NY 11362
DIFILIPPO, JOSEPH P, PHIL DEPT, UNIV OF WEST ONTARIO, LONDON ONT   CAN
DIFILIPPO, TERRY, PHIL DEPT, ST UNIV OF NY, AMHERST NY 14226
DIGGS, B J, PHIL DEPT, UNIV OF ILLINOIS, URBANA IL 61801

DIGIOVANNA, JOSEPH, PHIL DEPT, COL AT POTSDAM, POTSDAM NY 13676
DIGIOVANNI, GEORGE, PHILOSOPHY DEPT, MCGILL UNIVERSITY, MONTREAL QUE   CAN
DIIANNI, ALBERT R, PHIL DEPT, COL OF HOLY CROSS, WORCESTER MA 01610
DILASCIA, ALFRED P, PHIL DEPT, MANHATTAN COLLEGE, RIVERDALE NY 10471
DILLER, ELLIOT V N, PHIL DEPT, MILLS COLLEGE, OAKLAND CA 94613
DILLEY, FRANK B, PHILOSOPHY DEPT, UNIV OF DELAWARE, NEWARK DE 19711
DILLON, MARTIN C, PHIL DEPT, ST UNIV OF NY, BINGHAMTON NY 13901
DILLOW, TED, JOHN F KENNEDY COL, WAHOO, NE 68066
DILWORTH, DAVID, PHIL DEPT, ST UNIV OF NY, STONY BROOK NY 11790
DILWORTH, JOHN, PHIL DEPT, WEST MICHIGAN UNIV, KALAMAZOO MI 49001
DIMAS, THOMAS, PHIL DEPT, UNIV OF CALIFORNIA, IRVINE CA 92664
DINABURG, M P, PHIL DEPT, UNIV OF FLORIDA, GAINESVILLE FL 32611
DINAN, STEPHEN, PHIL & THEOL DIV, HOLY REDEEMER COL, WATERFORD WI 53185
DIOMBALA, A P, PHILOSOPHY DEPT, RICE UNIVERSITY, HOUSTON TX 77001
DION, D, COL DOM PHIL & THEOL, OTTAWA, ONT   CAN
DIONNE, GILBERT, PHILOSOPHY DEPT, UNIV DU QUEBEC, MONTREAL QUE   CAN
DIONNE, MAURICE, PHIL FACULTE, UNIVERSITE LAVAL, CITE UNIV QUE   CAN
DIPRE, GILIO, PHILOSOPHY DEPT, GANNON COLLEGE, ERIE PA 16501
DIRIG, WALTER F, PHILOSOPHY DEPT, ST JOHN VIANNEY SEM, MIAMI FL 33165
DITTES, JAMES E, YALE DIVINITY SCHOOL, NEW HAVEN, CT 06520
DIXON, PAUL R, PHILOSOPHY DEPT, UNIV OF S CAROLINA, COLUMBIA SC 29208
DJUTH, M, PHILOSOPHY DEPT, UNIV OF TORONTO, TORONTO ONT   CAN
DOAN, FRANK MELDOR, PHIL DEPT, LAKEHEAD UNIVERSITY, THUNDER BAY ONT   CAN
DOBBIN, JAY DEE, PHIL & REL STUD, COL OF GREAT FALLS, GREAT FALLS MT 59401
DOBOS, A, PHILOSOPHY DEPT, UNIV OF WATERLOO, WATERLOO ONT   CAN
DOCTORIAN, DAVID, SOC SCI DEPT, MOBERLY JUNIOR COL, MOBERLY MO 65270
DODSON, DAVE, PHILOSOPHY DEPT, CHAPMAN COLLEGE, ORANGE CA 92666
DOERING, MARY LOUANN, PHILOSOPHY DEPT, CLARKE COLLEGE, DUBUQUE IA 52001
DOHERTY, CORNELIUS, PHIL DEPT, QUINNIPIAC COLLEGE, HAMDEN CT 06518
DOHERTY, RICHARD, SOC SCI DEPT, REND LAKE COLLEGE, INA IL 62846
DOIG, JAMES C, HUMAN DIV, CLAYTON JR COLLEGE, MORROW GA 30260
DOIRON, NARCISSE, PHIL DEPT, COLLEGE DE BATHURST, BATHURST N B   CAN
DOLAN, JOHN M, PHIL DEPT, UNIV OF MINNESOTA, MINNEAPOLIS MN 55455
DOLAN, JOSEPH, PHIL DEPT, FORDHAM UNIVERSITY, BRONX NY 10458
DOLAN, S EDMUND, ST MARY'S COL OF CAL, MORAGA, CA 94575
DOLINSKY, PAUL, PHIL DEPT, ST UNIV OF NY, AMHERST NY 14226
DOLLAR, JAMES L, ANNE ARUNDEL COM COL, ARNOLD, MD 21012
DOMBROWIAK, DAVID, PHIL DEPT, UNIVERSITY OF DAYTON, DAYTON OH 45469
DOMMEYER, FREDERICK C, PHIL DEPT, CALIFORNIA ST UNIV, SAN JOSE CA 95114
DOMOTER, ZOLTON, PHILOSOPHY DEPT, UNIV OF PENN, PHILADELPHIA PA 19174
DONAGAN, ALAN, PHIL DEPT, UNIV OF CHICAGO, CHICAGO IL 60637
DONAGHY, KEVIN, PHIL DEPT, COLLEGE AT BROCKPORT, BROCKPORT NY 14420
DONAHOE, I M, PHILOSOPHY DEPT, UNIV OF ALBERTA, EDMONTON ALB   CAN
DONAHUE, EUGENE L, PHIL DEPT, CREIGHTON UNIV, OMAHA NE 68178
DONALDSON, GEORGE L, PHILOSOPHY DEPT, UNIV OF S ALABAMA, MOBILE AL 36688
DONCEL, JOSEPH F, PHIL DEPT, FORDHAM UNIVERSITY, BRONX NY 10458
DONEY, WILLIS, PHILOSOPHY DEPT, DARTMOUTH COLLEGE, HANOVER NH 03755
DONNELLAN, DEITH S, PHIL DEPT, UNIV OF CALIFORNIA, LOS ANGELES CA 90024
DONNELLY, JOHN, PHIL DEPT, FORDHAM UNIVERSITY, BRONX NY 10458
DONNER, WENDI, PHILOSOPHY DEPT, VICTORIA COLLEGE, TORONTO 5 ONT   CAN
DONOGHUE, JOHN D, PHIL DEPT, BOSTON COLLEGE, CHESTNUT HILL MA 02167
DONCHUE, KEVIN E, PHIL DEPT, MARIST COLLEGE, POUGHKEEPSIE NY 12601
DONCSO, ANTON, PHIL DEPT, UNIV OF DETROIT, DETROIT MI 48221
DONCUGHO, M, PHILOSOPHY DEPT, UNIV OF TORONTO, TORONTO ONT   CAN
DONOVAN, EDWARD L, INTEGRATED STUD, SACRED HEART COLLEGE, BELMONT NC 28012
DONOVAN, RICKART, PHIL DEPT, IONA COLLEGE, NEW ROCHELLE NY 10801
DOODY, JOHN A, PHILOSOPHY DEPT, VILLANOVA UNIV, VILLANOVA PA 19085
DOOLEY, PATRICK K, PHIL DEPT, ST BONAVENTURE UNIV, ST BONVENTURE NY 14778
DOOLEY, WILLIAM E, PHILOSOPHY DEPT, MARQUETTE UNIV, MILWAUKEE WI 53233
DORE, CLEMENT J, PHILOSOPHY DEPT, VANDERBILT UNIV, NASHVILLE TN 37235
DORE, J W, PHILOSOPHY DEPT, ST JOSEPH'S COLLEGE, EDMONTON 61 ALB   CAN
DORENENBURG, NOREEN, PHIL DEPT, SKIDMORE COLLEGE, SARATOGA SPGS NY 12886
DORFF, ELLIOT, PHIL OF RELIG, UNIV OF JUDAISM, LOS ANGELES CA 90028
DORION, MADELEINE, PHIL DEPT, COL BCIS-DE-BOULOGNE, MONTREAL QUE   CAN

DORMAN, LAURENCE, PHIL & HIST & SOC, SIMPSON COL, SAN FRANCISCO CA 94134
DORNAN, KEVIN, PHIL DEPT, UNIV OF N CAROLINA, CHAPEL HILL NC 27514
DORSEL, THOMAS N, UNIV OF ALBUQUERQUE, ALBUQUERQUE, NM 87120
DORSEY, WILLIAM R, PHILOSOPHY DEPT, RUTGERS UNIV, NEW BRUNSWICK NJ 08903
DORSTAL, ROBERT, PHILOSOPHY DEPT, PENN STATE UNIV, UNIV PARK PA 16802
DORTER, K N, PHILOSOPHY DEPT, UNIV OF GUELPH, GUELPH ONT   CAN
DOSS, R, PHIL OF REL & THEOL, AMER BAPTIST OF WEST, COVINA CA 91724
DOSS, SEALE R, PHILOSOPHY DEPT, RIPON COLLEGE, RIPON WI 54971
DOSSOGNE, VICTOR J, HUMAN DEPT, TRINIDAD ST JUN COL, TRINIDAD CO 81082
DOUDNA, JOHN CHARLES, REL & PHIL, BAKER UNIVERSITY, BALDWIN CITY KS 66006
DOUGHERTY, JUDE P, PHIL SCH, CATH UNIV OF AMER, WASHINGTON DC 20017
DOUGHERTY, THOMAS, PHIL DEPT, UNIV OF CINCINNATI, CINCINNATI OH 45221
DOUGLAS, N E, PHILOSOPHY DEPT, AMER BAPT THEOL SEM, NASHVILLE TN 37207
DOUGLAS, WALTER D, PHIL DEPT, SN BERNARDINO VALLEY, SN BERNARDINO CA 92403
DOUGLIN, ERNEST, PHIL DEPT, NORTHWESTERN UNIV, EVANSTON IL 60201
DOUILLARD, PAUL, PHIL DEPT, ASSUMPTION COLLEGE, WORCESTER MA 01609
DOVE, KENLEY, PHIL DEPT, NW SCH FOR SOC RES, NEW YORK NY 10003
DOW, J, PHIL DEPT, W CONNECTICUT ST COL, DANBURY CT 06810
DOWELL JR, ARTHUR N, PHIL DIV, FLORIDA COLLEGE, TEMPLE TER FL 33617
DOWEY, EDWARD A, THEOL DEPT, PRINCETON THEOL SEM, PRINCETON NJ 08540
DOWIS, JOE, PHIL & REL DEPT, UNIV OF GEORGIA, ATHENS GA 30602
DOWLING, DEAN E, ENG DEPT, U S MILITARY ACAD, WEST POINT NY 10996
DOWNES, CHAUNCEY, PHIL DEPT, NEW YORK UNIVERSITY, NEW YORK NY 10003
DOWNEY, LEO, PHIL & RELIG, INTERAMER UNIVERSITY, RAMEY AFB PR 00604
DOWNING, THOMAS, PHIL DEPT, W WASHINGTON ST COL, BELLINGHAM WA 98225
DOYLE, ANTOINETTE M, PHIL DEPT, LORETTO HEIGHTS COL, DENVER CO 80236
DOYLE, JAMES F, PHIL DEPT, UNIV OF MISSOURI, ST LOUIS MO 63121
DOYLE, JOHN J, PHIL DEPT, MARIAN COLLEGE, INDIANAPOLIS IN 46222
DOYLE, JOHN P, PHIL DEPT, ST LOUIS UNIVERSITY, ST LOUIS MO 63103
DOYLE, JOHN, PHILOSOPHY DEPT, LOYOLA COLLEGE, MONTREAL QUE   CAN
DOYLE, PATRICK, PHILOSOPHY DEPT, MARQUETTE UNIV, MILWAUKEE WI 53233
DOZORETZ, JERRY, PHIL DEPT, UNIV OF CALIFORNIA, SANTA BARBARA CA 93106
DRAGER, KENT, PHILOSOPHY DEPT, UNIV OF MASS, AMHERST MA 01002
DRAGHI, ROBERT A, PHIL & RELIG DEPT, MARYMOUNT COL, ARLINGTON VA 22207
DRAGSTEDT, JOHN ALBERT, ST MARY'S COL OF CAL, MORAGA, CA 94575
DRAKE, ALICE LYNN, PHIL DEPT, S METHODIST UNIV, DALLAS TX 75222
DRANE, JAMES, PHILOSOPHY DEPT, EDINBORO ST COL, EDINBORO PA 16412
DRANGE, THEODORE M, PHIL DEPT, WEST VIRGINIA UNIV, MORGANTOWN WV 26506
DRAY, WILLIAM H, PHIL DEPT, TRENT UNIVERSITY, PETERBOROUGH ONT   CAN
DREBEN, BURTON, PHIL DEPT, HARVARD UNIVERSITY, CAMBRIDGE MA 02138
DREHER, JOHN P, PHILOSOPHY DEPT, LAWRENCE UNIV, APPLETON WI 54911
DREHER, JOHN, PHIL SCH, UNIV OF S CALIFORNIA, LOS ANGELES CA 90007
DREISBACH, DONALD F, PHIL DEPT, N MICHIGAN UNIV, MARQUETTE MI 49855
DREISOERNER, CHARLES, PHIL DEPT, ST MARY'S UNIVERSITY, SAN ANTONIO TX 78228
DRENGSON, A R, PHILOSOPHY DEPT, UNIV OF VICTORIA, VICTORIA B C   CAN
DRENNAN, ELDON, PHILOSOPHY DEPT, COLUMBIA COLLEGE, COLUMBIA MO 65201
DRENNEN, D A, PHIL DEPT, MARIST COLLEGE, POUGHKEEPSIE NY 12601
DRETSKE, FREDERICK I, PHILOSOPHY DEPT, UNIV OF WISCONSIN, MADISON WI 53706
DREW-BEAR, ROBERT, 12 CHURCH STREET, NEW ROCHELLE, NY 10805
DREW, JOHN M, PHIL DEPT, UNIVERSITY OF TOLEDO, TOLEDO OH 43606
DREW, PHILIP, PHIL DEPT, EMORY UNIVERSITY, ATLANTA GA 30322
DREYFUS, HUBERT, PHIL DEPT, UNIV OF CALIFORNIA, BERKELEY CA 94720
DRISCOLL, D, PHIL DEPT, W CONNECTICUT ST COL, DANBURY CT 06810
DRISCOLL, DONALD J, PHIL DEPT, S COLORADO ST COL, PUEBLO CO 81001
DRISCOLL, EDWARD A, PHILOSOPHY DEPT, GEORGIAN COURT COL, LAKEWOOD NJ 08701
DRISDELLE, GERARD, COLLEGE D'AHUNTSIC, MONTREAL, QUE   CAN
DRTINA, RICHARD, PHIL DEPT, GEORGE WILLIAMS UNIV, MONTREAL 107 QUE   CAN
DRUCKMAN, AARON, PHILOSOPHY DEPT, PENN STATE UNIV, UNIV PARK PA 16802
DRUMIN, WILLIAM A, PHIL DEPT, KING'S COLLEGE, WILKES BARRE PA 18711
DRUMMER, MIRO M, PHIL DEPT, UNIV OF ILLINOIS, URBANA IL 61801
DRUMMOND, DOUGLAS, PHIL DEPT, UNIV OF SOUTH DAKOTA, VERMILLION SD 57069
DRUMMOND, JOHN J, PHIL DEPT, GEORGETOWN UNIV, WASHINGTON DC 20007
DRURY, GEORGE F, EMPIRE ST COL, SARATOGA SPGS, NY 12866
DRYDEN, LEE, PHIL DEPT, ST UNIV OF NY, AMHERST NY 14226

DRYER, D P, PHILOSOPHY DEPT, UNIV OF TORONTO, TORONTO ONT   CAN
DUBOIS, LAURISTON, PHILOSOPHY DEPT, NW NAZARENE COLLEGE, NAMPA ID 83651
DUBOSE, L SHANNON, PHILOSOPHY DEPT, UNIV OF S CAROLINA, COLUMBIA SC   29208
DUBRULE, D E, PHILOSOPHY DEPT, CARLETON UNIVERSITY, OTTAWA ONT   CAN
DUCE, LEONARD A, PHIL DEPT, TRINITY UNIVERSITY, SAN ANTONIO TX 78284
DUCHARME, LEONARD, PHIL FACULTY, UNIV OF OTTAWA, OTTAWA ONT   CAN
DUCHESNEAU, FRANCOIS, PHIL FACULTY, UNIV OF OTTAWA, OTTAWA ONT   CAN
DUCHON, STEVE, PHIL DEPT, ST UNIV OF NY, STONY BROOK NY   11790
DUCKETT, R E E, PHIL DEPT, UNIV OF N CAROLINA, WILMINGTON NC 28401
DUCLOS, MARCEL, ENG & SOC SCI DEPT, NW HAMPSHR TECH INST, CONCORD NH   03301
DUDA, GEORGE, PHIL DEPT, UNIVERSITY OF KANSAS, LAWRENCE KS 66044
DUDA, WILLIAM L, PHIL DEPT, ST UNIV OF NY, BINGHAMTON NY   13901
DUDECK, CAROLINE, PHILOSOPHY DEPT, UNIV OF WYOMING, LARAMIE WY 82071
DUDIK, EVAN MATTHEW, PHILOSOPHY DEPT, UNIV OF TEXAS, AUSTIN TX 78712
DUERLINGER, JAMES, PHIL DEPT, UNIVERSITY OF IOWA, IOWA CITY IA   52240
DUFEE, RICHARD, PHILOSOPHY DEPT, PENN STATE UNIV, UNIV PARK PA 16802
DUFFY, JOHN A, PHIL DEPT, ST ALPHONSUS COL, SUFFIELD CT   06078
DUFON, ROBERT D, PHIL DEPT, ST JOSEPH'S COLLEGE, EAST CHICAGO IN 46312
DUFRESNE, JACQUES, COLLEGE D'AHUNTSIC, MONTREAL, QUE   CAN
DUGAN, D KERRY, PHIL DEPT, TULANE UNIVERSITY, NEW ORLEANS LA 70118
DUGGAN, TIMOTHY J, PHILOSOPHY DEPT, DARTMOUTH COLLEGE, HANOVER NH   03755
DUGUAY, MICHEL, PHIL DEPT, COL RIVIERE DU LOUP, RIVIERE LOUP QUE   CAN
DUHAIME, MICHELINE, COL EDOUARD-MONTPETIT, LONGUEUIL, QUE   CAN
DUKELOW, OVEN W, PHILOSOPHY DEPT, WASH & JEFF COL, WASHINGTON PA 15301
DULAC, HENRI, PHIL DEPT, COL OF ST THOMAS, ST PAUL MN   55105
DULMAGE, HORACE, PHILOSOPHY DEPT, MCMASTER UNIVERSITY, HAMILTON ONT   CAN
DUM, GEORGE L, PHILOSOPHY DEPT, UNIV OF PORTLAND, PORTLAND OR   97203
DUMAS, CELINE, PHILOSOPHY DEPT, COL DE ROUYN-NORANDA, ROUYN QUE   CAN
DUMAS, DAVID, PHIL DEPT, KAN ST TEACHERS COL, EMPORIA KS   66801
DUMONT, FERNAND, PHIL FACULTE, UNIVERSITE LAVAL, CITE UNIV QUE   CAN
DUMONT, GUILBERT, AMERICAN RIVER COL, SACRAMENTO, CA   95841
DUMONT, MICHELE T, PHIL DEPT, MT ST MARY'S COL, LOS ANGELES CA 90049
DUMONT, RICHARD E, PHILOSOPHY DEPT, XAVIER UNIVERSITY, CINCINNATI OH   45207
DUMONT, ROGER, COL DE HAUTERIVE, HAUTERIVE, QUE   CAN
DUMOUCHEL, THERESE, PHIL DEPT, COL LIONEL-GROULX, STE-THERESE QUE   CAN
DUNAGAN, CLINTON, BIB & PHIL DEPT, HARDIN-SIMMONS UNIV, ABILENE TX 79601
DUNCAN, A R C, PHILOSOPHY DEPT, QUEEN'S UNIVERSITY, KINGSTON ONT   CAN
DUNCAN, ALEXANDER, PHIL DEPT, ST VIN DE PAUL SEM, BOYNTON FL 33435
DUNCAN, ELMER H, PHILOSOPHY DEPT, BAYLOR UNIVERSITY, WACO TX 76703
DUNCON, STANISLAUS J, PHIL DEPT, CAL POLYTECH ST U, SAN LUIS OBIS CA 93407
DUNGER, G A, HERITAGE & THT DIV, N AMERICAN BAPT SEM, SIOUX FALLS SD   57105
DUNHAM, BARROWS, MANNES COLLEGE, NEW YORK, NY   10021
DUNHAM, JOE LLOYD, AURORA COLLEGE, AURORA, IL   60507
DUNIK, PETER, PHIL & SOC DEPT, VANCOUVER CITY COL, VANCOUVER B C   CAN
DUNION, PAUL, HUMAN DEPT, MOHEGAN COM COL, NORWICH CT   06360
DUNLAP, JOHN T, HUMAN DEPT, COLUMBUS COLLEGE, COLUMBUS GA   31907
DUNLAVEY, JAMES L, PHIL DEPT, WASHINGTON UNIV, ST LOUIS MO   63130
DUNLAVEY, MARY, PHIL DEPT, WEST GEORGIA COLLEGE, CARROLLTON GA   30117
DUNLOP, CHARLES, PHIL DEPT, UNIV OF MICHIGAN, FLINT MI   48503
DUNMORE-LEIBOR, JUSTIN, PHIL DEPT, LEHMAN COLLEGE, BRONX NY   10468
DUNN, DOROTHY, IMMACULATE HEART COL, LOS ANGELES, CA   90027
DUNN, J MICHAEL, PHIL DEPT, INDIANA UNIVERSITY, BLOOMINGTON IN 47401
DUNN, ROSS DENISON, THEOL & HIST DEPT, AUSTIN THEOL SEM, AUSTIN TX 78705
DUNNE, MARY RACHEL, PHILOSOPHY DEPT, UNIV OF ST THOMAS, HOUSTON TX 77006
DUNNE, R, PHIL FACULTY, UNIV OF OTTAWA, OTTAWA ONT   CAN
DUNNING, H ROY, REL & PHIL DEPT, TREVECCA NAZ COL, NASHVILLE TN 37210
DUNPHY, RICHARD, PHIL DEPT, ST LOUIS UNIVERSITY, ST LOUIS MO 63103
DUNPHY, W B, UNIV OF ST MICHAEL'S, TORONTO 181, ONT   CAN
DUPONT, GERALD E, PHIL DEPT, ST MICHAEL'S COLLEGE, WINOOSKI VT   05404
DUPRE, LOUIS, PHIL DEPT, GEORGETOWN UNIV, WASHINGTON DC   20007
DUPRE, WILHELM, PHIL DEPT, DEPAUL UNIVERSITY, CHICAGO IL   60604
DUQUETTE, DAVID A, PHIL DEPT, RENSSELAER POLYTECH, TROY NY   12181
DURAND, CLIFFORD C, PHILOSOPHY DEPT, MORGAN STATE UNIV, BALTIMORE MD   21239
DURBIN, JACK D, PHIL DEPT, FLORIDA STATE UNIV, TALLAHASSEE FL   32306

DURBIN, PAUL T, PHILOSOPHY DEPT, UNIV OF DELAWARE, NEWARK DE 19711
DURFEE, HAROLD A, PHIL DEPT, THE AMERICAN UNIV, WASHINGTON DC 20016
DURKIN, THOMAS J, HUMAN DIV, KANSAS WESLEYAN UNIV, SALINA KS 67401
DURLAND, WILLIAM, PHIL DEPT, PURDUE UNIVERSITY, FORT WAYNE IN 46805
DUSEK, R V, PHILOSOPHY DEPT, UNIV OF NW HAMPSHIRE, DURHAM NH 03824
DUSKA, RONALD F, HUMANITIES DIV, ROSEMONT COLLEGE, ROSEMONT PA 19010
DUTTON, JOHN D, PHIL DEPT, CALIFORNIA ST UNIV, SAN JOSE CA 95114
DUZY, MICHAEL, SOC SCI DEPT, HARCUM JR COL, BRYN MAWR PA 19010
DWIGGINS, W CYRIL, PHILOSOPHY DEPT, DICKINSON COLLEGE, CARLISLE PA 17013
DWORKIN, GERALD, PHIL DEPT, UNIV OF ILLINOIS, CHICAGO IL 60680
DWYER, CHARLES, PHIL DEPT, UNIVERSITY OF DAYTON, DAYTON OH 45469
DWYER, HELENE, PHIL DEPT, NAZARETH COLLEGE, ROCHESTER NY 14610
DWYER, JOHN, PHILOSOPHY DEPT, QUEENS COLLEGE, FLUSHING NY 11367
DYAL, ROBERT A, PHILOSOPHY DEPT, KENT STATE UNIV, KENT OH 44242
DYBIKOWSKI, JAMES C, PHIL DEPT, UNIV BRIT COLUMBIA, VANCOUVER 8 B C   CAN
DYBOWSKI, BRIAN, HUMAN DEPT, COLLEGE OF SANTA FE, SANTA FE NM 87501
DYCHE, EUGENE I, PHIL DEPT, INDIANA ST UNIV, TERRE HAUTE IN 47809
DYE, JAMES W, PHIL DEPT, N ILLINOIS UNIV, DEKALB IL 60115
DYKE, CHARLES, PHIL DEPT, TEMPLE UNIVERSITY, PHILADELPHIA PA 19122
DYKEMAN, KING J, PHIL DEPT, FAIRFIELD UNIVERSITY, FAIRFIELD CT 06430
DYKES, DONNA, SOC & PHIL DEPT, TENN TECH UNIV, COOKEVILLE TN 38501
DYKHUIZEN, GEORGE, PHILOSOPHY DEPT, UNIV OF VERMONT, BURLINGTON VT 05401
DYKSTRA, D IVAN, PHILOSOPHY DEPT, HOPE COLLEGE, HOLLAND MI 49423
DYKSTRA, WESLEY C, PHILOSOPHY DEPT, ALMA COLLEGE, ALMA MI 48801
DYSON, VERENA, PHILOSOPHY DEPT, UNIV OF CALGARY, CALGARY 44 ALB   CAN
EAKER, CHARLES, PHIL DEPT, COL AT OSWEGO, OSWEGO NY 13126
EAMES, ELIZABETH R, PHIL DEPT, S ILLINOIS UNIV, CARBONDALE IL 62901
EAMES, S MORRIS, PHIL DEPT, S ILLINOIS UNIV, CARBONDALE IL 62901
EARL, R R, PHILOSOPHY DEPT, AMER BAPT THEOL SEM, NASHVILLE TN 37207
EARLE, WILLIAM A, PHIL DEPT, NORTHWESTERN UNIV, EVANSTON IL 60201
EARLE, WILLIAM J, PHIL DEPT, LONG ISLAND UNIV, BROOKLYN NY 11201
EARLY, FIRMAN A, PHIL DEPT, SIOUX FALLS COLLEGE, SIOUX FALLS SD 57101
EARLY, THOMAS, PHIL DEPT, CAL ST UNIV -HUMBOLDT, ARCATA CA 95521
EARMAN, JOHN S, PHIL DEPT, UNIV OF MINNESOTA, MINNEAPOLIS MN 55455
EASTERLING, MARVIN L, PHILOSOPHY DEPT, CALIFORNIA ST UNIV, CHICO CA 95926
EASTMAN JR, LUCIUS R, PHIL DEPT, CALIFORNIA ST UNIV, SAN JOSE CA 95114
EASTMAN, ROGER, PHILOSOPHY DEPT, REEDLEY COLLEGE, REEDLEY CA 93654
EASTMAN, W, PHILOSOPHY DEPT, UNIV OF ALBERTA, EDMONTON ALB   CAN
EASTON, LOYD D, PHIL DEPT, OHIO WESLEYAN UNIV, DELAWARE OH 43105
EASTON, RAYMOND, PHIL DEPT, UNIV OF KENTUCKY, LEXINGTON KY 40506
EATON, MARCIA, PHIL DEPT, UNIV OF MINNESOTA, MINNEAPOLIS MN 55455
EBACHER, ROGER, PHIL FACULTE, UNIVERSITE LAVAL, CITE UNIV QUE   CAN
EBBEN, JAMES, PHIL DEPT, THOMAS MORE COLLEGE, COVINGTON KY 41017
EBENRECK, CLYDE, PHIL DEPT, PRINCE GEORGE'S COM, LARGO MD 20870
EBENRECK, SARA, PHIL DEPT, PRINCE GEORGE'S COM, LARGO MD 20870
EBERENZ, JAMES H, PHIL DEPT, SPALDING COLLEGE, LOUISVILLE KY 40203
EBERHARDT, CHARLES R, PHIL & REL DEPT, TOWSON STATE COL, BALTIMORE MD 21204
EBERLE, JAMES, PHILOSOPHY DEPT, UNIV OF CALGARY, CALGARY 44 ALB   CAN
EBERLE, ROLF, PHIL DEPT, UNIV OF ROCHESTER, ROCHESTER NY 14627
EBERSOLE, FRANK B, PHILOSOPHY DEPT, UNIV OF OREGON, EUGENE OR 97403
EBERT, LOUIS, PHIL DEPT, UNIV OF S FLORIDA, TAMPA FL 33620
EBISCH, GLEN, PHIL DEPT, COLUMBIA UNIVERSITY, NEW YORK NY 10027
ECHELBARGER, CHARLES G, PHIL DEPT, COL AT OSWEGO, OSWEGO NY 13126
ECHEVARRIA, JOSE R, PHIL DEPT, CATHOLIC UNIVERSITY, PONCE PR 00731
ECHEVERRIA, JOSE, PHIL DEPT, UNIV OF PUERTO RICO, RIO PIEDRAS PR 00931
ECKHART, DENNIS, LOYOLA UNIVERSITY, LOS ANGELES, CA 90045
ECKROTH, RICHARD, PHIL DEPT, SAINT JOHN'S UNIV, COLLEGEVILLE MN 56321
ECKSTEIN, PAUL, PHIL DEPT, BOSTON COLLEGE, CHESTNUT HILL MA 02167
ECKSTEIN, STEPHEN, RELIG DEPT, E NEW MEXICO UNIV, PORTALES NM 88130
ECKSTRAND, B R, PHIL DEPT, JAMESTOWN COM COL, JAMESTOWN NY 14701
ECONOMOS, HOMER, ALMA WHITE COLLEGE, ZAREPHATH, NJ 08890
ECONOMOS, JOHN J, PHIL DEPT, UNIV OF ILLINOIS, CHICAGO IL 60680
ECSODI, JOHN, PHIL DEPT, ST JOSEPH'S COL, PHILADELPHIA PA 19131
EDDINS, BERKLEY, PHIL DEPT, ST UNIV OF NY, AMHERST NY 14226

EDDY, JANICE B, PHIL DEPT, FLORIDA ATLANTIC U, BOCA RATON FL 33432
EDDY, LYLE K, PHIL DEPT, UNIV OF NEBRASKA, LINCOLN NE 68502
EDDY, WILLARD O, PHIL DEPT, COLORADO ST UNIV, FORT COLLINS CO 80521
EDELENYI, ACHILLES, PHIL DEPT, UNIVERSITY OF DAYTON, DAYTON OH 45469
EDELSON, ZVI, PHIL & WORLD CULT, COM COL ALLEGHENY CO, MONROEVILLE PA 15146
EDELSTEIN, ROY S, PHILOSOPHY DEPT, OHIO STATE UNIV, COLUMBUS OH 43210
EDGAR, WILLIAM, PHIL DEPT, COL AT GENESEO, GENESEO NY 14454
EDGE, H L, REL & PHIL DEPT, ROLLINS COLLEGE, WINTER PARK FL 32789
EDIE, JAMES M, PHIL DEPT, NORTHWESTERN UNIV, EVANSTON IL 60201
EDISON, G, UNIV OF TRINITY COL, TORONTO 181, ONT   CAN
EDLER, MARIS, PHILOSOPHY DEPT, VILLANOVA UNIV, VILLANOVA PA 19085
EDLOW, R BLAIR, PHIL DEPT, UNIV OF MARYLAND, COLLEGE PARK MD 20742
EDMUNETTE, SISTER, REL STUD & PHIL, HILBERT COLLEGE, HAMBURG NY 14075
EDRINGTON, DEVON, ENGLISH & PHIL DEPT, TACOMA COM COL, TACOMA WA 98465
EDWARDS, CARL N, RELIG & PHIL DEPT, MARY BALDWIN COL, STAUNTON VA 24401
EDWARDS, CLIFFORD W, PHIL & RELIG, VA COMMONWEALTH UNIV, RICHMOND VA 23220
EDWARDS, JAMES C, PHILOSOPHY DEPT, FURMAN UNIVERSITY, GREENVILLE SC 29613
EDWARDS, JAMES, PHIL DEPT, NASSAU COM COL, GARDEN CITY NY 11530
EDWARDS, KENNETH C, PHIL DEPT, EAST KENTUCKY UNIV, RICHMOND KY 40475
EDWARDS, PAUL M, SOC SCI DIV, GRACELAND COLLEGE, LAMONI IA 50140
EDWARDS, PAUL, PHIL DEPT, BROOKLYN COLLEGE, BROOKLYN NY 11210
EDWARDS, REM B, PHIL DEPT, UNIV OF TENNESSEE, KNOXVILLE TN 37916
EDWARDS, RICHARD A, PHIL & RELIG, VA POLYTECH INST, BLACKSBURG VA 24061
EDWARDS, SANDRA S, PHIL DEPT, UNIV OF ARKANSAS, FAYETTEVILLE AR 72701
EDWARDS, WILLIAM F, PHIL DEPT, EMORY UNIVERSITY, ATLANTA GA 30322
EFFLER, ROY R, PHIL DEPT, DUNS SCOTUS COL, SOUTHFIELD MI 48075
EFROS, ISREAL, REL & PHIL DEPT, DROPSIE UNIVERSITY, PHILADELPHIA PA 19132
EGAN, EDMUND, PHILOSOPHY DEPT, LOYOLA COLLEGE, MONTREAL QUE   CAN
EGAN, WILLIAM T, PHILOSOPHY DEPT, ALVERNO COLLEGE, MILWAUKEE WI 53215
EGBUJIE, INNOCENT I, PHIL DEPT, BOSTON COLLEGE, CHESTNUT HILL MA 02167
EGERTSON, ERICK R, PHILOSOPHY DEPT, MIDLAND LUTH COL, FREMONT NE 68025
EGGAN, LLOYD A, PHILOSOPHY DEPT, UNIV OF WISCONSIN, MADISON WI 53706
EGGERMAN, RICHARD, PHIL DEPT, OKLAHOMA STATE UNIV, STILLWATER OK 74074
EGGERS, JOHN, PHIL DEPT, BENEDICTINE COLLEGE, ATCHISON KS 66002
EGGLETON, JOHN, RELIG DEPT, E NEW MEXICO UNIV, PORTALES NM 88130
EGGLETON, JOHN, HUMAN DEPT, MANHATTAN CHRIST COL, MANHATTAN KS 66502
EGYED, B I, PHILOSOPHY DEPT, CARLETON UNIVERSITY, OTTAWA ONT   CAN
EHLERS, HENRY J, PHIL DEPT, UNIV OF MINNESOTA, DULUTH MN 55812
EHMAN, MARK A, REL & PHIL DEPT, SPRINGFIELD COL, SPRINGFIELD MA 01109
EHMAN, ROBERT R, PHILOSOPHY DEPT, VANDERBILT UNIV, NASHVILLE TN 37235
EHRCKE, W F, PHILOSOPHY DEPT, UNIV OF TORONTO, TORONTO ONT   CAN
EHRHART, CARL Y, PHILOSOPHY DEPT, LEBANON VLY COL, ANNVILLE PA 17003
EHRLICH, LEONARD, PHILOSOPHY DEPT, UNIV OF MASS, AMHERST MA 01002
EICHHOEFER, GERALD W, PHIL DEPT, ST LOUIS UNIVERSITY, ST LOUIS MO 63103
EIKNER, ALLEN, PHIL & RELIG DEPT, DRURY COLLEGE, SPRINGFIELD MO 65802
EILSTEIN, HELENA, PHIL DEPT, UNIV OF NEW MEXICO, ALBUQUERQUE NM 87106
EISENBERG, J A, PHIL OF EDUC & HIST, ONTARIO INSTITUTE, TORONTO ONT   CAN
EISENBERG, PAUL D, PHIL DEPT, INDIANA UNIVERSITY, BLOOMINGTON IN 47401
EISENHOWER, MICHAEL C, PHIL DEPT, OCL AT OSWEGO, OSWEGO NY 13126
EKSTROM, SUSAN C, PHIL DEPT, MICHIGAN STATE UNIV, EAST LANSING MI 48823
ELBRECHT, JOYCE, PHIL & REL DEPT, ITHACA COLLEGE, ITHACA NY 14850
ELDERKIN, W R M, PHIL DEPT, UNIV OF NW BRUNSWICK, FREDERICTON N B   CAN
ELERDING, PHIL DEPT, ST FIDELIS COLLEGE, HERMAN, PA 16039
ELEVITCH, BERNARD, PHIL DEPT, BOSTON UNIVERSITY, BOSTON MA 02215
ELFSTROM, GERARD, PHIL DEPT, EMORY UNIVERSITY, ATLANTA GA 30322
ELGIN, CATHERINE Z, PHIL DEPT, BRANDEIS UNIVERSITY, WALTHAM MA 02154
ELIAS, JULIUS, PHIL DEPT, CITY COLLEGE, NEW YORK NY 10031
ELIAS, WILLIAM, PHIL & RELIG DEPT, UPSALA COL, EAST ORANGE NJ 07019
ELKATIP, SULE, PHIL DEPT, ST UNIV OF NY, AMHERST NY 14226
ELKINS, DEXTER, SOC SCI DIV, EL CENTRO COL, DALLAS TX 75202
ELKINS, J B, PHIL & RELIG, MUSKINGUM COLLEGE, NEW CONCORD OH 43762
ELLER, VERNARD, PHIL & RELIG DEPT, LA VERNE COLLEGE, LA VERNE CA 91750
ELLIN, JOSEPH, PHIL DEPT, WEST MICHIGAN UNIV, KALAMAZOO MI 49001
ELLINGBOE, JOHN, PHIL DEPT, UNIV OF MICHIGAN, ANN ARBOR MI 48104

ELLINGTON, J W, PHIL DEPT, UNIV OF CONNECTICUT, STORRS CT 06268
ELLIOT, CLYDE J, PHIL DEPT, SPRING HILL COLLEGE, MOBILE AL 36608
ELLIOTT, HERSCHEL, PHIL DEPT, UNIV CF FLORIDA, GAINESVILLE FL 32611
ELLIOTT, ROBERT, PHIL DEPT, TRINITY CHRIST COL, PALOS HEIGHTS IL 60463
ELLIS, FRANK, ST MARY'S COL OF CAL, MORAGA, CA 94575
ELLIS, M E, PHILOSOPHY DEPT, TAYLOR UNIVERSITY, UPLAND IN 46989
ELLIS, MATT L, PHILOSOPHY DEPT, HENDRIX COLLEGE, CONWAY AR 72032
ELLIS, R L, SOC SCI DEPT, AMARILLO COLLEGE, AMARILLO TX 79105
ELLISON, MARJORIE, PHIL DEPT, FORDHAM UNIVERSITY, BRONX NY 10458
ELLISTON, F, UNIV OF TRINITY COL, TORONTO 181, ONT   CAN
ELLISTON, FREDERICK A, PHIL DEPT, UNION COLLEGE, SCHENECTADY NY 12308
ELMEN, PAUL, PHIL THEOL DEPT, SEABURY W THEOL SEM, EVANSTON IN 60201
ELROD, JOHN, PHIL DEPT, IOWA STATE UNIV, AMES IA 50010
ELSNER, GARY A, ENG & HUM DEPT, LAKE MICHIGAN COL, BENTON HARBOR MI 49022
ELSTEIN, YOAV, PHIL OF RELIG, UNIV OF JUDAISM, LOS ANGELES CA 90028
ELUGARDO, R, PHILOSOPHY DEPT, UNIV CF ALBERTA, EDMONTON ALB   CAN
ELVETON, ROY O, PHIL DEPT, CARLETON COLLEGE, NORTHFIELD MN 55057
ELY, P, PHILOSOPHY DEPT, UNIV OF TORONTO, TORONTO ONT   CAN
EMAD, PARVIS, PHIL DEPT, DEPAUL UNIVERSITY, CHICAGO IL 60604
EMBLOM, WILLIAM J, PHIL STUD DEPT, S ILLINOIS UNIV, EDWARDSVILLE IL 62025
EMBREE, ALAN C, PHILOSOPHY DEPT, CEN YMCA COM COL, CHICAGO IL 60606
EMBREE, LESTER E, PHIL DEPT, N ILLINOIS UNIV, DEKALB IL 60115
EMINHIZER, EARL E, PHIL & REL STUD, YOUNGSTOWN ST UNIV, YOUNGSTOWN OH 44503
EMMONS, DONALD, PHIL & RELIG, JERSEY CITY ST COL, JERSEY CITY NJ 07305
EMRICK, HOWARD C, PHIL & REL DEPT, ADRIAN COLLEGE, ADRIAN MI 49221
ENC, BERENT, PHILOSOPHY DEPT, UNIV OF WISCONSIN, MADISON WI 53706
ENGEL, ELFRIEDE, HUMAN DEPT, LANSING COM COL, LANSING MI 48914
ENGEL, ELIZABETH, PHIL DEPT, CAL ST UNIV -HUMBOLDT, ARCATA CA 95521
ENGEL, S MORRIS, PHIL SCH, UNIV OF S CALIFORNIA, LOS ANGELES CA 90007
ENGLE, GALE, SOC OCI DIV, FOOTHILL COLLEGE, LOS ALTOS HLS CA 94022
ENGLEBRETSEN, G F, PHIL DEPT, BISHOP'S UNIVERSITY, LENNOXVILLE QUE   CAN
ENGLISH, JANE, PHIL DEPT, UNIV OF N CAROLINA, CHAPEL HILL NC 27514
ENJUTO-BERNAL, J, PHIL DEPT, UNIV OF PUERTO RICO, RIO PIEDRAS PR 00931
ENQUIST, ROY J, THEOL & PHIL DEPT, TEXAS LUTH COLLEGE, SEGUIN TX 78155
ENRIGHT, MICHAEL F, PHIL SCH, CATH UNIV OF AMER, WASHINGTON DC 20017
ENTEMAN, WILLARD F, PHIL DEPT, UNION COLLEGE, SCHENECTADY NY 12308
EPP, RONALD H, PHILOSOPHY DEPT, MEMPHIS ST UNIV, MEMPHIS TN 38152
EPSTEIN, JOSEPH, PHIL & REL DEPT, AMHERST COLLEGE, AMHERST MA 01002
EPSTEIN, RONALD B, PHIL DEPT, CALIFORNIA ST UNIV, SAN FRANCISCO CA 94132
EPTON, CHARLES, PHILOSOPHY DEPT, CLARK COLLEGE, VANCOUVER WA 98663
ERAMIAN, ROBERT, HUMAN DEPT, ST BERNARD COLLEGE, ST BERNARD AL 35138
ERDE, EDMUND L, PHIL DEPT, TRINITY UNIVERSITY, SAN ANTONIO TX 78284
ERDOS, EDWARD, SOC SCI DEPT, NEW YORK INST TECH, NEW YORK NY 10019
ERICKSON, GLENN, PHILOSOPHY DEPT, VANDERBILT UNIV, NASHVILLE TN 37235
ERICKSON, HARRIS, REL & PHIL, UNIV OF EVANSVILLE, EVANSVILLE IN 47701
ERICKSON, MILLARD J, CHRIST FAITH DEPT, BETHEL THEOL SEM, ST PAUL MN 55112
ERICKSON, STEPHEN A, PHILOSOPHY DEPT, POMONA COLLEGE, CLAREMONT CA 91711
ERICSON, RANDALL L, PHIL & REL DEPT, BEREA COLLEGE, BEREA KY 40403
ERIKSSON, VINCENT E, CAMROSE LUTH COL, CAMROSE, ALB   CAN
ERKOREKA, YON, PHIL DEPT, COL DE SHERBROOKE, SHERBROOKE QUE   CAN
ERLANDSON, DOUGLAS, PHIL DEPT, UNIV OF NEBRASKA, LINCOLN NE 68502
ERMAK, PAUL J, THEOL & PHIL, BRIAR CLIFF COLLEGE, SIOUX CITY IA 51104
ERMATINGER, CHARLES J, PHIL DEPT, ST LOUIS UNIVERSITY, ST LOUIS MO 63103
ERNEST, STEPHEN T, PHIL & THEOL, DIVINE WORD COLLEGE, EPWORTH IA 52045
ERPENBECK, JAMES, PHIL & THEOL DEPT, SAINT LEO COLLEGE, SAINT LEO FL 33574
ERTEL, PHILIP, PHIL DEPT, UNIVERSITY OF DAYTON, DAYTON OH 45469
ERWIN, EDWARD, PHIL DEPT, ST UNIV OF NY, STONY BROOK NY 11790
ESCARDO, MAURICIO E, COL OF VIRGIN ISLAND, SAINT THOMAS, VI 00801
ESHLEMAN, MARTIN, PHIL DEPT, CARLETON COLLEGE, NORTHFIELD MN 55057
ESHPETER, A, PHILOSOPHY DEPT, ST JOSEPH'S COLLEGE, EDMONTON 61 ALB   CAN
ESKRIDGE, JOHN, PHIL & EDUC DEPT, OCM COL ALLEGHENY CO, PITTSBURGH PA 15212
ESLICK, LEONARD J, PHIL DEPT, ST LOUIS UNIVERSITY, ST LOUIS MO 63103
ESPINA, JOSE R, PHIL DEPT, MOLLOY COLLEGE, ROCKVILLE NY 11570
ESPOSITO, JOAN, PHIL DEPT, ST UNIV CF NY, STONY BROOK NY 11790

ESPOSITO, JOSEPH L, PHIL DEPT, BRADLEY UNIVERSITY, PEORIA IL 61606
ESS, CHARLES, PHILOSOPHY DEPT, PENN STATE UNIV, UNIV PARK PA 16802
ESSMAN, SHIRLEY, PHIL DEPT, ST UNIV OF NY, STONY BROOK NY 11790
ESTALL, H M, PHILOSOPHY DEPT, QUEEN'S UNIVERSITY, KINGSTON ONT   CAN
ESTRADA, MANUEL, PHIL DEPT, CATHOLIC UNIVERSITY, PONCE PR 00731
ETCHEMENDY, JOHN, PHIL DEPT, UNIV OF NEVADA, RENO NV 89507
ETEROVICH, FRANCIS, PHIL DEPT, DEPAUL UNIVERSITY, CHICAGO IL 60604
ETZWILER, JAMES P, PHILOSOPHY DEPT, MARQUETTE UNIV, MILWAUKEE WI 53233
EURARD, PAULE, PHIL DEPT, COL FRANCOIS-X-GARN, QUEBEC CITY QUE   CAN
EVANGELIST, WILLIAM, PHIL DEPT, NORTHWESTERN UNIV, EVANSTON IL 60201
EVANS, C STEPHEN, PHILOSOPHY DEPT, TRINITY COLLEGE, DEERFIELD IL 60015
EVANS, C, PHIL DEPT, LOUISIANA ST UNIV, BATON ROUGE LA 70803
EVANS, CEDRIC A, PHIL DEPT, UNIV OF NEBRASKA, LINCOLN NE 68502
EVANS, CHARLES, PHIL DEPT, CITY COLLEGE, NEW YORK NY 10031
EVANS, CLYDE, PHILOSOPHY DEPT, UNIV OF MASS, BOSTON MA 02116
EVANS, D D, PHILOSOPHY DEPT, UNIV OF TORONTO, TORONTO ONT   CAN
EVANS, DAVID A, PHIL DEPT, WAYNE STATE UNIV, DETROIT MI 48202
EVANS, HENRY M, PHILOSOPHY DEPT, SOUTHEASTERN BIB COL, LAKELAND FL 33801
EVANS, JAMES, PHIL DEPT, WEBSTER COLLEGE, ST LOUIS MO 63119
EVANS, JOHN F, HUMAN DIV, PENINSULA COLLEGE, PORT ANGELES WA 98362
EVANS, JOSEPH, PHIL DEPT, IMMACULATA COLLEGE, IMMACULATA PA 19345
EVANS, JOSEPH, PHIL DEPT, UNIV OF NOTRE DAME, NOTRE DAME IN 46556
EVANS, L C, POLIT SCI & PHIL, WEBER STATE COLLEGE, OGDEN UT 84403
EVANS, LES, SOC SCI DEPT, MOHAWK COLLEGE, HAMILTON ONT   CAN
EVANS, LUTHER D, PHILOSOPHY DEPT, OHIO STATE UNIV, COLUMBUS OH 43210
EVANS, MELBORNE G, PHIL DEPT, UNIV OF NEW MEXICO, ALBUQUERQUE NM 87106
EVANS, MYRNA, HUMAN DIV, ILLINOIS VLY COM COL, OGLESBY IL 61348
EVANS, R CAMERON, PHIL DEPT, UNIV OF WEST ONTARIO, LONDON ONT   CAN
EVANS, ROBERT H, PHIL DEPT, UNIV OF MINNESOTA, DULUTH MN 55812
EVANS, ROBERT, THEOL DEPT, MCCORMICK THEOL SEM, CHICAGO IL 60614
EVANS, WILLIAM G, PHIL DEPT, UNIV OF CALIFORNIA, RIVERSIDE CA 92502
EVELETH, LOIS, PHIL DEPT, FORDHAM UNIVERSITY, BRONX NY 10458
EVERALL, DAVID G, PHIL DEPT, UNIV OF SN FRANCISCO, SAN FRANCISCO CA 94117
EVERALL, PATRICIA, SOC SCI DEPT, CITY COLLEGE, SAN FRANCISCO CA 94112
EWENS, THOMAS, PHIL DEPT, LE MOYNE COLLEGE, SYRACUSE NY 13214
EXDELL, JOHN B, PHIL DEPT, KANSAS ST UNIVERSITY, MANHATTAN KS 66506
EZORSKY, GERTRUDE, PHIL DEPT, BROOKLYN COLLEGE, BROOKLYN NY 11210
FAABORG, ROBERT W, PHIL DEPT, UNIV OF CINCINNATI, CINCINNATI OH 45221
FABIAN, ANDREW, PHIL DEPT, SAINT MARY'S COLLEGE, WINONA MN 55987
FACIONE, PETER, PHIL DEPT, BOWLING GREEN UNIV, BOWLING GREEN OH 43403
FACKENHEIM, E L, PHILOSOPHY DEPT, UNIV OF TORONTO, TORONTO ONT   CAN
FACTOR, R LANCE, PHIL & REL DEPT, KNOX COLLEGE, GALESBURG IL 61401
FAGAN, KENNETH, PHIL DEPT, EMORY UNIVERSITY, ATLANTA GA 30322
FAGOTHEY, AUSTIN, PHIL DEPT, UNIV OF SANTA CLARA, SANTA CLARA CA 95053
FAIN, HASKELL, PHILOSOPHY DEPT, UNIV OF WISCONSIN, MADISON WI 53706
FAIR, FRANK, PHIL DEPT, SAM HOUSTON ST UNIV, HUNTSVILLE TX 77340
FAIRBANKS, MATTHEW, PHILOSOPHY DEPT, UNIV OF SCRANTON, SCRANTON PA 18510
FAIRCHILD, DAVID, PHIL DEPT, PURDUE UNIVERSITY, FORT WAYNE IN 46805
FALES, KEVIN, PHIL DEPT, INDIANA UNIVERSITY, BLOOMINGTON IN 47401
FALK, ARTHUR, PHIL DEPT, WEST MICHIGAN UNIV, KALAMAZOO MI 49001
FALK, CONRAD, PHILOSOPHY DEPT, CONCEPTIONS SEM COL, CONCEPTION MO 64433
FALK, W D, PHIL DEPT, UNIV OF N CAROLINA, CHAPEL HILL NC 27514
FALLER, THOMPSON M, PHILOSOPHY DEPT, UNIV OF PORTLAND, PORTLAND OR 97203
FALLICO, ARTURO B, PHIL DEPT, CALIFORNIA ST UNIV, SAN JOSE CA 95114
FALLON, JAMES C, PHIL DEPT, LA SALLE COLLEGE, PHILADELPHIA PA 19141
FALLON, JEROME, PHIL & REL DEPT, HILLSDALE COLLEGE, HILLSDALE MI 49242
FALLON, TIMOTHY P, PHIL DEPT, UNIV OF SANTA CLARA, SANTA CLARA CA 95053
FALVO, EUGENIE G, PHIL DEPT, UNIV OF ILLINOIS, URBANA IL 61801
FANDOZZI, PHILLIP, PHIL DEPT, UNIV OF MONTANA, MISSOULA MT 59801
FANN, K T, PHILOSOPHY DEPT, ATKINSON COLLEGE, DOWNSVIEW ONT   CAN
FARALDO, FERNANDO, PHIL DEPT, XAVIER UNIVERSITY, NEW ORLEANS LA 70125
FARBER, MARVIN, PHIL DEPT, ST UNIV OF NY, AMHERST NY 14226
FARGEN, BRUCE, PHIL DEPT, UNIV OF WEST ONTARIO, LONDON ONT   CAN
FARKAS, LIVIA, PHIL DEPT, HUNTER COLLEGE, NEW YORK NY 10021

FARLEY, BEN, PHIL & RELIG DIV, LEES-MCRAE COLLEGE, BANNER ELK NC 28604
FARMER, CHARLES J, RELIG & PHIL DEPT, LOUISBURG COLLEGE, LOUISBURG NC 27549
FARRAR, JOHN, PHIL DEPT, CONCORDIA COLLEGE, MOORHEAD MN 56560
FARRE, GEORGE L, PHIL DEPT, GEORGETOWN UNIV, WASHINGTON DC 20007
FARRELL, DANIEL M, PHILOSOPHY DEPT, OHIO STATE UNIV, COLUMBUS OH 43210
FARRELL, EDWARD P, HUMAN DIV, ST JOHN'S UNIV, STATEN ISLAND NY 10301
FARRELL, HOBERT, COMMITMENT STUD, JOHN WESLEY COL, OWOSSO MI 48867
FARREN, C, PHILOSOPHY DEPT, LOS ANGELES HBR COL, WILMINGTON CA 90744
FARRIS, S ALLEN, PHIL DEPT, INDIANA UNIVERSITY, BLOOMINGTON IN 47401
FARRIS, W S J, REL PHIL & ETHICS, KNOX COLLEGE, TORONTO 181 ONT   CAN
FAULCONER, JAMES, PHILOSOPHY DEPT, PENN STATE UNIV, UNIV PARK PA 16802
FAULKNER, CHARLES, PHIL DEPT, ST UNIV OF NY, STONY BROOK NY 11790
FAUROT, JEAN H, PHIL DEPT, CALIFORNIA ST UNIV, SACRAMENTO CA 95819
FAUS, W ARTHUR, PHIL DEPT, LYCOMING COLLEGE, WILLIAMSPORT PA 17701
FAUSER, PATRICIA, PHILOSOPHY DEPT, ILL BENEDICTINE COL, LISLE IL 60532
FAUTH, MAE, HUMAN DIV, CHARLES CO COM COL, LA PLATA MD 20646
FAVA, PAUL DOMINIC, ST CATHERINE COL, ST CATHERINE, KY 40061
FAY, ABBOTT, SOC STUD DIV, WESTERN ST COLLEGE, GUNNISON CO 81230
FAY, BENJAMIN U, PHIL DEPT, PROVIDENCE COLLEGE, PROVIDENCE RI 02919
FAY, BRIAN, PHILOSOPHY DEPT, WESLEYAN UNIV, MIDDLETOWN CT 06457
FAY, CHARLES, PHILOSOPHY DEPT, CAL STATE COL, DOMINGUEZ HLS CA 90747
FAY, CORNELIUS, PHIL DEPT, ST BONAVENTURE UNIV, ST BONVENTURE NY 14778
FAY, FLORENCE, PHIL DEPT, LA SALLE COLLEGE, PHILADELPHIA PA 19141
FAY, JOHN, PHIL DEPT, S ILLINOIS UNIV, CARBONDALE IL 62901
FAY, MARTHA, PHIL DEPT, BOSTON UNIVERSITY, BOSTON MA 02215
FEAGIN, SUSAN L, PHILOSOPHY DEPT, UNIV OF WISCONSIN, MADISON WI 53706
FEAGINS, CARROLL, PHILOSOPHY DEPT, GUILFORD COLLEGE, GREENSBORO NC 27410
FEAVER, J CLAYTON, PHILOSOPHY DEPT, UNIV OF OKLAHOMA, NORMAN OK 73069
FEDELE, FRANK, PHIL DEPT, INDIANA UNIVERSITY, BLOOMINGTON IN 47401
FEDER, HENRY, PHIL DEPT, UNIV OF WEST ONTARIO, LONDON ONT   CAN
FEDERICI, SYLVIA, PHIL DEPT, ST UNIV OF NY, STONY BROOK NY 11790
FEDORYKA, DAMIAN, PHILOSOPHY DEPT, UNIV OF RHODE ISLAND, KINGSTON RI 02881
FEE, DIANA, PHILOSOPHY DEPT, COL OF NOTRE DAME, BELMONT CA 94002
FEEHAN, STEPHEN S, PHIL DEPT, IMMAC CONCEPTION SEM, DARLINGTON NJ 07430
FEEHAN, THOMAS, PHIL DEPT, COL OF HOLY CROSS, WORCESTER MA 01610
FEENBERG, ANDREW L, PHIL DEPT, CALIFORNIA ST UNIV, SAN DIEGO CA 92115
FEEZELL, LARRY, PHILOSOPHY DEPT, UNIV OF OKLAHOMA, NORMAN OK 73069
FEEZELL, RANDOLPH, PHILOSOPHY DEPT, UNIV OF OKLAHOMA, NORMAN OK 73069
FEFERMAN, SOLOMON, PHIL DEPT, STANFORD UNIVERSITY, STANFORD CA 94305
FEFFERMAN, MARK, PHIL DEPT, UNIV OF CALIFORNIA, LOS ANGELES CA 90024
FEHLER, J RICHARD, PHIL DEPT, COLUMBIA UNIVERSITY, NEW YORK NY 10027
FEIBLEMAN, JAMES K, PHIL DEPT, TULANE UNIVERSITY, NEW ORLEANS LA 70118
FEIEREISEN, JACK, ARTS & PHIL DEPT, NICOLET COLLEGE, RHINELANDER WI 54501
FEIGL, HERBERT, PHIL DEPT, UNIV OF MINNESOTA, MINNEAPOLIS MN 55455
FEINBERG, JOEL, PHIL DEPT, ROCKEFELLER UNIV, NEW YORK NY 10021
FEINGOLD, ELLIOT, SOC SCI DEPT, PACE COLLEGE, NEW YORK NY 10038
FEINSTEIN, SHERRYL, PHIL DEPT, BROOKLYN COLLEGE, BROOKLYN NY 11210
FEISS, HUGH, PHIL DEPT, MT ANGEL SEMINARY, ST BENEDICT OR 97373
FELCH, WILLIAM E, PHIL DEPT, UNIV OF WISCONSIN, LA CROSSE WI 54601
FELD, M, PHIL DEPT, UNIV OF MANITOBA, WINNIPEG 19 MAN   CAN
FELDMAN, FRED, PHILOSOPHY DEPT, UNIV OF MASS, AMHERST MA 01002
FELDMAN, RICHARD J, PHIL DEPT, UNIV OF WISCONSIN, STEVENS POINT WI 54481
FELDMAN, SEYMOUR, PHILOSOPHY DEPT, RUTGERS UNIV, NEW BRUNSWICK NJ 08903
FELDSTEIN, LEONARD, PHIL DEPT, FORDHAM UNIVERSITY, BRONX NY 10458
FELEPPA, ROBERT, PHIL DEPT, WASHINGTON UNIV, ST LOUIS MO 63130
FELKENES, SANDRA W, HUMAN DEPT, MILES COLLEGE, BIRMINGHAM AL 35208
FELL, ALBERT P, PHILOSOPHY DEPT, QUEEN'S UNIVERSITY, KINGSTON ONT   CAN
FELL, GILBERT S, PSYCH & PHIL, MONMOUTH COLLEGE, W LONG BRANCH NJ 07764
FELL, JOSEPH P, PHIL DEPT, BUCKNELL UNIVERSITY, LEWISBURG PA 17837
FELLOWS, WARD, COLLEGE OF SAN MATEO, SAN MATEO, CA 94402
FELS, LEONARD, PHIL DEPT, CALIFORNIA ST UNIV, LONG BEACH CA 90840
FELT, JAMES W, PHIL DEPT, UNIV OF SANTA CLARA, SANTA CLARA CA 95053
FELTZ, MERLIN, PHIL DEPT, DEPAUL UNIVERSITY, CHICAGO IL 60604
FENDRICH, ROGER P, PHILOSOPHY DEPT, BELOIT COLLEGE, BELOIT WI 53511

FENILI, J ROBERT, PHIL & THEOL DIV, HOLY REDEEMER COL, WATERFORD WI 53185
FENSKE, ALBERT W, PHIL DEPT, BEMIDJI STATE COL, BEMIDJI MN 56601
FENTON, NORMAN, PHIL DEPT, UNIVERSITY OF DALLAS, IRVING TX 75062
FEREJOHN, MICHAEL, PHIL DEPT, UNIV OF CALIFORNIA, IRVINE CA 92664
FERGUSON, ANN, PHILOSOPHY DEPT, UNIV OF MASS, AMHERST MA 01002
FERGUSON, EDWARD E, SOC SCI DEPT, HARRIS TEACHERS COL, ST LOUIS MO 63103
FERGUSON, JANE F, PHILOSOPHY DEPT, GEORGIAN COURT COL, LAKEWOOD NJ 08701
FERM, VERGILIUS, ASHLAND COLLEGE, ASHLAND, OH 44805
FERNANDEZ, MADELINA, PHIL DEPT, DEPAUL UNIVERSITY, CHICAGO IL 60604
FERNELIUS, CARL, ENG DEPT, KIRTLAND COM COL, ROSCOMMON MI 48653
FERRARA, FRANK D, PHIL DEPT, S ILLINOIS UNIV, CARBONDALE IL 62901
FERRARA, VINCENT, PHIL DEPT, INDIANA UNIV OF PENN, INDIANA PA 15701
FERRARI, LEO, PHIL DEPT, SAINT THOMAS UNIV, FREDERICTON N B   CAN
FERRATER-MORA, J, BRYN MAWR COLLEGE, BRYN MAWR, PA 19010
FERRE, FREDERICK, PHILOSOPHY DEPT, DICKINSON COLLEGE, CARLISLE PA 17013
FERREE, ROBERT F, BACONE COLLEGE, BACONE, OK 74420
FERRELL, DONALD R, PHIL & RELIG DEPT, DOANE COLLEGE, CRETE NE 68333
FESSLER, KATHRYN, PHIL DEPT, UNIV OF CINCINNATI, CINCINNATI OH 45221
FETHE, CHARLES B, PHIL DEPT, NEWARK STATE COL, UNION NJ 07083
FETLER, TIMOTHY, PHIL DEPT, SN BARBARA CY COL, SANTA BARBARA CA 93105
FETTERS, ROSS, SOC SCI DEPT, SHASTA COLLEGE, REDDING CA 96001
FETZER, JAMES H, PHIL DEPT, UNIV OF KENTUCKY, LEXINGTON KY 40506
FEY, WILLIAM, PHILOSOPHY DEPT, ST FIDELIS COLLEGE, HERMAN PA 16039
FEYERABEND, PAUL K, PHIL DEPT, UNIV OF CALIFORNIA, BERKELEY CA 94720
FIALA, DORIT, HUMAN DEPT, UNIV OF PUERTO RICO, MAYAGUEZ PR 00708
FICARRA, FRANK T, PHILOSOPHY DEPT, CALIFORNIA ST UNIV, CHICO CA 95926
FICCA, S CHARLES, PSYCH & PHIL, MONMOUTH COLLEGE, W LONG BRANCH NJ 07764
FIDALGO, MANUEL, PHIL DEPT, ST VIN DE PAUL SEM, BOYNTON FL 33435
FIELD, EDWIN, AMERICAN RIVER COL, SACRAMENTO, CA 95841
FIELD, HARTRY, PHIL DEPT, PRINCETON UNIVERSITY, PRINCETON NJ 08540
FIELD, JEFFREY, PHIL DEPT, UNIV OF MICHIGAN, ANN ARBOR MI 48104
FIELDEN, JOHN, SOC SCI DEPT, PHOENIX COLLEGE, PHOENIX AZ 85013
FIELDER, JOHN H, PHILOSOPHY DEPT, VILLANOVA UNIV, VILLANOVA PA 19085
FIGGE, FREDERICK W, SOC SCI DEPT, SOUTHEASTERN COM COL, KEOKUK IA 52632
FIGURSKI, LESHAK, PHIL & THEOL DEPT, FELICIAN COLLEGE, LODI NJ 07644
FILION, GERARD, PHIL DEPT, COL BOIS-DE-BOULOGNE, MONTREAL QUE   CAN
FILION, MAURICE, PHIL DEPT, COL VIEUX-MONTREAL, MONTREAL QUE   CAN
FINCH, HENRY LE ROY, PHIL DEPT, HUNTER COLLEGE, NEW YORK NY 10021
FINDLAY, JOHN, PHIL DEPT, BOSTON UNIVERSITY, BOSTON MA 02215
FINE, ARTHUR I, PHIL DEPT, UNIV OF ILLINOIS, CHICAGO IL 60680
FINE, CHARLES, PHIL DEPT, PURDUE UNIVERSITY, FORT WAYNE IN 46805
FINGARETTE, HERBERT, PHIL DEPT, UNIV OF CALIFORNIA, SANTA BARBARA CA 93106
FINK, JAMES R, PHILOSOPHY DEPT, SURRY COM COL, DOBSON NC 27017
FINK, PAUL F, SOC SCI DEPT, MOORPARK COLLEGE, MOORPARK CA 93021
FINK, RYCHARD, ARTS & HUMAN DEPT, SOMERSET COUNTY COL, SOMERVILLE NJ 08876
FINK, THOMAS, PHIL DEPT, UNIVERSITY OF IOWA, IOWA CITY IA 52240
FINKENBINDER, MICHAEL, PHIL DEPT, CALIFORNIA ST UNIV, LOS ANGELES CA 90032
FINLAY, LINDA, PHIL & REL DEPT, ITHACA COLLEGE, ITHACA NY 14850
FINN, D R, PHILOSOPHY DEPT, SIMON FRASER UNIV, BURNABY 2 B C   CAN
FINN, DANIELLE J, PHIL DEPT, COL VIEUX-MONTREAL, MONTREAL QUE   CAN
FINN, J, HUMAN DEPT, WESTMORELAND COM COL, YOUNGWOOD PA 15697
FINN, MARY LEROY, PHIL DEPT, NOTRE DAME COLLEGE, SOUTH EUCLID OH 44121
FINOCCHIARO, MAURICE A, PHIL DEPT, UNIV OF NEVADA, LAS VEGAS NV 89154
FINSEN, LAWRENCE, PHIL DEPT, ST UNIV OF NY, AMHERST NY 14226
FIORE, WILLIAM, PHIL DEPT, ST UNIV CF NY, STONY BROOK NY 11790
FIRTH, J J F, PHILOSOPHY DEPT, ST JOSEPH'S COLLEGE, EDMONTON 61 ALB   CAN
FIRTH, RODERICK, PHIL DEPT, HARVARD UNIVERSITY, CAMBRIDGE MA 02138
FISCELLA, JOAN, MARY MANSE COLLEGE, TOLEDO, OH 43620
FISCH, MAX H, PHIL DEPT, UNIV OF ILLINOIS, URBANA IL 61801
FISCHER, GILBERT R, PHIL DEPT, PURDUE UNIVERSITY, HAMMOND IN 46323
FISCHER, JAN B, HUMAN DIV, GLOUCESTER CO COL, SEWELL NJ 08080
FISCHER, KURT R, PHIL DEPT, MILLERSVILLE ST COL, MILLERSVILLE PA 17551
FISCHER, THOMAS GRIER, PHILOSOPHY DEPT, UNIV OF TEXAS, AUSTIN TX 78712
FISCHLER, PAUL, SAGE SCHOOL, CORNELL UNIVERSITY, ITHACA NY 14850

FISCHMANN, RUEL, PHIL DEPT, ST CLOUD ST COL, ST CLOUD MN 56301
FISER, KAREN, PHIL DEPT, SAINT OLAF COLLEGE, NORTHFIELD MN 55057
FISHER, GARY, PHIL DEPT, INDIANA-PURDUE UNIV, INDIANAPOLIS IN 46202
FISHER, JAMES V, PHIL DEPT, BENTLEY COLLEGE, WALTHAM MA 02154
FISHER, JOHN, PHIL DEPT, UNIV OF COLORADO, BOULDER CO 80302
FISHER, JOHN, PHIL DEPT, TEMPLE UNIVERSITY, PHILADELPHIA PA 19122
FISHMAN, STEPHEN M, PHIL DEPT, UNIV OF N CAROLINA, CHARLOTTE NC 28213
FISK, MILTON T, PHIL DEPT, INDIANA UNIVERSITY, BLOOMINGTON IN 47401
FITCH, FREDERIC, PHIL DEPT, YALE UNIVERSITY, NEW HAVEN CT 06520
FITCH, GREGORY, PHILOSOPHY DEPT, UNIV OF MASS, AMHERST MA 01002
FITTS, M PAULINE, PHIL DEPT, NIAGARA UNIVERSITY, NIAGARA UNIV NY 14109
FITZ, THOMAS R, COM SCI DEPT, UNIV OF WISCONSIN, RICE LAKE WI 54868
FITZGERALD, D J, PHIL DEPT, UNIV OF SN FRANCISCO, SAN FRANCISCO CA 94117
FITZGERALD, EUGENE J, PHIL DEPT, LA SALLE COLLEGE, PHILADELPHIA PA 19141
FITZGERALD, JANET, PHIL DEPT, MOLLOY COLLEGE, ROCKVILLE NY 11570
FITZGERALD, JOHN J, PHIL DEPT, SE MASS UNIV, N DARTMOUTH MA 02747
FITZGERALD, PAUL, PHIL DEPT, TEMPLE UNIVERSITY, PHILADELPHIA PA 19122
FITZGERALD, W C, PHIL & REL DEPT, N CAROLINA ST UNIV, RALEIGH NC 27607
FITZGIBBON, JOHN F, PHIL DEPT, ST AMBROSE COLLEGE, DAVENPORT IA 52803
FITZGIBBON, WILLIAM E, PHIL & THEOL, DIVINE WORD COLLEGE, EPWORTH IA 52045
FITZGIBBONS, ROBERT, PHIL DEPT, BRIDGEWATER ST COL, BRIDGEWATER MA 02324
FITZPATRICK, NOEL A, PHIL DEPT, SIENA COLLEGE, LOUDONVILLE NY 12211
FIVES, CARL J, PHIL DEPT, MT SAINT MARY'S COL, EMMITSBURG MD 21727
FLAGE, DANIEL, PHIL DEPT, UNIVERSITY OF IOWA, IOWA CITY IA 52240
FLANAGAN, JOSEPH, PHIL DEPT, BOSTON COLLEGE, CHESTNUT HILL MA 02167
FLANAGAN, OWEN, PHIL DEPT, BOSTON UNIVERSITY, BOSTON MA 02215
FLATT, CHARLES, PHIL & REL DEPT, COL OF THE DESERT, PALM DESERT CA 92260
FLAY, JOSEPH C, PHILOSOPHY DEPT, PENN STATE UNIV, UNIV PARK PA 16802
FLECKENSTEIN, M, PHIL DEPT, NIAGARA UNIVERSITY, NIAGARA UNIV NY 14109
FLEETWOOD, HUGH, PHIL DEPT, W WASHINGTON ST COL, BELLINGHAM WA 98225
FLEMING, DERWOOD, PHIL DEPT, SYRACUSE UNIVERSITY, SYRACUSE NY 13210
FLEMING, E, PHIL DEPT, UNIV OF MANITOBA, WINNIPEG 19 MAN   CAN
FLEMING, LEO, PHILOSOPHY DEPT, UNIV OF SCRANTON, SCRANTON PA 18510
FLEMING, NOEL, PHIL DEPT, UNIV OF CALIFORNIA, SANTA BARBARA CA 93106
FLEMING, PATRICIA A, PHIL DEPT, WASHINGTON UNIV, ST LOUIS MO 63130
FLEMING, ROBIN, PHIL DEPT, UNIV OF VIRGINIA, CHARLOTTESVL VA 22903
FLEMING, WILLIAM, LIT & LANG DEPT, DICKINSON STATE COL, DICKINSON ND 58601
FLEMMING, ARTHUR, PHIL DEPT, UNIV OF CALIFORNIA, LOS ANGELES CA 90024
FLESCHE, DAVID E, PHIL DEPT, BOSTON COLLEGE, CHESTNUT HILL MA 02167
FLETCHER, JAMES, HUMAN DEPT, GEORGE MASON UNIV, FAIRFAX VA 22030
FLEURY, GUY, PHIL DEPT, COL DE VALLEYFIELD, VALLEYFIELD QUE   CAN
FLICK, ROBERT, HUMAN DEPT, FLORIDA TECH UNIV, ORLANDO FL 32816
FLIPPEN, D, PHILOSOPHY DEPT, UNIV OF TORONTO, TORONTO ONT   CAN
FLOCSTROM, JOHN H, PHIL DEPT, UNIV OF LOUISVILLE, LOUISVILLE KY 40208
FLOOD, DAMIEN, REL STUD & PHIL, SPRINGFIELD COL, SPRINGFIELD IL 62702
FLOOD, PATRICK F, PHILOSOPHY DEPT, UNIV OF WINDSOR, WINDSOR ONT   CAN
FLORENTINE, THOMAS, SOC SCI DEPT, MT ALOYSIUS JR COL, CRESSON PA 16630
FLORES, ALBERT W, PHIL DEPT, RENSSELAER POLYTECH, TROY NY 12181
FLOWER, ELIZABETH, PHILOSOPHY DEPT, UNIV OF PENN, PHILADELPHIA PA 19174
FLOWER, ROBERT, PHIL DEPT, LE MOYNE COLLEGE, SYRACUSE NY 13214
FLOWERS, PETER, PHIL DEPT, BOSTON UNIVERSITY, BOSTON MA 02215
FLYNN, BERNARD C, EMPIRE ST COL, SARATOGA SPGS, NY 12866
FLYNN, FREDERICK E, PHIL DEPT, COL OF ST THOMAS, ST PAUL MN 55105
FLYNN, JOHN D, PHILOSOPHY DEPT, RUTGERS UNIV, NEW BRUNSWICK NJ 08903
FLYNN, THOMAS J, PHIL & RELIG, UNIV OF MISSISSIPPI, UNIVERSITY MS 38677
FLYNN, THOMAS R, PHIL SCH, CATH UNIV OF AMER, WASHINGTON DC 20017
FLYNN, THOMAS R, PHIL DEPT, THE AMERICAN UNIV, WASHINGTON DC 20016
FOA, PAMELA, PHIL DEPT, UNIV OF PITTSBURGH, PITTSBURGH PA 15260
FOARD, LAWRENCE C, PHIL DEPT, WESTFIELD STATE COL, WESTFIELD MA 01085
FOCHTMAN, VINCENT, PHIL DEPT, QUINCY COLLEGE, QUINCY IL 62301
FODOR, JERRY A, PHIL DEPT, MASS INST TECH, CAMBRIDGE MA 02139
FOGELIN, ROBERT, PHIL DEPT, YALE UNIVERSITY, NEW HAVEN CT 06520
FOGG, WALTER L, PHIL & REL DEPT, NORTHEASTERN UNIV, BOSTON MA 02115
FOHR, SAMUEL D, PHIL DEPT, UNIV OF PITTSBURGH, BRADFORD PA 16701

FOLEY, CORNELIUS, PHIL & REL STUD, COL OF GREAT FALLS, GREAT FALLS MT 59401
FOLEY, DANIEL P, PHILOSOPHY DEPT, XAVIER UNIVERSITY, CINCINNATI OH 45207
FOLEY, HELEN, PHIL & THEOL DEPT, MARILLAC COLLEGE, ST LOUIS MO 63121
FOLEY, JOHN P, PHIL DEPT, ST CHAS BORROMEO SEM, PHILADELPHIA PA 19151
FOLEY, LEO A, PHIL SCH, CATH UNIV OF AMER, WASHINGTON DC 20017
FOLEY, RICHARD, PHILOSOPHY DEPT, BROWN UNIVERSITY, PROVIDENCE RI 02912
FOLLESDAL, DAGFINN, PHIL DEPT, STANFORD UNIVERSITY, STANFORD CA 94305
FOLSE, HENRY J, PHIL DEPT, UNIV OF KENTUCKY, LEXINGTON KY 40506
FONTANA, THOMAS, PHIL DEPT, BROOKLYN COLLEGE, BROOKLYN NY 11210
FONTINELL, EUGENE, PHILOSOPHY DEPT, QUEENS COLLEGE, FLUSHING NY 11367
FOOT, PHILIPPA, PHIL DEPT, UNIV OF CALIFORNIA, LOS ANGELES CA 90024
FOOTE, CHARLES, PHIL DEPT, BOWLING GREEN UNIV, BOWLING GREEN OH 43403
FOOTE, EDWARD T, PHIL DEPT, ST LOUIS UNIVERSITY, ST LOUIS MO 63103
FORCE, JAMES E, PHIL DEPT, WASHINGTON UNIV, ST LOUIS MO 63130
FORD, CLIFTON, REL STUD DIV, OAKLAND CITY COLLEGE, OAKLAND CITY IN 47660
FORD, EDWARD, PHILOSOPHY DEPT, SOUTHWESTERN COL, CHULA VISTA CA 92010
FORD, J A, PHILOSOPHY DEPT, LAURENTIAN UNIV, SUDBURY ONT CAN
FORD, JOHN H, PHIL DEPT, UNIV OF LOUISVILLE, LOUISVILLE KY 40208
FORD, LEWIS S, PHILOSOPHY DEPT, PENN STATE UNIV, UNIV PARK PA 16802
FORD, ROBERT, SOC SCI DEPT, SAN DIEGO COM CY COL, SAN DIEGO CA 92101
FORD, THOMAS, PHIL DEPT, UNIV OF CALIFORNIA, IRVINE CA 92664
FORDERHASE, DUANE, PHIL DEPT, AUSTIN PEAY ST UNIV, CLARKSVILLE TN 37040
FOREE, ROBERT L, SOC SCI DEPT, INDEPENDENCE COM COL, INDEPENDENCE KS 67301
FOREMAN, ROBERT A, PHIL DEPT, CALIFORNIA ST UNIV, SACRAMENTO CA 95819
FORESTER, TIMOTHY, SOC SCI DIV, FLATHEAD VLY COM COL, KALISPELL MT 59901
FORGET, GILLES, PHIL DEPT, COL VIEUX-MONTREAL, MONTREAL QUE CAN
FORGET, MARIO, PHIL DEPT, COL TROIS-RIVIERES, 3 RIVIERES QUE CAN
FORGIE, J WILLIAM, PHIL DEPT, UNIV CF CALIFORNIA, SANTA BARBARA CA 93106
FORGUSON, L W, PHILOSOPHY DEPT, UNIV OF TORONTO, TORONTO ONT CAN
FORRESTER, JAMES, PHILOSOPHY DEPT, UNIV OF WYOMING, LARAMIE WY 82071
FORSHEY, GERALD, COMMUNIC ARTS DEPT, MALCOLM X COM COL, CHICAGO IL 60612
FORTH, DAVID, PHIL DEPT, E STROUDSBURG ST COL, E STROUDSBURG PA 18301
FORTIER, N, PHILOSOPHY DEPT, LAURENTIAN UNIV, SUDBURY ONT CAN
FORTIER, THEODORE L, PHIL DEPT, ASSUMPTION COLLEGE, WORCESTER MA 01609
FOSELA, MARIANO, PHIL & RELIG, INTERAMER UNIVERSITY, PONCE PR 00731
FOSS, JEFFREY, PHIL DEPT, UNIV OF WEST ONTARIO, LONDON ONT CAN
FOST, FREDERIC F, PHILOSOPHY DEPT, LINFIELD COLLEGE, MCMINNVILLE OR 97128
FOSTER JR, LEWIS A, PHIL DEPT, COL WILLIAM & MARY, WILLIAMSBURG VA 23185
FOSTER, A DURWOOD, SYST & PHIL, GRADUATE THEOL UNION, BERKELEY CA 94709
FOSTER, HAGUE D, PHILOSOPHY DEPT, CALIFORNIA ST UNIV, FRESNO CA 93740
FOSTER, JAMES, WILBERFORCE UNIV, WILBERFORCE, OH 45384
FOSTER, LAWRENCE, PHILOSOPHY DEPT, UNIV OF MASS, AMHERST MA 01002
FOSTER, MARGUERITE, PHILOSOPHY DEPT, DE ANZA COLLEGE, CUPERTINO CA 95014
FOSTER, ROSS A, PHIL & RELIG, GROVE CITY COLLEGE, GROVE CITY PA 16127
FOSTER, THOMAS, PHIL DEPT, BALL ST UNIVERSITY, MUNCIE IN 47306
FOTION, NICHOLAS, PHIL DEPT, EMORY UNIVERSITY, ATLANTA GA 30322
FOULK, GARY J, PHIL DEPT, INDIANA ST UNIV, TERRE HAUTE IN 47809
FOURNIER, JEAN-LOUIS, COLLEGE D'AHUNTSIC, MONTREAL, QUE CAN
FOURNIER, MARYLISE, COLLEGE D'AHUNTSIC, MONTREAL, QUE CAN
FOURNIER, S, PHIL FACULTY, UNIV OF OTTAWA, OTTAWA ONT CAN
FOUST, CONALD, PHIL PROGRAM, SANGAMON ST UNIV, SPRINGFIELD IL 62703
FOUTZ, KENNETH, CENTRAL WESLEYAN COL, CENTRAL, SC 29630
FOWKES, WILLIAM, PHIL DEPT, NORTHWESTERN UNIV, EVANSTON IL 60201
FOWLER, BILL G, PHIL & RELIG DEPT, ALDERSON BROADDUS COL, PHILIPPI WV 26416
FOWLER, J M, HUMAN DEPT, DYERSBURG ST COM COL, DYERSBURG TN 38024
FOWLER, JOHN S, PHIL DEPT, N ILLINOIS UNIV, DEKALB IL 60115
FOX, JOHN H, SOC SCI DEPT, SEATTLE CEN COM COL, SEATTLE WA 98122
FOX, JOSEF, PHIL & RELIG, UNIV OF NORTH IOWA, CEDAR FALLS IA 50613
FOX, M A, PHILOSOPHY DEPT, QUEEN'S UNIVERSITY, KINGSTON ONT CAN
FOX, MARIE C, PHIL DEPT, CALIFORNIA ST UNIV, SAN JOSE CA 95114
FOX, MARVIN, PHILOSOPHY DEPT, OHIO STATE UNIV, COLUMBUS OH 43210
FOX, RICHARD M, PHILOSOPHY DEPT, CLEVELAND ST UNIV, CLEVELAND OH 44115
FOX, ROBERT J, PHIL & REL STUD, COL OF GREAT FALLS, GREAT FALLS MT 59401
FOY, J, PHILOSOPHY DEPT, MT ST VINCENT UNIV, HALIFAX N S CAN

FOY, LINDA, PHIL DEPT, HARVARD UNIVERSITY, CAMBRIDGE MA 02138
FRAENKEL-CONRAT, JANE, EDUC & SCI DEPT, UNIV OF MAINE, MACHIAS ME 04654
FRAME, JOHN M, THEOL STUD FIELD, WESTMINSTER THEOL, PHILADELPHIA PA 19118
FRANCIS, RICHARD P, PHIL DEPT, UNIV OF COLORADO, COLORADO SPGS CO 80907
FRANCK, THOMAS, PHIL DEPT, COL RIVIERE DU LOUP, RIVIERE LOUP QUE   CAN
FRANCOEUR, ROBERT A, PHILOSOPHY DEPT, WALSH COLLEGE, CANTON OH 44720
FRANCOIS, GEORGES, PHILOSOPHY DEPT, UNIV DE MONCTON, MONCTON N B   CAN
FRANK, JAMES P, PHIL DEPT, UNIV OF COLORADO, BOULDER CO 80302
FRANK, KARL D, PHILOSOPHY DEPT, RUTGERS UNIV, NEW BRUNSWICK NJ 08903
FRANK, ROBERT F, HUMAN DEPT, MCHENRY CTY COLLEGE, CRYSTAL LAKE IL 60014
FRANK, ROBERT, AMERICAN RIVER COL, SACRAMENTO, CA 95841
FRANK, WILLIAM A, PHIL SCH, CATH UNIV OF AMER, WASHINGTON DC 20017
FRANK, WILLIAM F, PHIL DEPT, OREGON STATE UNIV, CORVALLIS OR 97331
FRANK, WILLIAM, ENG & PHIL DEPT, LONGWOOD COLLEGE, FARMVILLE VA 23901
FRANKE, J PAUL, PHILOSOPHY DEPT, BIRMINGHAM S COLLEGE, BIRMINGHAM AL 35204
FRANKEL, CHARLES, PHIL DEPT, COLUMBIA UNIVERSITY, NEW YORK NY 10027
FRANKEL, HENRY, PHIL DEPT, UNIV OF MISSOURI, KANSAS CITY MO 64110
FRANKENA, WILLIAM K, PHIL DEPT, UNIV OF MICHIGAN, ANN ARBOR MI 48104
FRANKFURT, HARRY, PHIL DEPT, ROCKEFELLER UNIV, NEW YORK NY 10021
FRANKLIN, MITCHELL, PHIL DEPT, ST UNIV OF NY, AMHERST NY 14226
FRANKLIN, STEPHEN T, PHIL DEPT, WM RAINEY HARPER COL, PALATINE IL 60067
FRANKS, DEAN K, PHIL DEPT, S ILLINOIS UNIV, CARBONDALE IL 62901
FRANKS, JOAN, PHILOSOPHY DEPT, OHIO DOMINICAN COL, COLUMBUS OH 43219
FRANKS, THOMAS, HIST & PHIL DEPT, E MICHIGAN UNIV, YPSILANTI MI 48197
FRANQUIZ, JOSE, PHILOSOPHY DEPT, W VA WESLEYAN COL, BUCKHANNON WV 26201
FRANZ, HAROLD J, HUMANITIES DIV, UNIV OF S CAROLINA, AIKEN SC 29801
FRANZ, LAWRENCE, PHILOSOPHY DEPT, OHIO STATE UNIV, COLUMBUS OH 43210
FRANZWA, GREGG, PHIL DEPT, UNIV OF ROCHESTER, ROCHESTER NY 14627
FRAPPIER, D, PHILOSOPHY DEPT, COLLEGE DE HULL, HULL QUE   CAN
FRAZER, CATHERINE, PHIL DEPT, UNIV CF DENVER, DENVER CO 80210
FRAZIER, A M, PHIL & RELIG DEPT, HOLLINS COLLEGE, HOLLINS COL VA 24020
FREASIER SR, BARNEY, PHIL & RELIG, VA COMMONWEALTH UNIV, RICHMOND VA 23220
FREDE, MICHAEL J, PHIL DEPT, UNIV OF CALIFORNIA, BERKELEY CA 94720
FREDERICK, JOE B, ALTUS JUNIOR COLLEGE, ALTUS, OK 73521
FREDERICK, NORRIS, PHIL & REL DEPT, UNIV OF GEORGIA, ATHENS GA 30602
FREDETTE, RAYMOND, COLLEGE D'AHUNTSIC, MONTREAL, QUE   CAN
FREED, R BRUCE, PHIL DEPT, UNIV OF WEST ONTARIO, LONDON ONT   CAN
FREEMAN, ALLEN J, PHIL & REL DEPT, MIDDLE GEORGIA COL, COCHRAN GA 31014
FREEMAN, DAVID H, PHILOSOPHY DEPT, UNIV OF RHODE ISLAND, KINGSTON RI 02881
FREEMAN, EUGENE, PHIL DEPT, CALIFORNIA ST UNIV, SAN JOSE CA 95114
FREEMAN, HILARY, PHIL DEPT, COL OF ST CATHERINE, SAINT PAUL MN 55105
FREEMAN, JOSEPH, PHIL DEPT, ROCKHURST COLLEGE, KANSAS CITY MO 64110
FREEMAN, KENNETH P, PHIL DEPT, COLORADO ST UNIV, FORT COLLINS CO 80521
FREEMAN, RODERICK, PHIL DEPT, WAYNE STATE UNIV, DETROIT MI 48202
FREIRE, ANTONIO, PHIL DEPT, COL FRANCOIS-X-GARN, QUEBEC CITY QUE   CAN
FRENCH, LOUISE, PHIL DEPT, MUNDELEIN COLLEGE, CHICAGO IL 60626
FRENCH, MERTON B, PHILOSOPHY DEPT, WASHBURN UNIVERSITY, TOPEKA KS 66621
FRENCH, PETER, HUMAN DIV, UNIV OF MINNESOTA, MORRIS MN 56267
FRENCH, STANLEY G, PHIL DEPT, GEORGE WILLIAMS UNIV, MONTREAL 107 QUE   CAN
FREPPERT, LUCAN, PHIL DEPT, QUINCY COLLEGE, QUINCY IL 62301
FREUND, E HANS, PHILOSOPHY DEPT, PENN STATE UNIV, UNIV PARK PA 16802
FRIED, DENNIS, PHILOSOPHY DEPT, UNIV OF MASS, AMHERST MA 01002
FRIED, MARLENE G, PHILOSOPHY DEPT, DARTMOUTH COLLEGE, HANOVER NH 03755
FRIEDLANDER, BRUCE, PHILOSOPHY DEPT, DUQUESNE UNIV, PITTSBURGH PA 15219
FRIEDMAN, HOWARD R, PHIL DEPT, UNIV OF CONNECTICUT, WATERBURY CT 06710
FRIEDMAN, JAMES W, PHIL DEPT, UNIV CF SANTA CLARA, SANTA CLARA CA 95053
FRIEDMAN, JOEL, PHIL DEPT, UNIV OF CALIFORNIA, DAVIS CA 95616
FRIEDMAN, KENNETH S, PHIL DEPT, COL AT OSWEGO, OSWEGO NY 13126
FRIEDMAN, MARILYN, PHILOSOPHY DEPT, DENISON UNIV, GRANVILLE OH 43023
FRIEDMAN, MOSHEH, JEWISH PHIL DEPT, RABBINICAL ACADEMY, BROOKLYN NY 11230
FRIEDMAN, PHIL DEPT, HARVARD UNIVERSITY, CAMBRIDGE, MA 02138
FRIEDMAN, WILLIAM, PHIL & RELIG, VA COMMONWEALTH UNIV, RICHMOND VA 23220
FRIEL, JAMES, ENG DEPT, AGR & TECH COLLEGE, FARMINGDALE NY 11735
FRIES, PAUL, SYST THEOL DEPT, NEW BRUNSWICK SEM, NEW BRUNSWICK NJ 08901

FRIESS, HORACE L, PHIL DEPT, COLUMBIA UNIVERSITY, NEW YORK NY 10027
FRINGS, MANFRED, PHIL DEPT, DEPAUL UNIVERSITY, CHICAGO IL 60604
FRIQUEGNON, MARIE L, PHILOSOPHY DEPT, PATERSON COL OF NJ, WAYNE NJ 07470
FRITH JR, HERBERT A, PHILOSOPHY DEPT, MANATEE JUN COL, BRADENTON FL 33505
FRITZ JR, C A, PHIL DEPT, UNIV OF CONNECTICUT, STORRS CT 06268
FRITZ, A D, PHIL DEPT, UNIV OF CONNECTICUT, STORRS CT 06268
FROMM, GEORG, PHIL DEPT, UNIV OF PUERTO RICO, RIO PIEDRAS PR 00931
FRONDIZI, RISIERI, PHIL DEPT, S ILLINOIS UNIV, CARBONDALE IL 62901
FRONTCZAK, DEIRDRE, PHIL DEPT, BOSTON COLLEGE, CHESTNUT HILL MA 02167
FROTHINGHAM, R, PHIL & RELIG DEPT, UNIV OF ARKANSAS, LITTLE ROCK AR 72204
FRY, GEORGE F, WEST NEVADA COM COL, CARSON CITY, NV 89701
FRY, MARION G, PHIL DEPT, TRENT UNIVERSITY, PETERBOROUGH ONT   CAN
FRY, THOMAS, PHILOSOPHY DEPT, COLLEGE OF WOOSTER, WOOSTER OH 44691
FRY, VIRGIL, REL STUD DIV, OAKLAND CITY COLLEGE, OAKLAND CITY IN 47660
FRYE, MARILYN, PHIL DEPT, UNIV OF PITTSBURGH, PITTSBURGH PA 15260
FRYE, ROBERT E, PHIL DEPT, INDIANA-PURDUE UNIV, INDIANAPOLIS IN 46202
FRYE, ROYAL M, PHILOSOPHY DEPT, BELKNAP COLLEGE, CENTER HARBOR NH 03226
FUCHS, ALAN E, PHIL DEPT, COL WILLIAM & MARY, WILLIAMSBURG VA 23185
FUCHS, JACK, PHIL DEPT, BOSTON UNIVERSITY, BOSTON MA 02215
FUCHS, JOANN, PHIL & REL DEPT, TOWSON STATE COL, BALTIMORE MD 21204
FUCHS, WALT, PHIL & REL DEPT, TOWSON STATE COL, BALTIMORE MD 21204
FUEHRER, MARK, PHIL DEPT, AUGSBURG COLLEGE, MINNEAPOLIS MN 55404
FUIR, GEORG R, PHIL DEPT, BOSTON COLLEGE, CHESTNUT HILL MA 02167
FUKSA, MICHAEL, PHIL DEPT, SLIPPERY ROCK ST COL, SLIPPERY ROCK PA 16057
FULLER, GARY, PHIL DEPT, UNIV OF FLORIDA, GAINESVILLE FL 32611
FULLINWIDER, ROBERT K, PHIL DEPT, ST UNIV OF NY, ALBANY NY 12203
FULMER, GILBERT, ENG & PHIL DEPT, SW TEXAS ST UNIV, SAN MARCOS TX 78666
FULTON III, CHARLES, HUMANITIES DEPT, JOHN A GUPTON COL, NASHVILLE TN 37920
FULTON, J S, PHILOSOPHY DEPT, RICE UNIVERSITY, HOUSTON TX 77001
FULTON, JAMES A, PHIL DEPT, WICHITA ST UNIV, WICHITA KS 67208
FULTON, ROBERT B, PARSONS COLLEGE, FAIRFIELD, IA 52803
FULTON, TRAVIS, PHIL & RELIG DEPT, WOOD JUNIOR COL, MATHISTON MS 39752
FUNG, RICHARD, PHIL DEPT, NORTHWESTERN UNIV, EVANSTON IL 60201
FUNK, NANETTE, PHIL DEPT, BROOKLYN COLLEGE, BROOKLYN NY 11210
FUNK, WARREN, PHIL DEPT, HUNTER COLLEGE, NEW YORK NY 10021
FURR, W HAL, PHIL & RELIG, UNIV OF MISSISSIPPI, UNIVERSITY MS 38677
FURTH, MONTGOMERY, PHIL DEPT, UNIV OF CALIFORNIA, LOS ANGELES CA 90024
FUSS, PETER, PHIL DEPT, UNIV OF MISSOURI, ST LOUIS MO 63121
GAA, JAMES C, PHIL DEPT, WASHINGTON UNIV, ST LOUIS MO 63130
GABBAY, DOV, PHIL DEPT, STANFORD UNIVERSITY, STANFORD CA 94305
GABERT, GLEN, HUMAN DIV, MORAINE VLY COM COL, PALOS HILLS IL 60465
GABOURY, P, PHILOSOPHY DEPT, LAURENTIAN UNIV, SUDBURY ONT   CAN
GADAMER, HANS G, PHILOSOPHY DEPT, MCMASTER UNIVERSITY, HAMILTON ONT   CAN
GADC, C D, PHILOSOPHY DEPT, QUEEN'S UNIVERSITY, KINGSTON ONT   CAN
GAFFNEY, RICHARD J, PHIL DEPT, BOSTON COLLEGE, CHESTNUT HILL MA 02167
GAGNE, CLAUDE, PHIL DEPT, COL THETFORD MINES, MEGANTIE QUE   CAN
GAGNE, JEANNE D'ARC, COL ST-JEAN VIANNEY, MONTREAL, QUE   CAN
GAGNE, PAUL, PHILOSOPHY DEPT, UNIV CU QUEBEC, 3-RIVIERES QUE   CAN
GAGNON, CLAUDE, COL EDOUARD-MONTPETIT, LONGUEUIL, QUE   CAN
GAGNON, DONAT, PHIL DEPT, COL TROIS-RIVIERES, 3 RIVIERES QUE   CAN
GAGNON, LAURENCE, PHIL & RELIG DEPT, COLGATE UNIVERSITY, HAMILTON NY 13346
GAGNON, LORRAINE MARIE, PHIL DEPT, ANNA MARIA COLLEGE, PAXTON MA 01612
GAGNON, LUC, PHIL DEPT, COL TROIS-RIVIERES, 3 RIVIERES QUE   CAN
GAGNON, MAURICE, PHIL DEPT, UNIV DE SHERBROOKE, SHERBROOKE QUE   CAN
GAGNON, RENALD, PHILOSOPHY DEPT, COL DE ROUYN-NORANDA, ROUYN QUE   CAN
GAHRINGER, ROBERT, PHIL DEPT, ST ANSELM'S COLLEGE, MANCHESTER NH 03102
GALBRAITH, WINSLOW H, PHIL DEPT, UNIV OF PITTSBURGH, TITUSVILLE PA 16354
GALBREATH, BURCE, PHILOSOPHY DEPT, BROWN UNIVERSITY, PROVIDENCE RI 02912
GALE, GEORGE, PHIL DEPT, UNIV OF MISSOURI, KANSAS CITY MO 64110
GALE, RICHARD, PHIL DEPT, UNIV OF PITTSBURGH, PITTSBURGH PA 15260
GALGAN, GERALD J, HUMAN DIV, ALPHONSUS COLLEGE, WOODCLIFF LK NJ 07675
GALINAITIS, JOHN, PHIL DEPT, UNIV OF WEST ONTARIO, LONDON ONT   CAN
GALIS, LEON, PHIL DEPT, FRANKLIN & MARSHALL, LANCASTER PA 17604
GALLA, JANE ELLEN, REL STUD & PHIL, VILLA MARIA COL, ERIE PA 16505

GALLAGHER, CORNELIUS, PHIL DEPT, ST UNIV OF NY, AMHERST NY 14226
GALLAGHER, DONALD K, PHIL DEPT, S ILLINOIS UNIV, CARBONDALE IL 62901
GALLAGHER, DONALD, PHIL FACULTY, UNIV OF OTTAWA, OTTAWA ONT CAN
GALLAGHER, IDELLA, PHIL FACULTY, UNIV OF OTTAWA, OTTAWA ONT CAN
GALLAGHER, KENNETH, PHIL DEPT, FORDHAM UNIVERSITY, BRONX NY 10458
GALLAGHER, WILLIAM, SOC SCI DEPT, MT ALOYSIUS JR COL, CRESSON PA 16630
GALLANT, CORINNE, PHILOSOPHY DEPT, UNIV DE MONCTON, MONCTON N B CAN
GALLIGAN, EDWARD M, PHIL DEPT, UNIV OF N CAROLINA, CHAPEL HILL NC 27514
GALLIGAN, WILLIAM G, HUMAN DIV, VINCENNES UNIV, VINCENNES IN 47591
GALLMAN, R LEE, DIV OF REL & PHIL, SAMFORD UNIV, BIRMINGHAM AL 35209
GALLOIS, ANDRE, PHIL DEPT, UNIV OF FLORIDA, GAINESVILLE FL 32611
GALLOP, DAVID, PHIL DEPT, TRENT UNIVERSITY, PETERBOROUGH ONT CAN
GALLOWAY, JOSEPH, PHIL DEPT, NORTHWESTERN UNIV, EVANSTON IL 60201
GALLUP, JOHN R, PHIL FACULTE, UNIVERSITE LAVAL, CITE UNIV QUE CAN
GALVIN, JAMES P, HUMAN DIV, ST MARY WOODS COL, ST MARY WOODS IN 47876
GAMBLE, HAROLD, PHILOSOPHY DEPT, MARAMEC COM COL, ST LOUIS MO 63122
GAMBLE, MARILYNN, PHIL DEPT, UNIV OF MINNESOTA, MINNEAPOLIS MN 55455
GANGADEAN, ASOKA, PHIL DEPT, HAVERFORD COLLEGE, HAVERFORD PA 19041
GANGADEAN, SURRENDRA, SOC SCI DEPT, PHOENIX COLLEGE, PHOENIX AZ 85013
GANNON, EDWARD, PHILOSOPHY DEPT, UNIV OF SCRANTON, SCRANTON PA 18510
GANNON, JOSEPH F, PHIL & REL STUD, MERCY COLLEGE, DOBBS FERRY NY 10522
GANNON, WILLIAM T, PHIL DEPT, NIAGARA UNIVERSITY, NIAGARA UNIV NY 14109
GANS, STEVEN, PHILOSOPHY DEPT, WINDHAM COLLEGE, PUTNEY VT 05346
GARCEAU, BENOIT, PHIL FACULTY, UNIV OF OTTAWA, OTTAWA ONT CAN
GARCIA CABAN, E, HUMAN DEPT, UNIV OF PUERTO RICO, CAYEY PR 00633
GARCIA HERRERA, E, HUMAN DEPT, UNIV OF PUERTO RICO, MAYAGUEZ PR 00708
GARCIA MARCHAND, J, HUMAN DEPT, UNIV OF PUERTO RICO, ARECIBO PR 00612
GARCIA-GOMEZ, JORGE, HUMAN DIV, LONG ISLAND UNIV, SOUTHAMPTON NY 11968
GARCIA, JESUS A, PHILOSOPHY DEPT, NM HIGHLANDS UNIV, LAS VEGAS NM 87701
GARDINER, SAM, PHIL DEPT, PURDUE UNIVERSITY, FORT WAYNE IN 46805
GARDNER, ROMAINE, PHIL DEPT, WAGNER COLLEGE, STATEN ISLAND NY 10301
GAREAU, SUZANNE, PHILOSOPHY DEPT, COL DE MAISONNEUVE, MONTREAL QUE CAN
GARELICK, HERBERT, PHIL DEPT, MICHIGAN STATE UNIV, EAST LANSING MI 48823
GAREY, JOCELYN, PHIL DEPT, ROSARY COLLEGE, RIVER FOREST IL 60305
GARFINKEL, ALAN, PHIL DEPT, CALIFORNIA ST UNIV, NORTHRIDGE CA 91324
GARIEPY, BENOIT, PHIL FACULTE, UNIVERSITE LAVAL, CITE UNIV QUE CAN
GARLAND, WILLIAM J, PHILOSOPHY DEPT, UNIV OF THE SOUTH, SEWANEE TN 37375
GARLOUGH, LOUANNA, PHIL DEPT, UNIV OF WEST ONTARIO, LONDON ONT CAN
GARMAN, SHARON, PHIL DEPT, UNIVERSITY OF MIAMI, CORAL GABLES FL 33124
GARNER, RICHARD T, PHILOSOPHY DEPT, OHIO STATE UNIV, COLUMBUS OH 43210
GARNIER, FRANCOIS, PHIL DEPT, UNIV OF N CAROLINA, WILMINGTON NC 28401
GARON, JEAN-DENIS, PHIL DEPT, COL DE SHERBROOKE, SHERBROOKE QUE CAN
GARRELTS, GEORGE, GEN STUDIES, QUINEBAUG VAL COM COL, DANIELSON CT 06239
GARRETT, BRAD, PHILOSOPHY DEPT, CARL ALBERT JR COL, POTEAU OK 74953
GARRETT, LEROY, HUMANITIES DIV, RICHLAND COLLEGE, DALLAS TX 75202
GARRETT, LESTER, PHIL DEPT, HUNTER COLLEGE, NEW YORK NY 10021
GARRETT, RICHARD, PHILOSOPHY DEPT, HOFSTRA UNIVERSITY, HEMPSTEAD NY 11550
GARRETT, ROLAND W, PHILOSOPHY DEPT, BALDWIN-WALLACE COL, BEREA OH 44017
GARRETT, THOMAS, PHILOSOPHY DEPT, UNIV OF SCRANTON, SCRANTON PA 18510
GARRETT, W EUGENE, PHIL DEPT, CENTRAL CONN ST COL, NEW BRITAIN CT 06050
GARRISON, GARY L, PHILOSOPHY DEPT, BETHANY COLLEGE, BETHANY WV 26032
GARRISON, GEORGE, PHIL DEPT, ST UNIV OF NY, AMHERST NY 14226
GARRY, ANN, PHIL DEPT, CALIFORNIA ST UNIV, LOS ANGELES CA 90032
GARRY, MARTIN, PHILOSOPHY DEPT, OHIO DOMINICAN COL, COLUMBUS OH 43219
GARSIDE, CHRISTINE, PHIL DEPT, GEORGE WILLIAMS UNIV, MONTREAL 107 QUE CAN
GARSON, JAMES, PHILOSOPHY DEPT, UNIV OF PENN, PHILADELPHIA PA 19174
GARVER, NEWTON, PHIL DEPT, ST UNIV OF NY, AMHERST NY 14226
GARVEY, CHARLES, PHIL DEPT, THOMAS MORE COLLEGE, COVINGTON KY 41017
GARVEY, EDWIN C, PHILOSOPHY DEPT, UNIV OF ST THOMAS, HOUSTON TX 77006
GARVEY, RITA, PHILOSOPHY DEPT, CLARKE COLLEGE, DUBUQUE IA 52001
GARVIN, NED, PHIL DEPT, BOSTON UNIVERSITY, BOSTON MA 02215
GARVIN, ROBERT M, PHIL DEPT, ST UNIV OF NY, ALBANY NY 12203
GARVIN, THOMAS, PHILOSOPHY DEPT, SEATTLE UNIVERSITY, SEATTLE WA 98122
GASKINS, RICHARD H, PHIL DEPT, CENTRAL CONN ST COL, NEW BRITAIN CT 06050

GASS, WILLIAM H, PHIL DEPT, WASHINGTON UNIV, ST LOUIS MO 63130
GATCHEL, RICHARD H, PHIL & RELIG STUD, CRAFTON HILLS COL, YUCAIPA CA 92399
GATES, JOHN F, PHIL DEPT, ST PAUL BIB COL, BIBLE COLLEGE MN 55375
GATTO, EDO, PHILOSOPHY DEPT, ST FRAN XAVIER UNIV, ANTIGONISH N S CAN
GATZKE, KEN, PHIL DEPT, S CONNECTICUT ST COL, NEW HAVEN CT 06515
GAUDET, MARCEL, PHIL DEPT, COL TROIS-RIVIERES, 3 RIVIERES QUE CAN
GAUGHAN, NORBERT, HUMANITIES DIV, UNIV OF PITTSBURGH, GREENSBURG PA 15601
GAUMOND, ANDRE, PHIL DEPT, COL DE LA POCATIERE, LA POCATIERE QUE CAN
GAUTHIER, D P, PHILOSOPHY DEPT, UNIV OF TORONTO, TORONTO ONT CAN
GAUTHIER, YVON, PHILOSOPHY DEPT, UNIV DE MONTREAL, MONTREAL QUE CAN
GAVIN, WILLIAM JOSEPH, PHIL DEPT, UNIV OF MAINE, PORTLAND ME 04103
GAVRILIS, NICHOLAS, PENN STATE UNIV, MCKEESPORT, PA 15132
GAVROGLU, KOSTA, PHIL DEPT, ST UNIV OF NY, STONY BROOK NY 11790
GAY, RALPH, GLENVILLE ST COL, GLENVILLE, WV 26351
GAY, RICHARD R, HUMAN DIV, ALASKA METHODIST U, ANCHORAGE AK 99504
GEACH, PETER, PHILOSOPHY DEPT, UNIV OF PENN, PHILADELPHIA PA 19174
GEAN, WILLIAM, PHIL DEPT, LAKE FOREST COLLEGE, LAKE FOREST IL 60045
GEDDES, LEONARD, PHILOSOPHY DEPT, UNIV OF OREGON, EUGENE OR 97403
GEEHAN, E ROBERT, PHIL DEPT, BARRINGTON COLLEGE, BARRINGTON RI 22806
GEEROMS, CLAUDE R, PHILOSOPHY DEPT, KENT STATE UNIV, KENT OH 44242
GEHMAN, JOHN, PHIL DEPT, UNIV OF ILLINOIS, URBANA IL 61801
GEHRING, OWEN, PHIL & THEOL, ST FRANCIS COLLEGE, FORT WAYNE IN 46808
GEIGER, GEORGE R, PHIL & RELIG DEPT, ANTIOCH COL, YELLOW SPGS OH 45387
GEISELMAN, LOUIS R, HUMAN DEPT, MT ANGEL COLLEGE, MT ANGEL OR 97362
GELBER, SIDNEY, PHIL DEPT, ST UNIV CF NY, STONY BROOK NY 11790
GELBLUM, EDWARD L, PHILOSOPHY DEPT, DUQUESNE UNIV, PITTSBURGH PA 15219
GELINAS, ELMER T, ST MARY'S COL OF CAL, MORAGA, CA 94575
GELINAS, GERARD, PHIL DEPT, COL VIEUX-MONTREAL, MONTREAL QUE CAN
GELLER, LEONARD, PHIL DEPT, ST BONAVENTURE UNIV, ST BONVENTURE NY 14778
GELPI, DONALD, PHIL DEPT, LOYOLA UNIVERSITY, NEW ORLEANS LA 70118
GELVEN, C MICHALE, PHIL DEPT, N ILLINOIS UNIV, DEKALB IL 60115
GELWICK, RICHARD L, REL & PHIL DEPT, STEPHENS COLLEGE, COLUMBIA MO 65201
GENAME, CAROLYN, PHIL DEPT, S ILLINOIS UNIV, CARBONDALE IL 62901
GENCO, PETER, PHILOSOPHY DEPT, EASTERN COLLEGE, ST DAVIDS PA 19087
GENDIN, SIDNEY, HIST & PHIL DEPT, E MICHIGAN UNIV, YPSILANTI MI 48197
GENDREAU, BERNARD, PHILOSOPHY DEPT, XAVIER UNIVERSITY, CINCINNATI OH 45207
GENDRON, CLEMENCE, COL DE HAUTERIVE, HAUTERIVE, QUE CAN
GENDRON, JOCELYN, PHIL DEPT, COL LIONEL-GROULX, STE-THERESE QUE CAN
GENDRON, MARC, PHILOSOPHY DEPT, MCGILL UNIVERSITY, MONTREAL QUE CAN
GENOVA, ANTHONY, PHIL DEPT, UNIVERSITY OF KANSAS, LAWRENCE KS 66044
GENOVA, JUDITH, PHIL DEPT, YALE UNIVERSITY, NEW HAVEN CT 06520
GENTRY JR, W C, DEPT OF PHIL & HUM, HENDERSON ST COL, ARKADELPHIA AR 71923
GENTRY, GEORGE, PHILOSOPHY DEPT, UNIV OF TEXAS, AUSTIN TX 78712
GEORGACARAKOS, GEORGE, PHIL DEPT, UNIV OF MISSOURI, COLUMBIA MO 65201
GEORGE, FERNANDO, PHIL DEPT, COL BOIS-DE-BOULOGNE, MONTREAL QUE CAN
GEORGE, FRANCIS E, PHIL DEPT, CREIGHTON UNIV, OMAHA NE 68178
GEORGE, RICHARD J, ARTS & SCI COL, UNIV OF SAN DIEGO, SAN DIEGO CA 92110
GEORGE, ROLF A, PHILOSOPHY DEPT, UNIV OF WATERLOO, WATERLOO ONT CAN
GEORGE, TIMOTHY, PHIL DEPT, UNIVERSITY OF KANSAS, LAWRENCE KS 66044
GEORGHRING, GEORGE, PHILOSOPHY DEPT, OHIO STATE UNIV, COLUMBUS OH 43210
GEORGIADIS, C, PHILOSOPHY DEPT, MCMASTER UNIVERSITY, HAMILTON ONT CAN
GEOTTER, R C, PHIL & RELIG, WEST KENTUCKY UNIV, BOWLING GREEN KY 42101
GEPFORD, WILLIAM G, PHIL & RELIG, MLSKINGUM COLLEGE, NEW CONCORD OH 43762
GERAETS, THEODORE, PHIL FACULTY, UNIV OF OTTAWA, OTTAWA ONT CAN
GERBER, DAVID, PHIL SCH, UNIV OF S CALIFORNIA, LOS ANGELES CA 90007
GERBER, WILLIAM, 4307 38TH ST NW, WASHINGTON, DC 20016
GERMAIN, PAUL, PHIL DEPT, GEORGE WILLIAMS UNIV, MONTREAL 107 QUE CAN
GERT, BERNARD, PHILOSOPHY DEPT, DARTMOUTH COLLEGE, HANOVER NH 03755
GERTNER, WILLIS, PHIL DEPT, UNIV OF WISCONSIN, EAU CLAIRE WI 54701
GERVAIS, BERNADETTE, COL ST-JEAN VIANNEY, MONTREAL, QUE CAN
GERVASI, JULIAN A, PHIL DEPT, MICHIGAN STATE UNIV, EAST LANSING MI 48823
GERWIN, M, PHIL DEPT, UNIV OF MANITCBA, WINNIPEG 19 MAN CAN
GERY, PAUL H, SOC STUD DIV, WESTERN ST COLLEGE, GUNNISON CO 81230
GETTIER, EDMUND, PHILOSOPHY DEPT, UNIV OF MASS, AMHERST MA 01002

GETTMAN, GARY L, PHIL & RELIG DEPT, YANKTON COLLEGE, YANKTON SD 57078
GETTNER, ALAN, PHIL BOARD STUD, COL AT PURCHASE, PURCHASE NY 10577
GEURAS, DEAN, ENG & PHIL DEPT, SW TEXAS ST UNIV, SAN MARCOS TX 78666
GEUSS, RAYMOND, PHIL DEPT, COLUMBIA UNIVERSITY, NEW YORK NY 10027
GEWIRTH, ALAN, PHIL DEPT, UNIV OF CHICAGO, CHICAGO IL 60637
GHANOTAKIS, G, PHILOSOPHY DEPT, UNIV OF TORONTO, TORONTO ONT CAN
GHOUGASSIAN, JOSEPH, ARTS & SCI COL, UNIV OF SAN DIEGO, SAN DIEGO CA 92110
GIACAMAN, GEORGE, PHIL DEPT, ST UNIV OF NY, AMHERST NY 14226
GIANNONI, C B, PHILOSOPHY DEPT, RICE UNIVERSITY, HOUSTON TX 77001
GIASSON, CLAUDE, COL EDOUARD-MONTPETIT, LONGUEUIL, QUE CAN
GIBBARD, ALAN F, PHIL DEPT, UNIV OF PITTSBURGH, PITTSBURGH PA 15260
GIBBARD, ALLAN, PHIL DEPT, UNIV OF CHICAGO, CHICAGO IL 60637
GIBBONS, ALAN C, PHILOSOPHY DEPT, EAST CAROLINA UNIV, GREENVILLE NC 27834
GIBBONS, JOHN F, PHIL DEPT, LA SALLE COLLEGE, PHILADELPHIA PA 19141
GIBBONS, JOSEPH P, PHIL & RELIG, LACYCLIFF COL, HIGHLAND FLS NY 10928
GIBBONS, THEODORE, PHILOSOPHY DEPT, E WASHINGTON ST COL, CHENEY WA 99004
GIBEAULT, MARCEL, PHIL DEPT, COL TROIS-RIVIERES, 3 RIVIERES QUE CAN
GIBIAN, BARBARA, PHIL DEPT, SYRACUSE UNIVERSITY, SYRACUSE NY 13210
GIBSON, DAVID E, PHIL DEPT, PEPPERDINE UNIVERSITY, LOS ANGELES CA 90044
GIBSON, GEOFFREY J, PHILOSOPHY DEPT, CALIFORNIA ST UNIV, FRESNO CA 93740
GIBSON, JOAN, UNIV OF ALBUQUERQUE, ALBUQUERQUE, NM 87120
GIBSON, LEONARD, PHILOSOPHY DEPT, UNIVERSITY OF TULSA, TULSA OK 74104
GIBSON, MARY, PHILOSOPHY DEPT, RUTGERS UNIV, NEW BRUNSWICK NJ 08903
GIBSON, ROBERT L, PHIL DEPT, LORETTO HEIGHTS COL, DENVER CO 80236
GIBSON, ROGER, PHIL DEPT, UNIV OF MISSOURI, COLUMBIA MO 65201
GIBSON, SHEILA, PHILOSOPHY DEPT, COL OF HOLY NAMES, OAKLAND CA 94619
GIEGENGACK, MARY, PHIL DEPT, LE MOYNE COLLEGE, SYRACUSE NY 13214
GIEGERICH, VINCENT E, BELLARMINE COLLEGE, LOUISVILLE, KY 40205
GIER, NICHOLAS, PHIL DEPT, UNIVERSITY OF IDAHO, MOSCOW ID 83843
GIERE, RONALD N, HIST & PHIL SCI, INDIANA UNIV, BLOOMINGTON IN 47401
GIERMEK, JOACHIM, PHIL DEPT, ST HYACINTH COLLEGE, GRANBY MA 01033
GIESCHEN, DONALD W, PHILOSOPHY DEPT, ARIZONA STATE UNIV, TEMPE AZ 85281
GIESE, ALBRECHT, ENG & PHIL DEPT, STEPHEN F AUSTIN U, NACOGDOCHES TX 75961
GIESELMAN, RICHARD W, PHILOSOPHY DEPT, UNIV OF ST THOMAS, HOUSTON TX 77006
GIESS, W, PHILOSOPHY DEPT, WARTBURG COLLEGE, WAVERLY IA 50677
GIETZ, WILLIAM, PHIL DEPT, UNIV OF ROCHESTER, ROCHESTER NY 14627
GIGUERE, JOHN, HUM & FINE ARTS DEPT, ST NORBERT COL, DE PERE WI 54115
GILBERT, JOSEPH, PHIL DEPT, COLLEGE AT BROCKPORT, BROCKPORT NY 14420
GILBERT, MICHAEL, PHILOSOPHY DEPT, UNIV OF WATERLOO, WATERLOO ONT CAN
GILBERT, NEAL W, PHIL DEPT, UNIV OF CALIFORNIA, DAVIS CA 95616
GILBERT, RUTH, PHILOSOPHY DEPT, UNIV OF WATERLOO, WATERLOO ONT CAN
GILBERT, THOMAS, PHIL DEPT, MORNINGSIDE COLLEGE, SIOUX CITY IA 51106
GILBERTSON, MARK, THEOL & PHIL DEPT, TEXAS LUTH COLLEGE, SEGUIN TX 78155
GILCHRIST, SHELLEY, PHILOSOPHY DEPT, RUTGERS UNIV, NEW BRUNSWICK NJ 08903
GILDIN, HILAIL, PHILOSOPHY DEPT, QUEENS COLLEGE, FLUSHING NY 11367
GILES, JAMES, PHIL DEPT, IONA COLLEGE, NEW ROCHELLE NY 10801
GILL, J, PHILOSOPHY DEPT, UNIV OF TORONTO, TORONTO ONT CAN
GILL, JERRY, LETTERS COLLEGIUM, ECKERD COLLEGE, ST PETERSBURG FL 33733
GILL, JOHN G, PHIL DEPT, CEN MICHIGAN UNIV, MT PLEASANT MI 48858
GILL, KERMODE F, PHILOSOPHY DEPT, KENT STATE UNIV, KENT OH 44242
GILLAN, GARTH J, PHIL DEPT, S ILLINOIS UNIV, CARBONDALE IL 62901
GILLASPIE, LEON, DIV OF GEN EDUC, S E BIBLE COL, BIRMINGHAM AL 35205
GILLESPIE, MALCOLM, WILBERFORCE UNIV, WILBERFORCE, OH 45384
GILLESPIE, MICHAEL, PHIL & REL DEPT, UNIV OF NEBRASKA, OMAHA NE 68132
GILLESPIE, NORMAN C, PHILOSOPHY DEPT, UNIV OF TEXAS, AUSTIN TX 78712
GILLILAND, JOE, HUMAN DEPT, COCHISE COLLEGE, DOUGLAS AZ 85228
GILLIS, EDWARD, PHIL DEPT, UNIV OF CALIFORNIA, IRVINE CA 92664
GILLMOR, WILEY G, PHIL & REL DEPT, N CAROLINA ST UNIV, RALEIGH NC 27607
GILMER, HARRY W, REL & PHIL DEPT, WESLEYAN COLLEGE, MACON GA 31201
GILMORE, THOMAS, PHILOSOPHY DEPT, GONZAGA UNIV, SPOKANE WA 99202
GILMOUR, JOHN C, HUMAN STUD DIV, ALFRED UNIVERSITY, ALFRED NY 14802
GILPATRICK, JEAN, PHIL DEPT, CEN VIRGINIA COM COL, LYNCHBURG VA 24502
GILPIN, R C, PHIL DEPT, BUTLER UNIVERSITY, INDIANAPOLIS IN 46205
GILROY JR, JOHN D, PHIL DEPT, ST LOUIS UNIVERSITY, ST LOUIS MO 63103

GILSON, E, UNIV OF ST MICHAEL'S, TORONTO 181, ONT   CAN
GINET, CARL, SAGE SCHOOL, CORNELL UNIVERSITY, ITHACA NY 14850
GINGRICH, JOHN, PHIL & RELIG DEPT, LA VERNE COLLEGE, LA VERNE CA 91750
GINI, ALFRED, PHIL DEPT, LOYOLA UNIVERSITY, CHICAGO IL 60626
GINSBERG, ROBERT, PHILOSOPHY DEPT, PENN STATE UNIV, MEDIA PA 19063
GIORGI, LOUIS P, CABRINI COLLEGE, RADNOR, PA 19087
GIROUX, JEAN-PAUL, PHIL DEPT, COL LIONEL-GROULX, STE-THERESE QUE   CAN
GIROUX, LAURENT, PHILOSOPHY DEPT, UNIV DU QUEBEC, 3-RIVIERES QUE   CAN
GIROUX, OSCAR, PHIL & THEOL DIV, ST FRANCIS COLLEGE, BIDDEFORD ME   04005
GIRCVARD, CLAUDE, COL EDOUARD-MONTPETIT, LONGUEUIL, QUE   CAN
GIRVETZ, HARRY, PHIL DEPT, UNIV OF CALIFORNIA, SANTA BARBARA CA 93106
GISSLER, ANTOINETTE, PHILOSOPHY DEPT, GAVILAN COL, GILROY CA 95020
GIUFFRIDA, ROBERT, PHIL DEPT, ST UNIV OF NY, AMHERST NY 14226
GIULIANO, JOHN, PHIL DEPT, UNIV OF CALIFORNIA, LOS ANGELES CA 90024
GIVNER, D, PHIL & CLASS DEPT, UNIV OF SASKATCHEWAN, REGINA SAS   CAN
GJORDING, CHRISTOPHER, PHILOSOPHY DEPT, GONZAGA UNIV, SPOKANE WA 99202
GLACKIN, JOHN J, HUMANITIES DIV, ROSEMONT COLLEGE, ROSEMONT PA 19010
GLADDEN, GARNET LEE, SOC SCI DEPT, RIVERSIDE CITY COL, RIVERSIDE CA 92506
GLANVILLE, JOHN J, PHIL DEPT, CALIFCRNIA ST UNIV, SAN FRANCISCO CA 94132
GLASS, ELYSE, PHIL DEPT, ST UNIV OF NY, STONY BROOK NY 11790
GLASS, M, PHILOSOPHY DEPT, CARLETON UNIVERSITY, OTTAWA ONT   CAN
GLASS, RONALD J, PHIL DEPT, UNIV OF WISCONSIN, LA CROSSE WI 54601
GLASSEN, P, PHIL DEPT, UNIV OF MANITOBA, WINNIPEG 19 MAN   CAN
GLASSHEIM, PATRICIA, PHIL DEPT, UNIV OF N DAKOTA, GRAND FORKS ND 58201
GLASSON, J, PHILOSOPHY DEPT, UNIV OF RHODE ISLAND, KINGSTON RI 02881
GLATHE, ALFRED, PHIL DEPT, CALIFORNIA ST UNIV, LOS ANGELES CA 90032
GLAVIN, JAMES M, ST JOHN'S COLLEGE, CAMARILLO, CA 93010
GLAZBROOK, JACK, LIBR STUD DIV, SENECA COLLEGE, WILLOWDALE ONT   CAN
GLAZEK, MARIANNE, PHIL DEPT, MERCY COLLEGE, DETROIT MI 48219
GLENN JR, JOHN D, PHIL DEPT, TULANE UNIVERSITY, NEW ORLEANS LA 70118
GLENN, ALFRED A, PHIL DEPT, BETHEL COLLEGE, ST PAUL MN 55112
GLESSNER, RICHARD H, PHIL DEPT, MOUNT IDA COLLEGE, NEWTON CENTRE MA 02135
GLICKMAN, JACK, PHIL DEPT, COLLEGE AT BROCKPORT, BROCKPORT NY 14420
GLIDDEN, DAVID K, PHIL DEPT, OCCIDENTAL COLLEGE, LOS ANGELES CA 90041
GLIDDEN, J C, POLIT SCI & PHIL, WEBER STATE COLLEGE, OGDEN UT 84403
GLISPIN, JAMES, PHIL DEPT, UNIV OF DETROIT, DETROIT MI 48221
GLOEKNER, MARTHA, PHIL DEPT, COL OF MT ST JOSEPH, MT ST JOSEPH OH 45051
GLOMB, JULIAN, HUMAN DIV, MORAINE VLY COM COL, PALOS HILLS IL 60465
GLOSSER, LAWRENCE, PHIL DEPT, UNIV OF CINCINNATI, CINCINNATI OH 45221
GLOSSOP, RONALD J, PHIL STUD DEPT, S ILLINOIS UNIV, EDWARDSVILLE IL 62025
GLOWIENKA, EMERINE, ARTS & SCI COL, UNIV OF SAN DIEGO, SAN DIEGO CA 92110
GLOYN, CYRIL K, PHIL DEPT, OCCIDENTAL COLLEGE, LOS ANGELES CA 90041
GLYMOUR, CLARK, PHIL DEPT, PRINCETON UNIVERSITY, PRINCETON NJ 08540
GNAGY, ALLEN S, HUMAN & PHIL DEPT, NE MISSOURI ST UNIV, MARYVILLE MO 64468
GNAU, DAYTON, LIBR ARTS, DETROIT COL BUSINESS, DEARBORN MI 48126
GOBAR, ASH, PHIL & RELIG, TRANSYLVANIA UNIV, LEXINGTON KY 40508
GOBLE, JONATHAN C, PHIL DEPT, UNIV CF N CAROLINA, CHAPEL HILL NC 27514
GODBOUT, LAURENT A, LANG & HUMAN DIV, COL UNIV ST JEAN, EDMONTON ALB   CAN
GODBOUT, ROBERT, REL & PHIL, UNIV OF EVANSVILLE, EVANSVILLE IN 47701
GODFREY, IAN, PHIL DEPT, UNIV OF WEST ONTARIO, LONDON ONT   CAN
GODIN, GUY, PHIL FACULTE, UNIVERSITE LAVAL, CITE UNIV QUE   CAN
GODLOVITCH, S, PHILOSOPHY DEPT, UNIV OF GUELPH, GUELPH ONT   CAN
GODOW JR, REW A, PHILOSOPHY DEPT, ILLINOIS ST UNIV, NORMAL IL 61761
GODSEY, R KIRBY, AVERETT COLLEGE, DANVILLE, VA 24541
GOECECKE, W ROBERT, PHIL DEPT, CEN WASH STATE COL, ELLENSBURG WA 98926
GOELLER, RICHARD, PHILOSOPHY DEPT, UNIV OF WATERLOO, WATERLOO ONT   CAN
GOFF, EDWIN L, PHILOSOPHY DEPT, VILLANOVA UNIV, VILLANOVA PA 19085
GOFF, ROBERT A, PHIL STUD BOARD, U OF CALIFORNIA, SANTA CRUZ CA 95060
GOHEEN, JOHN D, PHILOSOPHY DEPT, CALIFORNIA ST UNIV, HAYWARD CA 94542
GOICOECHEA, DAVID L, PHIL DEPT, BROCK UNIVERSITY, ST CATHARINES ONT   CAN
GOLASH, DEIRDRE K, PHIL DEPT, UNIV OF MARYLAND, COLLEGE PARK MD 20742
GOLD, JEFFREY, PHILOSOPHY DEPT, OHIO STATE UNIV, COLUMBUS OH 43210
GOLD, JONATHAN, PHIL DEPT, ST UNIV CF NY, STONY BROOK NY 11790
GOLDBERG, BARBARA, PHIL DEPT, GEORGE WILLIAMS UNIV, MONTREAL 107 QUE   CAN

GOLDBERG, BRUCE, PHIL DEPT, UNIV OF MARYLAND, BALTIMORE MD 21228
GOLDBERG, LARRY, PHIL DEPT, UNIVERSITY OF MIAMI, CORAL GABLES FL 33124
GOLDBLATT, DAVID A, PHILOSOPHY DEPT, DENISON UNIV, GRANVILLE OH 43023
GOLDEN, THOMAS, PHIL & REL STUD, HOLY FAMILY COL, MANITOWOC WI 54220
GOLDENBERG, SYDNEY, GLENDON COLLEGE, TORONTO, ONT   CAN
GOLDING, MARTIN, PHIL PROGRAM, GRADUATE SCH -CUNY, NEW YORK NY 10036
GOLDINGER, MILTON, PHILOSOPHY DEPT, UNIV OF WISONSIN, OSH KOSH WI 54901
GOLDMAN, ALAN H, PHILOSOPHY DEPT, OHIO UNIVERSITY, ATHENS OH 45701
GOLDMAN, ALVIN I, PHIL DEPT, UNIV OF MICHIGAN, ANN ARBOR MI 48104
GOLDMAN, HOLLY, PHIL DEPT, UNIV OF MICHIGAN, ANN ARBOR MI 48104
GOLDMAN, MICHAEL, PHILOSOPHY DEPT, MIAMI UNIVERSITY, OXFORD OH 45056
GOLDMAN, STEVEN, PHILOSOPHY DEPT, PENN STATE UNIV, UNIV PARK PA 16802
GOLDSMITH, DALE, PHIL & RELIG, MCPHERSON COLLEGE, MCPHERSON KS 67460
GOLDSTEIN, ALEX, PHIL & REL DEPT, ITHACA COLLEGE, ITHACA NY 14850
GOLDSTEIN, LEON J, PHIL DEPT, ST UNIV OF NY, BINGHAMTON NY 13901
GOLDSTEIN, MARC A, PHIL DEPT, NORTH ADAMS ST COL, NORTH ADAMS MA 01247
GOLDSTEIN, SIGNE B, HUMAN DIV, BENNETT COLLEGE, GREENSBORO NC 27420
GOLDSTICK, D, PHILOSOPHY DEPT, UNIV OF TORONTO, TORONTO ONT   CAN
GOLDTHWAIT, JOHN T, PHIL DEPT, COL AT PLATTSBURGH, PLATTSBURGH NY 12901
GOLDWASSER, S, SOC SCI DEPT, MERCER CO COM COL, TRENTON NJ 08690
GOLDWORTH, AMNON, PHIL DEPT, CALIFORNIA ST UNIV, SAN JOSE CA 95114
GOMBE, A, PHILOSOPHY DEPT, UNIV OF TORONTO, TORONTO ONT   CAN
GOMBERG, PAUL R, PHIL DEPT, UNIV OF MISSOURI, ST LOUIS MO 63121
GOMEZ, JOSE, PHILOSOPHY DEPT, CLARK COLLEGE, VANCOUVER WA 98663
GOMEZ, LUIS O, PHIL DEPT, UNIV OF PUERTO RICO, RIO PIEDRAS PR 00931
GOMEZ, NESTOR, PHIL DEPT, CATHOLIC UNIVERSITY, PONCE PR 00731
GOMEZ, SAMUEL, PHIL DEPT, NORTH ADAMS ST COL, NORTH ADAMS MA 01247
GONDA, JOSEPH P, GLENDON COLLEGE, TORONTO, ONT   CAN
GONSALVES, MILTON, PHIL DEPT, UNIV OF SANTA CLARA, SANTA CLARA CA 95053
GONZALEZ-LOBARRUB, J, PHILOSOPHY DEPT, DREW UNIVERSITY, MADISON NJ 07940
GONZALEZ, A, HUMAN DEPT, COL OF SACRED HEART, SANTURCE PR 00914
GONZALEZ, M J, PHIL DEPT, UNIV OF PUERTO RICO, RIO PIEDRAS PR 00931
GOOCH, P W, PHILOSOPHY DEPT, UNIV OF TORONTO, TORONTO ONT   CAN
GOOD, DONALD G, REL & PHIL DEPT, WILLIAM PENN COLLEGE, OSKALOOSA IA 52577
GOOD, ROBERT C, PHILOSOPHY DEPT, UNIV OF WISCONSIN, MADISON WI 53706
GOODE, TERRY M, PHILOSOPHY DEPT, UNIV OF S CAROLINA, COLUMBIA SC 29208
GOODENOUGH, IRENE, HUMAN DEPT, MASS BAY COM COL, WATERTOWN MA 02172
GOODFIELD, JUNE, PHIL DEPT, MICHIGAN STATE UNIV, EAST LANSING MI 48823
GOODING, WAYNE, PHIL DEPT, UNIV OF WEST ONTARIO, LONDON ONT   CAN
GOODMAN, CARTER, SOC SCI DEPT, CLAREMORE JR COL, CLAREMORE OK 74017
GOODMAN, LENN E, PHIL DEPT, UNIVERSITY OF HAWAII, HONOLULU HI 96822
GOODMAN, NELSON, PHIL DEPT, HARVARD UNIVERSITY, CAMBRIDGE MA 02138
GOODMAN, RUSSELL B, PHIL DEPT, UNIV OF NEW MEXICO, ALBUQUERQUE NM 87106
GOODMAN, STEVE, PHILOSOPHY DEPT, BROOKDALE COM COL, LINCROFT NJ 07738
GOODPASTER, KENNETH, PHIL DEPT, UNIV OF NOTRE DAME, NOTRE DAME IN 46556
GOODRUM, CRAIG R, PHILOSOPHY DEPT, ILLINOIS ST UNIV, NORMAL IL 61761
GOODWIN, GEORGE D, PHIL & REL DEPT, COL OF THE DESERT, PALM DESERT CA 92260
GOODWIN, JOHN, ASHLAND COM COLLEGE, ASHLAND, KY 41101
GOODWIN, JOHN, MARSHALL UNIVERSITY, HUNTINGTON, WV 25701
GOODWIN, ROBERT, PHIL DEPT, BOWLING GREEN UNIV, BOWLING GREEN OH 43403
GOOSENS, WILLIAM K, PHIL DEPT, UNIV OF VIRGINIA, CHARLOTTESVL VA 22903
GORDON, DALE H, UNIV OF MARYLAND, PRINCESS ANNE, MD 21853
GORDON, DANE, GEN STUD COL, ROCHESTER INST TECH, ROCHESTER NY 14623
GORDON, JACK, PHIL DEPT, UNIV OF SN FRANCISCO, SAN FRANCISCO CA 94117
GORDON, L D, PHIL DEPT, UNIV OF ILLINOIS, URBANA IL 61801
GORDON, ROBERT M, PHIL DEPT, UNIV OF MISSOURI, ST LOUIS MO 63121
GORMLEY, WILLIAM, HUMAN DIV, LONG ISLAND UNIV, SOUTHAMPTON NY 11968
GOROVITZ, SAMUEL, PHIL DEPT, UNIV OF MARYLAND, COLLEGE PARK MD 20742
GORR, MICHAEL, PHILOSOPHY DEPT, BROWN UNIVERSITY, PROVIDENCE RI 02912
GOSSELIN, GILLES, ART FACULTY, COLLEGE DE HEARST, HEARST ONT   CAN
GOSSELIN, PHILIP, PHILOSOPHY DEPT, BRANDON UNIVERSITY, BRANDON MAN   CAN
GOSSMAN, EVA REINITZ, PHIL DEPT, GOUCHER COLLEGE, TOWNSON MD 21204
GOTESKY, RUBIN, PHIL DEPT, N ILLINOIS UNIV, DEKALB IL 60115
GOTSHALK, RICHARD A, PHILOSOPHY DEPT, PENN STATE UNIV, UNIV PARK PA 16802

GOTTERBARN, DONALD, PHIL DEPT, WICHITA ST UNIV, WICHITA KS 67208
GOTTHELF, ALLAN, PHIL & RELIG DEPT, TRENTON STATE COL, TRENTON NJ 08625
GOTTLIEB, DALE, PHIL DEPT, JOHNS HOPKINS UNIV, BALTIMORE MD 21218
GOTTLIEB, DIANE, PHIL DEPT, PRINCE GEORGE'S COM, LARGO MD 20870
GOTTLIEB, ROGER, PHIL DEPT, BRANDEIS UNIVERSITY, WALTHAM MA 02154
GOUDGE, T A, PHILOSOPHY DEPT, UNIV OF TORONTO, TORONTO ONT CAN
GOUGH, JAMES E, PHILOSOPHY DEPT, UNIV OF WATERLOO, WATERLOO ONT CAN
GOUINLOCK, JAMES, PHIL DEPT, EMORY UNIVERSITY, ATLANTA GA 30322
GOULD, CAROL, PHIL DEPT, LEHMAN COLLEGE, BRONX NY 10468
GOULD, CHARLES, PHIL DEPT, UNIV OF WISCONSIN, MILWAUKEE WI 53201
GOULD, JAMES A, PHIL DEPT, UNIV OF S FLORIDA, TAMPA FL 33620
GOULD, JOSIAH B, PHIL DEPT, ST UNIV OF NY, ALBANY NY 12203
GOULD, WILLIAM DRUM, PHILOSOPHY DEPT, DICKINSON COLLEGE, CARLISLE PA 17013
GOULET, JEAN, PHIL DEPT, UNIV DE SHERBROOKE, SHERBROOKE QUE CAN
GOULET, RICHARD, PHIL DEPT, COL DE L'ASSOMPTION, L'ASSOMPTION QUE CAN
GOUR, GILLES, PHILOSOPHY DEPT, COL DE MAISONNEUVE, MONTREAL QUE CAN
GOUREVITCH, VICTOR, PHILOSOPHY DEPT, WESLEYAN UNIV, MIDDLETOWN CT 06457
GOVERT, MARY EVELYN, PHIL & THEOL, ST FRANCIS COLLEGE, FORT WAYNE IN 46808
GOVIER, TRUDY R, PHIL DEPT, TRENT UNIVERSITY, PETERBOROUGH ONT CAN
GOWEN, JULIE, PHILOSOPHY DEPT, ILLINOIS ST UNIV, NORMAL IL 61761
GRABAU, RICHARD F, PHIL DEPT, PURDUE UNIVERSITY, LAFAYETTE IN 47907
GRABER, GLENN C, PHIL DEPT, UNIV OF TENNESSEE, KNOXVILLE TN 37916
GRACE, JAMES H, PHIL & RELIG DEPT, GLASSBORO ST COL, GLASSBORO NJ 08028
GRACE, JAMES P, PHIL DEPT, CATH COL IMM CONCEPT, DOUGLASTON NY 11362
GRACIA, JORGE J, PHIL DEPT, ST UNIV OF NY, AMHERST NY 14226
GRAFF, JAMES A, PHILOSOPHY DEPT, VICTORIA COLLEGE, TORONTO 5 ONT CAN
GRAGG, ALAN W, PHIL DEPT, GEORGETOWN COLLEGE, GEORGETOWN KY 40215
GRAHAM, GEORGE A, PHIL DEPT, BRANDEIS UNIVERSITY, WALTHAM MA 02154
GRAHAM, JOSEPH M, PHILOSOPHY DEPT, UNIV OF ST THOMAS, HOUSTON TX 77006
GRAHAM, MARY JUDE, PHIL DEPT, COL OF ST MARY, OMAHA NE 68124
GRAHAM, STEVE, HUMANITIES DIV, RICHLAND COLLEGE, DALLAS TX 75202
GRAHAM, W C, PHILOSOPHY DEPT, UNIV OF TORONTO, TORONTO ONT CAN
GRAM, MOLTKE, PHIL DEPT, UNIVERSITY OF IOWA, IOWA CITY IA 52240
GRAM, RICHARD, PHILOSOPHY DEPT, PENN STATE UNIV, UNIV PARK PA 16802
GRAMLICH, FRANCIS W, PHILOSOPHY DEPT, DARTMOUTH COLLEGE, HANOVER NH 03755
GRANDSTRAND, KAREN, PHIL DEPT, SAINT OLAF COLLEGE, NORTHFIELD MN 55057
GRANDY, NORMAN, SOC SCI DIV, MCKENDREE COL, LEBANON IL 62254
GRANDY, RICHARD, PHIL DEPT, PRINCETON UNIVERSITY, PRINCETON NJ 08540
GRANEL, GERARD, PHILOSOPHY DEPT, UNIV DE MONTREAL, MONTREAL QUE CAN
GRANEY, MARC R, BRESCIA COLLEGE, OWENSBORO, KY 42301
GRANGE, JOSEPH, PHIL DEPT, UNIV OF MAINE, PORTLAND ME 04103
GRANGE, KATHLEEN, ENG & PHIL DEPT, COMPTON COLLEGE, COMPTON CA 90221
GRANGER, EDGAR HERBERT, PHILOSOPHY DEPT, UNIV OF TEXAS, AUSTIN TX 78712
GRANGER, G-G, PHIL DEPT, UNIV DE SHERBROOKE, SHERBROOKE QUE CAN
GRANROSE, JOHN T, PHIL & REL DEPT, UNIV OF GEORGIA, ATHENS GA 30602
GRANT, BRIAN, PHILOSOPHY DEPT, UNIV OF CALGARY, CALGARY 44 ALB CAN
GRANT, EDWARD, HIST & PHIL SCI, INDIANA UNIV, BLOOMINGTON IN 47401
GRANT, G G, PHIL DEPT, LOYOLA UNIVERSITY, CHICAGO IL 60626
GRANT, HECTOR J, PHIL & REL DEPT, HUSTON-TILLOTSON COL, AUSTIN TX 78702
GRANT, L R, PHIL FACULTY, UNIV OF OTTAWA, OTTAWA ONT CAN
GRANZOW, JAMES R, ENGLISH DEPT, NEW MEXICO MIL INST, ROSWELL NM 88201
GRASSI, CARLO, PHIL DEPT, UNIV OF DETROIT, DETROIT MI 48221
GRASSI, JOSEPH G, PHIL DEPT, FAIRFIELD UNIVERSITY, FAIRFIELD CT 06430
GRASSIAN, VICTOR, PHILOSOPHY DEPT, LOS ANGELES HBR COL, WILMINGTON CA 90744
GRATZ, ROBERT, HUMANITES DIV, LA ROCHE COLLEGE, PITTSBURGH PA 15237
GRAVANDER, JERRY W, PHIL DEPT, UNIV OF TENNESSEE, KNOXVILLE TN 37916
GRAVEL, PIERRE, PHILOSOPHY DEPT, UNIV DE MONTREAL, MONTREAL QUE CAN
GRAVELINE, ROBERT, PHIL & RELIG STUD, KING'S COLLEGE, LONDON ONT CAN
GRAVES, BERNARD, HUMAN DEPT, NICHOLS COLLEGE, DUDLEY MA 01570
GRAVES, DORSET, PHILOSOPHY DEPT, CHADRON ST COL, CHADRON NE 69337
GRAVES, JOHN C, PHIL DEPT, MASS INST TECH, CAMBRIDGE MA 02139
GRAY, CHRISTOPHER, PHILOSOPHY DEPT, LOYOLA COLLEGE, MONTREAL QUE CAN
GRAY, FRANCIS C, PHILOSOPHY DEPT, MANATEE JUN COL, BRADENTON FL 33505
GRAY, J GLENN, PHIL DEPT, COLORADO COLLEGE, COLORADO SPGS CO 80903

GRAY, PAUL, PHIL DEPT, CORNELL COLLEGE, MOUNT VERNON IA 52314
GRAY, PHILIP, PHILOSOPHY DEPT, WITTENBERG UNIV, SPRINGFIELD OH 45501
GRAY, WALLACE, PHIL & REL DEPT, SOUTHWESTERN COLLEGE, WINFIELD KS 67156
GRAY, WILLIAM D, HUMAN & PHIL DEPT, GROSSMONT COL, EL CAJON CA 92020
GRDINA, FRANK, HUMAN DEPT, DYKE COLLEGE, CLEVELAND OH 44114
GREAN, STANLEY, PHILOSOPHY DEPT, OHIO UNIVERSITY, ATHENS OH 45701
GRECO, JOSEPH, PHIL DEPT, S CONNECTICUT ST COL, NEW HAVEN CT 06515
GREEN, DENNIS C, SOC SCI DEPT, CITY COLLEGE, SAN FRANCISCO CA 94112
GREEN, LAWTON R, HUMAN DEPT, FLORIDA JUN COLLEGE, JACKSONVILLE FL 32205
GREEN, LUCILE W, MERRITT COLLEGE, OAKLAND, CA 94619
GREEN, MARSHALL, PHIL DEPT, ROOSEVELT UNIVERSITY, CHICAGO IL 60605
GREEN, MURRAY, PHIL DEPT, BERNARD BARUCH COL, NEW YORK NY 10010
GREEN, O HARVEY, PHIL DEPT, TULANE UNIVERSITY, NEW ORLEANS LA 70118
GREEN, REUBEN, PHIL & RELIG DEPT, LEMOYNE-OWEN COL, MEMPHIS TN 38126
GREEN, THOMAS F, PHIL DEPT, SYRACUSE UNIVERSITY, SYRACUSE NY 13210
GREEN, WILLIAM BAILLIE, THEOLOGY DEPT, EPISCOPAL THEOL SEM, AUSTIN TX 78767
GREEN, WILLIAM, HIST & PHIL & SOC SCI, SAN JOSE CITY COL, SAN JOSE CA 95114
GREENAWAY, MALCOLM, PHILOSOPHY DEPT, RUTGERS UNIV, NEW BRUNSWICK NJ 08903
GREENBERG, ARTHUR R, PHIL DEPT, KANSAS ST UNIVERSITY, MANHATTAN KS 66506
GREENBERG, GERSHON, PHIL DEPT, THE AMERICAN UNIV, WASHINGTON DC 20016
GREENBERG, ROBERT S, PHIL DEPT, BRANDEIS UNIVERSITY, WALTHAM MA 02154
GREENE JR, DAVID B, PHIL DEPT, WABASH COLLEGE, CRAWFORDSVL IN 47933
GREENE, JAMES, PHIL DEPT, N MICHIGAN UNIV, MARQUETTE MI 49855
GREENE, JEFFREY P, PHILOSOPHY DEPT, UNIV OF S CAROLINA, COLUMBIA SC 29208
GREENE, JESSE A, PHIL DEPT, UNIV OF ROCHESTER, ROCHESTER NY 14627
GREENE, JOSEPH, PHIL DEPT, FORDHAM UNIVERSITY, BRONX NY 10458
GREENE, MAXINE, PHIL & SOC SCI, TEACHERS COLLEGE, NEW YORK NY 10027
GREENE, MURRAY, PHIL PROGRAM, GRADUATE SCH -CUNY, NEW YORK NY 10036
GREENE, PHILIP B, PHIL DEPT, UNIV OF CALIFORNIA, SANTA BARBARA CA 93106
GREENE, RICHARD, PHIL DEPT, COLUMBIA UNIVERSITY, NEW YORK NY 10027
GREENE, ROBERT, PHIL DEPT, UNIVERSITY OF DAYTON, DAYTON OH 45469
GREENE, STEPHANIE, PHIL DEPT, BOWLING GREEN UNIV, BOWLING GREEN OH 43403
GREENE, VINCENT, SOC SCI DEPT, ST PETERSBURG JR COL, ST PETERSBURG FL 33733
GREENIA, DAVID, PHIL DEPT, CENTRAL CONN ST COL, NEW BRITAIN CT 06050
GREENLAND, VIRGINIA, PHILOSOPHY DEPT, VIRGINIA ST COL, PETERSBURG VA 23803
GREENLEE, DOUGLAS, PHIL DEPT, TEMPLE UNIVERSITY, PHILADELPHIA PA 19122
GREENLEE, W P, SOC SCI DEPT, MCNEESE STATE UNIV, LAKE CHARLES LA 70601
GREENMAN, MARTIN, PHIL & REL STUD, YOUNGSTOWN ST UNIV, YOUNGSTOWN OH 44503
GREENSPAN, PATRICIA S, PHIL DEPT, UNIV OF CHICAGO, CHICAGO IL 60637
GREENSTEIN, HAROLD, PHIL DEPT, COLLEGE AT BROCKPORT, BROCKPORT NY 14420
GREENWALD, H JONATHAN, PHIL DEPT, W CONNECTICUT ST COL, DANBURY CT 06810
GREENWELL, JAMES R, SCOTTSDALE COM COL, SCOTTSDALE, AZ 85252
GREENWELL, JAMES, SOC SCI DEPT, PHOENIX COLLEGE, PHOENIX AZ 85013
GREENWOOD, ROBERT L, PHILOSOPHY DEPT, UNIV OF S ALABAMA, MOBILE AL 36688
GREER, MELVIN E, PHIL DEPT, UNIV OF LOUISVILLE, LOUISVILLE KY 40208
GREER, YATES C, PHILOSOPHY DEPT, COL OF THE SISKIYOUS, WEED CA 96094
GREGG, W R, RELIG & PHIL DEPT, CLAFLIN UNIV, ORANGEBURG SC 29115
GREGORY, CARLTON H, PHIL DEPT, BARRINGTON COLLEGE, BARRINGTON RI 22806
GREGORY, DONALD R, PHILOSOPHY DEPT, N VIRGINIA COM COL, ANNANDALE VA 22003
GREGORY, HENRY, PHIL & RELIG DEPT, COTTEY COLLEGE, NEVADA MO 64772
GREGORY, JOHN, PHIL DEPT, FLORIDA STATE UNIV, TALLAHASSEE FL 32306
GREGORY, MARY S, PHILOSOPHY DEPT, N VIRGINIA COM COL, ANNANDALE VA 22003
GREGORY, THOMAS, REL & PHIL DEPT, WESTMINSTER COL, NW WILMINGTON PA 16142
GREGORY, WALTER, REL DEPT, UNIV OF GEORGIA, ATHENS GA 30602
GREIDER, JOHN C, HUMAN DIV, KENNESAW JR COLLEGE, MARIETTA GA 30060
GREIF, GARY, PHIL OPTION, UNIV OF WISCONSIN, GREEN BAY WI 54302
GREIG, GORDON M, PHILOSOPHY DEPT, UNIV OF CALGARY, CALGARY 44 ALB   CAN
GRENE, MARJORIE, PHIL DEPT, UNIV OF CALIFORNIA, DAVIS CA 95616
GRENIER, MONIQUE, PHIL DEPT, COL VIEUX-MONTREAL, MONTREAL QUE   CAN
GRENNAN, WAYNE, PHIL DEPT, DALHOUSIE UNIVERSITY, HALIFAX N S   CAN
GRESHAM, CHARLES R, KENTUCKY CHRIST COL, GRAYSON, KY 41143
GRESHAM, PERRY E, PHILOSOPHY DEPT, BETHANY COLLEGE, BETHANY WV 26032
GRESHAM, ROBERT W, PHIL DEPT, WASHINGTON UNIV, ST LOUIS MO 63130
GREWE, RUDOLF, PHIL DEPT, CITY COLLEGE, NEW YORK NY 10031

GRICE, H PAUL, PHIL DEPT, UNIV OF CALIFORNIA, BERKELEY CA 94720
GRIEG, JAMES A, PHIL DEPT, UNIV OF NEW MEXICO, ALBUQUERQUE NM 87106
GRIENER, GLENN, PHIL DEPT, UNIV OF WEST ONTARIO, LONDON ONT   CAN
GRIER, JAMES M, BIBL EDUC DEPT, CEDARVILLE COLLEGE, CEDARVILLE OH 45314
GRIER, PHILIP T, PHIL DEPT, NORTHWESTERN UNIV, EVANSTON IL 60201
GRIESBACH, MARC F, PHILOSOPHY DEPT, MARQUETTE UNIV, MILWAUKEE WI 53233
GRIESEDIECK, DAVID J, PHIL DEPT, UNIV OF MISSOURI, ST LOUIS MO 63121
GRIESEMER, MARY F, PHIL DEPT, ST LOUIS UNIVERSITY, ST LOUIS MO 63103
GRIFFIN JR, JUDSON S, PHIL DEPT, ST UNIV OF NY, BINGHAMTON NY 13901
GRIFFIN, BETTY S, REL & PHIL DEPT, ANDREW COLLEGE, CUTHBERT GA 31740
GRIFFIN, DAVID R, 1325 N COLLEGE, CLAREMONT, CA 91711
GRIFFIN, PHILLIP, PHIL DEPT, UNIV OF WISCONSIN, EAU CLAIRE WI 54701
GRIFFIN, ROBERT M, BETHANY NAZARENE COL, BETHANY, OK 73008
GRIFFIS, WILL, SOC SCI & HUM DEPT, MAUI COM COL, KAHULUI HI 96732
GRIFFISS, JAMES E, PHIL & SYST THEOL, NASHOTAH HOUSE SEM, NASHOTA WI 53058
GRIFFITH, STEPHEN R, PHIL DEPT, LYCOMING COLLEGE, WILLIAMSPORT PA 17701
GRIFFITH, WILLIAM B, PHIL DEPT, GEORGE WASHINGTON U, WASHINGTON DC 20006
GRIFFITH, WILLIAM J, BARD COLLEGE, ANNANDALE-HDSN, NY 12504
GRIFFITHS, L, PHIL & RELIG DEPT, UNIV OF ARKANSAS, LITTLE ROCK AR 72204
GRIGGS, C WILFRED, PHILOSOPHY DEPT, BRIGHAM YOUNG UNIV, PROVO UT 84601
GRIM, PATRICK, PHIL DEPT, BOSTON UNIVERSITY, BOSTON MA 02215
GRIMALDI, LEONARD N, ST PETER'S COLLEGE, JERSEY CITY, NJ 07306
GRIMES, PIERRE, SOC SCI DIV, GOLDEN WEST COL, HUNTINGTN BCH CA 92647
GRIMES, WILLIAM V, PHIL DEPT, ST UNIV OF NY, ALBANY NY 12203
GRIMM, RANDOLPH, PHIL DEPT, LE MOYNE COLLEGE, SYRACUSE NY 13214
GRIMM, ROBERT H, PHILOSOPHY DEPT, OBERLIN COLLEGE, OBERLIN OH 44074
GRISEZ, GERMAIN, CAMPION COLLEGE, REGINA, SAS   CAN
GRISWOLD, CHARLES, PHILOSOPHY DEPT, PENN STATE UNIV, UNIV PARK PA 16802
GRIVICICH, DONNA, GOGEBIC COM COL, IRONWOOD, MI 49938
GROB, RUTH, REL & PHIL DEPT, THE COLLEGE OF IDAHO, CALDWELL ID 83605
GROBY, GORDON L, HUMANITIES DIV, OHIO UNIVERSITY, LANCASTER OH 43130
GROHMAN, DONALD D, HIST RELIG & PHIL, KNOXVILLE COL, KNOXVILLE TN 37921
GRONTKOWSKI, CHRISTINE, PHIL DEPT, VASSAR COLLEGE, POUGHKEEPSIE NY 12601
GRONTKOWSKI, RAYMOND, PHIL DEPT, FORDHAM UNIVERSITY, BRONX NY 10458
GROSS, BARRY R, HUMAN DEPT, YORK COLLEGE, JAMAICA NY 11432
GROSS, BENNETT, PHIL DEPT, ST UNIV OF NY, STONY BROOK NY 11790
GROSS, DAMON J, PHIL DEPT, WICHITA ST UNIV, WICHITA KS 67208
GROSS, DWAYER D, PHILOSOPHY DEPT, EAST CAROLINA UNIV, GREENVILLE NC 27834
GROSS, HAROLD H, PHIL DEPT, BETHEL COLLEGE, NORTH NEWTON KS 67117
GROSS, RICHARD, PHIL DEPT, BOSTON COLLEGE, CHESTNUT HILL MA 02167
GROSS, SIDNEY, PHIL DEPT, ELMHURST COLLEGE, ELMHURST IL 60126
GROSSER, ELMER J, PHIL DEPT, SEM OF ST PIUS X, ERLANGER KY 41018
GROSSMAN, MORRIS, PHIL DEPT, FAIRFIELD UNIVERSITY, FAIRFIELD CT 06430
GROSSMAN, NEAL K, PHIL DEPT, UNIV OF ILLINOIS, CHICAGO IL 60680
GROSSMAN, ROSS, PHILOSOPHY DEPT, CAL STATE COL, DOMINGUEZ HLS CA 90747
GROSSMANN, R, PHIL DEPT, INDIANA UNIVERSITY, BLOOMINGTON IN 47401
GROSSO, MICHAEL, PHIL & RELIG, JERSEY CITY ST COL, JERSEY CITY NJ 07305
GROUNDS, VERNON, REL PHIL & APOL DEPT, CON BAPT THEOL SEM, DENVER CO 80210
GROVEN, BLAIR, HUMANITIES DEPT, COLLEGE OF MARIN, KENTFIELD CA 94904
GROVER, DOROTHY L, PHIL DEPT, UNIV CF ILLINOIS, CHICAGO IL 60680
GROVER, NORMAN L, PHIL & RELIG, VA POLYTECH INST, BLACKSBURG VA 24061
GROVER, ROBINSON A, PHIL DEPT, UNIV OF CONNECTICUT, TORRINGTON CT 06790
GROW, ANN E, PHIL & REL STUD, MERCY COLLEGE, DOBBS FERRY NY 10522
GRUEN JR, WILLIAM C, PHIL DEPT, UNIV OF LOUISVILLE, LOUISVILLE KY 40208
GRUENBAUM, ADOLF, PHIL DEPT, UNIV OF PITTSBURGH, PITTSBURGH PA 15260
GRUENDER, C DAVID, PHIL DEPT, FLORIDA STATE UNIV, TALLAHASSEE FL 32306
GRUENENFELDER, JACK, INDIANA UNIVERSITY, GARY, IN 46408
GRUGAN, ARTHUR, PHIL DEPT, HOLY FAMILY COLLEGE, PHILADELPHIA PA 19114
GRUNEBAUM, JAMES O, PHIL DEPT, COL AT BUFFALO, BUFFALO NY 14222
GRUVER, ERIC W, PHILOSOPHY DEPT, CYPRESS COLLEGE, CYPRESS CA 90630
GRUZALSKI, BART K, PHIL DEPT, UNIV CF MARYLAND, COLLEGE PARK MD 20742
GSCHWENDTNER, JOHN V G, HUMAN DIV, DOWLING COLLEGE, LONG ISLAND NY 11769
GUAGLIARDO, V, PHIL & THEOL, ST MARY'S DOMIN COL, NEW ORLEANS LA 70118
GUERETTE, JEAN-PAUL, PHIL DEPT, COL FRANCOIS-X-GARN, QUEBEC CITY QUE   CAN

GUERRIERI, DANIEL, PHIL DEPT, CALIFORNIA ST UNIV, LONG BEACH CA 90840
GUERRY, HERBERT, PHIL & RELIG DEPT, PEMBROKE ST UNIV, PEMBROKE NC 28372
GUILFOIL, DANIEL J, PHILOSOPHY DEPT, EDGEWOOD COLLEGE, MADISON WI   53711
GUILHAMET, JAMES, LOYOLA UNIVERSITY, LOS ANGELES, CA 90045
GUIN, PHILIP, PHIL DEPT, FRAMINGHAM STATE COL, FRAMINGHAM MA   01701
GUINAN, ST MICHAEL, PHILOSOPHY DEPT, BRESCIA COLLEGE, LONDON ONT   CAN
GUINIVEN, JOHN, PHILOSOPHY DEPT, UNIV OF MASS, AMHERST MA   01002
GUINN, RALPH A, PHIL & REL DEPT, TARKIO COLLEGE, TARKIO MO 64491
GUINN, TONEY, SAYRE JUNIOR COLLEGE, SAYRE, OK   73662
GUISTI, BRUCE, PHIL DEPT, S ILLINOIS UNIV, CARBONDALE IL 62901
GULESERIAN, THEODORE, PHILOSOPHY DEPT, ARIZONA STATE UNIV, TEMPE AZ   85281
GULL, RICHARD, PHIL DEPT, UNIV OF MICHIGAN, FLINT MI 48503
GULLEY, ANTHONY, PHILOSOPHY DEPT, IMMAC CONCEPTION SEM, TROY NY 12180
GUMP, M ARTHUR, PHILOSOPHY DEPT, SKYLINE COLLEGE, SAN BRUNO CA 94066
GUMZ, F A, PHILOSOPHY DEPT, WARTBURG COLLEGE, WAVERLY IA 50677
GUNDERSON, KEITH, PHIL DEPT, UNIV OF MINNESOTA, MINNEAPOLIS MN 55455
GUNT, JAMES D, PHIL & RELIG AREA, SHAW UNIVERSITY, RALEIGH NC 27602
GUNTER, PETE A Y, PHILOSOPHY DEPT, N TEXAS STATE UNIV, DENTON TX 76203
GUPTA, BINA, PHIL DEPT, S ILLINOIS UNIV, CARBONDALE IL 62901
GURCZAK, FRANCIS, HUMAN DIV, MOUNT ST MARY COL, HOOKSETT NH 03106
GURLAND, ROBERT, PHIL DEPT, NEW YORK UNIVERSITY, NEW YORK NY 10003
GURLEY, BETTY, PHIL DEPT, MOREHEAD STATE UNIV, MOREHEAD KY 40351
GURTHRIE, GEORGE, PHIL DEPT, UNIVERSITY OF TOLEDO, TOLEDO OH 43606
GUSTAFSON, DONALD F, PHIL DEPT, UNIV OF CINCINNATI, CINCINNATI OH 45221
GUSTAFSON, JAMES W, PHIL & FINE ARTS, N ESSEX COM COL, HAVERHILL MA 01830
GUSTAFSON, ROBERT, PHIL & RELIG DEPT, PEMBROKE ST UNIV, PEMBROKE NC 28372
GUSTASON, WILLIAM W, PHIL DEPT, PURDUE UNIVERSITY, LAFAYETTE IN 47907
GUSTAVSSON, ROGER, PHIL & REL, DEPAUW UNIVERSITY, GREENCASTLE IN 46135
GUTENSTEIN, LENORE L, PHILOSOPHY DEPT, UNIV OF WISCONSIN, MADISON WI 53706
GUTH, FRANCIS, PHILOSOPHY DEPT, ALGOMA COLLEGE, SALT ST MARIE ONT   CAN
GUTHRIE JR, S C, HIST-DOCTRINAL DEPT, COLUMBIA THEOL SEM, DECATUR GA   30031
GUTHRIE, GEORGE, PHIL DEPT, UNIVERSITY OF TOLEDO, TOLEDO OH 43606
GUTHRIE, HUNTER, PHIL DEPT, ST JOSEPH'S COL, PHILADELPHIA PA 19131
GUTMAN, A, PHILOSOPHY DEPT, UNIV OF TORONTO, TORONTO ONT   CAN
GUTMANN, JAMES, PHIL DEPT, COLUMBIA UNIVERSITY, NEW YORK NY 10027
GUTTING, GARY, PHIL DEPT, UNIV OF NOTRE DAME, NOTRE DAME IN 46556
GUY JR, ALFRED H, PHIL & REL DEPT, UNIV OF BALTIMORE, BALTIMORE MD   21201
GUY, FRITZ, LOMA LINDA UNIV, RIVERSIDE, CA 92505
GUYER, PAUL D, PHIL DEPT, UNIV OF PITTSBURGH, PITTSBURGH PA 15260
GUZIKOWSKI, MAX, PHIL DEPT, TRINITY COLLEGE, WASHINGTON DC 20017
GWALTNEY, MARILYN, PHILOSOPHY DEPT, MERCYHURST COLLEGE, ERIE PA 16501
HAACK, DUANE G, ENG DEPT, U S MILITARY ACAD, WEST POINT NY 10996
HAANSTAD, PAUL J, PHILOSOPHY DEPT, UNIV OF UTAH, SALT LAKE CTY UT   84112
HAAS, JAMES A, PHIL DEPT, KING'S COLLEGE, WILKES BARRE PA 18711
HAAS, KENNETH E, PHIL DEPT, HAMLINE UNIVERSITY, ST PAUL MN 55104
HABER, TED, PHILOSOPHY DEPT, EDINBORO ST COL, EDINBORO PA 16412
HABERMEHL, F, APPL ARTS SCH, NIAGARA COLLEGE, WELLAND ONT   CAN
HABERMEHL, LAWRENCE, PHIL DEPT, AMERICAN INTERNAT COL, SPRINGFIELD MA   01109
HACHEY, MERCEDES, PHIL DEPT, SAINT JOSEPH'S COL, NORTH WINDHAM ME   04062
HACKER, EDWARD A, PHIL & REL DEPT, NORTHEASTERN UNIV, BOSTON MA   02115
HACKETT, STUART C, PHIL DEPT, WHEATON COLLEGE, WHEATON IL   60187
HACKLER, CHRIS, PHIL DEPT, E TENNESSEE ST UNIV, JOHNSON CITY TN   37601
HACKMANN, E EDWARD, PHILOSOPHY DEPT, CAPITAL UNIV, COLUMBUS OH   43209
HACKSTAFF, L H, PHIL DEPT, WABASH COLLEGE, CRAWFORDSVL IN   47933
HADCAD, JAMIL, PHIL DEPT, COL VIEUX-MONTREAL, MONTREAL QUE   CAN
HADCOX, JACK, PHILOSOPHY DEPT, UNIV OF TEXAS, EL PASO TX 79968
HADDOX, M BRUCE, PHIL DEPT, SIMPSON COLLEGE, INDIANOLA IA 50125
HADEN, JAMES, PHILOSOPHY DEPT, COLLEGE OF WOOSTER, WOOSTER OH 44691
HADGOPOULOS, DEMETRIUS, PHIL DEPT, WAYNE STATE UNIV, DETROIT MI 48202
HAECKER, DOROTHY A, PHILOSOPHY DEPT, CALIFORNIA ST UNIV, CHICO CA 95926
HAGAN, WILLIAM, PHILOSOPHY DEPT, CAL STATE COL, DOMINGUEZ HLS CA 90747
HAGEN, CHARLES, PHIL DEPT, UNIV OF MICHIGAN, ANN ARBOR MI 48104
HAGEN, FRED W, PHILOSOPHY DEPT, UNIV OF UTAH, SALT LAKE CTY UT 84112
HAGEN, JOHN, PHILOSOPHY DEPT, UNIV OF TEXAS, AUSTIN TX 78712

HAGEN, LOREN, NORTHWEST COLLEGE, KIRKLAND, WA 98033
HAGENSICK, PAUL, SOC SCI DEPT, PORTLAND COM COLLEGE, PORTLAND OR 97219
HAGGARD, F P, PHIL & RELIG DEPT, NC WESLEYAN COLLEGE, ROCKY MOUNT NC 27801
HAGGERTY, WILLIAM J, PHIL DEPT, BOSTON COLLEGE, CHESTNUT HILL MA 02167
HAGIUS, HUGH, PHIL DEPT, COLUMBIA UNIVERSITY, NEW YORK NY 10027
HAGNER, DAVID, PHIL DEPT, UNIV OF CINCINNATI, CINCINNATI OH 45221
HAHN, LEWIS E, PHIL DEPT, S ILLINOIS UNIV, CARBONDALE IL 62901
HAHNFELD, JOHN H, HUMAN DIV, CURRY COLLEGE, MILTON MA 02186
HAHNLEN, LEE, REL & PHIL DIV, GRACE COLLEGE, WINONA LAKE IN 46590
HAIGHT, DAVID F, PHIL DEPT, PLYMOUTH STATE COL, PLYMOUTH NH 03264
HAIGHT, E F, PHILOSOPHY DEPT, BAPTIST COLLEGE, CHARLESTON SC 29411
HAILEY, J R, PHIL & RELIG DEPT, NC WESLEYAN COLLEGE, ROCKY MOUNT NC 27801
HAILPARN, MICHAEL, PHILOSOPHY DEPT, PATERSON COL OF NJ, WAYNE NJ 07470
HAINES, BYRON L, PHIL DEPT, PORTLAND ST UNIV, PORTLAND OR 97207
HAINES, SHARON, PHILOSOPHY DEPT, UNIV OF UTAH, SALT LAKE CTY UT 84112
HAINES, WAYNE, PHIL DEPT, LEWIS COLLEGE, LOCKPORT IL 60441
HALADUS, JEROME J, PHIL DEPT, PROVIDENCE COLLEGE, PROVIDENCE RI 02919
HALARD, PAUL, PHIL DEPT, ST XAVIER COLLEGE, CHICAGO IL 60655
HALBASCH, K E, PHIL DEPT, UNIV OF CONNECTICUT, STORRS CT 06268
HALBERSTADT, W H, PHIL DEPT, UNIV OF NEVADA, RENO NV 89507
HALBERSTAM, JOSHUA, PHILOSOPHY DEPT, BROOKDALE COM COL, LINCROFT NJ 07738
HALBFASS, WILHELM, PHIL DEPT, BROCK UNIVERSITY, ST CATHARINES ONT CAN
HALBROOK, STEPHEN P, PHIL DEPT, TUSKEGEE INSTITUTE, TUSKEGEE INST AL 36088
HALBROOKS, G THOMAS, HUMANITIES DIV, SOUTHSIDE VA COM COL, ALBERTA VA 23821
HALE, WIMBLEY, RELIG & PHIL DEPT, CLARK COLLEGE, ATLANTA GA 30314
HALEY, MARY ALICE, PHIL DEPT, CREIGHTON UNIV, OMAHA NE 68178
HALEY, S, PHILOSOPHY DEPT, UNIV OF ALBERTA, EDMONTON ALB CAN
HALFTER, WILLIAM, PHIL DEPT, ELMHURST COLLEGE, ELMHURST IL 60126
HALL JR, THOMAS O, PHIL & RELIG, VA COMMONWEALTH UNIV, RICHMOND VA 23220
HALL, B FRANK, PHIL DEPT, UNIV OF N CAROLINA, WILMINGTON NC 28401
HALL, CARL H, FINE ARTS DEPT, YUBA COLLEGE, MARYSVILLE CA 95901
HALL, DAVID, PHILOSOPHY DEPT, UNIV OF TEXAS, EL PASO TX 79968
HALL, ELTON A, PHILOSOPHY DEPT, CALIFORNIA ST UNIV, FRESNO CA 93740
HALL, HARRISON B, PHILOSOPHY DEPT, UNIV OF DELAWARE, NEWARK DE 19711
HALL, JAMES H, PHILOSOPHY DEPT, UNIV OF RICHMOND, RICHMOND VA 23173
HALL, JAY, HUMAN & PHIL, SANTA ROSA JR COL, SANTA ROSA CA 95401
HALL, JOHN DAVID, PHIL DEPT, OLIVET NAZARENE COL, KANKAKEE IL 60901
HALL, KENNETH H, PHIL DEPT, UNIV OF MARYLAND, COLLEGE PARK MD 20742
HALL, MICHAEL, PHILOSOPHY DEPT, OHIO STATE UNIV, NEWARK OH 43055
HALL, PATRICK, HIST & PHIL DEPT, FAIRLEIGH DICKINSON, MADISON NJ 07940
HALL, R A, PHILOSOPHY DEPT, UNIV OF LETHBRIDGE, LETHBRIDGE ALB CAN
HALL, RICHARD J, PHIL DEPT, MICHIGAN STATE UNIV, EAST LANSING MI 48823
HALL, RICHARD, PHIL DEPT, WAYNE STATE UNIV, DETROIT MI 48202
HALL, ROBERT W, PHILOSOPHY DEPT, UNIV OF VERMONT, BURLINGTON VT 05401
HALL, ROBERT, PHIL DEPT, UNIVERSITY OF KANSAS, LAWRENCE KS 66044
HALL, ROBERT, PHIL DEPT, COL OF STEUBENVILLE, STEUBENVILLE OH 43952
HALL, RONALD, SOC & PHIL DEPT, FRANCIS MARION COL, FLORENCE SC 29501
HALL, TERRY A, FINE ARTS DEPT, ALPENA COM COL, ALPENA MI 49707
HALL, TERRY R, PHIL DEPT, OKLAHOMA STATE UNIV, STILLWATER OK 74074
HALL, THOR, PHIL & RELIG, UNIV OF TENNESSEE, CHATTANOOGA TN 37401
HALLAM, R F D, PHIL DEPT, UNIV OF NW BRUNSWICK, FREDERICTON N B CAN
HALLBERG, FRED, PHIL & RELIG, UNIV OF NORTH IOWA, CEDAR FALLS IA 50613
HALLBORG, ROBERT, HUMAN DIV, D'YOUVILLE COLLEGE, BUFFALO NY 14201
HALLIE, PHILIP P, PHILOSOPHY DEPT, WESLEYAN UNIV, MIDDLETOWN CT 06457
HALLMAN, RALPH J, SOC SCI DEPT, PASADENA CY COLLEGE, PASADENA CA 91106
HALLSTEIN, JOSEPH, PHILOSOPHY DEPT, QUEENS COLLEGE, FLUSHING NY 11367
HALPIN, JOHN T, PHIL DEPT, HOLY APOSTLES COL, CROMWELL CT 06416
HALPIN, JOHN, PHIL DEPT, MANHATTAN COLLEGE, RIVERDALE NY 10471
HALPIN, MARLENE, PHIL DEPT, MOLLOY COLLEGE, ROCKVILLE NY 11570
HALVORSON, PHILLIP, CREATIVE ARTS DEPT, MUSKEGON COM COL, MUSKEGON MI 49443
HAMBLIN, FRANCES M, GEN STUD COL, ROCHESTER INST TECH, ROCHESTER NY 14623
HAMBLIN, PETER D, PHIL DEPT, UNIV OF ROCHESTER, ROCHESTER NY 14627
HAMBOURGER, ROBERT, PHILOSOPHY DEPT, UNIV OF WISCONSIN, MADISON WI 53706
HAMBURG, CARL H, PHIL DEPT, TULANE UNIVERSITY, NEW ORLEANS LA 70118

HAMBY, JAMES H, ENG & PHIL, SE MISSOURI ST COL, CAPE GIRARDEA MO 63701
HAMEL, ALBERT F, PHIL DEPT, UNIV OF HARTFORD, WEST HARTFORD CT 06117
HAMILTON, DAN, SOC SCI DEPT, ST PETERSBURG JR COL, ST PETERSBURG FL 33733
HAMILTON, J BROOKE, PHIL DEPT, TUSKEGEE INSTITUTE, TUSKEGEE INST AL 36088
HAMILTON, JAMES R, PHIL DEPT, KANSAS ST UNIVERSITY, MANHATTAN KS 66506
HAMILTON, JAMES, PHIL & REL DIV, ASBURY COLLEGE, WILMORE KY 40390
HAMILTON, ROBERT H, SOC SCI AREA, COLUMBIA JUNIOR COL, COLUMBIA CA 95310
HAMILTON, SAM M, PHILOSOPHY DEPT, FORT HAYS KAN ST COL, HAYS KS 67601
HAMILTON, WAYNE, PHIL & RELIG DEPT, FINDLAY COLLEGE, FINDLAY OH 45840
HAMILTON, WILLIAM F, PHIL DEPT, WASHINGTON UNIV, ST LOUIS MO 63130
HAMLIN, HOWARD P, PHIL DEPT, UNIV OF TENNESSEE, KNOXVILLE TN 37916
HAMMER, LOUIS Z, PHIL DEPT, RENSSELAER POLYTECH, TROY NY 12181
HAMMITT, VIRGINIA, PHIL & RELIG DEPT, COLGATE UNIVERSITY, HAMILTON NY 13346
HAMMOND, GUYTON B, PHIL & RELIG, VA POLYTECH INST, BLACKSBURG VA 24061
HAMMOND, JOHN L, PHIL DEPT, PORTLAND ST UNIV, PORTLAND OR 97207
HAMMOND, JOHN, PHILOSOPHY DEPT, ALVERNO COLLEGE, MILWAUKEE WI 53215
HAMMOND, LEWIS M, PHIL DEPT, UNIV OF VIRGINIA, CHARLOTTESVL VA 22903
HAMMOND, PHILLIP E, SOC DEPT, UNIV OF ARIZONA, TUCSON AZ 85721
HAMPSCH, GEORGE H, PHIL DEPT, COL OF HOLY CROSS, WORCESTER MA 01610
HAMPTON, MARIEL, PHILOSOPHY DEPT, JUDSON BAPTIST COL, PORTLAND OR 97220
HAMRE, JAMES, PHIL DIV, WALDORF COLLEGE, FOREST CITY IA 50436
HAMRICK, WILLIAM S, PHIL STUD DEPT, S ILLINOIS UNIV, EDWARDSVILLE IL 62025
HANAGAN, JOHN J, PHIL DEPT, ST MICHAEL'S COLLEGE, WINOOSKI VT 05404
HANAK, WALTER K, SOC SCI DIV, SHEPHERD COLLEGE, SHEPHERDTOWN WV 25443
HANCOCK, R N, PHIL DEPT, UNIV OF CONNECTICUT, STORRS CT 06268
HANCOCK, THOMAS, PHIL DEPT, UNIV OF ILLINOIS, URBANA IL 61801
HANDY, ROLLO L, PHIL DEPT, ST UNIV OF NY, AMHERST NY 14226
HANDY, T E D, PHILOSOPHY DEPT, QUEEN'S UNIVERSITY, KINGSTON ONT CAN
HANEN, MARSHA P, PHILOSOPHY DEPT, UNIV OF CALGARY, CALGARY 44 ALB CAN
HANEY, DOROTHY A, PHILOSOPHY DEPT, MARYWOOD COLLEGE, SCRANTON PA 18509
HANEY, M ESTES, PHIL & REL DIV, PASADENA COLLEGE, PASADENA CA 91104
HANEY, TERRENCE E, HUMAN DEPT, HONOLULU COM COL, HONOLULU HI 96817
HANFORD, JACK T, HUMAN DEPT, FERRIS ST COLLEGE, BIG RAPIDS MI 49307
HANG, PAUL, PHIL DEPT, NAZARETH COLLEGE, NAZARETH MI 49074
HANGERMAN SR, MANI G, PHIL DEPT, MARYGROVE COLLEGE, DETROIT MI 48221
HANINK, JAMES, PHIL DEPT, MICHIGAN STATE UNIV, EAST LANSING MI 48823
HANKE, JOHN W, PHILOSOPHY DEPT, UNIV OF RHODE ISLAND, KINGSTON RI 02881
HANKS, DONALD K, LOUISIANA ST UNIV, NEW ORLEANS, LA 70122
HANLEY, KATHARINE ROSE, PHIL DEPT, LE MOYNE COLLEGE, SYRACUSE NY 13214
HANLON, THOMAS JOSEPH, PHILOSOPHY DEPT, UNIV OF TEXAS, AUSTIN TX 78712
HANLY, C M T, PHILOSOPHY DEPT, UNIV OF TORONTO, TORONTO ONT CAN
HANLY, KEN, PHILOSOPHY DEPT, BRANDON UNIVERSITY, BRANDON MAN CAN
HANN, RICHARD K, IMPERIAL VALLEY COL, IMPERIAL, CA 92251
HANNA, ALLAN A, PHIL DEPT, UNIV OF WEST ONTARIO, LONDON ONT CAN
HANNA, JOSEPH F, PHIL DEPT, MICHIGAN STATE UNIV, EAST LANSING MI 48823
HANNA, THOMAS L, PHIL DEPT, UNIV OF FLORIDA, GAINESVILLE FL 32611
HANNAFORD, ROBERT, PHILOSOPHY DEPT, RIPON COLLEGE, RIPON WI 54971
HANNUM, HAROLD B, LOMA LINDA UNIV, RIVERSIDE, CA 92505
HANSEN, CARL L, REL & PHIL, BETHANY COLLEGE, LINDSBORG KS 67456
HANSEN, CHAD, PHIL DEPT, UNIV OF PITTSBURGH, PITTSBURGH PA 15260
HANSEN, CLIFFORD, WILBERFORCE UNIV, WILBERFORCE, OH 45384
HANSEN, FOREST, PHIL DEPT, LAKE FOREST COLLEGE, LAKE FOREST IL 60045
HANSEN, JAMES E, PHIL DEPT, BROCK UNIVERSITY, ST CATHARINES ONT CAN
HANSEN, LINDA, PHILOSOPHY DEPT, MARQUETTE UNIV, MILWAUKEE WI 53233
HANSEN, MICHAEL M, PHIL DEPT, UNIV OF NEBRASKA, LINCOLN NE 68502
HANSON, CLIFFORD, PHIL DEPT, DANA COLLEGE, BLAIR NE 68008
HANSON, DELBERT, PHILOSOPHY DEPT, BIOLA COLLEGE, LA MIRADA CA 90638
HANSON, LUTHER C, LANG & LIT DEPT, PLATTE JR COLLEGE, COLUMBUS NE 68601
HANSON, PHILIP, RELIG & PHIL DEPT, WILMINGTON COL, WILMINGTON OH 45177
HANSON, WILLIAM H, PHIL DEPT, UNIV OF MINNESOTA, MINNEAPOLIS MN 55455
HANTZ, HAROLD D, PHIL DEPT, UNIV OF ARKANSAS, FAYETTEVILLE AR 72701
HANU-S, JEROME, PHILOSOPHY DEPT, CONCEPTIONS SEM COL, CONCEPTION MO 64433
HARAN, JOHN P, PHIL DEPT, COL OF HOLY CROSS, WORCESTER MA 01610
HARBERT, DAVID L, PHIL DEPT, COL AT OSWEGO, OSWEGO NY 13126

HARBISON, WARREN, PHIL DEPT, SYRACUSE UNIVERSITY, SYRACUSE NY 13210
HARDER, ALLEN, PHIL DEPT, IOWA STATE UNIV, AMES IA 50010
HARDER, ROBERT L, HUMAN & PHIL DIV, UNIVERSITY OF TAMPA, TAMPA FL 33606
HARDGRAVE, HANNAH, PHIL DEPT, W ILLINOIS UNIV, MACOMB IL 61455
HARDIN, C L, PHIL DEPT, SYRACUSE UNIVERSITY, SYRACUSE NY 13210
HARDISON, RICHARD C, SOC SCI DIV, GLENDALE COM COL, GLENDALE CA 91208
HARDMAN, KEITH JORDAN, PHIL & RELIG, URSINUS COLLEGE, COLLEGEVILLE PA 19426
HARDWICH, CHARLEY D, PHIL DEPT, THE AMERICAN UNIV, WASHINGTON DC 20016
HARDWICK, CHARLES S, PHILOSOPHY DEPT, TEXAS TECH UNIV, LUBBOCK TX 79409
HARDWIG, JOHN R, PHIL DEPT, UNIV OF TENNESSEE, KNOXVILLE TN 37916
HARDY, GILBERT G, PHIL DEPT, UNIVERSITY OF DALLAS, IRVING TX 75062
HARDY, H, UNIV OF TRINITY COL, TORONTO 181, ONT CAN
HARDY, J G, SOC HIST & POLIT SCI, ALABAMA STATE UNIV, MONTGOMERY AL 36101
HARDY, LOUISE S, PHIL DEPT, UNIV OF N CAROLINA, CHAPEL HILL NC 27514
HARE, PETER H, PHIL DEPT, ST UNIV OF NY, AMHERST NY 14226
HARE, WILLIAM F, PHIL DEPT, DALHOUSIE UNIVERSITY, HALIFAX N S CAN
HARFORD, SAMUEL A, SOC SCI DIV, PARKERSBURG COM COL, PARKERSBURG WV 26101
HARGROVE, EUGENE, PHIL DEPT, UNIV OF MISSOURI, COLUMBIA MO 65201
HARING, ELLEN S, PHIL DEPT, UNIV OF FLORIDA, GAINESVILLE FL 32611
HARKINS, CYNTHIA, HUMANITIES DIV, SHERIDAN COLLEGE, SHERIDAN WY 82801
HARKINS, VERNON, PHILOSOPHY DEPT, SEATTLE UNIVERSITY, SEATTLE WA 98122
HARM, FREDERICK R, HUMAN DEPT, MCHENRY CTY COLLEGE, CRYSTAL LAKE IL 60014
HARMAN, GILBERT, PHIL DEPT, PRINCETON UNIVERSITY, PRINCETON NJ 08540
HARMAN, JOSEPH, COMMUNIC & HUMAN, OAKLAND COM COLLEGE, AUBURN HTS MI 48057
HARNISH, ROBERT M, PHILOSOPHY DEPT, UNIV OF ARIZONA, TUCSON AZ 85721
HARPER, DAVID, LIBR STUD & COMMUNIC, CAMBRIAN COLLEGE, SUDBURY ONT CAN
HARPER, J S, PHIL DEPT, UNIV OF FLORIDA, GAINESVILLE FL 32611
HARPER, MARY-ANGELA, PHIL DEPT, THE AMERICAN UNIV, WASHINGTON DC 20016
HARPER, VICKI, PHIL DEPT, UNIV OF MINNESOTA, MINNEAPOLIS MN 55455
HARPER, WILLIAM L, PHIL DEPT, UNIV OF WEST ONTARIO, LONDON ONT CAN
HARRAH, DAVID, PHIL DEPT, UNIV OF CALIFORNIA, RIVERSIDE CA 92502
HARRELL, JEAN G, PHILOSOPHY DEPT, CALIFORNIA ST UNIV, HAYWARD CA 94542
HARRIES, KARSTEN, PHIL DEPT, YALE UNIVERSITY, NEW HAVEN CT 06520
HARRIMAN, CHARLES J, HUMAN DEPT, COLLEGE OF SANTA FE, SANTA FE NM 87501
HARRINGTON, EUGENE J, PHIL DEPT, COL OF HOLY CROSS, WORCESTER MA 01610
HARRINGTON, JOHN, PHIL DEPT, LEWIS & CLARK COL, PORTLAND OR 97219
HARRINGTON, JOHN, PHILOSOPHY DEPT, UNIV OF OREGON, EUGENE OR 97403
HARRINGTON, KATHLEEN W, PHIL DEPT, EMORY UNIVERSITY, ATLANTA GA 30322
HARRINGTON, MICHAEL, PHIL & RELIG, UNIV OF MISSISSIPPI, UNIVERSITY MS 38677
HARRINGTON, R WARD, HUMAN DEPT, NEW YORK CY COM COL, BROOKLYN NY 11201
HARRION III, FRANK R, PHIL & REL DEPT, UNIV OF GEORGIA, ATHENS GA 30602
HARRIS JR, C E, PHIL & HUM DEPT, TEXAS A & M UNIV, COL STATION TX 77843
HARRIS, BENEDICT O, PHIL DEPT, CANISIUS COLLEGE, BUFFALO NY 14208
HARRIS, BOND, KENTUCKY WESLEYAN COL, OWENSBORO, KY 42301
HARRIS, CHARLES MOORE, MISSOURI WESTERN COL, ST JOSEPH, MO 64507
HARRIS, ERROL E, PHIL DEPT, NORTHWESTERN UNIV, EVANSTON IL 60201
HARRIS, FREDERICK P, PHIL DEPT, OREGON STATE UNIV, CORVALLIS OR 97331
HARRIS, GREGORY, PHILOSOPHY DEPT, DUQUESNE UNIV, PITTSBURGH PA 15219
HARRIS, H JOHN, PHIL DEPT, CEN WASH STATE COL, ELLENSBURG WA 98926
HARRIS, H S, GLENDON COLLEGE, TORONTO, ONT CAN
HARRIS, JAMES R, PHILOSOPHY DEPT, MARIETTA COLLEGE, MARIETTA OH 45750
HARRIS, M, PHIL OF EDUC & HIST, ONTARIO INSTITUTE, TORONTO ONT CAN
HARRIS, R BAINE, PHIL DEPT, EAST KENTUCKY UNIV, RICHMOND KY 40475
HARRIS, ROBERT T, PHIL DEPT, FRAMINGHAM STATE COL, FRAMINGHAM MA 01701
HARRIS, STEVEN, SOC SCI DEPT, BENNINGTON COLLEGE, BENNINGTON VT 05201
HARRIS, WILL C, PHIL DEPT, UNIV OF MISSOURI, ST LOUIS MO 63121
HARRISON III, FRANK R, PHIL & REL DEPT, UNIV OF GEORGIA, ATHENS GA 30602
HARRISON, A R, PHIL & HIST DEPT, EL RENO JUNIOR COL, EL RENO OK 73036
HARRISON, CHRISTIAN L, PHIL DEPT, ARK POLYTECH COL, RUSSELLVILLE AR 72801
HARRISON, CRAIG, PHIL DEPT, CALIFORNIA ST UNIV, SAN FRANCISCO CA 94132
HARRISON, E, HUMANITIES DIV, N VIRGINIA COM COL, ALEXANDRIA VA 22311
HARRISON, EDWARD H, HUMAN DIV, GLOUCESTER CO COL, SEWELL NJ 08080
HARRISON, JOAN, PHIL DEPT, HUNTER COLLEGE, NEW YORK NY 10021
HARRISON, STANLEY, PHIL DEPT, LE MOYNE COLLEGE, SYRACUSE NY 13214

HARRY, SHIRLEY A, PHIL & RELIG STUD, CRAFTON HILLS COL, YUCAIPA CA   92399
HART, ALAN, PHILOSOPHY DEPT, UNIV OF AKRON, AKRON OH 44325
HART, ALLAN, PHIL DEPT, MICHIGAN STATE UNIV, EAST LANSING MI   48823
HART, CARL, PHIL DEPT, UNIV OF MICHIGAN, ANN ARBOR MI 48104
HART, D S, PHILOSOPHY DEPT, QUEEN'S UNIVERSITY, KINGSTON ONT   CAN
HART, DONALD B, PHIL DEPT, UNIV OF N CAROLINA, CHAPEL HILL NC 27514
HART, JAMES, PHILOSOPHY DEPT, UNIV OF WATERLOO, WATERLOO ONT   CAN
HART, JOHN, PHIL DEPT, UNIV OF CINCINNATI, CINCINNATI OH 45221
HART, NANCY, PHIL DEPT, UNIV OF MICHIGAN, ANN ARBOR MI 48104
HART, RICHARD, PHIL DEPT, ST UNIV OF NY, STONY BROOK NY 11790
HART, SAMUEL L, FAIRLEIGH DICKINSON, TEANECK, NJ 07666
HART, WILBUR D, PHIL DEPT, UNIV OF MICHIGAN, ANN ARBOR MI 48104
HARTENBERG, SAM, HUMAN DEPT, YORK COLLEGE, JAMAICA NY 11432
HARTER, EDWARD D, PHIL DEPT, UNIVERSITY OF HAWAII, HONOLULU HI 96822
HARTLE, ANTHONY, ENG DEPT, U S MILITARY ACAD, WEST POINT NY 10996
HARTLEY, J, UNIV OF ST MICHAEL'S, TORONTO 181, ONT   CAN
HARTLEY, T J A, HUMANITIES DEPT, CENTENNIAL COLLEGE, SCARBOROUGH ONT   CAN
HARTMAN, DONALD T, PHILOSOPHY DEPT, JUNIATA COLLEGE, HUNTINGDON PA 16652
HARTMAN, EDWIN, PHILOSOPHY DEPT, UNIV OF PENN, PHILADELPHIA PA 19174
HARTMAN, RICHARD O, PHIL DEPT, FLORIDA SOUTHERN COL, LAKELAND FL 33802
HARTMAN, ROBERT H, WESTERN MARYLAND COL, WESTMINSTER, MD 21157
HARTNACK, JUSTUS, PHIL DEPT, COLLEGE AT BROCKPORT, BROCKPORT NY 14420
HARTNETT, JOHN K, PHIL DEPT, BOSTON COLLEGE, CHESTNUT HILL MA 02167
HARTNETT, RICHARD, ENG & PHIL DEPT, KIRKLAND HALL COL, OCEAN CITY MD   21842
HARTSHORNE, CHARLES, PHILOSOPHY DEPT, UNIV OF TEXAS, AUSTIN TX 78712
HARTSHORNE, M H, PHIL & RELIG DEPT, COLGATE UNIVERSITY, HAMILTON NY 13346
HARTSOCK, DONALD G, PHIL DEPT, COLORADO ST UNIV, FORT COLLINS CO 80521
HARTT, JOEL, PHIL DEPT, GEORGE WILLIAMS UNIV, MONTREAL 107 QUE   CAN
HARTWEG, NORMAN, PHIL DEPT, UNIV OF MICHIGAN, ANN ARBOR MI 48104
HARTWIG, H, PHILOSOPHY DEPT, UNIV OF TORONTO, TORONTO ONT   CAN
HARVEY, PETER J, PHILOSOPHY DEPT, WESLEYAN UNIV, MIDDLETOWN CT 06457
HARVEY, SAMUEL P, HUM & PHIL, SOUTH UNIV A & M COL, NEW ORLEANS LA 70126
HARVEY, W R C, PHILOSOPHY DEPT, VICTORIA UNIV, TORONTO 181 ONT   CAN
HARVEY, WARREN, PHILOSOPHY DEPT, MCGILL UNIVERSITY, MONTREAL QUE   CAN
HARWARD, DONALD W, PHILOSOPHY DEPT, UNIV OF DELAWARE, NEWARK DE 19711
HASHIMOTO, RENTARO, PHIL DEPT, MANHATTAN COLLEGE, RIVERDALE NY 10471
HASKELL, ELLERY B, PHILOSOPHY DEPT, ALBRIGHT COLLEGE, READING PA 19604
HASKELL, JONAN, HUMAN DEPT, SOUTHEASTERN COM COL, W BURLINGTON IA 52655
HASKER, WILLIAM, PHIL DEPT, HUNTINGTON COLLEGE, HUNTINGTON IN 46750
HASLETT, DAVID W, PHILOSOPHY DEPT, UNIV OF DELAWARE, NEWARK DE 19711
HASSEL, DAVID, PHIL DEPT, LOYOLA UNIVERSITY, CHICAGO IL 60626
HASSLER, CHRISTINE, PHILOSOPHY DEPT, MARQUETTE UNIV, MILWAUKEE WI 53233
HASSOL, MILTON, PHIL DEPT, LONG ISLAND UNIV, GREENVALE NY 11548
HATAB, LAWRENCE, PHIL DEPT, FORDHAM UNIVERSITY, BRONX NY 10458
HATCH, ORIN WALKER, BUSINESS & HUMAN, NEW MEXICO JR COL, HOBBS NM 88240
HATER, ROBERT J, LIBR ARTS FAC, ATHENAEUM OF OHIO, CINCINNATI OH 45230
HATFIELD, JOHN, SOC SCI DEPT, CAL ST POLYTECH UNIV, POMONA CA 91768
HATHAWAY, RONALD, PHIL DEPT, TEMPLE UNIVERSITY, PHILADELPHIA PA 19122
HATTIANGADI, J N, PHILOSOPHY DEPT, YORK UNIVERSITY, DOWNSVIEW ONT   CAN
HAUCK, FRED, PHIL DEPT, ATLANTIC UNION COL, S LANCASTER MA 01561
HAULE, JOHN, PHIL & REL DEPT, NORTHEASTERN UNIV, BOSTON MA 02115
HAUSER, JOHN DAVID, SOC SCI DEPT, CLATSOP COM COL, ASTORIA OR 97103
HAUSMAN, ALAN, PHILOSOPHY DEPT, OHIO STATE UNIV, COLUMBUS OH 43210
HAUSMAN, CARL R, PHILOSOPHY DEPT, PENN STATE UNIV, UNIV PARK PA 16802
HAUSMAN, DAVID B, PHIL DEPT, S METHODIST UNIV, DALLAS TX 75222
HAUSSER, HARRY, HIST & PHIL, MONTANA ST UNIV, BOZEMAN MT 59715
HAVER, RICHARD, PHIL DEPT, UNIV OF ROCHESTER, ROCHESTER NY 14627
HAVER, RONALD J, PHIL DEPT, ST UNIV OF NY, BINGHAMTON NY 13901
HAVERFIELD, ROGER, PHILOSOPHY DEPT, ALMA COLLEGE, ALMA MI 48801
HAVEY, WILLIAM B, PHILOSOPHY DEPT, UNIV OF S CAROLINA, COLUMBIA SC 29208
HAWI, SAMI S, PHIL DEPT, UNIV OF WISCONSIN, MILWAUKEE WI 53201
HAWKINS, DAVID, PHIL DEPT, UNIV OF COLORADO, BOULDER CO 80302
HAWKINS, JAMES P, SOC STUD DEPT, SANTA MONICA COL, SANTA MONICA CA 90405
HAWORTH, LAWRENCE L, PHILOSOPHY DEPT, UNIV OF WATERLOO, WATERLOO ONT   CAN

HAWTHORNE, JAMES, PHIL DEPT, UNIV OF MINNESOTA, MINNEAPOLIS MN 55455
HAY, GERALD C, PHIL DEPT, JOHN CARROLL UNIV, UNIVERSITY HT OH 44118
HAY, WILLIAM H, PHILOSOPHY DEPT, UNIV OF WISCONSIN, MADISON WI 53706
HAYDEN, VINCENT, PHIL DEPT, ST JOSEPH'S COL, PHILADELPHIA PA 19131
HAYES, PAUL, PHIL & RELIG DEPT, LEMOYNE-OWEN COL, MEMPHIS TN 38126
HAYES, VICTOR, PHIL & RELIG DEPT, DEFIANCE COLLEGE, DEFIANCE OH 43512
HAYES, WILLIAM H, PHILOSOPHY DEPT, CAL ST COL STANISLAUS, TURLOCK CA 95380
HAYMOND, WILLIAM S, PHIL DEPT, WEST VIRGINIA UNIV, MORGANTOWN WV 26506
HAYNES, L L, PHIL DEPT, SOUTH UNIV A & M COL, BATON ROUGE LA 70813
HAYNES, MARC, PHILOSOPHY DEPT, UNIV OF TEXAS, AUSTIN TX 78712
HAYNES, P, PHILOSOPHY DEPT, UNIV OF ALBERTA, EDMONTON ALB CAN
HAYNES, RICHARD P, PHIL DEPT, UNIV CF FLORIDA, GAINESVILLE FL 32611
HAYNES, THOMAS M, PHIL DEPT, LEHIGH UNIVERSITY, BETHLEHEM PA 18015
HAYS, BILL, PHIL DEPT, UNIV OF MISSOURI, COLUMBIA MO 65201
HAYWARD, JOHN FRANK, PHIL DEPT, S ILLINOIS UNIV, CARBONDALE IL 62901
HAZELTON, WILLIAM DEAN, PHIL DEPT, WHEATON COLLEGE, NORTON MA 02766
HAZEM, GEORGE A, ALLEGANY COM COL, CUMBERLAND, MD 21502
HEAGLE, JOHN, PHILOSOPHY DEPT, VITERBO COLLEGE, LA CROSSE WI 54601
HEALEY, JOSEPH, PHIL FACULTY, UNIV CF OTTAWA, OTTAWA ONT CAN
HEALY, MARGARET, HUMANITIES DIV, ROSEMONT COLLEGE, ROSEMONT PA 19010
HEANUE, H, ART & PHIL DEPT, LOS ANGELES TRADE COL, LOS ANGELES CA 90015
HEARD, GERALD C, REL & PHIL DEPT, LOUISIANA COLLEGE, PINEVILLE LA 71360
HEARN JR, THOMAS K, PHIL DEPT, COL WILLIAM & MARY, WILLIAMSBURG VA 23185
HEATH, PETER L, PHIL DEPT, UNIV OF VIRGINIA, CHARLOTTESVL VA 22903
HEATHERLY, CHERYL, PHIL DEPT, UNIV OF MISSOURI, COLUMBIA MO 65201
HEBERT, R L, PHILOSOPHY AREA, ROGER WILLIAMS COL, BRISTOL RI 02809
HECHT, F TORRENS, PHIL DEPT, LOYOLA UNIVERSITY, CHICAGO IL 60626
HECKMAN, JOHN H, BELLARMINE COLLEGE, LOUISVILLE, KY 40205
HEDMAN, CARL G, PHIL DEPT, UNIV OF WISCONSIN, MILWAUKEE WI 53201
HEELAN, PATRICK, PHIL DEPT, ST UNIV OF NY, STONY BROOK NY 11790
HEEREMA, ROBERT P, PHIL DEPT, CENTRAL UNIV OF IOWA, PELLA IA 50219
HEFFERMNAN, JAMES D, PHIL DEPT, UNIV OF THE PACIFIC, STOCKTON CA 95204
HEFFNER, JOHN H, PHILOSOPHY DEPT, LEBANON VLY COL, ANNVILLE PA 17003
HEGGIE, HENRY, LIBR STUD & COMMUNIC, CAMBRIAN COLLEGE, SUDBURY ONT CAN
HEICK, CECIL, SHORELINE COM COL, SEATTLE, WA 98133
HEIDE, PHILIP, SOC SCI DIV, MINOT STATE COL, MINOT ND 58701
HEIDELBERGER, HERBERT, PHILOSOPHY DEPT, UNIV OF MASS, AMHERST MA 01002
HEIDEMAN, EUGENE, PHIL DEPT, CENTRAL UNIV OF IOWA, PELLA IA 50219
HEIGES, KEN, PHILOSOPHY DEPT, UNIV CF WATERLOO, WATERLOO ONT CAN
HEIL, JOHN, PHIL DEPT, RANDOLPH-MACON COL, LYNCHBURG VA 24504
HEIM, MICHAEL R, PHIL DEPT, TULANE UNIVERSITY, NEW ORLEANS LA 70118
HEIMAN, ANBROSE, PHIL DEPT, ST JOSEPH'S COLLEGE, RENNSSELAER IN 47978
HEIN, HILDE S, PHIL DEPT, COL OF HOLY CROSS, WORCESTER MA 01610
HEIN, KARL, PHIL DEPT, UNIV OF WISCONSIN, STEVENS POINT WI 54481
HEINEN, JULITTA, ASSUMPTION COLLEGE, MENDHAM, NJ 07945
HEINTZ, JOHN, PHIL DEPT, UNIV OF N CAROLINA, CHAPEL HILL NC 27514
HEINTZ, LAWRENCE, PHIL DEPT, UNIV OF CALIFORNIA, SANTA BARBARA CA 93106
HEISER, JOHN H, PHIL DEPT, NIAGARA UNIVERSITY, NIAGARA UNIV NY 14109
HEISIG, JAMES W, PHIL & THEOL, DIVINE WORD COLLEGE, EPWORTH IA 52045
HEIZER, RUTH B, PHIL DEPT, GEORGETOWN COLLEGE, GEORGETOWN KY 40215
HELAL, GEORGES, PHILOSOPHY DEPT, UNIV DE MONTREAL, MONTREAL QUE CAN
HELBIG, ED, PHILOSOPHY DEPT, FOREST PARK COM COL, ST LOUIS MO 63110
HELBIG, FREDERICK, PHIL DEPT, FORDHAM UNIVERSITY, BRONX NY 10458
HELD, VIRGINIA, PHIL DEPT, HUNTER COLLEGE, NEW YORK NY 10021
HELCUSER, F J, PHIL DEPT, ST CHAS BORROMEO SEM, PHILADELPHIA PA 19151
HELEWA, JOHN, SETON HALL UNIV, SOUTH ORANGE, NJ 07079
HELLEGERS, FREDERICK, PHILOSOPHY DEPT, WASH & JEFF COL, WASHINGTON PA 15301
HELLENTHAL, MARC, PHIL DEPT, BOSTON UNIVERSITY, BOSTON MA 02215
HELLER, LORRAINE, PHILOSOPHY DEPT, OHIO STATE UNIV, COLUMBUS OH 43210
HELLMAN, GEOFFREY P, PHIL DEPT, INDIANA UNIVERSITY, BLOOMINGTON IN 47401
HELLYER, LORNE, PHIL DEPT, COL VIEUX-MONTREAL, MONTREAL QUE CAN
HELM, BERTRAND, POLIT SCI & PHIL, SW MISSOURI ST U, SPRINGFIELD MO 65802
HELM, PAUL, HUMAN DEPT, DAVIDSON CO COM COL, LEXINGTON NC 27292
HELM, ROBERT M, PHIL DEPT, WAKE FOREST UNIV, WINSTON-SALEM NC 27109

HELMERS, FREDERICK J, PHIL DEPT, ADELPHI UNIVERSITY, GARDEN CITY NY   11530
HEMMENDINGER, DAVID, HUMAN DIV, RICHMOND COLLEGE, STATEN ISLAND NY   10301
HEMPEL, CARL G, PHIL DEPT, PRINCETON UNIVERSITY, PRINCETON NJ   08540
HEMS, J M, PHILOSOPHY DEPT, UNIV OF GUELPH, GUELPH ONT   CAN
HENDEL, CHARLES, PHIL DEPT, YALE UNIVERSITY, NEW HAVEN CT   06520
HENDERSON, E, PHIL DEPT, LOUISIANA ST UNIV, BATON ROUGE LA   70803
HENDERSON, EDGAR H, PHIL DEPT, FLORIDA STATE UNIV, TALLAHASSEE FL   32306
HENDERSON, JAMES, PHIL DEPT, UNIVERSITY OF TOLEDO, TOLEDO OH   43606
HENDERSON, T Y, PHILOSOPHY DEPT, UNIV OF SASKATCHEWAN, SASKATOON SAS   CAN
HENDLEY, BRIAN P, PHILOSOPHY DEPT, UNIV OF WATERLOO, WATERLOO ONT   CAN
HENDRICKS, M ELTON, PHILOSOPHY DEPT, WOFFORD COLLEGE, SPARTANBURG SC   29301
HENDRICKSON, K E, HIST & PHIL DEPT, MIDWESTERN UNIV, WICHITA FALLS TX   76308
HENDRICKSON, W F, BELLARMINE COLLEGE, LOUISVILLE, KY   40205
HENDRY, HERBERT E, PHIL DEPT, MICHIGAN STATE UNIV, EAST LANSING MI   48823
HENGSTELER, V E, PHILOSOPHY DEPT, CERRITOS COLLEGE, NORWALK CA   90605
HENKE, UWE, PHIL DEPT, SWARTHMORE COLLEGE, SWARTHMORE PA   19081
HENLEY, KENNETH I, PHIL DEPT, UNIV OF KENTUCKY, LEXINGTON KY   40506
HENNESSEY, LEO F, PHIL DEPT, FORT LAUDERDALE UNIV, FT LAUDERDALE FL   33301
HENNING, ROBERT, THEOL & PHIL, VENNARD COLLEGE, UNIVERSITY PK IA   52595
HENNINGER, WILLIAM, MATH & PHIL DEPT, OAKLAND COM COL, FARMINGTON MI   48024
HENNUY, GUSTAVE, PHILOSOPHY DEPT, UNIV DE MONCTON, MONCTON N B   CAN
HENRICH, DIETER, PHIL DEPT, COLUMBIA UNIVERSITY, NEW YORK NY   10027
HENRY JR, GRANVILLE C, PHIL DEPT, CLAREMONT MEN'S COL, CLAREMONT CA   91711
HENRY, CARL F H, THEOL DEPT, E BAPT THEOL SEM, PHILADELPHIA PA   19151
HENRY, DENNIS R, PHILOSOPHY DEPT, UNIV OF WISCONSIN, MADISON WI   53706
HENRY, W CAMERON, PHIL DEPT, UNIV OF WEST ONTARIO, LONDON ONT   CAN
HENRY, WESLEY, SOC & PHIL DEPT, TENN TECH UNIV, COOKEVILLE TN   38501
HENSON, DONALD A, PHIL & REL STUD, WILKES COLLEGE, WILKES BARRE PA   18703
HENSON, JERRY, HUMANITIES DIV, EASTFIELD COLLEGE, DALLAS TX   75149
HENSON, RICHARD G, PHILOSOPHY DEPT, RUTGERS UNIV, NEW BRUNSWICK NJ   08903
HENZE, DONALD, PHIL DEPT, CALIFORNIA ST UNIV, NORTHRIDGE CA   91324
HEPP, MAYLON H, PHILOSOPHY DEPT, DENISON UNIV, GRANVILLE OH   43023
HERBENICK, RAYMOND M, PHIL DEPT, UNIVERSITY OF DAYTON, DAYTON OH   45469
HERBERG, WILL, PHILOSOPHY DEPT, DREW UNIVERSITY, MADISON NJ   07940
HERBERT, GARY, PHIL DEPT, LOYOLA UNIVERSITY, NEW ORLEANS LA   70118
HERBERT, ROBERT T, PHILOSOPHY DEPT, UNIV OF OREGON, EUGENE OR   97403
HERBST, P, PHILOSOPHY DEPT, SIMON FRASER UNIV, BURNABY 2 B C   CAN
HERBSTER, WILLIAM H, PHIL DEPT, N ILLINOIS UNIV, DEKALB IL   60115
HERMAN, ARTHUR, PHIL DEPT, UNIV OF WISCONSIN, STEVENS POINT WI   54481
HERMAN, BARBARA, PHIL DEPT, MASS INST TECH, CAMBRIDGE MA   02139
HERMAN, CARL, PHIL DEPT, UNIV OF MISSOURI, COLUMBIA MO   65201
HERMAN, DANIEL J, PHIL & REL STUD, UNIV OF W FLORIDA, PENSACOLA FL   32504
HERMAN, STEVEN, ENG & HUM DEPT, WEST NW ENGLAND COL, SPRINGFIELD MA   01119
HERMANN, ROBERT M, PHIL DEPT, INDIANA UNIV OF PENN, INDIANA PA   15701
HERNANDEZ, JOHN P, PHIL DEPT, BAKERSFIELD COLLEGE, BAKERSFIELD CA   93305
HEROD, JOHN, PHILOSOPHY DEPT, UNIV OF ARIZONA, TUCSON AZ   85721
HERRERA, ROBERT, SETON HALL UNIV, SOUTH ORANGE, NJ   07079
HERRING, OWEN F, PHIL DEPT, LYCOMING COLLEGE, WILLIAMSPORT PA   17701
HERRMANN, R, PHIL DEPT, UNIV OF TENNESSEE, KNOXVILLE TN   37916
HERRMANN, RICHARD E, HUMAN DIV, VOLUNTEER ST COM COL, GALLATIN TN   37066
HERSH, THOMAS, PHIL DEPT, CALIFORNIA ST UNIV, NORTHRIDGE CA   91324
HERSH, WILLIAM J, REFLECTIVE AREA, SALVE REGINA COLLEGE, NEWPORT RI   02840
HERSTON, VICTOR D, PHIL DEPT, UNIVERSITY OF MIAMI, CORAL GABLES FL   33124
HERTZ, RICHARD, HUM & SOC SCI DIV, CAL INST OF TECH, PASADENA CA   91101
HERTZBERG, LARS H, PHILOSOPHY DEPT, UNIV OF ARIZONA, TUCSON AZ   85721
HERX, FREDERICK C, PHIL DEPT, COL OF HOLY CROSS, WORCESTER MA   01610
HERZBERGER, H G, PHILOSOPHY DEPT, UNIV OF TORONTO, TORONTO ONT   CAN
HESCHEL, ABRAHAM J, PHIL & REL DEPT, JEWISH THEOL SEM, NEW YORK NY   10027
HESLEP, ROBERT D, PHIL & REL DEPT, UNIV OF GEORGIA, ATHENS GA   30602
HESS, P, PHILOSOPHY DEPT, VICTORIA UNIV, TORONTO 181 ONT   CAN
HESS, WELDON ROBERT, RELIG & PHIL DIV, MALONE COLLEGE, CANTON OH   44709
HESTER, JOSEPH P, PHILOSOPHY DEPT, CAMPBELL COLLEGE, BUIE'S CREEK NC   27506
HESTER, MARCUS B, PHIL DEPT, WAKE FOREST UNIV, WINSTON-SALEM NC   27109
HETKO, ALEX, PHILOSOPHY DEPT, RUSSELL SAGE COL, TROY NY   12180

HEWETT, DAVID G, SOC SCI DIV, ALBANY JR COLLEGE, ALBANY GA 31705
HEWITT, THOMAS, RELIG & PHIL DEPT, GARDNER-WEBB COL, BOILING SPGS NC 28017
HEYER JR, GEORGE S, THEOL & HIST DEPT, AUSTIN THEOL SEM, AUSTIN TX 78705
HICKEY, DENIS, PHILOSOPHY DEPT, CYPRESS COLLEGE, CYPRESS CA 90630
HICKEY, JOHN T, HUMANITIES DEPT, SINCLAIR COM COL, DAYTON OH 45402
HICKMAN, DAVID, PHIL DEPT, UNIVERSITY OF IOWA, IOWA CITY IA 52240
HICKMAN, LARRY, PHILOSOPHY DEPT, UNIV OF TEXAS, AUSTIN TX 78712
HICKMAN, RANDALL CLARK, PHILOSOPHY DEPT, UNIV OF TEXAS, AUSTIN TX 78712
HICKS, D C, PHILOSOPHY DEPT, UNIV OF ALBERTA, EDMONTON ALB CAN
HICKS, JOE H, PHIL DEPT, S METHODIST UNIV, DALLAS TX 75222
HICKS, WILLIAM N, PHIL & REL DEPT, N CAROLINA ST UNIV, RALEIGH NC 27607
HIEBERT, CLARENCE, BIB & PHIL DEPT, TABOR COLLEGE, HILLSBORO KS 67063
HIGGINBOTHAM, JAMES, PHIL DEPT, COLUMBIA UNIVERSITY, NEW YORK NY 10027
HIGGINS, DAVID J, PHIL DEPT, WEST GEORGIA COLLEGE, CARROLLTON GA 30117
HIGGINS, T J, PHILOSOPHY DEPT, LOYOLA COLLEGE, BALTIMORE MD 21210
HIGGINS, WILLIAM, PHILOSOPHY DEPT, UNIV OF RHODE ISLAND, KINGSTON RI 02881
HIGH, DALLAS M, PHIL DEPT, UNIV OF KENTUCKY, LEXINGTON KY 40506
HIGHBY, PATRICIA, SOC SCI DEPT, EASTERN ARIZONA COL, THATCHER AZ 85301
HILBE, JOSEPH, ARTS & HUM DIV, LEEWARD COM COL, PEARL CITY HI 96782
HILDEBRAND, C D W, PHIL & REL, DEPAUW UNIVERSITY, GREENCASTLE IN 46135
HILDRETH, CHARLES, PHIL DEPT, UNIV OF COLORADO, DENVER CO 80202
HILEY, DAVID R, PHILOSOPHY DEPT, MEMPHIS ST UNIV, MEMPHIS TN 38152
HILL JR, THOMAS E, PHIL DEPT, UNIV OF CALIFORNIA, LOS ANGELES CA 90024
HILL, CHRISTOPHER, PHIL DEPT, UNIV OF PITTSBURGH, PITTSBURGH PA 15260
HILL, DAVID, PHILOSOPHY DEPT, W VA WESLEYAN COL, BUCKHANNON WV 26201
HILL, JAMES J, PHIL & REL DEPT, TOWSON STATE COL, BALTIMORE MD 21204
HILL, JEROME, PHIL DEPT, UNIV OF MICHIGAN, ANN ARBOR MI 48104
HILL, JUDITH M, PHIL DEPT, UNIV OF N CAROLINA, CHAPEL HILL NC 27514
HILL, KNOX, PHIL DEPT, UNIV OF CHICAGO, CHICAGO IL 60637
HILL, MARY S, RELIG & PHIL DEPT, SALEM COLLEGE, WINSTON-SALEM NC 27108
HILL, MYLES, SOC SCI DEPT, PHOENIX COLLEGE, PHOENIX AZ 85013
HILL, PATRICK, PHIL DEPT, ST UNIV OF NY, STONY BROOK NY 11790
HILL, RONALD R, PHIL DEPT, UNIV OF CALIFORNIA, RIVERSIDE CA 92502
HILL, ROSCOE E, PHIL DEPT, UNIV OF DENVER, DENVER CO 80210
HILL, SHARON, PHIL DEPT, CALIFORNIA ST UNIV, LOS ANGELES CA 90032
HILL, THOMAS E, PHILOSOPHY DEPT, MACALESTER COLLEGE, ST PAUL MN 55101
HILLIARD, TRUETT L, SOC SCI DEPT, ODESSA COLLEGE, ODESSA TX 79760
HILLMAN, BRENT, PHILOSOPHY DEPT, UNIV OF ARIZONA, TUCSON AZ 85721
HILMY, SAMEER, PHIL DEPT, THE AMERICAN UNIV, WASHINGTON DC 20016
HILTY, E J, PHIL DEPT, UNIVERSITY OF KANSAS, LAWRENCE KS 66044
HILTZ, STEPHEN CHARLES, PHILOSOPHY DEPT, UNIV OF TEXAS, AUSTIN TX 78712
HIMES, CYNARA, PHIL DEPT, UNIVERSITY OF DAYTON, DAYTON OH 45469
HINCHCLIFF, JOHN, PHIL DEPT, HAMPDEN-SYDNEY COL, HAMPDEN-SYDNY VA 23943
HINCKLEY, DIANE, PHILOSOPHY DEPT, UNIV OF TEXAS, AUSTIN TX 78712
HINDERLITER, HAROLD H, PHIL & RELIG DEPT, OHIO NORTHERN UNIV, ADA OH 45810
HINER, KEITH, OAKTON COM COLLEGE, MORTON GROVE, IL 60053
HINES, JOHN N, SOC SCI DEPT, GEORGIA INST OF TECH, ATLANTA GA 30332
HINES, MARY E, PHIL SCH, CATH UNIV OF AMER, WASHINGTON DC 20017
HINKINS, JOHN P, COMMUNIC & HUMAN, OAKLAND COM COLLEGE, AUBURN HTS MI 48057
HINKLE, GERALD, RELIG & PHIL DEPT, AUSTIN COLLEGE, SHERMAN TX 75090
HINNERS, RICHARD, PHILOSOPHY DEPT, LOYOLA COLLEGE, MONTREAL QUE CAN
HINSHAW JR, VIRGIL, PHILOSOPHY DEPT, OHIO STATE UNIV, COLUMBUS OH 43210
HINSHAW, W B, PHIL & RELIG DEPT, ROANOKE COLLEGE, SALEM VA 24153
HINTIKKA, JAAKKO, PHIL DEPT, STANFORD UNIVERSITY, STANFORD CA 94305
HIRSCH, BRUCE A, PHILOSOPHY DEPT, UNIV OF DELAWARE, NEWARK DE 19711
HIRSCH, EDWARD WILLIAM, PHILOSOPHY DEPT, UNIV OF TEXAS, AUSTIN TX 78712
HIRSCH, ELI, PHIL DEPT, LONG ISLAND UNIV, BROOKLYN NY 11201
HIRSCH, ELIZABETH, PHIL & RELIG DEPT, TRENTON STATE COL, TRENTON NJ 08625
HIRSCHBEIN, RON L, PHILOSOPHY DEPT, CALIFORNIA ST UNIV, CHICO CA 95926
HIRSCHBEIN, SEVIN, PHIL DEPT, LEWIS & CLARK COL, PORTLAND OR 97219
HIRSCHMANN, DAVID, PHIL DEPT, UNIV OF NEVADA, RENO NV 89507
HITCHCOCK, DAVID, PHILOSOPHY DEPT, MCMASTER UNIVERSITY, HAMILTON ONT CAN
HITCHON, ROGER, PHIL DEPT, UNIV OF WEST ONTARIO, LONDON ONT CAN
HITTERDALE, LARRY, PHIL DEPT, CALIFORNIA ST UNIV, LOS ANGELES CA 90032

HIX JR, C EUGENE, PHILOSOPHY DEPT, CEN METHODIST COL, FAYETTE MO 65248
HJELM, RALPH O, PHIL DEPT, UNIV OF MAINE, ORONO ME 04773
HOAGLAND, SARAH, PHIL DEPT, VASSAR COLLEGE, POUGHKEEPSIE NY 12601
HOAGLUND, JOHN, PHILOSOPHY DEPT, CHR NEWPORT COL, NEWPORT NEWS VA 23606
HOAK, H PHILLIP, SYST THEOL DEPT, DALLAS THEOL SEM, DALLAS TX 75204
HOBAPP, P F, PHIL DEPT, UNIV OF N COLORADO, GREELEY CO 80631
HOBAUGH, REGINA, PHIL DEPT, HOLY FAMILY COLLEGE, PHILADELPHIA PA 19114
HOBBS, EDWARD, SYST & PHIL, GRADUATE THEOL UNION, BERKELEY CA 94709
HOBBS, HOYT, PHIL DEPT, LONG ISLAND UNIV, GREENVALE NY 11548
HOBBS, NANCY, HUMANITIES DEPT, NEW RIVER COM COL, DUBLIN VA 24084
HOBBS, WILLIAM G, PHIL DEPT, UNIV OF N CAROLINA, CHAPEL HILL NC 27514
HOBSON, MARY STILES, PHILOSOPHY DEPT, WASHINGTON ST UNIV, PULLMAN WA 99163
HOCHBERG, GARY H, PHIL DEPT, BUCKNELL UNIVERSITY, LEWISBURG PA 17837
HOCHBERG, HERBERT, PHIL DEPT, UNIV OF MINNESOTA, MINNEAPOLIS MN 55455
HOCK, RAYMOND, PHIL & REL, DRAKE UNIVERSITY, DES MOINES IA 50311
HOCKENOS, WARREN J, PHIL DEPT, SKIDMORE COLLEGE, SARATOGA SPGS NY 12886
HOCKING, RICHARD O'R, PHIL DEPT, EMORY UNIVERSITY, ATLANTA GA 30322
HOCKNEY, DONALD J, PHIL DEPT, UNIV OF WEST ONTARIO, LONDON ONT   CAN
HOCUTT, MAX O, PHIL DEPT, UNIV OF ALABAMA, UNIVERSITY AL 35486
HODGE, ELIZABETH J, HUMAN DEPT, NEWARK COL OF ENG, NEWARK NJ 07102
HODGE, JOHN L, PHILOSOPHY DEPT, CALIFORNIA ST UNIV, HAYWARD CA 94542
HODGEN, MAURICE D, LOMA LINDA UNIV, RIVERSIDE, CA 92505
HODGES, DONALD C, PHIL DEPT, FLORIDA STATE UNIV, TALLAHASSEE FL 32306
HODGES, MICHAEL P, PHILOSOPHY DEPT, VANDERBILT UNIV, NASHVILLE TN 37235
HODGKINS, GAIL, PHIL DEPT, UNIV OF SANTA CLARA, SANTA CLARA CA 95053
HODSON, JOHN, PHILOSOPHY DEPT, UNIV OF ARIZONA, TUCSON AZ 85721
HOEBING, PHILIBERT, PHIL DEPT, QUINCY COLLEGE, QUINCY IL 62301
HOEKSTRA, RAYMOND, SOC OF ARTS & CRAFTS, DETROIT, MI 48202
HOF, ROBERT M, PHIL DEPT, IMMACULATA COLLEGE, WASHINGTON DC 20016
HOFFECKER, ANDREW, PHIL & RELIG, GROVE CITY COLLEGE, GROVE CITY PA 16127
HOFFMAN, JOSHUA, PHIL DEPT, UNIV OF N CAROLINA, GREENSBORO NC 27412
HOFFMAN, LESTER, PHIL DEPT, LONG ISLAND UNIV, GREENVALE NY 11548
HOFFMAN, MARY, PHIL & REL STUD, HOLY FAMILY COL, MANITOWOC WI 54220
HOFFMAN, ROBERT, HUMAN DEPT, YORK COLLEGE, JAMAICA NY 11432
HOFFMAN, ROBERT, SOC SCI DEPT, SADDLEBACK COLLEGE, MISSION VIEJO CA 92675
HOFFMANN, W MICHAEL, PHILOSOPHY DEPT, HIRAM COLLEGE, HIRAM OH 44234
HOFFMANN, MARY, PHIL & REL STUD DEPT, SILVER LAKE COL, MANITOWOC WI 54220
HOFFMANN, WILLIAM, PHIL & REL DEPT, ITHACA COLLEGE, ITHACA NY 14850
HOFFMASTER, CHARLES B, PHIL DEPT, UNIV OF MINNESOTA, MINNEAPOLIS MN 55455
HOFMEISTER, HEIMO E, PHIL DEPT, THE AMERICAN UNIV, WASHINGTON DC 20016
HOFSTADTER, ALBERT, PHIL STUD BOARD, U OF CALIFORNIA, SANTA CRUZ CA 95060
HOGAN, DONALD J, PHILOSOPHY DEPT, XAVIER UNIVERSITY, CINCINNATI OH 45207
HOGAN, RICHARD, PHIL DEPT, SE MASS UNIV, N DARTMOUTH MA 02747
HOGAN, WILBUR C, PHIL DEPT, CAL POLYTECH ST U, SAN LUIS OBIS CA 93407
HOGANS, DONNA, PHILOSOPHY DEPT, MARQUETTE UNIV, MILWAUKEE WI 53233
HOHLT, DAVID T, ENG & PHIL DEPT, BLINN COLLEGE, BRENHAM TX 77833
HOISVEEN, TOM, PHILOSOPHY DEPT, UNIV OF WATERLOO, WATERLOO ONT   CAN
HOITENGA, DEWEY, PHIL DEPT, GRAND VALLEY ST COL, ALLENDALE MI 49401
HOITSMA, KENMONT, HUMANITIES DIV, CHABOT COLLEGE, HAYWARD CA 94545
HOLCOMB, HARMON R, PHIL DEPT, UNIV OF ROCHESTER, ROCHESTER NY 14627
HOLDER, FRED L, PHIL DEPT, SIMPSON COLLEGE, INDIANOLA IA 50125
HOLDSTOCK, ROGER, ENGLISH DEPT, WILLIAMSPORT COM COL, WILLIAMSPORT PA 17701
HOLDSWORTH, DAVID G, PHIL DEPT, UNIV OF WEST ONTARIO, LONDON ONT   CAN
HOLE, GEORGE T, PHIL DEPT, COL AT BUFFALO, BUFFALO NY 14222
HOLIEN, GERALD, PHIL DEPT, UNIV OF COLORADO, BOULDER CO 80302
HOLLADAY, JOHN, HUMAN DIV, MONROE CC COM COL, MONROE MI 48161
HOLLENBACH, PAUL, PHIL DEPT, IOWA STATE UNIV, AMES IA 50010
HOLLENHORST, G DONALD, PHIL DEPT, BARAT COLLEGE, LAKE FOREST IL 60045
HOLLEY, DAVID MARLIN, PHILOSOPHY DEPT, UNIV OF TEXAS, AUSTIN TX 78712
HOLLEY, ROBERT F, DANVILLE COM COL, DANVILLE, VA 24541
HOLLIDAY, CHRISTOPHER, PHIL DEPT, NORTHWESTERN UNIV, EVANSTON IL 60201
HOLLINGER, ROBERT, PHIL DEPT, CLARK UNIVERSITY, WORCESTER MA 01610
HOLLON JR, ELLIS, THEOL AREA, SE BAPTIST THEOL SEM, WAKE FOREST NC 27587
HOLLOWAY, ALVIN J, PHIL DEPT, LOYOLA UNIVERSITY, NEW ORLEANS LA 70118

HOLLOWAY, JAMES Y, PHIL & REL DEPT, BEREA COLLEGE, BEREA KY   40403
HOLLOWAY, MAURICE, PHILOSOPHY DEPT, EDINBORO ST COL, EDINBORO PA   16412
HOLLOWELL, REX, SOC SCI DEPT, SPOKANE FLS COM COL, SPOKANE WA   99202
HOLLOWMAN, HENRY, DETROIT BIB COLLEGE, DETROIT, MI   48235
HOLM, BRIAN, PHILOSOPHY DEPT, GODDARD COLLEGE, PLAINFIELD VT   05667
HOLMAN, ELIZABETH, PHIL DEPT, BOSTON UNIVERSITY, BOSTON MA   02215
HOLMAN, EMMETT, HUMAN DEPT, GEORGE MASON UNIV, FAIRFAX VA   22030
HOLMBERG, FRED B, WHITE PINES COLLEGE, CHESTER, NH   03036
HOLMES, ARTHUR F, PHIL DEPT, WHEATON COLLEGE, WHEATON IL   60187
HOLMES, C, PHILOSOPHY DEPT, UNIV PR EDWARD IS, CHARLOTTETOWN PEI   CAN
HOLMES, LARRY, PHIL DEPT, COL AT NEW PLATZ, NEW PLATZ NY   12561
HOLMES, RICHARD H, PHILOSOPHY DEPT, UNIV OF WATERLOO, WATERLOO ONT   CAN
HOLMES, ROBERT L, PHIL DEPT, UNIV OF ROCHESTER, ROCHESTER NY   14627
HOLMES, RONALD, PHIL DEPT, UNIVERSITY OF IDAHO, MOSCOW ID   83843
HOLMGREN, PHILIP S, HIST & PHIL DEPT, KEARNEY ST COL, KEARNEY NE   68847
HOLMSTROM, NANCY, PHILOSOPHY DEPT, UNIV OF WISCONSIN, MADISON WI   53706
HOLT, DAVID, PHILOSOPHY DEPT, OHIO STATE UNIV, COLUMBUS OH   43210
HOLTHAUS, REUBEN S, WESTERN MARYLAND COL, WESTMINSTER, MD   21157
HOLVECK, ELEANORE, PHILOSOPHY DEPT, DUQUESNE UNIV, PITTSBURGH PA   15219
HOLZAEPFEL, TODD, PHIL DEPT, BOWLING GREEN UNIV, BOWLING GREEN OH   43403
HOLZMAN, RICHARD, PHIL DEPT, UNIV OF CALIFORNIA, IRVINE CA   92664
HOMANN, FREDERICK A, PHIL DEPT, ST JOSEPH'S COL, PHILADELPHIA PA   19131
HOMBACH, FREDERICH A, COLLEGE OF DUPAGE, GLEN ELLYN, IL   60137
HOMLISH, JOHN, PHILOSOPHY DEPT, WASHBURN UNIVERSITY, TOPEKA KS   66621
HONER, STANLEY M, PHILOSOPHY DEPT, MT SAN ANTONIO COL, WALNUT CA   91789
HONEYWELL, J ARTHUR, PHIL DEPT, SKIDMORE COLLEGE, SARATOGA SPGS NY   12886
HONG, HOWARD, PHIL DEPT, SAINT OLAF COLLEGE, NORTHFIELD MN   55057
HOOD, C ELLSWORTH, PHIL DEPT, UNIV CF WISCONSIN, PLATTEVILLE WI   53818
HOOD, JO ROGERS, PHIL DEPT, UNIV OF ALABAMA, UNIVERSITY AL   35486
HOOD, MICHAEL, PHILOSOPHY DEPT, UNIV OF AKRON, AKRON OH   44325
HOOD, WEBSTER F, PHIL DEPT, CEN WASH STATE COL, ELLENSBURG WA   98926
HOOK, SIDNEY, PHIL DEPT, NEW YORK UNIVERSITY, NEW YORK NY   10003
HOOKER, CLIFFORD A, PHIL DEPT, UNIV OF WEST ONTARIO, LONDON ONT   CAN
HOOKER, JOHN, PHILOSOPHY DEPT, VANDERBILT UNIV, NASHVILLE TN   37235
HOOKER, MICHAEL, PHIL DEPT, HARVARD UNIVERSITY, CAMBRIDGE MA   02138
HOOPER, RACHEL, ROSARY HILL COLLEGE, BUFFALO, NY   14226
HOORMANN, CYRIL, PHILOSOPHY DEPT, UNIV OF TEXAS, AUSTIN TX   78712
HOOVER, MARY R, COMMUNIC & HUMAN, NAIROBI COLLEGE, E PALO ALTO CA   94303
HOPKINS JR, CLYDE L, PHILOSOPHY DEPT, PENN STATE UNIV, DUNMORE PA   18512
HOPKINS, JASPER, PHIL DEPT, UNIV OF MINNESOTA, MINNEAPOLIS MN   55455
HOPKINS, JOHN, HUMANITIES DEPT, POINT PARK COL, PITTSBURGH PA   15222
HOPKINS, ROBERT M, HUMAN DIV, JEFFERSON COLLEGE, HILLSBORO MO   63050
HOPSON, RONALD C, PHIL DEPT, FRANKLIN & MARSHALL, LANCASTER PA   17604
HORBACH, C FREDERICK, HUMAN DEPT, CUMBERLAND CO COL, VINELAND NJ   08360
HORBAN, PETER, PHIL DEPT, UNIV OF WEST ONTARIO, LONDON ONT   CAN
HORGAN, TERENCE L, PHIL & REL, DEPAUW UNIVERSITY, GREENCASTLE IN   46135
HORLICK, ROBERT, PHIL DEPT, UNIV OF MONTANA, MISSOULA MT   59801
HORN, ROBERT, PHIL DEPT, EARLHAM COLLEGE, RICHMOND IN   47374
HORNBECK, CHARLES E, SOC SCI DEPT, KEENE ST COLLEGE, KEENE NH   03431
HORNE, JAMES R, PHILOSOPHY DEPT, UNIV OF WATERLOO, WATERLOO ONT   CAN
HORNER, PAUL, BIB & REL EDUC, CAMPBELLSVILLE COL, CAMPBELLSVL KY   42718
HORNICK, M, PHIL DEPT, W CONNECTICUT ST COL, DANBURY CT   06810
HOROSZ, WILLIAM, PHILOSOPHY DEPT, UNIV OF OKLAHOMA, NORMAN OK   73069
HOROWITZ, LOUISE, PHIL DEPT, LONG ISLAND UNIV, BROOKLYN NY   11201
HOROWITZ, TAMARA, PHIL DEPT, MASS INST TECH, CAMBRIDGE MA   02139
HORRIGAN, KEVIN, PHIL DEPT, BENEDICTINE COLLEGE, ATCHISON KS   66002
HORSBURGH, H J N, PHILOSOPHY DEPT, UNIV OF VICTORIA, VICTORIA B C   CAN
HORTON, ERNEST, SOC SCI DIV, GLENDALE COM COL, GLENDALE CA   91208
HORTON, FRANK L, S CAL SCH OF THEOL, CLAREMONT, CA   91711
HORTON, WILLIAM H, GRAMBLING COLLEGE, GRAMBLING, LA   71245
HORVATH, NICHOLAS A, PHIL DEPT, JOHN CARROLL UNIV, UNIVERSITY HT OH   44118
HORWICH, PAUL, PHIL DEPT, MASS INST TECH, CAMBRIDGE MA   02139
HOSLER, DOUGLAS, ENGLISH LIT & PHIL, UNIV OF WISCONSIN, MADISON WI   53706
HOSPERS, JOHN, PHIL SCH, UNIV OF S CALIFORNIA, LOS ANGELES CA   90007

HOSTETLER, BARBARA, PHIL DEPT, UNIV OF NEW MEXICO, ALBUQUERQUE NM 87106
HOTZE, MARY H, PHILOSOPHY DEPT, NOTRE DAME COLLEGE, ST LOUIS MO 63125
HOUCHIN, THOMAS, HUMAN DIV, ST JOHN'S UNIV, STATEN ISLAND NY 10301
HOUDE, ROLAND, PHILOSOPHY DEPT, UNIV DE MONTREAL, MONTREAL QUE CAN
HOUGH JR, JOSEPH C, S CAL SCH OF THEOL, CLAREMONT, CA 91711
HOUGH, JOE, BEHAV SCI & SOC, PANOLA JR COL, CARTHAGE TX 75633
HOUGH, RONALD F, PHILOSOPHY DEPT, WRIGHT STATE UNIV, DAYTON OH 45431
HOUGHTALING, DAVID N, SOC SCI DIV, EVERETT COM COL, EVERETT WA 98201
HOUGHTON, RAYMOND, PHIL & EDUC DEPT, RHODE ISLAND COL, PROVIDENCE RI 02908
HOULE, ROLAND, PHIL DEPT, COL THETFORD MINES, MEGANTIE QUE CAN
HOULGATE, LAURENCE, HUMAN DEPT, GEORGE MASON UNIV, FAIRFAX VA 22030
HOULIHAN, TERESA, PHIL DEPT, AQUINAS COLLEGE, GRAND RAPIDS MI 49506
HOURANI, GEORGE F, PHIL DEPT, ST UNIV OF NY, AMHERST NY 14226
HOUSKA, R B, ARTS & SCI DIV, NATIONAL COL OF BUS, RAPID CITY SD 57701
HOUSTON, B, EDUCATION COLLEGE, ALTHOUSE COLLEGE, LONDON ONT CAN
HOUTS, RONALD, PHIL DEPT, UNIV OF CALIFORNIA, LOS ANGELES CA 90024
HOWALD, J THOMAS, PHIL & REL DEPT, FRANKLIN COL, FRANKLIN IN 46131
HOWARD, IVAN, WHITWORTH COLLEGE, BROOKHAVEN, MS 39601
HOWARD, JOHN, PHIL DEPT, SAINT JOHN'S UNIV, COLLEGEVILLE MN 56321
HOWARD, MICHAEL S, PHIL DEPT, ST UNIV OF NY, ALBANY NY 12203
HOWARD, RAYMOND, PHIL DEPT, JEFFERSON COM COL, LOUISVILLE KY 40205
HOWARD, RICHARD, PHIL DEPT, ST UNIV OF NY, STONY BROOK NY 11790
HOWARD, ROY J, PHIL DEPT, CALIFORNIA ST UNIV, SAN DIEGO CA 92115
HOWARD, V A, EDUCATION COLLEGE, ALTHOUSE COLLEGE, LONDON ONT CAN
HOWARD, WENDELL T, PHILOSOPHY DEPT, UNIV OF HOUSTON, HOUSTON TX 77004
HOWE, CLARENCE S, PHIL DEPT, CAL ST UNIV -HUMBOLDT, ARCATA CA 95521
HOWE, MARGARET, PHIL & RELIG, WEST KENTUCKY UNIV, BOWLING GREEN KY 42101
HOWE, NICHOLAS, FRANCONIA COLLEGE, FRANCONIA, NH 03580
HOWE, RICHARD, PHIL DEPT, LORAS COLLEGE, DUBUQUE IA 52001
HOWE, ROGER, PHIL DEPT, UNIV OF VIRGINIA, CHARLOTTESVL VA 22903
HOWELL, DAVID, PHILOSOPHY DEPT, MUHLENBERG COLLEGE, ALLENTOWN PA 18104
HOWELL, ROBERT, PHIL DEPT, STANFORD UNIVERSITY, STANFORD CA 94305
HOWELLS, EDMUND G, PHILOSOPHY DEPT, ARIZONA STATE UNIV, TEMPE AZ 85281
HOWEY, RICHARD, PHILOSOPHY DEPT, UNIV OF WYOMING, LARAMIE WY 82071
HOWIE, JOHN, PHIL DEPT, S ILLINOIS UNIV, CARBONDALE IL 62901
HOY, DANIEL J, PHIL & EDUC DEPT, RHODE ISLAND COL, PROVIDENCE RI 02908
HOY, DAVID, PHIL DEPT, PRINCETON UNIVERSITY, PRINCETON NJ 08540
HOYT III, WILLIAM R, REL & PHIL DEPT, BERRY COLLEGE, MOUNT BERRY GA 30149
HOYT, HAROLD B, PHIL DEPT, SAN ANTONIO COL, SAN ANTONIO TX 78284
HSIANG, PAUL, SETON HALL UNIV, SOUTH ORANGE, NJ 07079
HSIEH, SHAN-YUAN, PHIL DEPT, UNIV OF DENVER, DENVER CO 80210
HSU, SUNG-PENG, PHILOSOPHY DEPT, UNIV OF DELAWARE, NEWARK DE 19711
HUANG, EDWARD, PHIL & RELIG, JERSEY CITY ST COL, JERSEY CITY NJ 07305
HUANG, SIU-CHI, PHILOSOPHY DEPT, BEAVER COLLEGE, GLENSIDE PA 19038
HUBBARD, J MACOUBREY, PHIL DEPT, BENEDICTINE COLLEGE, ATCHISON KS 66002
HUBBARD, ROBERT R, PHILOSOPHY DEPT, GLENDALE COM COL, GLENDALE AZ 85301
HUBBART, JAMES R, PHIL DEPT, UNIV OF NEBRASKA, LINCOLN NE 68502
HUBBS, G, PHILOSOPHY DEPT, UNIV OF TORONTO, TORONTO ONT CAN
HUBER, CURTIS, PHILOSOPHY DEPT, PACIFIC LUTH UNIV, TACOMA WA 98447
HUBIN, DONALD, PHILOSOPHY DEPT, UNIV OF ARIZONA, TUCSON AZ 85721
HUCHINGSON, JAMES E, PHIL & REL DEPT, FLORIDA INTNL UNIV, MIAMI FL 33144
HUDDLESTUN, J R, PHILOSOPHY DEPT, REINHARDT COLLEGE, WALESKA GA 30183
HUDELSON, RICHARD, PHIL DEPT, UNIV OF MICHIGAN, ANN ARBOR MI 48104
HUDGINS, WALTER E, PHILOSOPHY DEPT, WOFFORD COLLEGE, SPARTANBURG SC 29301
HUDLIN, EDWARD W, PHIL STUD DEPT, S ILLINOIS UNIV, EDWARDSVILLE IL 62025
HUDSON, CHARLES L, HUMAN DEPT, WRIGHT CY COLLEGE, CHICAGO IL 60634
HUDSON, FREDERIC, PHIL DEPT, LONE MOUNTAIN COL, SAN FRANCISCO CA 94118
HUDSON, JAMES L, PHIL DEPT, N ILLINOIS UNIV, DEKALB IL 60115
HUDSON, STEPHEN D, PHIL DEPT, UNIV OF N CAROLINA, CHAPEL HILL NC 27514
HUDSON, YEAGER, PHIL & REL DEPT, COLBY COLLEGE, WATERVILLE ME 04901
HUEBNER, HARRY, CAN MENNONITE COL, WINNIPEG, MAN CAN
HUERTAS-JOURDA, JOSE, PHILOSOPHY DEPT, UNIV OF WATERLOO, WATERLOO ONT CAN
HUFF, DOUGLAS, PHIL DEPT, UNIV OF MISSOURI, COLUMBIA MO 65201
HUFF, THOMAS P, PHIL DEPT, UNIV OF MONTANA, MISSOULA MT 59801

HUFFMAN, ROBERT E, PARSONS COLLEGE, FAIRFIELD, IA 52803
HUG, PACIFIC L, PHIL DEPT, QUINCY COLLEGE, QUINCY IL 62301
HUGGETT, W J, PHILOSOPHY DEPT, UNIV OF TORONTO, TORONTO ONT   CAN
HUGHES, GRAHAM, NY UNIV LAW SCHOOL, NEW YORK, NY 10013
HUGHES, PATRICH, PHILOSOPHY DEPT, GAVILAN COL, GILROY CA 95020
HUGHES, RODERICK, PHIL DEPT, ST BONAVENTURE UNIV, ST BONVENTURE NY 14778
HUGHES, STEVEN P, PHIL DEPT, WASHINGTON UNIV, ST LOUIS MO 63130
HUGHES, W H, PHILOSOPHY DEPT, UNIV OF GUELPH, GUELPH ONT   CAN
HUGHLEY, WALTER C, PHIL & BIB DEPT, EAST MISS JUNIOR COL, SCOOBA MS 39358
HUGLY, P G, PHIL DEPT, UNIV OF ILLINOIS, URBANA IL 61801
HULL, DAVID L, PHIL DEPT, UNIV OF WISCONSIN, MILWAUKEE WI 53201
HULL, RICHARD T, PHIL DEPT, ST UNIV OF NY, AMHERST NY 14226
HULLETT, JAMES N, PHIL DEPT, BOSTON UNIVERSITY, BOSTON MA 02215
HULTGREN, LAWRENCE, PHIL & RELIG DEPT, VA WESLEYAN COL, NORFOLK VA 23502
HULTZEN, CARL, PHIL DEPT, WAYNE STATE UNIV, DETROIT MI 48202
HUMBER, JAMES M, PHIL DEPT, GEORGIA ST UNIV, ATLANTA GA 30303
HUMBERT, E ROYAL F, PHILOSOPHY DEPT, EUREKA COLLEGE, EUREKA IL 61530
HUMBERT, EARL R, FAIRLEIGH DICKINSON, TEANECK, NJ 07666
HUMPHREY, RICHARD A, APPALACHIAN ST UNIV, BOONE, NC 28607
HUMPHREY, THEODORE, PHILOSOPHY DEPT, ARIZONA STATE UNIV, TEMPE AZ 85281
HUMPHREYS, BURTON V, PHIL DEPT, FLAGLER COLLEGE, ST AUGUSTINE FL 32084
HUMPHREYS, FISHER, THEOL DIV, NEW ORLEANS BAPT SEM, NEW ORLEANS LA 70126
HUMPHRIES, BARBARA, PHIL DEPT, WAYNE STATE UNIV, DETROIT MI 48202
HUMPHRIES, HUGH, PHIL & HIST & SOC, SIMPSON COL, SAN FRANCISCO CA 94134
HUNAK, MIROSLAV JOHN, E TEXAS STATE UNIV, COMMERCE, TX 75428
HUND, WILLIAM B, PHILOSOPHY DEPT, UNIV OF PORTLAND, PORTLAND OR 97203
HUNDLEY, ROBERT, JOHNSON STATE COL, JOHNSON, VT 05656
HUNGERFORD, THOMAS, PHILOSOPHY DEPT, MCGILL UNIVERSITY, MONTREAL QUE   CAN
HUNGERLAND, ISABEL, PHIL DEPT, UNIV OF CALIFORNIA, BERKELEY CA 94720
HUNNEZ, MILTON, PHILOSOPHY DEPT, WILLIAMETTE UNIV, SALEM OR 97301
HUNT, C MURRAY, PHIL DEPT, SUSQUEHANNA UNIV, SELINSGROVE PA 17870
HUNT, LESTER, PHIL DEPT, UNIV OF CALIFORNIA, SANTA BARBARA CA 93106
HUNT, MARION, PHILOSOPHY DEPT, COL OF MT ST VINCENT, RIVERDALE NY 10471
HUNT, RALPH, MUS & HUM DEPT, PENSACOLA JUN COL, PENSACOLA FL 32504   -
HUNT, ROBERT W, PHIL DEPT, UNIV OF REDLANDS, REDLANDS CA 92373
HUNT, TERENCE J, PHIL DEPT, TRINITY UNIVERSITY, SAN ANTONIO TX 78284
HUNT, W MURRAY, SUSQUEHANNA UNIV, SELINSGROVE, PA 17870
HUNTER, CLARENCE V, PHIL & REL DIV, ASBURY COLLEGE, WILMORE KY 40390
HUNTER, DANIEL, PHIL DEPT, UNIV OF CALIFORNIA, IRVINE CA 92664
HUNTER, DAVID A, PHILOSOPHY DEPT, UNIV OF S CAROLINA, COLUMBIA SC 29208
HUNTER, J F M, PHILOSOPHY DEPT, UNIV OF TORONTO, TORONTO ONT   CAN
HUNTER, JOHN, PHIL DEPT, ST BONAVENTURE UNIV, ST BONVENTURE NY 14778
HUNTER, K, PHILOSOPHY DEPT, UNIV OF GUELPH, GUELPH ONT   CAN
HUNTER, MARY SUSAN, PHIL DEPT, S METHODIST UNIV, DALLAS TX 75222
HUNTINGTON, RON, PHILOSOPHY DEPT, CHAPMAN COLLEGE, ORANGE CA 92666
HUNTLEY, MARTIN A, PHILOSOPHY DEPT, UNIV OF WISCONSIN, MADISON WI 53706
HUNTLEY, TAZE, SOC SCI & ENG DEPT, AGR & TECH COLLEGE, MORRISVILLE NY 13408
HURDLE, BURTON, PHIL DEPT, UNIV OF ARKANSAS, FAYETTEVILLE AR 72701
HURLBUTT, ROBERT H, PHIL DEPT, UNIV OF NEBRASKA, LINCOLN NE 68502
HURLEY, PATRICK, ARTS & SCI COL, UNIV OF SAN DIEGO, SAN DIEGO CA 92110
HURREH, ISMAEL, PHIL DEPT, BOSTON UNIVERSITY, BOSTON MA 02215
HURRELL, PAUL, PHIL DEPT, MICHIGAN STATE UNIV, EAST LANSING MI 48823
HURST, CLYDE, BIB & PHIL DEPT, HARDIN-SIMMONS UNIV, ABILENE TX 79601
HURST, D R, PHIL FACULTY, UNIV OF OTTAWA, OTTAWA ONT   CAN
HURST, WILLIAM J, PHIL DEPT, DOMINICAN COLLEGE, BLAUVELT NY 10913
HURWITZ, GERALD Q, PHIL DEPT, LINCOLN UNIVERSITY, LINCOLN UNIV PA 19352
HUSAIN, MARTHA, PHIL DEPT, BROCK UNIVERSITY, ST CATHARINES ONT   CAN
HUSSON, KATHLEEN, PHILOSOPHY DEPT, VILLANOVA UNIV, VILLANOVA PA 19085
HUSTWIT, RONALD, PHILOSOPHY DEPT, COLLEGE OF WOOSTER, WOOSTER OH 44691
HUTCHEON, WILLARD, PHIL DEPT, CITY COLLEGE, NEW YORK NY 10031
HUTCHESON, PETER W, PHILOSOPHY DEPT, UNIV OF OKLAHOMA, NORMAN OK 73069
HUTCHINGS, PHIL DEPT, REEDLEY COLLEGE, REEDLEY, CA 93654
HUTCHISON, JOHN A, S CAL SCH OF THEOL, CLAREMONT, CA 91711
HUTCHISON, RUSSELL S, HIL & RELIG, MUSKINGUM COLLEGE, NEW CONCORD OH 43762

HYATT, MORNA, SWEDENBORG SCI ASSOC, BRYN ATHYN, PA 19009
HYLAND, DREW, PHIL DEPT, TRINITY COLLEGE, HARTFORD CT 06106
HYLAND, RICHARD, PHIL DEPT, UNIVERSITY OF DAYTON, DAYTON OH 45469
HYMAN, ARTHUR, PHIL DEPT, YESHIVA UNIVERSITY, NEW YORK NY 10033
HYMMEN, JAMES, PHILOSOPHY DEPT, UNIV OF WATERLOO, WATERLOO ONT   CAN
HYSONG, THOMAS, PHIL DEPT, UNIV OF CALIFORNIA, LOS ANGELES CA 90024
IANNONE, ABEL P, PHILOSOPHY DEPT, UNIV OF WISCONSIN, MADISON WI 53706
IANNONI, J E, PHIL FACULTY, UNIV OF OTTAWA, OTTAWA ONT   CAN
ICKES, KEITH, PHIL DEPT, INDIANA UNIVERSITY, BLOOMINGTON IN 47401
IEZZI, ANTHONY J, ST JOHN COLLEGE, CLEVELAND, OH 44114
IHARA, CRAIG K, PHIL DEPT, CALIFORNIA ST UNIV, FULLERTON CA 92634
IHDE, DON, PHIL DEPT, ST UNIV OF NY, STONY BROOK NY 11790
IHRIE, DALE, HUMAN DEPT, MACOMB CO COM COL, MOUNT CLEMENS MI 48043
IKAMAS, LEO, HUMAN DEPT, KASKASIA OCLLEGE, CENTRALIA IL 62801
ILLERT, W PAUL, PHILOSOPHY DEPT, MARAMEC COM COL, ST LOUIS MO 63122
IMBELLI, ROBERT P, SYST THEOL, ST JOSEPH'S SEM, YONKERS NY 10704
IMHOFF, CHRISTINE, PHIL DEPT, UNIV CF MONTANA, MISSOULA MT 59801
IMLAY, R A, PHILOSOPHY DEPT, UNIV OF TORONTO, TORONTO ONT   CAN
IMMERWAHR, JOHN, PHILOSOPHY DEPT, VILLANOVA UNIV, VILLANOVA PA 19085
IMMING, DONALD, RELIG & PHIL DEPT, MOUNT MARTY COL, YANKTON SD 57078
INADA, KENNETH K, PHIL DEPT, ST UNIV OF NY, AMHERST NY 14226
INGALLS, GORDON, ARTS & SCI, COL OF NEW CALEDONIA, PRINCE GEORGE B C   CAN
INGARDIA, RICHARD, PHILOSOPHY DEPT, EAST CAROLINA UNIV, GREENVILLE NC 27834
INGBER, WARREN, PHIL DEPT, UNIV OF MICHIGAN, ANN ARBOR MI 48104
INGLIS, BRIAN D, PHILOSOPHY DEPT, UNIV OF ST THOMAS, HOUSTON TX 77006
INGRAM, PAUL O, PHIL DEPT, SIMPSON COLLEGE, INDIANOLA IA 50125
INMAN, DAVID, PHILOSOPHY DEPT, SEM CF LADY OF PROV, WARWICK RI 02889
INMAN, FLOYD, PHILOSOPHY DEPT, HOFSTRA UNIVERSITY, HEMPSTEAD NY 11550
INNIS, ROBERT, PHIL DEPT, LOWELL STATE COLLEGE, LOWELL MA 01854
INVERSO, DONALD, PHILOSOPHY DEPT, UCL MISERICORDIA, DALLAS PA 18612
IOBET, PHILIP, PHILOSOPHY DEPT, PENN STATE UNIV, ERIE PA 16510
IORIO, DOMINICK, PHILOSOPHY DEPT, RIDER COLLEGE, TRENTON NJ 08602
IRANI, K D, PHIL DEPT, CITY COLLEGE, NEW YORK NY 10031
IRONS, THEODORE, PHILOSOPHY DEPT, UNIV OF ARIZONA, TUCSON AZ 85721
IRVINE, LANCE, PHILOSOPHY DEPT, ST JOSEPH'S COLLEGE, YORKTON SAS   CAN
IRWIN, JOHN P, ENG & PHIL DEPT, LOCK HAVEN ST COL, LOCK HAVEN PA 17745
IRWIN, KEITH W, LETTERS COLLEGIUM, ECKERD COLLEGE, ST PETERSBURG FL 33733
IRWIN, TERENCE, PHIL DEPT, HARVARD UNIVERSITY, CAMBRIDGE MA 02138
ISEMINGER, GARY, PHIL DEPT, CARLETON COLLEGE, NORTHFIELD MN 55057
ISHAM, GEORGE F, PHIL DEPT, CLARK CO COM COL, LAS VEGAS NV 89101
ISRAEL, DAVID, PHIL DEPT, TUFTS UNIVERSITY, MEDFORD MA 02155
ISRAELI, PHINEAS, PHIL DEPT, NORTHWESTERN UNIV, EVANSTON IL 60201
IVERSON, SHERWIN L, PHILOSOPHY DEPT, BALDWIN-WALLACE COL, BEREA OH 44017
IVERSON, VINCENT A, PHIL DEPT, HAMPDEN-SYDNEY COL, HAMPDEN-SYDNY VA 23943
IVEY, HERMAN V, ENG DEPT, U S MILITARY ACAD, WEST POINT NY 10996
IWANICKI, J A, PHIL DEPT, UNIV OF NW BRUNSWICK, FREDERICTON N B   CAN
IYER, ROJAM, PHIL DEPT, UNIV OF CINCINNATI, CINCINNATI OH 45221
JACINTA, MARY, ALVERNIA COLLEGE, READING, PA 19607
JACINTO, JOSE S, PHILOSOPHY DEPT, MT SAN ANTONIO COL, WALNUT CA 91789
JACK, H, PHIL & CLASS DEPT, UNIV OF SASKATCHEWAN, REGINA SAS   CAN
JACK, PERCIVAL J H, PHILOSOPHY DEPT, YORK UNIVERSITY, DOWNSVIEW ONT   CAN
JACKLIN, JOHN, PHIL DEPT, ST JOSEPH'S COL, PHILADELPHIA PA 19131
JACKLIN, PHILLIP D, PHIL DEPT, CALIFORNIA ST UNIV, SAN JOSE CA 95114
JACKMAN, FRANCIS, PHIL DEPT, ST JOSEPH SEM COL, ST BENEDICT LA 70457
JACKOWAY, MALKOM, PHILOSOPHY DEPT, FOREST PARK COM COL, ST LOUIS MO 63110
JACKSON, ARTHUR, PHIL DEPT, PROVIDENCE COLLEGE, PROVIDENCE RI 02919
JACKSON, DARRELL, PHILOSOPHY DEPT, COLLEGE OF WOOSTER, WOOSTER OH 44691
JACKSON, F L, PHILOSOPHY DEPT, MEMORIAL UNIV, ST JOHN'S N F   CAN
JACKSON, GILBERT, HUMAN DEPT, NEBRASKA S COM COL, FAIRBURY NE 68352
JACKSON, HOWARD O, PHIL DEPT, UNIV BRIT COLUMBIA, VANCOUVER 8 B C   CAN
JACKSON, JAMES C, PHILOSOPHY DEPT, VOORHEES COLLEGE, DENMARK SC 29042
JACKSON, M B, PHIL & CHRIST THT, KING COLLEGE, BRISTOL TN 37620
JACKSON, M J B, PHILOSOPHY DEPT, MEMORIAL UNIV, ST JOHN'S N F   CAN
JACKSON, TERRY, HUMAN DEPT, FLORIDA INST OF TECH, MELBOURNE FL 32901

JACKSON, THOMAS E, PHIL DEPT, UNIVERSITY OF HAWAII, HONOLULU HI 96822
JACOBOZZI, ELIO, LANG & HUMAN DEPT, LORAIN CO COM COL, ELYRIA OH 44035
JACOBS, JOHN, PHILOSOPHY DEPT, MANCHESTER COM COL, MANCHESTER CT 06040
JACOBSEN, R, PHILOSOPHY DEPT, UNIV OF ALBERTA, EDMONTON ALB   CAN
JACOBSON, DAVID, PHIL DEPT, PURDUE UNIVERSITY, FORT WAYNE IN 46805
JACOBSON, F A, PHIL DEPT, ROOSEVELT UNIVERSITY, CHICAGO IL 60605
JACOBSON, JOHN, EMPIRE ST COL, SARATOGA SPGS, NY 12866
JACOBSON, JOHN, PHILOSOPHY DEPT, WASH & JEFF COL, WASHINGTON PA 15301
JACOBSON, NOLAN P, PHIL & RELIG DEPT, WINTHROP COLLEGE, ROCKHILL SC 29730
JACOBSON, PAUL, PHILOSOPHY DEPT, MARYWOOD COLLEGE, SCRANTON PA 18509
JACOBSON, STEPHEN R, PHILOSOPHY DEPT, UNIV OF DELAWARE, NEWARK DE 19711
JACOBY, PAUL JOSEPH, PHILOSOPHY DEPT, SETON HILL COL, GREENSBURG PA 15601
JACOT, ROBERT E, BEHAV SCI, TRITON COLLEGE, RIVER GROVE IL 60171
JAEGER, ROBERT, PHIL DEPT, YALE UNIVERSITY, NEW HAVEN CT 06520
JAFFE, ERWIN A, HUMAN DIV, NEW ENGLAND COLLEGE, HENNIKER NH 03242
JAFFE, RAYMOND, PHIL DEPT, WELLS COLLEGE, AURORA NY 13026
JAFFEE, CHARLENE, PHIL DEPT, EMORY UNIVERSITY, ATLANTA GA 30322
JAGER, RONALD, PHIL DEPT, YALE UNIVERSITY, NEW HAVEN CT 06520
JAGGAR, ALISON, PHIL DEPT, UNIV OF CINCINNATI, CINCINNATI OH 45221
JAKEWAY, WADE, PHIL & THEOL DEPT, WARNER SOUTHERN COL, LAKE WALES FL 33853
JAKOVINA, JOHN A, PHILOSOPHY DEPT, UNIV OF WISCONSIN, MADISON WI 53706
JALBERT, GILLES, PHIL DEPT, COL DE VALLEYFIELD, VALLEYFIELD QUE   CAN
JAMALI, NASEEM Z, PHIL DEPT, ADELPHI UNIVERSITY, GARDEN CITY NY 11530
JAMES, EDWARD W, PHIL & REL DEPT, BATES COLLEGE, LEWISTON ME 04240
JAMES, F E, SOC HIST & POLIT SCI, ALABAMA STATE UNIV, MONTGOMERY AL 36101
JAMES, GENE G, PHILOSOPHY DEPT, MEMPHIS ST UNIV, MEMPHIS TN 38152
JAMES, PATRICIA A, PHILOSOPHY DEPT, KENT STATE UNIV, KENT OH 44242
JAMES, R E, PHIL & RELIG DEPT, NC WESLEYAN COLLEGE, ROCKY MOUNT NC 27801
JAMES, ROBERT, PHIL & EDUC DEPT, COM COL ALLEGHENY CO, PITTSBURGH PA 15212
JAMES, THEODORE E, PHIL DEPT, MANHATTAN COLLEGE, RIVERDALE NY 10471
JAMETON, ANDREW L, PHIL DEPT, ST UNIV OF NY, BINGHAMTON NY 13901
JAMIESON, DALE W, PHIL DEPT, UNIV OF N CAROLINA, CHAPEL HILL NC 27514
JANIK, ALLAN, PHIL DEPT, LA SALLE COLLEGE, PHILADELPHIA PA 19141
JANIK, LINDA, PHIL DEPT, LA SALLE COLLEGE, PHILADELPHIA PA 19141
JANNUSCH, BRUCE, PHIL DEPT, UNIV OF WISCONSIN, EAU CLAIRE WI 54701
JANSCH, RONALD, HUMAN STUD DEPT, MARIAN COLLEGE, FOND DU LAC WI 54935
JANTZ, ALBERT E, PHILOSOPHY DEPT, BCB JONES UNIV, GREENVILLE SC 29614
JAQUETTE, WILLIAM, POLIT SCI & PHIL, SW MISSOURI ST U, SPRINGFIELD MO 65802
JARDINE, JOHN G, PHIL & REL STUD, WILKES COLLEGE, WILKES BARRE PA 18703
JARDINE, JOSEPH, HUMAN DIV, CASTLETON STATE COL, CASTLETON VT 05735
JARMAN, JOHN, ARTS & SCI DIV, NATIONAL COL OF BUS, RAPID CITY SD 57701
JARRELL, JAMES A, NE STATE COLLEGE, TAHLEQUAH, OK 74464
JARVIE, IAN C, PHILOSOPHY DEPT, YORK UNIVERSITY, DOWNSVIEW ONT   CAN
JARVIS, DWIGHT C, HUMAN DEPT, DAVIDSON CO COM COL, LEXINGTON NC 27292
JARVIS, EDWARD, PHILOSOPHY DEPT, UNIV OF SCRANTON, SCRANTON PA 18510
JASON, GARY, PHIL DEPT, UNIV OF ILLINOIS, URBANA IL 61801
JEANMART, PIERRE, COL DE LEVIS-LAUZON, LAUZON, QUE   CAN
JEFFERS, JAMES, PHILOSOPHY DEPT, OHIO UNIVERSITY, ATHENS OH 45701
JEFFKO, WALTER G, PHIL DEPT, FITCHBURG STATE COL, FITCHBURG MA 01420
JEFFREY, A, PHILOSOPHY DEPT, CARLETON UNIVERSITY, OTTAWA ONT   CAN
JEFFREY, JEAN-RENE, PHIL DEPT, COL DE LA POCATIERE, LA POCATIERE QUE   CAN
JEFFREY, RICHARD, PHILOSOPHY DEPT, UNIV OF PENN, PHILADELPHIA PA 19174
JEFFREYS, JERI LYNN, PHIL DEPT, EMORY UNIVERSITY, ATLANTA GA 30322
JEFFRIES, STEPHEN, LOUISIANA ST UNIV, NEW ORLEANS, LA 70122
JEFKA, MYRON, PHIL DEPT, BROOKLYN COLLEGE, BROOKLYN NY 11210
JELINEK, JOHN P, PHIL DEPT, CREIGHTON UNIV, OMAHA NE 68178
JELLEMA, W HARRY, PHIL DEPT, GRAND VALLEY ST COL, ALLENDALE MI 49401
JELLICOE, ANDREA, PHILOSOPHY DEPT, QUEEN'S UNIVERSITY, KINGSTON ONT   CAN
JENEMANN, ALBERT H, PHILOSOPHY DEPT, WHEELING COLLEGE, WHEELING WV 26003
JENKINS, ANISE, PHIL DEPT, HOWARD UNIVERSITY, WASHINGTON DC 20001
JENKINS, I D, RELIG & PHIL DEPT, WILEY COLLEGE, MARSHALL TX 75670
JENKINS, IREDELL, PHIL DEPT, UNIV OF ALABAMA, UNIVERSITY AL 35486
JENKINS, ULYSSES, OMMUNIC ARTS DEPT, MALCOLM X COM COL, CHICAGO IL 60612
JENNER, T, PHILOSOPHY DEPT, UNIV OF RHODE ISLAND, KINGSTON RI 02881

JENNINGS, R J, PHILOSOPHY DEPT, SIMON FRASER UNIV, BURNABY 2 B C   CAN
JENSEN, A DEWEY, PHILOSOPHY DEPT, NORTH ARIZONA UNIV, FLAGSTAFF AZ 86001
JENSEN, HENNING, PHILOSOPHY DEPT, UNIV OF ARIZONA, TUCSON AZ 85721
JENSEN, JACK W, PHIL & RELIG DEPT, COLBY JR COLLEGE, NEW LONDON NH 03257
JENSEN, NEIL, SOC SCI DEPT, ESSEX CCM COL, BALTIMORE MD 21237
JENSEN, R M, PHILOSOPHY DEPT, MESA COMMUNITY COL, MESA AZ 85201
JENT, H CLAY, PHIL DEPT, CEN MISSOURI ST UNIV, WARRENSBURG MO 64093
JENTZ JR, ARTHUR H, PHILOSOPHY DEPT, HOPE COLLEGE, HOLLAND MI 49423
JERSTAD, MARK, RAINY RIV ST JR COL, INTNL FALLS, MN 56649
JEWELL, ROBERT D, PHILOSOPHY DEPT, UNIV OF CALGARY, CALGARY 44 ALB   CAN
JEWISON, LYNDA M, PHIL DEPT, UNIV OF WEST ONTARIO, LONDON ONT   CAN
JEZIERSKI, CAROL, PHIL DEPT, UNIV OF VIRGINIA, CHARLOTTESVL VA 22903
JIMENEZ, TOMAS M, INTERAMER UNIVERSITY, HATO REY, PR 00919
JOANNIDES, PETER, HUMAN DIV, JACKSONVILLE UNIV, JACKSONVILLE FL 32211
JOBE, EVAN, PHIL DEPT, IOWA STATE UNIV, AMES IA 50010
JOBES, JAMES W, PHIL DEPT, SOUTHWEST AT MEMPHIS, MEMPHIS TN 38112
JOHANN, ROBERT O, PHIL DEPT, FORDHAM UNIVERSITY, BRONX NY 10458
JOHANSON, ARNOLD, PHIL DEPT, MOORHEAD STATE COL, MOORHEAD MN 56560
JOHN SR, HELEN JAMES, PHIL DEPT, TRINITY COLLEGE, WASHINGTON DC 20017
JOHN, RICHARD T, PHIL & THEOL, ST FRANCIS COLLEGE, FORT WAYNE IN 46808
JOHNS, DONALD F, PHILOSOPHY DEPT, CENTRAL BIBLE COL, SPRINGFIELD MO 65802
JOHNSEN, BREDO C, PHILOSOPHY DEPT, UNIV OF HOUSTON, HOUSTON TX 77004
JOHNSON, ALLISON H, PHIL DEPT, UNIV OF WEST ONTARIO, LONDON ONT   CAN
JOHNSON, ARTHUR, HISTORY DEPT, W TEXAS STATE UNIV, CANYON TX 79015
JOHNSON, BAYLER L, PHIL DEPT, ST LAWRENCE UNIV, CANTON NY 13617
JOHNSON, CHARLES W, LANG & PHIL DEPT, UTAH STATE UNIV, LOGAN UT 84322
JOHNSON, CHARLES, PHIL DEPT, ST UNIV OF NY, STONY BROOK NY 11790
JOHNSON, CONRAD D, PHIL DEPT, UNIV OF MARYLAND, COLLEGE PARK MD 20742
JOHNSON, D, PHILOSOPHY DEPT, UNIV OF TORONTO, TORONTO ONT   CAN
JOHNSON, DAVID E, HIST DEPT, THE U S NAVAL ACAD, ANNAPOLIS MD 21402
JOHNSON, DAVID M, PHILOSOPHY DEPT, YORK UNIVERSITY, DOWNSVIEW ONT   CAN
JOHNSON, DEBORAH, PHIL DEPT, UNIVERSITY OF KANSAS, LAWRENCE KS 66044
JOHNSON, DON, CTR FOR THE PERSON, PRESCOTT COLLEGE, PRESCOTT AZ 86301
JOHNSON, DOUGLAS W, RELIG & PHIL DEPT, CLAFLIN UNIV, ORANGEBURG SC 29115
JOHNSON, FRED R, SOC SCI DEPT, FRIENDS BIBLE COL, HAVILAND KS 67059
JOHNSON, FREDERICK A, PHIL DEPT, COLORADO ST UNIV, FORT COLLINS CO 80521
JOHNSON, FREDERICK, ENG DEPT, ROCKLAND COM COL, SUFFERN NY 10901
JOHNSON, GALEN, PHIL DEPT, BOSTON UNIVERSITY, BOSTON MA 02215
JOHNSON, GLEN, HUMAN DIV, EAST MONTANA COL, BILLINGS MT 59101
JOHNSON, HAROLD J, PHIL DEPT, UNIV CF WEST ONTARIO, LONDON ONT   CAN
JOHNSON, HJALMAR W, THEOL DIV, LUTHERAN SCH OF THEO, CHICAGO IL 60615
JOHNSON, HOWARD R, ELMIRA COLLEGE, ELMIRA, NY 14901
JOHNSON, J GLOVER, PHILOSOPHY DEPT, MARIETTA COLLEGE, MARIETTA OH 45750
JOHNSON, J PRESCOTT, PHIL DEPT, MONMOUTH COLLEGE, MONMOUTH IL 61462
JOHNSON, JAMES R, FINE ARTS SCHOOL, UNIV OF CONNECTICUT, STORRS CT 06268
JOHNSON, JOHN F, PHIL DEPT, TEXAS CHRISTIAN UNIV, FORT WORTH TX 76129
JOHNSON, JOHN F, SYST THEOL DEPT, CCNCORDIA THEOL SEM, SPRINGFIELD IL 62702
JOHNSON, JOHN J, PHIL DEPT, COL OUR LADY OF ELMS, CHICOPEE MA 01013
JOHNSON, LARRY, PHIL & RELIG DEPT, TOUGALOO COLLEGE, TOUGLAOO MS 39174
JOHNSON, MAJOR, PHIL SCH, UNIV OF S CALIFORNIA, LOS ANGELES CA 90007
JOHNSON, MARY, HUMAN STUD DIV, UNIV OF WISCONSIN, KENOSHA WI 53140
JOHNSON, OLIVER A, PHIL DEPT, UNIV CF CALIFORNIA, RIVERSIDE CA 92502
JOHNSON, P, PHILOSOPHY DEPT, UNIV OF TORONTO, TORONTO ONT   CAN
JOHNSON, PATRICIA, PHIL DEPT, UNIV CF CALIFORNIA, SANTA BARBARA CA 93106
JOHNSON, PAUL, PHILOSOPHY DEPT, CAL STATE COL, SN BERNARDINO CA 92407
JOHNSON, R, PHIL DEPT, W CONNECTICUT ST COL, DANBURY CT 06810
JOHNSON, RALPH H, PHILOSOPHY DEPT, UNIV OF WINDSOR, WINDSOR ONT   CAN
JOHNSON, RICHARD C, PHIL & RELIG DEPT, TOUGALOO COLLEGE, TOUGLAOO MS 39174
JOHNSON, ROBERT L, RELIG & PHIL DIV, MALONE COLLEGE, CANTON OH 44709
JOHNSON, ROBERT, PHIL DEPT, UNIV OF CALIFORNIA, SANTA BARBARA CA 93106
JOHNSON, ROGER K, PHILOSOPHY DEPT, MT SAN ANTONIO COL, WALNUT CA 91789
JOHNSON, STEPHEN, PHILOSOPHY DEPT, UNIV OF TEXAS, AUSTIN TX 78712
JOHNSON, WALTER, HUMAN SCHOOL, SEATTLE PACIFIC COL, SEATTLE WA 98119
JOHNSON, WAYNE, HUMAN STUD DIV, UNIV OF WISCONSIN, KENOSHA WI 53140

JOHNSON, WILLIAM, PHIL DEPT, CALIFORNIA ST UNIV, LONG BEACH CA 90840
JOHNSTON, DALE A, PHIL & RELIG, WESTMINSTER COL, SALT LAKE CTY UT 84105
JOHNSTON, DAVID W, SOC SCI DEPT, ORANGE COAST COLLEGE, COSTA MESA CA 92626
JOHNSTON, HERBERT, PHIL DEPT, UNIV OF NOTRE DAME, NOTRE DAME IN 46556
JOHNSTON, JON J, SOC SCI DEPT, GEORGIA INST OF TECH, ATLANTA GA 30332
JOHNSTON, JULIA, PHIL DEPT, FAIRFIELD UNIVERSITY, FAIRFIELD CT 06430
JOHNSTON, PAT L, PHILOSOPHY DEPT, UNIV OF UTAH, SALT LAKE CTY UT 84112
JOHNSTON, THOMAS, PHIL & REL DEPT, UNIV OF GEORGIA, ATHENS GA 30602
JOHNSTONE, HENRY W, PHILOSOPHY DEPT, PENN STATE UNIV, UNIV PARK PA 16802
JOINES, KAREN R, DIV OF REL & PHIL, SAMFORD UNIV, BIRMINGHAM AL 35209
JOLIN, F R, SOC SCI DEPT, PORTLAND COM COLLEGE, PORTLAND OR 97219
JOLIN, STEPHEN T, PHILOSOPHY DEPT, UNIV OF PORTLAND, PORTLAND OR 97203
JOLY, PAUL T, PHIL TEACH AREA, WADHAMS HALL SEM, OGDENSBURG NY 13669
JOLY, RALPH P, PHIL DEPT, CANISIUS COLLEGE, BUFFALO NY 14208
JONAS, HANS, PHIL DEPT, NW SCH FOR SOC RES, NEW YORK NY 10003
JONES JR, ELBERT W, PHIL & REL, FLORIDA A & M UNIV, TALLAHASSEE FL 32307
JONES, ALFRED H, PHIL DEPT, UNIV OF ROCHESTER, ROCHESTER NY 14627
JONES, BARBARA, PHIL DEPT, PURDUE UNIVERSITY, FORT WAYNE IN 46805
JONES, BARRINGTON, PHIL DEPT, PRINCETON UNIVERSITY, PRINCETON NJ 08540
JONES, BARRY, ENGLISH DEPT, BELLEVILLE JR COL, BELLEVILLE IL 62221
JONES, BRYCE J, PHILOSOPHY DEPT, UNIV OF WISCONSIN, MADISON WI 53706
JONES, CHARLES, PHIL DEPT, UNIV OF ARKANSAS, FAYETTEVILLE AR 72701
JONES, DANIEL, RELIG & PHIL DEPT, ATHENS COLLEGE, ATHENS AL 35611
JONES, DAVID C, SYST THEOL DEPT, COVENANT THEOL SEM, ST LOUIS MO 63141
JONES, DAVID H, PHIL DEPT, COL WILLIAM & MARY, WILLIAMSBURG VA 23185
JONES, DAVID, PHILOSOPHY DEPT, WASHINGTON ST UNIV, PULLMAN WA 99163
JONES, DONALD F, HUMANITIES DEPT, HIGHLINE COM COL, MIDWAY WA 98031
JONES, DONALD, HUMAN DEPT, FLORIDA TECH UNIV, ORLANDO FL 32816
JONES, E D, LIBR ARTS DEPT, DOUGLAS COLLEGE, NW WESTMINSTR B C CAN
JONES, GEORGE, PHIL DEPT, GUSTAVUS ADOLPHUS COL, ST PETER MN 56082
JONES, GLYNIS, PHILOSOPHY DEPT, OHIO UNIVERSITY, ATHENS OH 45701
JONES, HARDY E, PHILOSOPHY DEPT, UNIV OF TEXAS, AUSTIN TX 78712
JONES, HARRY, REL & PHIL, UNIV OF EVANSVILLE, EVANSVILLE IN 47701
JONES, J WILLIAM, PHILOSOPHY DEPT, NW NAZARENE COLLEGE, NAMPA ID 83651
JONES, JAMES L, ENG & PHIL DEPT, ARMSTRONG ST COLLEGE, SAVANNAH GA 31406
JONES, JERE, PHIL DEPT, BROOKLYN COLLEGE, BROOKLYN NY 11210
JONES, JOHN D, PHIL DEPT, BOSTON COLLEGE, CHESTNUT HILL MA 02167
JONES, MARTIN M, PHILOSOPHY AREA, ROGER WILLIAMS COL, BRISTOL RI 02809
JONES, P, PHILOSOPHY DEPT, UNIV OF ALBERTA, EDMONTON ALB CAN
JONES, ROLAND B, WOODBURY COLLEGE, LOS ANGELES, CA 90017
JONES, ROYCE, RELIG & PHIL, UNION COLLEGE, BARBOURVILLE KY 40906
JONES, S MILTON, PHIL DEPT, UNIV OF ROCHESTER, ROCHESTER NY 14627
JONES, STEVEN CHARLES, PHILOSOPHY DEPT, UNIV OF TEXAS, AUSTIN TX 78712
JONES, STEVEN, PHILOSOPHY DEPT, UNIV OF WATERLOO, WATERLOO ONT CAN
JONES, T CANBY, RELIG & PHIL DEPT, WILMINGTON COL, WILMINGTON OH 45177
JONES, W GEORGE, DANVILLE COM COL, DANVILLE, VA 24541
JONES, WILLIAM A, PHILOSOPHY DEPT, XAVIER UNIVERSITY, CINCINNATI OH 45207
JONES, WILLIAM B, PHIL DEPT, UNIV OF FLORIDA, GAINESVILLE FL 32611
JONES, WILLIAM F, PHIL DEPT, EAST KENTUCKY UNIV, RICHMOND KY 40475
JONSEN, ALBERT R, PHIL DEPT, UNIV OF SN FRANCISCO, SAN FRANCISCO CA 94117
JOOS, ERNEST, PHILOSOPHY DEPT, LOYOLA COLLEGE, MONTREAL QUE CAN
JORDAHL, V TRUMAN, PHIL & RELIG DEPT, ROANOKE COLLEGE, SALEM VA 24153
JORDAK, FRANK, PHILOSOPHY DEPT, UNIV OF WATERLOO, WATERLOO ONT CAN
JORDAN, CHERIE, PHILOSOPHY DEPT, UNIV OF TEXAS, AUSTIN TX 78712
JORDAN, JAMES, PHILOSOPHY DEPT, QUEENS COLLEGE, FLUSHING NY 11367
JORDAN, ROBERT W, PHIL DEPT, CONNECTICUT COL, NEW LONDON CT 06320
JORDAN, ROBERT W, PHIL DEPT, COLORADO ST UNIV, FORT COLLINS CO 80521
JORGENSEN, OLE, GEN EDUC DEPT, DES MOINES COM COL, ANKENY IA 50021
JOSAITIS, MARVIN, HUMAN DIV, MONROE CO COM COL, MONROE MI 48161
JOSEPH, FRANCINE, PHIL DEPT, INDIANA UNIVERSITY, BLOOMINGTON IN 47401
JOSEPH, STEPHEN G, PHIL DEPT, BOSTON STATE COL, BOSTON MA 02115
JOSEPHSON, JOHN, PHILOSOPHY DEPT, OHIO STATE UNIV, COLUMBUS OH 43210
JOSEPHSON, SUSAN, PHILOSOPHY DEPT, OHIO STATE UNIV, COLUMBUS OH 43210
JOSHI, SUNDER, COLLEGE OF DUPAGE, GLEN ELLYN, IL 60137

JOST, LAWRENCE J, PHIL DEPT, UNIV OF CINCINNATI, CINCINNATI OH 45221
JOURDAIN, ALICE, PHIL DEPT, HUNTER COLLEGE, NEW YORK NY 10021
JOY, GLENN C, ENG & PHIL DEPT, SW TEXAS ST UNIV, SAN MARCOS TX 78666
JOY, M, PHIL OF EDUC & HIST, ONTARIC INSTITUTE, TORONTO ONT CAN
JOYAL, ACHILLE, PHIL DEPT, BRIDGEWATER ST COL, BRIDGEWATER MA 02324
JOYCE, ROBERT E, PHIL DEPT, SAINT JOHN'S UNIV, COLLEGEVILLE MN 56321
JOYNTON, O H, PHILOSOPHY DEPT, RICE UNIVERSITY, HOUSTON TX 77001
JUBIEN, MICHAEL, PHILOSOPHY DEPT, UNIV OF MASS, AMHERST MA 01002
JUCH, WILLIAM A, PHIL DEPT, BRANDEIS UNIVERSITY, WALTHAM MA 02154
JUFFRAS, ANGELO, PHILOSOPHY DEPT, PATERSON COL OF NJ, WAYNE NJ 07470
JUHASZ, LADISLAUS F, PHIL DEPT, CANISIUS COLLEGE, BUFFALO NY 14208
JUNG, MICHAEL, PHIL DEPT, ST JOSEPH SEM COL, ST BENEDICT LA 70457
JURENAS, ALGIRDAS, HUMAN DIV, UNIV OF MAINE, AUGUSTA ME 04330
JURKIEWICZ, HUGH, PHILOSOPHY DEPT, UNIV OF MASS, AMHERST MA 01002
JURKORIC, KATHRYN, PHILOSOPHY DEPT, CARTHAGE COLLEGE, KENOSHA WI 53140
JURSHEVESKI, S, PHILOSOPHY DEPT, UNIV OF TORONTO, TORONTO ONT CAN
JUSTICE, JOHN, PHILOSOPHY DEPT, UNIV OF TEXAS, AUSTIN TX 78712
KACHI, YUKIO, PHILOSOPHY DEPT, UNIV OF UTAH, SALT LAKE CTY UT 84112
KACZKOWSKI, CONRAD, PHIL DEPT, ST MARY'S UNIVERSITY, SAN ANTONIO TX 78228
KADING, DANIEL, PHILOSOPHY DEPT, KENYON COLLEGE, GAMBIER OH 43022
KADISH, MORTIMER, PHILOSOPHY DEPT, CASE WESTERN RESERVE, CLEVELAND OH 44106
KAELIN, EUGENE F, PHIL DEPT, FLORIDA STATE UNIV, TALLAHASSEE FL 32306
KAGAN, CONNIE B, PHILOSOPHY DEPT, UNIV OF OKLAHOMA, NORMAN OK 73069
KAHANE, HOWARD, PHIL DEPT, BERNARD BARUCH COL, NEW YORK NY 10010
KAHANE, JUDITH, PHIL DEPT, CENTRAL CONN ST COL, NEW BRITAIN CT 06050
KAHL, RUSSELL, PHIL DEPT, CALIFORNIA ST UNIV, SAN FRANCISCO CA 94132
KAHN, A, PHIL DEPT, W CONNECTICUT ST COL, DANBURY CT 06810
KAHN, CHARLES, PHILOSOPHY DEPT, UNIV OF PENN, PHILADELPHIA PA 19174
KAHN, STEVEN, PHIL DEPT, ST UNIV OF NY, AMHERST NY 14226
KAHN, THEODORE, REL & PHIL, IOWA WESLEYAN COL, MT PLEASANT IA 52641
KATN, PHILLIP J, HUMAN & PHIL DEPT, GROSSMONT COL, EL CAJON CA 92020
KAINZ, HOWARD P, PHILOSOPHY DEPT, MARQUETTE UNIV, MILWAUKEE WI 53233
KAISER, DONALD, SOC STUD DEPT, HIGHLAND PK COM COL, HIGHLAND PARK MI 48203
KAISER, NOLAN D, PHIL DEPT, CEN MICHIGAN UNIV, MT PLEASANT MI 48858
KALAL, LEONARD A, HUM & SOC SCI DEPT, COLO SCH OF MINES, GOLDEN CO 80401
KALI, BHASKARARAO, PHIL DEPT, UNIV OF BRIDGEPORT, BRIDGEPORT CT 06602
KALIKOW, THEODORA, PHIL DEPT, SE MASS UNIV, N DARTMOUTH MA 02747
KALIN, JESSE, PHIL DEPT, VASSAR COLLEGE, POUGHKEEPSIE NY 12601
KALIN, MARTIN, PHIL DEPT, DEPAUL UNIVERSITY, CHICAGO IL 60604
KALINSKI, W, PHILOSOPHY DEPT, UNIV OF TORONTO, TORONTO ONT CAN
KALISH, DONALD, PHIL DEPT, UNIV OF CALIFORNIA, LOS ANGELES CA 90024
KALKE, WILLIAM, PHIL DEPT, UNIV OF WISCONSIN, STEVENS POINT WI 54481
KALLAND, LLOYD A, THEOL DEPT, GORDON-CONWELL SEM, S HAMILTON MA 01982
KALLEN, HORACE M, PHIL DEPT, NW SCH FOR SOC RES, NEW YORK NY 10003
KALLES, JOHN D, PHILOSOPHY DEPT, FT STEILACOOM COL, TACOMA WA 98499
KALUPAHANA, DAVID J, PHIL DEPT, UNIVERSITY OF HAWAII, HONOLULU HI 96822
KAMBER, MATILD, SOC SCI AREA, COLUMBIA JUNIOR COL, COLUMBIA CA 95310
KAMBER, RICHARD, PHIL DEPT, SUSQUEHANNA UNIV, SELINSGROVE PA 17870
KAMINSKY, JACK, PHIL DEPT, ST UNIV OF NY, BINGHAMTON NY 13901
KAMLER, HOWARD, HIST & PHIL DEPT, E MICHIGAN UNIV, YPSILANTI MI 48197
KAMPE, CORNELIUS, PHILOSOPHY DEPT, ACADIA UNIVERSITY, WOLFVILLE N S CAN
KANATSKY, CHRISTOPHER, PHIL DEPT, UNIVERSITY OF DAYTON, DAYTON OH 45469
KANE, DENNIS C, PHIL DEPT, PROVIDENCE COLLEGE, PROVIDENCE RI 02919
KANE, FRANCES, PHILOSOPHY DEPT, CARDINAL GLENNON COL, ST LOUIS MO 63119
KANE, G STANLEY, PHILOSOPHY DEPT, MIAMI UNIVERSITY, OXFORD OH 45056
KANE, LOUIS, PHIL DEPT, ST HYACINTH COLLEGE, GRANBY MA 01033
KANE, ROBERT H, PHILOSOPHY DEPT, UNIV OF TEXAS, AUSTIN TX 78712
KANNWISHER, ARTHUR, PHIL DEPT, INDIANA UNIV OF PENN, INDIANA PA 15701
KANTOR, JAY, PHIL DEPT, CITY COLLEGE, NEW YORK NY 10031
KANTOR, SAMUEL, OHIO STATE UNIV, LIMA, OH 45804
KAPITAN, TOMIS, PHIL DEPT, INDIANA UNIVERSITY, BLOOMINGTON IN 47401
KAPLAN, DAVID, PHIL DEPT, UNIV OF CALIFORNIA, LOS ANGELES CA 90024
KAPLAN, MARK, PHIL DEPT, UNIV OF MICHIGAN, ANN ARBOR MI 48104
KAPLAN, SOLOMON M, PHIL & RELIG, CHATHAM COLLEGE, PITTSBURGH PA 15232

KAPPLER, A SERGE, PHIL DEPT, S METHODIST UNIV, DALLAS TX 75222
KARAHALIOS, GEORGE, PHIL & REL DEPT, HELLENIC COLLEGE, BROOKLINE MA 02146
KARASON, HALLDOR, PHIL DEPT, W WASHINGTON ST COL, BELLINGHAM WA 98225
KAREGA, CHUI, PHIL DEPT, MICHIGAN STATE UNIV, EAST LANSING MI 48823
KARELIS, CHARLES H, PHIL DEPT, WILLIAMS COLLEGE, WILLIAMSTOWN MA 01267
KARGOPOULOS, PHILLIP, PHIL DEPT, BOSTON UNIVERSITY, BOSTON MA 02215
KARLIN, LARRY, PHIL DEPT, UNIV OF CALIFORNIA, IRVINE CA 92664
KARNOS, DAVID, PHILOSOPHY DEPT, PENN STATE UNIV, UNIV PARK PA 16802
KARNOUTSOS, G, PHIL & RELIG, JERSEY CITY ST COL, JERSEY CITY NJ 07305
KARNS, C FRANKLIN, PHIL DEPT, CINCINNATI BIBLE SEM, CINCINNATI OH 45204
KARP, BARRIE, PHIL DEPT, CITY COLLEGE, NEW YORK NY 10031
KASACHKOFF, T, SOC SCI DEPT, MANHATTAN COM COL, NEW YORK NY 10019
KASHAP, S PAUL, PHIL STUD BOARD, U CF CALIFORNIA, SANTA CRUZ CA 95060
KASSIM, HUSAIN, HUMAN DEPT, FLORIDA TECH UNIV, ORLANDO FL 32816
KASTEN, VANCE R, PHILOSOPHY DEPT, RIPON COLLEGE, RIPON WI 54971
KASULIS, THOMAS P, PHIL DEPT, UNIVERSITY OF HAWAII, HONOLULU HI 96822
KATEN, TOM, HIST & PHIL, COM COL PHILADELPHIA, PHILADELPHIA PA 19107
KATES, CAROL, PHIL & REL DEPT, ITHACA COLLEGE, ITHACA NY 14850
KATES, LAWRENCE R, PHILOSOPHY DEPT, UNIV OF WISONSIN, OSH KOSH WI 54901
KATT, ROBERT, PHILOSOPHY DEPT, VANDERBILT UNIV, NASHVILLE TN 37235
KATZ, BERNARD, PHILOSOPHY DEPT, UNIV OF TEXAS, AUSTIN TX 78712
KATZ, ELEANOR F, SOC SCI DEPT, ORANGE COAST COLLEGE, COSTA MESA CA 92626
KATZ, JERROLD J, PHIL DEPT, MASS INST TECH, CAMBRIDGE MA 02139
KATZFEY, MARK, PHIL DEPT, UNIV OF WISCONSIN, MILWAUKEE WI 53201
KATZNER, LOUIS, PHIL DEPT, BOWLING GREEN UNIV, BOWLING GREEN OH 43403
KAUBER, PETER, PHIL DEPT, BOWLING GREEN UNIV, BOWLING GREEN OH 43403
KAUFFMAN, ALVIN H, PHIL DEPT, EAST NAZARENE COL, WOLLASTON MA 02170
KAUFMAN, HAROLD, SOC SCI DEPT, LAKE LAND COLLEGE, MATTOON IL 61938
KAUFMAN, LEO, PHILOSOPHY DEPT, SEATTLE UNIVERSITY, SEATTLE WA 98122
KAUFMAN, MARJORIE, PHIL DEPT, UNIV OF CALIFORNIA, LOS ANGELES CA 90024
KAUFMAN, PAUL S, PHIL DEPT, UNIV OF N CAROLINA, CHAPEL HILL NC 27514
KAUFMAN, STANLEY B, PHILOSOPHY DEPT, UNIV OF WISCONSIN, MADISON WI 53706
KAUFMANN, WALTER, PHIL DEPT, PRINCETON UNIVERSITY, PRINCETON NJ 08540
KAVALEC, NORMAN, HUMAN DEPT, OCEAN COUNTY COL, TOMS RIVER NJ 08753
KAVKA, GREGORY, PHIL DEPT, UNIV OF CALIFORNIA, LOS ANGELES CA 90024
KAWATSU, KIMIKO, PHIL DEPT, UNIVERSITY OF HAWAII, HONOLULU HI 96822
KAWCZAK, ANDREW, PHILOSOPHY DEPT, LOYOLA COLLEGE, MONTREAL QUE CAN
KAY, STANLEY B, PHIL & REL STUD, WILKES COLLEGE, WILKES BARRE PA 18703
KAY, TOOMB, REL & PHIL DEPT, TENN WESLEYAN COL, ATHENS TN 37303
KAYE, CLAIRE, PHILOSOPHY DEPT, CAL STATE COL, DOMINGUEZ HLS CA 90747
KEANE, ELLEN MARIE, PHIL DEPT, MARYMOUNT COLLEGE, TARRYTOWN NY 10591
KEANE, KEVIN P, PHIL DEPT, COLORADO ST UNIV, FORT COLLINS CO 80521
KEARLEY, CARROLL, LOYOLA UNIVERSITY, LOS ANGELES, CA 90045
KEARNEY, FRANCIS, PHIL DEPT, ST BONAVENTURE UNIV, ST BONVENTURE NY 14778
KEARNEY, JOHN, PHIL DEPT, ST JOSEPH'S COL, PHILADELPHIA PA 19131
KEARNS, JOHN T, PHIL DEPT, ST UNIV OF NY, AMHERST NY 14226
KEARNS, THOMAS J, PHIL DEPT, CHESTNUT HILL COL, PHILADELPHIA PA 19118
KEARNS, THOMAS R, PHIL & REL DEPT, AMHERST COLLEGE, AMHERST MA 01002
KEATHLEY, N, REL & PHIL, PALM BCH ATLANTIC COL, WEST PALM BCH FL 33401
KEATING, BERNARD, PHIL DEPT, UNIV OF VIRGINIA, CHARLOTTESVL VA 22903
KEATING, JAMES W, PHIL DEPT, DEPAUL UNIVERSITY, CHICAGO IL 60604
KEATON, ALVIN, GOV & PHIL DEPT, NEW MEXICO ST UNIV, LAS CRUCES NM 88003
KEDL, KENT, PHIL & REL DEPT, SOUTH DAKOTA ST UNIV, BROOKINGS SD 57006
KEEGAN, JOHN, THEOL PROGRAM, MARYKNOLL SEM, MARYKNOLL NY 10545
KEEHLEY, JAY T, MISSISSIPPI ST UNIV, ST COLLEGE, MS 39762
KEEL, OTHMAR, PHILOSOPHY DEPT, MCGILL UNIVERSITY, MONTREAL QUE CAN
KEELING, BRYANT, PHIL DEPT, W ILLINOIS UNIV, MACOMB IL 61455
KEELING, J KEITH, REL & PHIL DEPT, ROCKFORD COLLEGE, ROCKFORD IL 61101
KEEN, HEATHER, CTR FOR THE PERSON, PRESCOTT COLLEGE, PRESCOTT AZ 86301
KEEN, RAYMOND W, PHIL DEPT, CECIL COM COL, NORTH EAST MD 21901
KEEN, SAM, CTR FOR THE PERSON, PRESCOTT COLLEGE, PRESCOTT AZ 86301
KEEN, TOM, PHILOSOPHY DEPT, HEIDELBERG COLLEGE, TIFFIN OH 44883
KEENAN, BRIAN M, PHILOSOPHY DEPT, UNIV OF WINNIPEG, WINNIPEG MAN CAN
KEENAN, FRANCIS, ST UNIV OF NY, BROCKPORT, NY 14420

KEENE, CAROL A, PHIL STUD DEPT, S ILLINOIS UNIV, EDWARDSVILLE IL   62025
KEENE, J CALVIN, PHIL TEACH AREA, WADHAMS HALL SEM, OGDENSBURG NY   13669
KEGLEY, CHARLES W, PHIL & REL STUD, CAL STATE COL, BAKERSFIELD CA   93309
KEGLEY, JAQUELYN A K, PHIL & REL STUD, CAL STATE COL, BAKERSFIELD CA   93309
KEHEW, DONAL R, PHILOSOPHY DEPT, SEM OF LADY OF PROV, WARWICK RI   02889
KEHOE, E, SOC SCI DEPT, RYERSON POLYTECH U, TORONTO ONT   CAN
KEIM, ROBERT G, PHIL DEPT, UNIV OF WISCONSIN, MILWAUKEE WI   53201
KEIPER, RALPH, REL PHIL & APOL DEPT, CON BAPT THEOL SEM, DENVER CO   80210
KEISTER, J D, PHIL & RELIG DEPT, ROANOKE COLLEGE, SALEM VA   24153
KEKES, J, PHIL & CLASS DEPT, UNIV OF SASKATCHEWAN, REGINA SAS   CAN
KELBLEY, CHARLES, PHIL DEPT, FORDHAM UNIVERSITY, BRONX NY   10458
KELL, ROBIN, PHIL DEPT, PRINCE GEORGE'S COM, LARGO MD   20870
KELLEHER, JOHN R, HUMAN DEPT, LUZERNE CO COM COL, WILKES-BARRE PA   18711
KELLEHER, THOMAS B, ST PETER'S COLLEGE, JERSEY CITY, NJ   07306
KELLENBERGER, JAMES, PHIL DEPT, CALIFORNIA ST UNIV, NORTHRIDGE CA   91324
KELLER, CHESTER Z, PHIL DEPT, CEN WASH STATE COL, ELLENSBURG WA   98926
KELLER, JAMES A, PHILOSOPHY DEPT, WOFFORD COLLEGE, SPARTANBURG SC   29301
KELLER, JOHN, PHIL DEPT, ST JOSEPH'S COL, PHILADELPHIA PA   19131
KELLER, MARCIA L, PHIL DEPT, UNIV OF CALIFORNIA, RIVERSIDE CA   92502
KELLER, PAUL, HIST & PHIL DIV, TUSCULUM COLLEGE, GREENEVILLE TN   37743
KELLER, RICHARD P, SOC SCI DEPT, SEATTLE CEN COM COL, SEATTLE WA   98122
KELLEY, DICK, SOC SCI DEPT, LOWER COLUMBIA COL, LONGVIEW WA   98632
KELLEY, LEIGH B, PHIL DEPT, UNIV OF N CAROLINA, CHAPEL HILL NC   27514
KELLNER, DOUGLAS, PHILOSOPHY DEPT, UNIV OF TEXAS, AUSTIN TX   78712
KELLOWAY, WILLIAM, PHIL FACULTY, UNIV OF OTTAWA, OTTAWA ONT   CAN
KELLY JR, ARTHUR M, ENG DEPT, U S MILITARY ACAD, WEST POINT NY   10996
KELLY, CHARLES, PHIL DEPT, LE MOYNE COLLEGE, SYRACUSE NY   13214
KELLY, CORNELIUS J, PHIL DEPT, CARROLL COLLEGE, HELENA MT   59601
KELLY, DENIS RYAN, PHIL DEPT, MARIAN COLLEGE, INDIANAPOLIS IN   46222
KELLY, DEREK, PHILOSOPHY DEPT, HOFSTRA UNIVERSITY, HEMPSTEAD NY   11550
KELLY, EUGENE, SOC SCI DEPT, NEW YORK INST TECH, OLD WESTBURY NY   11568
KELLY, J M, UNIV OF ST MICHAEL'S, TORONTO 181, ONT   CAN
KELLY, JACK, PHIL DEPT, UNIV OF NEVADA, RENO NV   89507
KELLY, JAMES P, PHIL DEPT, PROVIDENCE COLLEGE, PROVIDENCE RI   02919
KELLY, JAMES PATRICK, PHILOSOPHY DEPT, LYNCHBURG COL, LYNCHBURG VA   24504
KELLY, JAMES T, PHILOSOPHY DEPT, URSULINE COLLEGE, CLEVELAND OH   44124
KELLY, JAMES V, PHIL DEPT, LOYOLA UNIVERSITY, CHICAGO IL   60626
KELLY, JOHN E, PHIL DEPT, CANISIUS COLLEGE, BUFFALO NY   14208
KELLY, MATTHEW JOHN, PHIL DEPT, S ILLINOIS UNIV, CARBONDALE IL   62901
KELLY, STEVEN D, PHIL DEPT, UNIV OF ILLINOIS, URBANA IL   61801
KELMACHTER, MARK, PHIL DEPT, EMORY UNIVERSITY, ATLANTA GA   30322
KELVINGTON, JAMES, PHILOSOPHY DEPT, GANNON COLLEGE, ERIE PA   16501
KEMERLING, GARTH, PHIL DEPT, UNIVERSITY OF IOWA, IOWA CITY IA   52240
KEMMIS, DANIEL, PHIL DEPT, UNIV OF MONTANA, MISSOULA MT   59801
KEMP, WILLIAM, PHIL DEPT, COL VIEUX-MONTREAL, MONTREAL QUE   CAN
KEMPNER, MARTIN, PHILOSOPHY DEPT, RUTGERS UNIV, NEW BRUNSWICK NJ   08903
KENDZIERSKI, LOTTIE H, PHILOSOPHY DEPT, MARQUETTE UNIV, MILWAUKEE WI   53233
KENEVAN, CHARLES A, PHIL DEPT, UNIV OF COLORADO, DENVER CO   80202
KENEVAN, PHILLIS, PHIL DEPT, UNIV OF COLORADO, BOULDER CO   80302
KENIG, HOWARD, PHIL DEPT, MILLERSVILLE ST COL, MILLERSVILLE PA   17551
KENNARD, GEORGE, PHILOSOPHY DEPT, GONZAGA UNIV, SPOKANE WA   99202
KENNARD, KENNETH C, PHILOSOPHY DEPT, ILLINOIS ST UNIV, NORMAL IL   61761
KENNEDY, BART F, PHIL & REL DEPT, TROY ST UNIVERSITY, TROY AL   36081
KENNEDY, CHARLES A, PHIL & RELIG, VA POLYTECH INST, BLACKSBURG VA   24061
KENNEDY, EARL W, PHIL DEPT, NORTHWESTERN COL, ORANGE CITY IA   51041
KENNEDY, EDWARD, PHIL DEPT, XAVIER UNIVERSITY, NEW ORLEANS LA   70125
KENNEDY, K M, SOUTH MISSIONARY COL, COLLEGEDALE, TN   37315
KENNEDY, LEONARD A, PHILOSOPHY DEPT, UNIV OF WINDSOR, WINDSOR ONT   CAN
KENNEDY, PHILIP C, SOC SCI DIV, MCKENDREE COL, LEBANON IL   62254
KENNEDY, SAMUEL, PHIL DEPT, ROCKHURST COLLEGE, KANSAS CITY MO   64110
KENNICK, WILLIAM E, PHIL & REL DEPT, AMHERST COLLEGE, AMHERST MA   01002
KENNINGTON, RICHARD H, PHILOSOPHY DEPT, PENN STATE UNIV, UNIV PARK PA   16802
KENNY, JOHN P, PHIL DEPT, PROVIDENCE COLLEGE, PROVIDENCE RI   02919
KENSHUR, DEBORAH, PHIL DEPT, UNIVERSITY OF IOWA, IOWA CITY IA   52240

KENT, BEVERLEY, PHILOSOPHY DEPT, UNIV OF WATERLOO, WATERLOO ONT   CAN
KENT, DALE, PHIL DEPT, MICHIGAN STATE UNIV, EAST LANSING MI 48823
KENT, E DARYL, PHILOSOPHY DEPT, GUILFORD COLLEGE, GREENSBORO NC 27410
KENT, EDWARD, PHIL DEPT, BROOKLYN COLLEGE, BROOKLYN NY 11210
KENT, OTIS, PHIL DEPT, UNIVERSITY OF IOWA, IOWA CITY IA 52240
KENT, THOMAS, PHIL DEPT, LE MOYNE COLLEGE, SYRACUSE NY 13214
KENYON, ROBERT, PHIL DEPT, NORTHWESTERN UNIV, EVANSTON IL 60201
KEON, JAMES J, PHILOSOPHY DEPT, UNIV OF ST THOMAS, HOUSTON TX 77006
KEPLER, JAMES H, WOODBURY COLLEGE, LOS ANGELES, CA 90017
KERINS, FRANK, PHIL DEPT, COL OF ST FRANCIS, JOLIET IL 60435
KERKHOFF, MANFRED, PHIL DEPT, UNIV OF PUERTO RICO, RIO PIEDRAS PR 00931
KERLIN, MICHAEL J, PHIL DEPT, LA SALLE COLLEGE, PHILADELPHIA PA 19141
KERN, RICHARD, PHIL & RELIG DEPT, FINDLAY COLLEGE, FINDLAY OH 45840
KERNER, GEORGE C, PHIL DEPT, MICHIGAN STATE UNIV, EAST LANSING MI 48823
KERR, HUGH T, THEOL DEPT, PRINCETON THEOL SEM, PRINCETON NJ 08540
KERR, STANLEY, NE ILLINOIS ST UNIV, CHICAGO, IL 60625
KERSTEN, FRED, PHIL OPTION, UNIV OF WISCONSIN, GREEN BAY WI 54302
KESMODEL, WILLIAM P, HUMAN DIV, CATONSVILLE COM COL, CATONSVILLE MD 21228
KESSLER, GARY E, PHIL & REL STUD, CAL STATE COL, BAKERSFIELD CA 93309
KESSLER, WARREN L, PHILOSOPHY DEPT, CALIFORNIA ST UNIV, FRESNO CA 93740
KETCHUM, RICHARD, PHIL DEPT, UNIV OF CALIFORNIA, SANTA BARBARA CA 93106
KETNER, KENNETH L, PHILOSOPHY DEPT, TEXAS TECH UNIV, LUBBOCK TX 79409
KETTLER, RONALD, PHIL DEPT, SEM OF ST PIUS X, ERLANGER KY 41018
KEYES, CHARLES D, PHILOSOPHY DEPT, DUQUESNE UNIV, PITTSBURGH PA 15219
KEYES, MARIE S T, PHIL DEPT, MARYMOUNT MANHATTAN, NEW YORK NY 10021
KEYES, RALPH, CTR FOR THE PERSON, PRESCOTT COLLEGE, PRESCOTT AZ 86301
KEYES, THOMAS, PHILOSOPHY DEPT, MARQUETTE UNIV, MILWAUKEE WI 53233
KEYES, WILLIAM T, PHIL DEPT, CALIFORNIA ST UNIV, SAN JOSE CA 95114
KEYS, JAMES M, HUMAN DIV, SOUTHEASTERN UNIV, WASHINGTON DC 20024
KEYS, MADELEINE, PHIL DEPT, UNIVERSITY OF IDAHO, MOSCOW ID 83843
KEYT, DAVID, PHILOSOPHY DEPT, UNIV OF WASHINGTON, SEATTLE WA 98195
KEYWORTH, DONALD, PHIL & REL, DRAKE UNIVERSITY, DES MOINES IA 50311
KHATCHADOURIAN, HAIG, PHIL DEPT, UNIV OF WISCONSIN, MILWAUKEE WI 53201
KIBBONS, JERRY, BIB & REL EDUC, CAMPBELLSVILLE COL, CAMPBELLSVL KY 42718
KIDDER, JOEL, PHIL DEPT, SYRACUSE UNIVERSITY, SYRACUSE NY 13210
KIEFER, HOWARD, PHIL DEPT, COLLEGE AT BROCKPORT, BROCKPORT NY 14420
KIELKOPF, CHARLES F, PHILOSOPHY DEPT, OHIO STATE UNIV, COLUMBUS OH 43210
KIERNAN, WILLIAM E, ST PETER'S COLLEGE, JERSEY CITY, NJ 07306
KIESAU, ROBERT F, PHIL DEPT, UNIV OF SOUTH DAKOTA, VERMILLION SD 57069
KIGER, BARRY W, PHIL & RELIG DEPT, UNIV OF ARKANSAS, LITTLE ROCK AR 72204
KIKER, FRANK, PHIL & RELIG DEPT, HAMPTON INST, HAMPTON VA 23368
KILEY, W PAUL, PHIL DEPT, CENTRAL CONN ST COL, NEW BRITAIN CT 06050
KILGORE, WILLIAM J, PHILOSOPHY DEPT, BAYLOR UNIVERSITY, WACO TX 76703
KILLEN, ALLEN, THEOLOGY DEPT, REFORMED THEOL SEM, JACKSON MS 39209
KILLORIN, JOSEPH, ENG & PHIL DEPT, ARMSTRONG ST COLLEGE, SAVANNAH GA 31406
KILZER, ERNEST, PHIL DEPT, SAINT JOHN'S UNIV, COLLEGEVILLE MN 56321
KILZER, PHILOMENE, RELIG & PHIL DEPT, MOUNT MARTY COL, YANKTON SD 57078
KIM, CHIN-TAI, PHILOSOPHY DEPT, CASE WESTERN RESERVE, CLEVELAND OH 44106
KIM, HA POONG, PHILOSOPHY DEPT, E ILLINOIS UNIV, CHARLESTON IL 61920
KIM, HA TAI, PHIL DEPT, WHITTIER COLLEGE, WHITTIER CA 90608
KIM, HYUNG I, PHIL DEPT, CALIFORNIA ST UNIV, LONG BEACH CA 90840
KIM, JAEGWON, PHIL DEPT, UNIV OF MICHIGAN, ANN ARBOR MI 48104
KIM, SANG-KI, PHIL STUD DEPT, S ILLINOIS UNIV, EDWARDSVILLE IL 62025
KIM, YONG CHOON, PHILOSOPHY DEPT, UNIV OF RHODE ISLAND, KINGSTON RI 02881
KIMBALL, ROBERT, SYST & PHIL, GRADUATE THEOL UNION, BERKELEY CA 94709
KIMBLE, JAMES P, PHIL DEPT, UNIV OF COLORADO, BOULDER CO 80302
KIMM, ROBERT, PHIL DEPT, DEPAUL UNIVERSITY, CHICAGO IL 60604
KIMMEL, LARRY D, PHIL DEPT, TRINITY UNIVERSITY, SAN ANTONIO TX 78284
KIMPEL, BENJAMIN, PHILOSOPHY DEPT, DREW UNIVERSITY, MADISON NJ 07940
KINCRED, SHEILA, PHIL DEPT, ST MARY'S UNIVERSITY, HALIFAX N S   CAN
KINCZIA, JOHN F, SOC SCI DEPT, COLORADO MT COL, LEADVILLE CO 80461
KING-FARLOW, J, PHILOSOPHY DEPT, UNIV OF ALBERTA, EDMONTON ALB   CAN
KING, C WAYNE, REL & PHIL DEPT, BLACKBURN COLLEGE, CARLINVILLE IL 62626
KING, CHARLES, PHILOSOPHY DEPT, POMONA COLLEGE, CLAREMONT CA 91711

KING, EDWARD G, PHIL DEPT, MARYGROVE COLLEGE, DETROIT MI 48221
KING, GUY O'GORMAN, PHILOSOPHY DEPT, OHIO STATE UNIV, COLUMBUS OH 43210
KING, JAMES T, PHIL DEPT, N ILLINOIS UNIV, DEKALB IL 60115
KING, JEFFREY, PHIL DEPT, ST UNIV OF NY, BINGHAMTON NY 13901
KING, JOHN, PHIL DEPT, ROCKEFELLER UNIV, NEW YORK NY 10021
KING, THOMAS W, HIST & PHIL DEPT, UNIV OF TEXAS, ARLINGTON TX 76010
KING, WILLIAM L, PHIL DEPT, IDAHO STATE UNIV, POCATELLO ID 83201
KING, WILLIAM, PHILOSOPHY DEPT, MCGILL UNIVERSITY, MONTREAL QUE   CAN
KING, WINSTON L, PHIL DEPT, COLORADO ST UNIV, FORT COLLINS CO 80521
KINGSBURY, LESLIE L, PHIL DEPT, ROCK VALLEY COLLEGE, ROCKFORD IL 61101
KINGSTON, F TEMPLE, PHILOSOPHY DEPT, UNIV OF WINDSOR, WINDSOR ONT   CAN
KINNAMAN, WILLIAM, SOC SCI DEPT, RHODE ISLAND JR COL, PROVIDENCE RI 02908
KINNIREY SR, ANN JULIA, PHIL DEPT, TRINITY COLLEGE, WASHINGTON DC 20017
KINSELLA, ARTHUR, ST EDWARD'S UNIV, AUSTIN, TX 78704
KINSELLA, NOEL, PHIL DEPT, SAINT THOMAS UNIV, FREDERICTON N B   CAN
KINZEL, MARGARET, SOC SCI DEPT, CAL ST POLYTECH UNIV, POMONA CA 91768
KIPNIS, KENNETH, PHIL DEPT, PURDUE UNIVERSITY, LAFAYETTE IN 47907
KIPPES, A, PHIL DEPT, OUR LADY OF LAKE COL, SAN ANTONIO TX 78285
KIRBY, BRIAN S, PHIL DEPT, ST LAWRENCE UNIV, CANTON NY 13617
KIRCHNER, LANDON, PHIL & REL DEPT, W LIBERTY ST COL, WEST LIBERTY WV 26074
KIRK, JAMES A, REL PHIL DEPT, ILIFF SCH OF THEOL, DENVER CO 80210
KIRK, JOHN, PHIL DEPT, COL AT NEW PLATZ, NEW PLATZ NY 12561
KIRK, ROBERT E, PHILOSOPHY DEPT, UNIV OF WASHINGTON, SEATTLE WA 98195
KIRK, SAMUEL A, PHILOSOPHY DEPT, OHIO STATE UNIV, COLUMBUS OH 43210
KIRKLAND, WILLIAM, REL & PHIL DEPT, MORRIS HARVEY COL, CHARLESTON WV 25304
KIRKPATRICK, DAVID, PHILOSOPHY DEPT, WAYLAND BAPT COL, PLAINVIEW TX 79072
KIRKPATRICK, R T, PHIL DEPT, UNIV OF SW LOUISIANA, LAFAYETTE LA 70501
KIRMANI, S, PHIL DEPT, UNIV OF CONNECTICUT, STORRS CT 06268
KIRSCHENMANN, FRED, HUMAN DIV, CURRY COLLEGE, MILTON MA 02186
KIRSHBAUM, HAROLD, PHIL & REL DEPT, COE COLLEGE, CEDAR RAPIDS IA 52402
KIRTLAND, ROBERT, PHIL & REL STUD DIV, LOURDES COL, SYLVANIA OH 43560
KISIEL, THEODORE J, PHIL DEPT, N ILLINOIS UNIV, DEKALB IL 60115
KISSIN, PETER P, PHILOSOPHY DEPT, CALIFORNIA ST UNIV, HAYWARD CA 94542
KITCHEL, MARY JEAN, PHIL DEPT, EMMANUEL COLLEGE, BOSTON MA 02115
KITCHENER, RICHARD F, PHIL DEPT, COLORADO ST UNIV, FORT COLLINS CO 80521
KITCHER, PHILIP, PHIL DEPT, VASSAR COLLEGE, POUGHKEEPSIE NY 12601
KITELEY, MURRAY, PHIL DEPT, SMITH COLLEGE, NORTHAMPTON MA 01060
KITZEROW, WALTER C, SOC SCI DEPT, MORTON COLLEGE, CICERO IL 60650
KIVY, PETER, PHILOSOPHY DEPT, RUTGERS UNIV, NEWARK NJ 07102
KLANN, RICHARD, SYST THEOL DEPT, CONCORDIA SEMINARY, ST LOUIS MO 63105
KLASING, SANDRA, PHIL DEPT, UNIVERSITY OF MIAMI, CORAL GABLES FL 33124
KLAUDER, FRANCIS J, PHILOSOPHY DEPT, DON BOSCO COLLEGE, NEWTON NJ 07860
KLEIN JR, TED E, PHIL DEPT, TEXAS CHRISTIAN UNIV, FORT WORTH TX 76129
KLEIN, BARBARA, PHIL DEPT, BOSTON UNIVERSITY, BOSTON MA 02215
KLEIN, DIANNA, PHILOSOPHY DEPT, RUTGERS UNIV, NEW BRUNSWICK NJ 08903
KLEIN, J THEODORE, PHIL OF RELIG DEPT, URBANA COLLEGE, URBANA OH 43078
KLEIN, KENNETH H, PHIL DEPT, VALPARAISO UNIV, VALPARAISO IN 46383
KLEIN, MARY K, PHIL OF RELIG DEPT, URBANA COLLEGE, URBANA OH 43078
KLEIN, PETER D, PHILOSOPHY DEPT, RUTGERS UNIV, NEW BRUNSWICK NJ 08903
KLEIN, SHERWIN, SOC SCI DEPT, BERGEN COM COL, PARAMUS NJ 07652
KLEINER, S A, PHIL & REL DEPT, UNIV OF GEORGIA, ATHENS GA 30602
KLEINMAN, LOWELL, PHIL DEPT, SUFFOLK CO COM COL, SELDEN NY 11784
KLEINMAN, ROBERT, MUS & HUM DEPT, PENSACOLA JUN COL, PENSACOLA FL 32504
KLEIS, SANDER, PHIL DEPT, ANDERSON COLLEGE, ANDERSON IN 46011
KLEITZ, PHILIP REX, HUMAN DEPT, COLLEGE OF SANTA FE, SANTA FE NM 87501
KLEMKE, E D, PHIL DEPT, ROOSEVELT UNIVERSITY, CHICAGO IL 60605
KLENK, VIRGINIA, PHILOSOPHY DEPT, UNIV OF HOUSTON, HOUSTON TX 77004
KLIMOV, ALEXIS, PHILOSOPHY DEPT, UNIV DE MONTREAL, MONTREAL QUE   CAN
KLINE, ALTON D, PHILOSOPHY DEPT, UNIV OF WISCONSIN, MADISON WI 53706
KLINE, C BENTON, HIST-DOCTRINAL DEPT, COLUMBIA THEOL SEM, DECATUR GA 30031
KLINE, CARL, LIBR STUD DEPT, BECKER JR COL, WORCESTER MA 01609
KLINE, GEORGE L, BRYN MAWR COLLEGE, BRYN MAWR, PA 19010
KLINE, ROBERT R, PHIL DEPT, MT SAINT MARY'S COL, EMMITSBURG MD 21727
KLINEFELTER, DONALD, PHIL & RELIG, UNIV OF TENNESSEE, CHATTANOOGA TN 37401

KLIVE, VISVALDIS, PHILOSOPHY DEPT, WITTENBERG UNIV, SPRINGFIELD OH 45501
KLOCKER, HARRY, PHIL DEPT, UNIV OF DENVER, DENVER CO 80210
KLOR DE ALVA, J JORGE, PHIL DEPT, CALIFORNIA ST UNIV, SAN JOSE CA 95114
KLUBACK, WILLIAM, HIST & POLIT SCI, KINGSBOROUGH COM COL, BROOKLYN NY 11235
KLUGE, E W, PHILOSOPHY DEPT, UNIV OF VICTORIA, VICTORIA B C CAN
KNAACK, JAY A, PHIL & REL STUD, UNIV OF W FLORIDA, PENSACOLA FL 32504
KNASES, J, PHILOSOPHY DEPT, UNIV OF TORONTO, TORONTO ONT CAN
KNECHT, PAUL, COMMITMENT STUD, JOHN WESLEY COL, OWOSSO MI 48867
KNEUPPER, THEODORE, PHIL DEPT, SLIPPERY ROCK ST COL, SLIPPERY ROCK PA 16057
KNIGHT, CHALMERS, PHIL DEPT, UNIV OF MICHIGAN, ANN ARBOR MI 48104
KNIGHT, JACK C, PHIL DEPT, UNIVERSITY OF MIAMI, CORAL GABLES FL 33124
KNIGHT, JOHN H, ENGLISH LIT & PHIL, UNIV OF WISCONSIN, MADISON WI 53706
KNIGHT, KIRBY, PHIL DEPT, UNIVERSITY OF DAYTON, DAYTON OH 45469
KNIGHT, THOMAS S, PHIL DEPT, ADELPHI UNIVERSITY, GARDEN CITY NY 11530
KNOBLOCK, JOHN H, PHIL DEPT, UNIVERSITY OF MIAMI, CORAL GABLES FL 33124
KNODELL JR, PRESTON, PHIL DEPT, ST MARY'S UNIVERSITY, SAN ANTONIO TX 78228
KNOTT, JOHN B, HUMAN DIV, OGLETHORPE UNIV, ATLANTA GA 30319
KNOTT, MOSES A, PHIL & RELIG, CENTENARY COL FOR WO, HACKETTSTOWN NJ 07840
KNOX JR, JOHN, PHILOSOPHY DEPT, DREW UNIVERSITY, MADISON NJ 07940
KNOX, ISRAEL, PHIL DEPT, NEW YORK UNIVERSITY, NEW YORK NY 10003
KNUDSEN, ROBERT, THEOL STUD FIELD, WESTMINSTER THEOL, PHILADELPHIA PA 19118
KOBELJA, CARL D, PHIL DEPT, SPRING HILL COLLEGE, MOBILE AL 36608
KOBER, MANFRED, GEN EDUC DEPT, FAITH BAPT BIB COL, ANKENY IA 50021
KOCH, DONALD F, PHIL DEPT, MICHIGAN STATE UNIV, EAST LANSING MI 48823
KOCH, MELVILLE L, PHILOSOPHY DEPT, CEN METHODIST COL, FAYETTE MO 65248
KOCH, P, PHILOSOPHY DEPT, UNIV PR EDWARD IS, CHARLOTTETOWN PEI CAN
KOCHER, JAMES C, FRANKLIN UNIVERSITY, COLUMBUS, OH 43215
KOCKELMANS, JOSEPH J, PHILOSOPHY DEPT, PENN STATE UNIV, UNIV PARK PA 16802
KOEHL, RICHARD A, PHIL DEPT, ST UNIV OF NY, AMHERST NY 14226
KOEHLER, CONRAD J, THIEL COLLEGE, GREENVILLE, PA 16125
KOEHN, DONALD R, PHIL DEPT, ILL WESLEYAN UNIV, BLOOMINGTON IL 61701
KOENEN, JANE, PHIL DEPT, NAZARETH COLLEGE, ROCHESTER NY 14610
KOENIG, THOMAS, PHIL DEPT, PURDUE UNIVERSITY, HAMMOND IN 46323
KOEPP, CYNTHIA J, PHIL DEPT, UNIVERSITY OF TOLEDO, TOLEDO OH 43606
KOERTGE, NORETTA, HIST & PHIL SCI, INDIANA UNIV, BLOOMINGTON IN 47401
KOESTENBAUM, PETER, PHIL DEPT, CALIFORNIA ST UNIV, SAN JOSE CA 95114
KOETHE, JOHN L, PHIL DEPT, UNIV OF WISCONSIN, MILWAUKEE WI 53201
KOHAK, ERAZIM, PHIL DEPT, BOSTON UNIVERSITY, BOSTON MA 02215
KOHL, MARVIN, PHIL DEPT, COL AT FREDONIA, FREDONIA NY 14063
KOHLENBERG, PHILIP, PHIL DEPT, ST CLOUD ST COL, ST CLOUD MN 56301
KOHLS, GERALD, PHILOSOPHY DEPT, GONZAGA UNIV, SPOKANE WA 99202
KOHLS, HARRY, PHILOSOPHY DEPT, SEATTLE UNIVERSITY, SEATTLE WA 98122
KOHLS, JOHN, PHIL DEPT, MT ANGEL SEMINARY, ST BENEDICT OR 97373
KOHN, JEROME, PHIL DEPT, NW SCH FOR SOC RES, NEW YORK NY 10003
KOLASNY, JOSEPH A, GEN EDUC DEPT, CLARK TECH COL, SPRINGFIELD OH 45501
KOLB, DAVID, PHIL DEPT, UNIV OF CHICAGO, CHICAGO IL 60637
KOLB, ROBERT W, PHIL DEPT, UNIV OF N CAROLINA, CHAPEL HILL NC 27514
KOLBE, HENRY E, PHIL OF RELIG, GARRETT THEOL SEM, EVANSTON IL 60201
KOLENDA, K, PHILOSOPHY DEPT, RICE UNIVERSITY, HOUSTON TX 77001
KOLIKOFF, FRED, PHIL DEPT, UNIV OF MICHIGAN, ANN ARBOR MI 48104
KOLITCH, DEAN, PHIL DEPT, LEHMAN COLLEGE, BRONX NY 10468
KOLLER, ALICE, PHILOSOPHY DEPT, EAST CAROLINA UNIV, GREENVILLE NC 27834
KOLLER, JOHN M, PHIL DEPT, RENSSELAER POLYTECH, TROY NY 12181
KOLLER, KERRY J, PHIL DEPT, UNIV OF SN FRANCISCO, SAN FRANCISCO CA 94117
KOLLMANN, EDWARD C, PHIL & RELIG DEPT, HAMPTON INST, HAMPTON VA 23368
KOMONCHAK, JOSEPH A, SYST THEOL, ST JOSEPH'S SEM, YONKERS NY 10704
KONDOLEON, THEODORE J, PHILOSOPHY DEPT, VILLANOVA UNIV, VILLANOVA PA 19085
KONECKY, STANLEY J, PHIL & RELIG DEPT, HARTWICK COLLEGE, ONEONTA NY 13820
KONECSNI, JOHNEMERY, CALDWELL COLLEGE, CALDWELL, NJ 07006
KONEFES, JAMES, PHIL DEPT, UNIVERSITY OF IOWA, IOWA CITY IA 52240
KONIGSBERG, JAN, PHIL DEPT, UNIV OF MONTANA, MISSOULA MT 59801
KONKEL, RICHARD H, PHIL & REL DEPT, FLORIDA INTNL UNIV, MIAMI FL 33144
KONRICH, EVA, PSYCH DEPT, EAST LOS ANGELES COL, LOS ANGELES CA 90022
KONYNDYK, KEN, PHIL DEPT, CALVIN COLLEGE, GRAND RAPIDS MI 49506

KOPPELMAN, WALTER, PHIL DEPT, CALIFORNIA ST UNIV, SAN DIEGO CA 92115
KORCIG, CARL R, PHIL DEPT, NORTHWESTERN UNIV, EVANSTON IL 60201
KORDUCAVICH, STEPHEN A, HUMAN DEPT, BROOME COM COL, BINGHAMTON NY 13902
KOREN, HENRY J, PHIL & THEOL DEPT, SAINT LEO COLLEGE, SAINT LEO FL 33574
KORN, FREDERICK, PHIL DEPT, BROOKLYN COLLEGE, BROOKLYN NY 11210
KORNER, STEPHAN, PHIL DEPT, YALE UNIVERSITY, NEW HAVEN CT 06520
KORNFEIN, ROGER, PHILOSOPHY DEPT, UNIV OF CALGARY, CALGARY 44 ALB CAN
KORNMUELLER, HELLMUTH, HUM DEPT, LK SUPERIOR ST COL, SALT ST MARIE MI 49783
KORSAK, RONALD, GOV & PHIL DEPT, NEW MEXICO ST UNIV, LAS CRUCES NM 88003
KORSMEYER, CAROLYN W, PHIL DEPT, ST UNIV OF NY, AMHERST NY 14226
KORT, LOUIS, PHIL DEPT, UNIV OF N CAROLINA, GREENSBORO NC 27412
KORTE, HERBERT, PHIL DEPT, UNIV OF WEST ONTARIO, LONDON ONT CAN
KORTIAN, GARBIS, PHILOSOPHY DEPT, UNIV DE MONTREAL, MONTREAL QUE CAN
KOSHOSHEK, RONALD, PHIL DEPT, UNIV OF WISCONSIN, EAU CLAIRE WI 54701
KOSLOW, ARNOLD, PHIL DEPT, BROOKLYN COLLEGE, BROOKLYN NY 11210
KOSMAN, L ARYEH, PHIL DEPT, HAVERFORD COLLEGE, HAVERFORD PA 19041
KOSNIK, ANTHONY, PHIL DEPT, ST MARY'S COLLEGE, ORCHARD LAKE MI 48034
KOSS, DONALD, PHIL DEPT, DEPAUL UNIVERSITY, CHICAGO IL 60604
KOSSEL, CLIFFORD, PHILOSOPHY DEPT, GONZAGA UNIV, SPOKANE WA 99202
KOSTED, PAUL, PHIL DEPT, UNIV OF CINCINNATI, CINCINNATI OH 45221
KOTTMAN, KARL, PHIL DEPT, IOWA STATE UNIV, AMES IA 50010
KOTZIN, RHODA H, PHIL DEPT, MICHIGAN STATE UNIV, EAST LANSING MI 48823
KOURANY, JANET A, PHILOSOPHY DEPT, UNIV OF UTAH, SALT LAKE CTY UT 84112
KOUTSOUVILIS, A P, EDUCATION COLLEGE, ALTHOUSE COLLEGE, LONDON ONT CAN
KOUX, YVON, PHILOSOPHY DEPT, COL DE MAISONNEUVE, MONTREAL QUE CAN
KOVACH, FRANCIS J, PHILOSOPHY DEPT, UNIV OF OKLAHOMA, NORMAN OK 73069
KOVACS, GEORGE, PHIL & REL DEPT, FLORIDA INTNL UNIV, MIAMI FL 33144
KOVALY, PAVEL, PHIL & REL DEPT, NORTHEASTERN UNIV, BOSTON MA 02115
KOVARIK, JAMES, PHIL DEPT, UNIVERSITY OF IOWA, IOWA CITY IA 52240
KOWALL, THOMAS W, PHILOSOPHY AREA, ROGER WILLIAMS COL, BRISTOL RI 02809
KOWALSKI, ANN M, PHILOSOPHY DEPT, UNIV OF RHODE ISLAND, KINGSTON RI 02881
KOWALSKI, JAMES G, PHILOSOPHY DEPT, UNIV OF RHODE ISLAND, KINGSTON RI 02881
KOZEL, CONSTANCE, PHILOSOPHY DEPT, COL MISERICORDIA, DALLAS PA 18612
KOZY JR, JOHN, PHILOSOPHY DEPT, EAST CAROLINA UNIV, GREENVILLE NC 27834
KRAEMER, WILLIAM S, PHIL DEPT, UNIV OF ARKANSAS, FAYETTEVILLE AR 72701
KRAFT, CHARLES, PHIL DEPT, UNIVERSITY OF DAYTON, DAYTON OH 45469
KRAKOW, IRVING, CAMDEN CO COLLEGE, ELACKWOOD, NJ 08012
KRAMER, SCOTT, PHIL DEPT, S ILLINOIS UNIV, CARBONDALE IL 62901
KRAMLINGER, THOMAS, PHIL DEPT, SIENA HEIGHTS COL, ADRIAN MI 49221
KRAMNICK, THOMAS, PHIL & RELIG, ENGLEWD CLIFFS COL, ENGLWD CLIFFS NJ 07632
KRANTZLER, ROBERT, PHIL DEPT, MIAMI-DADE JUN COL, MIAMI FL 33156
KRANZBERG, MELVIN, SOC SCI DEPT, GEORGIA INST OF TECH, ATLANTA GA 30332
KRASTEL, JOSEPH F, PHIL DEPT, ST ALPHONSUS COL, SUFFIELD CT 06078
KRAUS, ELIZABETH, PHIL DEPT, FORDHAM UNIVERSITY, BRONX NY 10458
KRAUS, RICHARD, PSYCH & SOC SCI, PACE COLLEGE, PLEASANTVILLE NY 10570
KRAUSE, KARL, PHIL DEPT, NORTHWESTERN UNIV, EVANSTON IL 60201
KRAUSZ, M, BRYN MAWR COLLEGE, BRYN MAWR, PA 19010
KRAUT, RICHARD H, PHIL DEPT, UNIV OF ILLINOIS, CHICAGO IL 60680
KREBBS, NORMAN A, PHILOSOPHY DEPT, WHITWORTH COLLEGE, SPOKANE WA 99251
KRECZ, CHARLES, PHIL DEPT, COL AT PLATTSBURGH, PLATTSBURGH NY 12901
KREEFT, PETER J, PHIL DEPT, BOSTON COLLEGE, CHESTNUT HILL MA 02167
KREILKAMP, DONALD, PHIL DEPT, ST JOSEPH'S COLLEGE, RENNSSELAER IN 47978
KREILKAMP, KARL, HUMAN DEPT, GEORGE MASON UNIV, FAIRFAX VA 22030
KREISEL, GEORG, PHIL DEPT, STANFORD UNIVERSITY, STANFORD CA 94305
KREISMAN, ARTHUR, HUMAN DIV, SOUTHERN OREGON COL, ASHLAND OR 97520
KRELLER, HERBERT J, SOC SCI DEPT, BUTLER CO COM JR COL, EL DORADO KS 67042
KREMER, E J, UNIV OF ST MICHAEL'S, TORONTO 181, ONT CAN
KRENIS, JOEL H, PHIL DEPT, UNIV OF ROCHESTER, ROCHESTER NY 14627
KRENTZ, ARTHUR, PHILOSOPHY DEPT, LUTHER COLLEGE, REGINA SAS CAN
KRESS, JERRY R, PHIL DEPT, UNIV OF MARYLAND, COLLEGE PARK MD 20742
KRETSCHMANN, PHILLIP, PHIL DEPT, BROOKLYN COLLEGE, BROOKLYN NY 11210
KRETZMANN, NORMAN, SAGE SCHOOL, CORNELL UNIVERSITY, ITHACA NY 14850
KRETZSCHMAR, BLAISE, PHIL DEPT, W ILLINOIS UNIV, MACOMB IL 61455
KREYCHE, GERALD F, PHIL DEPT, DEPAUL UNIVERSITY, CHICAGO IL 60604

KREYCHE, ROBERT J, PHILOSOPHY DEPT, UNIV OF ARIZONA, TUCSON AZ 85721
KRIKORIAN, YERVANT, PHIL DEPT, CITY COLLEGE, NEW YORK NY 10031
KRIMERMAN, L I, PHIL DEPT, UNIV OF CONNECTICUT, STORRS CT 06268
KRIMM, HANS, PHIL DEPT, COLORADO COLLEGE, COLORADO SPGS CO 80903
KRIMSKY, SHELDON, PHIL DEPT, UNIV OF S FLORIDA, TAMPA FL 33620
KRINSKY, RAYMOND, HUMAN DIV, PIEDMONT VA COM COL, CHARLOTTESVL VA 22903
KRIPKE, SAUL, PHIL DEPT, ROCKEFELLER UNIV, NEW YORK NY 10021
KRISTELLER, PAUL O, PHIL DEPT, COLUMBIA UNIVERSITY, NEW YORK NY 10027
KRISTOVICH, MICHAEL, LOYOLA UNIVERSITY, LOS ANGELES, CA 90045
KROIS, JOHN, PHILOSOPHY DEPT, PENN STATE UNIV, UNIV PARK PA 16802
KROLL, JOSEPH, PHILOSOPHY DEPT, CAL STATE COL, SN BERNARDINO CA 92407
KRONMAN, ANTHONY, PHIL DEPT, YALE UNIVERSITY, NEW HAVEN CT 06520
KRUMROY, KARL, PHILOSOPHY DEPT, KENT STATE UNIV, KENT OH 44242
KRUSE, CORNELIUS, PHILOSOPHY DEPT, WESLEYAN UNIV, MIDDLETOWN CT 06457
KRUTZEN, R W, PHILOSOPHY DEPT, UNIV OF SASKATCHEWAN, SASKATOON SAS CAN
KRYGER, HENRY, PHIL & THEOL DEPT, MARILLAC COLLEGE, ST LOUIS MO 63121
KRYTER, LAURENCE H, ENGLISH DEPT, JONES COUNTY JR COL, ELLISVILLE MS 39437
KRZYWICKI-HEBURT, G, PHILOSOPHY DEPT, QUEENS COLLEGE, FLUSHING NY 11367
KRZYWICKI-HERBURT, G, PHIL PROGRAM, GRADUATE SCH -CUNY, NEW YORK NY 10036
KUBARA, M P, PHILOSOPHY DEPT, UNIV OF LETHBRIDGE, LETHBRIDGE ALB CAN
KUBITZ, O A, PHIL DEPT, UNIV OF ILLINOIS, URBANA IL 61801
KUCHEMAN, CLARK A, PHIL DEPT, CLAREMONT MEN'S COL, CLAREMONT CA 91711
KUEHL, JAMES R, PHIL DEPT, NW SCH FOR SOC RES, NEW YORK NY 10003
KUEHN, B A, HUMANITIES DEPT, CENTENNIAL COLLEGE, SCARBOROUGH ONT CAN
KUFLIK, ARTHUR, PHIL DEPT, UNIV OF N CAROLINA, CHAPEL HILL NC 27514
KUHN, HAROLD B, THEOL & PHIL DIV, ASBURY THEOL SEM, WILMORE KY 40390
KUHNER, ROBERT, PHILOSOPHY DEPT, ANCHORAGE COM COL, ANCHORAGE AK 99503
KUHNS, RICHARD F, PHIL DEPT, COLUMBIA UNIVERSITY, NEW YORK NY 10027
KUIPER, JOHN, PHIL DEPT, UNIV OF KENTUCKY, LEXINGTON KY 40506
KULATHUNGAM, L C, PHIL DEPT, UNIV OF WEST ONTARIO, LONDON ONT CAN
KULTGEN, JOHN, PHIL DEPT, UNIV OF MISSOURI, COLUMBIA MO 65201
KUMAR, F L, PHILOSOPHY DEPT, MURRAY STATE UNIV, MURRAY KY 42071
KUMMEL, MARC S, PHIL DEPT, UNIV OF CALIFORNIA, SANTA BARBARA CA 93106
KUNG, GUIDO, PHIL DEPT, UNIV OF NOTRE DAME, NOTRE DAME IN 46556
KUNIN, JACK, PHIL & SOC DEPT, VANCOUVER CITY COL, VANCOUVER B C CAN
KUNKEL, JOSEPH C, PHIL DEPT, UNIVERSITY OF DAYTON, DAYTON OH 45469
KUNTZ, PAUL G, PHIL DEPT, EMORY UNIVERSITY, ATLANTA GA 30322
KUNZE, ROBERT W, PHILOSOPHY DEPT, UNIV OF PUGET SOUND, TACOMA WA 98416
KUO, DAVID, PHILOSOPHY DEPT, E WASHINGTON ST COL, CHENEY WA 99004
KUPERS, LAWRENCE, PHIL DEPT, ST UNIV OF NY, STONY BROOK NY 11790
KUPFER, JOSEPH, PHIL DEPT, IOWA STATE UNIV, AMES IA 50010
KURLANA, SAMUEL, GRATZ COLLEGE, PHILADELPHIA, PA 19141
KURTZ, JAMES E, N AMER BIB COLLEGE, DODGE CITY, KS 67801
KURTZ, PAUL W, PHIL DEPT, ST UNIV OF NY, AMHERST NY 14226
KUSHNER, THOMASINE, PHIL & REL DEPT, FLORIDA INTNL UNIV, MIAMI FL 33144
KUSMAN, STANLEY, PHIL DEPT, ST MARY'S UNIVERSITY, SAN ANTONIO TX 78228
KUSSACK, ALAN A, PHIL DEPT, UNIV OF N CAROLINA, CHAPEL HILL NC 27514
KUTTNAUER, MICHAEL V, SOC SCI DEPT, SAN DIEGO MESA COL, SAN DIEGO CA 92111
KUYKENDALL, ELEANOR, PHIL DEPT, COL AT NEW PLATZ, NEW PLATZ NY 12561
KVART, IGAL, PHIL DEPT, BRANDEIS UNIVERSITY, WALTHAM MA 02154
KWASNIAK, ARLENE, PHIL DEPT, WAYNE STATE UNIV, DETROIT MI 48202
KYBURG JR, HENRY E, PHIL DEPT, UNIV OF ROCHESTER, ROCHESTER NY 14627
L'HEUREUX, JACQUES, PHILOSOPHY DEPT, COL DE ROUYN-NORANDA, ROUYN QUE CAN
LA BOSSIERE, C R, PHIL DEPT, ROYAL RDS MIL COL, VICTORIA B C CAN
LA CORTE, JOHN, PHILOSOPHY DEPT, CAL STATE COL, DOMINGUEZ HLS CA 90747
LA CROIX, RICHARD R, PHIL DEPT, COL AT BUFFALO, BUFFALO NY 14222
LA MORE JR, GEORGE E, REL & PHIL, IOWA WESLEYAN COL, MT PLEASANT IA 52641
LA MOURE, SPENCER, HUMAN & PHIL DEPT, GROSSMONT COL, EL CAJON CA 92020
LA PLANTE, HARRY, DETROIT INST TECH, DETROIT, MI 48201
LA RUSCH, MICHELE, PHIL DEPT, UNIV OF CALIFORNIA, LOS ANGELES CA 90024
LABARRE, FRANCOISE, PHIL DEPT, COL LIONEL-GROULX, STE-THERESE QUE CAN
LABELLE, GENEVIEVE, COL EDOUARD-MONTPETIT, LONGUEUIL, QUE CAN
LABERGE, JACQUES, PHIL DEPT, COL DE LA POCATIERE, LA POCATIERE QUE CAN
LABERGE, PIERRE, PHIL FACULTY, UNIV OF OTTAWA, OTTAWA ONT CAN

LABINER, ELI, PHIL DIV, C S MOTT COM COL, FLINT MI 48503
LABOR, SUZANNE, PHILOSOPHY DEPT, VILLANOVA UNIV, VILLANOVA PA 19085
LABRECQUE, CLAUDE, PHIL DEPT, SEM DE SHERBROOKE, SHERBROOKE QUE   CAN
LABRIE, ROBERT, SEMINAIRE DE QUEBEC, QUEBEC, QUE   CAN
LABROUSSE, BERNARD, PHIL DEPT, COL VIEUX-MONTREAL, MONTREAL QUE   CAN
LACENTRA, WALTER, PHIL DEPT, ST JOHN FISHER COL, ROCHESTER NY 14618
LACEY, HUGH M, PHIL DEPT, SWARTHMORE COLLEGE, SWARTHMORE PA 19081
LACHANCE, J G, PHIL DEPT, COLLEGE SAINT-LOUIS, EDMUNDSTON N B   CAN
LACHARITE, NORMAND, PHILOSOPHY DEPT, UNIV DU QUEBEC, MONTREAL QUE   CAN
LACHENMAN, DANIEL, PHIL DEPT, ST UNIV OF NY, AMHERST NY 14226
LACHS, JOHN, PHILOSOPHY DEPT, VANDERBILT UNIV, NASHVILLE TN 37235
LACHTERMAN, DAVID, PHIL DEPT, SYRACUSE UNIVERSITY, SYRACUSE NY 13210
LACKEY, DOUGLAS, PHIL DEPT, BERNARD BARUCH COL, NEW YORK NY 10010
LACKEY, RONALD D, HUMAN DEPT, SOUTH GEORGIA COL, DOUGLAS GA 31533
LACKNER, HENRY, PHIL DEPT, ST MARY'S UNIVERSITY, HALIFAX N S   CAN
LACKOWSKI, PETER, SOC SCI DEPT, BENNINGTON COLLEGE, BENNINGTON VT 05201
LACOCK, DARRELL D, PHILOSOPHY DEPT, WESLEYAN UNIV, MIDDLETOWN CT 06457
LACROIX, B, COL DOM PHIL & THEOL, OTTAWA, ONT   CAN
LACROIX, WILLIAM, PHIL DEPT, ROCKHURST COLLEGE, KANSAS CITY MO 64110
LACY, ALLEN, PHIL OF RELIG, STOCTON STATE COL, POMONA NJ 08244
LACY, WILLIAM L, PHIL DEPT, SOUTHWEST AT MEMPHIS, MEMPHIS TN 38112
LADD, JOHN, PHILOSOPHY DEPT, BROWN UNIVERSITY, PROVIDENCE RI 02912
LADD, ROSALIND EKMAN, PHIL DEPT, WHEATON COLLEGE, NORTON MA 02766
LADEMAN, WILLIAM, PHIL DEPT, SACRED HEART UNIV, BRIDGEPORT CT 06604
LADENSON, ROBERT F, HUMAN DEPT, ILLINOIS INST TECH, CHICAGO IL 60616
LAFLEUR, JACQUES, PHIL DEPT, COL DE SHERBROOKE, SHERBROOKE QUE   CAN
LAFON, JAMES, PHIL & REL DIV, TEXAS WESLEYAN COL, FORT WORTH TX 76105
LAFRANCE, GERMAIN, PHIL DEPT, COL VIEUX-MONTREAL, MONTREAL QUE   CAN
LAFRANCE, GUY, PHIL FACULTY, UNIV OF OTTAWA, OTTAWA ONT   CAN
LAGADEC, CLAUDE, PHILOSOPHY DEPT, UNIV DE MONTREAL, MONTREAL QUE   CAN
LAGAULT, FRANCIS, SOC SCI DEPT, SPOKANE FLS COM COL, SPOKANE WA 99202
LAGUEUX, MAURICE, PHILOSOPHY DEPT, UNIV DE MONTREAL, MONTREAL QUE   CAN
LAHEY, L, PHILOSOPHY DEPT, UNIV OF ALBERTA, EDMONTON ALB   CAN
LAHOOD, GABRIEL, FAIRLEIGH DICKINSON, TEANECK, NJ 07666
LAHOOD, GABRIEL, PHIL DEPT, BOWLING GREEN UNIV, BOWLING GREEN OH 43403
LAI, T L, PHILOSOPHY DEPT, MEMORIAL UNIV, ST JOHN'S N F   CAN
LAKERS, JOHN JOSEPH, PHIL DEPT, QUINCY COLLEGE, QUINCY IL 62301
LAL, PURSHOTAM, PHILOSOPHY DEPT, OHIO UNIVERSITY, ATHENS OH 45701
LALIBERTE, FRANCOIS, PHIL DEPT, COL BOIS-DE-BOULOGNE, MONTREAL QUE   CAN
LALLIER, ALAIN, PHIL DEPT, COL TROIS-RIVIERES, 3 RIVIERES QUE   CAN
LALUMIA, J, PHILOSOPHY DEPT, HOFSTRA UNIVERSITY, HEMPSTEAD NY 11550
LAM, PHILIP, PHILOSOPHY DEPT, RUTGERS UNIV, NEW BRUNSWICK NJ 08903
LAMB, EDWARD, SOUTH MISSIONARY COL, COLLEGEDALE, TN 37315
LAMB, JAMES W, PHIL DEPT, S METHODIST UNIV, DALLAS TX 75222
LAMBERT, FRANK B, PHILOSOPHY DEPT, UNIV OF DELAWARE, NEWARK DE 19711
LAMBERT, JOSEPH, PHIL DEPT, UNIV OF CALIFORNIA, IRVINE CA 92664
LAMBERT, RICHARD T, PHIL DEPT, CARROLL COLLEGE, HELENA MT 59601
LAMBERT, ROGER, PHILOSOPHY DEPT, UNIV DU QUEBEC, MONTREAL QUE   CAN
LAMBROS, CHARLES, PHIL DEPT, ST UNIV OF NY, AMHERST NY 14226
LAMOUREUX, PHILIPPE, PHIL DEPT, COL VIEUX-MONTREAL, MONTREAL QUE   CAN
LAMPERT, LAURENCE A, PHIL DEPT, INDIANA-PURDUE UNIV, INDIANAPOLIS IN 46202
LAMPRECHT, STERLING P, PHIL & REL DEPT, AMHERST COLLEGE, AMHERST MA 01002
LANCIA, ELAINE, SOC SCI DEPT, NEW YORK INST TECH, OLD WESTBURY NY 11568
LANCTOT-BELANGER, M C, PHIL DEPT, CCL VIEUX-MONTREAL, MONTREAL QUE   CAN
LANDERS, BILLY, PHILOSOPHY DEPT, EAST CEN MO JR COL, UNION MO 63084
LANDESMAN JR, C, PHIL PROGRAM, GRADUATE SCH -CUNY, NEW YORK NY 10036
LANDESMAN, BRUCE M, PHILOSOPHY DEPT, UNIV OF UTAH, SALT LAKE CTY UT 84112
LANDESMAN, CHARLES, PHIL DEPT, HUNTER COLLEGE, NEW YORK NY 10021
LANDRUM, GEORGE, PHIL DEPT, W WASHINGTON ST COL, BELLINGHAM WA 98225
LANDRY, CECILE, PHIL DEPT, COL VIEUX-MONTREAL, MONTREAL QUE   CAN
LANDRY, JACQUELINE, PHIL DEPT, RIVIER COLLEGE, NASHUA NH 03060
LANE, GILLES, PHILOSOPHY DEPT, UNIV DU QUEBEC, 3-RIVIERES QUE   CAN
LANE, ROBERT D, HUMANITIES AREA, MALASPINA COLLEGE, NANAIMO B C   CAN
LANE, RONALD, PHIL DEPT, COL OF ST BENEDICT, ST JOSEPH MN 56374

LANFEAR, RAY, PHIL DEPT, UNIV OF MONTANA, MISSOULA MT 59801
LANG, ANTHONY, PHIL DEPT, LORAS COLLEGE, DUBUQUE IA 52001
LANG, BEREL, PHIL DEPT, UNIV OF COLORADO, BOULDER CO 80302
LANG, T J F, UNIV OF ST MICHAEL'S, TORONTO 181, ONT CAN
LANGAN, HUBERT E, HUMAN DIV, ORANGE CO COM COL, MIDDLETOWN NY 10940
LANGAN, T D, PHILOSOPHY DEPT, UNIV OF TORONTO, TORONTO ONT CAN
LANGAN, WILLIAM J, PHILOSOPHY DEPT, CALIFORNIA ST UNIV, HAYWARD CA 94542
LANGBAUER, DELMAR N, PHILOSOPHY DEPT, UNIV OF PUGET SOUND, TACOMA WA 98416
LANGE, ANN E, PHILOSOPHY DEPT, QUEENS COLLEGE, CHARLOTTE NC 28207
LANGE, JOHN, PHILOSOPHY DEPT, QUEENS COLLEGE, FLUSHING NY 11367
LANGEN, ROBERT, PHILOSOPHY DEPT, WATERLOO LUTH UNIV, WATERLOO ONT CAN
LANGENBACH, JOHN O, PHIL DEPT, UNIV OF MARYLAND, COLLEGE PARK MD 20742
LANGER, MONIKA, PHIL DEPT, YALE UNIVERSITY, NEW HAVEN CT 06520
LANGER, SUSANNE K, PHIL DEPT, CONNECTICUT COL, NEW LONDON CT 06320
LANGERAK, E, PHIL DEPT, SAINT OLAF COLLEGE, NORTHFIELD MN 55057
LANGFORD, M J, PHILOSOPHY DEPT, MEMORIAL UNIV, ST JOHN'S N F CAN
LANGHAM, P, PHIL DEPT, UNIV OF NW BRUNSWICK, SAINT JOHN N B CAN
LANGLEY, RAYMOND J, PHIL DEPT, MANHATTANVILLE COL, PURCHASE NY 10577
LANGO, JOHN, PHIL DEPT, HUNTER COLLEGE, NEW YORK NY 10021
LANGTON, BERNARD F, PHIL DEPT, PROVIDENCE COLLEGE, PROVIDENCE RI 02919
LANIGAN, JOSEPH F, ST MARY'S COL OF CAL, MORAGA, CA 94575
LANNING, GREGORY J, PHILOSOPHY DEPT, UNIV OF UTAH, SALT LAKE CTY UT 84112
LANNING, JAMES B, PHIL DEPT, UNIVERSITY OF MIAMI, CORAL GABLES FL 33124
LANSFORD, THERON, SOCIO-HUMAN STUD, TRI-STATE COLLEGE, ANGOLA IN 46703
LAPALME, ANDRE, COLLEGE D'AHUNTSIC, MONTREAL, QUE CAN
LAPAVA, NICHOLAS A, PHIL DEPT, LEHIGH UNIVERSITY, BETHLEHEM PA 18015
LAPEGNA, NICOLA, COL DE LEVIS-LAUZON, LAUZON, QUE CAN
LAPLANTE, NELSON, PHIL DEPT, LOYOLA UNIVERSITY, CHICAGO IL 60626
LAPLANTE, ROBERT, PHIL FACULTY, UNIV OF OTTAWA, OTTAWA ONT CAN
LAPOINTE, JOCELYNE, PHIL DEPT, COL VIEUX-MONTREAL, MONTREAL QUE CAN
LAPPIN, SHALOM, PHIL DEPT, BRANDEIS UNIVERSITY, WALTHAM MA 02154
LAPRISS, JEAN-PAUL, PHIL DEPT, COL DE SHERBROOKE, SHERBROOKE QUE CAN
LARGENT, CHRISTOPHER L, PHILOSOPHY DEPT, UNIV OF DELAWARE, NEWARK DE 19711
LARKIN, MIRIAM T, PHIL DEPT, MT ST MARY'S COL, LOS ANGELES CA 90049
LARKIN, RONALD, PHIL & THEOL DIV, ALLENTOWN COL, CENTER VALLEY PA 18034
LARMAN, MARIAN, PHIL DEPT, ST JOSEPH SEM COL, ST BENEDICT LA 70457
LARMI, OLIVER J, PHIL DEPT, BLOOMSBURG ST COL, BLOOMSBURG PA 17815
LAROCQUE, GUY, PHIL DEPT, COL DE VALLEYFIELD, VALLEYFIELD QUE CAN
LAROSE, JEAN-FRANCOIS, PHIL DEPT, SEM DE SHERBROOKE, SHERBROOKE QUE CAN
LAROUCHE, ROBERT, PHILOSOPHY DEPT, COL DE ROUYN-NORANDA, ROUYN QUE CAN
LARRABEE, HAROLD, PHIL DEPT, UNION COLLEGE, SCHENECTADY NY 12308
LARSEN, ALLAN, PHIL DEPT, SLIPPERY ROCK ST COL, SLIPPERY ROCK PA 16057
LARSEN, ANDRE, PHIL DEPT, COL BOIS-DE-BOULOGNE, MONTREAL QUE CAN
LARSON, BRUCE, PHIL DEPT, UNIV OF NOTRE DAME, NOTRE DAME IN 46556
LARSON, JOHN B, PHIL DEPT, SKAGIT VALLEY COL, MOUNT VERNON WA 98273
LARSON, LAWRENCE, PHIL DEPT, UNIV OF DENVER, DENVER CO 80210
LARSON, ROBERT, HUMAN DEPT, OKALOOSA-WALTON JR C, NICEVILLE FL 32578
LASCOLA, RUSSEL A, PHIL DEPT, CAL POLYTECH ST U, SAN LUIS OBIS CA 93407
LASHCHYK, EUGENE, PHIL DEPT, LA SALLE COLLEGE, PHILADELPHIA PA 19141
LASKA, PETER J, PHILOSOPHY DEPT, UNIV OF ARIZONA, TUCSON AZ 85721
LASKEY, DALLAS, PHIL DEPT, GEORGE WILLIAMS UNIV, MONTREAL 107 QUE CAN
LASLIE, ADELE, HUMAN DIV, KIRKLAND COLLEGE, CLINTON NY 13323
LASSETTER, CLARENCE R, SOC SCI, N KENTUCKY ST COL, HIGHLAND HTS KY 41076
LASZLO, ERVIN, PHIL DEPT, COL AT GENESEO, GENESEO NY 14454
LATANER, ALBERT, PHIL DEPT, NASSAU COM COL, GARDEN CITY NY 11530
LATAREWICZ, EDWARD, PHILOSOPHY DEPT, COL MISERICORDIA, DALLAS PA 18612
LATHROP, DONALD, BERKSHIRE COM COL, PITTSFIELD, MA 01201
LATKEWICZ, JOHN, PHIL DEPT, BOWLING GREEN UNIV, BOWLING GREEN OH 43403
LATRAVERSE, FRANCOIS, PHIL DEPT, COL LIONEL-GROULX, STE-THERESE QUE CAN
LATTA, BETSY C, PHIL DEPT, UNIV OF TENNESSEE, KNOXVILLE TN 37916
LAU, HERMAN, PHILOSOPHY DEPT, LOYOLA COLLEGE, MONTREAL QUE CAN
LAUDAN, LAURENS, PHIL DEPT, UNIV OF PITTSBURGH, PITTSBURGH PA 15260
LAUDER, ROBERT E, PHIL DEPT, CATH CCL IMM CONCEPT, DOUGLASTON NY 11362
LAUER, EUGENE F, HUMANITES DIV, LA ROCHE COLLEGE, PITTSBURGH PA 15237

LAUER, J QUENTIN, PHIL DEPT, FORDHAM UNIVERSITY, BRONX NY 10458
LAUER, ROSEMARY Z, PHIL DEPT, CALIFORNIA ST UNIV, SAN DIEGO CA 92115
LAUGHLIN, LLOYD, PHILOSOPHY DEPT, SN JOAQUIN DELTA COL, STOCKTON CA 95204
LAUGHLIN, RICHARD, PHIL DEPT, IDAHO STATE UNIV, POCATELLO ID 83201
LAURENT, GUY, COL MARGUERITE-BOURG, MONTREAL, QUE   CAN
LAURIE, W J, PHILOSOPHY DEPT, NOTRE DAME UNIV, NELSON B C   CAN
LAUTER, HERMAN A, PHIL DEPT, OCCIDENTAL COLLEGE, LOS ANGELES CA 90041
LAVALLEY, GERALD, PHIL DEPT, GEORGE WILLIAMS UNIV, MONTREAL 107 QUE   CAN
LAVELY, JOHN H, PHIL DEPT, BOSTON UNIVERSITY, BOSTON MA 02215
LAVERE, GEORGE J, PHIL DEPT, CANISIUS COLLEGE, BUFFALO NY 14208
LAVIGNE, JACQUES, PHIL DEPT, COL DE VALLEYFIELD, VALLEYFIELD QUE   CAN
LAVINE, T Z, PHIL DEPT, GEORGE WASHINGTON U, WASHINGTON DC 20006
LAVOIE, J, COL DOM PHIL & THEOL, OTTAWA, ONT   CAN
LAW, DAVID A, PHIL DEPT, SAN ANTONIC COL, SAN ANTONIO TX 78284
LAWLER, JAMES, PHIL DEPT, ST UNIV OF NY, AMHERST NY 14226
LAWRENCE, EDWIN G, PHIL STUD DEPT, S ILLINOIS UNIV, EDWARDSVILLE IL 62025
LAWRENCE, EDWIN, GEN STUD DIV, DELAWARE VLY COL, DOYLESTOWN PA 18901
LAWRENCE, JOHN, PHIL DEPT, MORNINGSIDE COLLEGE, SIOUX CITY IA 51106
LAWRENCE, NATHANIEL, PHIL DEPT, WILLIAMS COLLEGE, WILLIAMSTOWN MA 01267
LAWRENCE, PHILIP, PHIL DEPT, MT ANGEL SEMINARY, ST BENEDICT OR 97373
LAWRY, EDWARD G, PHIL DEPT, OKLAHOMA STATE UNIV, STILLWATER OK 74074
LAWRY, JOHN F, PHIL DEPT, UNIV OF MCNTANA, MISSOULA MT 59801
LAWS, JOHN W, LIB ARTS DEPT, THOMAS COLLEGE, WATERVILLE ME 04901
LAWSON, JACK, PHIL DEPT, MANKATO STATE COL, MANKATO MN 56001
LAWTON, E, PHILOSOPHY DEPT, UNIV OF ALBERTA, EDMONTON ALB   CAN
LAWTON, PHILIP N, HUMAN DIV, SPRINGFIELD TECH COL, SPRINGFIELD MA 01105
LAYCOCK, HENRY, PHILOSOPHY DEPT, QUEEN'S UNIVERSITY, KINGSTON ONT   CAN
LAYMAN, FRED D, THEOL & PHIL DIV, ASBURY THEOL SEM, WILMORE KY 40390
LAYMON, RONALD E, PHILOSOPHY DEPT, CHIO STATE UNIV, COLUMBUS OH 43210
LAZARUS, FRANCIS M, ENG DEPT, U S MILITARY ACAD, WEST POINT NY 10996
LE GRAND, M DAVID, PIEDMONT BIBLE CCL, WINSTON-SALEM, NC 27101
LEACH, JAMES J, PHIL DEPT, UNIV OF WEST ONTARIO, LONDON ONT   CAN
LEACH, RICHARD D, PHIL & RELIG DEPT, LAKELAND COL, SHEBOYGAN WI 53081
LEAN, MARTIN, PHIL DEPT, BROOKLYN COLLEGE, BROOKLYN NY 11210
LEAN, MARTIN, PHIL SCH, UNIV OF S CALIFORNIA, LOS ANGELES CA 90007
LEAR, GEORGE A, PHIL & REL DEPT, N CAROLINA ST UNIV, RALEIGH NC 27607
LEAR, JONATHON, PHIL DEPT, ROCKEFELLER UNIV, NEW YORK NY 10021
LEARNED, STEPHEN P, PHIL DEPT, INDIANA-PURDUE UNIV, INDIANAPOLIS IN 46202
LEARY, JOHN, HUMANE STUD, NEW COL OF CAL, SAUSALITO CA 94965
LEBEL, MARCELLE, PHILOSOPHY DEPT, COL DE MAISONNEUVE, MONTREAL QUE   CAN
LEBLANC, HUGHES, PHIL DEPT, TEMPLE UNIVERSITY, PHILADELPHIA PA 19122
LEBLANC, VALMOND, PHILOSOPHY DEPT, UNIV DE MONCTON, MONCTON N B   CAN
LEBLOND, BERNARD, COLLEGE D'AHUNTSIC, MONTREAL, QUE   CAN
LEBRATO, C MICHAEL, SOC SCI DEPT, KANSAS STATE COL, PITTSBURG KS 66762
LECHNER, ROBERT, PHIL DEPT, DEPAUL UNIVERSITY, CHICAGO IL 60604
LECLAIR, JEAN-CLAUDE, PHIL DEPT, COL TROIS-RIVIERES, 3 RIVIERES QUE   CAN
LECLERC, IVOR, PHIL DEPT, EMORY UNIVERSITY, ATLANTA GA 30322
LECLERC, MICHEL, PHILOSOPHY DEPT, UNIV DU QUEBEC, MONTREAL QUE   CAN
LECOMPTE, MICHEL, PHIL DEPT, COL DE VALLEYFIELD, VALLEYFIELD QUE   CAN
LEDBETTER, CHARLES, HUMAN DIV, THORNTON COM COL, SOUTH HOLLAND IL 60473
LEDOUX, ARTHUR J, PHIL DEPT, INDIANA UNIVERSITY, SOUTH BEND IN 46615
LEE, ARTHUR, PHILOSOPHY DEPT, UNIV CF WATERLOO, WATERLOO ONT   CAN
LEE, BERNARD J, PHILOSOPHY DEPT, MARYVILLE COLLEGE, ST LOUIS MO 63141
LEE, C RICHARD, PHIL DEPT, UNIV OF MARYLAND, COLLEGE PARK MD 20742
LEE, DONALD C, PHIL DEPT, UNIV OF NEW MEXICO, ALBUQUERQUE NM 87106
LEE, DONALD S, PHIL DEPT, TULANE UNIVERSITY, NEW ORLEANS LA 70118
LEE, EDWARD, PHIL DEPT, U OF CAL -SAN DIEGO, LA JOLLA CA 92037
LEE, GUN-WON, PHIL DEPT, UNIVERSITY OF HAWAII, HONOLULU HI 96822
LEE, HAROLD N, PHIL DEPT, TULANE UNIVERSITY, NEW ORLEANS LA 70118
LEE, JIG CHUEN, PHIL DEPT, UNIV OF CALIFORNIA, SANTA BARBARA CA 93106
LEE, KWANG-SAE, PHILOSOPHY DEPT, KENT STATE UNIV, KENT OH 44242
LEE, PAUL A, PHIL STUD BOARD, U OF CALIFORNIA, SANTA CRUZ CA 95060
LEE, RICHARD, PHIL DEPT, TRINITY COLLEGE, HARTFORD CT 06106
LEE, SUK KOO, PHIL DEPT, COLORADO ST UNIV, FORT COLLINS CO 80521

LEE, WILTON, SOUTH MISSIONARY COL, COLLEGEDALE, TN 37315
LEEDS, STEPHEN, PHILOSOPHY DEPT, BROWN UNIVERSITY, PROVIDENCE RI 02912
LEFEBVRE, GUY, PHIL DEPT, COL VIEUX-MONTREAL, MONTREAL QUE   CAN
LEFEVRE, JOSEPH, PHIL & REL DEPT, DILLARD UNIVERSITY, NEW ORLEANS LA 70122
LEFLAGUAIS, ROBERT, COLLEGE D'AHUNTSIC, MONTREAL, QUE   CAN
LEFLORE, RALPH B, PHIL DEPT, TEXAS CHRISTIAN UNIV, FORT WORTH TX 76129
LEGATE, JOHN J, LIBR STUD DIV, SENECA COLLEGE, WILLOWDALE ONT   CAN
LEGAULT, ALTON, PHIL DEPT, COL DE VALLEYFIELD, VALLEYFIELD QUE   CAN
LEGGETT, RICHARD C, PHILOSOPHY DEPT, N TEXAS STATE UNIV, DENTON TX 76203
LEHE, ROBERT T, PHIL DEPT, N ILLINOIS UNIV, DEKALB IL 60115
LEHMAN, H S, PHILOSOPHY DEPT, UNIV OF GUELPH, GUELPH ONT   CAN
LEHMANN JR, WILLIAM, PHIL DEPT, CONCORDIA TEACH COL, RIVER FOREST IL 60305
LEHMANN, S K, PHIL DEPT, UNIV OF CONNECTICUT, STORRS CT 06268
LEHOCKY, DANIEL L, PHIL DEPT, UNIV OF MISSOURI, ST LOUIS MO 63121
LEHRBASS, JUDITH A, HUMAN & FINE ARTS, W SHORE COM COL, SCOTTVILLE MI 49454
LEHRER, KEITH, PHIL DEPT, UNIV OF ROCHESTER, ROCHESTER NY 14627
LEIBOWITZ, CONSTANCE, PHIL DEPT, PLYMOUTH STATE COL, PLYMOUTH NH 03264
LEIGHTON, S, PHILOSOPHY DEPT, UNIV OF ALBERTA, EDMONTON ALB   CAN
LEINFELLNER, WERNER H, PHIL DEPT, UNIV OF NEBRASKA, LINCOLN NE 68502
LEININGER, C EARL, RELIG & PHIL DEPT, MARS HILL COLLEGE, MARS HILL NC 28754
LEISING, FRED, UNDERGRAD DEPT, ST JOHN VIANNEY SEM, E AURORA NY 14052
LEISSNER, GEORGE R, SOC & BEHAV SCI, BRENAU COLLEGE, GAINESVILLE GA 30501
LEITES, EDMUND, PHILOSOPHY DEPT, QUEENS COLLEGE, FLUSHING NY 11367
LEITH, JOHN, PHIL & RELIG, VA COMMONWEALTH UNIV, RICHMOND VA 23220
LEIVA, EMILIO, HUMAN DEPT, COL OF SACRED HEART, SANTURCE PR 00914
LELAND, JAMES, HUMAN DIV, EAST MONTANA COL, BILLINGS MT 59101
LELAND, K, PHILOSOPHY DEPT, UNIV OF TORONTO, TORONTO ONT   CAN
LEMIEUX, JACQUES, SEMINAIRE DE QUEBEC, QUEBEC, QUE   CAN
LEMIEUX, RAYMOND, COL EDOUARD-MONTPETIT, LONGUEUIL, QUE   CAN
LEMMEN, C, PHIL DEPT, W CONNECTICUT ST COL, DANBURY CT 06810
LEMOS, RAMON M, PHIL DEPT, UNIVERSITY OF MIAMI, CORAL GABLES FL 33124
LENGEL, LELAND, PHIL & RELIG, MCPHERSON COLLEGE, MCPHERSON KS 67460
LENHARDT, WAYNE, PHIL DEPT, UNIV OF WEST ONTARIO, LONDON ONT   CAN
LENKOWSKI, W JON, PHILOSOPHY DEPT, RUTGERS UNIV, NEW BRUNSWICK NJ 08903
LENNON, THOMAS M, PHIL DEPT, UNIV OF WEST ONTARIO, LONDON ONT   CAN
LENNOX, J, PHILOSOPHY DEPT, UNIV OF TORONTO, TORONTO ONT   CAN
LENSING, WILLIAM E, BARD COLLEGE, ANNANDALE-HDSN, NY 12504
LENSSEN, MARK, PHIL DEPT, NORTHWESTERN UNIV, EVANSTON IL 60201
LENZ, JOHN W, PHILOSOPHY DEPT, BROWN UNIVERSITY, PROVIDENCE RI 02912
LEONARD, LINDA, PHIL DEPT, UNIV OF COLORADO, DENVER CO 80202
LEONARD, R, PHILOSOPHY DEPT, UNIV OF ALBERTA, EDMONTON ALB   CAN
LEONARD, RICHARD, PHIL DEPT, INCARNATE WORD COL, SAN ANTONIO TX 78209
LEPAGE, DANIEL, PHILOSOPHY DEPT, COL DE MAISONNEUVE, MONTREAL QUE   CAN
LEPLEY, RAY, PHIL DEPT, BRADLEY UNIVERSITY, PEORIA IL 61606
LEPLIN, JARRETT, PHIL DEPT, UNIV OF N CAROLINA, GREENSBORO NC 27412
LERNER, ARTHUR, PHIL DEPT, LOS ANGELES CY COL, LOS ANGELES CA 90029
LERNER, MICHAEL, PHIL DEPT, TRINITY COLLEGE, HARTFORD CT 06106
LEROUX, GEORGES, PHILOSOPHY DEPT, UNIV DU QUEBEC, MONTREAL QUE   CAN
LESCOE, FRANCIS J, PHIL DEPT, ST JOSEPH COLLEGE, WEST HARTFORD CT 06117
LESHER, JAMES H, PHIL DEPT, UNIV OF MARYLAND, COLLEGE PARK MD 20742
LESLIE, J, PHILOSOPHY DEPT, UNIV OF GUELPH, GUELPH ONT   CAN
LESNOF-CARAVAGLIA, G, PHIL PROGRAM, SANGAMON ST UNIV, SPRINGFIELD IL 62703
LESPERANCE, SUZANNE, PHIL DEPT, COL LIONEL-GROULX, STE-THERESE QUE   CAN
LESSARD, ADELE, PHIL DEPT, COL TROIS-RIVIERES, 3 RIVIERES QUE   CAN
LESSES, GLENN W, PHIL DEPT, INDIANA UNIVERSITY, BLOOMINGTON IN 47401
LESSING, ABBA, PHIL DEPT, LAKE FOREST COLLEGE, LAKE FOREST IL 60045
LESSING, ALFRED, PHIL DEPT, OAKLAND UNIVERSITY, ROCHESTER MI 48063
LESTER, ROBERT, PHIL DEPT, UNIV OF COLORADO, BOULDER CO 80302
LESTER, RUSSELL, RELIG & PHIL DEPT, PAUL QUINN COLLEGE, WACO TX 76703
LESTER, TOM, HUM & SOC SCI, MONT COL OF MIN SCI, BUTTE MT 59701
LETENDRE, ROGER, PHILOSOPHY DEPT, CENTRE DES MAITRES, CAP-ROUGE QUE   CAN
LETHCOE, JAMES, HUMAN DIV, ALASKA METHODIST U, ANCHORAGE AK 99504
LETHCOE, N, PHILOSOPHY DEPT, UNIVERSITY OF ALASKA, FAIRBANKS AK 99701
LETSINGER, REED, PHIL DEPT, FLORIDA STATE UNIV, TALLAHASSEE FL 32306

LEUE, WILLIAM H, PHIL DEPT, ST UNIV OF NY, ALBANY NY 12203
LEVENBOOK, BARBARA, PHILOSOPHY DEPT, UNIV OF ARIZONA, TUCSON AZ 85721
LEVENSHON, IRA, PHIL DEPT, UNIVERSITY OF MIAMI, CORAL GABLES FL 33124
LEVENSOHN, STEPHEN, HUMAN DEPT, FLORIDA TECH UNIV, ORLANDO FL 32816
LEVENSON, BRUCE EDWARD, PHILOSOPHY DEPT, UNIV OF TEXAS, AUSTIN TX 78712
LEVER, OSCAR W, GEN EDUC DEPT, PALMER COLLEGE, COLUMBIA SC 29201
LEVESQUE, CLAUDE, PHILOSOPHY DEPT, UNIV DE MONTREAL, MONTREAL QUE   CAN
LEVESQUE, GYSLAIN, PHIL DEPT, COL TROIS-RIVIERES, 3 RIVIERES QUE   CAN
LEVEY, STEVE, PHIL DEPT, UNIV OF CALIFORNIA, LOS ANGELES CA 90024
LEVI, ALBERT WILLIAM, PHIL DEPT, WASHINGTON UNIV, ST LOUIS MO 63130
LEVI, DON S, PHILOSOPHY DEPT, UNIV CF OREGON, EUGENE OR 97403
LEVI, ISAAC, PHIL DEPT, COLUMBIA UNIVERSITY, NEW YORK NY 10027
LEVICH, MARVIN, REED COLLEGE, PORTLAND, OR 97202
LEVIN, DAVID M, PHIL DEPT, NORTHWESTERN UNIV, EVANSTON IL 60201
LEVIN, HAROLD D, PHIL & REL DEPT, N CAROLINA ST UNIV, RALEIGH NC 27607
LEVIN, JANET, PHIL DEPT, MASS INST TECH, CAMBRIDGE MA 02139
LEVIN, MICHAEL, PHIL DEPT, CITY COLLEGE, NEW YORK NY 10031
LEVINE, ANDREW, PHIL DEPT, UNIV BRIT COLUMBIA, VANCOUVER 8 B C   CAN
LEVINE, ELLIOTT M, PHILOSOPHY DEPT, UNIV OF WINNIPEG, WINNIPEG MAN   CAN
LEVINE, MAURIE, PHIL DEPT, UNIV OF CINCINNATI, CINCINNATI OH 45221
LEVINSON, JOEL, PHIL DEPT, LINCOLN LNIVERSITY, LINCOLN UNIV PA 19352
LEVIS, ROBERT C, SOC SCI DEPT, PASADENA CY COLLEGE, PASADENA CA 91106
LEVISON, ARNOLD B, PHIL DEPT, UNIV CF MARYLAND, BALTIMORE MD 21228
LEVIT, MARTIN, PHIL DEPT, UNIV OF MISSOURI, KANSAS CITY MO 64110
LEVY, DONALD, PHIL DEPT, BROOKLYN CCLLEGE, BROOKLYN NY 11210
LEVY, EDWIN, PHIL DEPT, UNIV BRIT COLUMBIA, VANCOUVER 8 B C   CAN
LEVY, GARY B, PHILOSOPHY DEPT, LOUISIANA ST UNIV, EUNICE LA 70535
LEVY, ROBERT, PHILOSOPHY DEPT, WITTENBERG UNIV, SPRINGFIELD OH 45501
LEVY, SANFORD, PHIL DEPT, UNIV OF MICHIGAN, ANN ARBOR MI 48104
LEVY, SOLOMON, PHIL DEPT, UNIV OF MISSOURI, KANSAS CITY MO 64110
LEVY, SYLVIA, HUMAN & FINE ARTS, S TEXAS JR COL, HOUSTON TX 77002
LEWIS, ALLISON L, PHIL DEPT, UNIV OF FLORIDA, GAINESVILLE FL 32611
LEWIS, BENJAMIN F, PHIL & RELIG, TRANSYLVANIA UNIV, LEXINGTON KY 40508
LEWIS, CHARLES M, PHIL DEPT, WAKE FOREST UNIV, WINSTON-SALEM NC 27109
LEWIS, CHESTER, PHILOSOPHY DEPT, WATERLOO LUTH UNIV, WATERLOO ONT   CAN
LEWIS, DAVID, PHIL DEPT, PRINCETON UNIVERSITY, PRINCETON NJ 08540
LEWIS, DONALD, PHILOSOPHY DEPT, CAL STATE COL, DOMINGUEZ HLS CA 90747
LEWIS, DOUGLAS, PHIL DEPT, UNIV OF MINNESOTA, MINNEAPOLIS MN 55455
LEWIS, EARL E, PHIL DEPT, FRANKLIN & MARSHALL, LANCASTER PA 17604
LEWIS, GEORGE, PHILOSOPHY DEPT, UNIV OF WATERLOO, WATERLOO ONT   CAN
LEWIS, GORDON, REL PHIL & APOL DEPT, CON BAPT THEOL SEM, DENVER CO 80210
LEWIS, GREGORY E, PHILOSOPHY DEPT, KENT STATE UNIV, KENT OH 44242
LEWIS, HERBERT, PHILOSOPHY DEPT, ACADIA UNIVERSITY, WOLFVILLE N S   CAN
LEWIS, JANET R, PHILOSOPHY DEPT, JUNIATA COLLEGE, HUNTINGDON PA 16652
LEWIS, JOHN U, PHILOSOPHY DEPT, UNIV OF WINDSOR, WINDSOR ONT   CAN
LEWIS, JONATHAN, PHIL DEPT, SYRACUSE UNIVERSITY, SYRACUSE NY 13210
LEWIS, JUDD W, HUMANITIES DEPT, CLINCH VALLEY COL, WISE VA 24293
LEWIS, KATHERINE, ENG DEPT, WAYNE STATE COL, WAYNE NE 68787
LEWIS, PIERS I, LIBR ARTS, MINN METRO ST COL, ST PAUL MN 55101
LEWIS, RANDY, PHILOSOPHY DEPT, UNIV OF TEXAS, AUSTIN TX 78712
LEY, MICHAEL, PHIL DEPT, LONG ISLAND UNIV, BROOKLYN NY 11201
LEYCEN, J W, PHILOSOPHY DEPT, CARLETON UNIVERSITY, OTTAWA ONT   CAN
LEZAN, WILLIAM, PHIL DEPT, PURDUE UNIVERSITY, FORT WAYNE IN 46805
LHOTA, BRIAN, PHIL DEPT, ST BONAVENTURE UNIV, ST BONVENTURE NY 14778
LIBBEY, EDWIN B, HUMAN DEPT, OKLA PANHANDLE ST COL, GOODWELL OK 73939
LICHENSTEIN, SANDRA, PHIL DEPT, SUFFOLK CO COM COL, SELDEN NY 11784
LICHTBLAU, DALE, PHILOSOPHY DEPT, OHIO STATE UNIV, COLUMBUS OH 43210
LIDDELL, ANNA FORBES, PHIL DEPT, FLCRIDA STATE UNIV, TALLAHASSEE FL 32306
LIDDELL, BRENDAN E A, PHIL DEPT, BRADLEY UNIVERSITY, PEORIA IL 61606
LIDDY, RICHARD M, PHIL DEPT, IMMAC CONCEPTION SEM, DARLINGTON NJ 07430
LIEB, IRWIN C, PHILOSOPHY DEPT, UNIV OF TEXAS, AUSTIN TX 78712
LIEBER, DAVID, PHIL OF RELIG, UNIV OF JUDAISM, LOS ANGELES CA 90028
LIEBERMAN, LEWIS R, HUMAN DEPT, COLLMBUS COLLEGE, COLUMBUS GA 31907
LIEBERSON, JONATHAN, PHIL DEPT, COLLMBIA UNIVERSITY, NEW YORK NY 10027

LIERO, STEVEN, PHILOSOPHY DEPT, VILLANOVA UNIV, VILLANOVA PA 19085
LIGGITT, O EUGENE, PHIL & RELIG, GROVE CITY COLLEGE, GROVE CITY PA 16127
LIGHT, LISSA, PHIL DEPT, ST UNIV OF NY, AMHERST NY 14226
LIGHTBODY, THOMAS P, PHILOSOHHY AREA, CUYAHOGA COM COL, CLEVELAND OH 44115
LILIENKAMP, PAUL, PHILOSOPHY DEPT, RANDOLPH-MACON COL, ASHLAND VA 23005
LILIENTHAL, ALFRED, PHIL DEPT, OLIVET NAZARENE COL, KANKAKEE IL 60901
LILJE, GERALD W, PHILOSOPHY DEPT, WASHINGTON ST UNIV, PULLMAN WA 99163
LILLEGARD, NORMAN S, PHIL DEPT, UNIV OF NEBRASKA, LINCOLN NE 68502
LIN, PAUL J, PHIL DEPT, SOUTH UNIV A & M COL, BATON ROUGE LA 70813
LIN, TIAN-MEIN, PHIL DEPT, INDIANA UNIV OF PENN, INDIANA PA 15701
LINCICOME, DAVID, PHILOSOPHY DEPT, OHIO UNIVERSITY, ATHENS OH 45701
LINCOURT, JOHN M, PHIL DEPT, UNIV OF N CAROLINA, CHARLOTTE NC 28213
LIND, RICHARD, PHILOSOPHY DEPT, UNIVERSITY OF TULSA, TULSA OK 74104
LINDAHL, ELDER, PHIL DEPT, NORTH PARK COLLEGE, CHICAGO IL 60625
LINDBECK, VIOLETTE, PHIL DEPT, S CONNECTICUT ST COL, NEW HAVEN CT 06515
LINDEMANN, KATHRYN, PHIL & REL STUD DIV, MT ST MARY COL, NEWBURGH NY 12550
LINDEN, G WILLIAM, PHIL STUD DEPT, S ILLINOIS UNIV, EDWARDSVILLE IL 62025
LINDENMUTH, DONALD C, PHIL DEPT, PENN STATE UNIV, SHUYKL HAVEN PA 17972
LINDER, M H, PHIL DEPT, BROWARD COM COL, FT LAUDERDALE FL 33314
LINDERMAYER, ERIC, PHILOSOPHY DEPT, RUTGERS UNIV, NEWARK NJ 07102
LINDGREN, J RALPH, PHIL DEPT, LEHIGH UNIVERSITY, BETHLEHEM PA 18015
LINDLEY, T F, PHIL DEPT, UNIV OF CONNECTICUT, STORRS CT 06268
LINDON, LUKE, PHIL DEPT, ST VIN DE PAUL SEM, BOYNTON FL 33435
LINDSEY JR, JAMES E, PHIL & RELIG, VA COMMONWEALTH UNIV, RICHMOND VA 23220
LINDSEY, JONATHAN A, PHIL & REL DEPT, JUDSON COLLEGE, MARION AL 36756
LINDSEY, WANDA, PHIL DEPT, FLORIDA STATE UNIV, TALLAHASSEE FL 32306
LINEBACK, RICHARD, PHIL DEPT, BOWLING GREEN UNIV, BOWLING GREEN OH 43403
LINGIS, ALPHONSO, PHILOSOPHY DEPT, PENN STATE UNIV, UNIV PARK PA 16802
LINGSWILER, ROBERT D, PHILOSOPHY DEPT, BALDWIN-WALLACE COL, BEREA OH 44017
LINK, S GORDDEN, HUMAN DIV, SOUTHEASTERN UNIV, WASHINGTON DC 20024
LINNELL, JOHN, PHIL DEPT, LUTHER COLLEGE, DECORAH IA 52101
LINSKY, LEONARD, PHIL DEPT, UNIV OF CHICAGO, CHICAGO IL 60637
LINVILLE, KENT, PHIL DEPT, OXFORD COLLEGE, OXFORD GA 30267
LION, ROBERTA, PHIL DEPT, ST UNIV OF NY, AMHERST NY 14226
LIOTTA, JAMES, PHILOSOPHY DEPT, CAL STATE COL, DOMINGUEZ HLS CA 90747
LIPMAN, M, PHIL & RELIG DEPT, MONTCLAIR ST COL, UPR MONTCLAIR NJ 07043
LIPMAN, MATTHEW, COL OF PHAR SCI, NEW YORK, NY 10027
LIPMAN, MATTHEW, PHIL DEPT, CITY COLLEGE, NEW YORK NY 10031
LIPSCHUTZ, SUSAN S, PHIL DEPT, UNIV OF DENVER, DENVER CO 80210
LIPTON, MICHAEL, PHIL & REL DEPT, NORTHEASTERN UNIV, BOSTON MA 02115
LISSKA, ANTHONY J, PHILOSOPHY DEPT, DENISON UNIV, GRANVILLE OH 43023
LIST, PETER C, PHIL DEPT, OREGON STATE UNIV, CORVALLIS OR 97331
LISZKA, JAMES, PHILOSOPHY DEPT, UNIV OF S CAROLINA, COLUMBIA SC 29208
LITCHENBERG, BENJAMIN, CALDWELL COLLEGE, CALDWELL, NJ 07006
LITHOWN, ROBERT, PHIL DEPT, UNIV OF WEST ONTARIO, LONDON ONT   CAN
LITKE, ROBERT F, PHIL DEPT, KALAMAZOO COLLEGE, KALAMAZOO MI 49001
LITTLE, BLAINE, PHIL DEPT, UNIV OF WEST ONTARIO, LONDON ONT   CAN
LITTLE, IVAN L, PHILOSOPHY DEPT, TEXAS TECH UNIV, LUBBOCK TX 79409
LITTLE, J FREDERICK, PHILOSOPHY DEPT, WATERLOO LUTH UNIV, WATERLOO ONT   CAN
LITTLEFIELD, LOY, PHIL DEPT, BOWLING GREEN UNIV, BOWLING GREEN OH 43403
LITTLETON, HAROLD E, RELIG & PHIL DEPT, MEREDITH COLLEGE, RALIEGH NC 27611
LITTLETON, WILLIAM H, PHIL & REL, GEORGIA COLLEGE, MILLEDGEVILLE GA 31061
LITZENBURG, THOMAS V, PHIL DEPT, WELLS COLLEGE, AURORA NY 13026
LIU, CHANG-YUAN, PHIL DEPT, S ILLINOIS UNIV, CARBONDALE IL 62901
LIU, JOSEPH, PHILOSOPHY DEPT, UNIV CE MONTREAL, MONTREAL QUE   CAN
LIU, SHU-HSIEN, PHIL DEPT, S ILLINOIS UNIV, CARBONDALE IL 62901
LIVERGOOD, NORMAN, HUMAN & PHIL, SANTA ROSA JR COL, SANTA ROSA CA 95401
LIVERNOIS, THOMAS, PHIL DEPT, SUSQUEHANNA UNIV, SELINSGROVE PA 17870
LIVINGSTON, DONALD W, PHIL DEPT, N ILLINOIS UNIV, DEKALB IL 60115
LLAMZON, BENJAMIN, PHIL DEPT, LOYOLA UNIVERSITY, CHICAGO IL 60626
LLEWELLYN, ROBERT R, PHIL DEPT, SOUTHWEST AT MEMPHIS, MEMPHIS TN 38112
LLOYD, LEWIS, SOC SCI DEPT, NORTHWOOD INSTITUTE, MIDLAND MI 48640
LLOYD, THOMAS, PHILOSOPHY DEPT, OHIO STATE UNIV, COLUMBUS OH 43210
LOAR, BRIAN, PHIL DEPT, UNIV OF MICHIGAN, ANN ARBOR MI 48104

LOBATO-MARTINES, R, PHIL DEPT, NORTHWESTERN UNIV, EVANSTON IL 60201
LOCHHEAD, D M, PHILOSOPHY DEPT, MEMORIAL UNIV, ST JOHN'S N F CAN
LOCKARD, HENRY C, PHIL DEPT, UNIV OF ILLINOIS, URBANA IL 61801
LOCKHART, TED W, PHIL DEPT, UNIV OF ROCHESTER, ROCHESTER NY 14627
LOCKHART, WALTER E, PHIL DEPT, SCHOOLCRAFT COLLEGE, LIVONIA MI 48151
LOCKLIN, DAVID K, PHIL DEPT, BOSTON STATE COL, BOSTON MA 02115
LOCKRIDGE, THOMAS F, PHIL DEPT, FLORIDA STATE UNIV, TALLAHASSEE FL 32306
LOCKWOOD, EUGENE DE V, OAKTON COM COLLEGE, MORTON GROVE, IL 60053
LOCKWOOD, MICHAEL, PHIL DEPT, NEW YORK UNIVERSITY, NEW YORK NY 10003
LODER, LESTER E, LIBR ARTS DEPT, PAUL SMITH'S COL, PAUL SMITH'S NY 12970
LOEB, MICHEL, PSYCH DEPT, UNIV OF LOUISVILLE, LOUISVILLE KY 40208
LOENKER, LEROY, PHIL DEPT, EMORY UNIVERSITY, ATLANTA GA 30322
LOEWER, BARRY M, PHILOSOPHY DEPT, UNIV OF S CAROLINA, COLUMBIA SC 29208
LOEWER, MARJORIE A, PHILOSOPHY DEPT, UNIV OF S CAROLINA, COLUMBIA SC 29208
LOFFBOURROW, R C, SOC SCI DIV, ANTELOPE VALLEY COL, LANCASTER CA 93554
LOFTIN, ROBERT W, PHIL DEPT, UNIV OF N FLORIDA, JACKSONVILLE FL 32216
LOFTUS, JOSEPH, PHIL DEPT, LOYOLA UNIVERSITY, CHICAGO IL 60626
LOGAN, ELEANOR, HUMANITIES DEPT, WIDENER COLLEGE, CHESTER PA 19013
LOGAN, MICHAEL, BRYN MAWR COLLEGE, BRYN MAWR, PA 19010
LOGUE, C W, HUMAN DEPT, COLUMBUS COLLEGE, COLUMBUS GA 31907
LOHMAN, PHILIP M, PHIL DEPT, UNIV OF CALIFORNIA, RIVERSIDE CA 92502
LOHR, JOHN, PHIL DEPT, DEPAUL UNIVERSITY, CHICAGO IL 60604
LOLLAR, JAMES, BEHAV SCI DEPT, PALOMAR COLLEGE, SAN MARCOS CA 92069
LOMBARD, LAWRENCE B, PHIL DEPT, WAYNE STATE UNIV, DETROIT MI 48202
LONDIS, JAMES J, PHIL DEPT, ATLANTIC UNION COL, S LANCASTER MA 01561
LONERGAN, J, PHIL DEPT, OUR LADY OF LAKE COL, SAN ANTONIO TX 78285
LONG, CHARLES, PHIL DEPT, UNIV OF CHICAGO, CHICAGO IL 60637
LONG, CYNTHIA, SOC SCI DEPT, RIVERSIDE CITY COL, RIVERSIDE CA 92506
LONG, DAVID W, PHIL DEPT, CALIFORNIA ST UNIV, SACRAMENTO CA 95819
LONG, DOUGLAS C, PHIL DEPT, UNIV OF N CAROLINA, CHAPEL HILL NC 27514
LONG, EUGENE T, PHILOSOPHY DEPT, UNIV OF S CAROLINA, COLUMBIA SC 29208
LONG, HARRY, PHIL & REL DEPT, HILLSDALE COLLEGE, HILLSDALE MI 49242
LONG, HERBERT, PHILOSOPHY DEPT, CASE WESTERN RESERVE, CLEVELAND OH 44106
LONG, JAMES, RELIG STUD DEPT, VILLA MARIA COLLEGE, BUFFALO NY 14225
LONG, JANELE BAKER, GEN EDUC DEPT, OWENS TECH COL, PERRYSBURG OH 43551
LONG, JEROME, PHILOSOPHY DEPT, E ILLINOIS UNIV, CHARLESTON IL 61920
LONG, JESSE C, COMMUNIC & LETTERS, WESTERN TEXAS COL, SNYDER TX 79549
LONG, JOHN E, PHIL & RELIG, WEST KENTUCKY UNIV, BOWLING GREEN KY 42101
LONG, MARY KATHERINE, PHILOSOPHY DEPT, ARIZONA STATE UNIV, TEMPE AZ 85281
LONG, PATRICIA S, PHIL DEPT, WEST VIRGINIA UNIV, MORGANTOWN WV 26506
LONG, PHILIP M, PHIL DEPT, UNIV OF ILLINOIS, URBANA IL 61801
LONG, R JAMES, PHIL DEPT, FAIRFIELD UNIVERSITY, FAIRFIELD CT 06430
LONG, ROBERT O, PHILOSOPHY DEPT, WITTENBERG UNIV, SPRINGFIELD OH 45501
LONG, ROBERT, PHILOSOPHY DEPT, UNIV OF WATERLOO, WATERLOO ONT CAN
LONG, THOMAS A, PHIL DEPT, UNIV OF CINCINNATI, CINCINNATI OH 45221
LONG, WILBUR, PHIL SCH, UNIV OF S CALIFORNIA, LOS ANGELES CA 90007
LONGACRE, LAWSON, PHIL DEPT, LONG ISLAND UNIV, BROOKLYN NY 11201
LONGERGAN, MARTIN, PHIL DEPT, CHAMINADE COLLEGE, HONOLULU HI 96816
LONGFELLOW, LAYNE, CTR FOR THE PERSON, PRESCOTT COLLEGE, PRESCOTT AZ 86301
LONGINO, HELEN, PHIL DEPT, U OF CAL -SAN DIEGO, LA JOLLA CA 92037
LONGLEY, DIANNE, PHILOSOPHY DEPT, UNIV OF OKLAHOMA, NORMAN OK 73069
LONGLEY, PETER, PHIL DEPT, HIBBING STATE JR COL, HIBBING MN 55746
LONGSTAFF, THOMAS R W, PHIL & REL DEPT, COLBY COLLEGE, WATERVILLE ME 04901
LONNES, JEROME L, PHIL & RELIG, VA COMMONWEALTH UNIV, RICHMOND VA 23220
LOOMER, BARNARD, SYST & PHIL, GRADUATE THEOL UNION, BERKELEY CA 94709
LOONEY, DAVID B, PHIL DEPT, HOWARD COM COLLEGE, COLUMBIA MD 21044
LOOSE, PATRICE, PHILOSOPHY DEPT, OHIO STATE UNIV, COLUMBUS OH 43210
LOPER, JOSEPH N, ADIRONDACK COM COL, GLENS FALLS, NY 12801
LOPEZ, PASCUAL, PHIL DEPT, COL DE SHERBROOKE, SHERBROOKE QUE CAN
LOPTSON, P J, PHILOSOPHY DEPT, UNIV OF SASKATCHEWAN, SASKATOON SAS CAN
LORD, ARTHUR, PHILOSOPHY DEPT, CENTRALIA COL, CENTRALIA WA 98531
LORD, CATHERINE, PHIL DEPT, SYRACUSE UNIVERSITY, SYRACUSE NY 13210
LORENZEN, PAUL, PHIL DEPT, BOSTON UNIVERSITY, BOSTON MA 02215
LOSASSO, ROSEMARIE, PHIL DEPT, MOLLOY COLLEGE, ROCKVILLE NY 11570

LOSEE, JOHN P, PHILOSOPHY DEPT, LAFAYETTE COLLEGE, EASTON PA   18042
LOSETH, PER O, HUMAN DEPT, OLIVE-HARVEY COM COL, CHICAGO IL   60628
LOSONCY, THOMAS A, PHILOSOPHY DEPT, VILLANOVA UNIV, VILLANOVA PA   19085
LOTHSTEIN, ARTHUR, PHIL DEPT, LONG ISLAND UNIV, GREENVALE NY   11548
LOTT, TOMMY, PHIL DEPT, UNIV OF CALIFORNIA, LOS ANGELES CA   90024
LOUCH, ALFRED, PHIL DEPT, CLAREMONT GRAD SCH, CLAREMONT CA   91711
LOUGHRAN, THOMAS J, PHIL DEPT, BOSTON COLLEGE, CHESTNUT HILL MA   02167
LOURO, MANUEL, COL DE LEVIS-LAUZON, LAUZON, QUE   CAN
LOUX, MICHAEL, PHIL DEPT, UNIV OF NOTRE DAME, NOTRE DAME IN   46556
LOVE JR, CHARLES E, PHIL & RELIG DEPT, ANTIOCH COL, YELLOW SPGS OH   45387
LOVE, CHARLES B, RELIG & PHIL DEPT, WILEY COLLEGE, MARSHALL TX   75670
LOVE, DAVID A, PHILOSOPHY DEPT, OBERLIN COLLEGE, OBERLIN OH   44074
LOVELACE, DAVID, PHIL DEPT, UNIV OF MICHIGAN, ANN ARBOR MI   48104
LOVELL, DAVID G, PHILOSOPHY DEPT, UNIV OF WISCONSIN, MADISON WI   53706
LOVIN, KEITH H, ENG & PHIL DEPT, SW TEXAS ST UNIV, SAN MARCOS TX   78666
LOVITT, C W, PHIL DEPT, CALIFORNIA ST UNIV, SACRAMENTO CA   95819
LOW, CLYDE M, SOC SCI DIV, SOLANO COLLEGE, SUISUN CITY CA   94585
LOWE, FLORENCE, PHIL DEPT, S CONNECTICUT ST COL, NEW HAVEN CT   06515
LOWE, JOHN, JOHNSON BIBLE COL, KNOXVILLE, TN   37920
LOWE, VICTOR, PHIL DEPT, JOHNS HOPKINS UNIV, BALTIMORE MD   21218
LOWER, RICHARD, ENG & PHIL DEPT, STEPHEN F AUSTIN U, NACOGDOCHES TX   75961
LOWN, JOHN, PHIL & REL DIV, PASADENA COLLEGE, PASADENA CA   91104
LOWRY, ATHERTON C, PHIL DEPT, LA SALLE COLLEGE, PHILADELPHIA PA   19141
LOWRY, JAMES, PHIL DEPT, ST MARY'S UNIVERSITY, HALIFAX N S   CAN
LOWRY, JON W, PHIL DEPT, LOYOLA UNIVERSITY, NEW ORLEANS LA   70118
LOY, HAROLD A, PHILOSOPHY DEPT, MT SAN ANTONIO COL, WALNUT CA   91789
LU, MATHIAS, PHILOSOPHY DEPT, JOHN F KENNEDY UNIV, MARTINEZ CA   94553
LUBOW, NEIL, PHIL DEPT, CALIFORNIA ST UNIV, LOS ANGELES CA   90032
LUC, LAURENT-PAUL, PHIL DEPT, UNIV DE SHERBROOKE, SHERBROOKE QUE   CAN
LUCAS JR, RAYMOND E, SOC SCI DEPT, KUTZTOWN STATE COL, KUTZTOWN PA   19530
LUCAS, BARBARA, PHIL DEPT, UNIV OF VIRGINIA, CHARLOTTESVL VA   22903
LUCAS, GERALD, COL OF PHAR SCI, NEW YORK, NY   10027
LUCAS, JOSEPH R, PHIL & REL STUD, YOUNGSTOWN ST UNIV, YOUNGSTOWN OH   44503
LUCAS, KAREN G, PHIL DEPT, WASHINGTON UNIV, ST LOUIS MO   63130
LUCASH, FRANK S, PHIL DEPT, UNIV OF NEVADA, RENO NV   89507
LUCE, DAVID R, PHIL DEPT, UNIV OF WISCONSIN, MILWAUKEE WI   53201
LUCEY, KENNETH, PHIL DEPT, COL AT FREDONIA, FREDONIA NY   14063
LUCHIES, JOHN E, PHIL & RELIG DEPT, DEFIANCE COLLEGE, DEFIANCE OH   43512
LUCIAN, MIRIAM, PHILOSOPHY DEPT, UNIV OF WASHINGTON, SEATTLE WA   98195
LUCIER, RUTH MILLER, HUMAN DIV, BENNETT COLLEGE, GREENSBORO NC   27420
LUCKENBACH, SIDNEY, PHIL DEPT, CALIFORNIA ST UNIV, NORTHRIDGE CA   91324
LUCKEY JR, GEORGE M, PHIL DEPT, MOREHEAD STATE UNIV, MOREHEAD KY   40351
LUCKHARDT, C GRANT, PHIL DEPT, GEORGIA ST UNIV, ATLANTA GA   30303
LUDLOW, L SPENCER, REL & PHIL, ST ANDREWS PRESB COL, LAURINBURG NC   28352
LUDWIG, JAN K, PHIL DEPT, UNION COLLEGE, SCHENECTADY NY   12308
LUEBKE, NEIL R, PHIL DEPT, OKLAHOMA STATE UNIV, STILLWATER OK   74074
LUEBKE, STEPHEN W, PHILOSOPHY DEPT, UNIV OF WISCONSIN, MADISON WI   53706
LUEGENBIEHL, HEINZ C, PHIL DEPT, PURDUE UNIVERSITY, LAFAYETTE IN   47907
LUEKER, ERWIN L, SYST THEOL DEPT, CONCORDIA SEMINARY, ST LOUIS MO   63105
LUGO, ELENA, HUMAN DEPT, UNIV OF PUERTO RICO, MAYAGUEZ PR   00708
LUGONES, MARIA, PHIL DEPT, CARLETON COLLEGE, NORTHFIELD MN   55057
LUISI, MIRIAM, SOC SCI DEPT, PACE COLLEGE, NEW YORK NY   10038
LUKNIC, ARNOLD, WORTHINGTON ST JR COL, WORTHINGTON, MN   56187
LUKNIC, JOHN, PHIL DEPT, NORMANDALE ST JR COL, BLOOMINGTON MN   55431
LUNCEFORD, W MABRY, DIV OF REL & PHIL, SAMFORD UNIV, BIRMINGHAM AL   35209
LUND, DAVID H, PHIL DEPT, BEMIDJI STATE COL, BEMIDJI MN   56601
LUNDEEN, LYMAN, SYST THEOL, LUTHERAN THEOL SEM, PHILADELPHIA PA   19119
LUNDGREN, GERALD, PHILOSOPHY DEPT, PENN STATE UNIV, UNIV PARK PA   16802
LUNSFORD, STEPHEN, PHILOSOPHY DEPT, OHIO STATE UNIV, COLUMBUS OH   43210
LUSCHEI, EUGENE C, PHILOSOPHY DEPT, BROWN UNIVERSITY, PROVIDENCE RI   02912
LUYSTER, R W, PHIL DEPT, UNIV OF CONNECTICUT, STORRS CT   06268
LUZ, EHUD, JEWISH THT DEPT, HEBREW COLLEGE, BROOKLINE MA   02146
LUZITANO, GEORGE, PHILOSOPHY DEPT, ST FIDELIS COLLEGE, HERMAN PA   16039
LYCAN, WILLIAM G, PHILOSOPHY DEPT, OHIO STATE UNIV, COLUMBUS OH   43210

LYDA, HAP, BEHAV SCI DEPT, TARRANT CO JR COL, FORT WORTH TX 76102
LYLE, WILLIAM E, PHILOSOPHY DEPT, KENT STATE UNIV, KENT OH 44242
LYNCH, JOHN J, PHIL DEPT, COL OF HOLY CROSS, WORCESTER MA 01610
LYNCH, L E M, UNIV OF ST MICHAEL'S, TORONTO 181, ONT CAN
LYNCH, RAYMOND, PHILOSOPHY DEPT, PENN STATE UNIV, UNIV PARK PA 16802
LYNES, JACK, PHIL DEPT, WAGNER COLLEGE, STATEN ISLAND NY 10301
LYONS, DANIEL D, PHIL DEPT, COLORADO ST UNIV, FORT COLLINS CO 80521
LYONS, DAVID, SAGE SCHOOL, CORNELL UNIVERSITY, ITHACA NY 14850
LYONS, LEONARD S, PHIL DEPT, UNIV OF SANTA CLARA, SANTA CLARA CA 95053
LYONS, RICHARD, PHIL DEPT, LOWELL STATE COLLEGE, LOWELL MA 01854
MAAT, HOWARD, HUMAN DIV, N COUNTRY COM COL, SARANAC LAKE NY 12983
MABE, ALAN R, PHIL DEPT, FLORIDA STATE UNIV, TALLAHASSEE FL 32306
MABRY, PAUL E, PHILOSOPHY DEPT, OLIVET COLLEGE, OLIVET MI 49076
MAC KAY, CHARLES, HUMANITIES DIV, KEYSTONE JR COL, LA PLUME PA 18440
MAC RAE, MAIRI, PHIL DEPT, ST UNIV CF NY, STONY BROOK NY 11790
MACADAM, JAMES I, PHIL DEPT, TRENT UNIVERSITY, PETERBOROUGH ONT CAN
MACALMON, EDWARD, PHIL DEPT, UNIV OF MISSOURI, COLUMBIA MO 65201
MACALUSO, CHRISTIE A, ST THOMAS SEM JUN C, BLOOMFIELD, CT 06002
MACANN, CHRISTOPHER, PHIL STUD BOARD, U OF CALIFORNIA, SANTA CRUZ CA 95060
MACBRYDE, DUNCAN, PHIL & RELIG DEPT, ESSEX COUNTY COL, NEWARK NJ 07102
MACCALLUM JR, GERALD, PHILOSOPHY DEPT, UNIV OF WISCONSIN, MADISON WI 53706
MACCORMAC, EARL L, PHILOSOPHY DEPT, DAVIDSON COLLEGE, DAVIDSON NC 28036
MACDONALD, C R, PHILOSOPHY DEPT, ST FRAN XAVIER UNIV, ANTIGONISH N S CAN
MACDONALD, C W, PHILOSOPHY DEPT, ST FRAN XAVIER UNIV, ANTIGONISH N S CAN
MACDONALD, DANIEL F, PHIL DEPT, ST MICHAEL'S COLLEGE, WINOOSKI VT 05404
MACDONALD, DOUGLAS, PHILOSOPHY DEPT, FURMAN UNIVERSITY, GREENVILLE SC 29613
MACDONALD, ERIC, PHILOSOPHY DEPT, UNIV OF WATERLOO, WATERLOO ONT CAN
MACDONALD, FRANK A, PHIL DEPT, COL WILLIAM & MARY, WILLIAMSBURG VA 23185
MACDONALD, JAMES, PHIL DEPT, INDIANA UNIVERSITY, BLOOMINGTON IN 47401
MACDONALD, LAUCHLIN D, PHIL DEPT, COL AT FREDONIA, FREDONIA NY 14063
MACDONALD, MICHAEL, HUMAN SCHOOL, SEATTLE PACIFIC COL, SEATTLE WA 98119
MACDONALD, R C, PHIL DEPT, UNIV OF NW BRUNSWICK, FREDERICTON N B CAN
MACDONALD, RONALD, PHILOSOPHY DEPT, MOUNT MARY COL, MILWAUKEE WI 53222
MACDOWELL, MARK E, PHIL DEPT, UNIVERSITY OF TOLEDO, TOLEDO OH 43606
MACGILL, N W, PHIL DEPT, UNIV OF NW BRUNSWICK, FREDERICTON N B CAN
MACGREGOR, GEDDES, PHIL SCH, UNIV OF S CALIFORNIA, LOS ANGELES CA 90007
MACGUIGAN, MARYELLEN, PHIL DEPT, UNIV OF DETROIT, DETROIT MI 48221
MACHADO, MICHAEL A, PHIL DEPT, FROSTBURG STATE COL, FROSTBURG MD 21532
MACHAMER, PETER K, PHILOSOPHY DEPT, OHIO STATE UNIV, COLUMBUS OH 43210
MACHAN, TIBOR R, PHIL DEPT, COL AT FREDONIA, FREDONIA NY 14063
MACHIN JR, HARRY, PHILOSOPHY DEPT, MARAMEC COM COL, ST LOUIS MO 36122
MACHINA, KENTON F, PHILOSOPHY DEPT, ILLINOIS ST UNIV, NORMAL IL 61761
MACHLE, EDWARD, PHIL DEPT, UNIV OF COLORADO, BOULDER CO 80302
MACINTIRE, GORDON, PHIL & RELIG DEPT, GLASSBORO ST COL, GLASSBORO NJ 08028
MACINTOSH, J J, PHILOSOPHY DEPT, UNIV OF CALGARY, CALGARY 44 ALB CAN
MACINTYRE, JANE, PHILOSOPHY DEPT, UNIV OF WATERLOO, WATERLOO ONT CAN
MACK, DARRYL, PHIL DEPT, UNIV OF CALIFORNIA, SANTA BARBARA CA 93106
MACK, ERIC, HUMAN DIV, EISENHOWER COLLEGE, SENECA FALLS NY 13148
MACKAY, ALFRED F, PHILOSOPHY DEPT, OBERLIN COLLEGE, OBERLIN OH 44074
MACKENSEN, WILLIAM, PHIL DEPT, UNIV OF MAINE, PORTLAND ME 04103
MACKENZIE, ANN W, GLENDON COLLEGE, TORONTO, ONT CAN
MACKENZIE, CHARLES S, PHIL & RELIG, GROVE CITY COLLEGE, GROVE CITY PA 16127
MACKENZIE, J C, PHILOSOPHY DEPT, UNIV OF ALBERTA, EDMONTON ALB CAN
MACKENZIE, NOLLAIG, GLENDON COLLEGE, TORONTO, ONT CAN
MACKENZIE, P T, PHILOSOPHY DEPT, UNIV OF SASKATCHEWAN, SASKATOON SAS CAN
MACKEY, LOUIS H, PHILOSOPHY DEPT, UNIV OF TEXAS, AUSTIN TX 78712
MACKINNON, BARBARA, PHIL DEPT, UNIV OF SN FRANCISCO, SAN FRANCISCO CA 94117
MACKINNON, EDWARD M, PHILOSOPHY DEPT, CALIFORNIA ST UNIV, HAYWARD CA 94542
MACKINTOSH, WILLIAM, PHILOSOPHY DEPT, REGIS COLLEGE, DENVER CO 80221
MACKLIN, RUTH, PHILOSOPHY DEPT, CASE WESTERN RESERVE, CLEVELAND OH 44106
MACLACHLAN, D L C, PHILOSOPHY DEPT, QUEEN'S UNIVERSITY, KINGSTON ONT CAN
MACLEAN, DOUGLAS, PHIL DEPT, YALE UNIVERSITY, NEW HAVEN CT 06520
MACLENNAN, IAN A, PHIL DEPT, DALHOUSIE UNIVERSITY, HALIFAX N S CAN
MACLEOD, A M, PHILOSOPHY DEPT, QUEEN'S UNIVERSITY, KINGSTON ONT CAN

MACLEOD, GREGORY, PHILOSOPHY DEPT, ST FRAN XAVIER UNIV, ANTIGONISH N S   CAN
MACLEOD, WILLIAM, PHIL DEPT, UNIV OF MAINE, PORTLAND ME 04103
MACMAHON, CHARLES E, MERRITT COLLEGE, OAKLAND, CA 94619
MACMANUS, O, PHILOSOPHY DEPT, ST FRAN XAVIER UNIV, SYDNEY N S   CAN
MACMILLAN, C J B, PHIL DEPT, FLORIDA STATE UNIV, TALLAHASSEE FL 32306
MACMILLAN, CLAUDE V, SOC SCI DEPT, ONONDAGA COM COL, SYRACUSE NY 13215
MACNIVEN, C DONALD, PHILOSOPHY DEPT, YORK UNIVERSITY, DOWNSVIEW ONT   CAN
MACORETTA, ORMAND, PHIL DEPT, LA SALLE COLLEGE, PHILADELPHIA PA 19141
MACOSKEY, ROBERT A, PHIL DEPT, SLIPPERY ROCK ST COL, SLIPPERY ROCK PA 16057
MACVEY, WAYNE, HIST & PHIL DEPT, E MICHIGAN UNIV, YPSILANTI MI 48197
MADDEN, A G, PHILOSOPHY DEPT, LOYOLA COLLEGE, BALTIMORE MD 21210
MADDEN, ARTHUR G, PHIL & REL DEPT, TOWSON STATE COL, BALTIMORE MD 21204
MADDEN, EDWARD H, PHIL DEPT, ST UNIV OF NY, AMHERST NY 14226
MADDEN, ROBERT E, PHILOSOPHY DEPT, DUQUESNE UNIV, PITTSBURGH PA 15219
MADDEN, S FRANCES, PHIL & RELIG DEPT, MARYLHURST COL, MARYLHURST OR 97036
MADIGAN, PATRICK, PHIL DEPT, LE MOYNE COLLEGE, SYRACUSE NY 13214
MADISON, G B, PHILOSOPHY DEPT, MCMASTER UNIVERSITY, HAMILTON ONT   CAN
MADSEN, PETER, PHILOSOPHY DEPT, DUQUESNE UNIV, PITTSBURGH PA 15219
MADSEN, TRUMAN G, PHILOSOPHY DEPT, BRIGHAM YOUNG UNIV, PROVO UT 84601
MAGANA, RICHARD, HUMAN DEPT, SULLIVAN CO COM COL, LOCH SHLDRAKE NY 12779
MAGAZ, THERESA, FLORIDA KEYS COM COL, KEY WEST, FL 33040
MAGEE, JOHN B, PHILOSOPHY DEPT, UNIV OF PUGET SOUND, TACOMA WA 98416
MAGEL, CHARLES R, PHIL DEPT, MOORHEAD STATE COL, MOORHEAD MN 56560
MAGID, CAROLYN, PHILOSOPHY DEPT, RUTGERS UNIV, NEW BRUNSWICK NJ 08903
MAGID, HENRY M, PHIL DEPT, CITY COLLEGE, NEW YORK NY 10031
MAGILOW, MOLLY RUTH, PHILOSOPHY DEPT, UNIV OF TEXAS, AUSTIN TX 78712
MAGNANO, PAUL, WHATCOM COM COL, FERNDALE, WA 98248
MAGNO, JOSEPH, PHILOSOPHY DEPT, EDGECLIFF COLLEGE, CINCINNATI OH 45206
MAGNUS, BERND, PHIL DEPT, UNIV OF CALIFORNIA, RIVERSIDE CA 92502
MAGRUDER, JAMES, ENG & PHIL DEPT, STEPHEN F AUSTIN U, NACOGDOCHES TX 75961
MAHAN, WALTER B, PHIL DEPT, S METHODIST UNIV, DALLAS TX 75222
MAHAN, WAYNE W, PHILOSOPHY DEPT, NORTH ARIZONA UNIV, FLAGSTAFF AZ 86001
MAHER, JOHN M, PHIL DEPT, FAIRFIELD UNIVERSITY, FAIRFIELD CT 06430
MAHER, MICHAEL, PHIL DEPT, SAINT MARY'S COLLEGE, WINONA MN 55987
MAHER, PAUL J, PHIL DEPT, MOLLOY COLLEGE, ROCKVILLE NY 11570
MAHLUM, ED, PHIL DEPT, UNIV OF MONTANA, MISSOULA MT 59801
MAHONEY, EDWARD, PHILOSOPHY DEPT, DUKE UNIVERSITY, DURHAM NC 27706
MAHONEY, MARY E, PHIL & REL STUD DIV, MT ST MARY COL, NEWBURGH NY 12550
MAIER, EUGENE, UNIV OF WISCONSIN, RIVER FALLS, WI 54022
MAIER, JOSEPH JOHN, PHIL DEPT, WHITMAN COLLEGE, WALLA WALLA WA 99362
MAILLOUX, N, COL DOM PHIL & THEOL, OTTAWA, ONT   CAN
MAINE, LEONARD, SOC SCI DIV, BREVARD COM COL, COCOA FL 32922
MAIRESSE, JEAN V, PSYCH DEPT, EAST LOS ANGELES COL, LOS ANGELES CA 90022
MAITLAND, JEFFREY A, PHIL DEPT, PURDUE UNIVERSITY, LAFAYETTE IN 47907
MAJCHRZAK, COLMAN, PHIL & THEOL DIV, HOLY REDEEMER COL, WATERFORD WI 53185
MAJORS, TROY E, PHIL DEPT, WICHITA ST UNIV, WICHITA KS 67208
MAKKREEL, RUDOLF, PHIL DEPT, EMORY UNIVERSITY, ATLANTA GA 30322
MAKRUSKI, EDWARD, PHILOSOPHY DEPT, OHIO STATE UNIV, COLUMBUS OH 43210
MALAMENT, DAVID, PHIL DEPT, ROCKEFELLER UNIV, NEW YORK NY 10021
MALCOLM, JOHN F, PHIL DEPT, UNIV OF CALIFORNIA, DAVIS CA 95616
MALCOLM, NORMAN, SAGE SCHOOL, CORNELL UNIVERSITY, ITHACA NY 14850
MALDONADO, JOSE M, INTERAMER UNIVERSITY, HATO REY, PR 00919
MALECEK, FRANCIS J, PHILOSOPHY DEPT, REGIS COLLEGE, DENVER CO 80221
MALETZ, WILLIAM, PHIL DEPT, NORTHWESTERN UNIV, EVANSTON IL 60201
MALHOTRA, ASHOK, PHIL DEPT, COL AT ONEONTA, ONEONTA NY 13820
MALIA, MARY, PHIL DEPT, ST UNIV OF NY, AMHERST NY 14226
MALIK, RAB N, PHIL & POLITICS DEPT, UNIV OF WISCONSIN, RICHLAND WI 53581
MALIN, GLEN P, PHIL DEPT, CALIFORNIA ST UNIV, LONG BEACH CA 90840
MALIN, JOHN, BEHAVIOR STUD DEPT, COLUMBUS TECH INST, COLUMBUS OH 43215
MALINO, JONATHAN, PHIL DEPT, COLUMBIA UNIVERSITY, NEW YORK NY 10027
MALITZ, RICHARD, PHIL DEPT, UNIV OF CALIFORNIA, LOS ANGELES CA 90024
MALLETT, MARCUS B, PHIL DEPT, UNIV OF VIRGINIA, CHARLOTTESVL VA 22903
MALLICK, KRISHNA, PHIL DEPT, BRANDEIS UNIVERSITY, WALTHAM MA 02154
MALLIN, S B, PHILOSOPHY DEPT, ATKINSON COLLEGE, DOWNSVIEW ONT   CAN

MALLORY, FRED C, PHIL & RELIG, VA COMMONWEALTH UNIV, RICHMOND VA 23220
MALLORY, WILLIAM, PHIL DEPT, WICHITA ST UNIV, WICHITA KS 67208
MALLOV, J A, PHILOSOPHY DEPT, QUEEN'S UNIVERSITY, KINGSTON ONT CAN
MALLOY, JOHN F, PHIL DEPT, LA SALLE COLLEGE, PHILADELPHIA PA 19141
MALLOY, JOHN, PHIL DEPT, IMMACULATA COLLEGE, IMMACULATA PA 19345
MALONE, MICHAEL E, PHILOSOPHY DEPT, NORTH ARIZONA UNIV, FLAGSTAFF AZ 86001
MALONE, ROBERT W, PHIL DEPT, BROCK UNIVERSITY, ST CATHARINES ONT CAN
MALONEY, CHARLES, PHILOSOPHY DEPT, RUTGERS UNIV, NEW BRUNSWICK NJ 08903
MALONEY, DANIEL, PHIL & THEOL DIV, MARY COLLEGE, BISMARCK ND 58501
MALONEY, JOHN, HUMAN DEPT, FLORIDA INST OF TECH, MELBOURNE FL 32901
MALONEY, JOSEPH MARIE, PHIL DEPT, TROCAIRE COLLEGE, BUFFALO NY 14220
MALONEY, WILLIAM, PHILOSOPHY DEPT, MARQUETTE UNIV, MILWAUKEE WI 53233
MALCUIN, HAREL, PHILOSOPHY DEPT, UNIV DU QUEBEC, MONTREAL QUE CAN
MAMO, P S, PHILOSOPHY DEPT, UNIV OF CALGARY, CALGARY 44 ALB CAN
MANDELBAUM, MAURICE, PHIL DEPT, JOHNS HOPKINS UNIV, BALTIMORE MD 21218
MANDT, ALMER J, PHILOSOPHY DEPT, VANDERBILT UNIV, NASHVILLE TN 37235
MANGRUM, FRANKLIN M, PHIL DEPT, MOREHEAD STATE UNIV, MOREHEAD KY 40351
MANICAS, PETER T, PHILOSOPHY DEPT, QUEENS COLLEGE, FLUSHING NY 11367
MANIER, EDWARD, PHIL DEPT, UNIV OF NOTRE DAME, NOTRE DAME IN 46556
MANIG, THOMAS O, PHIL DEPT, UNIV OF NEBRASKA, LINCOLN NE 68502
MANLEY, JAMES, PHIL OF RELIG, STOCTON STATE COL, POMONA NJ 08244
MANLEY, MICHAEL, HUMAN DIV, JEFFERSON COLLEGE, HILLSBORO MO 63050
MANN, JESSE A, PHIL DEPT, GEORGETOWN UNIV, WASHINGTON DC 20007
MANN, WILLIAM E, PHILOSOPHY DEPT, ILLINOIS ST UNIV, NORMAL IL 61761
MANNOIA, V JAMES, PHIL DEPT, WASHINGTON UNIV, ST LOUIS MO 63130
MANNOLINI, CAROL, PHIL DEPT, S ILLINOIS UNIV, CARBONDALE IL 62901
MANNS, JAMES W, PHIL DEPT, UNIV OF KENTUCKY, LEXINGTON KY 40506
MANOLAKOS, PETER, PHIL DEPT, SYRACUSE UNIVERSITY, SYRACUSE NY 13210
MANOR, RUTH, PHIL & RELIG, VA POLYTECH INST, BLACKSBURG VA 24061
MANSBRIDGE, C, DEAN OF ARTS, NOTRE DAME OF CAN, WILCOX SAS CAN
MANSON, RICHARD, PHIL DEPT, NORTHWESTERN UNIV, EVANSTON IL 60201
MANTAUTAS, V A, PHIL DEPT, GRT HARTFORD COM COL, HARTFORD CT 06106
MAPPES, TOM, PHIL DEPT, FROSTBURG STATE COL, FROSTBURG MD 21532
MAPSTONE, JAY, PHILOSOPHY DEPT, NYACK COLLEGE, NYACK NY 10931
MARA, JAMES, SYST & PHIL, GRADUATE THEOL UNION, BERKELEY CA 94709
MARBURY, CARL H, HIST & POLIT SCI, ALABAMA A & M UNIV, NORMAL AL 35762
MARCELL, NOAH, HUMAN DEPT, KENNEDY-KING COLLEGE, CHICAGO IL 60621
MARCHAL, JOSEPH, PHILOSOPHY DEPT, LAWRENCE UNIV, APPLETON WI 54911
MARCHAND, JEAN-PAUL, PHIL FACULTY, UNIV OF OTTAWA, OTTAWA ONT CAN
MARCIA, SISTER, REL STUD & PHIL, HILBERT COLLEGE, HAMBURG NY 14075
MARCIL, GEORGE, PHIL & THEOL DIV, ST FRANCIS COLLEGE, BIDDEFORD ME 04005
MARCIL, LOUISE, PHILOSOPHY DEPT, MCGILL UNIVERSITY, MONTREAL QUE CAN
MARCOLONGO, FRANCIS J, PHIL DEPT, UNIV OF CALIFORNIA, RIVERSIDE CA 92502
MARCUS, DEBBE, PHILOSOPHY DEPT, SKYLINE COLLEGE, SAN BRUNO CA 94066
MARCUS, RUTH, PHIL DEPT, YALE UNIVERSITY, NEW HAVEN CT 06520
MARCUSE, HERBERT, PHIL DEPT, U OF CAL -SAN DIEGO, LA JOLLA CA 92037
MARDIROS, A M, PHILOSOPHY DEPT, UNIV OF ALBERTA, EDMONTON ALB CAN
MARGENAU, HENRY, PHIL DEPT, YALE UNIVERSITY, NEW HAVEN CT 06520
MARGOLIS, JOSEPH, PHIL DEPT, TEMPLE UNIVERSITY, PHILADELPHIA PA 19122
MARIETTA, DON E, PHIL DEPT, FLORIDA ATLANTIC U, BCCA RATON FL 33432
MARINO, JOHN A, HUMAN DIV, HENDERSON COM COL, HENDERSON KY 42420
MARINO, JOHN, HUMAN DEPT, KENNEDY-KING COLLEGE, CHICAGO IL 60621
MARK, STEPHEN, COL OF NOTRE DAME, BALTIMORE, MD 21210
MARK, THOMAS, PHIL DEPT, U OF CAL -SAN DIEGO, LA JOLLA CA 92037
MARKER, EUGENE, HUMANITIES DIV, CHABOT COLLEGE, HAYWARD CA 94545
MARKGRAF, G K, BEHAV & SOC SCI DEPT, MODESTO JUNIOR COL, MODESTO CA 95350
MARKIE, PETER, PHILOSOPHY DEPT, UNIV OF MASS, AMHERST MA 01002
MARKLE, GILBERT SCOTT, PHIL DEPT, CLARK UNIVERSITY, WORCESTER MA 01610
MARKS, CHARLES, PHILOSOPHY DEPT, UNIV OF WASHINGTON, SEATTLE WA 98195
MARKS, JOE, SOC & BEHAV SCI DEPT, CENTRAL ARIZONA COL, COOLIDGE AZ 85228
MARKS, SANDRA, PHILOSOPHY DEPT, UNIV OF WASHINGTON, SEATTLE WA 98195
MARLETTE, WADE, LATIN & PHIL DEPT, NC CENTRAL UNIV, DURHAM NC 27707
MARLIN, JOSEPH, SOC SCI DEPT, ST PETERSBURG JR COL, ST PETERSBURG FL 33733
MARLIN, R R A, PHILOSOPHY DEPT, CARLETON UNIVERSITY, OTTAWA ONT CAN

MAROOSIS, J, PHILOSOPHY DEPT, UNIV CF TORONTO, TORONTO ONT   CAN
MARQUANDT, JAMES, PHIL DEPT, COPPIN STATE COLLEGE, BALTIMORE MD 21216
MARGUIS, DONALD, PHIL DEPT, UNIVERSITY OF KANSAS, LAWRENCE KS 66044
MARGUIS, JEAN-YVES, PHIL DEPT, COL CE SHERBROOKE, SHERBROOKE QUE   CAN
MARRAS, AUSONIO, PHIL DEPT, UNIV OF WEST ONTARIO, LONDON ONT   CAN
MARRERO, ALVIN C, PHILOSOPHY DEPT, XAVIER UNIVERSITY, CINCINNATI OH   45207
MARRON, JOHN, DELAWARE CO COM COL, MEDIA, PA 19063
MARSAN, GERNAIN, PHIL DEPT, COL LIONEL-GROULX, STE-THERESE QUE   CAN
MARSH, JAMES L, PHIL DEPT, ST LOUIS UNIVERSITY, ST LOUIS MO 63103
MARSH, JOSEPH, PHILOSOPHY DEPT, HUDSON VLY COM COL, TROY NY 12180
MARSHALL, DAVID, CABRINI COLLEGE, RADNOR, PA 19087
MARSHALL, DAVID, PHIL DEPT, ST JOSEPH'S COL, PHILADELPHIA PA 19131
MARSHALL, DONALD K, PHIL DEPT, MICHIGAN STATE UNIV, EAST LANSING MI   48823
MARSHALL, ERNEST, PHILOSOPHY DEPT, EAST CAROLINA UNIV, GREENVILLE NC   27834
MARSHALL, GEORGE J, CAMPION COLLEGE, REGINA, SAS   CAN
MARSHALL, GERALDINE, PHIL DEPT, BOSTON UNIVERSITY, BOSTON MA   02215
MARSHALL, JOHN M, SOC SCI DEPT, KANSAS STATE COL, PITTSBURG KS 66762
MARSHALL, JOHN P, PHIL DEPT, TRINITY UNIVERSITY, SAN ANTONIO TX 78284
MARSHALL, JOHN S, PHILOSOPHY DEPT, UNIV OF THE SOUTH, SEWANEE TN   37375
MARSHALL, JOHN, PHIL DEPT, UNIV OF VIRGINIA, CHARLOTTESVL VA   22903
MARSHALL, NORMAN, HIST & PHIL, MONTANA ST UNIV, BOZEMAN MT   59715
MARSHALL, ROWLAND C, PHIL DEPT, ST MARY'S UNIVERSITY, HALIFAX N S   CAN
MARSHBURN, ROBERT F, REL & PHIL DEPT, SOUTHWOOD COLLEGE, SALEMBURG NC   28385
MARTEL, JEAN-PAUL, COL MARGUERITE-BOURG, MONTREAL, QUE   CAN
MARTELLO, ERNEST, PHIL DEPT, PURDUE UNIVERSITY, FORT WAYNE IN   46805
MARTI, FRITZ, PHIL STUD DEPT, S ILLINOIS UNIV, EDWARDSVILLE IL 62025
MARTI, OSCAR, PHIL DEPT, CITY COLLEGE, NEW YORK NY 10031
MARTIN JR, WILLIAM M, PHIL DEPT, U S AIR FORCE ACAD, COLORADO SPGS CO   80840
MARTIN, B JOSEPH, NICHOLLS ST COLLEGE, THIBODAUX, LA 70301
MARTIN, C B, PHILOSOPHY DEPT, UNIV CF CALGARY, CALGARY 44 ALB   CAN
MARTIN, D C, RELIGION DEPT, GRAND CANYON COL, PHOENIX AZ 85017
MARTIN, DEAN, PHIL & REL STUD DEPT, U S INTNL UNIV, SAN DIEGO CA 92131
MARTIN, EDWARD, PHIL DEPT, THE AMERICAN UNIV, WASHINGTON DC 20016
MARTIN, EDWIN, PHIL DEPT, INDIANA UNIVERSITY, BLOOMINGTON IN 47401
MARTIN, F DAVID, PHIL DEPT, BUCKNELL UNIVERSITY, LEWISBURG PA 17837
MARTIN, GLEN O, HUM DEVEL DIV, SAINT MARY'S COL, ST MARY'S CY MD   20686
MARTIN, GLENN, REL & PHIL DIV, MARION COLLEGE, MARION IN 46952
MARTIN, GUY V, PHIL & RELIG DEPT, COLGATE UNIVERSITY, HAMILTON NY   13346
MARTIN, HILARY J, ST ALBERT'S COLLEGE, OAKLAND, CA 94618
MARTIN, J ALFRED, PHIL & RELIG DEPT, UNION THEOL SEM, NEW YORK NY   10027
MARTIN, JAMES, PHILOSOPHY DEPT, UNIV OF WYOMING, LARAMIE WY 82071
MARTIN, JANE, PHILOSOPHY DEPT, UNIV OF MASS, BOSTON MA 02116
MARTIN, JEAN-CLAUDE, COLLEGE D'AHUNTSIC, MONTREAL, QUE   CAN
MARTIN, JERRY, PHIL DEPT, UNIV OF COLORADO, BOULDER CO 80302
MARTIN, JOHN N, PHIL DEPT, UNIV OF CINCINNATI, CINCINNATI OH   45221
MARTIN, KENNETH F, PHIL DEPT, ST UNIV OF NY, BINGHAMTON NY 13901
MARTIN, MICHAEL, PHIL DEPT, BOSTON UNIVERSITY, BOSTON MA   02215
MARTIN, MICHAEL, PHIL DEPT, UNIV OF CALIFORNIA, IRVINE CA   92664
MARTIN, NORMAN M, PHILOSOPHY DEPT, UNIV OF TEXAS, AUSTIN TX 78712
MARTIN, RAMSEY, PHILOSOPHY DEPT, WASH & LEE UNIV, LEXINGTON VA   24450
MARTIN, RAYMOND F, PHIL DEPT, UNIV OF MARYLAND, COLLEGE PARK MD   20742
MARTIN, REX, PHIL DEPT, UNIVERSITY CF KANSAS, LAWRENCE KS 66044
MARTIN, RICHARD, PHIL DEPT, NORTHWESTERN UNIV, EVANSTON IL 60201
MARTIN, RICHARD, PHIL DEPT, INDIANA UNIVERSITY, BLOOMINGTON IN 47401
MARTIN, ROBERT L, PHILOSOPHY DEPT, RUTGERS UNIV, NEW BRUNSWICK NJ 08903
MARTIN, ROBERT M, PHIL DEPT, DALHOUSIE UNIVERSITY, HALIFAX N S   CAN
MARTIN, RONALD E, PHILOSOPHY DEPT, LYNCHBURG COL, LYNCHBURG VA   24504
MARTIN, STUART B, PHIL DEPT, BOSTON COLLEGE, CHESTNUT HILL MA   02167
MARTIN, WILLIAM O, PHILOSOPHY DEPT, UNIV OF RHODE ISLAND, KINGSTON RI   02881
MARTINE, BRIAN, PHILOSOPHY DEPT, PENN STATE UNIV, UNIV PARK PA 16802
MARTINEAU, JEAN-F, COLLEGE D'AHUNTSIC, MONTREAL, GUE   CAN
MARTINEZ, CHARLES, PHIL DEPT, WICHITA ST UNIV, WICHITA KS 67208
MARTINEZ, ERNEST R, SYST & PHIL, GRADUATE THEOL UNION, BERKELEY CA 94709
MARTINEZ, H S, MOD LANG DEPT, ANGELO STATE UNIV, SAN ANGELO TX 76901

MARTINEZ, MARIE L, PHILOSOPHY DEPT, MARYVILLE COLLEGE, ST LOUIS MO 63141
MARTINI, CLARE, HUMAN DEPT, AMUNDSEN-MAYFAIR COL, CHICAGO IL 60630
MARTINICH, ALOYSIUS, PHILOSOPHY DEPT, UNIV OF TEXAS, AUSTIN TX 78712
MARTINSON, PAUL V, SYST THEOL DEPT, LUTHER THEOL SEM, ST PAUL MN 55108
MARTINSON, PAUL, PHILOSOPHY DEPT, EDINBORO ST COL, EDINBORO PA 16412
MARTIRE, JOSEPH, PHIL DEPT, GOUCHER COLLEGE, TOWNSON MD 21204
MARTLAND, T R, PHIL DEPT, ST UNIV OF NY, ALBANY NY 12203
MARUNGI, ROBERT W, PHIL STUD DEPT, S ILLINOIS UNIV, EDWARDSVILLE IL 62025
MARVIN, E L, PHIL DEPT, UNIV OF MONTANA, MISSOULA MT 59801
MARX, JO ANN, PHIL DEPT, SOUTH UNIV A & M COL, BATON ROUGE LA 70813
MARY, GERALD, PHIL DEPT, CHESTNUT HILL COL, PHILADELPHIA PA 19118
MASCHNER, HORST G, PHILOSOPHY DEPT, DUQUESNE UNIV, PITTSBURGH PA 15219
MASHINTER, HARVEY, SOC SCI DEPT, LOWER COLUMBIA COL, LONGVIEW WA 98632
MASIELLO, RALPH J, PHIL DEPT, NIAGARA UNIVERSITY, NIAGARA UNIV NY 14109
MASON, AIMEE, HUM & COMMUNIC DIV, SEMINOLE JR COL, SANFORD FL 32771
MASON, HOMER E, PHIL DEPT, UNIV OF MINNESOTA, MINNEAPOLIS MN 55455
MASON, P C, PHIL DEPT, CARLETON COLLEGE, NORTHFIELD MN 55057
MASON, RICHARD G, HUMAN DEPT, MICHIGAN TECH UNIV, HOUGHTON MI 49931
MASSEY, G ERIC, PHIL DEPT, CALIFORNIA ST UNIV, LONG BEACH CA 90840
MASSEY, GERALD J, PHIL DEPT, UNIV OF PITTSBURGH, PITTSBURGH PA 15260
MASSIE, DAVID, PHIL DEPT, BROOKLYN COLLEGE, BROOKLYN NY 11210
MASSIEOTTE, GUY-PAUL, PHIL DEPT, COL THETFORD MINES, MEGANTIE QUE   CAN
MASSON, KEITH, PHIL DEPT, UNIV OF MICHIGAN, ANN ARBOR MI 48104
MASTROYANNIS, C, HUMANITIES DIV, CHABOT COLLEGE, HAYWARD CA 94545
MATES, BENSON, PHIL DEPT, UNIV OF CALIFORNIA, BERKELEY CA 94720
MATHEWS JR, BILL, HUMAN DEPT, UNIV OF MICHIGAN, DEARBORN MI 48128
MATHEWS, TUELIN M, PHIL DEPT, UNIV CF MARYLAND, COLLEGE PARK MD 20742
MATHUR, DINESH, PHIL DEPT, COLLEGE AT BROCKPORT, BROCKPORT NY 14420
MATICS, MARION, PHIL DEPT, BROOKLYN COLLEGE, BROOKLYN NY 11210
MATROSS, GERALD, PHIL DEPT, MERRIMACK COLLEGE, NORTH ANDOVER MA 01845
MATSEN, HERBERT S, PHILOSOPHY DEPT, UNIV OF S CAROLINA, COLUMBIA SC 29208
MATSON, WALLACE I, PHIL DEPT, UNIV CF CALIFORNIA, BERKELEY CA 94720
MATTEA, JAMES, PHILOSOPHY DEPT, MARQUETTE UNIV, MILWAUKEE WI 53233
MATTHEWS, GARETH, PHILOSOPHY DEPT, UNIV OF MASS, AMHERST MA 01002
MATTHEWS, LLOYD J, ENG DEPT, U S MILITARY ACAD, WEST POINT NY 10996
MATTHEWS, PAUL L, BELLARMINE COLLEGE, LOUISVILLE, KY 40205
MATTHEWS, ROBERT, RELIG & PHIL, UNION COLLEGE, BARBOURVILLE KY 40906
MATTHEWS, VICTOR, HUMAN DIV, GRND RAPIDS BAPT COL, GRAND RAPIDS MI 49505
MATTHIS, MICHAEL J, PHIL DEPT, FORDHAM UNIVERSITY, BRONX NY 10458
MATTINGLY, RICHARD E, PHIL DEPT, WESTMINSTER COLLEGE, FULTON MO 65251
MATTINGLY, SUSAN S, PHIL DEPT, LINCOLN UNIVERSITY, JEFFERSON CY MO 65101
MATTSON, ENOCH E, HUMANITIES DIV, TRINITY WEST COL, LANGLEY B C   CAN
MAUE, J BROOKS, PHIL DEPT, CALIFORNIA ST UNIV, LONG BEACH CA 90840
MAULDIN, DENISE E, PHIL DEPT, ST UNIV OF NY, BINGHAMTON NY 13901
MAULDIN, FRANK L, PSYCH & REL STUD, UNIV OF TENNESSEE, MARTIN TN 38237
MAULTSBY, HUBERT, PHIL OF RELIG, STOCTON STATE COL, POMONA NJ 08244
MAURER, A A, UNIV OF ST MICHAEL'S, TORONTO 181, ONT   CAN
MAVRODES, GEORGE I, PHIL DEPT, UNIV OF MICHIGAN, ANN ARBOR MI 48104
MAXWELL, D V, PHILOSOPHY DEPT, MEMORIAL UNIV, ST JOHN'S N F   CAN
MAXWELL, GROVER, PHIL DEPT, UNIV OF MINNESOTA, MINNEAPOLIS MN 55455
MAXWELL, PETER, PHIL DEPT, LOYOLA UNIVERSITY, CHICAGO IL 60626
MAY, H CLEVELAND, PHIL DEPT, UNIV OF N CAROLINA, CHAPEL HILL NC 27514
MAY, JAMES R, PHIL DEPT, BOSTON COLLEGE, CHESTNUT HILL MA 02167
MAY, T J, PHILOSOPHY DEPT, LOYOLA COLLEGE, BALTIMORE MD 21210
MAYBERRY, THOMAS, PHIL DEPT, UNIVERSITY OF TOLEDO, TOLEDO OH 43606
MAYER, CAROL, PHIL DEPT, QUINCY COLLEGE, QUINCY IL 62301
MAYER, DALMEN, BELLEVUE COM COL, BELLEVUE, WA 98007
MAYER, EDWARD F, PHIL DEPT, QUINCY COLLEGE, QUINCY IL 62301
MAYER, JOHN R A, PHIL DEPT, BROCK UNIVERSITY, ST CATHARINES ONT   CAN
MAYEROFF, MILTON, PHIL DEPT, COL AT CORTLAND, CORTLAND NY 13045
MAYERS, EUGENE D, PHILOSOPHY DEPT, CALIFORNIA ST UNIV, HAYWARD CA 94542
MAYERS, RONALD, HUMAN DIV, GRND RAPIDS BAPT COL, GRAND RAPIDS MI 49505
MAYFIELD, PAUL, PHIL DEPT, UNIV OF MARYLAND, BALTIMORE MD 21228
MAYFIELD, WILLIAM, HUMANE LEARNING, MILLIGAN COLLEGE, MILLIGAN COL TN 37682

MAYHALL JR, JAMES W, PHIL DEPT, WASHINGTON UNIV, ST LOUIS MO 63130
MAYHEW, LARRY D, PHIL & RELIG, WEST KENTUCKY UNIV, BOWLING GREEN KY 42101
MAYNARD, PATRICK L, PHIL DEPT, UNIV OF WEST ONTARIO, LONDON ONT   CAN
MAYO, DAVID J, PHIL DEPT, UNIV OF MINNESOTA, DULUTH MN 55812
MAYR, FRANZ K, PHILOSOPHY DEPT, UNIV OF PORTLAND, PORTLAND OR 97203
MAZAITIS, JOHN C, PHIL DEPT, GEORGETOWN UNIV, WASHINGTON DC 20007
MAZIARZ, EDWARD A, PHIL DEPT, LOYOLA UNIVERSITY, CHICAGO IL 60626
MAZURSKI, A A, PHILOSOPHY DEPT, QUEEN'S UNIVERSITY, KINGSTON ONT   CAN
MAZZOLA, JOHN, PHIL DEPT, S ILLINOIS UNIV, CARBONDALE IL 62901
MCADAM, RICHARD D, PHIL DEPT, BOSTON COLLEGE, CHESTNUT HILL MA 02167
MCALISTER, LINDA, PHIL PROGRAM, GRADUATE SCH -CUNY, NEW YORK NY 10036
MCALLEN, PETER, PHIL DEPT, UNIV OF CALIFORNIA, LOS ANGELES CA 90024
MCALLISTER, JAMES L, RELIG & PHIL DEPT, MARY BALDWIN COL, STAUNTON VA 24401
MCALLISTER, WINSTON K, PHIL DEPT, HOWARD UNIVERSITY, WASHINGTON DC 20001
MCANDREWS, J F, PHILOSOPHY DEPT, LOYOLA COLLEGE, BALTIMORE MD 21210
MCANINCH, ROBERT, SOC SCI DIV, PRESTONSBURG COM COL, PRESTONSBURG KY 41653
MCARDLE, ANN, PHILOSOPHY DEPT, QUEENS COLLEGE, FLUSHING NY 11367
MCARDLE, JOHN, PHIL DEPT, UNIV OF WEST ONTARIO, LONDON ONT   CAN
MCARTHUR, ROBERT P, PHIL & REL DEPT, COLBY COLLEGE, WATERVILLE ME 04901
MCARTHUR, RONALD P, ST MARY'S COL OF CAL, MORAGA, CA 94575
MCAVEY, JAMES R, PHIL DEPT, PROVIDENCE COLLEGE, PROVIDENCE RI 02919
MCAVOY, BERNARD L, PHILOSOPHY DEPT, UNIV OF PORTLAND, PORTLAND OR 97203
MCBETH, ALAN, PHIL DEPT, MICHIGAN STATE UNIV, EAST LANSING MI 48823
MCBRIDE, ROBERT E, PHILOSOPHY DEPT, ALBRIGHT COLLEGE, READING PA 19604
MCBRIDE, WILLIAM L, PHIL DEPT, PURDUE UNIVERSITY, LAFAYETTE IN 47907
MCCABE, BRENDAN, PHIL DEPT, JAMESTOWN COM COL, JAMESTOWN NY 14701
MCCABE, RUSSELL T, PHIL & RELIG, VA POLYTECH INST, BLACKSBURG VA 24061
MCCAFFREY, JOSEPH, PHIL DEPT, ST AMBROSE COLLEGE, DAVENPORT IA 52803
MCCALL, STORRS, PHIL DEPT, UNIV OF PITTSBURGH, PITTSBURGH PA 15260
MCCALLISTER, ALBERT, GEN EDUC DEPT, COLUMBIA BIBLE COL, COLUMBIA SC 29203
MCCANN JR, H J, PHIL & HUM DEPT, TEXAS A & M UNIV, COL STATION TX 77843
MCCARGAR, D, PHIL DEPT, BISHOP'S UNIVERSITY, LENNOXVILLE QUE   CAN
MCCARNEY, EVERETT F, SOC SCI DIV, SOLANO COLLEGE, SUISUN CITY CA 94585
MCCARTHY, D J, PHIL DEPT, UNIV OF MANITOBA, WINNIPEG 19 MAN   CAN
MCCARTHY, EDWARD, PHIL DEPT, ST JOSEPH'S COLLEGE, RENNSSELAER IN 47978
MCCARTHY, HAROLD E, PHIL DEPT, UNIVERSITY OF HAWAII, HONOLULU HI 96822
MCCARTHY, MICHAEL, PHIL DEPT, VASSAR COLLEGE, POUGHKEEPSIE NY 12601
MCCARTHY, THOMAS, PHIL DEPT, BOSTON UNIVERSITY, BOSTON MA 02215
MCCARTY, CHARLES L, PHIL & REL, COLLEGE OF EMPORIA, EMPORIA KS 66801
MCCARTY, DORAN, THEOL DEPT, MID W BAPT THEOL SEM, KANSAS CITY MO 64118
MCCLAIN, EDWARD F, ENGLISH LIT & PHIL, UNIV OF WISCONSIN, MADISON WI 53706
MCCLATCHEY, JOHN, REL & PHIL DEPT, CATAWBA COLLEGE, SALISBURY NC 28144
MCCLATCHY, JOHN, REL DEPT, UNIV OF GEORGIA, ATHENS GA 30602
MCCLEARY, RICHARD C, PHILOSOPHY DEPT, OLD DOMINION UNIV, NORFOLK VA 23508
MCCLELLAND, CHARLES, PHILOSOPHY DEPT, UNIV OF TEXAS, AUSTIN TX 78712
MCCLELLAND, WILLIAM, PHIL & RELIG, MUSKINGUM COLLEGE, NEW CONCORD OH 43762
MCCLENDON, JAMES, SYST & PHIL, GRADUATE THEOL UNION, BERKELEY CA 94709
MCCLENNEN, EDWARD, PHIL DEPT, WASHINGTON UNIV, ST LOUIS MO 63130
MCCLINTOCK, THOMAS, PHIL DEPT, TEMPLE UNIVERSITY, PHILADELPHIA PA 19122
MCCLOUD, LAWRENCE, PHIL DEPT, UNIVERSITY OF KANSAS, LAWRENCE KS 66044
MCCLURE, DONALD, PHIL & REL DEPT, TOCCOA FALLS INST, TOCCOA FALLS GA 30577
MCCLURE, GEORGE T, PHIL DEPT, S ILLINOIS UNIV, CARBONDALE IL 62901
MCCLURE, STEVE, SHORELINE COM COL, SEATTLE, WA 98133
MCCLURG, JACK, PHIL DEPT, CALIFORNIA ST UNIV, SAN DIEGO CA 92115
MCCLUSKY, JOSEPH B, PHIL DEPT, UNIVERSITY OF MIAMI, CORAL GABLES FL 33124
MCCOLLOUGH, J L, HIST & PHIL DEPT, CLEMSON UNIVERSITY, CLEMSON SC 29631
MCCOMMAS, BETTY JO, PHIL DEPT, QUACHITA BAPTIST U, ARKADELPHIA AR 71923
MCCONNELL JR, F, PHILOSOPHY DEPT, MORAVIAN COLLEGE, BETHLEHEM PA 18018
MCCONNELL, TERRANCE, PHIL DEPT, UNIV OF MINNESOTA, MINNEAPOLIS MN 55455
MCCOOL, GERALD A, PHIL DEPT, FORDHAM UNIVERSITY, BRONX NY 10458
MCCORD, JOAN, LIT & LANG DEPT, DREXEL UNIV, PHILADELPHIA PA 19104
MCCORMACK, J K, PHILOSOPHY DEPT, LOYOLA COLLEGE, BALTIMORE MD 21210
MCCORMICK, BERNARD P, LANG & LIT DEPT, MISSOURI S ST COL, JOPLIN MO 64801
MCCORMICK, HOWARD, PHIL DEPT, COL OUR LADY OF ELMS, CHICOPEE MA 01013

MCCORMICK, JANICE, PHIL DEPT, S ILLINOIS UNIV, CARBONDALE IL 62901
MCCORMICK, PETER, PHIL FACULTY, UNIV OF OTTAWA, OTTAWA ONT CAN
MCCORMICK, WILLIAM R, PHIL DEPT, MANHATTAN COLLEGE, RIVERDALE NY 10471
MCCOY, D B, PHILOSOPHY DEPT, AMER BAPT THEOL SEM, NASHVILLE TN 37207
MCCOY, GLENN, RELIG DEPT, E NEW MEXICO UNIV, PORTALES NM 88130
MCCRACKEN, CHARLES J, PHIL DEPT, MICHIGAN STATE UNIV, EAST LANSING MI 48823
MCCREADIE-ALBRIGHT, T, PHIL DEPT, BOSTON UNIVERSITY, BOSTON MA 02215
MCCREARY, JOHN, FLEMING COL APPL ARTS, PETERBOROUGH, ONT CAN
MCCRIMMON, MITCHELL, PHIL DEPT, UNIV OF WEST ONTARIO, LONDON ONT CAN
MCCUE, MARY WILLIAM, PHIL DEPT, MT ST CLARE COLLEGE, CLINTON IA 52732
MCCULLOCH, MICHAEL L, PHIL DEPT, COLORADO ST UNIV, FORT COLLINS CO 80521
MCCULLOUGH, DANIEL, LIBR ARTS SCH, GRAHME JR COLLEGE, BOSTON MA 02215
MCCULLOUGH, E J, PHILOSOPHY DEPT, ST THOMAS MORE COL, SASKATOON SAS CAN
MCCULLOUGH, LAURENCE, PHILOSOPHY DEPT, UNIV OF TEXAS, AUSTIN TX 78712
MCCUSKER, OWEN, PHIL DEPT, UNIVERSITY OF DAYTON, DAYTON OH 45469
MCDADE, JESSE N, PHIL DEPT, UNIV OF CALIFORNIA, RIVERSIDE CA 92502
MCDANIEL, BROOKS, COMMUNIC DIV, ILLINOIS CENTRAL COL, EAST PEORIA IL 61611
MCDANIEL, MICHAEL, PHILOSOPHY DEPT, LENOIR-RHYNE COLLEGE, HICKORY NC 28601
MCDANIEL, STANLEY, PHIL DEPT, CAL ST COL AT SONOMA, ROHNERT PARK CA 94928
MCDERMOTT, CHARLENE, PHIL DEPT, UNIV OF NEW MEXICO, ALBUQUERQUE NM 87106
MCDERMOTT, JOHN J, PHILOSOPHY DEPT, QUEENS COLLEGE, FLUSHING NY 11367
MCDERMOTT, JOHN, HUMAN DIV, EISENHOWER COLLEGE, SENECA FALLS NY 13148
MCDERMOTT, MICHAEL, HUMAN DEPT, GEORGE MASON UNIV, FAIRFAX VA 22030
MCDERMOTT, ROBERT, PHIL DEPT, BERNARD BARUCH COL, NEW YORK NY 10010
MCDONALD, CAROL, PHIL DEPT, N ILLINOIS UNIV, DEKALB IL 60115
MCDONALD, DURSTAN R, PHIL DEPT, HOBART & WM SMITH, GENEVA NY 14456
MCDONALD, JOHN W, PHILOSOPHY DEPT, WASH & JEFF COL, WASHINGTON PA 15301
MCDONALD, JOSEPH, PHIL DEPT, ST ANSELM'S COLLEGE, MANCHESTER NH 03102
MCDONALD, MICHAEL F, PHILOSOPHY DEPT, UNIV OF WATERLOO, WATERLOO ONT CAN
MCDONALD, PATRICK, PHIL DEPT, UNIV DE SHERBROOKE, SHERBROOKE QUE CAN
MCDONALD, ROBERT, PHIL DEPT, ST THOS AQUINAS COL, SPARKILL NY 10976
MCDONNELL, KEVIN, PHIL & REL DEPT, WASHINGTON COLLEGE, CHESTERLAND MD 21620
MCDONOUGH, J T, HUMANITIES DEPT, CENTENNIAL COLLEGE, SCARBOROUGH ONT CAN
MCDOWELL, EDWARD A, ENG & PHIL DEPT, MONTGOMERY COLLEGE, ROCKVILLE MD 20850
MCDOWELL, ELWOOD, PHILOSOPHY DEPT, UNIV OF OKLAHOMA, NORMAN OK 73069
MCELROY, ELLIOTT W, PHIL DEPT, VALDOSTA ST COL, VALDOSTA GA 31601
MCELVAIN, THOMAS, PSYCH & PHIL DEPT, TEXAS SOUTH UNIV, HOUSTON TX 77004
MCENEANY, GEORGE, PHIL DEPT, UNIV OF WEST ONTARIO, LONDON ONT CAN
MCENERNEY, DAVID, PHILOSOPHY DEPT, RUTGERS UNIV, NEW BRUNSWICK NJ 08903
MCEVILLY, WAYNE, HUMAN DEPT, COLLEGE OF SANTA FE, SANTA FE NM 87501
MCEVOY, JOHN G, PHIL DEPT, UNIV OF CINCINNATI, CINCINNATI OH 45221
MCEWEN, W P, PHILOSOPHY DEPT, HOFSTRA UNIVERSITY, HEMPSTEAD NY 11550
MCFADDEN, CHARLES J, PHILOSOPHY DEPT, VILLANOVA UNIV, VILLANOVA PA 19085
MCFADDEN, DANIEL, PHILOSOPHY DEPT, WHEELING COLLEGE, WHEELING WV 26003
MCFARLAND, JAMES, OHIO STATE UNIV, MARION, OH 43302
MCFARLAND, JOHN D, PHILOSOPHY DEPT, YORK UNIVERSITY, DOWNSVIEW ONT CAN
MCFARLAND, JOHN, PHIL DEPT, SPRING HILL COLLEGE, MOBILE AL 36608
MCFARLANE, L, PHILOSOPHY DEPT, QUEEN'S UNIVERSITY, KINGSTON ONT CAN
MCFARLANE, WILLIAM H, HUMAN DEPT, GEORGE MASON UNIV, FAIRFAX VA 22030
MCGANN, THOMAS F, ST PETER'S COLLEGE, JERSEY CITY, NJ 07306
MCGARY, HOWARD, PHIL DEPT, UNIV OF MINNESOTA, MINNEAPOLIS MN 55455
MCGARY, KEITH, PHIL & RELIG DEPT, ANTIOCH COL, YELLOW SPGS OH 45387
MCGEE, C DOUGLAS, BOWDOIN COLLEGE, BRUNSWICK, ME 04011
MCGEE, HAROLD F, E SHORE COM COL, WALLOPS IS, VA 23337
MCGEE, KAREN J, PHIL DEPT, UNIV OF MARYLAND, COLLEGE PARK MD 20742
MCGEOUGH, JOSEPH, PHIL DEPT, HUNTER COLLEGE, NEW YORK NY 10021
MCGHAN, BARBARA, PHIL & RELIG, VA COMMONWEALTH UNIV, RICHMOND VA 23220
MCGHAN, HARLAN P, PHIL & RELIG, VA COMMONWEALTH UNIV, RICHMOND VA 23220
MCGILL, V JERAULD, PHIL DEPT, CALIFORNIA ST UNIV, SAN FRANCISCO CA 94132
MCGILP, I, PHILOSOPHY DEPT, UNIV OF ALBERTA, EDMONTON ALB CAN
MCGILVRAY, JAMES, PHILOSOPHY DEPT, MCGILL UNIVERSITY, MONTREAL QUE CAN
MCGINLEY, JOHN, PHILOSOPHY DEPT, UNIV OF SCRANTON, SCRANTON PA 18510
MCGINNISS, JOHN, FINE ARTS DEPT, TALLAHASSEE COM COL, TALLAHASSEE FL 32304
MCGLINCHY, EDWARD H, ST PETER'S COLLEGE, JERSEY CITY, NJ 07306

MCGLYNN, FRED, PHIL DEPT, UNIV OF MONTANA, MISSOULA MT 59801
MCGLYNN, JAMES, PHIL DEPT, UNIV OF DETROIT, DETROIT MI 48221
MCGOVERN, ARTHUR, PHIL DEPT, UNIV OF DETROIT, DETROIT MI 48221
MCGOVERN, KENNETH C, CAMPION COLLEGE, REGINA, SAS CAN
MCGOWAN, JAMES K, PHIL DEPT, UNIV OF N CAROLINA, WILMINGTON NC 28401
MCGOWAN, JOHN, PHIL & RELIG, JERSEY CITY ST COL, JERSEY CITY NJ 07305
MCGRADE, A S, PHIL DEPT, UNIV OF CONNECTICUT, STORRS CT 06268
MCGRATH, JAMES, PHIL DEPT, THE AMERICAN UNIV, WASHINGTON DC 20016
MCGRAW, GERALD E, PHIL & REL DEPT, TOCCOA FALLS INST, TOCCOA FALLS GA 30577
MCGRAW, JOHN B, ST PETER'S COLLEGE, JERSEY CITY, NJ 07306
MCGRAW, JOHN, PHILOSOPHY DEPT, LOYOLA COLLEGE, MONTREAL QUE CAN
MCGRAW, MINERVA, HUMAN DEPT, TRI-COUNTY TECH INST, MURPHY NC 28906
MCGRAW, RENE, PHIL DEPT, SAINT JOHN'S UNIV, COLLEGEVILLE MN 56321
MCGREAL, IAN P, PHIL DEPT, CALIFORNIA ST UNIV, SACRAMENTO CA 95819
MCGREGOR, JAMES E, PHIL DEPT, BOSTON STATE COL, BOSTON MA 02115
MCGREGOR, ROBERT, PHIL DEPT, UNIV OF DENVER, DENVER CO 80210
MCGUIGAN, JAMES, PHILOSOPHY DEPT, SEATTLE UNIVERSITY, SEATTLE WA 98122
MCGUINNESS, FRANK, PHIL DEPT, CALIFORNIA ST UNIV, NORTHRIDGE CA 91324
MCGUIRE, JAMES E, PHIL DEPT, UNIV OF PITTSBURGH, PITTSBURGH PA 15260
MCGUIRE, MARCIE M, PHIL DEPT, HOWARD UNIVERSITY, WASHINGTON DC 20001
MCGUIRE, RICHARD, PHIL DEPT, COLLEGE AT BROCKPORT, BROCKPORT NY 14420
MCHALE, ELWYN, PHIL DEPT, ROSARY COLLEGE, RIVER FOREST IL 60305
MCHAN, GEORGE L, SOC STUD & EDUC DIV, JACKSON ST COM COL, JACKSON TN 38301
MCHARRY, JOHN, PHIL DEPT, UNIV OF ILLINOIS, URBANA IL 61801
MCHCLLAND, LARRY, FINE & APPL ARTS, PIMA COLLEGE, TUCSON AZ 85721
MCILVAIN, CHERRY, ENGLISH DEPT, BLACK HAWK COLLEGE, MOLINE IL 61265
MCINERNEY, PETER, PHILOSOPHY DEPT, UNIV OF TEXAS, AUSTIN TX 78712
MCINERNY, RALPH, PHIL DEPT, UNIV OF NOTRE DAME, NOTRE DAME IN 46556
MCINNIS, S PETER M, PHIL & RELIG DEPT, MARYLHURST COL, MARYLHURST OR 97036
MCINTIRE, MARK DENNIS, PHIL DEPT, WESTFIELD STATE COL, WESTFIELD MA 01085
MCINTIRE, RUSSELL M, RELIG & PHIL DEPT, LAMBUTH COLLEGE, JACKSON TN 38301
MCINTIRE, STEPHEN J, PHIL DEPT, UNIV OF ROCHESTER, ROCHESTER NY 14627
MCINTYRE, JANE L, PHILOSOPHY DEPT, CLEVELAND ST UNIV, CLEVELAND OH 44115
MCINTYRE, RONALD, PHILOSOPHY DEPT, CASE WESTERN RESERVE, CLEVELAND OH 44106
MCKAY, CLIFFORD, PHIL & RELIG DEPT, DRURY COLLEGE, SPRINGFIELD MO 65802
MCKAY, JOHN T, PHIL DEPT, BARRY COLLEGE, MIAMI SHORES FL 33153
MCKAY, THOMAS, PHIL DEPT, SYRACUSE UNIVERSITY, SYRACUSE NY 13210
MCKEAN, WILLIAM B, HUM DEPT, ST JOHNS RIV JR COL, PALATKA FL 32077
MCKEE, PATRICK L, PHIL DEPT, COLORADO ST UNIV, FORT COLLINS CO 80521
MCKELLIGAN, MARCIA, PHILOSOPHY DEPT, UNIV OF MASS, AMHERST MA 01002
MCKELVEY, MIKE, PHIL DEPT, S ILLINOIS UNIV, CARBONDALE IL 62901
MCKENNA, MICHAEL, PHIL DEPT, UNIV OF MINNESOTA, MINNEAPOLIS MN 55455
MCKENNA, WILLIAM, PHIL DEPT, NW SCH FOR SOC RES, NEW YORK NY 10003
MCKENNEY, JOHN L, PHIL & RELIG, MUSKINGUM COLLEGE, NEW CONCORD OH 43762
MCKENZIE, LEO, PHIL DEPT, ST CHAS BORROMEO SEM, PHILADELPHIA PA 19151
MCKENZIE, MARIAN, PHIL DEPT, CENTRAL CONN ST COL, NEW BRITAIN CT 06050
MCKEON, RICHARD, PHIL DEPT, UNIV OF CHICAGO, CHICAGO IL 60637
MCKIE, WILLIAM, PHIL DEPT, SN BERNARDINO VALLEY, SN BERNARDINO CA 92403
MCKILLIP, THOMAS, PHIL DEPT, PRAIRIE ST COLLEGE, CHICAGO HTS IL 60411
MCKIM, VAUGHN, PHIL DEPT, UNIV OF NOTRE DAME, NOTRE DAME IN 46556
MCKINNEY, DAPHNE, PHIL DEPT, HUNTER COLLEGE, NEW YORK NY 10021
MCKINNEY, RICHARD, PHILOSOPHY DEPT, MORGAN STATE UNIV, BALTIMORE MD 21239
MCKINNON, ALASTAIR, PHILOSOPHY DEPT, MCGILL UNIVERSITY, MONTREAL QUE CAN
MCKINNON, LAWRENCE, PHIL DEPT, ST JOSEPH'S COL, PHILADELPHIA PA 19131
MCKIRAHAN, RICHARD, PHILOSOPHY DEPT, POMONA COLLEGE, CLAREMONT CA 91711
MCKNIGHT, DAVID, REL & PHIL DEPT, BLUE RIDGE COM COL, WEYERS CAVE VA 24486
MCKNIGHT, EUGENE C, PHIL DEPT, LOS ANGELES CY COL, LOS ANGELES CA 90029
MCKOWN, D B, PHILOSOPHY DEPT, AUBURN UNIVERSITY, AUBURN AL 36830
MCLAIN, F MICHAEL, PHIL DEPT, SOUTHWEST AT MEMPHIS, MEMPHIS TN 38112
MCLANE, H EARL, PHIL DEPT, COL WILLIAM & MARY, WILLIAMSBURG VA 23185
MCLAREN, ROBERT B, CAL STATE COLLEGE, FULLERTON, CA 92634
MCLAREN, RONALD, PHILOSOPHY DEPT, KENYON COLLEGE, GAMBIER OH 43022
MCLAUGHLIN, ANDREW, PHIL DEPT, LEHMAN COLLEGE, BRONX NY 10468
MCLAUGHLIN, BERNARD, PHIL DEPT, ST JOHN'S SEM COL, BRIGHTON MA 02135

MCLAUGHLIN, JOHN D, CRITICAL STUD DEPT, MASS COL OF ART, BOSTON MA   02215
MCLAUGHLIN, JOHN, ELMIRA COLLEGE, ELMIRA, NY   14901
MCLAUGHLIN, MICHAEL, PHIL DEPT, PURDUE UNIVERSITY, LAFAYETTE IN   47907
MCLAUGHLIN, ROBERT J, PHIL DEPT, ST JOHN FISHER COL, ROCHESTER NY   14618
MCLEAN, CHARLES J, PHILOSOPHY DEPT, BROWN UNIVERSITY, PROVIDENCE RI   02912
MCLEAN, GEORGE F, PHIL SCH, CATH UNIV OF AMER, WASHINGTON DC   20017
MCLEAN, M, PHILOSOPHY DEPT, UNIV OF ALBERTA, EDMONTON ALB   CAN
MCLEAN, MURDITH, LIBR EDUC DEPT, GRANDE PR REG COL, GRANDE PR ALB   CAN
MCLELLAN, JOHN M, PHILOSOHHY AREA, CUYAHOGA COM COL, CLEVELAND OH   44115
MCLELLAND, REGINALD F, BIB & PHIL, COVENANT COLLEGE, LOOKOUT MTN TN   37350
MCLENDON, HIRAM, PHIL DEPT, NEW YORK UNIVERSITY, NEW YORK NY   10003
MCLENDON, VONCEIL, SOC SCI DIV, PARKERSBURG COM COL, PARKERSBURG WV   26101
MCMAHON, ARNOLD, PHILOSOPHY DEPT, CAL STATE COL, DOMINGUEZ HLS CA   90747
MCMAHON, DEANNA, HUMAN STUD DIV, UNIV OF WISCONSIN, KENOSHA WI   53140
MCMAHON, FRANCIS, PHIL DEPT, ROOSEVELT UNIVERSITY, CHICAGO IL   60605
MCMAHON, JOSEPH, HUMAN DIV, HARRIMAN COLLEGE, HARRIMAN NY   10926
MCMAHON, M BRIAN, HUMAN STUD DIV, UNIV OF WISCONSIN, KENOSHA WI   53140
MCMAHON, ROBERTA, PHILOSOPHY DEPT, SEATTLE UNIVERSITY, SEATTLE WA   98122
MCMAHON, WILLIAM E, PHILOSOPHY DEPT, UNIV OF AKRON, AKRON OH   44325
MCMASTER, R K, PHIL & THEOL, MOUNT MERCY COLLEGE, CEDAR RAPIDS IA   52402
MCMICHAEL, JACK R, PHILOSOPHY DEPT, CONCORD COLLEGE, ATHENS WV   24712
MCMILLAN, ELIZABETH, PHILOSOPHY DEPT, CARLOW COLLEGE, PITTSBURGH PA   15213
MCMILLION, PHIL, RELIG DEPT, E NEW MEXICO UNIV, PORTALES NM   88130
MCMINN, J B, PHIL DEPT, UNIV OF ALABAMA, UNIVERSITY AL   35486
MCMORROW, GEORGE, PHIL DEPT, NAZARETH COLLEGE, NAZARETH MI   49074
MCMULLEN, GEORGE, PHILOSOPHY DEPT, MOUNT MARY COL, MILWAUKEE WI   53222
MCMULLEN, W A, PHIL DEPT, TRENT UNIVERSITY, PETERBOROUGH ONT   CAN
MCMULLIN, ERNAN, PHIL DEPT, UNIV OF NOTRE DAME, NOTRE DAME IN   46556
MCMURRY, MORELAND, ENG & HUM DEPT, MONROE COM COL, ROCHESTER NY   14623
MCMURRY, WILLIAM L, PHIL DEPT, OKLAHOMA STATE UNIV, STILLWATER OK   74074
MCMURTRY, J, PHILOSOPHY DEPT, UNIV CF GUELPH, GUELPH ONT   CAN
MCNABB, JAMES R, HUMAN DEPT, ERIE COM COLLEGE, BUFFALO NY   14221
MCNALLY, PATRICK H, PHIL DEPT, BOSTON COLLEGE, CHESTNUT HILL MA   02167
MCNAMARA, VINCENT, PHILOSOPHY DEPT, LOYOLA COLLEGE, MONTREAL QUE   CAN
MCNEAL, B L, PHIL DEPT, UNIV OF FLORIDA, GAINESVILLE FL   32611
MCNEIL, THOMAS W, PHIL & RELIG, INTERAMER UNIVERSITY, RAMEY AFB PR   00604
MCNEIL, THOMAS, PHIL DEPT, INTERAMER UNIVERSITY, RAMEY AFB PR   00604
MCPEAK, MARGARET, PHIL DEPT, DEPAUL UNIVERSITY, CHICAGO IL   60604
MCPECK, J E, EDUCATION COLLEGE, ALTHOUSE COLLEGE, LONDON ONT   CAN
MCRAE, R F, PHILOSOPHY DEPT, UNIV OF TORONTO, TORONTO ONT   CAN
MCRIAVY, J, PHILOSOPHY DEPT, ST THOMAS MORE COL, SASKATOON SAS   CAN
MCTIGHE, THOMAS P, PHIL DEPT, GEORGETOWN UNIV, WASHINGTON DC   20007
MCWHINNEY, RUSSELL, PHILOSOPHY DEPT, BEAVER COLLEGE, GLENSIDE PA   19038
MEACHAM, MARION, SOC SCI DIV, EDMONDS COM COL, LYNNWOOD WA   98036
MEAGHER, ROBERT E, HUMAN & ARTS SCH, HAMPSHIRE COLLEGE, AMHERST MA   01002
MEAGHER, WILLIAM, HUMAN DEPT, FELICIAN COLLEGE, CHICAGO IL   60659
MEANS, BLANCHARD, PHIL DEPT, TRINITY COLLEGE, HARTFORD CT   06106
MECHANIC, JANEVIVE, HIST & PHIL DEPT, FAIRLEIGH DICKINSON, MADISON NJ   07940
MEDINA, ANGEL DE L, PHIL DEPT, GEORGIA ST UNIV, ATLANTA GA   30303
MEDLOCK, GORDON, PHILOSOPHY DEPT, COLLEGE OF WOOSTER, WOOSTER OH   44691
MEE, THOMAS ALAN, PHILOSOPHY DEPT, UNIV OF TEXAS, AUSTIN TX   78712
MEEHL, PAUL, PHIL DEPT, UNIV OF MINNESOTA, MINNEAPOLIS MN   55455
MEEKO IV, JOSEPH G, PHIL DEPT, U S AIR FORCE ACAD, COLORADO SPGS CO   80840
MEERBOTE, RALF, PHIL DEPT, UNIV OF ILLINOIS, CHICAGO IL   60680
MEGILL, KENNETH A, PHIL DEPT, UNIV CF FLORIDA, GAINESVILLE FL   32611
MEHL, PAUL, REL & PHIL DEPT, HOOD COLLEGE, FREDERICK MD   21701
MEHLBERG, HENRY, PHIL DEPT, UNIV OF FLORIDA, GAINESVILLE FL   32611
MEHLBERG, HENRYK, PHIL DEPT, UNIV OF CHICAGO, CHICAGO IL   60637
MEIER, CARL, PHIL DEPT, FRANKLIN & MARSHALL, LANCASTER PA   17604
MEIERDING, LOREN, PHILOSOPHY DEPT, UNIV OF TEXAS, AUSTIN TX   78712
MEIKLEJOHN, DONALD, PHIL DEPT, SYRACUSE UNIVERSITY, SYRACUSE NY   13210
MEILACH, MICHAEL, PHIL DEPT, SIENA COLLEGE, LOUDONVILLE NY   12211
MEILAND, JACK W, PHIL DEPT, UNIV OF MICHIGAN, ANN ARBOR MI   48104
MELAKOPIDES, C J, PHILOSOPHY DEPT, QUEEN'S UNIVERSITY, KINGSTON ONT   CAN

MELCHERT, NORMAN P, PHIL DEPT, LEHIGH UNIVERSITY, BETHLEHEM PA 18015
MELDEN, A I, PHIL DEPT, UNIV OF CALIFORNIA, IRVINE CA 92664
MELLEMA, GREGORY, PHILOSOPHY DEPT, UNIV OF MASS, AMHERST MA 01002
MELLEMA, PAUL, PHIL DEPT, UNIV OF NOTRE DAME, NOTRE DAME IN 46556
MELLICAN, R EUGENE, PHIL DEPT, BOSTON STATE COL, BOSTON MA 02115
MELLINGER, MATTHEW, PHIL DEPT, HUNTER COLLEGE, NEW YORK NY 10021
MELLO, MICHAEL, PHILOSOPHY DEPT, MERCED COLLEGE, MERCED CA 95340
MELNICK, ARTHUR, PHIL DEPT, UNIV OF ILLINOIS, URBANA IL 61801
MELOKOPIDES, C J, PHIL DEPT, UNIV OF WEST ONTARIO, LONDON ONT CAN
MELSER, TERRY, PHILOSOPHY DEPT, ARIZONA STATE UNIV, TEMPE AZ 85281
MELTON, RICHARD, LIBR ARTS, MINN METRO ST COL, ST PAUL MN 55101
MELVILLE, MICHAEL J, SOC SCI DIV, GOLDEN WEST COL, HUNTINGTN BCH CA 92647
MENDELSOHN, RICHARD, PHIL DEPT, LEHMAN COLLEGE, BRONX NY 10468
MENDENHALL, MARY, PHIL DEPT, CALIFORNIA ST UNIV, SAN DIEGO CA 92115
MENDENHALL, VANCE, PHIL FACULTY, UNIV OF OTTAWA, OTTAWA ONT CAN
MENKITI, IFEANI, PHIL DPET, WELLESLEY COLLEGE, WELLESLEY MA 02181
MENMUIR, RONALD J, PHIL DEPT, MONTEREY PNSLA COL, MONTEREY CA 93940
MENY, JAMES, PHILOSOPHY DEPT, ST VINCENT COLLEGE, LATROBE PA 15650
MENZA, VICTOR G, PHILOSOPHY DEPT, DARTMOUTH COLLEGE, HANOVER NH 03755
MENZEL, PAUL, PHILOSOPHY DEPT, PACIFIC LUTH UNIV, TACOMA WA 98447
MERCER, DAVID, PHILOSOPHY DEPT, UNIV OF CALGARY, CALGARY 44 ALB CAN
MERCIER, SUZANNE, PHIL DEPT, COL DE VICTORIAVILLE, VICTORIAVILLE QUE CAN
MERCKEN, H PAUL F, PHIL DEPT, FLORIDA STATE UNIV, TALLAHASSEE FL 32306
MERCURE, GUY, COL DE HAUTERIVE, HAUTERIVE, QUE CAN
MERCURIO, FRANK X, PHILOSOPHY DEPT, XAVIER UNIVERSITY, CINCINNATI OH 45207
MERRILL, DANIEL D, PHILOSOPHY DEPT, OBERLIN COLLEGE, OBERLIN OH 44074
MERRILL, GARY, PHIL CEPT, LOYOLA UNIVERSITY, CHICAGO IL 60626
MERRILL, JANET, GEN ARTS DIV, BERKSHIRE CHRIST COL, LENOX MA 01240
MERRILL, KENNETH R, PHILOSOPHY DEPT, UNIV OF OKLAHOMA, NORMAN OK 73069
MERRIMAN, KATE, PHILOSOPHY DEPT, UNIV OF WATERLOO, WATERLOO ONT CAN
MERRITT, ROBERT K, PHILOSOPHY DEPT, SACRAMENTO CY COL, SACRAMENTO CA 95822
MESSENGER, THEODORE, PHIL DEPT, UNIV OF N DAKOTA, GRAND FORKS ND 58201
MESSER, JOHN, REL DEPT, UNIV OF GEORGIA, ATHENS GA 30602
MESSERICH, VALERIUS, PHIL DEPT, QUINCY COLLEGE, QUINCY IL 62301
MESSIER, R, PHILOSOPHY DEPT, UNIV OF RHODE ISLAND, KINGSTON RI 02881
MESTER, JOHN L, PHIL DEPT, N ILLINOIS UNIV, DEKALB IL 60115
MESTER, RICHARD, PHILOSOPHY DEPT, PENN STATE UNIV, ERIE PA 16510
METAYER, MICHEL, PHIL DEPT, COL LIONEL-GROULX, STE-THERESE QUE CAN
METIVIER, P, COL DOM PHIL & THEOL, OTTAWA, ONT CAN
METRICK, DENNIS L, PHILOSOPHY DEPT, MARIETTA COLLEGE, MARIETTA OH 45750
METZEL, NANCY L, PHIL DEPT, N ILLINOIS UNIV, DEKALB IL 60115
METZGER, KENNETH H, ENG & PHIL, SE MISSOURI ST COL, CAPE GIRARDEA MO 63701
METZGER, ROBERT S, PHIL & REL DEPT, N CAROLINA ST UNIV, RALEIGH NC 27607
MEUNIER, JEAN-GUY, PHILOSOPHY DEPT, UNIV DU QUEBEC, MONTREAL QUE CAN
MEUSSLING, HERBERT, LIBR ARTS, INDIANA INST OF TECH, FORT WAYNE IN 46803
MEYER, ALLAN, HUMAN DEPT, COCHISE COLLEGE, DOUGLAS AZ 85228
MEYER, CHARLES, PHIL DEPT, W ILLINOIS UNIV, MACOMB IL 61455
MEYER, DAVID P, THEOL DEPT, CONCORDIA TEACH COL, SEWARD NE 68434
MEYER, HERBERT H, PHIL DEPT, MERRIMACK COLLEGE, NORTH ANDOVER MA 01845
MEYER, JEFFREY, PHILOSOPHY DEPT, UNIV OF OREGON, EUGENE OR 97403
MEYER, LEROY, PHIL DEPT, UNIV OF VIRGINIA, CHARLOTTESVL VA 22903
MEYER, MARCIA E, PHIL DEPT, UNIV OF ILLINOIS, URBANA IL 61801
MEYER, MYRON, MISSOURI WESTERN COL, ST JOSEPH, MO 64507
MEYER, ROBERT, PHIL DEPT, UNIV OF PITTSBURGH, PITTSBURGH PA 15260
MEYER, THERESA A, PHIL DEPT, BOSTON COLLEGE, CHESTNUT HILL MA 02167
MEYERS, DORIS, PHIL DEPT, ILL WESLEYAN UNIV, BLOOMINGTON IL 61701
MEYERS, LEONARD L, PHILOSOPHY DEPT, OTTAWA UNIVERSITY, OTTAWA KS 66067
MEYERS, ORVIL FLOYD, PHIL DEPT, LOS ANGELES CY COL, LOS ANGELES CA 90029
MEYERS, ROBERT G, PHIL DEPT, ST UNIV OF NY, ALBANY NY 12203
MEYERSON, BARBARA, PHIL DEPT, COLUMBIA UNIVERSITY, NEW YORK NY 10027
MEYN, HENNING L, PHIL DEPT, ST UNIV OF NY, ALBANY NY 12203
MICALLEF, JOHN, HUMAN DEPT, MT ANGEL COLLEGE, MT ANGEL OR 97362
MICALLEF, P J, PHILOSOPHY DEPT, NOTRE DAME UNIV, NELSON B C CAN
MICHAEL, EMILY, PHIL DEPT, BROOKLYN COLLEGE, BROOKLYN NY 11210

MICHAEL, GARY, PHIL DEPT, METROPOLITAN ST COL, DENVER CO 80202
MICHALOS, A C, PHILOSOPHY DEPT, UNIV OF GUELPH, GUELPH ONT   CAN
MICHALSKI, MELVIN E, PHIL DEPT, ST FRANCIS DE SALES, MILWUAKEE WI   53207
MICHAUD, REGIS, PHIL DEPT, COL DE LA POCATIERE, LA POCATIERE QUE   CAN
MICHELSEN, J M, PHILOSOPHY DEPT, UNIV OF VICTORIA, VICTORIA B C   CAN
MICKUNAS, ALGIS, PHILOSOPHY DEPT, OHIO UNIVERSITY, ATHENS OH 45701
MIELKE, ROBERT H, PHIL DEPT, E TENNESSEE ST UNIV, JOHNSON CITY TN 37601
MIENERT, R W, ALMA WHITE COLLEGE, ZAREPHATH, NJ 08890
MIETZELFELD, RICHARD A, PHIL DEPT, HOLY APOSTLES COL, CROMWELL CT 06416
MIGAUD, RONALD, ENG & PHIL DEPT, COMPTON COLLEGE, COMPTON CA 90221
MIGLIORE, DANIEL L, THEOL DEPT, PRINCETON THEOL SEM, PRINCETON NJ 08540
MIGLORIE JR, FRANK S, COL OF ST JOSEPH, RUTLAND, VT 05701
MIHALICH, JOSEPH C, PHIL DEPT, LA SALLE COLLEGE, PHILADELPHIA PA 19141
MIJUSKOVIC, BEN L, PHIL DEPT, S ILLINOIS UNIV, CARBONDALE IL 62901
MILAM, THOMAS R, ABRAHAM BALDWIN, AGRICULTURAL COLLEGE, TIFTON GA 31794
MILBURN, MYRA M, PHIL DEPT, UNIV OF SANTA CLARA, SANTA CLARA CA 95053
MILDRAM, ROBERT, PHIL & RELIG, UNIV OF TENNESSEE, CHATTANOOGA TN 37401
MILES, ROBERT, FORT VALLEY ST COL, FORT VALLEY, GA 31030
MILKMAN, KENNETH, PHILOSOPHY DEPT, DAWSON COLLEGE, MONTREAL QUE   CAN
MILLER III, JOHN F, PHILOSOPHY DEPT, N TEXAS STATE UNIV, DENTON TX 76203
MILLER, ALVIN, PHIL & REL DEPT, UNIV OF GEORGIA, ATHENS GA 30602
MILLER, ARTHUR, PHIL DEPT, MICHIGAN STATE UNIV, EAST LANSING MI 48823
MILLER, BRUCE K, 17 ST JAMES PARK, LOS ANGELES, CA 90007
MILLER, BRUCE L, PHIL DEPT, MICHIGAN STATE UNIV, EAST LANSING MI 48823
MILLER, C T, REL & PHIL DEPT, MORRIS HARVEY COL, CHARLESTON WV 25304
MILLER, CECIL H, PHIL DEPT, KANSAS ST UNIVERSITY, MANHATTAN KS 66506
MILLER, CLYDE LEE, PHIL DEPT, ST UNIV OF NY, STONY BROOK NY 11790
MILLER, DALE, PHIL & REL, DRAKE UNIVERSITY, DES MOINES IA 50311
MILLER, DAVID L, PHILOSOPHY DEPT, UNIV OF TEXAS, AUSTIN TX 78712
MILLER, DAVID L, PHIL DEPT, UNIV OF WISCONSIN, LA CROSSE WI 54601
MILLER, DOUGLAS, PHIL DEPT, UNIV OF BRIDGEPORT, BRIDGEPORT CT 06602
MILLER, EDDIE L, PHIL DEPT, UNIV OF COLORADO, BOULDER CO 80302
MILLER, FRANKLIN, PHIL DEPT, COLUMBIA UNIVERSITY, NEW YORK NY 10027
MILLER, FRED, PHIL DEPT, BOWLING GREEN UNIV, BOWLING GREEN OH 43403
MILLER, GEORGE, PHIL DEPT, UNIV OF CINCINNATI, CINCINNATI OH 45221
MILLER, HARLAN B, PHIL & RELIG, VA POLYTECH INST, BLACKSBURG VA 24061
MILLER, HERSCHEL, JOHNSON STATE COL, JOHNSON, VT 05656
MILLER, HUGH, PHIL DEPT, UNIV OF CALIFORNIA, LOS ANGELES CA 90024
MILLER, IZCHAK, PHIL DEPT, MASS INST TECH, CAMBRIDGE MA 02139
MILLER, J C, PHIL & REL AREA, FAYETTEVILLE ST UNIV, FAYETTEVILLE NC 28301
MILLER, J ROBERT, PHIL DEPT, EAST KENTUCKY UNIV, RICHMOND KY 40475
MILLER, JACK E, PHIL DEPT, TULANE UNIVERSITY, NEW ORLEANS LA 70118
MILLER, JEROME A, PHIL DEPT, SALISBURY STATE COL, SALISBURY MD 21801
MILLER, JOHN A, PHIL & REL DEPT, WASHINGTON COLLEGE, CHESTERLAND MD 21620
MILLER, JOHN WILLIAM, PHIL DEPT, WILLIAMS COLLEGE, WILLIAMSTOWN MA 01267
MILLER, KAREN, PHILOSOPHY DEPT, DELAWARE ST COL, DOVER DE 19901
MILLER, L G, PHILOSOPHY DEPT, UNIV OF SASKATCHEWAN, SASKATOON SAS   CAN
MILLER, LARRY W, PHIL DEPT, TULANE UNIVERSITY, NEW ORLEANS LA 70118
MILLER, LEON, PHIL DEPT, MILLERSVILLE ST COL, MILLERSVILLE PA 17551
MILLER, MARJORIE, PHIL DEPT, ST UNIV OF NY, STONY BROOK NY 11790
MILLER, MARV H, PHIL & RELIG DEPT, DAKOTA WESLEYAN UNIV, MITCHELL SD 57301
MILLER, MITCHELL, PHIL DEPT, VASSAR COLLEGE, POUGHKEEPSIE NY 12601
MILLER, MYRON, PHILOSOPHY DEPT, NYACK COLLEGE, NYACK NY 10931
MILLER, PAUL J W, PHIL DEPT, UNIV OF COLORADO, BOULDER CO 80302
MILLER, R H, ACADEMIC STUD DEPT, NC SCH OF THE ARTS, WINSTON-SALEM NC 27107
MILLER, RICHARD W, HUMAN DEPT, UNIV OF MISSOURI, ROLLA MO 65401
MILLER, RICHARD, SAGE SCHOOL, CORNELL UNIVERSITY, ITHACA NY 14850
MILLER, ROBERT G, PHIL DEPT, ST JOHN FISHER COL, ROCHESTER NY 14618
MILLER, ROBERT J, PHIL DEPT, NAZARETH COLLEGE, ROCHESTER NY 14610
MILLER, T H, RELIG & PHIL DEPT, WILEY COLLEGE, MARSHALL TX 75670
MILLER, THOMAS, PHIL DEPT, UNIVERSITY OF DAYTON, DAYTON OH 45469
MILLER, W PETER, PHILOSOPHY DEPT, UNIV OF WINNIPEG, WINNIPEG MAN   CAN
MILLER, WILLARD, PHILOSOPHY DEPT, UNIV OF VERMONT, BURLINGTON VT 05401
MILLER, WILLIAM M, PHILOSOPHY DEPT, KENT STATE UNIV, KENT OH 44242

MILLER, WILLIAM, HIST & PHIL DEPT, E MICHIGAN UNIV, YPSILANTI MI 48197
MILLEY, C ROSS, RELIG & PHIL, BETHUNE-COOKMAN COL, DAYTONA FL 32015
MILLHOLLAND, DONALD, PHILOSOPHY DEPT, GUILFORD COLLEGE, GREENSBORO NC 27410
MILLIGAN, CHARLES S, REL PHIL DEPT, ILIFF SCH OF THEOL, DENVER CO 80210
MILLS, KENNETH, PHIL DEPT, YALE UNIVERSITY, NEW HAVEN CT 06520
MILLS, STEPHEN, PHIL DEPT, UNIV OF VIRGINIA, CHARLOTTESVL VA 22903
MILLS, WATSON E, AVERETT COLLEGE, DANVILLE, VA 24541
MILMED, BELLA, FAIRLEIGH DICKINSON, TEANECK, NJ 07666
MILNE, ERIC, SOC SCI & HUMAN DIV, FANSHANE COLLEGE, LONDON ONT   CAN
MILNE, GRETCHEN, PHIL DEPT, CALIFORNIA ST UNIV, SAN FRANCISCO CA 94132
MILO, RONALD D, PHILOSOPHY DEPT, UNIV OF ARIZONA, TUCSON AZ 85721
MILTON, DONALD, PHIL DEPT, WEST MICHIGAN UNIV, KALAMAZOO MI 49001
MINAHAN, JOHN P, PHIL DEPT, COL AT BUFFALO, BUFFALO NY 14222
MINAS, ANNE C, PHILOSOPHY DEPT, UNIV OF WATERLOO, WATERLOO ONT   CAN
MINAS, J SAYER, PHILOSOPHY DEPT, UNIV OF WATERLOO, WATERLOO ONT   CAN
MINCH, LARRY, PHIL DEPT, BOSTON UNIVERSITY, BOSTON MA 02215
MINHINNICK, J, PHIL FACULTY, UNIV OF OTTAWA, OTTAWA ONT   CAN
MINICHINO, CAMILLE, PHIL DEPT, EMMANUEL COLLEGE, BOSTON MA 02115
MININNI, FRANK J, PHILOSOPHY DEPT, MARSHALL UNIV, HUNTINGTON WV 25701
MINK, LOUIS O, PHILOSOPHY DEPT, WESLEYAN UNIV, MIDDLETOWN CT 06457
MINKIEL, STEPHEN, PHILOSOPHY DEPT, GANNON COLLEGE, ERIE PA 16501
MINKUS, PETER A, PHILOSOPHY DEPT, YORK UNIVERSITY, DOWNSVIEW ONT   CAN
MINOGGIO, FERRANDO, PHIL DEPT, BORROMEO SEM OF OHIO, WICKLIFFE OH 44092
MINOR, GENE, COMMUNIC & HUM, COLORADO MT COL, GLENWOOD SPGS CO 81601
MINOR, WILLIAM S, 303 S TOWER ROAD, CARBONDALE, IL 62901
MINTON, ARTHUR, PHIL DEPT, UNIV OF MISSOURI, KANSAS CITY MO 64110
MINTON, VIRGINIA, REL & PHIL, DONNELLY COLLEGE, KANSAS CITY KS 66102
MINTZ, MAX, EDUC & PSYCH DEPTS, LEWIS & CLARK ST COL, LEWISTON ID 83501
MIRACCHI, SYLVANO, PHIL DEPT, BALL ST UNIVERSITY, MUNCIE IN 47306
MIRARCHI, LAWRENCE, PHIL DEPT, UNIV OF ROCHESTER, ROCHESTER NY 14627
MIRITELLO, FRANK, PHIL DEPT, DEPAUL UNIVERSITY, CHICAGO IL 60604
MIRVISH, ADRIAN, PHIL DEPT, UNIV OF CINCINNATI, CINCINNATI OH 45221
MISCH, EDWARD J, SOC STUD DEPT, SIMON'S ROCK, GR BARRINGTON MA 01230
MISCHEL, THEODORE, PHIL DEPT, ST UNIV OF NY, BINGHAMTON NY 13901
MISGELD, D, PHILOSOPHY DEPT, LAURENTIAN UNIV, SUDBURY ONT   CAN
MISH'ALANI, JAMES, PHILOSOPHY DEPT, UNIV OF WASHINGTON, SEATTLE WA 98195
MISSIRAS, ANDREW, BEHAVIOR SCI DEPT, ATLANTIC COM COL, MAYS LNDG NJ 08330
MISSNER, MARSHALL, PHILOSOPHY DEPT, UNIV OF WISONSIN, OSH KOSH WI 54901
MISTRO, ANGEL, HUMANITIES DEPT, ROBERT MORRIS COL, CORAOPOLIS PA 15108
MITCHELL, DONALD W, PHIL DEPT, PURDUE UNIVERSITY, LAFAYETTE IN 47907
MITCHELL, R LLOYD, PHILOSOPHY DEPT, WASH & JEFF COL, WASHINGTON PA 15301
MITCHELL, THOMAS, PHIL DEPT, TROCAIRE COLLEGE, BUFFALO NY 14220
MITIAS, MICHAEL H, PHIL DEPT, MILLSAPS COLLEGE, JACKSON MS 39210
MITTLER, BERT I, PHIL DEPT, EMORY UNIVERSITY, ATLANTA GA 30322
MIX, L, PHILOSOPHY DEPT, UNIV OF ALBERTA, EDMONTON ALB   CAN
MIXSON JR, WILLIAM C, PHIL DEPT, WASHINGTON UNIV, ST LOUIS MO 63130
MIZE, JOHN, SOC SCI DEPT, LONG BEACH CY COL, LONG BEACH CA 90808
MIZICKO, MELORY, PHIL DEPT, DEPAUL UNIVERSITY, CHICAGO IL 60604
MIZZI, CHARLES E, HUMAN DIV, DOWLING COLLEGE, LONG ISLAND NY 11769
MOATS, GAIL, PHIL DEPT, UNIV OF NEBRASKA, LINCOLN NE 68502
MOBERG, DALE, PHIL DEPT, NORTHWESTERN UNIV, EVANSTON IL 60201
MOCKBEE, JIM MICHAEL, PHILOSOPHY DEPT, ARIZONA STATE UNIV, TEMPE AZ 85281
MODERBACHER, J, PHILOSOPHY DEPT, COL OF NOTRE DAME, BELMONT CA 94002
MOELLER, NORMAN, PHIL DEPT, UNIV OF DETROIT, DETROIT MI 48221
MOELLERING, H ARMIN, RELIG & PHIL DEPT, LUTHER COLLEGE, TEANECK NJ 07666
MOES, MARK MATTHEW, PHILOSOPHY DEPT, UNIV OF TEXAS, AUSTIN TX 78712
MOHAN, P KRISHNA, PHIL DEPT, S CONNECTICUT ST COL, NEW HAVEN CT 06515
MOHAN, ROBERT P, PHIL SCH, CATH UNIV OF AMER, WASHINGTON DC 20017
MOHAN, WILLIAM, PHILOSOPHY DEPT, MARYWOOD COLLEGE, SCRANTON PA 18509
MOHANTY, JITENDRA N, PHILOSOPHY DEPT, UNIV OF OKLAHOMA, NORMAN OK 73069
MOHL, OSCAR, HUMAN DEPT, NEW YORK CY COM COL, BROOKLYN NY 11201
MOHR, R, PHILOSOPHY DEPT, UNIV OF TORONTO, TORONTO ONT   CAN
MOHR, SIMON, RELIG STUD, MARIA REGINA COL, SYRACUSE NY 13208
MOISAN, JAMES V, SOC SCI DEPT, UMPQUA COM COLLEGE, ROSEBURG OR 97470

MOJICA, AGUEDO, PHIL DEPT, UNIV OF PUERTO RICO, RIO PIEDRAS PR 00931
MOLDRUP, WILLIAM, PHILOSOPHY DEPT, MERCED COLLEGE, MERCED CA 95340
MOLENKAMP, HAROLD, SOC SCI DEPT, LANE COM COLLEGE, EUGENE OR 97405
MOLINA, FERNANO, PHIL DEPT, SYRACUSE UNIVERSITY, SYRACUSE NY 13210
MOLINE, JON N, PHILOSOPHY DEPT, UNIV OF WISCONSIN, MADISON WI 53706
MOLLOY, FRANCIS P, PHIL DEPT, BOSTON COLLEGE, CHESTNUT HILL MA 02167
MOMEYER, RICHARD, PHILOSOPHY DEPT, MIAMI UNIVERSITY, OXFORD OH 45056
MONAHAN, ARTHUR P, PHIL DEPT, ST MARY'S UNIVERSITY, HALIFAX N S CAN
MONAHAN, E J, PHILOSOPHY DEPT, LAURENTIAN UNIV, SUDBURY ONT CAN
MONARCH, IRA A, PHIL & REL DEPT, FLORIDA INTNL UNIV, MIAMI FL 33144
MONASTERIO, XAVIER O, PHIL DEPT, UNIVERSITY OF DAYTON, DAYTON OH 45469
MONCADORI, FABRIZIO, PHILOSOPHY DEPT, UNIV OF PENN, PHILADELPHIA PA 19174
MONCINI, RAYMOND, PHILOSOPHY DEPT, COL OF HOLY NAMES, OAKLAND CA 94619
MONETA, GIUSEPPINA, PHILOSOPHY DEPT, UNIV OF VERMONT, BURLINGTON VT 05401
MONETTE, LISE, PHILOSOPHY DEPT, UNIV DU QUEBEC, MONTREAL QUE CAN
MONGEAU, YVES, COLLEGE D'AHUNTSIC, MONTREAL, QUE CAN
MONICAL, DAVID, PHIL DEPT, UNIV OF MINNESOTA, MINNEAPOLIS MN 55455
MONK, ROBERT, PHIL DEPT, UNIV OF ILLINOIS, URBANA IL 61801
MONNIN, LLOYD N, GEN EDUC DEPT, CLARK TECH COL, SPRINGFIELD OH 45501
MONROE, CRAIG J, PHIL DEPT, ST UNIV OF NY, BINGHAMTON NY 13901
MONROE, LEE J, PHIL DEPT, BORROMEO SEM OF OHIO, WICKLIFFE OH 44092
MONROE, WARNER, RELIG DEPT, WARNER PACIFIC COL, PORTLAND OR 97215
MONSON, CHARLES H, PHILOSOPHY DEPT, UNIV OF UTAH, SALT LAKE CTY UT 84112
MONTAGUE, K, PHILOSOPHY DEPT, UNIV OF GUELPH, GUELPH ONT CAN
MONTAGUE, PHILLIP, PHIL DEPT, W WASHINGTON ST COL, BELLINGHAM WA 98225
MONTALVO, JOSEFINA, HUMAN DEPT, COL OF SACRED HEART, SANTURCE PR 00914
MONTANARI, GIOVANNI, PHILOSOPHY DEPT, GANNON COLLEGE, ERIE PA 16501
MONTECINO, HENRY, PHIL DEPT, LOYOLA UNIVERSITY, NEW ORLEANS LA 70118
MONTEFIORE, ALAN, PHILOSOPHY DEPT, MCGILL UNIVERSITY, MONTREAL QUE CAN
MONTGOMERY, JEFFREY, PHIL DEPT, S ILLINOIS UNIV, CARBONDALE IL 62901
MONTGOMERY, MARTHA B, LIT & LANG DEPT, DREXEL UNIV, PHILADELPHIA PA 19104
MONTGOMERY, SHARON, PHIL DEPT, INDIANA UNIV OF PENN, INDIANA PA 15701
MOODY, ERNEST A, PHIL DEPT, UNIV OF CALIFORNIA, LOS ANGELES CA 90024
MOODY, F KENNEN, BEHAV & SOC SCI, BENNETT COLLEGE, MILLBROOK NY 12545
MOODY, THOMAS, PHIL DEPT, UNIV OF MINNESOTA, MINNEAPOLIS MN 55455
MOON, JESSE K, CHRIST MINISTRY, SW ASSEM GOD COL, WAXANACHIE TX 75165
MOONEY, CHRISTOPHER, PHIL DEPT, NASSAU COM COL, GARDEN CITY NY 11530
MOONEY, DONALD, PHIL DEPT, SIENA COLLEGE, LOUDONVILLE NY 12211
MOONEY, EDWARD, PHIL DEPT, CAL ST COL AT SONOMA, ROHNERT PARK CA 94928
MOOR, DONALD R, PHIL DEPT, PORTLAND ST UNIV, PORTLAND OR 97207
MOOR, JAMES H, PHILOSOPHY DEPT, DARTMOUTH COLLEGE, HANOVER NH 03755
MOORE JR, ERNEST E, PHIL DEPT, MORRIS BROWN COLLEGE, ATLANTA GA 30314
MOORE, ANNE R, FAYETTEVILLE TECH, FAYETTEVILLE, NC 28303
MOORE, ASHER, PHILOSOPHY DEPT, UNIV OF NW HAMPSHIRE, DURHAM NH 03824
MOORE, BROOKE N, PHILOSOPHY DEPT, CALIFORNIA ST UNIV, CHICO CA 95926
MOORE, CURTIS, FINE ARTS DEPT, YUBA COLLEGE, MARYSVILLE CA 95901
MOORE, DARELL, REL & PHIL DIV, SPRING ARBOR COL, SPRING ARBOR MI 49283
MOORE, DOROTHY, SOC SCI DEPT, DAYTONA BCH COM COL, DAYTONA BEACH FL 32015
MOORE, EDWARD C, PHIL DEPT, INDIANA-PURDUE UNIV, INDIANAPOLIS IN 46202
MOORE, G, PHIL DEPT, W CONNECTICUT ST COL, DANBURY CT 06810
MOORE, J T, REL & PHIL DEPT, PHILLIPS UNIVERSITY, ENID OK 73701
MOORE, J W, PHIL & RELIG DEPT, NC WESLEYAN COLLEGE, ROCKY MOUNT NC 27801
MOORE, JOHN BRUCE, PHIL DEPT, NORTHWESTERN UNIV, EVANSTON IL 60201
MOORE, JOHN, HUMAN DEPT, OREGON COL OF EDUC, MONMOUTH OR 97361
MOORE, JOHN, PHIL DEPT, SWARTHMORE COLLEGE, SWARTHMORE PA 19081
MOORE, MARK A, PHIL DEPT, SALISBURY STATE COL, SALISBURY MD 21801
MOORE, MERRITT H, PHIL DEPT, UNIV OF TENNESSEE, KNOXVILLE TN 37916
MOORE, ROBERT E, PHIL DEPT, BOSTON STATE COL, BOSTON MA 02115
MOORE, RONALD M, PHIL DEPT, UNIVERSITY OF HAWAII, HONOLULU HI 96822
MOORE, STANLEY R, PHIL DEPT, UNIV OF WISCONSIN, PLATTEVILLE WI 53818
MOORE, STANLEY, PHIL DEPT, U OF CAL -SAN DIEGO, LA JOLLA CA 92037
MOORE, TERRY, PHIL DEPT, UNIV OF N CAROLINA, CHAPEL HILL NC 27514
MOORE, WILLIS, PHIL DEPT, S ILLINOIS UNIV, CARBONDALE IL 62901
MOOREFIELD, DAVID R, RELIG & PHIL DEPT, PRESBYTERIAN COL, CLINTON SC 29325

PHILOSOPHERS

MOORHEAD, HUGH, NE ILLINOIS ST UNIV, CHICAGO, IL 60625
MOORMAN, JOSEPH G, PHILOSOPHY DEPT, XAVIER UNIVERSITY, CINCINNATI OH 45207
MOORMAN, LAWRENCE A, FINE ARTS DEPT, YUBA COLLEGE, MARYSVILLE CA 95901
MORA, ANTONIA, HUMAN DEPT, COL OF SACRED HEART, SANTURCE PR 00914
MORALES, GOLDIEB, PSYCH DEPT, EAST LOS ANGELES COL, LOS ANGELES CA 90022
MORALES, W, PHILOSOPHY DEPT, CENTRE DES MAITRES, CAP-ROUGE QUE CAN
MORAN, JAMES, ROSARY HILL COLLEGE, BUFFALO, NY 14226
MORAN, JAN, POLIT SCI & PHIL, SW MISSOURI ST U, SPRINGFIELD MO 65802
MORAN, JOHN H, PHIL DEPT, MANHATTAN COLLEGE, RIVERDALE NY 10471
MORAN, JUDITH, PHIL & THEOL DEPT, MARILLAC COLLEGE, ST LOUIS MO 63121
MORAN, LAWRENCE, PHIL FACULTY, UNIV OF OTTAWA, OTTAWA ONT CAN
MORAN, VINCENT, PHIL DEPT, UNIV OF SN FRANCISCO, SAN FRANCISCO CA 94117
MORAVCSIK, J M, PHIL DEPT, STANFORD UNIVERSITY, STANFORD CA 94305
MORAWETZ, THOMAS, PHIL DEPT, YALE UNIVERSITY, NEW HAVEN CT 06520
MORAZAIN, ANDRE, PHILOSOPHY DEPT, UNIV OF WATERLOO, WATERLOO ONT CAN
MORDEN, MICHAEL, PHILOSOPHY DEPT, BELOIT COLLEGE, BELOIT WI 53511
MOREL, DENISE, PHILOSOPHY DEPT, MCGILL UNIVERSITY, MONTREAL QUE CAN
MOREL, RAYMOND, PHIL DEPT, COL FRANCOIS-X-GARN, QUEBEC CITY QUE CAN
MORELAND, JOHN M, PHIL DEPT, AUGUSTANA COLLEGE, ROCK ISLAND IL 61201
MORELLI, E, PHILOSOPHY DEPT, UNIV OF TORONTO, TORONTO ONT CAN
MORELLI, FRANK H, PHIL DEPT, UNIV OF N COLORADO, GREELEY CO 80631
MORELLI, M, PHILOSOPHY DEPT, UNIV OF TORONTO, TORONTO ONT CAN
MORELLI, MARIO, PHIL DEPT, W ILLINOIS UNIV, MACOMB IL 61455
MORENO-ELOSEQUI, A, ST ALBERT'S COLLEGE, OAKLAND, CA 94618
MOREWEDGE, PARVIS, PHIL DEPT, BERNARD BARUCH COL, NEW YORK NY 10010
MORGAN, C G, PHILOSOPHY DEPT, UNIV OF ALBERTA, EDMONTON ALB CAN
MORGAN, C SHANNON, REL & PHIL DEPT, PIEDMONT COLLEGE, DEMOREST GA 30535
MORGAN, DAVID, PHIL & RELIG, UNIV OF NORTH IOWA, CEDAR FALLS IA 50613
MORGAN, G M, PHIL DEPT, ROYAL RDS MIL COL, VICTORIA B C CAN
MORGAN, JAMES S, PHILOSOPHY DEPT, PENN STATE UNIV, DUBOIS PA 15801
MORGAN, JOHN, PHIL DEPT, QUINNIPIAC COLLEGE, HAMDEN CT 06518
MORGAN, JOHN, PHILOSOPHY DEPT, LOYOLA COLLEGE, MONTREAL QUE CAN
MORGAN, KATHRYN, PHIL DEPT, BOSTON UNIVERSITY, BOSTON MA 02215
MORGAN, KENNETH, PHIL & RELIG DEPT, COLGATE UNIVERSITY, HAMILTON NY 13346
MORGAN, METALEEN, HUM & SOC SCI DEPT, CALDWELL COM COL, LENOIR NC 28645
MORGAN, MILES, PHIL DEPT, MASS INST TECH, CAMBRIDGE MA 02139
MORGAN, RAYMOND E, PHILOSOPHY DEPT, LYNCHBURG COL, LYNCHBURG VA 24504
MORGAREIDGE, CLAYTON, PHIL DEPT, LEWIS & CLARK COL, PORTLAND OR 97219
MORGENBESSER, SIDNEY, PHIL DEPT, COLUMBIA UNIVERSITY, NEW YORK NY 10027
MORIARTY, FRANCIS J, PHILOSOPHY DEPT, REGIS COLLEGE, DENVER CO 80221
MORICK, HAROLD, PHIL DEPT, ST UNIV CF NY, ALBANY NY 12203
MORILLO, CAROLYN R, LOUISIANA ST UNIV, NEW ORLEANS, LA 70122
MORIN, DENIS, PHILOSOPHY DEPT, MCGILL UNIVERSITY, MONTREAL QUE CAN
MORIN, MICHEL, COL EDOUARD-MONTPETIT, LONGUEUIL, QUE CAN
MORIN, SERGE, PHILOSOPHY DEPT, UNIV DE MONCTON, MONCTON N B CAN
MORIN, Y, PHILOSOPHY DEPT, COL DE MAISONNEUVE, MONTREAL QUE CAN
MORIONES, FRANCIS, REL & PHIL, DONNELLY COLLEGE, KANSAS CITY KS 66102
MORITZ, K, PHILOSOPHY DEPT, UNIV OF TORONTO, TORONTO ONT CAN
MORKOVSKY, MARY, PHIL DEPT, OUR LADY OF LAKE COL, SAN ANTONIO TX 78285
MORNEAU, ROBERT, PHIL & REL STUD DEPT, SILVER LAKE COL, MANITOWOC WI 54220
MORREALL, J, PHILOSOPHY DEPT, UNIV CF TORONTO, TORONTO ONT CAN
MORRILL, RICHARD L, PHIL & RELIG, CHATHAM COLLEGE, PITTSBURGH PA 15232
MORRIS, BERTRAM, PHIL DEPT, UNIV OF COLORADO, BOULDER CO 80302
MORRIS, CHARLES W, PHIL DEPT, UNIV CF FLORIDA, GAINESVILLE FL 32611
MORRIS, DANIEL J, PHIL DEPT, UNIV OF ILLINOIS, CHICAGO IL 60680
MORRIS, DONALD, COMMUNIC & HUM DEPT, JOHN A LOGAN COL, CARTERVILLE IL 62918
MORRIS, HERBERT, PHIL DEPT, UNIV OF CALIFORNIA, LOS ANGELES CA 90024
MORRIS, JOHN S, PHIL & RELIG DEPT, COLGATE UNIVERSITY, HAMILTON NY 13346
MORRIS, PHYLLIS S, HUMAN DIV, KIRKLAND COLLEGE, CLINTON NY 13323
MORRIS, RICHARD, LOYOLA UNIVERSITY, LOS ANGELES, CA 90045
MORRIS, WILLIAM E, PHIL DEPT, UNIV OF CINCINNATI, CINCINNATI OH 45221
MORRIS, WILLIAM S, PHIL DEPT, LAKEHEAD UNIVERSITY, THUNDER BAY ONT CAN
MORRISEY, BRIAN, PHIL FACULTY, UNIV OF OTTAWA, OTTAWA ONT CAN
MORRISON II, ROY D, PHIL OF RELIG, WESLEY THEOL SEM, WASHINGTON DC 20016

MORRISON, J C, PHILOSOPHY DEPT, UNIV OF TORONTO, TORONTO ONT   CAN
MORRISON, LINDA, PHIL DEPT, ST UNIV OF NY, STONY BROOK NY   11790
MORRISON, MARY JANE, PHIL DEPT, UNIV OF ILLINOIS, URBANA IL   61801
MORRISON, PAUL W, SOC SCI DIV, MINOT STATE COL, MINOT ND   58701
MORRISON, PAUL, PHIL DEPT, COLLEGE AT BROCKPORT, BROCKPORT NY   14420
MORRISTON, WESLEY, PHIL DEPT, UNIV OF COLORADO, BOULDER CO   80302
MORRITT, RONALD, PHIL DEPT, BROOKLYN COLLEGE, BROOKLYN NY   11210
MORROW, FRANK, PHIL DEPT, W WASHINGTON ST COL, BELLINGHAM WA   98225
MORROW, HUBERT W, RELIG & PHIL DIV, BETHEL COLLEGE, MCKENZIE TN   38201
MORROW, RICHARD, PHIL DEPT, UNIV OF CALIFORNIA, LOS ANGELES CA   90024
MORRY, MATTHEW F, PHIL DEPT, PROVIDENCE COLLEGE, PROVIDENCE RI   02919
MORSE, MARK, SOC SCI DEPT, KIRKWOOD COM COL, CEDAR RAPIDS IA   52406
MORSE, WARNER, PHIL DEPT, UNIVERSITY OF KANSAS, LAWRENCE KS   66044
MORSINK, JOHANNES, PHILOSOPHY DEPT, DREW UNIVERSITY, MADISON NJ   07940
MORTIMER, ROBERT, PHIL DEPT, UNIV OF S FLORIDA, TAMPA FL   33620
MORTIMER, RODERICK, PHIL DEPT, UNIVERSITY OF TOLEDO, TOLEDO OH   43606
MORTON, BRUCE N, PHIL DEPT, WAYNE STATE UNIV, DETROIT MI   48202
MORTON, CHARLES E, PHIL DEPT, OAKLAND UNIVERSITY, ROCHESTER MI   48063
MORTON, EDMUND, PHILOSOPHY DEPT, SEATTLE UNIVERSITY, SEATTLE WA   98122
MORTON, JOHN ADAM, PHIL DEPT, PRINCETON UNIVERSITY, PRINCETON NJ   08540
MORTON, JOSEPH, PHIL DEPT, GOUCHER COLLEGE, TOWNSON MD   21204
MOSCA, AMEDIO, PHIL DEPT, FORDHAM UNIVERSITY, BRONX NY   10458
MOSEDALE, FRED, PHILOSOPHY DEPT, MILLIKIN UNIVERSITY, DECATUR IL   62522
MOSELEY, MATILDA H, GEN EDUC DEPT, PALMER COLLEGE, CHARLESTON SC   29401
MOSER, SHIA, PHIL DEPT, ST UNIV OF NY, AMHERST NY   14226
MOSHER, D L, PHILOSOPHY DEPT, UNIV OF TORONTO, TORONTO ONT   CAN
MOSKOP, JOHN CHARLES, PHILOSOPHY DEPT, UNIV OF TEXAS, AUSTIN TX   78712
MOSLEY, ALBERT, HIST & PHIL DEPT, FEDERAL CY COL, WASHINGTON DC   20001
MOSLEY, ELIS G, RELIG & PHIL DEPT, ARKANSAS COLLEGE, BATESVILLE AR   72501
MOSLEY, J L, PHILOSOPHY DEPT, RICE UNIVERSITY, HOUSTON TX   77001
MOSS, HENRY, HUMANITIES DIV, ROSEMONT COLLEGE, ROSEMONT PA   19010
MOSS, J E, PHILOSOPHY DEPT, ST AUGUSTINE'S SEM, SCARBOROUGH ONT   CAN
MOTHERSHEAD, JOHN, PHIL DEPT, STANFORD UNIVERSITY, STANFORD CA   94305
MOULDS, GEORGE H, PHILOSOPHY DEPT, KENT STATE UNIV, KENT OH   44242
MOULTON, EBEN, PHILOSOPHY DEPT, VANDERBILT UNIV, NASHVILLE TN   37235
MOULTON, JANICE, PHIL DEPT, TEMPLE UNIVERSITY, PHILADELPHIA PA   19122
MOULTON, JOHN R, PHILOSOPHY DEPT, UNIV OF WISCONSIN, MADISON WI   53706
MOULTON, PHILLIPS P, PHIL & REL DEPT, ADRIAN COLLEGE, ADRIAN MI   49221
MOUNCE, ROBERT H, PHIL & RELIG, WEST KENTUCKY UNIV, BOWLING GREEN KY   42101
MOUNTCASTLE JR, W W, PHIL & REL STUD, UNIV OF W FLORIDA, PENSACOLA FL   32504
MOURANT, JOHN A, PHILOSOPHY DEPT, PENN STATE UNIV, UNIV PARK PA   16802
MOURELATOS, ALEXANDER, PHILOSOPHY DEPT, UNIV OF TEXAS, AUSTIN TX   78712
MOUTAFAKIS, N J, PHILOSOPHY DEPT, CLEVELAND ST UNIV, CLEVELAND OH   44115
MOUTON, DAVID, PHIL DEPT, ROOSEVELT UNIVERSITY, CHICAGO IL   60605
MOUW, RICHARD, PHIL DEPT, CALVIN COLLEGE, GRAND RAPIDS MI   49506
MOW, JOSEPH B, PHILOSOPHY DEPT, W VA WESLEYAN COL, BUCKHANNON WV   26201
MOWAT, H, PHILOSOPHY DEPT, SHERIDAN COLLEGE, OAKVILLE ONT   CAN
MOWRY, DAVID, PHIL DEPT, COL AT PLATTSBURGH, PLATTSBURGH NY   12901
MUCKLOW, NEALE H, PHILOSOPHY DEPT, UNIV OF RICHMOND, RICHMOND VA   23173
MUEHLMANN, ROBERT G, PHIL DEPT, UNIV OF WEST ONTARIO, LONDON ONT   CAN
MUELLER, DONALD, PHIL DEPT, BARTLESVILLE WES COL, BARTLESVILLE OK   74003
MUELLER, GUSTAV E, PHILOSOPHY DEPT, UNIV OF OKLAHOMA, NORMAN OK   73069
MUELLER, IAN, PHIL DEPT, UNIV OF CHICAGO, CHICAGO IL   60637
MUELLER, JOSEPH P, PHIL DEPT, ST LOUIS UNIVERSITY, ST LOUIS MO   63103
MUELLER, ROBERT, PHIL DEPT, BALL ST UNIVERSITY, MUNCIE IN   47306
MUGERAUER, ROBERT, PHIL DEPT, GRAND VALLEY ST COL, ALLENDALE MI   49401
MUGGE, GEORGE A, HIST & GOV DEPT, MITCHELL COLLEGE, NEW LONDON CT   06320
MUHRER, VERLE, SOC SCI DEPT, PENN VLY COM COL, KANSAS CITY MO   64111
MUIR, DAVID G, SOC SCI DEPT, ONONDAGA COM COL, SYRACUSE NY   13215
MULHERN, JOHN, BRYN MAWR COLLEGE, BRYN MAWR, PA   19010
MULHOLLAND, L A, PHILOSOPHY DEPT, MEMORIAL UNIV, ST JOHN'S N F   CAN
MULHOLLAND, ROYAL, PHIL & REL, GREENVILLE COLLEGE, GREENVILLE IL   62246
MULLALLY, JOSEPH P, PHILOSOPHY DEPT, QUEENS COLLEGE, FLUSHING NY   11367
MULLANE, HARVEY P, PHIL DEPT, UNIV OF CINCINNATI, CINCINNATI OH   45221

MULLEN, JOHN D, HUMAN DIV, DOWLING COLLEGE, LONG ISLAND NY 11769
MULLEN, LAWRENCE, RELIG & PHIL DEPT, HOUGHTON COLLEGE, HOUGHTON NY 14744
MULLEN, MICHAEL J, PHILOSOPHY DEPT, UNIV OF THE SOUTH, SEWANEE TN 37375
MULLEN, PHILIP, PHIL DEPT, LA SALLE COLLEGE, PHILADELPHIA PA 19141
MULLEN, WILBUR H, PHIL DEPT, EAST NAZARENE COL, WOLLASTON MA 02170
MULLETT, SHEILA, PHIL DEPT, GEORGE WILLIAMS UNIV, MONTREAL 107 QUE   CAN
MULLIGAN, ROBERT W, PHILOSOPHY DEPT, XAVIER UNIVERSITY, CINCINNATI OH 45207
MULLIGAN, THOMAS, PHIL DEPT, NORTHWESTERN UNIV, EVANSTON IL 60201
MULLIN, JAMES T, HUMAN & PHIL DEPT, GROSSMONT COL, EL CAJON CA 92020
MULLIN, RICHARD, HUMAN DEPT, CULLMAN COLLEGE, CULLMAN AL 35055
MULLINS, ROBERT, PHIL DEPT, UNIV OF N DAKOTA, GRAND FORKS ND 58201
MULLINS, WARREN J, PHIL DEPT, UNIV BRIT COLUMBIA, VANCOUVER 8 B C   CAN
MULVANEY, ROBERT J, PHILOSOPHY DEPT, UNIV OF S CAROLINA, COLUMBIA SC 29208
MUNDAY, DANIEL P, PHIL DEPT, NIAGARA UNIVERSITY, NIAGARA UNIV NY 14109
MUNDSTOCK, L, PHILOSOPHY DEPT, LOS ANGELES HBR COL, WILMINGTON CA 90744
MUNITZ, LENORE B, HIST & PHIL DEPT, BRIARCLIFF COL, BRIARCLF MNR NY 10510
MUNITZ, MILTON, PHIL DEPT, BERNARD BARUCH COL, NEW YORK NY 10010
MUNK, ARTHUR, PHIL DEPT, ALBION COLLEGE, ALBION MI 49224
MUNRO, BRAD, PHILOSOPHY DEPT, UNIV OF WATERLOO, WATERLOO ONT   CAN
MUNRO, DONALD J, PHIL DEPT, UNIV OF MICHIGAN, ANN ARBOR MI 48104
MUNRO, JAMES, PHILOSOPHY DEPT, EDINBORO ST COL, EDINBORO PA 16412
MUNSAT, STANLEY, PHIL DEPT, UNIV OF N CAROLINA, CHAPEL HILL NC 27514
MUNSON, J RONALD, PHIL DEPT, UNIV OF MISSOURI, ST LOUIS MO 63121
MUNSON, THOMAS, PHIL DEPT, DEPAUL UNIVERSITY, CHICAGO IL 60604
MUNSTER, RALF F, PHIL DEPT, GEORGIA ST UNIV, ATLANTA GA 30303
MURAWSKI, E, PHIL DEPT, LA SALLE COLLEGE, PHILADELPHIA PA 19141
MURCHISON, ANNA, GEN EDUC DEPT, PALMER COLLEGE, CHARLESTON SC 29401
MURCHLAND, BERNARD, PHIL DEPT, OHIO WESLEYAN UNIV, DELAWARE OH 43105
MURIN, CHARLES, PHILOSOPHY DEPT, UNIV DE MONTREAL, MONTREAL QUE   CAN
MURNION, WILLIAM, AMER STUD SCHOOL, RAMAPO COLLEGE, MAHWAH NJ 07430
MURPH, DWIGHT, PHILOSOPHY DEPT, RUTGERS UNIV, NEW BRUNSWICK NJ 08903
MURPHREE, IDUS L, PHILOSOPHY DEPT, OHIO UNIVERSITY, ATHENS OH 45701
MURPHREE, WALLACE, MISSISSIPPI ST UNIV, ST COLLEGE, MS 39762
MURPHY, CLIFFORD H, PHIL DEPT, ROCKY MTN COLLEGE, BILLINGS MT 59102
MURPHY, EDWARD, LOYOLA CY COLLEGE, NEW ORLEANS, LA 70118
MURPHY, FRANK J, PHILOSOPHY DEPT, EAST CAROLINA UNIV, GREENVILLE NC 27834
MURPHY, JACK, DIABLO VALLEY COL, PLEASANT HILL, CA 94523
MURPHY, JAMES, ENG & GEN STUD, SPRING GARDEN COL, CHESTNUT HILL PA 19118
MURPHY, JEFFRIE G, PHILOSOPHY DEPT, UNIV OF ARIZONA, TUCSON AZ 85721
MURPHY, JOHN F, PHIL DEPT, BORROMEO SEM OF OHIO, WICKLIFFE OH 44092
MURPHY, JOHN P, PHILOSOPHY DEPT, UNIV OF TEXAS, AUSTIN TX 78712
MURPHY, RICHARD T, PHIL DEPT, BOSTON COLLEGE, CHESTNUT HILL MA 02167
MURPHY, ROBERT M, PHIL & REL DEPT, FRANKLIN COL, FRANKLIN IN 46131
MURPHY, WALTER Y, PHIL DEPT, FLORIDA SOUTHERN COL, LAKELAND FL 33802
MURRAY, CLAYTON J, PHIL DEPT, CANISIUS COLLEGE, BUFFALO NY 14208
MURRAY, J ATHOL, DEAN OF ARTS, NOTRE DAME OF CAN, WILCOX SAS   CAN
MURRAY, J PATRICK, PHIL DEPT, ST LOUIS UNIVERSITY, ST LOUIS MO 63103
MURRAY, JOHN P, GEN EDUC DEPT, CLARK TECH COL, SPRINGFIELD OH 45501
MURRAY, JOHN, PHILOSOPHY AREA, COUNTY COL OF MORRIS, RANDOLPH NJ 07801
MURRAY, MICHAEL, PHIL DEPT, VASSAR COLLEGE, POUGHKEEPSIE NY 12601
MURRAY, NOLAND P, PHILOSOPHY DEPT, ST COL OF ARKANSAS, CONWAY AR 72032
MURRAY, R, SOC SCI DEPT, RYERSON POLYTECH U, TORONTO ONT   CAN
MURRAY, THOMAS, COL OF THE SEQUOIAS, VISALIA, CA 93277
MURRAY, WARREN J, PHIL FACULTE, UNIVERSITE LAVAL, CITE UNIV QUE   CAN
MURUNGI, JOHN, PHIL & REL DEPT, TOWSON STATE COL, BALTIMORE MD 21204
MUSE, KENNETH, PHIL DEPT, CREIGHTON UNIV, OMAHA NE 68178
MUSKA, RUDOLPH, PHILOSOPHY DEPT, HEIDELBERG COLLEGE, TIFFIN OH 44883
MUSSARD, RICHARD R, HUMAN DIV, INDIANA ST UNIV, EVANSVILLE IN 47712
MUSSMAN, EMANUEL, GEN EDUC DEPT, MOHAWK VLY COM COL, UTICA NY 13501
MUYSKENS, JAMES, PHIL DEPT, HUNTER COLLEGE, NEW YORK NY 10021
MYATT, RODNEY, PHILOSOPHY DEPT, PATERSON COL OF NJ, WAYNE NJ 07470
MYER, RAWLEY, JOHN F KENNEDY COL, WAHOO, NE 68066
MYERS, C MASON, PHIL DEPT, N ILLINOIS UNIV, DEKALB IL 60115
MYERS, CHARLES R, PHIL DEPT, U S AIR FORCE ACAD, COLORADO SPGS CO 80840

MYERS, DAVID, PHIL DEPT, MOORHEAD STATE COL, MOORHEAD MN 56560
MYERS, GERALD, PHILOSOPHY DEPT, QUEENS COLLEGE, FLUSHING NY 11367
MYERS, JOHN, PHIL DEPT, COPPIN STATE COLLEGE, BALTIMORE MD 21216
MYERS, JOSEPH, PHIL DEPT, FAIRFIELD UNIVERSITY, FAIRFIELD CT 06430
MYERS, LEWIS A, PHILOSOPHY DEPT, STETSON UNIVERSITY, DELAND FL 32720
MYERS, ROBERT E, PHILOSOPHY DEPT, BETHANY COLLEGE, BETHANY WV 26032
MYERS, ROBERT, RELIG & PHIL DEPT, CLARK COLLEGE, ATLANTA GA 30314
MYERS, WILLIAM, PHILOSOPHY DEPT, VILLANOVA UNIV, VILLANOVA PA 19085
MYRBO, GUNNULF, PHILOSOPHY DEPT, PACIFIC LUTH UNIV, TACOMA WA 98447
MYRO, GEORGE, PHIL DEPT, UNIV OF CALIFORNIA, BERKELEY CA 94720
NABAKWE, W, PHIL FACULTY, UNIV OF OTTAWA, OTTAWA ONT CAN
NABBE, H, PHIL OF EDUC & HIST, ONTARIO INSTITUTE, TORONTO ONT CAN
NACHBAHR, B A, PHILOSOPHY DEPT, LOYOLA COLLEGE, BALTIMORE MD 21210
NADAL, JUAN, PHIL DEPT, CATHOLIC UNIVERSITY, PONCE PR 00731
NADEAU, JEAN, PHIL DEPT, LE SEM ST GEORGES, VL-ST-GEORGES QUE CAN
NADEAU, LOUIS V, SOC SCI DEPT, ELIZABETH CY ST UNIV, ELIZABETH CY NC 27909
NADEAU, ROBERT, PHILOSOPHY DEPT, UNIV DU QUEBEC, MONTREAL QUE CAN
NADLER, CHARLES H, PHIL DEPT, CEN WASH STATE COL, ELLENSBURG WA 98926
NADON, BENOIT, PHIL DEPT, COL DE SHERBROOKE, SHERBROOKE QUE CAN
NAGEL, ERNEST, PHIL DEPT, COLUMBIA UNIVERSITY, NEW YORK NY 10027
NAGEL, G, PHILOSOPHY DEPT, UNIV OF TORONTO, TORONTO ONT CAN
NAGEL, RICHARD I, PHIL & REL DEPT, N CAROLINA ST UNIV, RALEIGH NC 27607
NAGEL, THOMAS, PHIL DEPT, PRINCETON UNIVERSITY, PRINCETON NJ 08540
NAGEOTTE, G, PHILOSOPHY DEPT, UNIV OF TORONTO, TORONTO ONT CAN
NAGLE, LINDA, PHILOSOPHY DEPT, RUTGERS UNIV, NEW BRUNSWICK NJ 08903
NAGLE, ROBERT, HUMAN & PHIL DEPT, NE MISSOURI ST UNIV, MARYVILLE MO 64468
NAGLEE, DAVID I, RELIG & PHIL DEPT, LAGRANGE COLLEGE, LAGRANGE GA 30240
NAGLEY, WINFIELD E, PHIL DEPT, UNIVERSITY OF HAWAII, HONOLULU HI 96822
NAGY, PAUL, PHIL DEPT, INDIANA-PURDUE UNIV, INDIANAPOLIS IN 46202
NAHM, IHRU, PHIL DEPT, UNIV OF ILLINOIS, CHICAGO IL 60680
NAHM, MILTON C, BRYN MAWR COLLEGE, ERYN MAWR, PA 19010
NAHRA, JOSEPH A, PHILOSOPHY DEPT, MARYCREST COLLEGE, DAVENPORT IA 52804
NAJM, SAMI, PHILOSOPHY DEPT, MCMASTER UNIVERSITY, HAMILTON ONT CAN
NAKHNIKIAN, GEORGE, PHIL DEPT, INDIANA UNIVERSITY, BLOOMINGTON IN 47401
NAMMOUR, JAMIL, PHIL DEPT, CALIFORNIA ST UNIV, SACRAMENTO CA 95819
NARBUTAS, JONAS, PHILOSOPHY DEPT, UNIV OF SCRANTON, SCRANTON PA 18510
NARCONE, HENRY F, PHIL DEPT, KING'S COLLEGE, WILKES BARRE PA 18711
NARGAJ, ANDREW, PHIL DEPT, SAINT JOSEPH'S COL, NORTH WINDHAM ME 04062
NARUM, W H K, PHIL DEPT, SAINT OLAF COLLEGE, NORTHFIELD MN 55057
NARVESON, JAN F, PHILOSOPHY DEPT, UNIV OF WATERLOO, WATERLOO ONT CAN
NASH, LEWIS, HUMANITIES DIV, COL OF THE REDWOODS, EUREKA CA 95501
NASH, P W, CAMPION COLLEGE, REGINA, SAS CAN
NASH, R L, PHILOSOPHY DEPT, LAURENTIAN UNIV, SUDBURY ONT CAN
NASH, RONALD H, PHIL & RELIG, WEST KENTUCKY UNIV, BOWLING GREEN KY 42101
NASR, WADDAH N, PHIL DEPT, BEMIDJI STATE COL, BEMIDJI MN 56601
NATANSON, HARVEY, PHIL DEPT, STATEN IS COM COL, STATEN ISLAND NY 10301
NATANSON, MAURICE A, PHIL STUD BOARD, U OF CALIFORNIA, SANTA CRUZ CA 95060
NATHAN, DANIEL O, PHILOSOPHY DEPT, TEXAS TECH UNIV, LUBBOCK TX 79409
NATHAN, GEORGE J, PHIL DEPT, BROCK UNIVERSITY, ST CATHARINES ONT CAN
NATHANSON, STEPHEN L, PHIL & REL DEPT, NORTHEASTERN UNIV, BOSTON MA 02115
NAU, JOHN F, PHIL & RELIG DEPT, UNIV OF S MISS, HATTIESBURG MS 39401
NAUD, JULIEN, PHILOSOPHY DEPT, UNIV DU QUEBEC, 3-RIVIERES QUE CAN
NAUGHTON, E RUSSELL, PHIL DEPT, LA SALLE COLLEGE, PHILADELPHIA PA 19141
NAUGLE, M H, PHILOSOPHY DEPT, RICE UNIVERSITY, HOUSTON TX 77001
NAUMAN JR, ST ELMO, PHILOSOPHY DEPT, CHR NEWPORT COL, NEWPORT NEWS VA 23606
NAUS, JOHN E, PHILOSOPHY DEPT, MARQUETTE UNIV, MILWAUKEE WI 53233
NAVIA, LUIS E, SOC SCI DEPT, NEW YORK INST TECH, OLD WESTBURY NY 11568
NAVICKAS, JOSEPH L, PHIL DEPT, BOSTON COLLEGE, CHESTNUT HILL MA 02167
NAYLOR, ANDREW, PHIL DEPT, INDIANA UNIVERSITY, SOUTH BEND IN 46615
NAYLOR, J, PHILOSOPHY DEPT, UNIV PR EDWARD IS, CHARLOTTETOWN PEI CAN
NEALE SR, ANN, PHIL DEPT, GEORGETOWN UNIV, WASHINGTON DC 20007
NEALE, PHILIP, PHILOSOPHY DEPT, VANDERBILT UNIV, NASHVILLE TN 37235
NEARING, HOMER, HUMANITIES DEPT, WIDENER COLLEGE, CHESTER PA 19013
NEARING, KATHLEEN, PHIL DEPT, BOSTON UNIVERSITY, BOSTON MA 02215

NEBLETT, WILLIAM R, PHIL DEPT, OCCIDENTAL COLLEGE, LOS ANGELES CA   90041
NEDZYNSKI, THOMAS, PHILOSOPHY DEPT, EAST CAROLINA UNIV, GREENVILLE NC   27834
NEEDHAM, DAVID L, PHIL DEPT, N ILLINOIS UNIV, DEKALB IL   60115
NEEDLEMAN, JACOB, PHIL DEPT, CALIFORNIA ST UNIV, SAN FRANCISCO CA   94132
NEELANDS, D, UNIV OF TRINITY COL, TORONTO 181, ONT   CAN
NEELY, F WRIGHT, PHIL DEPT, UNIV OF ILLINOIS, URBANA IL   61801
NEGLEY, GLENN R, PHILOSOPHY DEPT, DUKE UNIVERSITY, DURHAM NC   27706
NEHAMAS, ALEXANDER, PHIL DEPT, UNIV OF PITTSBURGH, PITTSBURGH PA   15260
NEILSON, BRYAN, PHILOSOPHY DEPT, BROWN UNIVERSITY, PROVIDENCE RI   02912
NELKIN, NORTON, LOUISIANA ST UNIV, NEW ORLEANS, LA   70122
NELSON, BONNIE A, PHILOSOPHY DEPT, GLENDALE COM COL, GLENDALE AZ   85301
NELSON, DAVID S, PHIL & REL DEPT, SCUTH DAKOTA ST UNIV, BROOKINGS SD   57006
NELSON, EVERETT J, PHILOSOPHY DEPT, OHIO STATE UNIV, COLUMBUS OH   43210
NELSON, FRANCIS G, PHILOSOPHY DEPT, LINFIELD COLLEGE, MCMINNVILLE OR   97128
NELSON, HERBERT J, PHIL DEPT, CANISIUS COLLEGE, BUFFALO NY   14208
NELSON, JAMES, PHIL DEPT, NORTH PARK COLLEGE, CHICAGO IL   60625
NELSON, JOHN, PHIL DEPT, UNIV OF COLORADO, BOULDER CO   80302
NELSON, JOHN, PHIL DEPT, TEMPLE UNIVERSITY, PHILADELPHIA PA   19122
NELSON, PAUL, SOC SCI & ENG DEPT, AGR & TECH COLLEGE, MORRISVILLE NY   13408
NELSON, RAYMOND, PHILOSOPHY DEPT, CASE WESTERN RESERVE, CLEVELAND OH   44106
NELSON, SHERWOOD M, PHIL DEPT, CALIFORNIA ST UNIV, SAN DIEGO CA   92115
NELSON, TIM B, RELIG & PHIL DEPT, MISSOURI VALLEY COL, MARSHALL MO   65340
NELSON, WILLIAM N, PHILOSOPHY DEPT, UNIV OF HOUSTON, HOUSTON TX   77004
NEMETH, THOMAS, PHIL DEPT, UNIVERSITY OF KANSAS, LAWRENCE KS   66044
NEMETZ, ANTHONY A, PHIL & REL DEPT, UNIV OF GEORGIA, ATHENS GA   30602
NENON, THOMAS J, PHIL DEPT, BOSTON COLLEGE, CHESTNUT HILL MA   02167
NEPHEW, ALBERT H, PHIL DEPT, COL ST SCHOLASTICA, DULUTH MN   55811
NERON, ROMEO, PHILOSOPHY DEPT, CENTRE DES MAITRES, CAP-ROUGE QUE   CAN
NERSOYAN, H JAMES, PHIL DEPT, UNIVERSITY OF DAYTON, DAYTON OH   45469
NESBITT, LAVERNE FRED, ROCKMONT COLLEGE, DENVER, CO   80226
NESBY, ROBERT, PHILOSOPHY DEPT, MESA COMMUNITY COL, MESA AZ   85201
NETZKY, RALPH, GEORGE WILLIAMS COL, DOWNERS GROVE, IL   60615
NEUDSTADT, ROBERT, DIABLO VALLEY COL, PLEASANT HILL, CA   94523
NEUFELD, ELMER, PHILOSOPHY DEPT, BLUFFTON COLLEGE, BLUFFTON OH   45817
NEUJUHR, PHILLIP N, HUMAN DIV, OGLETHORPE UNIV, ATLANTA GA   30319
NEUMAIER, JOHN, EMPIRE ST COL, SARATOGA SPGS, NY   12866
NEUMANN, FRANKE J, PHIL & RELIG, VA POLYTECH INST, BLACKSBURG VA   24061
NEUMANN, HARRY, PHILOSOPHY DEPT, SCRIPPS COLLEGE, CLAREMONT CA   91711
NEUSCHAEFER, WOLFGANG, SOC SCI DEPT, PENN VLY COM COL, KANSAS CITY MO   64111
NEVILLE, MARIE-SUZANNE, PHIL DEPT, UNIV OF HARTFORD, WEST HARTFORD CT   06117
NEVILLE, MICHAEL R, PENN STATE UNIV, YORK, PA   17403
NEVILLE, MICHAEL, PHILOSOPHY DEPT, WASHINGTON ST UNIV, PULLMAN WA   99163
NEVILLE, ROBERT, PHIL BOARD STUD, COL AT PURCHASE, PURCHASE NY   10577
NEWBURGER, STANLEY, PHIL DEPT, COL AT NEW PLATZ, NEW PLATZ NY   12561
NEWELL, J DAVID, PHIL & REL DEPT, WASHINGTON COLLEGE, CHESTERLAND MD   21620
NEWELL, THOMAS G, PHIL DEPT, U S AIR FORCE ACAD, COLORADO SPGS CO   80840
NEWGARDEN, ARTHUR, PHIL DEPT, COL AT PLATTSBURGH, PLATTSBURGH NY   12901
NEWHALL, DAVID H, PHIL DEPT, PORTLAND ST UNIV, PORTLAND OR   97207
NEWLON, ROBERT E, EDUC DEPT, WEST MONTANA COL, DILLON MT   59725
NEWMAN, CHARLES, PHIL DEPT, UNIV OF N CAROLINA, GREENSBORO NC   27412
NEWMAN, IRA, PHIL DEPT, MANSFIELD ST COLLEGE, MANSFIELD PA   16933
NEWMAN, J, PHILOSOPHY DEPT, UNIV OF GUELPH, GUELPH ONT   CAN
NEWMAN, ROBERT G, REL & PHIL DEPT, MORRIS HARVEY COL, CHARLESTON WV   25304
NEWMAN, STEWART A, PHILOSOPHY DEPT, CAMPBELL COLLEGE, BUIE'S CREEK NC   27506
NEWMAN, WILLIAM, PHIL DEPT, UNIV OF MICHIGAN, ANN ARBOR MI   48104
NEWPORT, JOHN, SW BAPT THEOL SEM, FORT WORTH, TX   76122
NEWTON, LISA, PHIL DEPT, FAIRFIELD UNIVERSITY, FAIRFIELD CT   06430
NEWTON, TIKA, PHIL DEPT, ST UNIV OF NY, STONY BROOK NY   11790
NEYER, JOSEPH, PHILOSOPHY DEPT, RUTGERS UNIV, NEW BRUNSWICK NJ   08903
NICHOLAS, JOAN, PHIL DEPT, ALBERTUS MAGNUS COL, NEW HAVEN CT   06511
NICHOLAS, JOHN M, PHIL DEPT, UNIV OF WEST ONTARIO, LONDON ONT   CAN
NICHOLL, LARIMORE L, PHIL DEPT, S COLORADO ST COL, PUEBLO CO   81001
NICHOLS, HOWARD, STATE COM COLLEGE, EAST ST LOUIS, IL   62201
NICHOLS, JOHN, PHIL DEPT, ST JOSEPH'S COLLEGE, RENNSSELAER IN   47978

NICHOLSON, G A, PHILOSOPHY DEPT, UNIV OF TORONTO, TORONTO ONT   CAN
NICHOLSON, SUSAN T, PHIL & RELIG, CHATHAM COLLEGE, PITTSBURGH PA 15232
NICKEL, JACOB, KANSAS NEWMAN COL, WICHITA, KS 67213
NICKEL, JAMES W, PHIL DEPT, WICHITA ST UNIV, WICHITA KS 67208
NICKEL, WALTER R, PHIL DEPT, SIOUX FALLS COLLEGE, SIOUX FALLS SD 57101
NICKELL, JAMES, PHIL & REL DEPT, PARK COLLEGE, KANSAS CITY MO 64152
NICKLES, T J, PHIL DEPT, UNIV OF ILLINOIS, URBANA IL 61801
NIDA, MELVIN, RELIG & PHIL DEPT, SALEM COLLEGE, SALEM WV 26426
NIEDBALSKI, TERRENCE, PHIL DEPT, ST MARY'S COLLEGE, ORCHARD LAKE MI 48034
NIECZWIECKI, HAROLD, PHIL DEPT, COL OF ST FRANCIS, JOLIET IL 60435
NIELKE, DAVID, HUM & SOC SCI, KAPIOLANI COM COL, HONOLULU HI 96814
NIELSEN, HARRY A, PHILOSOPHY DEPT, UNIV OF WINDSOR, WINDSOR ONT   CAN
NIELSEN, JOHN, PHIL DEPT, DANA COLLEGE, BLAIR NE 68008
NIELSEN, KAI, PHILOSOPHY DEPT, UNIV OF CALGARY, CALGARY 44 ALB   CAN
NIELSEN, MAURICE, PHIL DEPT, W ILLINOIS UNIV, MACOMB IL 61455
NIELSEN, W H, PHIL DEPT, UNIV OF MANITOBA, WINNIPEG 19 MAN   CAN
NIELSEN, WILLIAM, PHIL DEPT, BAKERSFIELD COLLEGE, BAKERSFIELD CA 93305
NIELSON, ROBERT L, HUMAN DIV, D'YOUVILLE COLLEGE, BUFFALO NY 14201
NIETMANN, W F, PHILOSOPHY DEPT, NORTH ARIZONA UNIV, FLAGSTAFF AZ 86001
NIETMANN, WILLIAM D, PHIL DEPT, UNIV OF THE PACIFIC, STOCKTON CA 95204
NIGREEN, WILLIAM, PHIL DEPT, UNIV OF VIRGINIA, CHARLOTTESVL VA 22903
NILSON, DONALD, PHIL DEPT, EMORY UNIVERSITY, ATLANTA GA 30322
NINER, ELAINE C, HUMANITIES DIV, N VIRGINIA COM COL, ALEXANDRIA VA 22311
NISHI, SHUNJI, SYST & PHIL, GRADUATE THEOL UNION, BERKELEY CA 94709
NISHIMURA, KEN, HUMAN DIV, OGLETHORPE UNIV, ATLANTA GA 30319
NISSEN, LOWELL A, PHIL DEPT, UNIV OF ARKANSAS, FAYETTEVILLE AR 72701
NISSIM-SABAT, MARILYN, PHIL DEPT, DEPAUL UNIVERSITY, CHICAGO IL 60604
NIVISON, DAVID, PHIL DEPT, STANFORD UNIVERSITY, STANFORD CA 94305
NIXON, MARK R, PHIL DEPT, UNIV OF N CAROLINA, CHAPEL HILL NC 27514
NOAH, ARIS, PHILOSOPHY DEPT, PATERSON COL OF NJ, WAYNE NJ 07470
NOBLE, CHERYL N, PHIL DEPT, PURDUE UNIVERSITY, LAFAYETTE IN 47907
NOBLE, RICHARD S, PHIL STUD BOARD, U OF CALIFORNIA, SANTA CRUZ CA 95060
NOBO, JORGE L, PHILOSOPHY DEPT, WASHBURN UNIVERSITY, TOPEKA KS 66621
NOEBEL, DAVID, HUMANITIES DIV, AMERICAN CHRIST COL, TULSA OK 74129
NOLAN, JUSTIN, PHILOSOPHY DEPT, ST VINCENT COLLEGE, LATROBE PA 15650
NOLAN, PAUL, PHIL SCH, CATH UNIV OF AMER, WASHINGTON DC 20017
NOLAN, RICHARD T, MATTATUCK COM COL, WATERBURY, CT 06708
NOLAN, RITA, PHIL DEPT, UNIV OF N CAROLINA, CHAPEL HILL NC 27514
NOLEN, DONALD M, SOC SCI DEPT, PARKLAND COLLEGE, CAMPAIGN IL 61820
NOONAN, FLORENCE, PHIL DEPT, UNITY COLLEGE, UNITY ME 04988
NOONAN, MARK L, PHIL DEPT, ST JOHN'S SEM COL, BRIGHTON MA 02135
NOONE, JOHN B, PHILOSOPHY DEPT, QUEENS COLLEGE, FLUSHING NY 11367
NORAGON, PATRICIA A, PHILOSOPHY DEPT, BALDWIN-WALLACE COL, BEREA OH 44017
NORD, WARREN A, PHIL DEPT, UNIV OF N CAROLINA, CHAPEL HILL NC 27514
NORDBERG, KEVIN, PHILOSOPHY DEPT, UNIV OF SCRANTON, SCRANTON PA 18510
NORDBY, JON, PHILOSOPHY DEPT, UNIV OF MASS, AMHERST MA 01002
NORDELL, VERONICA, PHIL DEPT, GEORGE WILLIAMS UNIV, MONTREAL 107 QUE   CAN
NORDENHAUG, THEODORE D, PHILOSOPHY DEPT, MERCER UNIVERSITY, MACON GA 31207
NORDGULEN, GEORGE S, PHIL DEPT, EAST KENTUCKY UNIV, RICHMOND KY 40475
NORDQUIST, ROGER F, PHIL DEPT, WILSON COLLEGE, CHAMBERSBURG PA 17201
NORDSTROM, LOUIS, PHIL DEPT, MARYMOUNT COLLEGE, TARRYTOWN NY 10591
NOREN, STEPHEN, PHIL DEPT, CALIFORNIA ST UNIV, LONG BEACH CA 90840
NORMAN, JOHN E, PHIL DEPT, UNIV OF WISCONSIN, MILWAUKEE WI 53201
NORMANDEAU, G YANNICK, PHIL DEPT, COL VIEUX-MONTREAL, MONTREAL QUE   CAN
NORMORE, CALVIN G, PHILOSOPHY DEPT, YORK UNIVERSITY, DOWNSVIEW ONT   CAN
NORRIS, STEPHEN E, PHIL DEPT, UNIV OF MISSOURI, ST LOUIS MO 63121
NORTH, JAMES, GEN EDUC DEPT, SAN JOSE BIBLE COL, SAN JOSE CA 95108
NORTHRUP, FILMER, PHIL DEPT, YALE UNIVERSITY, NEW HAVEN CT 06520
NORTHUP, A B, GEN ARTS DIV, BERKSHIRE CHRIST COL, LENOX MA 01240
NORTHWALL, JOHN, PHIL DEPT, DANA COLLEGE, BLAIR NE 68008
NORTON, BRYAN, PHILOSOPHY DEPT, NEW COLLEGE, SARASOTA FL 33578
NORTON, DAVID L, PHILOSOPHY DEPT, UNIV OF DELAWARE, NEWARK DE 19711
NORTON, RICHARD H, SOC SCI DEPT, OLYMPIC COLLEGE, BREMERTON WA 98310
NOSICH, GERALD M, LOUISIANA ST UNIV, NEW ORLEANS, LA 70122

NOSS, GEORGE, PHIL & REL DEPT, BEREA COLLEGE, BEREA KY 40403
NOSS, JOHN B, PHIL DEPT, FRANKLIN & MARSHALL, LANCASTER PA 17604
NOTA, JOHN H, PHIL DEPT, BROCK UNIVERSITY, ST CATHARINES ONT   CAN
NOVAK, DAVID, PHIL DEPT, OKLAHOMA CITY COL, OKLAHOMA CITY OK 73106
NOVOTNEY, ANDREW J, PHIL DEPT, GEORGETOWN UNIV, WASHINGTON DC 20007
NOWELL-SMITH, P H, PHILOSOPHY DEPT, YORK UNIVERSITY, DOWNSVIEW ONT   CAN
NOXON, JAMES, PHILOSOPHY DEPT, MCMASTER UNIVERSITY, HAMILTON ONT   CAN
NOZICK, ROBERT, PHIL DEPT, HARVARD UNIVERSITY, CAMBRIDGE MA 02138
NUCKOLS, THOMAS W, RELIG & PHIL DEPT, AUSTIN COLLEGE, SHERMAN TX 75090
NUGENT, FRANCIS R, PHIL DEPT, UNIV CF SN FRANCISCO, SAN FRANCISCO CA 94117
NUMAGHI, PHIL DEPT, DOMINICAN COLLEGE, SAN RAFAEL, CA 94901
NURNBERGER, LOTHAR, PHIL DEPT, LOYOLA UNIVERSITY, CHICAGO IL 60626
NUSENOFF, RONALD, PHILOSOPHY DEPT, OHIO STATE UNIV, COLUMBUS OH 43210
NUTE JR, DONALD E, PHIL & REL DEPT, UNIV OF GEORGIA, ATHENS GA 30602
NUTTAL, STEVEN R, PHIL DEPT, N ILLINOIS UNIV, DEKALB IL 60115
NUTTER, TERRY, PHIL DEPT, ST UNIV OF NY, AMHERST NY 14226
NUTTING, KURT, PHILOSOPHY DEPT, UNIV OF UTAH, SALT LAKE CTY UT 84112
NWODO, CHRISTOPHER S, PHILOSOPHY DEPT, VILLANOVA UNIV, VILLANOVA PA 19085
NYGREN, E HERBERT, PHILOSOPHY DEPT, TAYLOR UNIVERSITY, UPLAND IN 46989
NYMAN, JAMES, PHIL DEPT, TRINITY UNIVERSITY, SAN ANTONIO TX 78284
O'BLENES, GARY E, PHIL DEPT, UNIVERSITY OF HAWAII, HONOLULU HI 96822
O'BRIANT, WALTER H, PHIL & REL DEPT, UNIV OF GEORGIA, ATHENS GA 30602
O'BRIEN, EDWARD, GEN STUD DIV, DELAWARE VLY COL, DOYLESTOWN PA 18901
O'BRIEN, GEORGE, PHIL DEPT, MIDDLEBURY COLLEGE, MIDDLEBURY VT 05753
O'BRIEN, GERARD C, PHIL DEPT, BOSTON COLLEGE, CHESTNUT HILL MA 02167
O'BRIEN, JAMES A, PHILOSOPHY DEPT, WHEELING COLLEGE, WHEELING WV 26003
O'BRIEN, JAMES F, PHILOSOPHY DEPT, VILLANOVA UNIV, VILLANOVA PA 19085
O'BRIEN, JOHN F, PHIL DEPT, IMMAC CONCEPTION SEM, DARLINGTON NJ 07430
O'BRIEN, JOSEPH, PHIL DEPT, BENEDICTINE COLLEGE, ATCHISON KS 66002
O'BRIEN, LOUIS D, ENG & PHIL DEPT, SW TEXAS ST UNIV, SAN MARCOS TX 78666
O'BRIEN, ROBERT J, PHIL DEPT, MONTEREY PNSLA COL, MONTEREY CA 93940
O'BROCHTA, THOMAS, PHIL DEPT, MUNDELEIN COLLEGE, CHICAGO IL 60626
O'CALLAGHAN, W, HUM & FINE ARTS DEPT, ST NORBERT COL, DE PERE WI 54115
O'CONNELL, DESMOND, HUMAN DEPT, COCHISE COLLEGE, DOUGLAS AZ 85228
O'CONNELL, JOSEPH, PHIL & REL DEPT, UNIV OF GEORGIA, ATHENS GA 30602
O'CONNELL, ROBERT J, PHIL DEPT, FORDHAM UNIVERSITY, BRONX NY 10458
O'CONNOR, C R, PHIL & RELIG, ENGLEWD CLIFFS COL, ENGLWD CLIFFS NJ 07632
O'CONNOR, DANIEL D, PHIL DEPT, WILLIAMS COLLEGE, WILLIAMSTOWN MA 01267
O'CONNOR, DENNIS, PHILOSOPHY DEPT, LOYOLA COLLEGE, MONTREAL QUE   CAN
O'CONNOR, FINBARR W, PHILOSOPHY DEPT, BEAVER COLLEGE, GLENSIDE PA 19038
O'CONNOR, JOHN, ST CATHERINE COL, ST CATHERINE, KY 40061
O'CONNOR, JOHN, PHILOSOPHY DEPT, CASE WESTERN RESERVE, CLEVELAND OH 44106
O'CONNOR, PAUL, HUMAN DIV, CONCORDIA SENIOR COL, FORT WAYNE IN 46825
O'CONNOR, RICHARD, PHIL DEPT, SIENA COLLEGE, LOUDONVILLE NY 12211
O'CONNOR, ROBERT F, PHIL DEPT, TEXAS CHRISTIAN UNIV, FORT WORTH TX 76129
O'CONNOR, THOMAS F, PHIL DEPT, BOSTON COLLEGE, CHESTNUT HILL MA 02167
O'DONNELL, PATRICK J, PHILOSOPHY DEPT, UNIV OF DELAWARE, NEWARK DE 19711
O'GRADY, DENNIS J, ST PETER'S COLLEGE, JERSEY CITY, NJ 07306
O'GRADY, DONALD, PHIL DEPT, LOYOLA UNIVERSITY, CHICAGO IL 60626
O'HANLEY, LEONARD, PHILOSOPHY DEPT, LOYOLA COLLEGE, MONTREAL QUE   CAN
O'HANLON, DANIEL, SYST & PHIL, GRADUATE THEOL UNION, BERKELEY CA 94709
O'HARA, JOHN J, HUMAN DIV, NOTRE DAME COLLEGE, MANCHESTER NH 03104
O'HARA, MARY L, PHIL DEPT, COL OF ST CATHERINE, SAINT PAUL MN 55105
O'HARE, WILLIAM T, PHIL DEPT, COL ST SCHOLASTICA, DULUTH MN 55811
O'KEEFE, LUCIENNE, PHILOSOPHY DEPT, URSULINE COLLEGE, CLEVELAND OH 44124
O'KEEFE, MARTIN D, PHIL DEPT, ST LOUIS UNIVERSITY, ST LOUIS MO 63103
O'KELLEY, TOM A, SOC SCI DEPT, ST PETERSBURG JR COL, ST PETERSBURG FL 33733
O'LEARY, JAMES F, ROSARY HILL COLLEGE, BUFFALO, NY 14226
O'LEARY, P T, EDUCATION COLLEGE, ALTHOUSE COLLEGE, LONDON ONT   CAN
O'MALLEY-KEYES, A, PHILOSOPHY DEPT, MCGILL UNIVERSITY, MONTREAL QUE   CAN
O'MALLEY, JOSEPH J, PHILOSOPHY DEPT, MARQUETTE UNIV, MILWAUKEE WI 53233
O'MANIQUE, J T, PHILOSOPHY DEPT, CARLETON UNIVERSITY, OTTAWA ONT   CAN
O'MEARA, WILLIAM M, PHIL & RELIG DEPT, MADISON COL, HARRISONBURG VA 22801
O'MEARA, WILLIAM, PHIL DEPT, UNIV OF CHICAGO, CHICAGO IL 60637

O'NEIL, BRIAN E, PHIL DEPT, UNIV OF NEW MEXICO, ALBUQUERQUE NM 87106
O'NEIL, CHARLES J, PHILOSOPHY DEPT, VILLANOVA UNIV, VILLANOVA PA 19085
O'NEIL, MICHAEL P, PHIL DEPT, KANSAS ST UNIVERSITY, MANHATTAN KS 66506
O'NEIL, RICHARD A, RELIG & PHIL DEPT, EMORY & HENRY COL, EMORY VA 24327
O'NEILL, JOHN J, PHIL DEPT, BOSTON STATE COL, BOSTON MA 02115
O'NEILL, PATRICK, PHILOSOPHY DEPT, ST VINCENT COLLEGE, LATROBE PA 15650
O'NEILL, PETER, PHIL DEPT, IONA COLLEGE, NEW ROCHELLE NY 10801
O'NEILL, REGINALD F, PHIL DEPT, FITCHBURG STATE COL, FITCHBURG MA 01420
O'NEILL, ROBERT E, PHIL DEPT, PLYMOUTH STATE COL, PLYMOUTH NH 03264
O'NEILL, WILLIAM, PHIL DEPT, IONA COLLEGE, NEW ROCHELLE NY 10801
O'REILLY, PETER, PHIL DEPT, CALIFORNIA ST UNIV, SAN DIEGO CA 92115
O'ROURKE, JAMES, PHIL DEPT, ST ANSELM'S COLLEGE, MANCHESTER NH 03102
O'SHEA, MICHAEL, SOC SCI DEPT, NAPA COLLEGE, NAPA CA 94558
O'SHEA, ROBERT, PHIL DEPT, SACRED HEART UNIV, BRIDGEPORT CT 06604
O'SULLIVAN, DANIEL, PHIL DEPT, UNIV OF SN FRANCISCO, SAN FRANCISCO CA 94117
O'SULLIVAN, JOAN, PHIL DEPT, BOSTON STATE COL, BOSTON MA 02115
O'SULLIVAN, JOHN, HUMAN DIV, HARTFORD COM COLLEGE, BEL AIR MD 21014
O'SULLIVAN, MAUREEN, PHIL DEPT, ELIZABETH SETON COL, YONKERS NY 10701
O'TOOLE, EDWARD, PHIL & RELIG, ENGLEWD CLIFFS COL, ENGLWD CLIFFS NJ 07632
O'TOOLE, FREDERICK, PHIL DEPT, CAL POLYTECH ST U, SAN LUIS OBIS CA 93407
OAKES, GUY B, PSYCH & PHIL, MONMOUTH COLLEGE, W LONG BRANCH NJ 07764
OAKES, ROBERT A, HUMAN DEPT, UNIV OF MISSOURI, ROLLA MO 65401
OAKLANDER, NATHAN, PHIL DEPT, UNIV OF MICHIGAN, FLINT MI 48503
OASTLER, JOHN, COLLEGE OF DUPAGE, GLEN ELLYN, IL 60137
OBA, WILLIAM I, HIST GOV & PHIL, ADAMS STATE COL, ALAMOSA CO 81101
OBEE, THOMAS F, ENG DEPT, ST CLAIR CO COM COL, PORT HURON MI 48060
OBERDIEK, HANS, PHIL DEPT, SWARTHMORE COLLEGE, SWARTHMORE PA 19081
OBITTS, STANLEY, REL STUD & PHIL, WESTMONT COLLEGE, SANTA BARBARA CA 93108
OBSTFELD, KAILA, PHIL DEPT, BROOKLYN COLLEGE, BROOKLYN NY 11210
OCCHIO, JOSEPH M, PHILOSOPHY DEPT, DON BOSCO COLLEGE, NEWTON NJ 07860
OCHOCO, SEVERINO, HUMAN DIV, UNIV OF PITTSBURGH, JOHNSTOWN PA 15904
OCHS, CAROL, PHILOSOPHY DEPT, SIMMONS COLLEGE, BOSTON MA 02115
ODEGARD, D, PHILOSOPHY DEPT, UNIV OF GUELPH, GUELPH ONT CAN
ODELL, S JACK, PHIL DEPT, UNIV OF MARYLAND, COLLEGE PARK MD 20742
ODENDAHL, THEODORE L, PHIL DEPT, N ILLINOIS UNIV, DEKALB IL 60115
ODSCHLAEGER, MAX F, HIST & PHIL DEPT, UNIV OF TEXAS, ARLINGTON TX 76010
OEI, LEE, ST FRANCIS COL, LORETTO, PA 15940
OEN, BING, MAUNA OLU COLLEGE, PAIA, HI 96779
OESTERLE, JOHN, PHIL DEPT, UNIV OF NOTRE DAME, NOTRE DAME IN 46556
OFFENBACH, ELIZABETH, PHILOSOPHY DEPT, MCGILL UNIVERSITY, MONTREAL QUE CAN
OGDEN, MARGUERITE, HUMANITIES DIV, SOUTHSIDE VA COM COL, ALBERTA VA 23821
OGDEN, MILDRED C, AIMS COLLEGE, GREELEY, CO 80631
OGILVY, JAMES, PHIL DEPT, YALE UNIVERSITY, NEW HAVEN CT 06520
OGUAH, BENJAMIN E, PHILOSOPHY DEPT, UNIV OF UTAH, SALT LAKE CTY UT 84112
OHAN, FARID, LIBR STUD DIV, SENECA COLLEGE, WILLOWDALE ONT CAN
OKACIGBO, CHUBA, HIST & PHIL DEPT, FEDERAL CY COL, WASHINGTON DC 20001
OKE, JENUDO U, PHIL DEPT, TUSKEGEE INSTITUTE, TUSKEGEE INST AL 36088
OKLU, SAMUEL, HUMAN DEPT, KENNEDY-KING COLLEGE, CHICAGO IL 60621
OKNENT, MARK, PHIL & REL DEPT, BATES COLLEGE, LEWISTON ME 04240
OKRENT, KATHY, PHIL DEPT, QUINNIPIAC COLLEGE, HAMDEN CT 06518
OLAFSON, FREDERICK, PHIL DEPT, U OF CAL -SAN DIEGO, LA JOLLA CA 92037
OLBRICHT, T H, BIBLE DEPT, ABILENE CHRIST COL, ABILENE TX 79601
OLDENQUIST, ANDREW G, PHILOSOPHY DEPT, OHIO STATE UNIV, COLUMBUS OH 43210
OLDFIELD, JOHN J, REL & PHIL, DONNELLY COLLEGE, KANSAS CITY KS 66102
OLDS, MASON, REL & PHIL DEPT, SPRINGFIELD COL, SPRINGFIELD MA 01109
OLIN, DORIS, GLENDON COLLEGE, TORONTO, ONT CAN
OLIVE, DON H, PHILOSOPHY DEPT, WAYLAND BAPT COL, PLAINVIEW TX 79072
OLIVER, G BENJAMIN, PHIL DEPT, HOBART & WM SMITH, GENEVA NY 14456
OLIVER, JAMES W, PHILOSOPHY DEPT, UNIV OF S CAROLINA, COLUMBIA SC 29208
OLIVER, RICHARD L, PHIL DEPT, SAN ANTONIO COL, SAN ANTONIO TX 78284
OLIVER, W DONALD, PHIL DEPT, UNIV OF MISSOURI, COLUMBIA MO 65201
OLIVEROS, ANTONIO, INTERAMER UNIVERSITY, HATO REY, PR 00919
OLIVIER, ANN, PHIL DEPT, XAVIER UNIVERSITY, NEW ORLEANS LA 70125
OLIVIER, NICOLE, PHIL DEPT, COL VIELX-MONTREAL, MONTREAL QUE CAN

OLMSTED, RICHARD, PHIL DEPT, COL OF ST CATHERINE, SAINT PAUL MN 55105
OLSCAMP, PAUL, PHIL DEPT, SYRACUSE UNIVERSITY, SYRACUSE NY 13210
OLSEN, E C, PHIL OF EDUC & HIST, ONTARIO INSTITUTE, TORONTO ONT CAN
OLSEN, RICHARD E, PHIL DEPT, ADELPHI UNIVERSITY, GARDEN CITY NY 11530
OLSHEWSKY, THOMAS M, PHIL DEPT, UNIV OF KENTUCKY, LEXINGTON KY 40506
OLSON, CARL W, PHIL DEPT, UNIV OF NEBRASKA, LINCOLN NE 68502
OLSCN, GEORGE, PHIL DEPT, UNIV OF CINCINNATI, CINCINNATI OH 45221
OLSCN, GORDON, PHILOSOPHY DEPT, NE COL BIBLE INST, ESSEX FELLS NJ 07021
OLSCN, J G, POLIT SCI & PHIL, WEBER STATE COLLEGE, OGDEN UT 84403
OLSON, ROBERT G, PHIL DEPT, LONG ISLAND UNIV, BROOKLYN NY 11201
OLTMAN, JOHN M, PHIL DEPT, WEST VIRGINIA ST COL, INSTITUTE WV 25112
OMAN, WILLIAM, PHIL DEPT, SLIPPERY ROCK ST COL, SLIPPERY ROCK PA 16057
OMATZE, JAMES, PHIL & RELIG, WEST KENTUCKY UNIV, BOWLING GREEN KY 42101
OMUNDSON, BRUCE, HUMAN DEPT, LANSING COM COL, LANSING MI 48914
ONDERDONK, VIRGINIA, PHIL DPET, WELLESLEY COLLEGE, WELLESLEY MA 02181
ONOFRIO, TERESINA, REL STUD & PHIL, VILLA MARIA COL, ERIE PA 16505
OPPACHER, FRANZ, PHIL DEPT, WASHINGTON UNIV, ST LOUIS MO 63130
OPPENHEIM, DAVID, PHILOSOPHY DEPT, UNIV OF WISCONSIN, MADISON WI 53706
OPPENHEIM, FELIX, PHILOSOPHY DEPT, UNIV OF MASS, AMHERST MA 01002
OPPENHEIM, FRANK M, PHILOSOPHY DEPT, XAVIER UNIVERSITY, CINCINNATI OH 45207
OPPITZ, JOSEPH, PHIL DEPT, ST HYACINTH COLLEGE, GRANBY MA 01033
ORANGE, S DONNA, PHIL & RELIG DEPT, MARYLHURST COL, MARYLHURST OR 97036
ORENDUFF, JESS M, ENG & PHIL DEPT, SW TEXAS ST UNIV, SAN MARCOS TX 78666
ORENSTEIN, ALAN, PHIL DEPT, TRENT UNIVERSITY, PETERBOROUGH ONT CAN
ORENSTEIN, ALEX, PHILOSOPHY DEPT, QUEENS COLLEGE, FLUSHING NY 11367
ORGAN, TROY W, PHILOSOPHY DEPT, OHIO UNIVERSITY, ATHENS OH 45701
ORGEL, GARY S, PHIL DEPT, BOSTON COLLEGE, CHESTNUT HILL MA 02167
ORIANNE, ANDRE P, PHILOSOPHY DEPT, PENN STATE UNIV, UNIV PARK PA 16802
ORLEBEKE, CLIFTON, PHIL DEPT, CALVIN COLLEGE, GRAND RAPIDS MI 49506
ORMISTON, GAYLE L, PHIL DEPT, UNIV OF WEST ONTARIO, LONDON ONT CAN
ORNSTEIN, JACK, PHIL DEPT, GEORGE WILLIAMS UNIV, MONTREAL 107 QUE CAN
ORPINELA, ROBERT R, RAYMOND COLLEGE, STOCKTON, CA 95204
ORR, ALEXANDER R, CROWDER COLLEGE, NEOSHO, MO 64850
ORR, DAVID A, PHIL DEPT, UNIV OF LOUISVILLE, LOUISVILLE KY 40208
ORR, WILLIAM M, PHIL & RELIG, CENTENARY COL FOR WO, HACKETTSTOWN NJ 07840
ORTEGON, SAMUEL, RELIGION DEPT, CALIFORNIA BAPT COL, RIVERSIDE CA 92504
OSANA, ZDENCKO A, PHIL DEPT, COL VIEUX-MONTREAL, MONTREAL QUE CAN
OSBCRNE, CLIFFORD, PHIL DEPT, UNIVERSITY OF KANSAS, LAWRENCE KS 66044
OSBCRNE, KENAN, SYST & PHIL, GRADUATE THEOL UNION, BERKELEY CA 94709
OSBORNE, MARTHA L, PHIL DEPT, UNIV OF TENNESSEE, KNOXVILLE TN 37916
OSCANYAN, FREDERICK, PHIL DEPT, YALE UNIVERSITY, NEW HAVEN CT 06520
OSHEROFF, STEVEN S, PHIL DEPT, GEORGETOWN UNIV, WASHINGTON DC 20007
OSQNIACH, AUGUSTINE, PHILOSOPHY DEPT, ST MARTIN'S COLLEGE, OLYMPIA WA 98503
OST, DAVID, PHILOSOPHY DEPT, UNIV OF TEXAS, AUSTIN TX 78712
OSTIEN, PHILIP, PHIL DEPT, UNIVERSITY OF IOWA, IOWA CITY IA 52240
OSTLE, ROBERT, MATH & PHIL DEPT, OAKLAND COM COL, FARMINGTON MI 48024
OSTRANDER, THOMAS P, PHIL DEPT, GEORGETOWN UNIV, WASHINGTON DC 20007
OSWALT, JERRY, RELIG & PHIL DEPT, WILLIAM CAREY COL, HATTIESBURG MS 39401
OTIS, MARIO, PHIL DEPT, COL VIEUX-MONTREAL, MONTREAL QUE CAN
OTT, PHILIP, REL & PHIL, UNIV OF EVANSVILLE, EVANSVILLE IN 47701
OTTO, HERBERT R, PHIL DEPT, PLYMOUTH STATE COL, PLYMOUTH NH 03264
OUELLET, ALAIN, PHIL DEPT, COL TROIS-RIVIERES, 3 RIVIERES QUE CAN
OURSLER, BARNEY, PHIL DEPT, ST UNIV OF NY, AMHERST NY 14226
OUTLAW, I LUCIUS T, RELIG & PHIL DEPT, FISK UNIVERSITY, NASHVILLE TN 37203
OUTWATER, DENIS, PHIL DEPT, SUFFOLK UNIVERSITY, BOSTON MA 02114
OVERFIELD, MARY BRIAN, PHILOSOPHY DEPT, MOUNT MARY COL, MILWAUKEE WI 53222
OVERHOLT, THOMAS W, PHIL & RELIG DEPT, YANKTON COLLEGE, YANKTON SD 57078
OVERVOLD, GARY E, PHIL DEPT, CLARK UNIVERSITY, WORCESTER MA 01610
OVERVOLD, MARK, PHIL DEPT, UNIV OF MICHIGAN, ANN ARBOR MI 48104
OWEN, DAVID, PHILOSOPHY DEPT, UNIV OF WINNIPEG, WINNIPEG MAN CAN
OWEN, DENNIS, PHIL & RELIG DEPT, TRENTON STATE COL, TRENTON NJ 08625
OWEN, ROBERT, CULT & SOC SERVICES, TULSA JUNIOR COL, TULSA OK 74119
OWEN, WILLIAM A, HUMAN DEPT, UNIV OF PUERTO RICO, MAYAGUEZ PR 00708
OWENS, J, UNIV OF ST MICHAEL'S, TORONTO 181, ONT CAN

OWENS, L GARY, PHIL DEPT, INDIANA-PURDUE UNIV, INDIANAPOLIS IN 46202
OWENS, THOMAS J, PHIL DEPT, BOSTON COLLEGE, CHESTNUT HILL MA 02167
OWENS, WAYNE, PHIL DEPT, DEPAUL UNIVERSITY, CHICAGO IL 60604
OWINGS JR, HARRY E, PHILOSOPHY DEPT, UNIVERSITY OF GUAM, AGANA GU 96910
OWSLEY, RICHARD M, PHILOSOPHY DEPT, N TEXAS STATE UNIV, DENTON TX 76203
OZAR, DAVID, PHIL DEPT, LOYOLA UNIVERSITY, CHICAGO IL 60626
OZMUN, LETITIA J, PHILOSOPHY DEPT, UNIV OF OKLAHOMA, NORMAN OK 73069
PAAS, DAVID E, PHIL DEPT, UNIV OF NEBRASKA, LINCOLN NE 68502
PADERON, EDUARDO S, PHIL DEPT, ELIZABETH SETON COL, YONKERS NY 10701
PADGETT, JACK F, PHIL DEPT, ALBION COLLEGE, ALBION MI 49224
PAGE, F HILTON, PHIL DEPT, DALHOUSIE UNIVERSITY, HALIFAX N S CAN
PAGE, ROBERT R, PHIL DEPT, UNIV OF ILLINOIS, CHICAGO IL 60680
PAGEE, SAM, PHIL & SOC DEPT, VANCOUVER CITY COL, VANCOUVER B C CAN
PAGELER, JOHN, PHIL DEPT, WM RAINEY HARPER COL, PALATINE IL 60067
PAGLIUSO, SAVERIO, PHILOSOPHY DEPT, UNIV OF WATERLOO, WATERLOO ONT CAN
PAHEL, KENNETH R, PHIL & REL DEPT, KNOX COLLEGE, GALESBURG IL 61401
PAHI, BISWAMBHAR, PHIL DEPT, UNIV OF NOTRE DAME, NOTRE DAME IN 46556
PAI, YOUNG, EDUCATION SCHOOL, UNIV OF MISSOURI, KANSAS CITY MO 64110
PAIGE, R DOUGLAS, PHILOSOPHY DEPT, UNIV OF AKRON, AKRON OH 44325
PAILLE, YVON, PHIL DEPT, COL TROIS-RIVIERES, 3 RIVIERES QUE CAN
PAIN, JAMES H, PHILOSOPHY DEPT, DREW UNIVERSITY, MADISON NJ 07940
PAINTER, ALFRED W, SOC SCI DEPT, ORANGE COAST COLLEGE, COSTA MESA CA 92626
PALEY, BRUCE, PHIL DEPT, CAMBRIDGE JR COLLEGE, CAMBRIDGE MA 02140
PALLIN, JEFFREY J, PHILOSOPHY DEPT, UNIV OF WISCONSIN, MADISON WI 53706
PALMER JR, T VAIL, RIO GRANDE COLLEGE, RIO GRANDE, OH 45674
PALMER, DONALD, HUMANITIES DEPT, COLLEGE OF MARIN, KENTFIELD CA 94904
PALMER, L, PHIL OF EDUC & HIST, ONTARIO INSTITUTE, TORONTO ONT CAN
PALMER, LUCIA M, PHILOSOPHY DEPT, UNIV OF DELAWARE, NEWARK DE 19711
PALMER, R DAVID, PHIL DEPT, COL AT FREDONIA, FREDONIA NY 14063
PALMER, RICHARD W, PHIL & RELIG, MACMURRAY COLLEGE, JACKSONVILLE IL 62650
PALTER, ROBERT, PHILOSOPHY DEPT, UNIV OF TEXAS, AUSTIN TX 78712
PAMPUSCH, ANITA, PHIL DEPT, COL OF ST CATHERINE, SAINT PAUL MN 55105
PANAGIOTOU, S, PHILOSOPHY DEPT, UNIV OF GUELPH, GUELPH ONT CAN
PANARO, GERARD P, PHIL DEPT, BOSTON COLLEGE, CHESTNUT HILL MA 02167
PANICHAS, GEORGE, PHILOSOPHY DEPT, UNIV OF ARIZONA, TUCSON AZ 85721
PANISH, THEODORE M, PHILOSOPHY DEPT, UNIV OF S CAROLINA, COLUMBIA SC 29208
PANNILL, H BURNELL, PHILOSOPHY DEPT, RANDOLPH-MACON COL, ASHLAND VA 23005
PANUSH, IRVING, HUMAN DIV, MACOMB CO COM COL, WARREN MI 48093
PAPACOSTAS, GEORGE A, HUMANITIES DEPT, YORK COL OF PENN, YORK PA 17405
PAPADAKIS, BASIL, PHIL DEPT, ROSARY COLLEGE, RIVER FOREST IL 60305
PAPADIS, DEMETRIOS, PHIL DEPT, THE AMERICAN UNIV, WASHINGTON DC 20016
PAPAGEORGOPOULOS, N, PHILOSOPHY DEPT, KENT STATE UNIV, KENT OH 44242
PAPARELLA, BENEDICT A, PHILOSOPHY DEPT, VILLANOVA UNIV, VILLANOVA PA 19085
PAPAY, JOSEPH L, ST PETER'S COLLEGE, JERSEY CITY, NJ 07306
PAPE, TIM, PHIL & REL DEPT, UNIV OF GEORGIA, ATHENS GA 30602
PAPPAS, GEORGE S, PHILOSOPHY DEPT, OHIO STATE UNIV, COLUMBUS OH 43210
PAPPIN III, JOSEPH L, PHILOSOPHY DEPT, UNIV OF OKLAHOMA, NORMAN OK 73069
PAQUET, LEONCE, PHIL FACULTY, UNIV OF OTTAWA, OTTAWA ONT CAN
PARADIS, ANDRE, PHILOSOPHY DEPT, UNIV DU QUEBEC, MONTREAL QUE CAN
PARCELS, JOHN L, ENGLISH DEPT, GEORGIA SOUTHERN COL, STATESBORO GA 30458
PAREJKO, JAMES, SOC SCI DEPT, CHICAGO ST UNIV, CHICAGO IL 60628
PARENT, WILLIAM, PHIL DEPT, UNIV OF SANTA CLARA, SANTA CLARA CA 95053
PARK II, C, PHILOSOPHY DEPT, PENN STATE UNIV, MONACA PA 15061
PARK, DESIREE, PHILOSOPHY DEPT, LOYOLA COLLEGE, MONTREAL QUE CAN
PARK, YNHUI, PHILOSOPHY DEPT, SIMMONS COLLEGE, BOSTON MA 02115
PARKER, BERNARD S, EMPIRE ST COL, SARATOGA SPGS, NY 12866
PARKER, CLARENCE M, PHILOSOPHY DEPT, CENTRAL ST UNIV, EDMUND OK 73034
PARKER, EARL H, RELIG & PHIL DEPT, CHOWAN COLLEGE, MURFREESBORO NC 27855
PARKER, EUGENE, PHILOSOPHY DEPT, OHIO STATE UNIV, COLUMBUS OH 43210
PARKER, FRANCIS H, PHIL & REL DEPT, COLBY COLLEGE, WATERVILLE ME 04901
PARKER, GEORGE F, PHIL & REL DEPT, BEREA COLLEGE, BEREA KY 40403
PARKER, HAROLD L, PHIL DEPT, MIDDLE TENN ST UNIV, MURFREESBORO TN 37130
PARKER, JOSEPH, PHILOSOPHY DEPT, ST MARTIN'S COLLEGE, OLYMPIA WA 98503
PARKER, RICHARD B, PHILOSOPHY DEPT, CALIFORNIA ST UNIV, CHICO CA 95926

PARKER, STEVEN H, PHIL DEPT, PURDUE UNIVERSITY, LAFAYETTE IN 47907
PARKER, THOMAS, THEOL DEPT, MCCORMICK THEOL SEM, CHICAGO IL 60614
PARKER, WILLIAM L, SOC SCI DIV, GLENDALE COM COL, GLENDALE CA 91208
PARKINSON, MICHAEL, PHIL DEPT, UNIV OF WEST ONTARIO, LONDON ONT   CAN
PARKS, R ZANE, PHILOSOPHY DEPT, UNIV OF WISCONSIN, MADISON WI 53706
PARMENTER, JAMES, PHILOSOPHY DEPT, KENT STATE UNIV, KENT OH 44242
PARNELL JR, WALTER, LAKE CITY COM COL, LAKE CITY, FL 32055
PAROSKI, MARY, PHILOSOPHY DEPT, MOUNTAIN VIEW COL, DALLAS TX 75211
PARR, WILMA R, BEHAVIOR STUD DEPT, COLUMBUS TECH INST, COLUMBUS OH 43215
PARRISH, THOMAS, PHIL DEPT, WAYNE STATE UNIV, DETROIT MI 48202
PARRY, RICHARD D, PHIL DEPT, AGNES SCOTT COLLEGE, DECATUR GA 30030
PARRY, WILLIAM T, PHIL DEPT, ST UNIV OF NY, AMHERST NY 14226
PARSISSON, DONALD, HUMANITIES DEPT, LAKELAND COM COL, MENTOR OH 44060
PARSONS, BARBARA, PHIL DEPT, UNIV OF WISCONSIN, PLATTEVILLE WI 53818
PARSONS, CHARLES D, PHIL DEPT, COLUMBIA UNIVERSITY, NEW YORK NY 10027
PARSONS, HOWARD L, PHIL DEPT, UNIV OF BRIDGEPORT, BRIDGEPORT CT 06602
PARSONS, KATHRYN PYNE, PHIL DEPT, SMITH COLLEGE, NORTHAMPTON MA 01060
PARSONS, TERENCE, PHILOSOPHY DEPT, UNIV OF MASS, AMHERST MA 01002
PARTEE, BARBARA, PHILOSOPHY DEPT, UNIV OF MASS, AMHERST MA 01002
PARTEE, CHARLES B, REL & PHIL, BUENA VISTA COLLEGE, STORM LAKE IA 50588
PASCALE, ELMO, HUMAN DIV, LINCOLN COLLEGE, LINCOLN IL 62656
PASCH, ALAN, PHIL DEPT, UNIV OF MARYLAND, COLLEGE PARK MD 20742
PASCUAL, RICARDO R, PHIL DEPT, BRADLEY UNIVERSITY, PEORIA IL 61606
PASHMAN, JON, PHIL DEPT, LONG ISLAND UNIV, BROOKLYN NY 11201
PASHMAN, SUSAN, PHIL DEPT, ADELPHI UNIVERSITY, GARDEN CITY NY   11530
PASKE, GERALD H, PHIL DEPT, WICHITA ST UNIV, WICHITA KS 67208
PASKOW, ALAN, PHILOSOPHY DEPT, UNIV OF VERMONT, BURLINGTON VT 05401
PASOTTI, ROBERT N, PHIL DEPT, ADELPHI UNIVERSITY, GARDEN CITY NY   11530
PASQUARELLO, ANTHONY, OHIO STATE UNIV, MANSFIELD, OH 44906
PASS, HARRY B, PHIL DEPT, ST UNIV OF NY, BINGHAMTON NY 13901
PASSELL, DAN, PHIL DEPT, PORTLAND ST UNIV, PORTLAND OR 97207
PASTERK, CYRILL, PHIL DEPT, UNIV OF NEVADA, LAS VEGAS NV 89154
PASTIN, MARK, PHIL DEPT, INDIANA UNIVERSITY, BLOOMINGTON IN 47401
PATAR, BENOIT, COL EDOUARD-MONTPETIT, LONGUEUIL, QUE CAN
PATEL, RAMESH, PHIL DEPT, LAKE FOREST COLLEGE, LAKE FOREST IL 60045
PATERSON, ANTOINETTE M, PHIL DEPT, COL AT BUFFALO, BUFFALO NY 14222
PATERSON, G M, PHILOSOPHY DEPT, LAURENTIAN UNIV, SUDBURY ONT   CAN
PATOINE, YVON, PHIL DEPT, COL THETFORD MINES, MEGANTIE QUE   CAN
PATON, THOMAS, HIST & PHIL DIV, TUSCULUM COLLEGE, GREENEVILLE TN 37743
PATRICK, FORREST, SHORELINE COM COL, SEATTLE, WA 98133
PATRICK, WALTER T, PHILOSOPHY DEPT, UNIV OF AKRON, AKRON OH 44325
PATRIK, LINDA, PHIL DEPT, NORTHWESTERN UNIV, EVANSTON IL 60201
PATRY, JACQUES, PHIL DEPT, COL TROIS-RIVIERES, 3 RIVIERES QUE   CAN
PATTEN, S C, PHILOSOPHY DEPT, UNIV CF LETHBRIDGE, LETHBRIDGE ALB   CAN
PATTERSON, CHARLES H, PHIL DEPT, UNIV OF NEBRASKA, LINCOLN NE 68502
PATTERSON, RICHARD, PIEDMONT BIBLE COL, WINSTON-SALEM, NC 27101
PATTESON JR, ROY K, LIBR ARTS DIV, S SEMINARY JR COL, BUENA VISTA VA 24416
PATTESON, DRURY, PHIL DEPT, CARSON-NEWMAN COL, JEFFERSON CY TN 37760
PATTI, DORIS E, PHILOSOPHY DEPT, OHIO UNIVERSITY, ATHENS OH 45701
PATTON, THOMAS E, PHIL DEPT, UNIV BRIT COLUMBIA, VANCOUVER 8 B C   CAN
PAUCHERI, L U, PHILOSOPHY DEPT, AUBURN UNIVERSITY, AUBURN AL 36830
PAUL, CONRAD, PHIL DEPT, N ILLINOIS UNIV, DEKALB IL 60115
PAUL, JEAN, PHIL DEPT, MANKATO STATE COL, MANKATO MN 56001
PAUL, RICHARD, PHIL DEPT, CAL ST COL AT SONOMA, ROHNERT PARK CA 94928
PAUL, ROBERT, REED COLLEGE, PORTLANC, OR 97202
PAUL, WILFORD N, GOV & PHIL DEPT, NEW MEXICO ST UNIV, LAS CRUCES NM 88003
PAUL, WILLIAM W, PHIL DEPT, CENTRAL UNIV OF IOWA, PELLA IA 50219
PAULEY, EDWARD H, PHILOSOPHY DEPT, UNIV OF RHODE ISLAND, KINGSTON RI 02881
PAULI, JAMES M, PHIL DEPT, ST ALPHONSUS COL, SUFFIELD CT 06078
PAULIDIS, JOHN, PHIL DEPT, LONG ISLAND UNIV, GREENVALE NY 11548
PAULIE, M JULITA, HUMAN DIV, ST MARY PLAINS COL, DODGE CITY KS 67801
PAULIN, M, SOC SCI DEPT, RYERSON POLYTECH U, TORONTO ONT   CAN
PAULSEN, DAVID L, PHILOSOPHY DEPT, ERIGHAM YOUNG UNIV, PROVO UT 84601
PAULSEN, DAVID, PHIL DEPT, BELLEVUE COLLEGE, BELLEVUE NE 68005

PAULSON, LAWRENCE, PHIL DEPT, WICHITA ST UNIV, WICHITA KS 67208
PAULUS, AGENS L, HUMAN STUD DEPT, MARIAN COLLEGE, FOND DU LAC WI 54935
PAULY, HERTA, PHIL & RELIG DEPT, UPSALA COL, EAST ORANGE NJ 07019
PAULY, THOMAS, HUMAN DIV, JACKSONVILLE UNIV, JACKSONVILLE FL 32211
PAUTZ, ZANE E W, PHIL & RELIG DEPT, MILTON COLLEGE, MILTON WI 53563
PAV, PETER, LETTERS COLLEGIUM, ECKERD COLLEGE, ST PETERSBURG FL 33733
PAVLAT, JOHN R, PHILOSOPHY DEPT, UNIV OF WISCONSIN, MADISON WI 53706
PAVLIK, R M, PHILOSOPHY DEPT, RICE UNIVERSITY, HOUSTON TX 77001
PAX, CLYDE V, PHIL DEPT, COL OF HOLY CROSS, WORCESTER MA 01610
PAXSON JR, THOMAS D, PHIL STUD DEPT, S ILLINOIS UNIV, EDWARDSVILLE IL 62025
PAYER, MARY, PHIL DEPT, COLUMBIA UNIVERSITY, NEW YORK NY 10027
PAYER, P, PHILOSOPHY DEPT, MT ST VINCENT UNIV, HALIFAX N S CAN
PAYNE, LA VETA, SOUTH MISSIONARY COL, COLLEGEDALE, TN 37315
PAYNE, MICHAEL A, GRAMBLING COLLEGE, GRAMBLING, LA 71245
PAYNE, PERRELL F, PHIL DEPT, HOBART & WM SMITH, GENEVA NY 14456
PAYZANT, G B, PHILOSOPHY DEPT, UNIV OF TORONTO, TORONTO ONT CAN
PEACH, BERNARD, PHILOSOPHY DEPT, DUKE UNIVERSITY, DURHAM NC 27706
PEACOCK, LELON J, UNIV OF GEORGIA, ATHENS, GA 30601
PEAK, IRA, PHIL DEPT, UNIV OF LOUISVILLE, LOUISVILLE KY 40208
PEAL, JANET, CALDWELL COLLEGE, CALDWELL, NJ 07006
PEARCE, DONALD, PHIL DEPT, UNIV OF N DAKOTA, GRAND FORKS ND 58201
PEARCE, GLENN A, PHIL DEPT, UNIV OF WEST ONTARIO, LONDON ONT CAN
PEARL, LEON, PHILOSOPHY DEPT, HOFSTRA UNIVERSITY, HEMPSTEAD NY 11550
PEARL, PHILIP D, PHIL DEPT, SUFFOLK UNIVERSITY, BOSTON MA 02114
PEARSON, LEON, PHIL FACULTY, UNIV OF OTTAWA, OTTAWA ONT CAN
PEASE, KENNETH R, PHILOSOPHY DEPT, UNIV OF DUBUQUE, DUBUQUE IA 52001
PECCORINI, FRANCISCO L, PHIL DEPT, CALIFORNIA ST UNIV, LONG BEACH CA 90840
PECHARROMEN, O, PHIL & REL STUD, COL OF GREAT FALLS, GREAT FALLS MT 59401
PECK, WILLIAM, REED COLLEGE, PORTLAND, OR 97202
PEDEN, CREIGHTON, AUGUSTA COLLEGE, AUGUSTA, GA 30904
PEDEN, JAMES B, ARTS & SCI DEPT, CHAMPLAIN COLLEGE, BURLINGTON VT 05401
PEDERSON, LAMOYNE, PHILOSOPHY DEPT, AUGUSTANA COLLEGE, SIOUX FALLS SD 57102
PEDRIZETTI, RAYMOND, PHIL DEPT, SAINT JOHN'S UNIV, COLLEGEVILLE MN 56321
PEDTKE, WILLIAM, PHIL DEPT, MARIAN COLLEGE, INDIANAPOLIS IN 46222
PEEL, MALCOLM L, PHIL & REL DEPT, COE COLLEGE, CEDAR RAPIDS IA 52402
PEERY, REBECCA S, PHIL & RELIG DEPT, RADFORD COLLEGE, RADFORD VA 24141
PEET, JAMES M, ENG & PHIL DEPT, MONTGOMERY COLLEGE, ROCKVILLE MD 20850
PEGIS, A C, UNIV OF ST MICHAEL'S, TORONTO 181, ONT CAN
PEIKOFF, LEONARD, ENG DEPT, POLYTECH INSTITUTE, BROOKLYN NY 11201
PEINADO, FIRMIN, PHIL DEPT, MARYGROVE COLLEGE, DETROIT MI 48221
PELAEZ, MARTHA, PHIL DEPT, XAVIER UNIVERSITY, NEW ORLEANS LA 70125
PELLAUER, DAVID, PHIL DEPT, BARAT COLLEGE, LAKE FOREST IL 60045
PELLETIER, A, PHILOSOPHY DEPT, UNIV OF ALBERTA, EDMONTON ALB CAN
PELLETIER, F J, PHILOSOPHY DEPT, UNIV OF ALBERTA, EDMONTON ALB CAN
PELLETIER, J J, COL DE LEVIS-LAUZON, LAUZON, QUE CAN
PELLETIER, JACQUES, SEMINAIRE DE QUEBEC, QUEBEC, QUE CAN
PELLETIER, JACQUES, PHIL DEPT, COL DE SHERBROOKE, SHERBROOKE QUE CAN
PELLETIER, RENE, PHIL DEPT, COL DE SHERBROOKE, SHERBROOKE QUE CAN
PELLETIER, YVES, PHIL DEPT, COL RIVIERE DU LOUP, RIVIERE LOUP QUE CAN
PELON, MICHAEL P, PHIL & REL DEPT, NORWICH UNIVERSITY, NORTHFIELD VT 05663
PELOQUIN, CLAUDE, PHIL DEPT, COL BOIS-DE-BOULOGNE, MONTREAL QUE CAN
PELTZ, RICHARD W, PHIL DEPT, UNIV OF WISCONSIN, MILWAUKEE WI 53201
PEMBERTON, HARRISON, PHILOSOPHY DEPT, WASH & LEE UNIV, LEXINGTON VA 24450
PENCE, CAROL L, PHILOSOPHY DEPT, UNIV OF OKLAHOMA, NORMAN OK 73069
PENCE, GREG, PHILOSOPHY DEPT, BROOKDALE COM COL, LINCROFT NJ 07738
PENDLETON, BILLY, SOC SCI DEPT, LONG BEACH CY COL, LONG BEACH CA 90808
PENDLETON, GENE, PHILOSOPHY DEPT, KENT STATE UNIV, KENT OH 44242
PENELHUM, T M, PHILOSOPHY DEPT, UNIV OF CALGARY, CALGARY 44 ALB CAN
PENELHUM, TERENCE M, PHILOSOPHY DEPT, UNIV OF WATERLOO, WATERLOO ONT CAN
PENFIELD, KATHERINE S, LANG & LIT DEPT, CAZENOVIA COL, CAZENOVIA NY 13035
PENN, STUART, PHILOSOPHY DEPT, E ILLINOIS UNIV, CHARLESTON IL 61920
PENNA, J, PHILOSOPHY DEPT, ST THOMAS MORE COL, SASKATOON SAS CAN
PENNER, TERRENCE, PHILOSOPHY DEPT, UNIV OF WISCONSIN, MADISON WI 53706
PENNINGTON, WILLIAM A, SOC SCI DEPT, DELTA STATE COL, CLEVELAND MS 38732

PENNOCK, ROBERT E, HUMAN DEPT, FINGER LAKES COM COL, CANANDAIGUA NY 14424
PEPIN, JEAN, PHILOSOPHY DEPT, UNIV DE MONTREAL, MONTREAL QUE   CAN
PEPPER, GEORGE, PHIL DEPT, IONA COLLEGE, NEW ROCHELLE NY 10801
PEPPER, HENRY, SOC SCI DEPT, SHAWNEE COLLEGE, ULLIN IL 62992
PEPPER, MICHAEL A, PHIL DEPT, BOSTON COLLEGE, CHESTNUT HILL MA 02167
PERERA, P E H, PHIL FACULTY, UNIV OF OTTAWA, OTTAWA ONT   CAN
PEREZ-MARCHAND, M, PHIL DEPT, UNIV OF PUERTO RICO, RIO PIEDRAS PR 00931
PERKINS, HUEL D, PHIL DEPT, SOUTH UNIV A & M COL, BATON ROUGE LA 70813
PERKINS, MORELAND, PHIL DEPT, UNIV OF MARYLAND, COLLEGE PARK MD 20742
PERKINS, ROBERT L, PHILOSOPHY DEPT, UNIV OF S ALABAMA, MOBILE AL 36688
PERKINS, WAYNE R, REL & PHIL, UNIV OF EVANSVILLE, EVANSVILLE IN 47701
PERLMUTTER, MARTIN, PHILOSOPHY DEPT, UNIV OF TEXAS, AUSTIN TX 78712
PERLOFF, MICHAEL N, PHIL DEPT, UNIV OF WISCONSIN, MILWAUKEE WI 53201
PERNA, ALBERT F, PHIL DEPT, BAY ST JR COLLEGE, BOSTON MA 02116
PERNU, DAVID, PHILOSOPHY DEPT, UNIV OF WATERLOO, WATERLOO ONT   CAN
PEROTTI, JAMES, PHILOSOPHY DEPT, OHIO UNIVERSITY, ATHENS OH 45701
PERREIAH, ALAN R, PHIL DEPT, UNIV OF KENTUCKY, LEXINGTON KY 40506
PERRIN, RONALD, PHIL DEPT, UNIV OF MONTANA, MISSOULA MT 59801
PERROIS, CHARLES, PHILOSOPHY DEPT, COL DE MAISONNEUVE, MONTREAL QUE   CAN
PERRY, CHARNER, PHIL DEPT, UNIV OF CHICAGO, CHICAGO IL 60637
PERRY, DAVID, PHIL DEPT, UNIV OF COLORADO, BOULDER CO 80302
PERRY, JOHN R, PHIL DEPT, UNIV OF CALIFORNIA, LOS ANGELES CA 90024
PERRY, THOMAS D, PHIL DEPT, ST UNIV OF NY, AMHERST NY 14226
PERSICH, HAROLD B, PHILOSOPHY DEPT, CARDINAL GLENNON COL, ST LOUIS MO 63119
PERZ, JOSEPH, ARTS & HUM DIV, LEEWARD COM COL, PEARL CITY HI 96782
PESCA, DENNIS, PHIL DEPT, UNIV OF MICHIGAN, ANN ARBOR MI 48104
PETERFREUND, SHELDON, PHIL DEPT, SYRACUSE UNIVERSITY, SYRACUSE NY 13210
PETERKIN, JOHN M, PHIL DEPT, CREIGHTON UNIV, OMAHA NE 68178
PETERS, AL, PHIL DEPT, PURDUE UNIVERSITY, FORT WAYNE IN 46805
PETERS, CURTIS, HUMAN DIV, CONCORDIA SENIOR COL, FORT WAYNE IN 46825
PETERS, EUGENE H, PHILOSOPHY DEPT, HIRAM COLLEGE, HIRAM OH 44234
PETERS, HAVEN, PHIL DEPT, ST UNIV OF NY, AMHERST NY 14226
PETERS, LEROY, PHIL DEPT, WICHITA ST UNIV, WICHITA KS 67208
PETERS, MARY NIVARD, PHIL DEPT, NOTRE DAME COLLEGE, SOUTH EUCLID OH 44121
PETERS, THEODORE F, RELIG & PHIL DEPT, NEWBERRY COLLEGE, NEWBERRY SC 29108
PETERSEN, BREDAHL, PHILOSOPHY DEPT, MORGAN STATE UNIV, BALTIMORE MD 21239
PETERSEN, E J, PHILOSOPHY DEPT, MERCED COLLEGE, MERCED CA 95340
PETERSON JR, J L, HUMAN DEPT, SUE BENNETT COL, LONDON KY 40741
PETERSON, FORREST, PHIL DEPT, S CONNECTICUT ST COL, NEW HAVEN CT 06515
PETERSON, GILBERT, ENVIRON STUD, PHILA COL OF BIB, PHILADELPHIA PA 19103
PETERSON, JAMES C, ENG DEPT, U S MILITARY ACAD, WEST POINT NY 10996
PETERSON, JOHN F, PHILOSOPHY DEPT, UNIV OF RHODE ISLAND, KINGSTON RI 02881
PETERSON, MICHAEL, PHIL DEPT, UNIV OF KENTUCKY, LEXINGTON KY 40506
PETERSON, PAUL, PHIL DEPT, UNIV OF MICHIGAN, FLINT MI 48503
PETERSON, PHILLIP, PHIL DEPT, SYRACUSE UNIVERSITY, SYRACUSE NY 13210
PETERSON, RICHARD, PHIL DEPT, ST UNIV OF NY, AMHERST NY 14226
PETERSON, S, PHILOSOPHY DEPT, UNIV OF TORONTO, TORONTO ONT   CAN
PETERSON, SANDRA, PHIL DEPT, UNIV OF MINNESOTA, MINNEAPOLIS MN 55455
PETERSON, SVEN R, PHIL DEPT, UNION COLLEGE, SCHENECTADY NY 12308
PETERSON, THOMAS R, PHIL DEPT, PROVIDENCE COLLEGE, PROVIDENCE RI 02919
PETOCK, STUART J, PHIL DEPT, UNIV OF NEVADA, RENO NV 89507
PETRAROJA, SERGE, PHIL FACULTY, UNIV OF OTTAWA, OTTAWA ONT   CAN
PETRICK, EILEEN, PHILOSOPHY DEPT, COL OF CHARLESTON, CHARLESTON SC 29401
PETRICK, JOSEPH, PHILOSOPHY DEPT, COL OF CHARLESTON, CHARLESTON SC 29401
PETRIE, HUGH G, 503 S CHICAGO AVE, CHAMPAIGN, IL 61820
PETROPOULOS, GUS J, PHILOSOPHY DEPT, SKYLINE COLLEGE, SAN BRUNO CA 94066
PETRUSZ, GUSTAV W, TARRANT CO JR COL, HURST, TX 76053
PETTY, BENJAMIN A, PHIL DEPT, S METHODIST UNIV, DALLAS TX 75222
PETTY, SAM, PHIL DEPT, UNIV OF KENTUCKY, LEXINGTON KY 40506
PEZZOLO, PETER E, PHIL DEPT, NEWARK STATE COL, UNION NJ 07083
PFEFFER, ROSE, HUMAN DIV, DOWLING COLLEGE, LONG ISLAND NY 11769
PFEFFER, WILLIAM, NEBRASKA WES UNIV, LINCOLN, NE 68504
PFEIFER, DAVID, PHIL DEPT, W ILLINOIS UNIV, MACOMB IL 61455
PFEIFFER, W M, PHILOSOPHY DEPT, UNIV OF WINNIPEG, WINNIPEG MAN   CAN

PFISTERER, ROBERT, SYST & PHIL, GRADUATE THEOL UNION, BERKELEY CA 94709
PFITSCH, JOHN, PHIL & REL DEPT, UNIV OF GEORGIA, ATHENS GA 30602
PFUNTER, CARL H, PHIL DEPT, GEORGE WASHINGTON U, WASHINGTON DC 20006
PHAKATHI, C, PHIL FACULTY, UNIV OF OTTAWA, OTTAWA ONT CAN
PHARR, WALTER M, HIST & PHIL DEPT, CLEMSON UNIVERSITY, CLEMSON SC 29631
PHEARSON, GEORGE, PHILOSOPHY DEPT, MESA COMMUNITY COL, MESA AZ 85201
PHELAN, GERARD, ENG DEPT, AGR & TECH COLLEGE, FARMINGDALE NY 11735
PHELAN, THOMAS, HUM & FINE ARTS DEPT, ST NORBERT COL, DE PERE WI 54115
PHELPS, H L, PHILOSOPHY DEPT, AMER BAPT THEOL SEM, NASHVILLE TN 37207
PHELPS, JOHN J, PHIL DEPT, UNIV OF NEBRASKA, LINCOLN NE 68502
PHELPS, MARY, PHIL DEPT, ST LOUIS UNIVERSITY, ST LOUIS MO 63103
PHENIX, PHILIP, PHIL & SOC SCI, TEACHERS COLLEGE, NEW YORK NY 10027
PHILIPS, MICHAEL L, PHIL DEPT, PORTLAND ST UNIV, PORTLAND OR 97207
PHILLIPS, ALAN, PHIL DEPT, ST CLOUD ST COL, ST CLOUD MN 56301
PHILLIPS, ANNE H, HIST DEPT, THE U S NAVAL ACAD, ANNAPOLIS MD 21402
PHILLIPS, C, PHIL DEPT, METROPOLITAN ST COL, DENVER CO 80202
PHILLIPS, G R, HUMANE LEARNING, MILLIGAN COLLEGE, MILLIGAN COL TN 37682
PHILLIPS, J DAVID, LIBR STUD DIV, SENECA COLLEGE, WILLOWDALE ONT CAN
PHILLIPS, JOHN F, PHILOSOPHY DEPT, OHIO UNIVERSITY, ATHENS OH 45701
PHILLIPS, JOHN, PHIL DEPT, ST CLOUD ST COL, ST CLOUD MN 56301
PHILLIPS, LEO H, PHIL & REL DEPT, HILLSDALE COLLEGE, HILLSDALE MI 49242
PHILLIPS, NADINE, PHIL DEPT, WAYNE STATE UNIV, DETROIT MI 48202
PHILLIPS, R M, ENG & HUM DEPT, WEST NW ENGLAND COL, SPRINGFIELD MA 01119
PHILLIPS, ROBERT L, PHILOSOPHY DEPT, WESLEYAN UNIV, MIDDLETOWN CT 06457
PHILLIPS, THOMAS R, PHIL DEPT, LA SALLE COLLEGE, PHILADELPHIA PA 19141
PHIPPS, WILLIAM E, RELIG & PHIL DEPT, DAVIS & ELKINS COL, ELKINS WV 26241
PIC'L, ANN, PHIL DEPT, UNIV OF MAINE, PORTLAND ME 04103
PICARD, EMY, ST JOHN COLLEGE, CLEVELAND, OH 44114
PICHE, DONALD R, UNIV OF ALBUQUERQUE, ALBUQUERQUE, NM 87120
PICHETTE, MICHEL, PHILOSOPHY DEPT, UNIV DU QUEBEC, MONTREAL QUE CAN
PICIRILLI, R E, PHIL & COMP RELIG, FREE WILL BAPT COL, NASHVILLE TN 37205
PICKARD, RICHARD D, PHIL DEPT, UNIVERSITY OF TOLEDO, TOLEDO OH 43606
PICKARD, SUE M, PHIL DEPT, WAYNE STATE UNIV, DETROIT MI 48202
PICKUP, IAN, LIBR STUD DIV, SENECA COLLEGE, WILLOWDALE ONT CAN
PIDGEON, PATRICK F, SOC SCI DEPT, SAN DIEGO MESA COL, SAN DIEGO CA 92111
PIELKE, ROBERT G, HUMAN DEPT, GEORGE MASON UNIV, FAIRFAX VA 22030
PIEPKORN, ARTHUR C, SYST THEOL DEPT, CONCORDIA SEMINARY, ST LOUIS MO 63105
PIERCE, CHRISTINE M, PHIL DEPT, COL AT OSWEGO, OSWEGO NY 13126
PIERRE, S, COL DOM PHIL & THEOL, OTTAWA, ONT CAN
PIERSON, EILENE C, COASTAL CAR COM COL, JACKSONVILLE, NC 28540
PIERZCHALSKI, R J, PHIL DEPT, LA SALLE COLLEGE, PHILADELPHIA PA 19141
PIETERSMA, H, PHILOSOPHY DEPT, VICTORIA UNIV, TORONTO 181 ONT CAN
PIETERSMA, H, PHILOSOPHY DEPT, VICTORIA COLLEGE, TORONTO 5 ONT CAN
PIETRZAK, DANIEL, PHIL DEPT, ST HYACINTH COLLEGE, GRANBY MA 01033
PIGGUSH, JAMES R, PHIL DEPT, CANISIUS COLLEGE, BUFFALO NY 14208
PIJNENBURG, PETRUS, HUMAN DEPT, UNIV OF PUERTO RICO, PONCE PR 00731
PIKE, NELSON, PHIL DEPT, UNIV OF CALIFORNIA, IRVINE CA 92664
PILLOTE, JOYCE H, PHIL DEPT, CEN MICHIGAN UNIV, MT PLEASANT MI 48858
PINCOFFS, EDMUND L, PHILOSOPHY DEPT, UNIV OF TEXAS, AUSTIN TX 78712
PINE, RON, HUM & SOC SCI, KAPIOLANI COM COL, HONOLULU HI 96814
PING, CHARLES J, PHIL DEPT, CEN MICHIGAN UNIV, MT PLEASANT MI 48858
PINKARD, TERRY, PHIL DEPT, ST UNIV OF NY, STONY BROOK NY 11790
PINTER, ALEXANDER E, SOC SCI EDUC DEPT, JACKSON STATE COL, JACKSON MS 39217
PINTO, ROBERT C, PHILOSOPHY DEPT, UNIV OF WINDSOR, WINDSOR ONT CAN
PINTO, WILLA, PHIL DEPT, UNIV OF COLORADO, BOULDER CO 80302
PINTON, GIORGIO, PHIL DEPT, UNIV OF HARTFORD, WEST HARTFORD CT 06117
PION, D, PHILOSOPHY DEPT, LAURENTIAN UNIV, SUDBURY ONT CAN
PIPPIN, ROBERT, PHILOSOPHY DEPT, PENN STATE UNIV, UNIV PARK PA 16802
PISCITELLI, EMILE, PHILOSOPHY DEPT, N VIRGINIA COM COL, ANNANDALE VA 22003
PITCHER, GEORGE, PHIL DEPT, PRINCETON UNIVERSITY, PRINCETON NJ 08540
PITT, JACK A, PHILOSOPHY DEPT, CALIFORNIA ST UNIV, FRESNO CA 93740
PITT, JOSEPH C, PHIL & RELIG, VA POLYTECH INST, BLACKSBURG VA 24061
PITT, WILLIAM B, PHIL DEPT, GEORGETOWN UNIV, WASHINGTON DC 20007
PITTMAN, DAVID, HUM & SOC SCI DEPT, CALDWELL COM COL, LENOIR NC 28645

PIXLER, PAUL W, PHIL & POLIT SCI, FORT LEWIS COLLEGE, DURANGO CO   81301
PIZANTE, WILLIAM, PHIL DEPT, ST UNIV OF NY, BINGHAMTON NY   13901
PLACE, JAMES, PHIL DEPT, SE MASS UNIV, N DARTMOUTH MA   02747
PLAMONDON, ANN, PHIL DEPT, LOYOLA UNIVERSITY, NEW ORLEANS LA   70118
PLAMONDON, JACQUES, PHIL DEPT, UNIV DE SHERBROOKE, SHERBROOKE QUE   CAN
PLANTE, ROBERT, PHIL FACULTE, UNIVERSITE LAVAL, CITE UNIV QUE   CAN
PLANTINGA, ALVIN, PHIL DEPT, CALVIN COLLEGE, GRAND RAPIDS MI   49506
PLATT, DAVID S, PHIL DEPT, WILSON COLLEGE, CHAMBERSBURG PA   17201
PLATT, ROBERT M, BEHAV SCI DEPT, TARRANT CO JR COL, FORT WORTH TX   76102
PLATT, THOMAS W, PHIL DEPT, WEST CHESTER ST COL, WEST CHESTER PA   19380
PLECNIK, JOHN, PHILOSOPHY DEPT, MARQUETTE UNIV, MILWAUKEE WI   53233
PLETCHER, GALEN K, PHIL STUD DEPT, S ILLINOIS UNIV, EDWARDSVILLE IL   62025
PLOCHMANN, GEORGE K, PHIL DEPT, S ILLINOIS UNIV, CARBONDALE IL   62901
PLOTT, JOHN C, PHILOSOPHY DEPT, MARSHALL UNIV, HUNTINGTON WV   25701
PLUMLEY, BOYD, POTOMAC STATE COL, KEYSER, WV   26726
PLYLER, LORENZO P, RELIG & PHIL, METHODIST COLLEGE, FAYETTEVILLE NC   28301
POCKLINGTON, STEPHEN L, PHILOSOPHY DEPT, OHIO UNIVERSITY, ATHENS OH   45701
POETKER, JOSEPH L, HIST & GOV DEPT, NE LOUISIANA UNIV, MONROE LA   71201
POHLE, WILLIAM, PHIL DEPT, LEHMAN COLLEGE, BRONX NY   10468
POHMEA, TIM, HUMANITIES DEPT, BUTLER CO COM COL, BUTLER PA   16001
POINLANE, EVELYNE, PHIL DEPT, COL FRANCOIS-X-GARN, QUEBEC CITY QUE   CAN
POIRIER, JEAN-GUY, PHIL DEPT, COL VIEUX-MONTREAL, MONTREAL QUE   CAN
POISSANT, LEEWARD J, PHIL TEACH AREA, WADHAMS HALL SEM, OGDENSBURG NY   13669
POISSON, LOUISE, PHIL DEPT, COL LIONEL-GROULX, STE-THERESE QUE   CAN
POLAN, STANLEY M, PHIL & RELIG DEPT, FRANKLIN PIERCE COL, RINDGE NH   03461
POLANSKY, RONALD M, PHIL DEPT, BOSTON COLLEGE, CHESTNUT HILL MA   02167
POLE, NELSON, PHILOSOPHY DEPT, CLEVELAND ST UNIV, CLEVELAND OH   44115
POLISH, DAVID, PHIL OF RELIG, GARRETT THEOL SEM, EVANSTON IL   60201
POLITELLA, JOSEPH, PHILOSOPHY DEPT, KENT STATE UNIV, KENT OH   44242
POLK, DAVID P, LEXINGTON THEOL SEM, LEXINGTON, KY   40508
POLKOWSKI, WILLIAM, PHIL DEPT, UNIV OF MICHIGAN, ANN ARBOR MI   48104
POLLARD, MARTIN, PHIL DEPT, MT ANGEL SEMINARY, ST BENEDICT OR   97373
POLLOCK, A, PHIL FACULTY, UNIV OF OTTAWA, OTTAWA ONT   CAN
POLLOCK, JOHN, PHIL DEPT, UNIV OF ROCHESTER, ROCHESTER NY   14627
POLLOCK, LANSING, PHIL DEPT, COL AT BUFFALO, BUFFALO NY   14222
POLLOCK, ROBERT C, SOC SCI DEPT, PACE COLLEGE, NEW YORK NY   10038
POLONEY, WILLIAM, PHIL DEPT, UNIV OF MICHIGAN, ANN ARBOR MI   48104
POLCNOFF, IRVING I, PHIL DEPT, PORTLAND ST UNIV, PORTLAND OR   97207
POLS, EDWARD, BOWDOIN COLLEGE, BRUNSWICK, ME   04011
POMEDLI, MICHAEL M, PHILOSOPHY DEPT, ST PETER'S JR COL, MUENSTER SAS   CAN
POMERLEAU, WAYNE, PHIL DEPT, NORTHWESTERN UNIV, EVANSTON IL   60201
POND, GARDNER, SOC SCI DEPT, ESSEX COM COL, BALTIMORE MD   21237
PONNECH, BEN, ENG & PHIL DEPT, COMPTON COLLEGE, COMPTON CA   90221
PONTON, LIONEL, PHIL FACULTE, UNIVERSITE LAVAL, CITE UNIV QUE   CAN
POOLE, C F, PHILOSOPHY DEPT, MT ALLISON UNIV, SACKVILLE N B   CAN
POPICH, MICHAEL A, PHIL DEPT, ST UNIV OF NY, BINGHAMTON NY   13901
POPIK, KRISTIN, PHIL DEPT, NIAGARA UNIVERSITY, NIAGARA UNIV NY   14109
POPKIN, RICHARD H, PHIL DEPT, WASHINGTON UNIV, ST LOUIS MO   63130
POPOVICH, RICHARD E, PHIL STUD DEPT, S ILLINOIS UNIV, EDWARDSVILLE IL   62025
POPOVICH, THOMAS E, PHILOSOPHY DEPT, UNIV OF WISCONSIN, MADISON WI   53706
POPF, MICHELE, PHIL DEPT, UNIV OF CINCINNATI, CINCINNATI OH   45221
PORRECO, ROCCO E, PHIL DEPT, GEORGETOWN UNIV, WASHINGTON DC   20007
PORTER, BURTON, PHILOSOPHY DEPT, RUSSELL SAGE COL, TROY NY   12180
PORTER, DONALD, COLLEGE OF SAN MATEO, SAN MATEO, CA   94402
PORTER, FRED STEVEN, HUMAN DEPT, CLARKSON COL OF TECH, POTSDAM NY   13676
PORTNOY, JULIUS, PHIL DEPT, BROOKLYN COLLEGE, BROOKLYN NY   11210
POSPESEL, HOWARD A, PHIL DEPT, UNIVERSITY OF MIAMI, CORAL GABLES FL   33124
POST, JOHN F, PHILOSOPHY DEPT, VANDERBILT UNIV, NASHVILLE TN   37235
POSTMA, HANS, PHIL DEPT, DEPAUL UNIVERSITY, CHICAGO IL   60604
POSTMA, JOHN, PHIL & SOC DEPT, VANCOUVER CITY COL, VANCOUVER B C   CAN
POSY, CARL J, PHIL DEPT, UNIV OF PITTSBURGH, PITTSBURGH PA   15260
POTTER, JEAN, BRYN MAWR COLLEGE, BRYN MAWR, PA   19010
POTTER, KARL, PHILOSOPHY DEPT, UNIV OF WASHINGTON, SEATTLE WA   98195
POTTER, NELSON T, PHIL DEPT, UNIV OF NEBRASKA, LINCOLN NE   68502

POTTER, VINCENT G, PHIL DEPT, FORDHAM UNIVERSITY, BRONX NY   10458
POTTHOFF, HARVEY H, REL PHIL DEPT, ILIFF SCH OF THEOL, DENVER CO   80210
POTTINGER, GARREL, PHIL DEPT, CARNEGIE-MELLON UNIV, PITTSBURGH PA   15213
POTVIN, GERARD, PHILOSOPHY DEPT, UNIV DE MONTREAL, MONTREAL QUE   CAN
POULAIN, JACQUES, PHILOSOPHY DEPT, UNIV DE MONTREAL, MONTREAL QUE   CAN
POULIN, LOUIS, PHIL DEPT, COL DE SHERBROOKE, SHERBROOKE QUE   CAN
POURCH, STEPHEN, PHIL DEPT, DEPAUL UNIVERSITY, CHICAGO IL   60604
POUSSON, LEON, PHIL DEPT, ST MARY'S UNIVERSITY, SAN ANTONIO TX   78228
POWELL, ALLAN, HUMAN DEPT, HAGERSTOWN JR COL, HAGERSTOWN MD   21740
POWELL, ARTHUR J, LANG ARTS DEPT, PCLK COM COLLEGE, WINTER HAVEN FL   33880
POWELL, J L, PHILOSOPHY DEPT, AMER BAPT THEOL SEM, NASHVILLE TN   37207
POWELL, R E, HERITAGE & THT DIV, N AMERICAN BAPT SEM, SIOUX FALLS SD   57105
POWELL, RALPH, PHILOSOPHY DEPT, AQUINAS INST THEOL, DUBUQUE IA   52001
POWER, ROBERT J, PHILOSOPHY DEPT, WRIGHT STATE UNIV, DAYTON OH   45431
POWERS, JOSEPH, SYST & PHIL, GRADUATE THEOL UNION, BERKELEY CA   94709
POWERS, LAWRENCE H, PHIL DEPT, WAYNE STATE UNIV, DETROIT MI   48202
POZZI, HECTOR R, PHILOSOPHY DEPT, UNIV OF HOUSTON, HOUSTON TX   77004
PRABHU, JOSEPH, PHIL DEPT, BOSTON UNIVERSITY, BOSTON MA   02215
PRADO, C G, PHILOSOPHY DEPT, QUEEN'S UNIVERSITY, KINGSTON ONT   CAN
PRAETORIUS, MICHAEL, PHIL DEPT, WHITTIER COLLEGE, WHITTIER CA   90608
PRAH, JOHN, PHILOSOPHY DEPT, GANNON COLLEGE, ERIE PA   16501
PRATER, FRANCINE, PHIL DEPT, UNIV OF NEBRASKA, LINCOLN NE   68502
PRATT, RONALD L, PHIL DEPT, JOHN CARROLL UNIV, UNIVERSITY HT OH   44118
PRATTE, RICHARD, 145 RAMSEYER HALL, OHIO STATE UNIV, COLUMBUS OH   43210
PREACHER, THOMAS, PHILOSOPHY DEPT, BROWN UNIVERSITY, PROVIDENCE RI   02912
PREGEANT, W RUSSELL, HUMAN DIV, CURRY COLLEGE, MILTON MA   02186
PREHER, LEO MARIE, ST CATHERINE COL, ST CATHERINE, KY   40061
PREMO, BLANCHE, PHIL DEPT, SAINT MARY'S COLLEGE, WINONA MN   55987
PRENDERGAST, AGNES C, PHIL DEPT, BARRY COLLEGE, MIAMI SHORES FL   33153
PRENDERGAST, THOMAS, PHILOSOPHY DEPT, MARQUETTE UNIV, MILWAUKEE WI   53233
PRESLER, JUDITH L, PHIL DEPT, UNIV CF N CAROLINA, CHARLOTTE NC   28213
PRESS, GERALD, PHILOSOPHY DEPT, PENN STATE UNIV, UNIV PARK PA   16802
PRESS, HOWARD, PHIL DEPT, LONG ISLAND UNIV, GREENVALE NY   11548
PRESSEAULT, JACQUES, PHIL DEPT, COL LIONEL-GROULX, STE-THERESE QUE   CAN
PREUS, ANTHONY, PHIL DEPT, ST UNIV OF NY, BINGHAMTON NY   13901
PREUS, ROBERT D, SYST THEOL DEPT, CONCORDIA SEMINARY, ST LOUIS MO   63105
PREUSS, P S, PHILOSOPHY DEPT, UNIV CF LETHBRIDGE, LETHBRIDGE ALB   CAN
PREVALLET, ELAINE M, REL PHIL DEPT, ILIFF SCH OF THEOL, DENVER CO   80210
PREWETT, ARIS, PHILOSOPHY DEPT, CENTRAL ST UNIV, EDMUND OK   73034
PRICE, BRUCE W, PHILOSOPHY DEPT, DELAWARE ST COL, DOVER DE   19901
PRICE, CONNIE C, PHIL DEPT, TUSKEGEE INSTITUTE, TUSKEGEE INST AL   36088
PRICE, J THOMAS, PHIL DEPT, TUSKEGEE INSTITUTE, TUSKEGEE INST AL   36088
PRICE, JOAN, PHILOSOPHY DEPT, MESA COMMUNITY COL, MESA AZ   85201
PRICE, KENNETH, HUMAN DIV, WYTHEVILLE COM COL, WYTHEVILLE VA   24382
PRICE, KINGSLEY, PHIL DEPT, JOHNS HOPKINS UNIV, BALTIMORE MD   21218
PRICE, ROBERT G, PHILOSOPHY DEPT, PENN STATE UNIV, UNIV PARK PA   16802
PRICE, SHEILA, PHIL DEPT, CALIFORNIA ST UNIV, LOS ANGELES CA   90032
PRICE, THOMAS, PHILOSOPHY DEPT, LOS ANGELES BAPT COL, NEWHALL CA   91321
PRIGGE, NORMAN K, PHIL & REL STUD, CAL STATE COL, BAKERSFIELD CA   93309
PRILEY, JEANNE M, PHIL & RELIG DEPT, OHIO NORTHERN UNIV, ADA OH   45810
PRINCE, GRAY, HUM & FINE ARTS DEPT, W LOS ANGELES COL, CULVER CITY CA   90230
PRINCE, HERBERT, PHIL & REL DIV, PASADENA COLLEGE, PASADENA CA   91104
PRING, ROBERT K, HUMAN DIV, HERKIMER CO COM COL, HERKIMER NY   13350
PRINS, TUNIS, PHIL DEPT, CALVIN COLLEGE, GRAND RAPIDS MI   49506
PRIOR, WILLIAM JAMES, PHILOSOPHY DEPT, UNIV OF TEXAS, AUSTIN TX   78712
PRITCHARD, GREGORY D, PHIL DEPT, WAKE FOREST UNIV, WINSTON-SALEM NC   27109
PRITCHARD, ILONA, PHIL DEPT, ST UNIV OF NY, STONY BROOK NY   11790
PRITCHARD, MICHAEL, PHIL DEPT, WEST MICHIGAN UNIV, KALAMAZOO MI   49001
PROCTOR, GEORGE, PHIL DEPT, CAL ST COL AT SONOMA, ROHNERT PARK CA   94928
PROCTOR, ROBERT J, PHIL DEPT, COLORADO ST UNIV, FORT COLLINS CO   80521
PROCTOR, THOMAS H, PHIL DPET, WELLESLEY COLLEGE, WELLESLEY MA   02181
PROKOPCZYK, CZESLAW, PHIL DEPT, ST UNIV OF NY, BINGHAMTON NY   13901
PROSCH, HARRY, PHIL DEPT, SKIDMORE COLLEGE, SARATOGA SPGS NY   12886
PROSPERI, A O, HUMAN DEPT, WESTMORELAND COM COL, YOUNGWOOD PA   15697

PROUDFOOT, CHARLES M, PHIL & REL DEPT, PARK COLLEGE, KANSAS CITY MO   64152
PROULX, BERNARD, COLLEGE D'AHUNTSIC, MONTREAL, QUE   CAN
PROULX, CAROLE, PHIL DEPT, COL DE VALLEYFIELD, VALLEYFIELD QUE   CAN
PROULX, JEAN, COLLEGE D'AHUNTSIC, MONTREAL, QUE   CAN
PROUSSIS, COSTAS M, PHIL & REL DEPT, HELLENIC COLLEGE, BROOKLINE MA   02146
PROUT, WILLIAM E, PHIL & RELIG DEPT, MISS ST COL WOMEN, COLUMBUS MS   39701
PROVENCE, DONALD L, PHIL DEPT, CALIFORNIA ST UNIV, SAN FRANCISCO CA   94132
PROVENCE, MERRILL B, PHIL DEPT, MILLS COLLEGE, OAKLAND CA   94613
PROVOST, PAUL E, PHIL DEPT, AMERICAN INTERNAT COL, SPRINGFIELD MA   01109
PRUCHE, BENOIT, PHIL DEPT, UNIV DE SHERBROOKE, SHERBROOKE QUE   CAN
PRUETT, GORDON E, PHIL & REL DEPT, NORTHEASTERN UNIV, BOSTON MA   02115
PRUFER, THOMAS, PHIL SCH, CATH UNIV OF AMER, WASHINGTON DC   20017
PRUITT, RICHARD, PHIL DEPT, BOSTON UNIVERSITY, BOSTON MA   02215
PRUITT, SYLVIA, PHIL DEPT, UNIV OF REDLANDS, REDLANDS CA   92373
PRUST, RICHARD C, REL & PHIL, ST ANDREWS PRESB COL, LAURINBURG NC   28352
PRYSTANSKI, A H, PHIL FACULTY, UNIV OF OTTAWA, OTTAWA ONT   CAN
PSITTAS, NICHOLAS, HUMAN DIV, MACOMB CO COM COL, WARREN MI   48093
PUBLOW, RICHARD, HUMAN DIV, ILLINOIS VLY COM COL, OGLESBY IL   61348
PUCCETTI, PETER, PHILOSOPHY DEPT, DUQUESNE UNIV, PITTSBURGH PA   15219
PUCCETTI, ROLAND, PHIL DEPT, DALHOUSIE UNIVERSITY, HALIFAX N S   CAN
PUCKETT, J NILES, RELIGION DEPT, GRAND CANYON COL, PHOENIX AZ   85017
PUECHNER, WILLIAM E, PHIL DEPT, ST FRANCIS DE SALES, MILWUAKEE WI   53207
PUETT, WILLIAM, PHILOSOPHY DEPT, CAL STATE COL, DOMINGUEZ HLS CA   90747
PUFFENBERGER, W V, RELIG & PHIL, ELIZABETHTOWN COL, ELIZABETHTOWN PA   17022
PUGH, JOHN K, PHIL DEPT, JOHN CARROLL UNIV, UNIVERSITY HT OH   44118
PUHR, BARRY, PHIL DEPT, UNIV OF KENTUCKY, LEXINGTON KY   40506
PULASKI, RICHARD, PHIL DEPT, WEST MICHIGAN UNIV, KALAMAZOO MI   49001
PULIGANDLA, R, PHIL DEPT, UNIVERSITY OF TOLEDO, TOLEDO OH   43606
PULLEN, PAUL T, HUMANITIES DEPT, VA WESTERN COM COL, ROANOKE VA   24015
PULLIUM, RAY CARL, ALEXANDER CY JR COL, ALEXANDER CY, AL   35010
PULSIFER, JACK R, SOC SCI DIV, FAIRMONT ST COL, FAIRMONT WV   26554
PUNZO, VINCENT C, PHIL DEPT, ST LOUIS UNIVERSITY, ST LOUIS MO   63103
PUOLIN, LOUIS-PHILIPE, PHIL DEPT, LE SEM ST GEORGES, VL-ST-GEORGES QUE   CAN
PURCELL JR, E G, RELIG & PHIL DEPT, ATLANTIC CHRIST COL, WILSON NC   27893
PURCY, ROBERT D, PHIL DEPT, UNIV OF WEST ONTARIO, LONDON ONT   CAN
PURNELL, FREDERICK, PHILOSOPHY DEPT, QUEENS COLLEGE, FLUSHING NY   11367
PURTILL, RICHARD, PHIL DEPT, W WASHINGTON ST COL, BELLINGHAM WA   98225
PURTON, A C, PHIL & CLASS DEPT, UNIV OF SASKATCHEWAN, REGINA SAS   CAN
PUTNAM, HILARY, PHIL DEPT, HARVARD UNIVERSITY, CAMBRIDGE MA   02138
PUTNAM, LEON, PHILOSOPHY DEPT, HEIDELBERG COLLEGE, TIFFIN OH   44883
PUTNAM, RUTH ANNA, PHIL DPET, WELLESLEY COLLEGE, WELLESLEY MA   02181
PYNE, THOMAS, PHILOSOPHY DEPT, CAL STATE COL, DOMINGUEZ HLS CA   90747
QUANBECK, WARREN A, SYST THEOL DEPT, LUTHER THEOL SEM, ST PAUL MN   55108
QUAST, WERNER C, HUMAN DIV, PENINSULA COLLEGE, PORT ANGELES WA   98362
QUAYLE, THOMAS, ENGLISH DEPT, BLACK HAWK COLLEGE, MOLINE IL   61265
QUEST, EDWARD, PHIL DEPT, CALIFORNIA ST UNIV, LONG BEACH CA   90840
QUIGLEY, JAMES, PHIL & THEOL DEPT, MARILLAC COLLEGE, ST LOUIS MO   63121
QUIKO, EDUARD, PHIL & RELIG, SCHOOL OF THE OZARKS, POINT LOOKOUT MO   65726
QUILL, JAMES E, PHIL DEPT, SEM OF ST PIUS X, ERLANGER KY   41018
QUINE, W V, PHIL DEPT, HARVARD UNIVERSITY, CAMBRIDGE MA   02138
QUINN, DENNIS, PHILOSOPHY DEPT, ST VINCENT COLLEGE, LATROBE PA   15650
QUINN, JOHN F, PHIL DEPT, UNIVERSITY OF DAYTON, DAYTON OH   45469
QUINN, MICHAEL S, PHIL DEPT, S METHODIST UNIV, DALLAS TX   75222
QUINN, PHILIP L, PHILOSOPHY DEPT, BROWN UNIVERSITY, PROVIDENCE RI   02912
QUINN, WARREN S, PHIL DEPT, UNIV OF CALIFORNIA, LOS ANGELES CA   90024
QUINN, WILFRED, PHIL DEPT, IONA COLLEGE, NEW ROCHELLE NY   10801
QUINNELL, W, PHIL DEPT, W CONNECTICUT ST COL, DANBURY CT   06810
QUINNELLY, JAMES D, GEN EDUC DEPT, GRACE BIB INST, OMAHA NE   68108
QUINONES, LEONCIO, INTERAMER UNIVERSITY, HATO REY, PR   00919
QUIROS, CARLOS S, PHIL & RELIG, INTERAMER UNIVERSITY, PONCE PR   00731
QURESHI, TUFAIL, PHIL & RELIG DEPT, ANTIOCH COL, YELLOW SPGS OH   45387
RAAB, FRANCIS V, PHILOSOPHY DEPT, UNIV OF ARIZONA, TUCSON AZ   85721
RABAY, CHRISTOPHER, PHIL DEPT, UNIVERSITY OF DALLAS, IRVING TX   75062
RABB, JAMES DOUGLAS, PHIL DEPT, LAKEHEAD UNIVERSITY, THUNDER BAY ONT   CAN

RABBIN, HARVEY, PHIL DEPT, COLORADO COLLEGE, COLORADO SPGS CO 80903
RABE, VIRGIL W, RELIG & PHIL DEPT, MISSOURI VALLEY COL, MARSHALL MO 65340
RABIN, CATHERINE P, PHIL DEPT, GEORGETOWN UNIV, WASHINGTON DC 20007
RABINOWITZ, JOSHUA, PHIL DEPT, UNIV OF ILLINOIS, CHICAGO IL 60680
RABINOWITZ, REA, PHILOSOPHY DEPT, LAFAYETTE COLLEGE, EASTON PA 18042
RACHELS, JAMES W, PHIL DEPT, UNIVERSITY OF MIAMI, CORAL GABLES FL 33124
RACINE, ALBERT J, GRAD NATIVE AMER STUD, D-Q UNIVERSITY, DAVIS CA 95616
RADCLIFF, PETER E, PHIL DEPT, CALIFORNIA ST UNIV, SAN FRANCISCO CA 94132
RADDEN, JENNIFER, PHIL DEPT, TUFTS UNIVERSITY, MEDFORD MA 02155
RADEMACHER, PAUL G, PHIL DEPT, EVANGELICAL THEO SEM, NAPERVILLE IL 60540
RADER, MELVIN, PHILOSOPHY DEPT, UNIV OF WASHINGTON, SEATTLE WA 98195
RADEST, HOWARD, AMER STUD SCHOOL, RAMAPO COLLEGE, MAHWAH NJ 07430
RADFORD, ROBERT T, PHIL DEPT, OKLAHOMA STATE UNIV, STILLWATER OK 74074
RADNER, DAISIE, PHIL DEPT, ST UNIV OF NY, AMHERST NY 14226
RADNER, MICHAEL, PHILOSOPHY DEPT, MCMASTER UNIVERSITY, HAMILTON ONT   CAN
RADTKE, WILLIAM, SETON HALL UNIV, SOUTH ORANGE, NJ 07079
RAE, JOHN B, HUM & SOC SCI DEPT, HARVEY MUDD COLLEGE, CLAREMONT CA 91711
RAFF, CHARLES, PHIL DEPT, SWARTHMORE COLLEGE, SWARTHMORE PA 19081
RAFTERY, PAUL, SYST & PHIL, GRADUATE THEOL UNION, BERKELEY CA 94709
RAGEN, DAVID, PHIL & RELIG, VA COMMONWEALTH UNIV, RICHMOND VA 23220
RAGLAND, O J, HUMAN DEPT, KITTRELL COLLEGE, KITTRELL NC 27544
RAINES, DOUGLAS, PHIL DEPT, UNIV OF MISSOURI, COLUMBIA MO 65201
RAINONE, FRANCINE, PHIL DEPT, GEORGETOWN UNIV, WASHINGTON DC 20007
RAINVILLE, FREDERIC, PHIL DEPT, COL THETFORD MINES, MEGANTIE QUE   CAN
RAINVILLE, MAURICE, PHILOSOPHY DEPT, UNIV DE MONCTON, MONCTON N B   CAN
RAITT, JILL, DUKE DIVINITY SCHOOL, DUKE UNIVERSITY, DURHAM NC 27706
RAJANI, KARL, PHIL DEPT, UNIV OF WISCONSIN, MILWAUKEE WI 53201
RAJCHMAN, JOHN, PHIL DEPT, COLUMBIA UNIVERSITY, NEW YORK NY 10027
RAJNOVICH, J, PHILOSOPHY DEPT, UNIV OF TORONTO, TORONTO ONT   CAN
RAJU, P T, PHIL DEPT, LEHMAN COLLEGE, BRONX NY 10468
RALEY, ADAM, PHILOSOPHY DEPT, E WASHINGTON ST COL, CHENEY WA 99004
RALPH, SIMEONE, PHILOSOPHY DEPT, DON BOSCO TECH INST, ROSEMEAD CA 91770
RAMA RAO, P S S, PHILOSOPHY DEPT, MIAMI UNIVERSITY, OXFORD OH 45056
RAMASHANKER, KARUNA L, PHIL DEPT, UNIVERSITY OF HAWAII, HONOLULU HI 96822
RAMBUSH, ARLENE, HUMAN DEPT, FULTON-MONTGOMERY C, JOHNSTOWN NY 12095
RAMIREZ, J ROLAND, PHILOSOPHY DEPT, DUQUESNE UNIV, PITTSBURGH PA 15219
RAMM, B, PHIL OF REL & THEOL, AMER BAPT SEM WEST, COVINA CA 91724
RAMOS, CARLOS, HUMAN DEPT, UNIV OF PUERTO RICO, PONCE PR 00731
RAMSAY, WILLIAM M, PHIL & CHRIST THT, KING COLLEGE, BRISTOL TN 37620
RAMSDELL, ROBERT D, PHIL DEPT, FRAMINGHAM STATE COL, FRAMINGHAM MA 01701
RAMSPERGER, ALBERT G, PHILOSOPHY DEPT, UNIV OF WISCONSIN, MADISON WI 53706
RAMSTETTER, P V, PHIL DEPT, DUNS SCOTUS COL, SOUTHFIELD MI 48075
RAND, ELBRIDGE N, PHIL DEPT, UNIV BRIT COLUMBIA, VANCOUVER 8 B C   CAN
RANDALL, ALBERT, PHIL DEPT, AUSTIN PEAY ST UNIV, CLARKSVILLE TN 37040
RANDALL, JOHN H, PHIL DEPT, COLUMBIA UNIVERSITY, NEW YORK NY 10027
RANDLE, D CRAIG, PHILOSOPHY DEPT, UNIV OF UTAH, SALT LAKE CTY UT 84112
RANGER, PHILIPPE, PHIL DEPT, COL VIEUX-MONTREAL, MONTREAL QUE   CAN
RANKEN, NANI L, HUMAN DIV, INDIANA UNIVERSITY, KOKOMO IN 46901
RANKLIN, K W, PHILOSOPHY DEPT, UNIV OF VICTORIA, VICTORIA B C   CAN
RANLY, ERNEST, PHIL DEPT, ST JOSEPH'S COLLEGE, RENNSSELAER IN 47978
RANSOM, GENE, PHILOSOPHY DEPT, UNIV OF UTAH, SALT LAKE CTY UT 84112
RANSOM, KEVIN T, HUMAN DEPT, MEDAILLE COLLEGE, BUFFALO NY 14214
RAO, D V, HIST & POLIT SCI, ALABAMA A & M UNIV, NORMAL AL 35762
RAO, RAJA, PHILOSOPHY DEPT, UNIV OF TEXAS, AUSTIN TX 78712
RAPACZYNSKI, ANDREZEJ, PHIL DEPT, COLUMBIA UNIVERSITY, NEW YORK NY 10027
RAPAPORT, ELIZABETH, PHIL DEPT, BOSTON UNIVERSITY, BOSTON MA 02215
RAPAPORT, WILLIAM, PHIL DEPT, INDIANA UNIVERSITY, BLOOMINGTON IN 47401
RAPHAEL, LEYLA, PHILOSOPHY DEPT, MCGILL UNIVERSITY, MONTREAL QUE   CAN
RAPPAPORT, MARK, PHIL DEPT, BOWLING GREEN UNIV, BOWLING GREEN OH 43403
RAPPEPORT, D, SOC & BEHAV SCI DEPT, WESTARK COM COL, FORT SMITH AR 72901
RASHID, A, PHIL FACULTY, UNIV OF OTTAWA, OTTAWA ONT   CAN
RASMUSSEN, DAVID M, PHIL DEPT, BOSTON COLLEGE, CHESTNUT HILL MA 02167
RASMUSSEN, DENNIS F, PHILOSOPHY DEPT, BRIGHAM YOUNG UNIV, PROVO UT 84601
RASMUSSEN, DOUGLAS, PHILOSOPHY DEPT, MARQUETTE UNIV, MILWAUKEE WI 53233

RASMUSSEN, PAUL C, PHIL DEPT, S ILLINOIS UNIV, CARBONDALE IL   62901
RASMUSSEN, PAUL E, PHIL DEPT, UNIV OF WISCONSIN, LA CROSSE WI   54601
RATHBUN, TIMOTHY, PHIL DEPT, UNIV OF CALIFORNIA, LOS ANGELES CA   90024
RATHMAN, STEVE, SOC SCI DEPT, PORTLAND COM COLLEGE, PORTLAND OR   97219
RATOWSKY, HENRY, PHIL DEPT, CITY COLLEGE, NEW YORK NY   10031
RATZLAFF, RUBEN, GEN EDUC DEPT, SAN JOSE BIBLE COL, SAN JOSE CA   95108
RATZLAFF, VERNON, PHIL DEPT, MENNONITE BRETH COL, WINNIPEG MAN   CAN
RATZSCH, DELVIN, PHILOSOPHY DEPT, UNIV OF MASS, AMHERST MA   01002
RAUP, BRUCE, PHIL & SOC SCI, TEACHERS COLLEGE, NEW YORK NY   10027
RAUSCH, ERVIN J, PHIL & THEOL, ST FRANCIS COLLEGE, FORT WAYNE IN   46808
RAUTENKRANZ, K R, PHIL DEPT, TRENT UNIVERSITY, PETERBOROUGH ONT   CAN
RAVEKES, JOHN E, SOC SCI DEPT, DUNDALK COM COL, BALTIMORE MD   21222
RAWLINSON, MARY, PHIL DEPT, NORTHWESTERN UNIV, EVANSTON IL   60201
RAWLS, JOHN, PHIL DEPT, HARVARD UNIVERSITY, CAMBRIDGE MA   02138
RAY, ALAN CHAD, PHIL DEPT, NORTHWESTERN UNIV, EVANSTON IL   60201
RAY, KENNETH, PHIL DEPT, UNIV OF CINCINNATI, CINCINNATI OH   45221
RAY, R K, PHIL DEPT, UNIV OF NW BRUNSWICK, FREDERICTON N B   CAN
RAYFIELD, DAVID, PHIL DEPT, SAGINAW VALLEY COL, UNIV CENTER MI   48710
RAYMOND, G, COL DOM PHIL & THEOL, OTTAWA, ONT   CAN
READ, LESLIE C, PHILOSOPHY DEPT, SACRAMENTO CY COL, SACRAMENTO CA   95822
READ, RALPH H, SOC SCI DEPT, LAWRENCE INST TECH, SOUTHFIELD MI   48075
READ, WALDEMER P, PHILOSOPHY DEPT, UNIV OF UTAH, SALT LAKE CTY UT   84112
REAGAN, CHARLES E, PHIL DEPT, KANSAS ST UNIVERSITY, MANHATTAN KS   66506
REAGAN, JAMES T, PHIL DEPT, ST LOUIS UNIVERSITY, ST LOUIS MO   63103
REARDON, JOSEPH, PHIL & THEOL, DOMINICAN COLLEGE, HOUSTON TX   77021
REBELLO, ALFRED, PHIL DEPT, COL TROIS-RIVIERES, 3 RIVIERES QUE   CAN
REBOUL, OLIVIER, PHILOSOPHY DEPT, UNIV DE MONTREAL, MONTREAL QUE   CAN
RECHTIN, LISBETH, PHIL DEPT, UNIV OF CINCINNATI, CINCINNATI OH   45221
RECK, ANDREW J, PHIL DEPT, TULANE UNIVERSITY, NEW ORLEANS LA   70118
RECKER, DOREN A, PHIL STUD DEPT, S ILLINOIS UNIV, EDWARDSVILLE IL   62025
RECCOB, JAMES, RELIG & PHIL DEPT, OTTERBEIN COL, WESTERVILLE OH   43081
REDDING, DAVID A, PHIL DEPT, FLAGLER COLLEGE, ST AUGUSTINE FL   32084
REDDITT, PAUL, RELIG & PHIL DEPT, OTTERBEIN COL, WESTERVILLE OH   43081
REDLON, REGINALD, PHIL DEPT, ST BONAVENTURE UNIV, ST BONVENTURE NY   14778
REDMAN, DELMAR R, PHILOSOPHY DEPT, VANDERBILT UNIV, NASHVILLE TN   37235
REDMON JR, ROBERT B, PHIL DEPT, MONMOUTH COLLEGE, MONMOUTH IL   61462
REDMOND, HOWARD A, PHILOSOPHY DEPT, WHITWORTH COLLEGE, SPOKANE WA   99251
REDMOND, PAUL V, PHIL DEPT, MT SAINT MARY'S COL, EMMITSBURG MD   21727
REDPATH, PETER A, ENG & PHIL DEPT, LOCK HAVEN ST COL, LOCK HAVEN PA   17745
REED, DAVID A, PHILOSOPHY DEPT, MUHLENBERG COLLEGE, ALLENTOWN PA   18104
REED, ELIZABETH S, PHIL DEPT, COL WILLIAM & MARY, WILLIAMSBURG VA   23185
REED, MARGARET, PHILOSOPHY DEPT, UNIVERSITY OF TULSA, TULSA OK   74104
REED, OSCAR, RELIG & ETHICS DEPT, NAZARENE THEOL SEM, KANSAS CITY MO   64131
REED, RICHARD, HUMAN DEPT, OLIVE-HARVEY COM COL, CHICAGO IL   60628
REED, RONALD, PHIL DEPT, UNIV OF WEST ONTARIO, LONDON ONT   CAN
REED, SYLVIA, HUMANITIES DEPT, MIDLANDS TECH CTR, COLUMBIA SC   29205
REED, T M, PHILOSOPHY DEPT, UNIV OF UTAH, SALT LAKE CTY UT   84112
REED, TED, DIABLO VALLEY COL, PLEASANT HILL, CA   94523
REEDER, HARRY, PHILOSOPHY DEPT, UNIV OF WATERLOO, WATERLOO ONT   CAN
REEDER, PAUL A, PHIL DEPT, LOS ANGELES CY COL, LOS ANGELES CA   90029
REESE, GEORGE C, THIEL COLLEGE, GREENVILLE, PA   16125
REESE, WILLIAM L, PHIL DEPT, ST UNIV OF NY, ALBANY NY   12203
REEVES, C, PHILOSOPHY DEPT, UNIV OF GUELPH, GUELPH ONT   CAN
REEVES, GENE, WILBERFORCE UNIV, WILBERFORCE, OH   45384
REEVES, M FRANCIS, PHIL DEPT, BENTLEY COLLEGE, WALTHAM MA   02154
REEVES, SANDRA, SOC SCI DEPT, PASADENA CY COLLEGE, PASADENA CA   91106
REGAN, ANSELM, PHIL DEPT, ST ANSELM'S COLLEGE, MANCHESTER NH   03102
REGAN, BRIAN, PHIL DEPT, NORTHWESTERN UNIV, EVANSTON IL   60201
REGAN, DANIEL T, PHILOSOPHY DEPT, VILLANOVA UNIV, VILLANOVA PA   19085
REGAN, JAMES T, HUM & FINE ARTS DEPT, ST NORBERT COL, DE PERE WI   54115
REGAN, THOMAS H, PHIL & REL DEPT, N CAROLINA ST UNIV, RALEIGH NC   27607
REGIS JR, EDWARD, PHIL DEPT, HOWARD UNIVERSITY, WASHINGTON DC   20001
REGIS, L, COL DOM PHIL & THEOL, OTTAWA, ONT   CAN
REGIS, LOUIS-MARIE, PHILOSOPHY DEPT, UNIV DE MONTREAL, MONTREAL QUE   CAN

REICH, STEPHEN, PHIL DEPT, BROOKLYN COLLEGE, BROOKLYN NY 11210
REICHE, HAROLD, PHIL DEPT, SUFFOLK UNIVERSITY, BOSTON MA 02114
REICHENBACH, BRUCE R, PHIL DEPT, AUGSBURG COLLEGE, MINNEAPOLIS MN 55404
REICHENBACH, MARIA M, PHIL DEPT, LOS ANGELES CY COL, LOS ANGELES CA 90029
REICHMANN, JAMES B, PHILOSOPHY DEPT, SEATTLE UNIVERSITY, SEATTLE WA 98122
REID, ALBERT C, PHIL DEPT, WAKE FOREST UNIV, WINSTON-SALEM NC 27109
REID, CHARLES L, PHIL & REL STUD, YOUNGSTOWN ST UNIV, YOUNGSTOWN OH 44503
REID, MALCOLM A, PHILOSOPHY DEPT, GORDON COLLEGE, WENHAM MA 01984
REIDY, MARTIN, PHILOSOPHY DEPT, LOYOLA COLLEGE, MONTREAL QUE CAN
REIF, PATRICIA, IMMACULATE HEART COL, LOS ANGELES, CA 90027
REIF, WALTER F, PHIL DEPT, PACIFIC UNIVERSITY, FOREST GROVE OR 97116
REIFF, ALLAN, HUMANITIES DIV, CHABOT COLLEGE, HAYWARD CA 94545
REILLY, JAMES, PHIL DEPT, INDIANA UNIVERSITY, BLOOMINGTON IN 47401
REILLY, RICHARD, PHIL DEPT, ST BONAVENTURE UNIV, ST BONVENTURE NY 14778
REILLY, WILLIAM F, PHIL DEPT, MOLLOY COLLEGE, ROCKVILLE NY 11570
REILLY, WILLIAM F, PHIL DEPT, MANHATTAN COLLEGE, RIVERDALE NY 10471
REINHERR, OTTO, PHIL DEPT, SUSQUEHANNA UNIV, SELINSGROVE PA 17870
REIN'L, ROBERT, PHILOSOPHY DEPT, ARIZONA STATE UNIV, TEMPE AZ 85281
REINELT, HERBERT R, PHIL DEPT, UNIV OF THE PACIFIC, STOCKTON CA 95204
REINES, ALVIN, HEBREW UNION COL, CINCINNATI, OH 45220
REINHARDT, LLOYD, PHIL DEPT, UNIV OF CALIFORNIA, SANTA BARBARA CA 93106
REIS, LINCOLN, PHIL DEPT, LONG ISLAND UNIV, BROOKLYN NY 11201
REISER, OLIVER L, PHIL DEPT, UNIV OF PITTSBURGH, PITTSBURGH PA 15260
REISIG, JOSEPH, PHIL DEPT, FORDHAM UNIVERSITY, BRONX NY 10458
REISS, LESTER J, PHIL DEPT, CONNECTICUT COL, NEW LONDON CT 06320
REISS, RICHARD, PHIL DEPT, ROCKEFELLER UNIV, NEW YORK NY 10021
REIST, BENJAMIN, SYST & PHIL, GRADUATE THEOL UNION, BERKELEY CA 94709
REIST, IRWIN, RELIG & PHIL DEPT, HOUGHTON COLLEGE, HOUGHTON NY 14744
REITER, JAMES E, AURORA COLLEGE, AURORA, IL 60507
REITH, HERMAN, PHIL DEPT, UNIV OF NOTRE DAME, NOTRE DAME IN 46556
REITHER, WILLIAM H, PHILOSOPHY DEPT, OHIO STATE UNIV, COLUMBUS OH 43210
REITZNER, MELVIN K, PHILOSOPHY DEPT, MARYVILLE COLLEGE, ST LOUIS MO 63141
REMICK, OSCAR E, PHIL DEPT, COL AT FREDONIA, FREDONIA NY 14063
REMINGTON, DAVID, GEN EDUC DEPT, JAMES SPRUNT INST, KENANSVILLE NC 28398
REMNANT, PETER, PHIL DEPT, UNIV BRIT COLUMBIA, VANCOUVER 8 B C CAN
REMSBERG, ROBERT, PHILOSOPHY DEPT, WITTENBERG UNIV, SPRINGFIELD OH 45501
REMY, THERESE, COL ANDRE-GRASSET, MONTREAL, QUE CAN
RENAUD, LAURENT, PHILOSOPHY DEPT, CCL DE MAISONNEUVE, MONTREAL QUE CAN
RENAULT, MARC, PHILOSOPHY DEPT, UNIV DU QUEBEC, 3-RIVIERES QUE CAN
RENSHAW, RICHARD W, PHIL DEPT, SAINT THOMAS UNIV, FREDERICTON N B CAN
RENSMA, PATRICIA, PHILOSOPHY DEPT, PENN STATE UNIV, MONT ALTO PA 17237
RENZ, FRANCIS, PHIL DEPT, ST JOSEPH'S COL, PHILADELPHIA PA 19131
RESCHER, NICHOLAS, PHIL DEPT, UNIV OF PITTSBURGH, PITTSBURGH PA 15260
RESNICK, L, PHILOSOPHY DEPT, SIMON FRASER UNIV, BURNABY 2 B C CAN
RESNIK, MICHAEL D, PHIL DEPT, UNIV OF N CAROLINA, CHAPEL HILL NC 27514
RETHIS, MICHAEL, PHIL DEPT, S CONNECTICUT ST COL, NEW HAVEN CT 06515
RETHY, ROBERT, PHILOSOPHY DEPT, PENN STATE UNIV, UNIV PARK PA 16802
REUBEN, ROBERT, COMMUNIC ARTS DIV, WASHTENAW COM COL, ANN ARBOR MI 48107
REUMAN, ROBERT E, PHIL & REL DEPT, COLBY COLLEGE, WATERVILLE ME 04901
REUSCHER, JOHN A, PHIL DEPT, GEORGETOWN UNIV, WASHINGTON DC 20007
REYES, RAUL, SOC SCI DIV, PARKERSBURG COM COL, PARKERSBURG WV 26101
REYMOND, ROBERT L, SYST THEOL DEPT, COVENANT THEOL SEM, ST LOUIS MO 63141
REYNOLDS JR, L, PHIL DEPT, PACIFIC UNIVERSITY, FOREST GROVE OR 97116
REYNOLDS, ANN C, SOC SCI DEPT, PASADENA CY COLLEGE, PASADENA CA 91106
REYNOLDS, BERNARD, PHIL DEPT, THE AMERICAN UNIV, WASHINGTON DC 20016
REYNOLDS, CECIL, PHIL DEPT, NORTHWESTERN UNIV, EVANSTON IL 60201
REYNOLDS, FERRIS E, PHILOSOPHY DEPT, ELON COLLEGE, ELON COLLEGE NC 27244
REYNOLDS, H, PHILOSOPHY DEPT, SHERIDAN COLLEGE, OAKVILLE ONT CAN
REYNOLDS, NOEL B, PHILOSOPHY DEPT, BRIGHAM YOUNG UNIV, PROVO UT 84601
REYNOLDS, PAUL A, PHILOSOPHY DEPT, WESLEYAN UNIV, MIDDLETOWN CT 06457
REZENDE, ANTONIO, PHIL DEPT, COL TROIS-RIVIERES, 3 RIVIERES QUE CAN
RHEA, DAVID, PHIL DEPT, BAKERSFIELD COLLEGE, BAKERSFIELD CA 93305
RHINELANDER, PHILIP, PHIL DEPT, STANFORD UNIVERSITY, STANFORD CA 94305
RHOADES, DAN D, S CAL SCH OF THEOL, CLAREMONT, CA 91711

RHOADES, DONALD D, S CAL SCH OF THEOL, CLAREMONT, CA 91711
RHOADES, STEPHEN, HUMAN DIV, ILLINOIS VLY COM COL, OGLESBY IL 61348
RHODES, ANN ADAMS, RELIG & PHIL DEPT, ARKANSAS COLLEGE, BATESVILLE AR 72501
RHODES, EDMUND M, PHIL DEPT, UNIVERSITY OF DAYTON, DAYTON OH 45469
RHODES, MARGARET, PHILOSOPHY DEPT, SIMMONS COLLEGE, BOSTON MA 02115
RHODES, WILLIAM E, PHIL DEPT, METROPOLITAN ST COL, DENVER CO 80202
RIANI, PETER R, PHIL TEACH AREA, WACHAMS HALL SEM, OGDENSBURG NY 13669
RICCARDO, EDWARD, BEHAV SCI, TRITON COLLEGE, RIVER GROVE IL 60171
RICCI, LOUIS M, HUMAN DEPT, ERIE COM COLLEGE, BUFFALO NY 14221
RICCI, PAUL O, PHILOSOPHY DEPT, CYPRESS COLLEGE, CYPRESS CA 90630
RICE, DAN, PHIL & RELIG DEPT, DAKOTA WESLEYAN UNIV, MITCHELL SD 57301
RICE, DANIEL, PHIL DEPT, UNIV OF WISCONSIN, EAU CLAIRE WI 54701
RICE, DONALD C, PHIL DEPT, UNIV OF WEST ONTARIO, LONDON ONT CAN
RICE, K CRAIG, PHIL DEPT, UNIV OF ILLINOIS, URBANA IL 61801
RICE, LEE C, PHILOSOPHY DEPT, MARQUETTE UNIV, MILWAUKEE WI 53233
RICE, ROBERT, PHILOSOPHY DEPT, UNIV OF VERMONT, BURLINGTON VT 05401
RICH, GREGORY, PHIL DEPT, UNIVERSITY OF MIAMI, CORAL GABLES FL 33124
RICHARD, A, PHIL FACULTY, UNIV OF OTTAWA, OTTAWA ONT CAN
RICHARD, ARSENE, PHILOSOPHY DEPT, UNIV DE MONCTON, MONCTON N B CAN
RICHARD, JOSEPH, PHILOSOPHY DEPT, UNIV OF ARIZONA, TUCSON AZ 85721
RICHARDS, BENJAMIN A, PHIL & REL DEPT, ITHACA COLLEGE, ITHACA NY 14850
RICHARDS, BEVERLY, PHIL DEPT, PURDUE UNIVERSITY, FORT WAYNE IN 46805
RICHARDS, DAVID H, SOC SCI DEPT, AUBURN COM COLLEGE, AUBURN NY 13021
RICHARDS, JERALD H, SOC SCI, N KENTUCKY ST COL, HIGHLAND HTS KY 41076
RICHARDS, JERRY, REL & PHIL, IOWA WESLEYAN COL, MT PLEASANT IA 52641
RICHARDS, JOHN, PHIL & REL DEPT, UNIV OF GEORGIA, ATHENS GA 30602
RICHARDS, NORVIN W, PHIL DEPT, UNIV OF ALABAMA, UNIVERSITY AL 35486
RICHARDS, RICHARD C, SOC SCI DEPT, CAL ST POLYTECH UNIV, POMONA CA 91768
RICHARDS, ROBERT J, PHIL DEPT, CREIGHTON UNIV, OMAHA NE 68178
RICHARDS, WILLIAM M, PHIL DEPT, UNIVERSITY OF DAYTON, DAYTON OH 45469
RICHARDSON, BRIAN, BIBL STUD & PHIL DIV, BRYAN COLLEGE, DAYTON TN 37321
RICHARDSON, CHARLES C, PHIL DEPT, S ILLINOIS UNIV, CARBONDALE IL 62901
RICHARDSON, DAVID, PHILOSOPHY DEPT, EDINBORO ST COL, EDINBORO PA 16412
RICHARDSON, HENRY V M, PHIL DEPT, WALLA WALLA COM COL, WALLA WALLA WA 99362
RICHARDSON, NORMAN E, PHIL DEPT, GETTYSBURG COLLEGE, GETTYSBURG PA 17325
RICHARDSON, T, PHIL & RELIG DEPT, MONTCLAIR ST COL, UPR MONTCLAIR NJ 07043
RICHARDSON, WILLIAM, PHIL DEPT, FORDHAM UNIVERSITY, BRONX NY 10458
RICHER, RONALD, PHIL DEPT, COL BOIS-DE-BOULOGNE, MONTREAL QUE CAN
RICHEY, FRANCIS A, PHIL DEPT, COL OF ST ELIZABETH, CONVENT STA NJ 07961
RICHFIELD, JEROME, PHIL DEPT, CALIFORNIA ST UNIV, NORTHRIDGE CA 91324
RICHMAN, ROBERT J, PHILOSOPHY DEPT, UNIV OF WASHINGTON, SEATTLE WA 98195
RICHMOND, SAMUEL A, PHILOSOPHY DEPT, CLEVELAND ST UNIV, CLEVELAND OH 44115
RICHTER, MARY ANN, APPALACHIAN ST UNIV, BOONE, NC 28607
RICKERT, RICHARD, PHIL DEPT, MERRIMACK COLLEGE, NORTH ANDOVER MA 01845
RICKERT, TRUDY, PHILOSOPHY DEPT, WASHINGTON ST UNIV, PULLMAN WA 99163
RICKERTSEN, BRYAN C, PHIL DEPT, UNIV OF NEBRASKA, LINCOLN NE 68502
RICKS, WILLIAM, PHIL & REL DEPT, UNIV OF GEORGIA, ATHENS GA 30602
RICOEUR, PAUL, PHIL DEPT, UNIV OF CHICAGO, CHICAGO IL 60637
RICPLEY, ROBERT C, PHIL DEPT, LAKEHEAD UNIVERSITY, THUNDER BAY ONT CAN
RIDDLE, CHAUNCEY C, PHILOSOPHY DEPT, BRIGHAM YOUNG UNIV, PROVO UT 84601
RIDDLE, GLENN K, PHIL DEPT, UNIV OF WISCONSIN, MILWAUKEE WI 53201
RIECEL, MARCUS E, PHIL DEPT, INDIANA ST UNIV, TERRE HAUTE IN 47809
RIEMAN, T WAYNE, REL & PHIL, MANCHESTER COLLEGE, N MANCHESTER IN 46962
RIEMER, NEAL, PHILOSOPHY DEPT, DREW UNIVERSITY, MADISON NJ 07940
RIEPE, DALE M, PHIL DEPT, ST UNIV OF NY, AMHERST NY 14226
RIEPER, BYRON M, PHIL DEPT, UNIVERSITY OF HAWAII, HONOLULU HI 96822
RIESS, CHESTER L, HUMAN DEPT, LONG ISLAND UNIV, BROOKLYN NY 11216
RIFE, WILLIAM C, PHIL DEPT, NORTH CENTRAL COL, NAPERVILLE IL 60540
RIFORGIATO, LEONARD, LIBR ARTS & SOC SCI, PENN STATE UNIV, SHARON PA 16146
RIGBY, HARRY W, PHIL DEPT, SAINT THOMAS UNIV, FREDERICTON N B CAN
RIGGIN, DONALD L, ARTS & SCI DEPT, MINNESOTA BIB COL, ROCHESTER MN 55901
RIGGS, DONALD R, PHIL DEPT, UNIV OF ILLINOIS, URBANA IL 61801
RIGGS, MICHAEL D, PHIL DEPT, WASHINGTON UNIV, ST LOUIS MO 63130
RIGNEY, ELEANOR, SOC & BEHAV SCI, BRENAU COLLEGE, GAINESVILLE GA 30501

RIGTERINK, ROGER J, ENGLISH LIT & PHIL, UNIV OF WISCONSIN, MADISON WI 53706
RIKER, JOHN, PHIL DEPT, COLORADO COLLEGE, COLORADO SPGS CO 80903
RIKKERS, ROBERT, PHIL DEPT, MANKATO STATE COL, MANKATO MN 56001
RILA, JAMES S, PHILOSOPHY DEPT, HURON COLLEGE, HURON SD 57350
RILEY JR, T D, PHIL & HUM DEPT, TEXAS A & M UNIV, COL STATION TX 77843
RILEY, BRUCE T, PHIL & REL STUD, YOUNGSTOWN ST UNIV, YOUNGSTOWN OH 44503
RILEY, GRESHAM, PHILOSOPHY DEPT, NEW COLLEGE, SARASOTA FL 33578
RILEY, JAMES, PHILOSOPHY DEPT, SEATTLE UNIVERSITY, SEATTLE WA 98122
RINCERLY, ALLEN V, PHIL DEPT, UNIVERSITY OF DAYTON, DAYTON OH 45469
RINEHART, B, PHILOSOPHY DEPT, UNIV CF TORONTO, TORONTO ONT CAN
RING, BENJAMIN, PHIL DEPT, UNIV OF N DAKOTA, GRAND FORKS ND 58201
RING, ELIZABETH M, PHIL DEPT, HAMILTON COLLEGE, CLINTON NY 13323
RING, GILL, PHIL DIV, ST MEINRAD COLLEGE, SAINT MEINRAD IN 47577
RING, MERRILL, PHIL DEPT, CALIFORNIA ST UNIV, FULLERTON CA 92634
RING, WILLIAM, PHIL & RELIG STUD, KING'S COLLEGE, LONDON ONT CAN
RINGELHEIM, JOAN, PHIL DEPT, UNIV OF BRIDGEPORT, BRIDGEPORT CT 06602
RINGEN, JON D, PHIL DEPT, INDIANA UNIVERSITY, SOUTH BEND IN 46615
RINGER, VIRGINIA H, PHIL DEPT, CALIFORNIA ST UNIV, LONG BEACH CA 90840
RINGLE, MARTIN, PHIL DEPT, ST UNIV CF NY, BINGHAMTON NY 13901
RIORDAN, JOSEPH D, PHIL DEPT, FORDHAM UNIVERSITY, BRONX NY 10458
RIORDAN, TIM, SHORELINE COM COL, SEATTLE, WA 98133
RIOS, ROBERTO, PHILOSOPHY DEPT, UNIV OF HOUSTON, HOUSTON TX 77004
RIOUX, BERTRAND, PHILOSOPHY DEPT, UNIV DE MONTREAL, MONTREAL QUE CAN
RISER, JOHN, HUMAN DEPT, FLORIDA TECH UNIV, ORLANDO FL 32816
RISHER, CHARLES A, SOC SCI DEPT, DALTON JR COLLEGE, DALTON GA 30720
RITERIS, JOHN M, PHIL DEPT, INDIANA-PURDUE UNIV, INDIANAPOLIS IN 46202
RITTER, G A, PHIL & RELIG DEPT, ROANOKE COLLEGE, SALEM VA 24153
RITTERSPACH, A D, RELIG & PHIL, ELIZABETHTOWN COL, ELIZABETHTOWN PA 17022
RIUKAS, STANLEY, PHIL DEPT, WEST CHESTER ST COL, WEST CHESTER PA 19380
RIVENBARK, W H, SOC SCI DEPT, DAYTONA BCH COM COL, DAYTONA BEACH FL 32015
RIVETT, DAVID, PHIL DEPT, UNIV OF WEST ONTARIO, LONDON ONT CAN
RIZIK, JAMES, NE ILLINOIS ST UNIV, CHICAGO, IL 60625
ROACH, CORWIN, PHILOSOPHY DEPT, N DAKOTA ST UNIV, FARGO ND 58102
ROACH, DEWEY R, PHIL & RELIG DEPT, MISS ST COL WOMEN, COLUMBUS MS 39701
ROARK, DALLAS M, PHIL DEPT, KAN ST TEACHERS COL, EMPORIA KS 66801
ROARK, WILLIAM W, HUMAN DIV, MISSOURI BAPT COL, ST LOUIS MO 63141
ROBB, JAMES H, PHILOSOPHY DEPT, MARQUETTE UNIV, MILWAUKEE WI 53233
ROBB, KEVIN, PHIL SCH, UNIV OF S CALIFORNIA, LOS ANGELES CA 90007
ROBBINS, DENNIS A, PHIL DEPT, BOSTON COLLEGE, CHESTNUT HILL MA 02167
ROBBINS, J WESLEY, PHIL DEPT, INDIANA UNIVERSITY, SOUTH BEND IN 46615
ROBERSON, C C, GEN EDUC DEPT, NE BIBLE INST, GREEN LANE PA 18054
ROBERT, ROLAND, PHILOSOPHY DEPT, COL DE ROUYN-NORANDA, ROUYN QUE CAN
ROBERT, SERGE, COL EDOUARD-MONTPETIT, LONGUEUIL, QUE CAN
ROBERTS, ARTHUR O, RELIG DIV, GEORGE FOX COLLEGE, NEWBERG OR 97132
ROBERTS, DON D, PHILOSOPHY DEPT, UNIV OF WATERLOO, WATERLOO ONT CAN
ROBERTS, GEORGE W, PHILOSOPHY DEPT, DUKE UNIVERSITY, DURHAM NC 27706
ROBERTS, JAMES B, PHIL DEPT, S ILLINOIS UNIV, CARBONDALE IL 62901
ROBERTS, JOHN, PHIL & REL DEPT, HILLSDALE COLLEGE, HILLSDALE MI 49242
ROBERTS, KLINE, PHIL & RELIG DEPT, COLGATE UNIVERSITY, HAMILTON NY 13346
ROBERTS, LAWRENCE D, PHIL DEPT, ST UNIV OF NY, BINGHAMTON NY 13901
ROBERTS, LOUISE N, PHIL DEPT, TULANE UNIVERSITY, NEW ORLEANS LA 70118
ROBERTS, M, PHILOSOPHY DEPT, UNIV OF RHODE ISLAND, KINGSTON RI 02881
ROBERTS, VICTOR, HUMANITIES DIV, SAINT GREGORY'S COL, SHAWNEE OK 74801
ROBERTS, WESLEY A, THEOL DEPT, GORDON-CONWELL SEM, S HAMILTON MA 01982
ROBERTSON, ANN, PHIL DEPT, ST UNIV OF NY, AMHERST NY 14226
ROBERTSON, BRUCE, PHIL & REL DEPT, TOWSON STATE COL, BALTIMORE MD 21204
ROBERTSON, DONALD R, WOODBURY COLLEGE, LOS ANGELES, CA 90017
ROBERTSON, J C, PHIL DEPT, UNIV OF NW BRUNSWICK, SAINT JOHN N B CAN
ROBERTSON, JOHN E, PHIL DEPT, UNIV BRIT COLUMBIA, VANCOUVER 8 B C CAN
ROBERTSON, ROBERT E, PHIL DEPT, BALL ST UNIVERSITY, MUNCIE IN 47306
ROBERTSON, THOMAS, PHIL DEPT, UNIV OF ILLINOIS, URBANA IL 61801
ROBILLARD, GEORGE M, PHIL DEPT, PROVIDENCE COLLEGE, PROVIDENCE RI 02919
ROBIN, RICHARD, MT HOLYOKE COLLEGE, SOUTH HADLEY, MA 01075
ROBINS, MICHAEL, PHIL DEPT, BOWLING GREEN UNIV, BOWLING GREEN OH 43403

ROBINSON, ANDREW, PHIL DEPT, ST ANSELM'S COLLEGE, MANCHESTER NH 03102
ROBINSON, B, PHILOSOPHY DEPT, UNIV OF RHODE ISLAND, KINGSTON RI 02881
ROBINSON, BLAINE, LANG & SOC SCI DEPT, SD SCH OF MINES, RAPID CITY SD 57701
ROBINSON, DANIEL, PHIL SCH, UNIV OF S CALIFORNIA, LOS ANGELES CA 90007
ROBINSON, F E, PHILOSOPHY DEPT, MURRAY STATE UNIV, MURRAY KY 42071
ROBINSON, H J, PHILOSOPHY DEPT, UNIV OF GUELPH, GUELPH ONT CAN
ROBINSON, J ALAN, PHIL DEPT, SYRACUSE UNIVERSITY, SYRACUSE NY 13210
ROBINSON, JENEFER M, PHIL DEPT, UNIV OF CINCINNATI, CINCINNATI OH 45221
ROBINSON, JOHN MANSLEY, PHILOSOPHY DEPT, WINDHAM COLLEGE, PUTNEY VT 05346
ROBINSON, JONATHAN, PHILOSOPHY DEPT, MCGILL UNIVERSITY, MONTREAL QUE CAN
ROBINSON, P R, PHIL DEPT, UNIV OF NW BRUNSWICK, FREDERICTON N B CAN
ROBINSON, PETER, PHIL DEPT, UNIV OF TEXAS, EL PASO TX 79968
ROBINSON, R N, PHILOSOPHY DEPT, UNIV OF S CAROLINA, CONWAY SC 29526
ROBINSON, RICHARD E, PHIL DEPT, UNIV BRIT COLUMBIA, VANCOUVER 8 B C CAN
ROBINSON, T M, PHILOSOPHY DEPT, UNIV OF TORONTO, TORONTO ONT CAN
ROBINSON, THOMAS H, PHILOSOPHY DEPT, QUEEN'S UNIVERSITY, KINGSTON ONT CAN
ROBINSON, WILLIAM, PHIL DEPT, IOWA STATE UNIV, AMES IA 50010
ROBINSON, WILLIAM, PHIL & RELIG, VA COMMONWEALTH UNIV, RICHMOND VA 23220
ROBISON, ANDREW, PHIL DEPT, UNIV OF ILLINOIS, URBANA IL 61801
ROBISON, JOHN, PHILOSOPHY DEPT, UNIV OF MASS, AMHERST MA 01002
ROBISON, WADE L, PHILOSOPHY DEPT, OHIO STATE UNIV, COLUMBUS OH 43210
ROBLIN, RONALD E, PHIL DEPT, COL AT BUFFALO, BUFFALO NY 14222
ROBSON, KENT E, LANG & PHIL DEPT, UTAH STATE UNIV, LOGAN UT 84322
ROBSON, WESLEY, PHIL DEPT, UNIV OF CALIFORNIA, LOS ANGELES CA 90024
ROBY, THOMAS W, HUMAN DEPT, KENNEDY-KING COLLEGE, CHICAGO IL 60621
ROCA, OCTAVIO, PHIL DEPT, GEORGETOWN UNIV, WASHINGTON DC 20007
ROCCO, THOMAS, PHIL DEPT, UNIV OF WISCONSIN, EAU CLAIRE WI 54701
ROCHE, EVAN, PHIL DEPT, SIENA COLLEGE, LOUDONVILLE NY 12211
ROCHE, THERESE A, PHIL DEPT, COL OF ST ELIZABETH, CONVENT STA NJ 07961
ROCHELEAU, MAURICE, PHIL DEPT, OBLATE COLLEGE & SEM, NATICK MA 01760
ROCK, GLORIA, PHIL DEPT, CALIFORNIA ST UNIV, FULLERTON CA 92634
ROCK, JOHN P, PHIL DEPT, BOSTON COLLEGE, CHESTNUT HILL MA 02167
ROCKMORE, TOM, PHIL DEPT, YALE UNIVERSITY, NEW HAVEN CT 06520
ROCKWELL, PAUL H, HIST & PHIL DEPT, MIDWESTERN UNIV, WICHITA FALLS TX 76308
RODA, ANTHONY, PHIL DEPT, COL AT ONEONTA, ONEONTA NY 13820
RODEWALD, RICHARD, PHIL DEPT, UNIV OF CALIFORNIA, LOS ANGELES CA 90024
RODGERS, ARTHUR E, PHIL DEPT, ST CHAS BORROMEO SEM, PHILADELPHIA PA 19151
RODGERS, B W, DEPT OF HUM, FREDERICK COM COL, FREDERICK MD 21701
RODIER, DAVID F, PHIL DEPT, THE AMERICAN UNIV, WASHINGTON DC 20016
RODRIGUE, MARCEL, PHIL DEPT, LE SEM ST GEORGES, VL-ST-GEORGES QUE CAN
RODRIGUE, REAL, COL EDOUARD-MONTPETIT, LONGUEUIL, QUE CAN
RODRIGUEZ, F C, PHILOSOPHY DEPT, RICE UNIVERSITY, HOUSTON TX 77001
RODRIGUEZ, V, PHIL DEPT, AQUINAS COLLEGE, GRAND RAPIDS MI 49506
RODRIQUEZ, BENJAMIN, PHIL & RELIG, INTERAMER UNIVERSITY, RAMEY AFB PR 00604
ROEDEL, FRANCIS, LIBR ARTS FAC, ATHENAEUM OF OHIO, CINCINNATI OH 45230
ROELOFS, RICHARD, HUMAN DIV, KIRKLAND COLLEGE, CLINTON NY 13323
ROELOFS, ROBERT T, PHIL DEPT, UNIV OF NEVADA, RENO NV 89507
ROGERS, BEN F, PHIL DEPT, WICHITA ST UNIV, WICHITA KS 67208
ROGERS, C THOMAS, PHIL DEPT, INDIANA UNIVERSITY, SOUTH BEND IN 46615
ROGERS, DAVID L, PHILOSOPHY DEPT, UNIV OF HOUSTON, HOUSTON TX 77004
ROGERS, HERBERT F, RELIG & PHIL DEPT, CLARK COLLEGE, ATLANTA GA 30314
ROGERS, KIM, PHIL DEPT, E TENNESSEE ST UNIV, JOHNSON CITY TN 37601
ROGERS, LEWIS M, PHILOSOPHY DEPT, UNIV OF UTAH, SALT LAKE CTY UT 84112
ROGERS, ROBERT, PHIL DEPT, UNIV OF COLORADO, BOULDER CO 80302
ROGERS, THOMAS, KENTUCKY WESLEYAN COL, OWENSBORO, KY 42301
ROHATYN, DENNIS A, PHIL DEPT, ROOSEVELT UNIVERSITY, CHICAGO IL 60605
ROHR, MICHAEL, PHILOSOPHY DEPT, RUTGERS UNIV, NEWARK NJ 07102
ROHR, VINCENT, PHILOSOPHY DEPT, ST FIDELIS COLLEGE, HERMAN PA 16039
ROJAS OSSORIO, C, PHIL DEPT, CATHOLIC UNIVERSITY, PONCE PR 00731
ROJAS, BILLY, HUMAN DEPT, ALICE LLOYD COLLEGE, PIPPA PASSES KY 41844
ROJO SEIJAS, JOSE, PHIL DEPT, CATHOLIC UNIVERSITY, PONCE PR 00731
ROJO SEIJAS, LUIS, HUMAN DEPT, UNIV OF PUERTO RICO, MAYAGUEZ PR 00708
ROLFE, RHEA, SOUTH MISSIONARY COL, COLLEGEDALE, TN 37315
ROLLIN, BERNARD E, PHIL DEPT, COLORADO ST UNIV, FORT COLLINS CO 80521

ROLLINS, C D, PHIL DEPT, UNIV OF CONNECTICUT, STORRS CT 06268
ROLSTON III, HOLMES, PHIL DEPT, COLORADO ST UNIV, FORT COLLINS CO 80521
ROLSTON, HOWARD L, PHIL DEPT, GEORGETOWN UNIV, WASHINGTON DC 20007
ROLSTON, J S, POLIT SCI & PHIL, WEBER STATE COLLEGE, OGDEN UT 84403
ROMA III, EMILIO, PHIL DEPT, ST UNIV OF NY, BINGHAMTON NY 13901
ROMAN, MARK D, PHIL DEPT, ST LOUIS UNIVERSITY, ST LOUIS MO 63103
ROMANE, JOSEPH J, CABRINI COLLEGE, RADNOR, PA 19087
ROMANELL, PATRICK, PHILOSOPHY DEPT, UNIV OF TEXAS, EL PASO TX 79968
ROMANO, CHRISTOPHER, PHIL DEPT, THE AMERICAN UNIV, WASHINGTON DC 20016
ROMANOS, GEORGE, PHIL DEPT, BOSTON UNIVERSITY, BOSTON MA 02215
ROMANSKI, RONALD, PHIL DEPT, DEPAUL UNIVERSITY, CHICAGO IL 60604
ROMINGER, ROBERT, SOC STUD DEPT, MISS GULF COAST JR C, PERKINSTON MS 39573
ROOD, HAROLD J, PHILOSOPHY DEPT, WASHBURN UNIVERSITY, TOPEKA KS 66621
ROOKS, CHARLES, PHIL DEPT, THOMAS MORE COLLEGE, COVINGTON KY 41017
ROONEY, MATTHEW A, ST PETER'S COLLEGE, JERSEY CITY, NJ 07306
ROOT, DAVID, PHILOSOPHY DEPT, ATLANTA CHRIST COL, EAST POINT GA 30344
ROOT, MICHAEL, PHIL DEPT, UNIV OF MINNESOTA, MINNEAPOLIS MN 55455
ROPER, JAMES E, PHIL DEPT, MICHIGAN STATE UNIV, EAST LANSING MI 48823
ROQUE, ALICIA, PHIL DEPT, CALIFORNIA ST UNIV, SAN FRANCISCO CA 94132
RORTY, AMELIE O, PHILOSOPHY DEPT, RUTGERS UNIV, NEW BRUNSWICK NJ 08903
RORTY, RICHARD, PHIL DEPT, PRINCETON UNIVERSITY, PRINCETON NJ 08540
ROSE, BEA, CHAFFEY COLLEGE, ALTA LOMA, CA 91701
ROSE, DELBERT R, THEOL & PHIL DIV, ASBURY THEOL SEM, WILMORE KY 40390
ROSE, DUDLEY C, LIBR ARTS DEPT, NORTHAMPTON JR COL, NORTHAMPTON MA 01060
ROSE, LARRY, REL & PHIL, BAKER UNIVERSITY, BALDWIN CITY KS 66006
ROSE, LYNN E, PHIL DEPT, ST UNIV OF NY, AMHERST NY 14226
ROSE, MARY CARMAN, PHIL DEPT, GOUCHER COLLEGE, TOWNSON MD 21204
ROSE, ROBERT, PHILOSOPHY DEPT, UNIV DU QUEBEC, 3-RIVIERES QUE CAN
ROSEN, BERNARD, PHILOSOPHY DEPT, OHIO STATE UNIV, COLUMBUS OH 43210
ROSEN, DEBORAH, LOUISIANA ST UNIV, NEW ORLEANS, LA 70122
ROSEN, IRA, PHIL DEPT, ST UNIV OF NY, STONY BROOK NY 11790
ROSEN, JAY, PHIL DEPT, MICHIGAN STATE UNIV, EAST LANSING MI 48823
ROSEN, JEFFREY, PHILOSOPHY DEPT, RUTGERS UNIV, NEW BRUNSWICK NJ 08903
ROSEN, STANLEY, PHILOSOPHY DEPT, PENN STATE UNIV, UNIV PARK PA 16802
ROSENBAUM, DOROTHY H, PHIL DEPT, HOWARD UNIVERSITY, WASHINGTON DC 20001
ROSENBAUM, STEPHEN E, PHILOSOPHY DEPT, ILLINOIS ST UNIV, NORMAL IL 61761
ROSENBAUM, STUART, PHIL DEPT, GUSTAVUS ADOLPHUS COL, ST PETER MN 56082
ROSENBERG, ALEXANDER, PHIL DEPT, DALHOUSIE UNIVERSITY, HALIFAX N S CAN
ROSENBERG, FRED C, PHIL DEPT, UNIV OF N CAROLINA, CHAPEL HILL NC 27514
ROSENBERG, JAY F, PHIL DEPT, UNIV OF N CAROLINA, CHAPEL HILL NC 27514
ROSENBERG, JEAN, COL OF NOTRE DAME, BALTIMORE, MD 21210
ROSENBERG, MILTON, HUMAN DEPT, COL OF LAKE COUNTY, GRAYSLAKE IL 60030
ROSENBERG, RICHARD, ST MARY'S COL OF CAL, MORAGA, CA 94575
ROSENKRANTZ, GARY, PHILOSOPHY DEPT, BROWN UNIVERSITY, PROVIDENCE RI 02912
ROSENKRANTZ, ROGER, PHILOSOPHY DEPT, UNIV OF S CAROLINA, COLUMBIA SC 29208
ROSENSTEIN, LEON, PHIL DEPT, CALIFORNIA ST UNIV, SAN DIEGO CA 92115
ROSENTHAL, A, PHILOSOPHY DEPT, UNIV OF TORONTO, TORONTO ONT CAN
ROSENTHAL, ABIGAIL, PHIL DEPT, BROOKLYN COLLEGE, BROOKLYN NY 11210
ROSENTHAL, CHARLES, PHIL DEPT, BOWLING GREEN UNIV, BOWLING GREEN OH 43403
ROSENTHAL, DAVID, PHIL DEPT, LEHMAN COLLEGE, BRONX NY 10468
ROSENTHAL, ROBERT J, PHIL DEPT, HANOVER COLLEGE, HANOVER IN 47243
ROSENTHAL, SANDRA, PHIL DEPT, LOYOLA UNIVERSITY, NEW ORLEANS LA 70118
ROSS, DAVID ANTHONY, PHILOSOPHY DEPT, UNIV OF TEXAS, AUSTIN TX 78712
ROSS, DAVID L, PHILOSOPHY DEPT, UNIV OF DELAWARE, NEWARK DE 19711
ROSS, DAVID, PHILOSOPHY DEPT, DUKE UNIVERSITY, DURHAM NC 27706
ROSS, FLOYD H, SOC SCI DEPT, CAL ST POLYTECH UNIV, POMONA CA 91768
ROSS, GARY M, LOMA LINDA UNIV, RIVERSIDE, CA 92505
ROSS, GREGORY A, PHILOSOPHY DEPT, EAST CAROLINA UNIV, GREENVILLE NC 27834
ROSS, JAMES F, PHILOSOPHY DEPT, UNIV OF PENN, PHILADELPHIA PA 19174
ROSS, KELLEY L, PHIL DEPT, UNIVERSITY OF HAWAII, HONOLULU HI 96822
ROSS, M, PHILOSOPHY DEPT, UNIV OF ALBERTA, EDMONTON ALB CAN
ROSS, RALPH, PHILOSOPHY DEPT, SCRIPPS COLLEGE, CLAREMONT CA 91711
ROSS, ROBERT, PHIL & PSYCH DEPT, LINCOLN CHRIST COL, LINCOLN IL 62656
ROSS, STEPHEN, PHIL DEPT, ST UNIV OF NY, BINGHAMTON NY 13901

ROSS, W GORDON, PHIL & REL DEPT, BEREA COLLEGE, BEREA KY   40403
ROSS, WALTER B, HIST DEPT, DUTCHESS COM COL, POUGHKEEPSIE NY 12601
ROSSI, PHILIP JOSEPH, PHILOSOPHY DEPT, UNIV OF TEXAS, AUSTIN TX   78712
ROSSINI, F A, SOC SCI DEPT, GEORGIA INST OF TECH, ATLANTA GA   30332
ROSSNER, WILLIAM, PHIL DEPT, ROCKHURST COLLEGE, KANSAS CITY MO 64110
ROSTHAL, ROBERT, PHIL DEPT, UNIV OF N CAROLINA, GREENSBORO NC 27412
ROTH, JOHN K, PHIL DEPT, CLAREMONT MEN'S COL, CLAREMONT CA 91711
ROTH, JOSEPH S, PHIL DEPT, CANISIUS COLLEGE, BUFFALO NY 14208
ROTH, MICHAEL, PHIL DEPT, FRANKLIN & MARSHALL, LANCASTER PA 17604
ROTH, ROBERT J, PHIL DEPT, FORDHAM UNIVERSITY, BRONX NY 10458
ROTH, ROBERT, SYST THEOL DEPT, NW LUTH THEOL SEM, ST PAUL MN 55108
ROTH, SOL, PHIL DEPT, YESHIVA UNIVERSITY, NEW YORK NY 10033
ROTHBART, DANIEL, PHIL DEPT, ST UNIV OF NY, BINGHAMTON NY 13901
ROTHBERY, DONALD, PHIL DEPT, BOSTON UNIVERSITY, BOSTON MA 02215
ROTHENBERG, ALBERT, PHILOSOPHY DEPT, PENN STATE UNIV, UNIV PARK PA 16802
ROTHERMEL, DENNIS, PHIL DEPT, NORTHWESTERN UNIV, EVANSTON IL 60201
ROTHSCHILD, FRITZ, PHIL & REL DEPT, JEWISH THEOL SEM, NEW YORK NY 10027
ROTHWELL, MEL THOMAS, BETHANY NAZARENE COL, BETHANY, OK 73008
ROTONDO, JOSEPH T, PHIL DEPT, UNIV OF ROCHESTER, ROCHESTER NY 14627
ROTTMAYER, WILLIAM, PHILOSOPHY DEPT, E WASHINGTON ST COL, CHENEY WA 99004
ROTTSCHAEFER, WILLIAM, PHIL DEPT, CCL AT PLATTSBURGH, PLATTSBURGH NY 12901
ROULEAU, M CELESTE, PHILOSOPHY DEPT, RUSSELL COLLEGE, BURLINGAME CA 94010
ROUPAS, T G, PHIL DEPT, UNIV OF CONNECTICUT, STORRS CT 06268
ROUSE, DAVID, PHILOSOPHY DEPT, VANDERBILT UNIV, NASHVILLE TN 37235
ROUSE, JOSEPH, PHIL DEPT, NORTHWESTERN UNIV, EVANSTON IL 60201
ROUSSEAU, EDWARD L, PHILOSOPHY DEPT, MARQUETTE UNIV, MILWAUKEE WI 53233
ROUZER, NANCY C, HUMAN DEPT, CEN PIEDMONT COM COL, CHARLOTTE NC 28204
ROWAN, ROBERT J, PHIL DEPT, UNIV BRIT COLUMBIA, VANCOUVER B B C   CAN
ROWE, JOHN P, DIV OF EDUC, PACIFIC CHRISTIAN COL, LONG BEACH CA 90804
ROWE, WILLIAM L, PHIL DEPT, PURDUE UNIVERSITY, LAFAYETTE IN 47907
ROY, EUGENE, PHILOSOPHY DEPT, LOYOLA COLLEGE, MONTREAL QUE   CAN
ROY, JACQUES, PHIL DEPT, COL RIVIERE DU LOUP, RIVIERE LOUP QUE   CAN
ROY, JEAN, PHILOSOPHY DEPT, UNIV DE MONTREAL, MONTREAL QUE   CAN
ROY, MAYO RAE, PHIL DEPT, CLACKAMAS COM COL, OREGON CITY OR 97045
ROY, SUBODH, PHIL DEPT, STATEN IS COM COL, STATEN ISLAND NY 10301
ROY, YVES, PHIL DEPT, COL TROIS-RIVIERES, 3 RIVIERES QUE   CAN
ROYCE, THOMAS R, PHILOSOPHY DEPT, GONZAGA UNIV, SPOKANE WA 99202
ROYER, TORRENCE L, PHILOSOPHY DEPT, ARIZONA STATE UNIV, TEMPE AZ 85281
ROYSE, JAMES R, PHIL DEPT, CALIFORNIA ST UNIV, SAN FRANCISCO CA 94132
RUANE, ED, ST EDWARD'S UNIV, AUSTIN, TX 78704
RUANE, T J, PHIL FACULTY, UNIV OF OTTAWA, OTTAWA ONT   CAN
RUANO, ARGIMIRO, HUMAN DEPT, UNIV OF PUERTO RICO, MAYAGUEZ PR 00708
RUBIN, ALVAN D, PHIL DEPT, ST LOUIS UNIVERSITY, ST LOUIS MO 63103
RUBIN, RICHARD M, PHIL DEPT, WASHINGTON UNIV, ST LOUIS MO 63130
RUBIN, RONALD G, PHIL DEPT, PITZER COLLEGE, CLAREMONT CA 91750
RUBINOFF, M L, PHIL DEPT, TRENT UNIVERSITY, PETERBOROUGH ONT   CAN
RUBINSTEIN, R, PHILOSOPHY DEPT, UNIV OF TORONTO, TORONTO ONT   CAN
RUBLE, RAYMOND S, APPALACHIAN ST UNIV, BOONE, NC 28607
RUBY, LIONEL, PHIL DEPT, ROOSEVELT UNIVERSITY, CHICAGO IL 60605
RUCHTI, WARREN, PHILOSOPHY DEPT, OHIO UNIVERSITY, ATHENS OH 45701
RUCKER, DARNELL, PHIL DEPT, SKIDMORE COLLEGE, SARATOGA SPGS NY 12886
RUDAVSKY, TAMAR, PHIL DEPT, BRANDEIS UNIVERSITY, WALTHAM MA 02154
RUDDICK, C T, PHIL DEPT, LAKE ERIE COLLEGE, PAINESVILLE OH 44077
RUDDICK, WILLIAM, PHIL DEPT, NEW YORK UNIVERSITY, NEW YORK NY 10003
RUDE, RICHARD, PHILOSOPHY DEPT, UNIV OF TEXAS, AUSTIN TX 78712
RUDINOW, JOEL, PHIL DEPT, UNIV OF WEST ONTARIO, LONDON ONT   CAN
RUDNER, RICHARD S, PHIL DEPT, WASHINGTON UNIV, ST LOUIS MO 63130
RUDOFF, JOHN, PHILOSOPHY DEPT, MARQUETTE UNIV, MILWAUKEE WI 53233
RUESHOFF, AGNES V, PHIL DEPT, COL OF ST ELIZABETH, CONVENT STA NJ 07961
RUEST, PAUL, PHIL DEPT, COL RIVIERE DU LOUP, RIVIERE LOUP QUE   CAN
RUF, HENRY, PHIL DEPT, COL AT OSWEGO, OSWEGO NY 13126
RUGGERI, JOHN, GWYNEDD-MERCY COL, GWYNEDD VLY, PA 19437
RUGGIERO, VINCENT RYAN, HUMAN DEPT, AGR & TECH COLLEGE, DELHI NY 13753
RUHLEN, RALPH, REL & PHIL, BAKER UNIVERSITY, BALDWIN CITY KS 66006

RUIZ CORDOBES, S, HUMAN DEPT, UNIV OF PUERTO RICO, PONCE PR 00731
RUJA, HARRY, PHIL DEPT, CALIFORNIA ST UNIV, SAN DIEGO CA 92115
RUKAVINA, THOMAS, PHILOSOPHY DEPT, GONZAGA UNIV, SPOKANE WA 99202
RUMBAUGH, LIELA M, PHIL DEPT, NORTH CENTRAL COL, NAPERVILLE IL 60540
RUMSEY, WILLIAM, PHIL DEPT, COLUMBIA UNIVERSITY, NEW YORK NY 10027
RUNKLE, GERALD J T, PHIL STUD DEPT, S ILLINOIS UNIV, EDWARDSVILLE IL 62025
RUNNER, EVAN, PHIL DEPT, CALVIN COLLEGE, GRAND RAPIDS MI 49506
RUNYAN, MARY, PHIL DEPT, BALL ST UNIVERSITY, MUNCIE IN 47306
RUSE, M E, PHILOSOPHY DEPT, UNIV OF GUELPH, GUELPH ONT CAN
RUSH, VINCENT E, PHIL DEPT, COL OF ST THOMAS, ST PAUL MN 55105
RUSK, JERRY, REL & PHIL, UNIV OF EVANSVILLE, EVANSVILLE IN 47701
RUSSELL, ANTHONY, PHIL FACULTY, UNIV OF OTTAWA, OTTAWA ONT CAN
RUSSELL, CHRISTOPHER, PHILOSOPHY DEPT, MORAVIAN COLLEGE, BETHLEHEM PA 18018
RUSSELL, J MICHAEL, PHIL DEPT, CALIFORNIA ST UNIV, FULLERTON CA 92634
RUSSELL, JOSEPH, PHILOSOPHY DEPT, QUEEN'S UNIVERSITY, KINGSTON ONT CAN
RUSSELL, MICHAEL, PHIL DEPT, UNIV OF MICHIGAN, ANN ARBOR MI 48104
RUSSELL, RICHARD, PHIL DEPT, TRINITY CHRIST COL, PALOS HEIGHTS IL 60463
RUSSELL, ROBERT P, PHILOSOPHY DEPT, VILLANOVA UNIV, VILLANOVA PA 19085
RUSSELL, WILLIAM, PHIL DEPT, UNIV OF CINCINNATI, CINCINNATI OH 45221
RUSSELLO, JAMES J, PHIL DEPT, ST UNIV OF NY, BINGHAMTON NY 13901
RUSSMAN, THOMAS, PHILOSOPHY DEPT, ST FIDELIS COLLEGE, HERMAN PA 16039
RUST, ERIC C, CHRIST PHIL DEPT, S BAPTIST THEOL SEM, LOUISVILLE KY 40206
RUTENBER, C, PHIL OF REL & THEOL, AMER BAPT SEM WEST, COVINA CA 91724
RUTH JR, LESTER R, HUM & SOC SCI, LAKE-SUMTER COM COL, LEESBURG FL 32748
RUTH, SHEILA, PHIL STUD DEPT, S ILLINOIS UNIV, EDWARDSVILLE IL 62025
RUTTENBERG, HOWARD, HUMAN DEPT, YORK COLLEGE, JAMAICA NY 11432
RYAN, ALLISON, PHIL DEPT, ROCKEFELLER UNIV, NEW YORK NY 10021
RYAN, ANDREW, PHIL DEPT, UNIV OF VIRGINIA, CHARLOTTESVL VA 22903
RYAN, BERNARD M, PHIL DEPT, MANHATTAN COLLEGE, RIVERDALE NY 10471
RYAN, CHEYNEY, PHIL DEPT, BOSTON UNIVERSITY, BOSTON MA 02215
RYAN, EUGENE E, PHILOSOPHY DEPT, EAST CAROLINA UNIV, GREENVILLE NC 27834
RYAN, JOHN J, PHIL DEPT, ST ANSELM'S COLLEGE, MANCHESTER NH 03102
RYAN, JOHN K, PHIL SCH, CATH UNIV OF AMER, WASHINGTON DC 20017
RYAN, MARY M, PHIL & THEOL, MOUNT MERCY COLLEGE, CEDAR RAPIDS IA 52402
RYAN, MICHAEL, PHIL & RELIG STUD, KING'S COLLEGE, LONDON ONT CAN
RYAN, WILLIAM, PHILOSOPHY DEPT, GONZAGA UNIV, SPOKANE WA 99202
RYAN, XAVIER, PHIL DEPT, MARIST COLLEGE, POUGHKEEPSIE NY 12601
RYBKA, HESTER W, PHIL DEPT, PALMER JR COLLEGE, DAVENPORT IA 52501
RYER, JOSEPH, PHILOSOPHY DEPT, ST VINCENT COLLEGE, LATROBE PA 15650
RYKER, KENNETH W, NORTHWOOD INSTITUTE, CEDAR HILL, TX 75104
RYNIN, DAVID, PHIL DEPT, UNIV OF CALIFORNIA, BERKELEY CA 94720
SAATKAMP, HERMAN J, HUMAN & PHIL DIV, UNIVERSITY OF TAMPA, TAMPA FL 33606
SABRI, JEAN, PHIL DEPT, COL DE VICTORIAVILLE, VICTORIAVILLE QUE CAN
SACHS, DAVID, PHIL DEPT, JOHNS HOPKINS UNIV, BALTIMORE MD 21218
SACHS, SANDRA, PHILOSOPHY DEPT, UNIV OF WATERLOO, WATERLOO ONT CAN
SACK, SUSAN, PHILOSOPHY DEPT, UNIV OF ARIZONA, TUCSON AZ 85721
SACKS, JOE, PHILOSOPHY DEPT, PENN STATE UNIV, UNIV PARK PA 16802
SACKSTEDER, WILLIAM, PHIL DEPT, UNIV OF COLORADO, BOULDER CO 80302
SADOWSKY, JAMES, PHIL DEPT, FORDHAM UNIVERSITY, BRONX NY 10458
SAETTI, JOHN A, HUMAN & PHIL DEPT, GROSSMONT COL, EL CAJON CA 92020
SAFFER, CHARLES A, BRESCIA COLLEGE, OWENSBORO, KY 42301
SAFFORD, BETTY C, PHIL DEPT, CALIFORNIA ST UNIV, FULLERTON CA 92634
SAFRAN, THEODORE R, PHIL DEPT, ARK POLYTECH COL, RUSSELLVILLE AR 72801
SAGAL, PAUL, PHIL DEPT, BOSTON UNIVERSITY, BOSTON MA 02215
SAGER, GENE, BEHAV SCI DEPT, PALOMAR COLLEGE, SAN MARCOS CA 92069
SAGOFF, MARK, PHILOSOPHY DEPT, UNIV OF PENN, PHILADELPHIA PA 19174
SAHAKIAN, WILLIAM S, PHIL DEPT, SUFFOLK UNIVERSITY, BOSTON MA 02114
SAIJO, HISAYO, P O BOX 857, SAUSALITO, CA 94965
SAIN, DANIEL D, HUM & SOC SCI, EMBRY-RIDDLE AERO U, DAYTONA BEACH FL 32015
SAINT-DENIS, HENRY, PHIL FACULTY, UNIV OF OTTAWA, OTTAWA ONT CAN
SAINT-JACQUES, A, PHIL FACULTE, UNIVERSITE LAVAL, CITE UNIV QUE CAN
SAINT-PIERRE, GAETAN, PHILOSOPHY DEPT, UNIV DU QUEBEC, MONTREAL QUE CAN
SALE, WILLIAM F, SOC SCI, GULF COAST COM COL, PANAMA CITY FL 32401
SALGADO, JOSE, PHIL DEPT, CATHOLIC UNIVERSITY, PONCE PR 00731

SALLIS, JOHN C, PHILOSOPHY DEPT, DUQUESNE UNIV, PITTSBURGH PA 15219
SALLSTROM, JOHN E, PHIL & REL, GEORGIA COLLEGE, MILLEDGEVILLE GA 31061
SALMON, ELIZABETH G, PHIL DEPT, FORDHAM UNIVERSITY, BRONX NY 10458
SALMON, MERRILEE H, PHILOSOPHY DEPT, UNIV OF ARIZONA, TUCSON AZ 85721
SALMON, WESLEY C, PHILOSOPHY DEPT, UNIV OF ARIZONA, TUCSON AZ 85721
SALOMON, HILEL B, PHILOSOPHY DEPT, UNIV OF S CAROLINA, COLUMBIA SC 29208
SALTER, DONALD, PHIL DEPT, CALIFORNIA ST UNIV, NORTHRIDGE CA 91324
SALTZMAN, GERALD, PHIL DEPT, CALIFORNIA ST UNIV, NORTHRIDGE CA 91324
SALZBERGER, RONALD, PHIL DEPT, SAINT MARY'S COLLEGE, WINONA MN 55987
SAMARANCH, FRANCISCO, HUMAN DEPT, COL OF SACRED HEART, SANTURCE PR 00914
SAMAY, SEBASTIAN, PHILOSOPHY DEPT, ST VINCENT COLLEGE, LATROBE PA 15650
SAMSON, ANDRE, PHIL DEPT, COLLEGE SAINT-LOUIS, EDMUNDSTON N B   CAN
SAMUEL, PETER, PHILOSOPHY DEPT, WASHBURN UNIVERSITY, TOPEKA KS 66621
SANABRIA, MIGUEL, PHIL DEPT, UNIVERSITY OF MIAMI, CORAL GABLES FL 33124
SANBORN, DONALD H, HUMAN DEPT, WRIGHT CY COLLEGE, CHICAGO IL 60634
SANCHEZ, HALLEY, HUMAN DEPT, UNIV OF PUERTO RICO, MAYAGUEZ PR 00708
SANDBERG, ERIC, PHILOSOPHY DEPT, PENN STATE UNIV, UNIV PARK PA 16802
SANDERS, J P, HUMAN DIV, COLUMBIAN CHRIST COL, PORTLAND OR 97220
SANDERS, JACK, PHIL DEPT, BOSTON UNIVERSITY, BOSTON MA 02215
SANDERS, STEVEN, PHIL DEPT, BRIDGEWATER ST COL, BRIDGEWATER MA 02324
SANDERS, VICTOR, PHIL DEPT, DEPAUL UNIVERSITY, CHICAGO IL 60604
SANDERSON, DONALD, PHILOSOPHY DEPT, UNIV OF TEXAS, AUSTIN TX 78712
SANDERSON, G, PHILOSOPHY DEPT, ST FRAN XAVIER UNIV, ANTIGONISH N S   CAN
SANDERSON, JOHN W, BIB & PHIL, COVENANT COLLEGE, LOOKOUT MTN TN 37350
SANDLER, ARTHUR M, PHIL DEPT, WEBSTER COLLEGE, ST LOUIS MO 63119
SANDROCK, MARQUE, PHILOSOPHY DEPT, KENT STATE UNIV, KENT OH 44242
SANDSTROM, PETER G, PHILOSOPHY DEPT, OTTAWA UNIVERSITY, OTTAWA KS 66067
SANFORD, DAVID, PHILOSOPHY DEPT, DUKE UNIVERSITY, DURHAM NC 27706
SANKER, LOUIS M, PHIL DEPT, DELTA COLLEGE, UNIV CENTER MI 48710
SANKOWSKI, EDWARD, PHIL DEPT, NORTHWESTERN UNIV, EVANSTON IL 60201
SANTACRUZ, BENEDICTO, PHIL DEPT, CATHOLIC UNIVERSITY, PONCE PR 00731
SANTAS, GERASIMOS, PHIL DEPT, UNIV OF CALIFORNIA, IRVINE CA 92664
SANTILLI, PAUL C, PHIL DEPT, BOSTON COLLEGE, CHESTNUT HILL MA 02167
SANTONI, RONALD E, PHILOSOPHY DEPT, DENISON UNIV, GRANVILLE OH 43023
SANTOS, ANTONIO, PHIL DEPT, UNIV OF CINCINNATI, CINCINNATI OH 45221
SANTULLI, MICHAEL, PHILOSOPHY DEPT, PENN STATE UNIV, HAZLETON PA 18201
SAPADIN, EUGENE, JOHNSON STATE COL, JOHNSON, VT 05656
SAPONTZIS, STEVE F, PHILOSOPHY DEPT, CALIFORNIA ST UNIV, HAYWARD CA 94542
SAPP, C L, HUMAN AFFAIRS INST, S OKLAHOMA CY JR COL, OKLAHOMA CY OK 73159
SARENAC, VESILIN, RELIG & PHIL, METHODIST COLLEGE, FAYETTEVILLE NC 28301
SARGENT, BENJAMIN, PHIL DEPT, UNIV OF SN FRANCISCO, SAN FRANCISCO CA 94117
SARGENT, ROBERT, GEN EDUC DEPT, SAN JOSE BIBLE COL, SAN JOSE CA 95108
SARKAR, ANIL K, PHILOSOPHY DEPT, CALIFORNIA ST UNIV, HAYWARD CA 94542
SARRACINO, MIA, PHIL DEPT, MILLERSVILLE ST COL, MILLERSVILLE PA 17551
SARTORELLI, LINDA M, PHIL DEPT, INDIANA UNIVERSITY, SOUTH BEND IN 46615
SARTORIUS, ROLF, PHIL DEPT, UNIV OF MINNESOTA, MINNEAPOLIS MN 55455
SASSO, JAMES, PHIL & RELIG, JERSEY CITY ST COL, JERSEY CITY NJ 07305
SATRE, THOMAS, PHIL DEPT, SAM HOUSTON ST UNIV, HUNTSVILLE TX 77340
SAUCIER, JEAN, PHIL DEPT, COL LIONEL-GROULX, STE-THERESE QUE   CAN
SAUDADE, GIL, ENGLISH DEPT, BELLEVILLE JR COL, BELLEVILLE IL 62221
SAUER, HAROLD, PHILOSOPHY DEPT, EDINBORO ST COL, EDINBORO PA 16412
SAULNIER, DENYSE, PHIL DEPT, COL LIONEL-GROULX, STE-THERESE QUE   CAN
SAULNIER, THERESE, PHIL DEPT, COL DE VICTORIAVILLE, VICTORIAVILLE QUE   CAN
SAUNDERS, JASON L, PHIL DEPT, CITY COLLEGE, NEW YORK NY 10031
SAUNDERS, JOHN TURK, PHIL DEPT, CALIFORNIA ST UNIV, NORTHRIDGE CA 91324
SAUVAGEOT, WILLIAM, PHIL DEPT, UNIV OF CALIFORNIA, IRVINE CA 92664
SAVAGE, C WADE, PHIL DEPT, UNIV OF MINNESOTA, MINNEAPOLIS MN 55455
SAVAGE, DENIS D, PHILOSOPHY DEPT, MARQUETTE UNIV, MILWAUKEE WI 53233
SAVAGE, HELEN, ENG & PHIL DEPT, LONGWOOD COLLEGE, FARMVILLE VA 23901
SAVAGE, R R, PHILOSOPHY DEPT, QUEEN'S UNIVERSITY, KINGSTON ONT   CAN
SAVAGE, TERRY, PHIL DEPT, BOSTON UNIVERSITY, BOSTON MA 02215
SAVAN, D, PHILOSOPHY DEPT, UNIV OF TORONTO, TORONTO ONT   CAN
SAVARY, CLAUDE, PHILOSOPHY DEPT, UNIV DU QUEBEC, 3-RIVIERES QUE   CAN
SAVAS, SAZAN, PHIL DEPT, ST UNIV OF NY, STONY BROOK NY 11790

SAVERY, BARNETT, PHIL DEPT, UNIV BRIT COLUMBIA, VANCOUVER 8 B C   CAN
SAVIGNAC, FRANCOIS, COLLEGE D'AHUNTSIC, MONTREAL, QUE   CAN
SAVITT, STEVEN, PHIL DEPT, UNIV BRIT COLUMBIA, VANCOUVER 8 B C   CAN
SAWYER, EDWARD H, CULVER-STOCKTON OCL, CANTON, MO 63435
SAYDAH, J ROGER, PHILOSOPHY DEPT, OHIO UNIVERSITY, ATHENS OH 45701
SAYERS, B W, PHILOSOPHY DEPT, QUEEN'S UNIVERSITY, KINGSTON ONT   CAN
SAYLES, EDWARD M, HUMAN DEPT, UNIV OF MICHIGAN, DEARBORN MI 48128
SAYRE, KENNETH, PHIL DEPT, UNIV OF NOTRE DAME, NOTRE DAME IN 46556
SAYWARD JR, CHARLES W, PHIL DEPT, UNIV OF NEBRASKA, LINCOLN NE 68502
SCALES, RONALD, PHIL DEPT, U OF CAL -SAN DIEGO, LA JOLLA CA 92037
SCALON, JOHN D, PHILOSOPHY DEPT, DUQUESNE UNIV, PITTSBURGH PA 15219
SCANLAN, JAMES P, PHILOSOPHY DEPT, OHIO STATE UNIV, COLUMBUS OH 43210
SCANLON JR, THOMAS M, PHIL DEPT, PRINCETON UNIVERSITY, PRINCETON NJ 08540
SCARBOROUGH, JOHN R, LEICESTER JR OCL, LEICESTER, MA 01524
SCARLETT, B, PHILOSOPHY DEPT, UNIV OF TORONTO, TORONTO ONT   CAN
SCARROW, DAVID S, PHIL DEPT, KALAMAZOO COLLEGE, KALAMAZOO MI 49001
SCHAAFT, GRETCHEN, PHIL DEPT, MONTGOMERY COLLEGE, TAKOMA PARK MD 20012
SCHACHT, RICHARD L, PHIL DEPT, UNIV OF ILLINOIS, URBANA IL 61801
SCHAEFER, MICHAEL P, PHILOSOPHY DEPT, UNIV OF OKLAHOMA, NORMAN OK 73069
SCHAFER, A M, PHIL DEPT, UNIV OF MANITOBA, WINNIPEG 19 MAN   CAN
SCHAFER, H, PHILOSOPHY DEPT, UNIV OF ALBERTA, EDMONTON ALB   CAN
SCHAFF, DION, PSYCH DEPT, WORCESTER STATE COL, WORCESTER MA 01602
SCHAFFNER, KENNETH, PHIL DEPT, UNIV OF PITTSBURGH, PITTSBURGH PA 15260
SCHAGLMAN, HERMAN E, PHIL OF RELIG, GARRETT THEOL SEM, EVANSTON IL 60201
SCHAGRIN, MORTON L, PHIL DEPT, COL AT FREDONIA, FREDONIA NY 14063
SCHAJOWICZ, LUDWIG, PHIL DEPT, UNIV OF PUERTO RICO, RIO PIEDRAS PR 00931
SCHALDENBRAND, MARY, PHIL DEPT, LOYOLA UNIVERSITY, CHICAGO IL 60626
SCHAMIS, JEFFREY, HUMAN DEPT, KENNEDY-KING COLLEGE, CHICAGO IL 60621
SCHANKULA, HENRY A S, PHIL DEPT, UNIV OF KENTUCKY, LEXINGTON KY 40506
SCHAPKER, HOWARD, PHIL & RELIG, JERSEY CITY ST COL, JERSEY CITY NJ 07305
SCHARFE, RONALD, GEN STUD DIV, FT WAYNE BIBLE COL, FORT WAYNE IN 46807
SCHARFF, ROBERT, PHILOSOPHY DEPT, UNIV OF NW HAMPSHIRE, DURHAM NH 03824
SCHARLE, THEODORE, PHIL DEPT, BRADLEY UNIVERSITY, PEORIA IL 61606
SCHATTLE, BRYANT, PHILOSOPHY DEPT, EDINBORO ST COL, EDINBORO PA 16412
SCHAUB, THOMAS, PHIL DEPT, INDIANA UNIV OF PENN, INDIANA PA 15701
SCHECTER, JOSEPH, COM COL OF BALTIMORE, BALTIMORE, MD 21215
SCHEDLER, NORBERT, PHIL DEPT, PURDUE UNIVERSITY, FORT WAYNE IN 46805
SCHEER, RICHARD K, PHIL DEPT, KANSAS ST UNIVERSITY, MANHATTAN KS 66506
SCHEFFLER, ISRAEL, PHIL DEPT, HARVARD UNIVERSITY, CAMBRIDGE MA 02138
SCHEIMANN, RICHARD, PHIL DEPT, VALPARAISO UNIV, VALPARAISO IN 46383
SCHEINBERG, PATRICIA, PHILOSOPHY DEPT, UNIV OF CALGARY, CALGARY 44 ALB   CAN
SCHELL, JOSEPH O, PHIL DEPT, JOHN CARROLL UNIV, UNIVERSITY HT OH 44118
SCHER, STEPHEN, PHILOSOPHY DEPT, BROWN UNIVERSITY, PROVIDENCE RI 02912
SCHERER, DONALD, PHIL DEPT, BOWLING GREEN UNIV, BOWLING GREEN OH 43403
SCHERMER, MARSHA, PHILOSOPHY DEPT, KENYON COLLEGE, GAMBIER OH 43022
SCHETTLER, JOHN, BEHAV SCI DEPT, PALOMAR COLLEGE, SAN MARCOS CA 92069
SCHEU, MARINA, PHIL & REL STUD DEPT, SILVER LAKE COL, MANITOWOC WI 54220
SCHICK, FREDERIC, PHILOSOPHY DEPT, RUTGERS UNIV, NEW BRUNSWICK NJ 08903
SCHICK, LESTER, PHIL DEPT, MICHIGAN STATE UNIV, EAST LANSING MI 48823
SCHIEVELLA, P S, PHIL & RELIG, JERSEY CITY ST COL, JERSEY CITY NJ 07305
SCHIFF, DANIEL, PHIL DEPT, COL AT GENESEO, GENESEO NY 14454
SCHIFFER, STEPHEN R, PHIL DEPT, UNIV OF CALIFORNIA, BERKELEY CA 94720
SCHILLER, JEROME P, PHIL DEPT, WASHINGTON UNIV, ST LOUIS MO 63130
SCHILPP, PAUL ARTHUR, PHIL DEPT, NORTHWESTERN UNIV, EVANSTON IL 60201
SCHIMMEL, SOL, JEWISH THT DEPT, HEBREW COLLEGE, BROOKLINE MA 02146
SCHIMOLER, ROBERT, PHIL DEPT, MARY MOUNT COLLEGE, SALINA KS 67401
SCHINSTOCK, JIM, ARTS & HUMAN, HUTCHINSON COM COL, HUTCHINSON KS 67501
SCHIPPER, GERRIT, PHIL DEPT, UNIVERSITY OF MIAMI, CORAL GABLES FL 33124
SCHIRMER, K E, SOC SCI DEPT, KELLOGG COM COLLEGE, BATTLE CREEK MI 49016
SCHLABACH, ANNE, SOC SCI DEPT, BENNINGTON COLLEGE, BENNINGTON VT 05201
SCHLAFER, DAVID J, PHILOSOPHY DEPT, TRINITY COLLEGE, DEERFIELD IL 60015
SCHLAGEL, RICHARD H, PHIL DEPT, GEORGE WASHINGTON U, WASHINGTON DC 20006
SCHLARETZKI, W ERNEST, PHIL DEPT, UNIV OF MARYLAND, COLLEGE PARK MD 20742
SCHLECHT, LUDWIG, PHILOSOPHY DEPT, MUHLENBERG COLLEGE, ALLENTOWN PA 18104

SCHLEE, CHARLES, PHIL DEPT, UNIVERSITY OF KANSAS, LAWRENCE KS 66044
SCHLEGEL, EDWARD R, PHIL DEPT, COL CF STEUBENVILLE, STEUBENVILLE OH 43952
SCHLEIFER, MICHAEL, PHILOSOPHY DEPT, MCGILL UNIVERSITY, MONTREAL QUE CAN
SCHLESINGER, GEORGE, PHIL DEPT, UNIV OF N CAROLINA, CHAPEL HILL NC 27514
SCHLESINGER, STEVEN A, PHILOSOPHY DEPT, ARIZONA STATE UNIV, TEMPE AZ 85281
SCHMELTEKOPF, DONALD, HISTORY DEPT, UNION COLLEGE, CRANFORD NJ 07016
SCHMIDKE, CHARLES, HUMAN DIV, NIAGARA CO COM COL, NIAGARA FALLS NY 14303
SCHMIDT-RAGHAVAN, M, PHIL DEPT, LONG ISLAND UNIV, GREENVALE NY 11548
SCHMIDT, DAVID, PHIL DEPT, UNIVERSITY OF KANSAS, LAWRENCE KS 66044
SCHMIDT, DELPHINE, KANSAS NEWMAN COL, WICHITA, KS 67213
SCHMIDT, MICHAEL F, PHIL DEPT, CALIFORNIA ST UNIV, SAN JOSE CA 95114
SCHMIDT, PAUL F, PHIL DEPT, UNIV OF NEW MEXICO, ALBUQUERQUE NM 87106
SCHMIDT, ROBERT W, PHILOSOPHY DEPT, XAVIER UNIVERSITY, CINCINNATI OH 45207
SCHMIDT, ROGER, PHIL DEPT, SN BERNARDINO VALLEY, SN BERNARDINO CA 92403
SCHMIEGE, OSCAR, PHIL & REL STUD DEPT, U S INTNL UNIV, SAN DIEGO CA 92131
SCHMITT, FREDERICH, PHIL DEPT, UNIV OF MICHIGAN, ANN ARBOR MI 48104
SCHMITT, RICHARD, PHILOSOPHY DEPT, BROWN UNIVERSITY, PROVIDENCE RI 02912
SCHMITT, S ROSINA, PHIL DEPT, COL OF ST BENEDICT, ST JOSEPH MN 56374
SCHMITZ, ALFRED O, HUMANITIES DIV, CONVERSE COLLEGE, SPARTANBURG SC 29301
SCHMITZ, K, UNIV OF TRINITY COL, TORONTO 181, ONT CAN
SCHMUCKER, LARRY A, PHIL DEPT, UNIV OF SOUTH DAKOTA, VERMILLION SD 57069
SCHNABEL, ROBERT V, PHILOSOPHY DEPT, CONCORDIA COLLEGE, BRONXVILLE NY 10708
SCHNALL, IRA, PHIL DEPT, YESHIVA UNIVERSITY, NEW YORK NY 10033
SCHNEEBECK, PAUL, PHIL DEPT, ST MARY'S SEM COL, PERRYVILLE MO 63775
SCHNEEBECK, PAUL, PHILOSOPHY DEPT, CARDINAL GLENNON COL, ST LOUIS MO 63119
SCHNEEWIND, JEROME, PHIL DEPT, UNIV OF PITTSBURGH, PITTSBURGH PA 15260
SCHNEIDER, HERBERT W, PHIL DEPT, COLUMBIA UNIVERSITY, NEW YORK NY 10027
SCHNEIDER, HUBERT H, PHIL DEPT, UNIV OF NEBRASKA, LINCOLN NE 68502
SCHNEIDER, MARIUS G, PHIL SCH, CATH UNIV OF AMER, WASHINGTON DC 20017
SCHNEIDER, MONICA, PHIL DEPT, MARY MOUNT COLLEGE, SALINA KS 67401
SCHNEIDER, PAUL A, PHILOSOPHY DEPT, UNIV OF OREGON, EUGENE OR 97403
SCHNEIDER, PAUL M, UNIV OF ALBUQUERQUE, ALBUQUERQUE, NM 87120
SCHNEIDER, RICHARD, SOC SCI DEPT, RIVERSIDE CITY COL, RIVERSIDE CA 92506
SCHNEITER, FRANCES, PHIL DEPT, JEFFERSON COM COL, LOUISVILLE KY 40205
SCHNETZER, O DALE, PHILOSOPHY DEPT, BOWLING GREEN UNIV, HURON OH 44839
SCHOCHET, IMMANUEL, PHILOSOPHY DEPT, UNIV OF WATERLOO, WATERLOO ONT CAN
SCHOEDINGER, ANDREW B, PHIL & POLIT SCI, BOISE ST COLLEGE, BOISE ID 83707
SCHOEMAN, FERDINAND D, PHIL DEPT, LYCOMING COLLEGE, WILLIAMSPORT PA 17701
SCHOENHOFEN, DARR, PHIL DEPT, SYRACUSE UNIVERSITY, SYRACUSE NY 13210
SCHOENIG, RICHARD K, PHIL DEPT, INDIANA UNIVERSITY, BLOOMINGTON IN 47401
SCHOENLY, STEVEN, PHIL DEPT, S ILLINOIS UNIV, CARBONDALE IL 62901
SCHOFEILD, JAMES L, SOC SCI DEPT, ONONDAGA COM COL, SYRACUSE NY 13215
SCHOLZ, DONALD, PHIL DEPT, BENEDICTINE COLLEGE, ATCHISON KS 66002
SCHORP, FRANZ, PHIL DEPT, ST MARY'S UNIVERSITY, SAN ANTONIO TX 78228
SCHOTCH, PETER K, PHIL DEPT, DALHOUSIE UNIVERSITY, HALIFAX N S CAN
SCHOUBORG, GARY ROBERT, PHILOSOPHY CEPT, UNIV OF TEXAS, AUSTIN TX 78712
SCHOULS, P A, PHILOSOPHY DEPT, UNIV OF ALBERTA, EDMONTON ALB CAN
SCHRADER, GEORGE, PHIL DEPT, YALE UNIVERSITY, NEW HAVEN CT 06520
SCHRADER, ROBERT W, HUMAN STUD DIV, UNIV OF WISCONSIN, KENOSHA WI 53140
SCHRAG, BRIAN, PHIL DEPT, HAMPDEN-SYDNEY COL, HAMPDEN-SYDNY VA 23943
SCHRAG, CALVIN O, PHIL DEPT, PURDUE UNIVERSITY, LAFAYETTE IN 47907
SCHRAG, FRANCIS K, PHILOSOPHY DEPT, UNIV OF WISCONSIN, MADISON WI 53706
SCHRAG, O OSWALD, RELIG & PHIL DEPT, FISK UNIVERSITY, NASHVILLE TN 37203
SCHRENK, LAURA, PHIL DEPT, GEORGE WASHINGTON U, WASHINGTON DC 20006
SCHROEDER, DAVID, CAN MENNONITE COL, WINNIPEG, MAN CAN
SCHUBART, W RICHARD, PHIL DEPT, GETTYSBURG COLLEGE, GETTYSBURG PA 17325
SCHUBERT, RICHARD E, PHIL DEPT, UNIV OF ILLINOIS, URBANA IL 61801
SCHUBERT, ROBERT J, PHIL DIV, PONT COL JOSEPHINUM, WORTHINGTON OH 43085
SCHUELER, G FREDERIC, PHIL DEPT, UNIV OF NEW MEXICO, ALBUQUERQUE NM 87106
SCHUERMANN, REINER, PHILOSOPHY DEPT, DUQUESNE UNIV, PITTSBURGH PA 15219
SCHUETT, JOHN T, PHIL DEPT, UNIV OF DETROIT, DETROIT MI 48221
SCHUETZINGER, C E, PHIL DEPT, MERCY COLLEGE, DETROIT MI 48219
SCHUFREIDER, GREGORY, PHIL DEPT, UNIV OF CALIFORNIA, SANTA BARBARA CA 93106
SCHUG, FRED, PHIL DEPT, COPPIN STATE COLLEGE, BALTIMORE MD 21216

SCHUH, EDWARD W, PHIL DEPT, UNIVERSITY OF MIAMI, CORAL GABLES FL 33124
SCHULDENFREI, RICHARD, PHIL DEPT, SWARTHMORE COLLEGE, SWARTHMORE PA 19081
SCHULER, JEANNE A, PHIL DEPT, WASHINGTON UNIV, ST LOUIS MO 63130
SCHULER, JOSEPH L, PHIL DEPT, UNIV OF WISCONSIN, STEVENS POINT WI 54481
SCHLLLER, PETER, PHILOSOPHY DEPT, MIAMI UNIVERSITY, OXFORD OH 45056
SCHULMEISTER, LAWRENCE, REL DEPT, UNIV OF GEORGIA, ATHENS GA 30602
SCHULTE, LYLE, PHILOSOPHY DEPT, VITERBO COLLEGE, LA CROSSE WI 54601
SCHULTZ, FREDERICK, EDUCATION COLLEGE, UNIV OF AKRON, AKRON OH 44325
SCHLLTZ, ROBERT C, PHIL DEPT, UNIV CF DENVER, DENVER CO 80210
SCHULTZ, ROBERT, PHIL DEPT, UNIV OF PITTSBURGH, PITTSBURGH PA 15260
SCHULWEIS, HAROLD, PHIL OF RELIG, UNIV OF JUDAISM, LOS ANGELES CA 90028
SCHUMACHER, JOHN A, PHIL DEPT, RENSSELAER POLYTECH, TROY NY 12181
SCHLMAKER, MILLARD, QUEEN'S THEOL CCL, KINGSTON, ONT   CAN
SCHUMM, GEORGE F, PHILOSOPHY DEPT, CHIO STATE UNIV, COLUMBUS OH 43210
SCHURR, GEORGE, PHIL PROGRAM, SANGAMON ST UNIV, SPRINGFIELD IL 62703
SCHLSTER, CYNTHIA, PHIL DEPT, UNIV CF MONTANA, MISSOULA MT 59801
SCHUTTS, E, PHIL DEPT, W CONNECTICUT ST COL, DANBURY CT 06810
SCHLWER, ANDRE, PHILOSOPHY DEPT, DUQUESNE UNIV, PITTSBURGH PA 15219
SCHUYLER, WILLIAM M, PHIL DEPT, UNIV OF LOUISVILLE, LOUISVILLE KY 40208
SCHWAGER, ROBERT L, PHIL DEPT, COL AT CORTLAND, CORTLAND NY 13045
SCHWANAUER, FRANCIS, PHIL DEPT, UNIV OF MAINE, PORTLAND ME 04103
SCHWANKL, P R, PHILOSOPHY DEPT, UNIV OF TORONTO, TORONTO ONT   CAN
SCHWARCZ, ERNEST, PHILOSOPHY DEPT, QUEENS COLLEGE, FLUSHING NY 11367
SCHWARTZ, ADINA, PHIL DEPT, ROCKEFELLER UNIV, NEW YORK NY 10021
SCHWARTZ, GERALD M, PHIL DEPT, UNIVERSITY OF HAWAII, HONOLULU HI 96822
SCHWARTZ, LEWIS, PHIL DEPT, LEHMAN COLLEGE, BRONX NY 10468
SCHWARTZ, ROBERT D, PHIL DEPT, ST UNIV OF NY, BINGHAMTON NY 13901
SCHWARTZ, ROBERT J, PHIL DEPT, WASHINGTON UNIV, ST LOUIS MO 63130
SCHWARTZ, ROBERT, PHIL DEPT, BROOKLYN COLLEGE, BROOKLYN NY 11210
SCHWARTZ, STEPHEN, PHIL & REL DEPT, ITHACA COLLEGE, ITHACA NY 14850
SCHWARTZ, THOMAS, PHIL DEPT, CARNEGIE-MELLON UNIV, PITTSBURGH PA 15213
SCHWARZ, ROBERT, PHIL DEPT, FLORIDA ATLANTIC U, BOCA RATON FL 33432
SCHWARZ, STEPHEN, PHILOSOPHY DEPT, UNIV OF RHODE ISLAND, KINGSTON RI 02881
SCHWARZSCHILD, S S, PHIL DEPT, WASHINGTON UNIV, ST LOUIS MO 63130
SCHWEDER, WILLIAM H, PHIL DEPT, GEORGETOWN UNIV, WASHINGTON DC 20007
SCHWEICKART, CHARLES, PHILOSOPHY DEPT, OHIO STATE UNIV, COLUMBUS OH 43210
SCHWIMMER, SEYMOUR, PHIL DEPT, BLOOMSBURG ST COL, BLOOMSBURG PA 17815
SCHWYZER, HUBERT, PHIL DEPT, UNIV OF CALIFORNIA, SANTA BARBARA CA 93106
SCLAFANI, R J, PHILOSOPHY DEPT, RICE UNIVERSITY, HOUSTON TX 77001
SCOFIELD, RUSSELL G, LESLEY COLLEGE, CAMBRIDGE, MA 02183
SCORE II, JOHN N R, RELIG & PHIL, SOUTHWESTERN UNIV, GEORGETOWN TX 78626
SCOTT-CRAIG, T S K, PHILOSOPHY DEPT, DARTMOUTH COLLEGE, HANOVER NH 03755
SCOTT, BRUCE A, PHIL DEPT, BOSTON STATE COL, BOSTON MA 02115
SCOTT, CHARLES E, PHILOSOPHY DEPT, VANDERBILT UNIV, NASHVILLE TN 37235
SCOTT, EDWARD, PHILOSOPHY DEPT, DUQLESNE UNIV, PITTSBURGH PA 15219
SCOTT, FRANCES, PHIL DEPT, COL OF ST FRANCIS, JOLIET IL 60435
SCOTT, FREDERICK J D, PHIL DEPT, CALIFORNIA ST UNIV, SAN JOSE CA 95114
SCOTT, GEORGE E, PHILOSOPHY DEPT, WARREN WILSON COL, SWANNANOA NC 28778
SCOTT, J JULIUS, PHIL & RELIG, WEST KENTUCKY UNIV, BOWLING GREEN KY 42101
SCOTT, JAMES H, PHIL DEPT, UNIV OF ARKANSAS, FAYETTEVILLE AR 72701
SCOTT, STEVEN, PHILOSOPHY DEPT, E WASHINGTON ST COL, CHENEY WA 99004
SCOTT, T KERMIT, PHIL DEPT, PURDUE UNIVERSITY, LAFAYETTE IN 47907
SCOTT, ULRIC, PHIL DEPT, SAINT MARY'S COLLEGE, WINONA MN 55987
SCOTT, WALTER G, PHIL DEPT, OKLAHOMA STATE UNIV, STILLWATER OK 74074
SCRIBNER, PHILLIP H, PHIL DEPT, THE AMERICAN UNIV, WASHINGTON DC 20016
SCRIVEN, MICHAEL, PHIL DEPT, UNIV OF CALIFORNIA, BERKELEY CA 94720
SCUDDER JR, JOHN R, PHILOSOPHY DEPT, LYNCHBURG COL, LYNCHBURG VA 24504
SCULLY, EDWARD, PHIL FACULTY, UNIV CF OTTAWA, OTTAWA ONT   CAN
SCULLY, JOHN, PHILOSOPHY DEPT, UNIV OF DELAWARE, NEWARK DE 19711
SEAMAN, FRANCIS, PHIL DEPT, UNIVERSITY OF IDAHO, MOSCOW ID 83843
SEARLE, JOHN R, PHIL DEPT, UNIV OF CALIFORNIA, BERKELEY CA 94720
SEARLES, HERBERT L, PHIL SCH, UNIV CF S CALIFORNIA, LOS ANGELES CA 90007
SEBESTYEN, PAUL, PHIL DEPT, NORTH PARK COLLEGE, CHICAGO IL 60625
SEDEY, DANIEL, PHIL DEPT, CALIFORNIA ST UNIV, NORTHRIDGE CA 91324

SEDHI, ZIAOLLAH, PHIL DEPT, UNIVERSITY OF DAYTON, DAYTON OH 45469
SEEBALDT, DOROTHY, PHIL DEPT, MERCY COLLEGE, DETROIT MI 48219
SEEBOHM, THOMAS M, PHILOSOPHY DEPT, PENN STATE UNIV, UNIV PARK PA 16802
SEEBURGER, FRANCIS, PHIL DEPT, UNIV OF DENVER, DENVER CO 80210
SEERVELD, CALVIN, PHIL DEPT, TRINITY CHRIST COL, PALOS HEIGHTS IL 60463
SEESKIN, KENNETH R, PHIL DEPT, NORTHWESTERN UNIV, EVANSTON IL 60201
SEFLER, GEORGE, PHIL DEPT, MANSFIELD ST COLLEGE, MANSFIELD PA 16933
SEGAL, JEROME L, HUMAN DEPT, WRIGHT CY COLLEGE, CHICAGO IL 60634
SEIDEL, ASHER, PHILOSOPHY DEPT, MIAMI UNIVERSITY, OXFORD OH 45056
SEIDEL, GEORGE J, PHILOSOPHY DEPT, ST MARTIN'S COLLEGE, OLYMPIA WA 98503
SEIDENSTICKER, W D, ENG & PHIL, SE MISSOURI ST COL, CAPE GIRARDEA MO 63701
SEIDLER, MICHAEL J, PHIL DEPT, ST LOUIS UNIVERSITY, ST LOUIS MO 63103
SEIFERT, HARVEY J, S CAL SCH OF THEOL, CLAREMONT, CA 91711
SEIFERT, JOSEF, PHIL DEPT, UNIVERSITY OF DALLAS, IRVING TX 75062
SEIGFRIED, HANS, PHIL DEPT, LOYOLA UNIVERSITY, CHICAGO IL 60626
SEIZ, MARK A, PHIL DEPT, ST UNIV OF NY, BINGHAMTON NY 13901
SELCIN, IRVING, PHIL DEPT, UNIV OF MICHIGAN, ANN ARBOR MI 48104
SELEMAN, STEPHEN, PHIL DEPT, HOLY APOSTLES COL, CROMWELL CT 06416
SELF, E B, HUMAN DIV, HOPKINSVILLE COM COL, HOPKINSVILLE KY 42240
SELF, J M, PHIL DEPT, UNIV OF FLORIDA, GAINESVILLE FL 32611
SELIGMAN, DAVID B, PHIL DEPT, N ILLINOIS UNIV, DEKALB IL 60115
SELIGMAN, PAUL, PHILOSOPHY DEPT, UNIV OF WATERLOO, WATERLOO ONT   CAN
SELK, EUGENE E, PHIL DEPT, CREIGHTON UNIV, OMAHA NE 68178
SELL JR, RALPH W, LANG ARTS DEPT, LEHIGH CO COM COL, SCHNECKSVILLE PA 18078
SELLARS, WILFRID, PHIL DEPT, UNIV OF PITTSBURGH, PITTSBURGH PA 15260
SELTZER, EDWARD, QUEENSBOROUGH COM COL, NEW YORK, NY 11364
SEMAN, PAUL, HUMANITIES DEPT, SINCLAIR COM COL, DAYTON OH 45402
SEMERARO, RICHARD P, PHIL DIV, PONT COL JOSEPHINUM, WORTHINGTON OH 43085
SENDAYDIEGO, HENRY B, PHILOSOPHY DEPT, WHEELING COLLEGE, WHEELING WV 26003
SENDRY, JEANETTE, PHIL DEPT, UNIV OF CALIFORNIA, LOS ANGELES CA 90024
SENECAL, FRANCE, COL EDOUARD-MONTPETIT, LONGUEUIL, QUE   CAN
SENESCHAL, THEODORE, HUMANITIES DIV, SAINT GREGORY'S COL, SHAWNEE OK 74801
SENIOR, ROBERT C, SOC SCI DEPT, NEWTON JR COL, NEWTONVILLE MA 02160
SENSAT, JULIUS, PHILOSOPHY DEPT, UNIV OF TEXAS, AUSTIN TX 78712
SENSKI, NORMAN, HUMAN DEPT, AMUNDSEN-MAYFAIR COL, CHICAGO IL 60630
SENTER, NELL W, PHIL DEPT, TEXAS CHRISTIAN UNIV, FORT WORTH TX 76129
SERAFINI, ANTHONY L, PHIL DEPT, BOSTON STATE COL, BOSTON MA 02115
SERAN, WILLIAM, PHIL DEPT, WAYNE STATE UNIV, DETROIT MI 48202
SERAN, WILLIAM, PHIL DEPT, ST CLOUD ST COL, ST CLOUD MN 56301
SEREN, MARJORIE, PHIL & RELIG DEPT, NATIONAL COL OF EDUC, EVANSTON IL 60201
SERENE, EILEEN, PHIL DEPT, STANFORD UNIVERSITY, STANFORD CA 94305
SERTIC, JOHN, AMERICAN RIVER COL, SACRAMENTO, CA 95841
SESEK, RAPHAEL, PHIL DEPT, IMMACULATA COLLEGE, IMMACULATA PA 19345
SESONSKE, ALEX, PHIL DEPT, UNIV OF CALIFORNIA, SANTA BARBARA CA 93106
SESSIONS, GEORGE S, PHILOSOPHY DEPT, SIERRA COLLEGE, ROCKLIN CA 95677
SESSIONS, LAD, PHILOSOPHY DEPT, WASH & LEE UNIV, LEXINGTON VA 24450
SETTLE, EDWIN T, PHIL & REL DEPT, CCE COLLEGE, CEDAR RAPIDS IA 52402
SETTLE, T W, PHILOSOPHY DEPT, UNIV OF GUELPH, GUELPH ONT   CAN
SEUNG, THOMAS K, PHILOSOPHY DEPT, UNIV OF TEXAS, AUSTIN TX 78712
SEVENSKY, ROBERT L, PHIL DEPT, BOSTON COLLEGE, CHESTNUT HILL MA 02167
SEVERENS, RICHARD H, PHIL & REL DEPT, UNIV OF GEORGIA, ATHENS GA 30602
SEWARD, ROBERT, PHIL DEPT, CEN VIRGINIA COM COL, LYNCHBURG VA 24502
SFEKAS, STANELY, PHIL DEPT, BROOKLYN COLLEGE, BROOKLYN NY 11210
SH-VEEV, CHARLES L, LIBR ARTS SCH, HAWAII PACIFIC COL, HONOLULU HI 96813
SHACKELFORD III, E A, SOC SCI DEPT, KUTZTOWN STATE COL, KUTZTOWN PA 19530
SHAFER, CAROLYN, REL DEPT, UNIV OF GEORGIA, ATHENS GA 30602
SHAFFER, J A, PHIL DEPT, UNIV OF CONNECTICUT, STORRS CT 06268
SHAHAN, ROBERT W, PHILOSOPHY DEPT, UNIV OF OKLAHOMA, NORMAN OK 73069
SHAIKUN, GLENN, PHIL DEPT, COLLEGE AT BROCKPORT, BROCKPORT NY 14420
SHALOM, ALBERT, PHILOSOPHY DEPT, MCMASTER UNIVERSITY, HAMILTON ONT   CAN
SHALVEY, THOMAS, PHIL DEPT, S CONNECTICUT ST COL, NEW HAVEN CT 06515
SHAMEAM, ARIFA, PHIL DEPT, UNIVERSITY OF HAWAII, HONOLULU HI 96822
SHANEY, KATHERINE, SOC STUD DEPT, SANTA MONICA COL, SANTA MONICA CA 90405
SHANEY, KATHY, PHIL DEPT, UNIV OF CALIFORNIA, LOS ANGELES CA 90024

SHANDALOW, NEIL, PHIL DEPT, COL AT ONEONTA, ONEONTA NY 13820
SHANG, PAUL, PHIL DEPT, FLORIDA STATE UNIV, TALLAHASSEE FL 32306
SHANKER, GEORGE, PSYCH & SOC SCI, PACE COLLEGE, PLEASANTVILLE NY 10570
SHANKS, JAMES, PHIL DEPT, MICHIGAN STATE UNIV, EAST LANSING MI 48823
SHAPERE, DUDLEY, PHIL DEPT, UNIV OF ILLINOIS, URBANA IL 61801
SHAPIRA, MICHAEL S, PHIL DEPT, UNIV OF ILLINOIS, URBANA IL 61801
SHAPIRO, DANIEL, PHIL DEPT, HUNTER COLLEGE, NEW YORK NY 10021
SHAPIRO, DAVID, PHIL & REL DEPT, HEBREW THEOL COL, SKOKIE IL 60076
SHAPIRO, DAVID, JEWISH THT DEPT, HEBREW COLLEGE, BROOKLINE MA 02146
SHAPIRO, GARY, PHIL DEPT, UNIVERSITY OF KANSAS, LAWRENCE KS 66044
SHAPIRO, HENRY L, PHIL DEPT, UNIV OF MISSOURI, ST LOUIS MO 63121
SHAPIRO, HERMAN, PHIL DEPT, CALIFORNIA ST UNIV, SAN JOSE CA 95114
SHAPIRO, VIVIAN M, LIT & LANG DEPT, DREXEL UNIV, PHILADELPHIA PA 19104
SHAPLEY, SUSAN, PHIL DEPT, HUNTER COLLEGE, NEW YORK NY 10021
SHARKEY, PAUL W, PHIL DEPT, MT ST MARY'S COL, LOS ANGELES CA 90049
SHARKEY, ROBERT, PHILOSOPHY DEPT, MCGILL UNIVERSITY, MONTREAL QUE CAN
SHARMA, VED P, PHIL DEPT, CALIFORNIA ST UNIV, SAN JOSE CA 95114
SHARP, G, PHILOSOPHY DEPT, UNIV OF ALBERTA, EDMONTON ALB CAN
SHARP, W D, PHILOSOPHY DEPT, UNIV OF ALBERTA, EDMONTON ALB CAN
SHARPE, CHARLES, SOC & PHIL DEPT, TENN TECH UNIV, COOKEVILLE TN 38501
SHARTIN, DANIEL, PHIL DEPT, UNIV OF CALIFORNIA, LOS ANGELES CA 90024
SHARVY, RICHARD, PHIL DEPT, SWARTHMORE COLLEGE, SWARTHMORE PA 19081
SHAVER, JOHN, PHILOSOPHY DEPT, DUQUESNE UNIV, PITTSBURGH PA 15219
SHAW, ALBERT C, PHIL & RELIG DEPT, GLASSBORO ST COL, GLASSBORO NJ 08028
SHAW, BRIAN A, PHIL DEPT, HOLY APOSTLES COL, CROMWELL CT 06416
SHAW, DANIEL C, PHIL DEPT, N ILLINOIS UNIV, DEKALB IL 60115
SHAW, JAMES R, PHIL DEPT, UNIV OF ROCHESTER, ROCHESTER NY 14627
SHAW, JOHN P, PHIL DEPT, UNIV OF NEBRASKA, LINCOLN NE 68502
SHAW, JOHN, PHIL DEPT, BELLEVUE COLLEGE, BELLEVUE NE 68005
SHEA, DENNIS, PHIL DEPT, HUNTER COLLEGE, NEW YORK NY 10021
SHEA, HOWARD, PHILOSOPHY DEPT, ST FRAN XAVIER UNIV, ANTIGONISH N S CAN
SHEA, W WINSLOW, PHIL DEPT, UNIVERSITY OF MIAMI, CORAL GABLES FL 33124
SHEA, WILLIAM, PHILOSOPHY DEPT, MCGILL UNIVERSITY, MONTREAL QUE CAN
SHEARIN, JESSE E, THIEL COLLEGE, GREENVILLE, PA 16125
SHEARSON, W A, PHIL DEPT, BISHOP'S UNIVERSITY, LENNOXVILLE QUE CAN
SHEEHAN, ROBERT, PHIL DEPT, WINONA STATE COL, WINONA MN 55987
SHEEHAN, THOMAS, PHIL DEPT, LOYOLA UNIVERSITY, CHICAGO IL 60626
SHEEKS, R W, PHILOSOPHY DEPT, MURRAY STATE UNIV, MURRAY KY 42071
SHEHADI, FADLOU, PHILOSOPHY DEPT, RUTGERS UNIV, NEW BRUNSWICK NJ 08903
SHEITOYAN, VICTOR, PHIL DEPT, COL VIEUX-MONTREAL, MONTREAL QUE CAN
SHELBURNE, W A, PHIL DEPT, UNIV OF FLORIDA, GAINESVILLE FL 32611
SHELDON, J G, ENG & HUM DEPT, WEST NW ENGLAND COL, SPRINGFIELD MA 01119
SHELDON, WILMON, PHIL DEPT, YALE UNIVERSITY, NEW HAVEN CT 06520
SHELLEY, BRUCE, REL PHIL & APOL DEPT, CON BAPT THEOL SEM, DENVER CO 80210
SHELLEY, JOHN C, PHIL & REL DEPT, FRANKLIN COL, FRANKLIN IN 46131
SHELLY, HAROLD, PHILOSOPHY DEPT, NYACK COLLEGE, NYACK NY 10931
SHELTON, JIMMY DALE, PHILOSOPHY DEPT, ST COL OF ARKANSAS, CONWAY AR 72032
SHENK, J PAUL, PHILOSOPHY DEPT, BELKNAP COLLEGE, CENTER HARBOR NH 03226
SHENKMAN, MICHAEL H, PHIL DEPT, BOSTON COLLEGE, CHESTNUT HILL MA 02167
SHEPARD, DARRELL R, PHILOSOPHY DEPT, WASHBURN UNIVERSITY, TOPEKA KS 66621
SHEPARD, NOLAN, PHIL & RELIG, UNIV OF MISSISSIPPI, UNIVERSITY MS 38677
SHEPARD, PAUL B, PHILOSOPHY DEPT, EL CAMINO COLLEGE, TORRENCE CA 90506
SHEPARD, PHILIP T, PHIL DEPT, MICHIGAN STATE UNIV, EAST LANSING MI 48823
SHEPHERD, ROBERT T, HUMANITIES DEPT, LANEY COLLEGE, OAKLAND CA 94606
SHER, GEORGE, FAIRLEIGH DICKINSON, TEANECK, NJ 07666
SHERBURNE, DONALD W, PHILOSOPHY DEPT, VANDERBILT UNIV, NASHVILLE TN 37235
SHERIDAN, DIANE, PHILOSOPHY DEPT, BROWN UNIVERSITY, PROVIDENCE RI 02912
SHERIDAN, GREGORY, PHIL DEPT, WEST MICHIGAN UNIV, KALAMAZOO MI 49001
SHERIDAN, JAMES F, PHIL & REL DEPT, ALLEGHENY COLLEGE, MEADVILLE PA 16335
SHERLOCK, MAUREEN, PHILOSOPHY DEPT, EDINBORO ST COL, EDINBORO PA 16412
SHERMAN, ERNEST, PSYCH & SOC SCI, PACE COLLEGE, PLEASANTVILLE NY 10570
SHERMAN, FRANKLIN E, THEOL DIV, LUTHERAN SCH OF THEO, CHICAGO IL 60615
SHERMAN, MERTON E, PHILOSOPHY DEPT, HURON COLLEGE, HURON SD 57350
SHERMAN, NANCY, PHIL DEPT, BOSTON UNIVERSITY, BOSTON MA 02215

SHEROUSE, MARK, PHILOSOPHY DEPT, OHIO STATE UNIV, COLUMBUS OH 43210
SHEROVER, CHARLES, PHIL DEPT, HUNTER COLLEGE, NEW YORK NY 10021
SHEROVER, ERICA, PHIL DEPT, UNIV OF PITTSBURGH, PITTSBURGH PA 15260
SHEVACH, DAVID R, PHIL DEPT, UNIV OF WISCONSIN, MILWAUKEE WI 53201
SHIAO, LOUIS, PHIL DEPT, ST MARY'S UNIVERSITY, SAN ANTONIO TX 78228
SHIBLES, WARREN A, PHILOSOPHY DEPT, UNIV OF WISCONSIN, WHITEWATER WI 53190
SHIELDS, ALLAN E, PHIL DEPT, CALIFORNIA ST UNIV, SAN DIEGO CA 92115
SHIELDS, JAMES, PHILOSOPHY DEPT, HOWARD PAYNE COL, BROWNWOOD TX 76801
SHIGEFUJI, SHENIE, PHIL DEPT, UNIV OF WISCONSIN, EAU CLAIRE WI 54701
SHIH, YUANG-KANG, PHILOSOPHY DEPT, CHIO STATE UNIV, COLUMBUS OH 43210
SHIMIZU, VICTOR Y, PHILOSOPHY DEPT, UNIV OF WINNIPEG, WINNIPEG MAN   CAN
SHINOMISSE, EIICHI, PHILOSOPHY DEPT, CAL STATE COL, DOMINGUEZ HLS CA 90747
SHIMONY, ABNER, PHIL DEPT, BOSTON UNIVERSITY, BOSTON MA 02215
SHIN, OH HYUN, PHIL DEPT, UNIV OF MICHIGAN, ANN ARBOR MI 48104
SHINE, DANIEL J, PHIL DEPT, BOSTON COLLEGE, CHESTNUT HILL MA 02167
SHINER, LARRY, PHIL PROGRAM, SANGAMON ST UNIV, SPRINGFIELD IL 62703
SHINER, R A, PHILOSOPHY DEPT, UNIV CF ALBERTA, EDMONTON ALB   CAN
SHINN, EARL W, PHILOSOPHY DEPT, UNIV OF S CAROLINA, COLUMBIA SC 29208
SHINN, GERALD H, PHIL DEPT, UNIV OF N CAROLINA, WILMINGTON NC 28401
SHINN, ROBERT W, PHILOSOPHY DEPT, EASTERN COLLEGE, ST DAVIDS PA 19087
SHIPKA, THOMAS, PHIL & REL STUD, YOUNGSTOWN ST UNIV, YOUNGSTOWN OH 44503
SHIPLEY, WILLIAM L, ARTS & SCI COL, UNIV OF SAN DIEGO, SAN DIEGO CA 92110
SHIPPEE, ARTHUR, PHIL DEPT, UNIV OF HARTFORD, WEST HARTFORD CT 06117
SHIRAHAMA, YUKIO, PHIL DEPT, SAN ANTONIO COL, SAN ANTONIO TX 78284
SHIREY, KEITH, SOC SCI DEPT, AZUSA PACIFIC COL, AZUSA CA 91702
SHIRK, EVELYN, PHILOSOPHY DEPT, HOFSTRA UNIVERSITY, HEMPSTEAD NY 11550
SHIRLEY, E, PHIL DEPT, LOUISIANA ST UNIV, BATON ROUGE LA 70803
SHISHIDO, MILES, PHIL DEPT, PACIFIC UNIVERSITY, FOREST GROVE OR 97116
SHITAMA, G A, PHIL DEPT, UNIV OF FLORIDA, GAINESVILLE FL 32611
SHMIDMAN, JOSHUA, PHIL DEPT, YESHIVA UNIVERSITY, NEW YORK NY 10033
SHMUELI, EFRAIM, PHILOSOPHY DEPT, CLEVELAND ST UNIV, CLEVELAND OH 44115
SHOEMAKER, ROBERT G, PHILOSOPHY DEPT, HENDRIX COLLEGE, CONWAY AR 72032
SHOEMAKER, SYDNEY, SAGE SCHOOL, CORNELL UNIVERSITY, ITHACA NY 14850
SHOENFIELD, JOSEPH R, MATH DEPT, DUKE UNIVERSITY, DURHAM NC 27706
SHOLL, WILLIAM, PHIL DEPT, UNIV OF NEW HAVEN, WEST HAVEN CT 06516
SHONSHECK, JONATHAN C, PHILOSOPHY DEPT, OHIO STATE UNIV, COLUMBUS OH 43210
SHOPE, ROBERT K, PHILOSOPHY DEPT, UNIV OF MASS, BOSTON MA 02116
SHORT, MORRIS R, PSYCH & PHIL, MONMOUTH COLLEGE, W LONG BRANCH NJ 07764
SHORT, THOMAS, PHILOSOPHY DEPT, KENYON COLLEGE, GAMBIER OH 43022
SHORTEN, SARAH J, PHIL DEPT, UNIV OF WEST ONTARIO, LONDON ONT   CAN
SHOUERY, IMAD T, PHIL DEPT, INDIANA ST UNIV, TERRE HAUTE IN 47809
SHOWALTER, JERRY, REL & PHIL DIV, MARION COLLEGE, MARION IN 46952
SHOWS, CHARLES R, SOC STUD DEPT, MISS GULF COAST JR C, HANDSBORO MS 39554
SHUCY, JOHN, PHIL DEPT, UNIV OF MISSOURI, COLUMBIA MO 65201
SHUE, HENRY G, PHIL DPET, WELLESLEY COLLEGE, WELLESLEY MA 02181
SHUFORD, HAYWOOD R, PHILOSOPHY DEPT, UNIV OF HOUSTON, HOUSTON TX 77004
SHUKAIR, ALI, FORT VALLEY ST COL, FORT VALLEY, GA 31030
SHULAK, ALLEN, PHILOSOPHY DEPT, JOHN F KENNEDY UNIV, MARTINEZ CA 94553
SHULER, ROBERT, PHILOSOPHY DEPT, EL CAMINO COLLEGE, TORRENCE CA 90506
SHUMAKER, JAMES D, PHIL DEPT, UNIV CF N CAROLINA, CHARLOTTE NC 28213
SHUMAN, KILIAN, ST FRANCIS COL, LORETTO, PA 15940
SHURDEN, ROBERT, PHIL DEPT, MISSISSIPPI COLLEGE, CLINTON MS 39058
SHUTE, CLARENCE, PHILOSOPHY DEPT, UNIV OF MASS, AMHERST MA 01002
SHWARZE, SHARON, CABRINI COLLEGE, RADNOR, PA 19087
SHWAYDER, DAVID S, PHIL DEPT, UNIV OF ILLINOIS, URBANA IL 61801
SIBLEY, FRANCIS, PHIL & REL DEPT, PARK COLLEGE, KANSAS CITY MO 64152
SIBLEY, JACK, PHIL & PSYCH DEPT, TEXAS WOMAN'S UNIV, DENTON TX 76201
SIBLEY, MYRON K, HUMAN STUD DIV, ALFRED UNIVERSITY, ALFRED NY 14802
SIBLEY, S FLOYD, NW STATE COLLEGE, ALVA, OK 73717
SIBLEY, W M, PHIL DEPT, UNIV OF MANITOBA, WINNIPEG 19 MAN   CAN
SICHA, JEFFREY, PHIL DEPT, CALIFORNIA ST UNIV, NORTHRIDGE CA 91324
SIDES, CHERY, PHIL DEPT, CEN MISSOURI ST UNIV, WARRENSBURG MO 64093
SIDES, HENRY, COLLEGE OF SAN MATEO, SAN MATEO, CA 94402
SIDORAK, STEVE, REL PHIL DEPT, ILIFF SCH OF THEOL, DENVER CO 80210

SIDORSKY, DAVID, PHIL DEPT, COLUMBIA UNIVERSITY, NEW YORK NY 10027
SIEGEL, KENNETH, PHILOSOPHY DEPT, PATERSON COL OF NJ, WAYNE NJ 07470
SIEGEL, SEYMOUR, PHIL & REL DEPT, JEWISH THEOL SEM, NEW YORK NY 10027
SIEGLER, FREDERICK A, PHILOSOPHY DEPT, UNIV OF WASHINGTON, SEATTLE WA 98195
SIEGMANN, WILLIAM L, PHIL DEPT, UNIVERSITY OF MIAMI, CORAL GABLES FL 33124
SIEVERT, DONALD, PHIL DEPT, UNIV OF MISSOURI, COLUMBIA MO 65201
SIEWERT, DONALD J, PHIL SCH, CATH UNIV OF AMER, WASHINGTON DC 20017
SIGNER, MARCUS G, PHILOSOPHY DEPT, UNIV OF WISCONSIN, MADISON WI 53706
SIKES, DOUG, PHIL & RELIG DEPT, OKLA COL OF LIBR ARTS, CHICKASHA OK 73018
SIKORA, RICHARD, PHIL DEPT, UNIV BRIT COLUMBIA, VANCOUVER 8 B C CAN
SILBER, JOHN, PHIL DEPT, BOSTON UNIVERSITY, BOSTON MA 02215
SILBERG, JACK, ENG & PHIL DEPT, LOCK HAVEN ST COL, LOCK HAVEN PA 17745
SILBERMANN, EILEEN, SOC SCI DEPT, ESSEX COM COL, BALTIMORE MD 21237
SILL, JAMES D, GEN EDUC DEPT, SOUTHWESTERN ST COL, WEATHERFORD OK 73096
SILVER, MITCHEL H, PHIL DEPT, ST UNIV OF NY, BINGHAMTON NY 13901
SILVERBLATT, BARRY, PHIL DEPT, UNIV OF MISSOURI, COLUMBIA MO 65201
SILVERMAN, DAVID W, PHIL & REL DEPT, JEWISH THEOL SEM, NEW YORK NY 10027
SILVERMAN, ROBERT, PHILOSOPHY DEPT, RUTGERS UNIV, NEW BRUNSWICK NJ 08903
SILVERS, ANITA, PHIL DEPT, CALIFORNIA ST UNIV, SAN FRANCISCO CA 94132
SILVERSTEIN, HARRY S, PHILOSOPHY DEPT, WASHINGTON ST UNIV, PULLMAN WA 99163
SILVEY, FRANK, PHIL DEPT, UNIV OF CALIFORNIA, LOS ANGELES CA 90024
SIMARD, YVON, PHIL DEPT, COL VIEUX-MONTREAL, MONTREAL QUE CAN
SIMAS, EDWARD, PHILOSOPHY DEPT, SEM OF LADY OF PROV, WARWICK RI 02889
SIMCO, NANCY D, PHILOSOPHY DEPT, MEMPHIS ST UNIV, MEMPHIS TN 38152
SIMEC, MARY, PHILOSOPHY DEPT, ALVERNO COLLEGE, MILWAUKEE WI 53215
SIMKINS, RONALD, PHIL DEPT, UNIV OF ILLINOIS, URBANA IL 61801
SIMMONDS, KENT, PHIL DEPT, LUTHER COLLEGE, DECORAH IA 52101
SIMMONS, EDWARD D, PHILOSOPHY DEPT, MARQUETTE UNIV, MILWAUKEE WI 53233
SIMMONS, JOSEPH, PHILOSOPHY DEPT, SACRAMENTO CY COL, SACRAMENTO CA 95822
SIMMONS, K MURRAY, PHILOSOPHY DEPT, BRANDON UNIVERSITY, BRANDON MAN CAN
SIMMONS, VALERIE, SOC SCI DEPT, PORTLAND COM COLLEGE, PORTLAND OR 97219
SIMMONS, WILLIAM J, SPEECH & DRAMA, TENN STATE UNIV, NASHVILLE TN 37203
SIMON, HOWARD L, PHIL & REL, DEPAUW UNIVERSITY, GREENCASTLE IN 46135
SIMON, JEROME, PHIL DEPT, CALIFORNIA ST UNIV, LOS ANGELES CA 90032
SIMON, LARRY, PHIL DEPT, BOSTON UNIVERSITY, BOSTON MA 02215
SIMON, M A, PHIL DEPT, UNIV OF CONNECTICUT, STORRS CT 06268
SIMON, ROBERT L, PHIL DEPT, HAMILTON COLLEGE, CLINTON NY 13323
SIMON, ST SIMON, MARY MANSE COLLEGE, TOLEDO, OH 43620
SIMON, STEPHEN, PHIL DEPT, CALIFORNIA ST UNIV, FULLERTON CA 92634
SIMON, THOMAS W, PHIL DEPT, UNIV OF FLORIDA, GAINESVILLE FL 32611
SIMONDS, ROGER T, PHIL DEPT, THE AMERICAN UNIV, WASHINGTON DC 20016
SIMONS, JOSEPH, PHIL DEPT, UNIV OF WISCONSIN, MILWAUKEE WI 53201
SIMONS, LEO, PHIL DEPT, UNIV OF CINCINNATI, CINCINNATI OH 45221
SIMONS, MARGARET, PHIL DEPT, PURDUE UNIVERSITY, LAFAYETTE IN 47907
SIMONSEN, KENNETH, HUMAN DEPT, COL OF LAKE COUNTY, GRAYSLAKE IL 60030
SIMONSON, JOHN F, REL & PHIL DEPT, SUOMI COLLEGE, HANCOCK MI 49930
SIMPSON JR, HOKE S, HUMAN & PHIL DEPT, GROSSMONT COL, EL CAJON CA 92020
SIMPSON, J E, PHILOSOPHY DEPT, MCMASTER UNIVERSITY, HAMILTON ONT CAN
SIMPSON, RICHARD, PHIL DEPT, DEPAUL UNIVERSITY, CHICAGO IL 60604
SIMPSON, ROBERT E, PHILOSOPHY DEPT, YORK UNIVERSITY, DOWNSVIEW ONT CAN
SIMPSON, ROBERT L, REL & PHIL DEPT, PHILLIPS UNIVERSITY, ENID OK 73701
SIMPSON, WALTER, PHIL DEPT, ST UNIV OF NY, AMHERST NY 14226
SIMS, JOHN, BIBL & HIST STUD, LEE COLLEGE, CLEVELAND TN 37311
SINATRA, RICHARD L, PHIL DEPT, TEXAS CHRISTIAN UNIV, FORT WORTH TX 76129
SINCLAIR, JON, HUMAN DIV, ALASKA METHODIST U, ANCHORAGE AK 99504
SINGER, BETH, BROOKLYN COLLEGE, BROCKLYN, NY 11210
SINGER, IRVING, PHIL DEPT, MASS INST TECH, CAMBRIDGE MA 02139
SINGER, LINDA, PHIL DEPT, ST UNIV OF NY, BINGHAMTON NY 13901
SINGER, PETER, PHIL DEPT, NEW YORK UNIVERSITY, NEW YORK NY 10003
SINGH, BHAGWAN B, PHIL DEPT, S ILLINOIS UNIV, CARBONDALE IL 62901
SINGH, SURJIT, SYST & PHIL, GRADUATE THEOL UNION, BERKELEY CA 94709
SINGLETARY, REBECCA, HUMAN & PHIL DIV, UNIVERSITY OF TAMPA, TAMPA FL 33606
SINISI, VITO F, PHIL DEPT, ST UNIV OF NY, BINGHAMTON NY 13901
SINKS, JOHN, HUMAN DEPT, GEORGE MASON UNIV, FAIRFAX VA 22030

SINZ, EUGENE, PHIL & THEOL DEPT, MARILLAC COLLEGE, ST LOUIS MO 63121
SIPFLE, DAVID A, PHIL DEPT, CARLETON COLLEGE, NORTHFIELD MN 55057
SIRCELLO, GUY, PHIL DEPT, UNIV OF CALIFORNIA, IRVINE CA 92664
SIRRIDGE, MARY, PHILOSOPHY DEPT, UNIV OF MASS, AMHERST MA 01002
SITTE, MARTIN, PHILOSOPHY DEPT, PENN STATE UNIV, UNIV PARK PA 16802
SIZEMORE, WARNER, PHIL & RELIG DEPT, GLASSBORO ST COL, GLASSBORO NJ 08028
SJURSEN, HAROLD, PHIL DEPT, AUGUSTANA COLLEGE, ROCK ISLAND IL 61201
SKADDEN, STUART, PHILOSOPHY DEPT, UNIV OF S CAROLINA, COLUMBIA SC 29208
SKEEN, NANCY N, PHIL DEPT, UNIV OF SOUTH DAKOTA, VERMILLION SD 57069
SKELLY, ALAN, PHIL DEPT, LONG ISLAND UNIV, GREENVALE NY 11548
SKELTON, KENNETH T, HIST DEPT, DUTCHESS COM COL, POUGHKEEPSIE NY 12601
SKIDMORE, ARTHUR, PHIL DEPT, UNIVERSITY OF KANSAS, LAWRENCE KS 66044
SKINNER, JOHN E, THEOL DEPT, DIV SCH PROT CHURCH, PHILADELPHIA PA 19104
SKLAR, JUDITH B, PHIL DEPT, WASHINGTON UNIV, ST LOUIS MO 63130
SKLAR, LAWRENCE, PHIL DEPT, UNIV OF MICHIGAN, ANN ARBOR MI 48104
SKODACEK, AUGUST, PHIL & REL STUD, YOUNGSTOWN ST UNIV, YOUNGSTOWN OH 44503
SKOGLUND, HENRY L, PHIL DEPT, NORTH CENTRAL COL, NAPERVILLE IL 60540
SKORPEN, ERLING R, PHIL DEPT, UNIV OF MAINE, ORONO ME 04473
SKOTTEGAARD, ROBERT, HUMAN DEPT, ANOKA-RAMSEY ST COL, COON RAPIDS MN 55433
SKRUPSKELIS, IGNAS, PHILOSOPHY DEPT, UNIV OF S CAROLINA, COLUMBIA SC 29208
SKYRUMS, BRIAN F, PHIL DEPT, UNIV OF ILLINOIS, CHICAGO IL 60680
SLAATTE, HOWARD A, PHILOSOPHY DEPT, MARSHALL UNIV, HUNTINGTON WV 25701
SLACK, RANSOM, PHIL DEPT, UNIV OF WEST ONTARIO, LONDON ONT CAN
SLAGHT, RALPH, PHILOSOPHY DEPT, LAFAYETTE COLLEGE, EASTON PA 18042
SLATER, J G, PHILOSOPHY DEPT, UNIV OF TORONTO, TORONTO ONT CAN
SLATTERY, KENNETH F, PHIL DEPT, NIAGARA UNIVERSITY, NIAGARA UNIV NY 14109
SLATTERY, MICHAEL P, PHILOSOPHY DEPT, VILLANOVA UNIV, VILLANOVA PA 19085
SLAUGHTER, TOM, PHIL DEPT, ST UNIV OF NY, STONY BROOK NY 11790
SLALSON, WILLIAM L, PHIL DEPT, COLORADO ST UNIV, FORT COLLINS CO 80521
SLEEP, R, SOC SCI DEPT, RYERSON POLYTECH U, TORONTO ONT CAN
SLEEPER, RALPH, PHILOSOPHY DEPT, QUEENS COLLEGE, FLUSHING NY 11367
SLEIGH, ROBERT, PHILOSOPHY DEPT, UNIV OF MASS, AMHERST MA 01002
SLINGER, JAMES W, PHILOSOPHY DEPT, CALIFORNIA ST UNIV, FRESNO CA 93740
SLINKARD, R T, RELIG & PHIL DEPT, PHILANDER SMITH COL, LITTLE ROCK AR 72203
SLIVINSKI, DENNIS, PHILOSOPHY DEPT, VANDERBILT UNIV, NASHVILLE TN 37235
SLOTE, MICHAEL, PHIL DEPT, ST UNIV OF NY, STONY BROOK NY 11790
SLUGA, HANS, PHIL DEPT, UNIV OF CALIFORNIA, BERKELEY CA 94720
SLUITER, PAUL, PHIL DEPT, ST UNIV OF NY, STONY BROOK NY 11790
SMABY, JOHN, PHIL DEPT, CAL ST COL AT SONOMA, ROHNERT PARK CA 94928
SMALE, PETER G W, PHILOSOPHY DEPT, ACADIA UNIVERSITY, WOLFVILLE N S CAN
SMALL, KENNETH, PHILOSOPHY DEPT, UNIV OF WASHINGTON, SEATTLE WA 98195
SMART, HAROLD R, SAGE SCHOOL, CORNELL UNIVERSITY, ITHACA NY 14850
SMELSER, PHILIP S, PHILOSOPHY DEPT, GLENDALE COM COL, GLENDALE AZ 85301
SMERUD, WARREN, PHIL DEPT, CONCORDIA COLLEGE, MOORHEAD MN 56560
SMIARD, LOUIS, PHIL DEPT, COL DE L'ASSOMPTION, L'ASSOMPTION QUE CAN
SMITH III, SAMUEL, PHIL & RELIG DEPT, DRURY COLLEGE, SPRINGFIELD MO 65802
SMITH JR, PAUL E, PHIL & RELIG DEPT, RICHARD BLAND COL, PETERSBURG VA 23803
SMITH, ALBERT E, LOMA LINDA UNIV, RIVERSIDE, CA 92505
SMITH, ALBERT J, PHIL DEPT, UNIV OF SN FRANCISCO, SAN FRANCISCO CA 94117
SMITH, BOBBY L, SOC SCI DEPT, HOWARD COM JR COL, BIG SPRING TX 79720
SMITH, CAMILLA, HUMAN DEPT, AGR & TECH COLLEGE, DELHI NY 13753
SMITH, CAROL ANN, HUMAN DEPT, UNIV OF MISSOURI, ROLLA MO 65401
SMITH, CHARLES, PHILOSOPHY DEPT, VANDERBILT UNIV, NASHVILLE TN 37235
SMITH, CHRISTOPHER, PHIL DEPT, LOWELL STATE COLLEGE, LOWELL MA 01854
SMITH, D, PHILOSOPHY DEPT, UNIV OF ALBERTA, EDMONTON ALB CAN
SMITH, DANIEL M, ENG DEPT, U S MILITARY ACAD, WEST POINT NY 10996
SMITH, DAVID, PHIL DEPT, UNIV OF CALIFORNIA, IRVINE CA 92664
SMITH, E DIANE, PHIL DEPT, CALIFORNIA ST UNIV, FULLERTON CA 92634
SMITH, EDWARD G, PHILOSOPHY DEPT, MARYVILLE COLLEGE, ST LOUIS MO 63141
SMITH, EDWARD T, PHIL DEPT, UNIV OF DENVER, DENVER CO 80210
SMITH, ELIZABETH, PHILOSOPHY DEPT, OHIO UNIVERSITY, ATHENS OH 45701
SMITH, ERIC, PHIL DEPT, MICHIGAN STATE UNIV, EAST LANSING MI 48823
SMITH, G ROSS, PHIL DEPT, ARAPAHOE COM COL, LITTLETON CO 80120
SMITH, GENE WARD, PHIL DEPT, INDIANA UNIVERSITY, BLOOMINGTON IN 47401

SMITH, GEORGE, PHIL & SOC DEPT, VANCOUVER CITY COL, VANCOUVER B C   CAN
SMITH, GERARD, PHILOSOPHY DEPT, MARQUETTE UNIV, MILWAUKEE WI 53233
SMITH, GERRIT, PHIL DEPT, FORDHAM UNIVERSITY, BRONX NY 10458
SMITH, HUSTON, PHIL DEPT, SYRACUSE UNIVERSITY, SYRACUSE NY 13210
SMITH, IAN, HUMAN DEPT, MIDDLESEX CC COL, EDISON NJ 08817
SMITH, J WELDON, PHIL & RELIG, MACMURRAY COLLEGE, JACKSONVILLE IL 62650
SMITH, J, PHILOSOPHY DEPT, MCGILL UNIVERSITY, MONTREAL QUE   CAN
SMITH, JAMES L, PHILOSOPHY DEPT, EAST CAROLINA UNIV, GREENVILLE NC 27834
SMITH, JAMES M, PHILOSOPHY DEPT, CALIFORNIA ST UNIV, FRESNO CA 93740
SMITH, JAMES P, PHIL DEPT, UNIV OF MINNESOTA, MINNEAPOLIS MN 55455
SMITH, JAMES R, PHIL DEPT, PURDUE UNIVERSITY, LAFAYETTE IN 47907
SMITH, JAMES WARD, PHIL DEPT, PRINCETON UNIVERSITY, PRINCETON NJ 08540
SMITH, JANET FARRELL, PHIL DEPT, LAKE FOREST COLLEGE, LAKE FOREST IL 60045
SMITH, JODY, MUS & HUM DEPT, PENSACOLA JUN COL, PENSACOLA FL 32504
SMITH, JOHN L, PHIL DEPT, VALPARAISO UNIV, VALPARAISO IN 46383
SMITH, JOHN SYLVESTER, FLORIDA KEYS COM COL, KEY WEST, FL 33040
SMITH, JOHN, PHIL DEPT, YALE UNIVERSITY, NEW HAVEN CT 06520
SMITH, K, PHIL DEPT, LOUISIANA ST UNIV, BATON ROUGE LA 70803
SMITH, KEVIN, BIBL LIT & PHIL DIV, BETHANY BIBLE COL, SANTA CRUZ CA 95060
SMITH, LINDA, PHIL DEPT, MICHIGAN STATE UNIV, EAST LANSING MI 48823
SMITH, MALCOLM B E, PHIL DEPT, SMITH COLLEGE, NORTHAMPTON MA 01060
SMITH, MARC E, PHIL DEPT, SAINT THOMAS UNIV, FREDERICTON N B   CAN
SMITH, MARILYN, PHIL DEPT, QUINNIPIAC COLLEGE, HAMDEN CT 06518
SMITH, MICHAEL F, PHIL DEPT, INDIANA UNIVERSITY, BLOOMINGTON IN 47401
SMITH, MILTON S, HUMANITIES DEPT, VA WESTERN COM COL, ROANOKE VA 24015
SMITH, P J, PHILOSOPHY DEPT, MCGILL UNIVERSITY, MONTREAL QUE   CAN
SMITH, PATRICIA, HUMANITIES AREA, MALASPINA COLLEGE, NANAIMO B C   CAN
SMITH, PETER FOX, CANAAN COLLEGE, CANAAN, NH 03741
SMITH, PHILIP, CALDWELL COLLEGE, CALDWELL, NJ 07006
SMITH, R W, PHILOSOPHY DEPT, MESA COMMUNITY COL, MESA AZ 85201
SMITH, RICHARD A, PHIL DEPT, PURDUE UNIVERSITY, LAFAYETTE IN 47907
SMITH, RICHARD B, REL STUD DIV, OAKLAND CITY COLLEGE, OAKLAND CITY IN 47660
SMITH, RICHARD C, PHIL DEPT, UNIV OF LOUISVILLE, LOUISVILLE KY 40208
SMITH, RICHARD L, PHIL DEPT, CALIFORNIA ST UNIV, FULLERTON CA 92634
SMITH, ROBERT S, PHIL DEPT, CATH COL IMM CONCEPT, DOUGLASTON NY 11362
SMITH, ROBERT V, PHIL & RELIG DEPT, COLGATE UNIVERSITY, HAMILTON NY 13346
SMITH, ROBERT, PHIL & RELIG DEPT, TRENTON STATE COL, TRENTON NJ 08625
SMITH, ROBIN, PHIL DEPT, OCCIDENTAL COLLEGE, LOS ANGELES CA 90041
SMITH, ROGER, COMMUNIC & ARTS, HARRISBURG COM COL, HARRISBURG PA 17110
SMITH, S ENID, PHIL DEPT, COL OF ST BENEDICT, ST JOSEPH MN 56374
SMITH, S ROBERT, ST MARY'S COL OF CAL, MORAGA, CA 94575
SMITH, STEVEN A, PHIL DEPT, CLAREMONT MEN'S COL, CLAREMONT CA 91711
SMITH, T DAVID, PHIL DEPT, FLAGLER COLLEGE, ST AUGUSTINE FL 32084
SMITH, TERRY L, PHILOSOPHY DEPT, UNIV OF WISCONSIN, MADISON WI 53706
SMITH, THOMAS M, PHIL & RELIG DEPT, UNIV OF ARKANSAS, LITTLE ROCK AR 72204
SMITH, TIMOTHY H, HOFSTRA UNIVERSITY, HEMPSTEAD, NY 11550
SMITH, W ROBERT, PHIL DEPT, BETHEL COLLEGE, ST PAUL MN 55112
SMITH, WILLIAM A, SETON HALL UNIV, SOUTH ORANGE, NJ 07079
SMITH, WILLIAM G, PHIL DEPT, UNIV OF NEW MEXICO, ALBUQUERQUE NM 87106
SMITH, WILLIE J, PHILOSOPHY DEPT, RUTGERS UNIV, NEW BRUNSWICK NJ 08903
SMITHENAN, V, PHILOSOPHY DEPT, UNIV PR EDWARD IS, CHARLOTTETOWN PEI   CAN
SMITHURST, MICHAEL, PHIL DEPT, BROOKLYN COLLEGE, BROOKLYN NY 11210
SMITS, HENRY, SOC SCI DEPT, NE MISSOURI ST UNIV, KIRKSVILLE MO 63501
SMOKLER, HOWARD, PHIL DEPT, UNIV OF COLORADO, BOULDER CO 80302
SMOLKO, JOHN F, PHIL DEPT, UNIV OF MARYLAND, COLLEGE PARK MD 20742
SMOCK, R, PHILOSOPHY DEPT, UNIV OF GUELPH, GUELPH ONT   CAN
SMOCT II, WILLIAM R, PHILOSOPHY DEPT, MIAMI UNIVERSITY, OXFORD OH 45056
SMOTHERS, THOMAS, REL & PHIL, PALM BCH ATLANTIC COL, WEST PALM BCH FL 33401
SMUCKER, JAN, PHIL DEPT, HANOVER COLLEGE, HANOVER IN 47243
SMULLYAN, ARTHUR F, PHILOSOPHY DEPT, RUTGERS UNIV, NEW BRUNSWICK NJ 08903
SMYTH, RICHARD A, PHIL DEPT, UNIV OF N CAROLINA, CHAPEL HILL NC 27514
SMYTHE, JEANNE P, PHIL DEPT, UNIV OF N CAROLINA, CHAPEL HILL NC 27514
SMYTHE, THOMAS, PHIL DEPT, UNIV OF N CAROLINA, GREENSBORO NC 27412
SNARE, FRANCIS, PHIL DEPT, UNIVERSITY OF IOWA, IOWA CITY IA 52240

SNEDDEN, JAMES A, PARSONS COLLEGE, FAIRFIELD, IA 52803
SNOCK, LEE E, SYST THEOL DEPT, LUTHER THEOL SEM, ST PAUL MN 55108
SNOWDEN, ARMON, RELIG & PHIL, ELIZABETHTOWN COL, ELIZABETHTOWN PA 17022
SNOWDEN, B F, SOC SCI DEPT, NW STATE UNIVERSITY, NATCHITOCHES LA 71457
SNOWDEN, THOMAS G, SOC RELATIONS, MONTGOMERY COM COL, BLUE BELL PA 19422
SNYDER, AARON, HUMAN STUD DIV, UNIV OF WISCONSIN, KENOSHA WI 53140
SNYDER, D PAUL, PHIL DEPT, TEMPLE UNIVERSITY, PHILADELPHIA PA 19122
SNYDER, JOHN J, PHIL & RELIG STUD, KING'S COLLEGE, LONDON ONT   CAN
SNYDER, JOHN, PHILOSOPHY DEPT, MARYWOOD COLLEGE, SCRANTON PA 18509
SNYDER, LEE, PHIL DEPT, ST UNIV OF NY, AMHERST NY 14226
SNYDER, PETER V, PHIL DEPT, MARY WASHINGTON COL, FREDERICKSBG VA 22401
SNYDER, WILLIAM S, PHIL DEPT, CALIFORNIA ST UNIV, SAN DIEGO CA 92115
SOBEL, J H, PHILOSOPHY DEPT, UNIV OF TORONTO, TORONTO ONT   CAN
SOBEL, JERRY, PHIL DEPT, TUFTS UNIVERSITY, MEDFORD MA 02155
SOBLE, ALAN, PHIL DEPT, ST UNIV OF NY, AMHERST NY 14226
SOBOCINSKI, BOLESLAW, PHIL DEPT, UNIV OF NOTRE DAME, NOTRE DAME IN 46556
SOCCIO, DOUGLAS, PHILOSOPHY DEPT, MARAMEC COM COL, ST LOUIS MO 63122
SODERLIND, KAREN, PHILOSOPHY DEPT, UNIV OF MASS, AMHERST MA 01002
SOFFER, WALTER, PHIL DEPT, GEORGE WASHINGTON U, WASHINGTON DC 20006
SOKOLOWSKI, ROBERT, PHIL SCH, CATH UNIV OF AMER, WASHINGTON DC 20017
SOKOLOWSKI, W R, PHIL DEPT, GRT HARTFORD COM COL, HARTFORD CT 06106
SOLES, DAVID, KANSAS NEWMAN COL, WICHITA, KS 67213
SOLES, DEBORAH, PHIL DEPT, WICHITA ST UNIV, WICHITA KS 67208
SOLGANICK, HARVEY, HUMANITIES DIV, EASTFIELD COLLEGE, DALLAS TX 75149
SOLL, A IVAN, PHILOSOPHY DEPT, UNIV OF WISCONSIN, MADISON WI 53706
SOLLAZZO, GARY J, PHIL DEPT, UNIV OF MARYLAND, COLLEGE PARK MD 20742
SOLLISH, MARTIN, BEHAVIOR SCI DEPT, ATLANTIC COM COL, MAYS LNDG NJ 08330
SOLOMON, DAVID, PHIL DEPT, UNIV OF NOTRE DAME, NOTRE DAME IN 46556
SOLOMON, HOWARD, PHIL DEPT, N ILLINOIS UNIV, DEKALB IL 60115
SOLOMON, ROBERT, PHILOSOPHY DEPT, UNIV OF TEXAS, AUSTIN TX 78712
SOLOMON, TED, PHIL DEPT, IOWA STATE UNIV, AMES IA 50010
SOLTIS, JONAS, PHIL & SOC SCI, TEACHERS COLLEGE, NEW YORK NY 10027
SOMERVILLE, JAMES, PHILOSOPHY DEPT, XAVIER UNIVERSITY, CINCINNATI OH 45207
SOMMER, JOHN, THE WESTERN COLLEGE, OXFORD, OH 45056
SOMMER, STEPHANIE, PHILOSOPHY DEPT, UNIV OF MASS, AMHERST MA 01002
SOMMERS, FREDERIC T, PHIL DEPT, BRANDEIS UNIVERSITY, WALTHAM MA 02154
SOMMESE, REBECCA R, PHIL DEPT, UNIV OF CONNECTICUT, GROTON CT 06340
SONESON, J MELBURN, PHIL DEPT, NORTH PARK COLLEGE, CHICAGO IL 60625
SONTAG, FREDERICK, PHILOSOPHY DEPT, POMONA COLLEGE, CLAREMONT CA 91711
SOO, FRANCIS Y, PHIL DEPT, BOSTON COLLEGE, CHESTNUT HILL MA 02167
SOOVIK, MIHKEL, HUMAN DIV, CONCORDIA SENIOR COL, FORT WAYNE IN 46825
SOPER, WILLIAM WAYNE, PHIL DEPT, WHITMAN COLLEGE, WALLA WALLA WA 99362
SOPHOCLES, SOPHOCLES, HUMANITIES DEPT, WIDENER COLLEGE, CHESTER PA 19013
SORENSON, MARTIN, PHIL DEPT, ST PATRICK'S COLLEGE, MOUNTAIN VIEW CA 94040
SOSA, ERNEST, PHILOSOPHY DEPT, BROWN UNIVERSITY, PROVIDENCE RI 02912
SOSENSKY, IRVING, PHIL DEPT, PURDUE UNIVERSITY, LAFAYETTE IN 47907
SOSNA, NORMAN, HUMAN DEPT, DYKE COLLEGE, CLEVELAND OH 44114
SOSNIN, CARL H, PHIL DEPT, UNIV OF ALABAMA, UNIVERSITY AL 35486
SOTO, CARLOS, PHIL DEPT, UNIV OF PUERTO RICO, RIO PIEDRAS PR 00931
SOTO, JUAN, PHIL DEPT, UNIV OF PUERTO RICO, RIO PIEDRAS PR 00931
SOUCOUP, D G, PHIL DEPT, UNIV OF NW BRUNSWICK, FREDERICTON N B   CAN
SOUCY, ARMAND, PHILOSOPHY DEPT, ST FRAN XAVIER UNIV, ANTIGONISH N S   CAN
SOUCY, MARCEL, PHILOSOPHY DEPT, COL DE MAISONNEUVE, MONTREAL QUE   CAN
SOWELL, JESSE J, PHIL & RELIG DEPT, WOOD JUNIOR COL, MATHISTON MS 39752
SPADE, PAUL V, PHIL DEPT, INDIANA UNIVERSITY, BLOOMINGTON IN 47401
SPADER, PETER H, PHILOSOPHY DEPT, LYNCHBURG COL, LYNCHBURG VA 24504
SPADONI, CARL, PHILOSOPHY DEPT, UNIV OF WATERLOO, WATERLOO ONT   CAN
SPAIN, ARNOLD, PHIL & THEOL DIV, MARY COLLEGE, BISMARCK ND 58501
SPANGLER, A, PHILOSOPHY DEPT, UNIV OF ALBERTA, EDMONTON ALB   CAN
SPANGLER, G A, PHIL DEPT, CALIFORNIA ST UNIV, LONG BEACH CA 90840
SPARSHOTT, F E, PHILOSOPHY DEPT, VICTORIA COLLEGE, TORONTO 5 ONT   CAN
SPARSHOTT, R, PHILOSOPHY DEPT, VICTORIA UNIV, TORONTO 181 ONT   CAN
SPAULDING, OLIVIA, LIVINGSTONE COLLEGE, SALISBURY, NC 28144
SPEAR, MARTIN, HIST & PHIL, COM COL PHILADELPHIA, PHILADELPHIA PA 19107

SPEARS, GEORGE J, PHILOSOPHY DEPT, MANATEE JUN COL, BRADENTON FL 33505
SPECTOR, JONATHAN M, PHILOSOPHY DEPT, UNIV OF TEXAS, AUSTIN TX 78712
SPECTOR, MARSHALL, PHIL DEPT, ST UNIV OF NY, STONY BROOK NY 11790
SPEEGLE, LYLE, SOC SCI DEPT, LONG BEACH CY COL, LONG BEACH CA 90808
SPEIER, THOMAS O, PHIL DEPT, DUNS SCOTUS COL, SOUTHFIELD MI 48075
SPELLMAN, A LYNNE, PHIL DEPT, UNIV OF ILLINOIS, URBANA IL 61801
SPELLMAN, JAMES, PHIL DEPT, UNIV OF ILLINOIS, URBANA IL 61801
SPELMAN, ELIZABETH V, PHIL & REL DEPT, AMHERST COLLEGE, AMHERST MA 01002
SPENCER, JAMES C, HUMAN DEPT, CUYAHOGA COM COL, PARMA HEIGHTS OH 44130
SPENCER, JOHN, PHILOSOPHY DEPT, DAWSON COLLEGE, MONTREAL QUE CAN
SPENCER, THEODORE, PHIL DEPT, UNIVERSITY OF IOWA, IOWA CITY IA 52240
SPERD, SHUBERT, ACADEMIC STUD, CLEVELAND ART INST, CLEVELAND OH 44106
SPICKER, STUART, SCH OF MEDICINE, UNIV OF CONNECTICUT, FARMINGTON CT 06032
SPIEGEL, RICHARD, PHILOSOPHY DEPT, UNIV OF WISCONSIN, WHITEWATER WI 53190
SPIEGELBERG, HERBERT, PHIL DEPT, WASHINGTON UNIV, ST LOUIS MO 63130
SPIELER, DAVID A, PHIL & REL DEPT, ADRIAN COLLEGE, ADRIAN MI 49221
SPIELMAN, STEPHEN, PHIL DEPT, LEHMAN COLLEGE, BRONX NY 10468
SPIER, CARL, PHIL DEPT, UNIV OF VIRGINIA, CHARLOTTESVL VA 22903
SPINNENWEBER, ANDREW, PHIL DEPT, COL OF STEUBENVILLE, STEUBENVILLE OH 43952
SPIRES, T GRADY, PHILOSOPHY DEPT, GORDON COLLEGE, WENHAM MA 01984
SPIRO, JACK D, PHIL & RELIG, VA COMMONWEALTH UNIV, RICHMOND VA 23220
SPITZER, ADELE, PHIL & RELIG DEPT, COLGATE UNIVERSITY, HAMILTON NY 13346
SPITZIG, NORMAN, PHILOSOPHY DEPT, OHIO STATE UNIV, COLUMBUS OH 43210
SPONHEIM, PAUL R, SYST THEOL DEPT, LUTHER THEOL SEM, ST PAUL MN 55108
SPOON, JERRY W, HUMAN DIV, NORTHEASTERN JUN COL, STERLING CO 80751
SPRAGINS, C F, RELIG & PHIL DEPT, ARKANSAS COLLEGE, BATESVILLE AR 72501
SPRAGUE, ELMER, PHIL DEPT, BROOKLYN COLLEGE, BROOKLYN NY 11210
SPRAGUE, ROSAMOND, PHILOSOPHY DEPT, UNIV OF S CAROLINA, COLUMBIA SC 29208
SPRING, CHARLES, REL & PHIL DEPT, CCLO WOMEN'S COL, DENVER CO 80220
SPRINGER, HUGH B, SOC SCI DIV, FAIRMONT ST COL, FAIRMONT WV 26554
SPRINGER, R, REL STUD & PHIL, WESTMONT COLLEGE, SANTA BARBARA CA 93108
SPRINGER, WILLIAM, PHILOSOPHY DEPT, UNIV OF TEXAS, EL PASO TX 79968
SPRINTZEN, DAVID, PHIL DEPT, LONG ISLAND UNIV, GREENVALE NY 11548
SPROULE, JOHN, DIV OF GEN EDUC, S E BIBLE COL, BIRMINGHAM AL 35205
SPROULL, JERRY, PHIL & REL DEPT, TOCCOA FALLS INST, TOCCOA FALLS GA 30577
SPRUNG, C MERVYN C, PHIL DEPT, BROCK UNIVERSITY, ST CATHARINES ONT CAN
SPRUNGER, MEREDITH J, LIBR ARTS, INDIANA INST OF TECH, FORT WAYNE IN 46803
SPRUNK, RALPH, THEOL & PHIL, VENNARD COLLEGE, UNIVERSITY PK IA 52595
SPURNEY, RICHARD, SOC SCI DEPT, LONG BEACH CY COL, LONG BEACH CA 90808
SPURRELL, LLOYD A C, PHIL DEPT, UNIV OF WEST ONTARIO, LONDON ONT CAN
SQUADRITO, KATHLEEN, PHIL DEPT, PURDUE UNIVERSITY, FORT WAYNE IN 46805
SQUIER, ROBERT, PHILOSOPHY DEPT, REGIS COLLEGE, DENVER CO 80221
SRYGLEY JR, EDGAR V, PHIL DIV, FLORIDA COLLEGE, TEMPLE TER FL 33617
SSEKASOZI, ENGLEBERT, PHIL DEPT, UNIVERSITY OF KANSAS, LAWRENCE KS 66044
ST CLAIR, JUDITH, PHIL DEPT, TULANE UNIVERSITY, NEW ORLEANS LA 70118
ST CLAIR, REGINALD, HUMAN DIV, PIEDMONT VA COM COL, CHARLOTTESVL VA 22903
ST CLAIR, UTE H, PHILOSOPHY DEPT, OHIO STATE UNIV, COLUMBUS OH 43210
ST PIERRE, PAUL, PHILOSOPHY DEPT, MARQUETTE UNIV, MILWAUKEE WI 53233
ST-ANTOINE, JUDE, PHIL DEPT, COL BOIS-DE-BOULOGNE, MONTREAL QUE CAN
ST-JEAN, ROBERT, PHIL DEPT, COL VIEUX-MONTREAL, MONTREAL QUE CAN
STAAL, JOHAN F, PHIL DEPT, UNIV OF CALIFORNIA, BERKELEY CA 94720
STABILE, KATINA, QUEENSBOROUGH COM COL, NEW YORK, NY 11364
STACER, JOHN, PHIL DEPT, SPRING HILL COLLEGE, MOBILE AL 36608
STACK, GEORGE J, PHIL DEPT, COLLEGE AT BROCKPORT, BROCKPORT NY 14420
STACK, JOHN, PHILOSOPHY DEPT, VILLANOVA UNIV, VILLANOVA PA 19085
STACK, M, PHIL DEPT, UNIV OF MANITOBA, WINNIPEG 19 MAN CAN
STACY, JAMES W, PHILOSOPHY DEPT, UNIV OF OKLAHOMA, NORMAN OK 73069
STADELMAN, RICHARD, PHIL & HUM DEPT, TEXAS A & M UNIV, COL STATION TX 77843
STADLER, INGRID, PHIL DPET, WELLESLEY COLLEGE, WELLESLEY MA 02181
STAFFORD, OTTILIE, PHIL DEPT, ATLANTIC UNION COL, S LANCASTER MA 01561
STAFFORD, ROBERT H, PHIL DEPT, COL CUR LADY OF ELMS, CHICOPEE MA 01013
STAFFORD, SIDNEY, RELIG & PHIL DEPT, LOUISBURG COLLEGE, LOUISBURG NC 27549
STAFFORD, SUE, PHIL DEPT, TRINITY COLLEGE, HARTFORD CT 06106
STAGER, JAY R, PHILOSOPHY DEPT, MANCHESTER COM COL, MANCHESTER CT 06040

STAGMAN, DAVID, SYST THEOL DEPT, JESUIT SCH OF THEOL, BERKELEY CA   94709
STAHL, GARY, PHIL DEPT, UNIV OF COLORADO, BOULDER CO   80302
STAHL, GERALD, PHIL DEPT, NORTHWESTERN UNIV, EVANSTON IL   60201
STAHL, JOHN T, PHIL & RELIG, WEST KENTUCKY UNIV, BOWLING GREEN KY   42101
STAHL, ROLAND C, PHILOSOPHY DEPT, NATH HAWTHORNE COL, ANTRIM NH   03440
STAIRS, ALLEN E, PHIL DEPT, UNIV OF WEST ONTARIO, LONDON ONT   CAN
STAKELUM, JAMES W, PHIL DEPT, ST MARY'S SEM COL, PERRYVILLE MO   63775
STALKER, DOUGLAS F, PHIL DEPT, UNIV OF N CAROLINA, CHAPEL HILL NC   27514
STALL, ROSANNA, PHIL DEPT, GEORGE WILLIAMS UNIV, MONTREAL 107 QUE   CAN
STALNAKER, C L, PHIL & REL DEPT, N CAROLINA ST UNIV, RALEIGH NC   27607
STALNAKER, ROBERT, SAGE SCHOOL, CORNELL UNIVERSITY, ITHACA NY   14850
STAM, JAMES H, PHIL & RELIG DEPT, UPSALA COL, EAST ORANGE NJ   07019
STAMBAUGH, JOAN, PHIL DEPT, HUNTER COLLEGE, NEW YORK NY   10021
STANEY, JOSEPH D, PHILOSOPHY DEPT, MCMURRAY COLLEGE, ABILENE TX   79605
STAMPE, DENNIS W, PHILOSOPHY DEPT, UNIV OF WISCONSIN, MADISON WI   53706
STANAGE, SHERMAN M, PHIL DEPT, N ILLINOIS UNIV, DEKALB IL   60115
STANDLEY, GERALD B, PHIL DEPT, UNIV OF FLORIDA, GAINESVILLE FL   32611
STANFIELD, JESSE A, RELIG & PHIL DEPT, WILMINGTON COL, WILMINGTON OH   45177
STANGER, RICHARD L, PHIL & RELIG, MACMURRAY COLLEGE, JACKSONVILLE IL   62650
STANKIEWICZ, ANN, PHIL & REL STUD DIV, MT ST MARY COL, NEWBURGH NY   12550
STANTON, W, PHIL & RELIG DEPT, MONTCLAIR ST COL, UPR MONTCLAIR NJ   07043
STANTON, WILLIAM, PHIL DEPT, NASSAU COM COL, GARDEN CITY NY   11530
STANWAY, R A, PHILOSOPHY DEPT, MT ALLISON UNIV, SACKVILLE N B   CAN
STARK, BRUCE C, ASHLAND COLLEGE, ASHLAND, OH   44805
STARK, THOMAS, HUMAN DEPT, LOOP COLLEGE, CHICAGO IL   60601
STARKEY, LAWRENCE H, 519 COLLEGE LANE, JAMESTOWN, ND   58401
STARKEY, LAWRENCE H, PHILOSOPHY DEPT, JAMESTOWN COL, JAMESTOWN ND   58401
STARKS, MICHAEL W, PHILOSOPHY DEPT, UNIV OF TEXAS, AUSTIN TX   78712
STARNES, RONALD WARE, PHILOSOPHY DEPT, WESLEY COLLEGE, DOVER DE   19901
STARR, B S, BEHAV & SOC SCI DEPT, MODESTO JUNIOR COL, MODESTO CA   95350
STARR, ROGER, PHIL DEPT, MICHIGAN STATE UNIV, EAST LANSING MI   48823
STARR, WILLIAM C, PHILOSOPHY DEPT, UNIV OF WISCONSIN, MADISON WI   53706
STARR, ZACHARY, PHIL DEPT, BRANDEIS UNIVERSITY, WALTHAM MA   02154
START, LESTER J, PHIL DEPT, KALAMAZOO COLLEGE, KALAMAZOO MI   49001
STASSEN, GLEN, PHIL & REL DEPT, BEREA COLLEGE, BEREA KY   40403
STATHAM, DENIS, HUMANITIES DIV, SAINT GREGORY'S COL, SHAWNEE OK   74801
STAUDE, MITCHELL, PHIL DEPT, UNIV OF MARYLAND, COLLEGE PARK MD   20742
STAUDENBAUR, RONALD, PHIL DEPT, MICHIGAN STATE UNIV, EAST LANSING MI   48823
STAVRIDES, RIA, REL & PHIL DEPT, COLO WOMEN'S COL, DENVER CO   80220
STAVROS, PETER, PHIL DEPT, RENSSELAER POLYTECH, TROY NY   12181
STAWINSKI, ARTHUR W, HUMAN DEPT, ILLINOIS INST TECH, CHICAGO IL   60616
STAYTON, WILLIAM H, PHIL DEPT, U S AIR FORCE ACAD, COLORADO SPGS CO   80840
STE MARIE, LOUIS, PHILOSOPHY DEPT, GONZAGA UNIV, SPOKANE WA   99202
STEADY, LEO J, PHILOSOPHY DEPT, TRINITY COLLEGE, BURLINGTON VT   05401
STEARNS, ISABEL, BRYN MAWR COLLEGE, BRYN MAWR, PA   19010
STEARNS, J BRENTON, PHILOSOPHY DEPT, UNIV OF WINNIPEG, WINNIPEG MAN   CAN
STECK, ROBERT, PHIL DEPT, COLORADO COLLEGE, COLORADO SPGS CO   80903
STEEL, MARGARET, PHILOSOPHY DEPT, KENT STATE UNIV, KENT OH   44242
STEELE, DENNIS, SOC SCI DIV, GRACELAND COLLEGE, LAMONI IA   50140
STEELMAN, EDMUND H, RELIG & PHIL, SOUTHWESTERN UNIV, GEORGETOWN TX   78626
STEEN, FREDERICK, PHILOSOPHY DEPT, UNIV OF S CAROLINA, COLUMBIA SC   29208
STEEN, PETER, PHIL & BIB DEPT, GENEVA COLLEGE, BEAVER FALLS PA   15010
STEGEMAN, BEATRICE, STATE COM COLLEGE, EAST ST LOUIS, IL   62201
STEIN, GEORGE P, PHILOSOPHY DEPT, BLOOMFIELD COLLEGE, BLOOMFIELD NJ   07003
STEIN, HOWARD, PHIL DEPT, COLUMBIA UNIVERSITY, NEW YORK NY   10027
STEIN, KENNETH E, LIBR ARTS DEPT, WORCESTER JR COL, WORCESTER MA   01608
STEINBERG, ALAN, PHIL DEPT, MASS INST TECH, CAMBRIDGE MA   02139
STEINBERG, DANNY, PHIL DEPT, UNIV OF WEST ONTARIO, LONDON ONT   CAN
STEINBERG, ERIC, PHIL DEPT, BROOKLYN COLLEGE, BROOKLYN NY   11210
STEINBUCH, THOMAS, PHILOSOPHY DEPT, UNIV OF MASS, AMHERST MA   01002
STEINER, KENNETH M, PHIL DEPT, ST UNIV OF NY, BINGHAMTON NY   13901
STEINER, MARK, PHIL DEPT, COLUMBIA UNIVERSITY, NEW YORK NY   10027
STEINKE, JOSEPH T, OHLONE COMMUNITY COL, FREMONT, CA   94537
STEINKRAUS, WARREN E, PHIL DEPT, COL AT OSWEGO, OSWEGO NY   13126

STEINLE, JAMES, PHIL & REL STUD DIV, LOURDES COL, SYLVANIA OH 43560
STEINMAN, DIANE, PHIL DEPT, UNIV OF COLORADO, BOULDER CO 80302
STELL, LANCE K, PHILOSOPHY DEPT, ILLINOIS ST UNIV, NORMAL IL 61761
STELZER, JOHN, PHIL DEPT, PRINCE GEORGE'S COM, LARGO MD 20870
STENERSON, ORVILLE, HUMAN DEPT, BISMARCK JR COL, BISMARCK ND 58501
STENGREN, GEORGE L, PHIL DEPT, CEN MICHIGAN UNIV, MT PLEASANT MI 48858
STENNER, ALFRED J, PHIL DEPT, WASHINGTON UNIV, ST LOUIS MO 63130
STENSAGER, EUGENE F, GRAYS HARBOR COL, ABERDEEN, WA 98520
STEPELEVICH, LAWRENCE, PHILOSOPHY DEPT, VILLANOVA UNIV, VILLANOVA PA 19085
STEPHENS, GAYLE, PHILOSOPHY DEPT, UNIV OF MASS, AMHERST MA 01002
STEPHENS, KENNETH D, PHIL DEPT, GEORGIA ST UNIV, ATLANTA GA 30303
STEPHENS, WALTER'S, PHIL & RELIG DEPT, KEUKA COLLEGE, KEUKA PARK NY 14478
STEPHENSON, GERALD H, PHIL DEPT, INDIANA UNIVERSITY, SOUTH BEND IN 46615
STEPHENSON, WELDON LEE, SOC SCI DEPT, SOUTH PLAINS COL, LEVELLAND TX 79336
STERBA, JAMES, PHIL DEPT, UNIV OF NOTRE DAME, NOTRE DAME IN 46556
STERGIADES, JOHN W, PHILOSOPHY DEPT, WALSH COLLEGE, CANTON OH 44720
STERLING, JOSEPH W, PHIL SCH, CATH UNIV OF AMER, WASHINGTON DC 20017
STERLING, MARVIN C, PHIL DEPT, UNIV OF CALIFORNIA, RIVERSIDE CA 92502
STERN, ALFRED, HUMAN DEPT, UNIV OF PUERTO RICO, MAYAGUEZ PR 00708
STERN, CARL, PHIL DEPT, UNIV OF NEW MEXICO, ALBUQUERQUE NM 87106
STERN, H WILLARD, PHIL DEPT, NEWARK STATE COL, UNION NJ 07083
STERN, KENNETH, PHIL DEPT, ST UNIV OF NY, ALBANY NY 12203
STERN, LAURENT, PHILOSOPHY DEPT, RUTGERS UNIV, NEW BRUNSWICK NJ 08903
STERN, LAWRENCE I, PHIL DEPT, CITY COLLEGE, NEW YORK NY 10031
STERNFELD, ROBERT, PHIL DEPT, ST UNIV OF NY, STONY BROOK NY 11790
STEVENS, ATLEE, HUM & COMMUNIC DIV, SEMINOLE JR COL, SANFORD FL 32771
STEVENS, EDWARD V, PHIL DEPT, CANISIUS COLLEGE, BUFFALO NY 14208
STEVENS, JOHN C, PHIL DEPT, PURDUE UNIVERSITY, LAFAYETTE IN 47907
STEVENS, MORRIS L, SOC SCI DEPT, KANSAS STATE COL, PITTSBURG KS 66762
STEVENS, REX P, PHILOSOPHY DEPT, MERCER UNIVERSITY, MACON GA 31207
STEVENS, RICHARD M, PHIL DEPT, BOSTON COLLEGE, CHESTNUT HILL MA 02167
STEVENSON, CHARLES, PHIL DEPT, UNIV OF MICHIGAN, ANN ARBOR MI 48104
STEVENSON, DON R, PHILOSOPHY DEPT, ERSKINE COLLEGE, DUE WEST SC 29639
STEVENSON, J T, PHILOSOPHY DEPT, UNIV OF TORONTO, TORONTO ONT   CAN
STEVENSON, JOHN G, PHIL DEPT, PURDUE UNIVERSITY, LAFAYETTE IN 47907
STEWART, C, PHILOSOPHY DEPT, UNIV OF GUELPH, GUELPH ONT   CAN
STEWART, CALVIN G, PHIL DEPT, CALIFORNIA ST UNIV, SAN JOSE CA 95114
STEWART, CLAUDE, PHIL & RELIG DEPT, MARYVILLE COL, MARYVILLE TN 37801
STEWART, D B, PHILOSOPHY DEPT, UNIV OF GUELPH, GUELPH ONT   CAN
STEWART, DONALD L, PHIL DEPT, UNIVERSITY OF HAWAII, HONOLULU HI 96822
STEWART, J DAVID, PHILOSOPHY DEPT, OHIO UNIVERSITY, ATHENS OH 45701
STEWART, JOHN P, PHIL DEPT, UNIV BRIT COLUMBIA, VANCOUVER B B C   CAN
STEWART, MAE, ENVIRON STUD, PHILA COL OF BIB, PHILADELPHIA PA 19103
STEWART, MALCOLM F, PHIL & RELIG, ILLINOIS COLLEGE, JACKSONVILLE IL 62650
STEWART, MELVILLE, PHIL DEPT, BETHEL COLLEGE, ST PAUL MN 55112
STEWART, P A G, RELIG & PHIL DEPT, MISS INDUST COL, HOLLY SPRINGS MS 38635
STEWART, RODERICK, PHIL DEPT, SYRACUSE UNIVERSITY, SYRACUSE NY 13210
STEWART, W F M, PHILOSOPHY DEPT, UNIV OF CALGARY, CALGARY 44 ALB   CAN
STEWART, WILLIAM A, PHIL DEPT, ST MARY'S UNIVERSITY, HALIFAX N S   CAN
STICH, ELIZABETH, PHIL DEPT, COL ST SCHOLASTICA, DULUTH MN 55811
STICH, STEPHEN P, PHIL DEPT, UNIV OF MICHIGAN, ANN ARBOR MI 48104
STIERNOTTE, ALFRED, PHIL DEPT, QUINNIPIAC COLLEGE, HAMDEN CT 06518
STIETZEL, ERIC, SOC SCI DIV, FOOTHILL COLLEGE, LOS ALTOS HLS CA 94022
STIKKERS, KENNETH, PHIL DEPT, DEPAUL UNIVERSITY, CHICAGO IL 60604
STILES, GRACE ELLEN, UNIV OF MAINE, FARMINGTON, ME 04938
STILLWELL, SHELLEY L, PHIL DEPT, PURDUE UNIVERSITY, LAFAYETTE IN 47907
STINE, GAIL C, PHIL DEPT, WAYNE STATE UNIV, DETROIT MI 48202
STINE, WILLIAM D, PHIL DEPT, WAYNE STATE UNIV, DETROIT MI 48202
STINES, JAMES W, APPALACHIAN ST UNIV, BOONE, NC 28607
STITCH, ELIZABETH, PHIL DEPT, COL OF ST CATHERINE, SAINT PAUL MN 55105
STITES, DEL E, PHIL DEPT, BELLEVUE COLLEGE, BELLEVUE NE 68005
STIVER, JAMES L, PHILOSOPHY DEPT, UNIV OF S CAROLINA, COLUMBIA SC 29208
STOCK, JEROLD, HUMANITIES DIV, S W VA COM COL, LOGAN WV 25601
STOCKTON, C N, UNIV OF WISCONSIN, RIVER FALLS, WI 54022

STOHRER, WALTER, PHILOSOPHY DEPT, MARQUETTE UNIV, MILWAUKEE WI 53233
STOKES, THOMAS J, PHILOSOPHY DEPT, UNIV OF WINDSOR, WINDSOR ONT CAN
STOLNITZ, JEROME, PHIL DEPT, LEHMAN COLLEGE, BRONX NY 10468
STONE, FRANK F, PHIL & RELIG, SCHOOL OF THE OZARKS, POINT LOOKOUT MO 65726
STONE, JEROME A, PHIL DEPT, KENDALL COLLEGE, EVANSTON IL 60204
STONE, JOHN DAVID, PHILOSOPHY DEPT, UNIV OF TEXAS, AUSTIN TX 78712
STONE, ROBERT, PHIL DEPT, LONG ISLAND UNIV, GREENVALE NY 11548
STONE, RONALD H, CHURCH & MINISTRY, PITTS THEOL SEM, PITTSBURGH PA 15206
STOCL, MATTHEW, PHILOSOPHY DEPT, RUTGERS UNIV, NEW BRUNSWICK NJ 08903
STORMER, GERALD D, PHIL DEPT, N ILLINOIS UNIV, DEKALB IL 60115
STOTT, GILMORE, PHIL DEPT, SWARTHMORE COLLEGE, SWARTHMORE PA 19081
STOLGH, CHARLOTTE, PHIL DEPT, UNIV CF CALIFORNIA, SANTA BARBARA CA 93106
STOLGH, ROBERT, PHILOSOPHY DEPT, OHIO STATE UNIV, COLUMBUS OH 43210
STOUT, F, PHILOSOPHY DEPT, LOYOLA COLLEGE, BALTIMORE MD 21210
STOUT, SHARON, PHILOSOPHY DEPT, UNIV OF MASS, AMHERST MA 01002
STOUTLAND, F, PHIL DEPT, SAINT OLAF COLLEGE, NORTHFIELD MN 55057
STRAHAN, ARCHIE, SOC STUD DEPT, MISS GULF COAST JR C, GAUTIER MS 39553
STRAHL, PAULA, PHILOSOPHY DEPT, PATERSON COL OF NJ, WAYNE NJ 07470
STRAND, DAVID, PHILOSOPHY DEPT, UNIV OF CALGARY, CALGARY 44 ALB CAN
STRANG, JOHN, PHILOSOPHY DEPT, DUQUESNE UNIV, PITTSBURGH PA 15219
STRASSER, MICHAEL W, PHILOSOPHY DEPT, DUQUESNE UNIV, PITTSBURGH PA 15219
STRATH, FREDERICK, PHIL DEPT, MARYMCUNT COLLEGE, TARRYTOWN NY 10591
STRATTON, J, SOC SCI DEPT, RYERSON POLYTECH U, TORONTO ONT CAN
STRAUCH, ALEX, ROCKMONT COLLEGE, DENVER, CO 80226
STRAUMANIS, ERIC, PHILOSOPHY DEPT, CAPITAL UNIV, COLUMBUS OH 43209
STRAUMANIS, JOAN, PHILOSOPHY DEPT, CENISON UNIV, GRANVILLE OH 43023
STRAUSS, JAMES D, PHIL & PSYCH DEPT, LINCOLN CHRIST COL, LINCOLN IL 62656
STREADWICK, ROBERT L, MID MICHIGAN COM COL, HARRISON, MI 48625
STREVELER, PAUL, PHIL DEPT, WEST CHESTER ST COL, WEST CHESTER PA 19380
STRICKLAND, WILLIAM, REL & PHIL DEPT, TREVECCA NAZ COL, NASHVILLE TN 37210
STRICKLER, GERALD B, PHIL DEPT, CALIFORNIA ST UNIV, LONG BEACH CA 90840
STRIMPLE, PATRICIA A, PHIL DEPT, BOSTON COLLEGE, CHESTNUT HILL MA 02167
STRINGER, VARNES, RELIG & SOC SCI, CONCORDIA LUTH COL, AUSTIN TX 78705
STRINGFIELD, LEROY P, PHIL & REL DEPT, JUDSON COLLEGE, MARION AL 36756
STRIPLING, SCOTT, PHILOSOPHY DEPT, PENN STATE UNIV, UNIV PARK PA 16802
STROH, GUY, PHILOSOPHY DEPT, RIDER COLLEGE, TRENTON NJ 08602
STROICK, CLEMENS, PHIL FACULTY, UNIV OF OTTAWA, OTTAWA ONT CAN
STRCLL, AVRUM, PHIL DEPT, U OF CAL -SAN DIEGO, LA JOLLA CA 92037
STROM, ELISABETH, PHIL DEPT, IMMACULATA COLLEGE, IMMACULATA PA 19345
STROMBERG, JAMES S, PHIL DEPT, COL OF ST THOMAS, ST PAUL MN 55105
STRCMSETH, W A, PHIL DEPT, SAINT OLAF COLLEGE, NORTHFIELD MN 55057
STRONG, CARSON, PHIL DEPT, UNIVERSITY OF DAYTON, DAYTON OH 45469
STRONG, EDWARD W, PHIL DEPT, UNIV OF CALIFORNIA, BERKELEY CA 94720
STRONG, JOHN V, ST PETER'S COLLEGE, JERSEY CITY, NJ 07306
STROSSER, RICHARD F, PHIL DEPT, LA SALLE COLLEGE, PHILADELPHIA PA 19141
STROUD-DRINKWATER, C, PHILOSOPHY DEPT, UNIV OF TORONTO, TORONTO ONT CAN
STROUD, BARRY G, PHIL DEPT, UNIV OF CALIFORNIA, BERKELEY CA 94720
STROUD, BILL, ENG PHIL & LANG DIV, ARKANSAS ST U, ST UNIVERSITY AR 72467
STROUD, WILLAIM, RELIG & PHIL DEPT, SALEM COLLEGE, SALEM WV 26426
STROUP, MICHAEL, ARTS & HUM DIV, LEEWARD COM COL, PEARL CITY HI 96782
STRUCKMAN, ROBERT, SOC SCI DEPT, CITY COLLEGE, SAN FRANCISCO CA 94112
STRUCKMEYER, F R, PHIL DEPT, WEST CHESTER ST COL, WEST CHESTER PA 19380
STRUHL, KARSTEN J, PHIL DEPT, LONG ISLAND UNIV, BROOKLYN NY 11201
STRUPL, MILOS, PHIL & RELIG DEPT, DEFIANCE COLLEGE, DEFIANCE OH 43512
STUART, ALBERT, PHIL DEPT, DEPAUL UNIVERSITY, CHICAGO IL 60604
STUART, JAMES, PHIL DEPT, BOWLING GREEN UNIV, BOWLING GREEN OH 43403
STUART, WILLIAM JAMES, PHIL & REL, GREENVILLE COLLEGE, GREENVILLE IL 62246
STUBER, JOHN W, HUM & SOC STUD, LETCURNEAU COL, LONGVIEW TX 75601
STUCKEL, RUTH, THEOL & PHIL DEPT, AVILA COLLEGE, KANSAS CITY MO 64145
STUDDARD, ALBERT, PHIL & RELIG DEPT, PEMBROKE ST UNIV, PEMBROKE NC 28372
STUHR, CHRISTIAN A, APPL ARTS DIV, CONFEDERATION COL, THUNDER BAY ONT CAN
STUHR, JOHN JEREMY, PHILOSOPHY DEPT, UNIV OF TEXAS, AUSTIN TX 78712
STULBERG, JOSEPH B, PHIL DEPT, UNIV OF ROCHESTER, ROCHESTER NY 14627
STURDIVANT, ROBERT V, REL & PHIL DEPT, BERRY COLLEGE, MOUNT BERRY GA 30149

STURGEON, NICHOLAS, SAGE SCHOOL, CORNELL UNIVERSITY, ITHACA NY 14850
STURM, FRED GILETTE, THE WESTERN COLLEGE, OXFORD, OH 45056
STURM, WILLIAM, PHIL & RELIG DEPT, VA WESLEYAN COL, NORFOLK VA 23502
SUBER, PETER, PHIL DEPT, NORTHWESTERN UNIV, EVANSTON IL 60201
SUGALSKI, J R, PHIL DEPT, UNIV OF FLORIDA, GAINESVILLE FL 32611
SUGARMAN, RICHARD, PHILOSOPHY DEPT, UNIV OF VERMONT, BURLINGTON VT 05401
SUITS, BERNARD H, PHILOSOPHY DEPT, UNIV OF WATERLOO, WATERLOO ONT   CAN
SUITS, DAVID, PHILOSOPHY DEPT, UNIV OF WATERLOO, WATERLOO ONT   CAN
SUKALE, MICHAEL, PHIL DEPT, PRINCETON UNIVERSITY, PRINCETON NJ 08540
SULLINS, MAX, LABETTE COM JR COL, PARSONS, KS 67357
SULLIVAN, ARTHUR F, PHIL DEPT, NORTH ADAMS ST COL, NORTH ADAMS MA 01247
SULLIVAN, F RUSSELL, CULT ARTS DEPT, N SHORE COM COL, BEVERLY MA 01915
SULLIVAN, HENRY B, HUMAN DIV, GLOUCESTER CO COL, SEWELL NJ 08080
SULLIVAN, JAY L, PHIL DEPT, UNIV OF N CAROLINA, CHAPEL HILL NC 27514
SULLIVAN, JOHN EDWARD, ST ALBERT'S COLLEGE, OAKLAND, CA 94618
SULLIVAN, JOHN G, PHILOSOPHY DEPT, ELON COLLEGE, ELON COLLEGE NC 27244
SULLIVAN, JOHN, SYST & PHIL, GRADUATE THEOL UNION, BERKELEY CA 94709
SULLIVAN, MARK, PHILOSOPHY DEPT, COL OF NOTRE DAME, BELMONT CA 94002
SULLIVAN, MARY JANE, PHILOSOPHY DEPT, DUQUESNE UNIV, PITTSBURGH PA 15219
SULLIVAN, NEAL, PHILOSOPHY DEPT, UNIV OF S CAROLINA, CONWAY SC 29526
SULLIVAN, ROBERT P, PHIL DEPT, NIAGARA UNIVERSITY, NIAGARA UNIV NY 14109
SULLIVAN, ROGER, PHILOSOPHY DEPT, UNIV OF S CAROLINA, COLUMBIA SC 29208
SULLIVAN, STEPHEN E, PHIL & THEOL, ST FRANCIS COLLEGE, FORT WAYNE IN 46808
SULLIVAN, THOMAS D, PHIL DEPT, COL OF ST THOMAS, ST PAUL MN 55105
SULLIVAN, WILLIAM A, PHILOSOPHY DEPT, UNIV OF CINCINNATI, BLUE ASH OH 45236
SULLIVAN, WILLIAM, PHILOSOPHY DEPT, UNIV OF S CAROLINA, COLUMBIA SC 29208
SULLIVAN, WILLIAM, PHIL & THEOL DIV, ALLENTOWN COL, CENTER VALLEY PA 18034
SUMMERS, JAMES W, PHIL DEPT, TULANE UNIVERSITY, NEW ORLEANS LA 70118
SUMNER, L W, PHILOSOPHY DEPT, UNIV OF TORONTO, TORONTO ONT   CAN
SUN, G C H, PHILOSOPHY DEPT, UNIV OF S ALABAMA, MOBILE AL 36688
SUNCHEIM, FRANK, HUMAN & PHIL DIV, UNIVERSITY OF TAMPA, TAMPA FL 33606
SUPPE, BERNARD, PHILOSOPHY DEPT, UNIV OF SCRANTON, SCRANTON PA 18510
SUPPE, FREDERICK R, PHIL DEPT, UNIV OF MARYLAND, COLLEGE PARK MD 20742
SUPPES, PATRICK, PHIL DEPT, STANFORD UNIVERSITY, STANFORD CA 94305
SURBER, JERE, PHILOSOPHY DEPT, PENN STATE UNIV, UNIV PARK PA 16802
SURJIT, SINGH, CHRIST PHIL DEPT, SAN FRAN THEOL SEM, SAN ANSELMO CA 94960
SURRATT, JERRY L, RELIG & PHIL DEPT, WINGATE COLLEGE, WINGATE NC 28174
SUSAK, MICHAEL, PHILOSOPHY DEPT, KENT STATE UNIV, KENT OH 44242
SUSKY, JOHN E, PHIL DEPT, OKLAHOMA STATE UNIV, STILLWATER OK 74074
SUTER, RONALD, PHIL DEPT, MICHIGAN STATE UNIV, EAST LANSING MI 48823
SUTFIN, EDWARD, PHIL & REL DEPT, NORWICH UNIVERSITY, NORTHFIELD VT 05663
SUTHERLAND, ROBERT S, HUMAN DIV, MISSOURI BAPT COL, ST LOUIS MO 63141
SUTPHIN, JOHN E, MISSISSIPPI ST UNIV, ST COLLEGE, MS 39762
SUTPHIN, STANLEY T, RELIG & PHIL, ELIZABETHTOWN COL, ELIZABETHTOWN PA 17022
SUTTON JR, PAUL W, PHIL DEPT, UNIV OF CINCINNATI, CINCINNATI OH 45221
SUTULA, JOHN, PHILOSOPHY DEPT, OHIO STATE UNIV, COLUMBUS OH 43210
SVENONIUS, DIANE, PHIL DEPT, UNIV OF MARYLAND, COLLEGE PARK MD 20742
SVENONIUS, LARS S, PHIL DEPT, UNIV OF MARYLAND, COLLEGE PARK MD 20742
SVITAK, IVAN, PHILOSOPHY DEPT, CALIFORNIA ST UNIV, CHICO CA 95926
SWADLEY, ELLIS C, EDUC & SCI DEPT, UNIV OF MAINE, MACHIAS ME 04654
SWAIN, MARSHALL W, PHILOSOPHY DEPT, OHIO STATE UNIV, COLUMBUS OH 43210
SWAN, P, PHILOSOPHY DEPT, ST THOMAS MORE COL, SASKATOON SAS   CAN
SWANKE, JOHN W, ARTS & SCI COL, UNIV OF SAN DIEGO, SAN DIEGO CA 92110
SWANSON, GERALD, PHILOSOPHY DEPT, UNIV OF VERMONT, BURLINGTON VT 05401
SWANSON, LYNN, PHIL & RELIG DEPT, COLBY JR COLLEGE, NEW LONDON NH 03257
SWANSON, MYRON R, PHIL DEPT, BEMIDJI STATE COL, BEMIDJI MN 56601
SWANSON, REUBEN J, RELIG & PHIL DEPT, W CAROLINA UNIV, CULLOWHEE NC 28723
SWANSON, STANLEY H, REL & PHIL, BETHANY COLLEGE, LINDSBORG KS 67456
SWARTZ, N M, PHILOSOPHY DEPT, SIMON FRASER UNIV, BURNABY 2 B C   CAN
SWARTZ, PHIL DEPT, UNIV OF MASS, BOSTON, MA 02116
SWARTZ, THOMAS, PHIL DEPT, BOWLING GREEN UNIV, BOWLING GREEN OH 43403
SWEARINGER, JACK, ENG DEPT, SW OREGON COM COL, COOS BAY OR 97420
SWEENEY, JAMES J, PHIL DEPT, MERRIMACK COLLEGE, NORTH ANDOVER MA 01845
SWEENEY, JOHN, PHILOSOPHY DEPT, RIDER COLLEGE, TRENTON NJ 08602

SWEENEY, KEVIN W, PHILOSOPHY DEPT, UNIV OF WISCONSIN, MADISON WI 53706
SWEENEY, LEO, PHIL DEPT, LOYOLA UNIVERSITY, CHICAGO IL 60626
SWEENEY, ROBERT D, PHIL DEPT, JOHN CARROLL UNIV, UNIVERSITY HT OH 44118
SWEENEY, TIMOTHY, PHIL DIV, ST MEINRAD COLLEGE, SAINT MEINRAD IN 47577
SWEET, ALBERT, PHILOSOPHY DEPT, RUTGERS UNIV, NEWARK NJ 07102
SWEET, DOLORES M, PHIL DEPT, CAL POLYTECH ST U, SAN LUIS OBIS CA 93407
SWEET, DONALD G, ENGLISH LIT & PHIL, UNIV OF WISCONSIN, MADISON WI 53706
SWEIGART, JOHN, PHIL & RELIG DEPT, MADISON COL, HARRISONBURG VA 22801
SWIATEK, STANLEY, REL STUD & PHIL, SPRINGFIELD COL, SPRINGFIELD IL 62702
SWITALSKI, BRUNO, PHIL DEPT, DEPAUL UNIVERSITY, CHICAGO IL 60604
SWOL, GABRIEL, REL STUD & PHIL, HILBERT COLLEGE, HAMBURG NY 14075
SYFERS, JAMES W, PHIL DEPT, CALIFORNIA ST UNIV, SAN FRANCISCO CA 94132
SYLVESTER, C BERNARD, PHIL DEPT, NIAGARA UNIVERSITY, NIAGARA UNIV NY 14109
SYLVESTER, R P, HUMAN DIV, NEW ENGLAND COLLEGE, HENNIKER NH 03242
SYNAN, E A, UNIV OF ST MICHAEL'S, TORONTO 181, ONT   CAN
SYNNESTVEDT, JUSTIN, HUMAN DIV, MORAINE VLY COM COL, PALOS HILLS IL 60465
SZATHMARY, ARTHUR, PHIL DEPT, PRINCETON UNIVERSITY, PRINCETON NJ 08540
TABOR, JOHN, PHIL DEPT, UNIVERSITY OF KANSAS, LAWRENCE KS 66044
TAIT, FOSTER E, PHILOSOPHY DEPT, UNIV OF S CAROLINA, COLUMBIA SC 29208
TAIT, WILLIAM, PHIL DEPT, UNIV OF CHICAGO, CHICAGO IL 60637
TAKEI, FRANKLIN S, SOC SCI DEPT, CLARION STATE COL, CLARION PA 16214
TALARSKY, JOSEPH W, HUMAN DEPT, LUZERNE CO COM COL, WILKES-BARRE PA 18711
TALBERT, ROBERT M, PHIL & RELIG, VA COMMONWEALTH UNIV, RICHMOND VA 23220
TALBOT, FRANCOIS, PHILOSOPHY DEPT, COL DE MAISONNEUVE, MONTREAL QUE   CAN
TALBOTT, SHERIDAN, PHIL DEPT, S ILLINOIS UNIV, CARBONDALE IL 62901
TALBOTT, THOMAS, PHILOSOPHY DEPT, WILLIAMETTE UNIV, SALEM OR 97301
TALBUTT JR, PALMER C, PHIL & RELIG, VA POLYTECH INST, BLACKSBURG VA 24061
TALLON, ANDREW, PHILOSOPHY DEPT, MARQUETTE UNIV, MILWAUKEE WI 53233
TALLON, JAMES, PHIL DEPT, UNIV OF WEST ONTARIO, LONDON ONT   CAN
TALMAGE, RONALD R, PHIL DEPT, ST LOUIS UNIVERSITY, ST LOUIS MO 63103
TALMAGE, S, PHILOSOPHY DEPT, CARLETON UNIVERSITY, OTTAWA ONT   CAN
TAMASHIRO, DAVID M, PHIL DEPT, WHEATON COLLEGE, WHEATON IL 60187
TAMINIAUX, JACQUES M, PHIL DEPT, BOSTON COLLEGE, CHESTNUT HILL MA 02167
TAMNY, MARTIN, PHIL DEPT, CITY COLLEGE, NEW YORK NY 10031
TAMPKE, ROBERT A, ENG & PHIL DEPT, SW TEXAS ST UNIV, SAN MARCOS TX 78666
TAMTE, JAMES, SOC SCI DEPT, MESABI COM COLLEGE, VIRGINIA MN 55792
TANENZAPH, STANLEY, PHIL DEPT, MIAMI-DADE JUN COL, MIAMI FL 33156
TANGUAY, JEAN-CHARLES, PHIL DEPT, COL VIEUX-MONTREAL, MONTREAL QUE   CAN
TANNENBAUM, JERRY, PHIL DEPT, UNIV OF CALIFORNIA, SANTA BARBARA CA 93106
TANNER, ROBERT C, PHILOSOPHY DEPT, UNIV OF UTAH, SALT LAKE CTY UT 84112
TANNER, SOC SCI DEPT, ALGONQUIN COL ARTS, OTTAWA, ONT   CAN
TANNER, STEVEN, PHIL DEPT, UNIV OF ILLINOIS, URBANA IL 61801
TAPKE, PETER F, PHIL & REL DEPT, WASHINGTON COLLEGE, CHESTERLAND MD 21620
TAPSCOTT, BANGS L, PHILOSOPHY DEPT, UNIV OF UTAH, SALT LAKE CTY UT 84112
TARASEVITCH, C, PHILOSOPHY DEPT, ILL BENEDICTINE COL, LISLE IL 60532
TARCIF, GERMAIN, PHIL DEPT, COL THETFORD MINES, MEGANTIE QUE   CAN
TARR, PATRICK H, PHIL DEPT, UNIV OF N CAROLINA, CHAPEL HILL NC 27514
TASSI, A G, PHILOSOPHY DEPT, LOYOLA COLLEGE, BALTIMORE MD 21210
TATALOVICH, ROBERT, PHIL DEPT, CONCORDIA COLLEGE, MOORHEAD MN 56560
TATE, DONALD S, PHILOSOPHY DEPT, UNIV OF OKLAHOMA, NORMAN OK 73069
TATTERSHALL, PHIL DEPT, FLORIDA STATE UNIV, TALLAHASSEE, FL 32306
TAUREK, JOHN, PHIL DEPT, NEW YORK UNIVERSITY, NEW YORK NY 10003
TAYLOR, CHARLES D, PHIL & RELIG DEPT, RADFORD COLLEGE, RADFORD VA 24141
TAYLOR, CHARLES, PHILOSOPHY DEPT, MCGILL UNIVERSITY, MONTREAL QUE   CAN
TAYLOR, CRAIG, PHIL DEPT, UNIV OF ILLINOIS, URBANA IL 61801
TAYLOR, DARRELL, PHILOSOPHY DEPT, QUEENS COLLEGE, FLUSHING NY 11367
TAYLOR, DONALD M, REL & PHIL DIV, BETHEL COLLEGE, MISHAWAKA IN 46544
TAYLOR, DOUGLAS, PHIL DEPT, FLORIDA STATE UNIV, TALLAHASSEE FL 32306
TAYLOR, FRANK, PHILOSOPHY DEPT, E ILLINOIS UNIV, CHARLESTON IL 61920
TAYLOR, GENE F, HIST & POLIT SCI, ALABAMA A & M UNIV, NORMAL AL 35762
TAYLOR, IDEL W, PHILOSOPHY DEPT, MORGAN STATE UNIV, BALTIMORE MD 21239
TAYLOR, JEFFREY, REL DEPT, UNIV OF GEORGIA, ATHENS GA 30602
TAYLOR, JOHN F, PHIL DEPT, MICHIGAN STATE UNIV, EAST LANSING MI 48823
TAYLOR, LOUIS H, VA INTERMONT COL, BRISTOL, VA 24201

TAYLOR, PAUL, PHIL DEPT, BROOKLYN COLLEGE, BROOKLYN NY 11210
TAYLOR, RICHARD N, PHIL DEPT, UNIV CF S FLORIDA, TAMPA FL 33620
TAYLOR, RICHARD, PHIL DEPT, UNIV OF ROCHESTER, ROCHESTER NY 14627
TAYLOR, ROBERT, PHIL DEPT, SLIPPERY ROCK ST COL, SLIPPERY ROCK PA 16057
TAYLOR, S WALLACE, RELIG & PHIL DEPT, LIMESTONE COLLEGE, GAFFNEY SC 29340
TAYLOR, STEPHEN, PHIL DEPT, UNIVERSITY OF TOLEDO, TOLEDO OH 43606
TAYLOR, THELMA W, HUMANITIES DEPT, POINT PARK COL, PITTSBURGH PA 15222
TAYLOR, TIMOTHY, PHIL DEPT, MANKATO STATE COL, MANKATO MN 56001
TAYLOR, W S, HIST OF THEOL DIV, VANCOUVER SCH THEOL, VANCOUVER 8 B C   CAN
TAYLOR, WILLIAM G, RELIG DEPT, MARTIN COLLEGE, PULASKI TN 38478
TCHAO, JOSEPH HO-JOU, PHIL DEPT, UNIV DE SHERBROOKE, SHERBROOKE QUE   CAN
TEETER, LURA S, PHIL DEPT, SE MASS UNIV, N DARTMOUTH MA 02747
TEGHRARIAN, SOUREN, PHILOSOPHY DEPT, PATERSON COL OF NJ, WAYNE NJ 07470
TEHENNEPE, EUGENE, PHIL DEPT, CONNECTICUT COL, NEW LONDON CT 06320
TEICHERT, HARRY W, PHIL DEPT, INDIANA UNIVERSITY, BLOOMINGTON IN 47401
TEIGEN, BJARNE W, BETHANY LUTHERAN COL, MANKATO, MN 56001
TEITELMAN, MICHAEL, PHIL DEPT, COLUMBIA UNIVERSITY, NEW YORK NY 10027
TEJERA, VICTOR, PHIL DEPT, ST UNIV CF NY, STONY BROOK NY 11790
TELFORD, KENNETH A, HUMAN DEPT, WRIGHT CY COLLEGE, CHICAGO IL 60634
TELLER, PAUL R, PHIL DEPT, UNIV OF ILLINOIS, CHICAGO IL 60680
TEMIN, MARC, PHIL DEPT, MIDDLEBURY COLLEGE, MIDDLEBURY VT 05753
TEMKO, PHILIP, PHIL DEPT, CAL ST COL AT SONOMA, ROHNERT PARK CA 94928
TEMPEST, ALBERT E, PHIL DEPT, UNIV CF WEST ONTARIO, LONDON ONT   CAN
TEMPLE, DENNIS, PHIL DEPT, ROOSEVELT UNIVERSITY, CHICAGO IL 60605
TEMPLIN, J ALTON, REL PHIL DEPT, ILIFF SCH OF THEOL, DENVER CO 80210
TENNESSEN, H, PHILOSOPHY DEPT, UNIV OF ALBERTA, EDMONTON ALB   CAN
TENNEY, CHARLES D, PHIL DEPT, S ILLINOIS UNIV, CARBONDALE IL 62901
TENZIS, LOUIS, PHIL DEPT, ROSARY COLLEGE, RIVER FOREST IL 60305
TEO, WESLEY, SOC SCI DEPT, CHICAGO ST UNIV, CHICAGO IL 60628
TERAKAWA, SHUNSHO, PHIL DEPT, CALIFORNIA ST UNIV, SAN JOSE CA 95114
TERDAL, ROY, HUMAN DIV, NW MICHIGAN COLLEGE, TRAVERSE CITY MI 49684
TERRELL, D BURNHAM, PHIL DEPT, UNIV OF MINNESOTA, MINNEAPOLIS MN 55465
TERRELL, DAVID, HUMAN DIV, NW MICHIGAN COLLEGE, TRAVERSE CITY MI 49684
TERRELL, H, PHIL & RELIG DEPT, COLGATE UNIVERSITY, HAMILTON NY 13346
TESCHNER, GEORGE, PHILOSOPHY DEPT, BLOOMFIELD COLLEGE, BLOOMFIELD NJ 07003
TEST, ROBERT, PHIL DEPT, N ILLINOIS UNIV, DEKALB IL 60115
TETRAULT, GERALD EMILE, PHIL DEPT, WESTFIELD STATE COL, WESTFIELD MA 01085
TEUTSCH, RALPH J, PHIL DEPT, UNIV OF N CAROLINA, CHAPEL HILL NC 27514
THACKERAY, WILLIAM W, LANG & LIT, NORTH MONTANA COL, HAVRE MT 59501
THALBERG, IRVIN G, PHIL DEPT, UNIV CF ILLINOIS, CHICAGO IL 60680
THARP, LYNN H, PHILOSOPHY DEPT, UNIV OF WISCONSIN, MADISON WI 53706
THAU, STEWART, PHIL DEPT, SYRACUSE UNIVERSITY, SYRACUSE NY 13210
THAYER, H S, PHIL DEPT, CITY COLLEGE, NEW YORK NY 10031
THEAU, JEAN, PHIL FACULTY, UNIV OF OTTAWA, OTTAWA ONT   CAN
THEBERGE, GUY, PHIL DEPT, COL DE LA POCATIERE, LA POCATIERE QUE   CAN
THECE, DIDRIK O, PHIL DEPT, PURDUE UNIVERSITY, LAFAYETTE IN 47907
THECPHANOUS, ANDREW, PHIL DEPT, UNIV OF NEVADA, RENO NV 89507
THERRIEN, VINCENT, PHILOSOPHY DEPT, UNIV DU QUEBEC, 3-RIVIERES QUE   CAN
THIBAULT, SERGE, PHIL DEPT, COL TROIS-RIVIERES, 3 RIVIERES QUE   CAN
THICH, THIEN-AN, PHIL DEPT, LOS ANGELES CY COL, LOS ANGELES CA 90029
THIESSEN, ELMER J, HUMAN & SOC SCI, MEDICINE HAT COL, MEDICINE HAT ALB   CAN
THIESSEN, ELMER, PHILOSOPHY DEPT, UNIV OF WATERLOO, WATERLOO ONT   CAN
THIRKEL, W EDMUND, PHIL DEPT, JOHN CARROLL UNIV, UNIVERSITY HT OH 44118
THIROUX, JACQUES P, PHIL DEPT, BAKERSFIELD COLLEGE, BAKERSFIELD CA 93305
THIRY, LEON, PHILOSOPHY DEPT, WATERLOO LUTH UNIV, WATERLOO ONT   CAN
THOCE, RICHARD, PHILOSOPHY DEPT, UNIV OF WATERLOO, WATERLOO ONT   CAN
THOMAS JR, SID B, PHIL DEPT, ST UNIV OF NY, BINGHAMTON NY 13901
THOMAS-MOORE, GAR, PHIL DEPT, RENSSELAER POLYTECH, TROY NY 12181
THOMAS, A J, PHILOSOPHY DEPT, MARQUETTE UNIV, MILWAUKEE WI 53233
THOMAS, C C, PHIL & REL AREA, FAYETTEVILLE ST UNIV, FAYETTEVILLE NC 28301
THOMAS, C T, PHILOSOPHY DEPT, PFEIFFER COLLEGE, MISENHEIMER NC 28109
THOMAS, CARLA R, PHILOSOPHY DEPT, GODDARD COLLEGE, PLAINFIELD VT 05667
THOMAS, DEBORAH R, PHIL DEPT, RENSSELAER POLYTECH, TROY NY 12181
THOMAS, EDMUND, HUMAN DIV, NIAGARA CO COM COL, NIAGARA FALLS NY 14303

THOMAS, GEORGE B, PHIL DEPT, UNIV OF VIRGINIA, CHARLOTTESVL VA   22903
THOMAS, GEORGE H, RELIG & PHIL DEPT, MOUNT UNION COLLEGE, ALLIANCE OH   44601
THOMAS, HERMAN E, REL & PHIL DEPT, SPRINGFIELD COL, SPRINGFIELD MA   01109
THOMAS, IVO, PHIL DEPT, UNIV OF NOTRE DAME, NOTRE DAME IN   46556
THOMAS, J D, BIBLE DEPT, ABILENE CHRIST COL, ABILENE TX   79601
THOMAS, JAMES A, PHIL DEPT, ST UNIV OF NY, ALBANY NY   12203
THOMAS, JAMES A, PHIL & RELIG DEPT, UNIV OF S MISS, HATTIESBURG MS   39401
THOMAS, JAMES, PHILOSOPHY DEPT, MT SAN ANTONIO COL, WALNUT CA   91789
THOMAS, JOHN C, PHILOSOPHY DEPT, UNIV OF OREGON, EUGENE OR   97403
THOMAS, JOHN E, PHILOSOPHY DEPT, MCMASTER UNIVERSITY, HAMILTON ONT   CAN
THOMAS, JOHN W, PHIL & REL DEPT, ELLEN CUSHING JR COL, BRYN MAWR PA   19010
THOMAS, JOSEPH, PHIL DIV, ST MEINRAD COLLEGE, SAINT MEINRAD IN   47577
THOMAS, LARRY L, PHIL DEPT, TUSKEGEE INSTITUTE, TUSKEGEE INST AL   36088
THOMAS, NORMAN L, PHIL DEPT, SIMPSON COLLEGE, INDIANOLA IA   50125
THOMAS, STEPHEN N, PHILOSOPHY DEPT, UNIV OF WASHINGTON, SEATTLE WA   98195
THOMAS, THOMAS A, APOLOGETICS DEPT, BAPTIST BIB COL, CLARKS SUMMIT PA   18411
THOMAS, WILLIAM W, PHIL & RELIG DEPT, MADISON COL, HARRISONBURG VA   22801
THOMAS, WILLIAM W, PHIL & RELIG, LINDENWOOD COLLEGES, ST CHARLES MO   63301
THOMASON, RICHMOND, PHIL DEPT, UNIV OF PITTSBURGH, PITTSBURGH PA   15260
THOMPSON III, H, PHILOSOPHY DEPT, UNIV OF SASKATCHEWAN, SASKATOON SAS   CAN
THOMPSON, CAMERON, PHIL & REL, PINE MANOR JR COL, CHESTNUT HILL MA   02167
THOMPSON, CHARLES W, HUMAN DIV, UNIV OF ALABAMA, BIRMINGHAM AL   35233
THOMPSON, D L, PHILOSOPHY DEPT, MEMORIAL UNIV, ST JOHN'S N F   CAN
THOMPSON, DORA, SOC SCI DIV, EL CENTRO COL, DALLAS TX   75202
THOMPSON, EDWARD, PHILOSOPHY DEPT, UNIV OF TEXAS, AUSTIN TX   78712
THOMPSON, FRANK, PHIL DEPT, INDIANA UNIVERSITY, BLOOMINGTON IN   47401
THOMPSON, FRED, HUM & SOC SCI DIV, CAL INST OF TECH, PASADENA CA   91101
THOMPSON, G O, PHIL & RELIG, WESTMAR COLLEGE, LEMARS IA   51031
THOMPSON, GEORGE, PHIL DEPT, E STROUDSBURG ST COL, E STROUDSBURG PA   18301
THOMPSON, HUGO, PHILOSOPHY DEPT, MILLIKIN UNIVERSITY, DECATUR IL   62522
THOMPSON, J M, PHILOSOPHY DEPT, CARLETON UNIVERSITY, OTTAWA ONT   CAN
THOMPSON, JOHN G, PHIL DEPT, UNIVERSITY OF DAYTON, DAYTON OH   45469
THOMPSON, JOSIAH D, PHIL DEPT, HAVERFORD COLLEGE, HAVERFORD PA   19041
THOMPSON, KENNETH, PHIL DEPT, LOYOLA UNIVERSITY, CHICAGO IL   60626
THOMPSON, MANLEY, PHIL DEPT, UNIV OF CHICAGO, CHICAGO IL   60637
THOMPSON, R DUANE, REL & PHIL DIV, MARION COLLEGE, MARION IN   46952
THOMPSON, ROBERT F, PHILOSOPHY DEPT, MEMPHIS ST UNIV, MEMPHIS TN   38152
THOMPSON, ROBERT N, HUMANITIES DIV, TRINITY WEST COL, LANGLEY B C   CAN
THOMPSON, SAMUEL M, PHIL DEPT, MONMOUTH COLLEGE, MONMOUTH IL   61462
THOMPSON, STEPHEN, PHIL & REL, PINE MANOR JR COL, CHESTNUT HILL MA   02167
THOMPSON, THOMAS, PHIL & RELIG, UNIV OF NORTH IOWA, CEDAR FALLS IA   50613
THOMPSON, TYLER, PHIL OF RELIG, GARRETT THEOL SEM, EVANSTON IL   60201
THOMPSON, WARREN K A, PHILOSOPHY DEPT, LEBANON VLY COL, ANNVILLE PA   17003
THOMPSON, WILLIAM, PHIL DEPT, COL AT POTSDAM, POTSDAM NY   13676
THOMSETT, DEREK, PHILOSOPHY DEPT, UNIV OF WATERLOO, WATERLOO ONT   CAN
THOMSON, JAMES F, PHIL DEPT, MASS INST TECH, CAMBRIDGE MA   02139
THOMSON, JUDITH J, PHIL DEPT, MASS INST TECH, CAMBRIDGE MA   02139
THOMTE, REIDAR, PHIL DEPT, CONCORDIA COLLEGE, MOORHEAD MN   56560
THORN, LAURLEE, PHIL DEPT, TRINITY UNIVERSITY, SAN ANTONIO TX   78284
THORNBRUGH, JOHN, PHIL DEPT, DEPAUL UNIVERSITY, CHICAGO IL   60604
THORNTON, M T, PHILOSOPHY DEPT, VICTORIA UNIV, TORONTO 181 ONT   CAN
THORPE, DERRICK G S, PHIL DEPT, UNIV OF WEST ONTARIO, LONDON ONT   CAN
THORWALDSEN, ROLAND E, PHIL & REL DEPT, COLBY COLLEGE, WATERVILLE ME   04901
THRANE, GARY A, HUMAN DEPT, ILLINOIS INST TECH, CHICAGO IL   60616
THREN, CHRISTINE, PHIL DEPT, UNIV OF MICHIGAN, ANN ARBOR MI   48104
THRO, LINUS J, PHIL DEPT, ST LOUIS UNIVERSITY, ST LOUIS MO   63103
THURESON, JOAN I, PHILOSOPHY DEPT, EL CAMINO COLLEGE, TORRENCE CA   90506
THURN, RICHARD, PHILOSOPHY DEPT, COL OF HOLY NAMES, OAKLAND CA   94619
THURSBY, VINCENT V, PHIL DEPT, FLORIDA STATE UNIV, TALLAHASSEE FL   32306
TIBBETTS, PAUL, PHIL DEPT, UNIVERSITY OF DAYTON, DAYTON OH   45469
TIBOLLA, PATRICIA, PHILOSOPHY DEPT, UNIV OF UTAH, SALT LAKE CTY UT   84112
TICAC, WAYNE, PHIL DEPT, LINCOLN UNIVERSITY, JEFFERSON CY MO   65101
TICE, JOHN K, LOUISIANA ST UNIV, NEW ORLEANS, LA   70122
TICH, JOHN G, PHILOSOPHY DEPT, VILLANOVA UNIV, VILLANOVA PA   19085

TICKEMYER, GARLAND E, PHIL DEPT, CEN MISSOURI ST UNIV, WARRENSBURG MO 64093
TIDWELL, JACQUELINE, REL & PHIL DEPT, TENN WESLEYAN COL, ATHENS TN 37303
TIEBOUT, H M, PHIL DEPT, UNIV OF ILLINOIS, URBANA IL 61801
TIEDEMAN, KENT, PHILOSOPHY DEPT, CALIFORNIA ST UNIV, CHICO CA 95926
TIEFEL, HANS O, REL & PHIL DEPT, THE COLLEGE OF IDAHO, CALDWELL ID 83605
TIEN, SHEN, PHILOSOPHY DEPT, UNIV OF WATERLOO, WATERLOO ONT CAN
TIENSON, JOHN L, PHIL DEPT, INDIANA UNIVERSITY, BLOOMINGTON IN 47401
TIETZ, J H, PHILOSOPHY DEPT, SIMON FRASER UNIV, BURNABY 2 B C CAN
TIEWS, KENNETH, PHIL DEPT, UNIV OF MICHIGAN, ANN ARBOR MI 48104
TIGNER, STEVEN, PHIL DEPT, UNIVERSITY OF TOLEDO, TOLEDO OH 43606
TILDEN, NANCY L, PHIL DEPT, CALIFORNIA ST UNIV, SAN FRANCISCO CA 94132
TILFORD, JAMES, PHIL DEPT, WICHITA ST UNIV, WICHITA KS 67208
TILGHMAN, BENJAMIN R, PHIL DEPT, KANSAS ST UNIVERSITY, MANHATTAN KS 66506
TILLERY, THOMAS D, SOC SCI DEPT, NORTHERN STATE COL, ABERDEEN SD 57401
TILLEY, W CLYDE, RELIG & PHIL DEPT, UNION UNIVERSITY, JACKSON TN 38301
TILLMAN, FRANK, PHIL DEPT, VASSAR COLLEGE, POUGHKEEPSIE NY 12601
TILLMAN, STANLEY C, PHILOSOPHY DEPT, XAVIER UNIVERSITY, CINCINNATI OH 45207
TILLMANN, GEORGE D, PHILOSOPHY DEPT, RUTGERS UNIV, NEW BRUNSWICK NJ 08903
TILLOTSON, ELROY E, SOC SCI DEPT, ALLEN CO COM JR COL, IOLA KS 66749
TILSON, LEE, PHIL DEPT, WAYNE STATE UNIV, DETROIT MI 48202
TIMM, ROGER E, PHILOSOPHY DEPT, CONCORDIA COLLEGE, BRONXVILLE NY 10708
TIMMONS, MARK C, PHILOSOPHY DEPT, ARIZONA STATE UNIV, TEMPE AZ 85281
TINSLEY, WILLIAM, SOC SCI DIV, FOOTHILL COLLEGE, LOS ALTOS HLS CA 94022
TINTES, PETER, PHIL DEPT, WILLMAR ST JR COL, WILLMAR MN 56201
TIPPEY, BYRON L, REL & PHIL DIV, MARION COLLEGE, MARION IN 46952
TISCHER, D H, PHILOSOPHY DEPT, UNIV OF TORONTO, TORONTO ONT CAN
TISDALE, NOEL, PHILOSOPHY DEPT, RUTGERS UNIV, NEW BRUNSWICK NJ 08903
TITCHENER, JOHN, PHIL DEPT, UNIV OF MARYLAND, BALTIMORE MD 21228
TITIEV, ROBERT J, PHIL DEPT, WAYNE STATE UNIV, DETROIT MI 48202
TITUS, HAROLD H, PHILOSOPHY DEPT, DENISON UNIV, GRANVILLE OH 43023
TLUMAK, JEFFREY, PHILOSOPHY DEPT, VANDERBILT UNIV, NASHVILLE TN 37235
TOBEY, HERBERT, PHIL DEPT, LONE MOUNTAIN COL, SAN FRANCISCO CA 94118
TOBIN, JOHN P, HUMAN DEPT, EDISON CCM COL, FORT MYERS FL 33091
TOBIN, JOHN, PHIL DEPT, S ILLINOIS UNIV, CARBONDALE IL 62901
TOBIN, RICHARD J, PHILOSOPHY DEPT, UNIV OF WISCONSIN, MADISON WI 53706
TODD, D D, PHILOSOPHY DEPT, SIMON FRASER UNIV, BURNABY 2 B C CAN
TODD, G F, PHILOSOPHY DEPT, UNIV OF GUELPH, GUELPH ONT CAN
TODD, JAMES A, PHIL DEPT, LAKE ERIE COLLEGE, PAINESVILLE OH 44077
TODD, JENNIFER, PHIL DEPT, BOSTON UNIVERSITY, BOSTON MA 02215
TODD, WILLIAM L, PHIL DEPT, UNIV OF CINCINNATI, CINCINNATI OH 45221
TODES, SAMUEL J, PHIL DEPT, NORTHWESTERN UNIV, EVANSTON IL 60201
TODRANK, GUSTAVE H, PHIL & REL DEPT, COLBY COLLEGE, WATERVILLE ME 04901
TOENJES, RICHARD H, PHIL DEPT, UNIV OF N CAROLINA, CHARLOTTE NC 28213
TOKERUD, B, PHILOSOPHY DEPT, UNIV OF ALBERTA, EDMONTON ALB CAN
TOLAN, EDWIN K, PHIL DEPT, UNION COLLEGE, SCHENECTADY NY 12308
TOLAND, WILLIAM G, PHILOSOPHY DEPT, BAYLOR UNIVERSITY, WACO TX 76703
TOLLEFSEN, OLAF P, PHIL DEPT, MT SAINT MARY'S COL, EMMITSBURG MD 21727
TOLLEFSON, ROBERT J, REL & PHIL, BUENA VISTA COLLEGE, STORM LAKE IA 50588
TOLLINCHI, ESTEBAN, PHIL DEPT, UNIV OF PUERTO RICO, RIO PIEDRAS PR 00931
TOMAS, VINCENT, PHILOSOPHY DEPT, BROWN UNIVERSITY, PROVIDENCE RI 02912
TOMASIC, THOMAS M, PHIL DEPT, JOHN CARROLL UNIV, UNIVERSITY HT OH 44118
TOMBERLIN, JAMES, PHIL DEPT, CALIFORNIA ST UNIV, NORTHRIDGE CA 91324
TOMINAGA, THOMAS T, PHIL DEPT, UNIV OF NEVADA, LAS VEGAS NV 89154
TOMLINSON, ARLINE, WRIGHT STATE UNIV, CELINA, OH 45822
TOMLINSON, MARTHA, HUM & FINE ARTS, NORTH FLORIDA JR COL, MADISON FL 32340
TOMLINSON, THOMAS, PHIL DEPT, MICHIGAN STATE UNIV, EAST LANSING MI 48823
TOMPKINS, ROBERT, HUMAN DEPT, OREGON COL OF EDUC, MONMOUTH OR 97361
TOMSONS, GUNARS, PHIL DEPT, CEN MICHIGAN UNIV, MT PLEASANT MI 48858
TONELLI, GIORGIO, PHIL DEPT, ST UNIV OF NY, BINGHAMTON NY 13901
TONG, LIK KUEN, PHIL DEPT, FAIRFIELD UNIVERSITY, FAIRFIELD CT 06430
TONG, PAUL K, PHIL & RELIG DEPT, GLASSBORO ST COL, GLASSBORO NJ 08028
TOOLE, ROBERT J, PHIL DEPT, ST UNIV OF NY, BINGHAMTON NY 13901
TOOLEY, MICHAEL, PHIL DEPT, STANFORD UNIVERSITY, STANFORD CA 94305
TOOMEY, CHARLES B, PHIL DEPT, BOSTON COLLEGE, CHESTNUT HILL MA 02167

TOON, MARK, PHIL DIV, ST MEINRAD COLLEGE, SAINT MEINRAD IN 47577
TORGESON, JON, PHIL & REL, DRAKE UNIVERSITY, DES MOINES IA 50311
TORINSKY, NORMAN, PHILOSOPHY DEPT, DUQUESNE UNIV, PITTSBURGH PA 15219
TORMEY, ALAN, PHIL DEPT, UNIV OF MARYLAND, BALTIMORE MD 21228
TORMEY, ANTHONY, PHILOSOPHY DEPT, IMMAC CONCEPTION SEM, TROY NY 12180
TORMEY, JUDITH, PHIL DEPT, TEMPLE UNIVERSITY, PHILADELPHIA PA 19122
TORPPA, ALAN J, PHIL DEPT, UNIV OF N CAROLINA, CHAPEL HILL NC 27514
TORRES, DANIEL, HUMAN DEPT, OLIVE-HARVEY COM COL, CHICAGO IL 60628
TORRETTI, ROBERTO, PHIL DEPT, UNIV CF PUERTO RICO, RIO PIEDRAS PR 00931
TORZALA, HENRY, PHIL DEPT, ST MARY'S COLLEGE, ORCHARD LAKE MI 48034
TOTTEN, JOHN, PHIL DEPT, ST MARY'S UNIVERSITY, SAN ANTONIO TX 78228
TOUEY, JOHN V, PHIL DEPT, CHESTNUT HILL COL, PHILADELPHIA PA 19118
TOULMIN, STEPHEN E, PHIL DEPT, MICHIGAN STATE UNIV, EAST LANSING MI 48823
TOULOUSE, MICHAEL, PHILOSOPHY DEPT, SEATTLE UNIVERSITY, SEATTLE WA 98122
TOURANGEAU, BERNARD, PHIL DEPT, COL VIEUX-MONTREAL, MONTREAL QUE CAN
TOUSSAINT, BERNARD, PHILOSOPHY DEPT, ILL BENEDICTINE COL, LISLE IL 60532
TOVO, JEROME C, PHILOSOPHY DEPT, UNIV OF DELAWARE, NEWARK DE 19711
TOWNSEND JR, DABNEY, HIST & PHIL DEPT, UNIV OF TEXAS, ARLINGTON TX 76010
TOWNSEND, BURKE, PHIL DEPT, UNIV OF MONTANA, MISSOULA MT 59801
TOWNSLEY, GALE A, PHILOSOPHY DEPT, PENN STATE UNIV, UNIONTOWN PA 15401
TRACY, NAT, PHILOSOPHY DEPT, HOWARD PAYNE COL, BROWNWOOD TX 76801
TRAFICANTO, DENISE C, PHIL DEPT, UNIV OF CALIFORNIA, RIVERSIDE CA 92502
TRAHAN, LOUISE, PHIL DEPT, COL BOIS-DE-BOULOGNE, MONTREAL QUE CAN
TRAINOR, ROSALEEN, PHILOSOPHY DEPT, SEATTLE UNIVERSITY, SEATTLE WA 98122
TRAMEL, STEPHEN G, PHILOSOPHY DEPT, FORT HAYS KAN ST COL, HAYS KS 67601
TRAMMELL, RICHARD L, PHIL & RELIG, GROVE CITY COLLEGE, GROVE CITY PA 16127
TRANT, EDWARD J, PHIL DEPT, MANHATTAN COLLEGE, RIVERDALE NY 10471
TRATEBAS, EDMUND W, PHIL DEPT, NORTHWESTERN COL, ORANGE CITY IA 51041
TRAUB, DONALD, PSYCH DEPT, WORCESTER STATE COL, WORCESTER MA 01602
TRAVERS, DAVID, HUMAN DIV, NASSON COLLEGE, SPRINGVALE ME 04083
TRAVERSO, EVERETT, HUMAN & PHIL, SANTA ROSA JR COL, SANTA ROSA CA 95401
TRAVIS, CHARLES, PHILOSOPHY DEPT, UNIV OF CALGARY, CALGARY 44 ALB CAN
TRAVIS, JANET L, PHIL DEPT, UNIV OF NEVADA, LAS VEGAS NV 89154
TRAXL, WILLIAM L, PHIL DEPT, HOLY APOSTLES COL, CROMWELL CT 06416
TRAYNOR, W T, SOC SCI & HUMAN DIV, FANSHANE COLLEGE, LONDON ONT CAN
TREADWAY, DOUGLAS, MAUNA OLU COLLEGE, PAIA, HI 96779
TREANOR, JAMES, ENG & PHIL DEPT, SW TEXAS ST UNIV, SAN MARCOS TX 78666
TREASH, G S, PHILOSOPHY DEPT, MT ALLISON UNIV, SACKVILLE N B CAN
TREBILCOT, JOYCE, PHIL DEPT, WASHINGTON UNIV, ST LOUIS MO 63130
TREDWELL, ROBERT F, PHIL DEPT, UNIV OF MAINE, ORONO ME 04773
TREEN, D, PHILOSOPHY DEPT, UNIV OF TORONTO, TORONTO ONT CAN
TRELO, VIRGIL, PHILOSOPHY DEPT, ILL BENEDICTINE COL, LISLE IL 60532
TRELOAR, JOHN, PHIL DEPT, MICHIGAN STATE UNIV, EAST LANSING MI 48823
TRELOGAN, THOMAS K, PHILOSOPHY DEPT, OBERLIN COLLEGE, OBERLIN OH 44074
TREMBLAY, ANDRE, ART FACULTY, COLLEGE DE HEARST, HEARST ONT CAN
TREMBLAY, JACQUES, COL EDOUARD-MONTPETIT, LONGUEUIL, QUE CAN
TREMBLAY, NORMAND, COL EDOUARD-MONTPETIT, LONGUEUIL, QUE CAN
TREPANIER, EMMANUEL, PHIL FACULTE, UNIVERSITE LAVAL, CITE UNIV QUE CAN
TREPP, LEO, SOC SCI DEPT, NAPA COLLEGE, NAPA CA 94558
TRESCA, INA K, PHIL DEPT, FLORIDA STATE UNIV, TALLAHASSEE FL 32306
TRETMAN, JOHN A, PHILOSOPHY DEPT, MCGILL UNIVERSITY, MONTREAL QUE CAN
TREVAS, ROBERT, PHILOSOPHY DEPT, OHIO UNIVERSITY, ATHENS OH 45701
TRIEBEWASSER, HAROLD, PHIL DEPT, BOWLING GREEN UNIV, BOWLING GREEN OH 43403
TRIMBERGER, CHRISTINE, PHILOSOPHY DEPT, ALVERNO COLLEGE, MILWAUKEE WI 53215
TRIMBLE, THOMAS M, PHILOSOPHY DEPT, MERCER UNIVERSITY, MACON GA 31207
TRINKLE, JOSEPH, PHIL DEPT, FAIRFIELD UNIVERSITY, FAIRFIELD CT 06430
TRIPLETT, JANET C, PHILOSOPHY DEPT, NM HIGHLANDS UNIV, LAS VEGAS NM 87701
TRIPODES, PETER, PHIL DEPT, MT ST MARY'S COL, LOS ANGELES CA 90049
TRITSCHLER, ALAN, PHIL DEPT, UNIV OF MISSOURI, COLUMBIA MO 65201
TRIVUS, SIDNEY, PHIL DEPT, CALIFORNIA ST UNIV, LOS ANGELES CA 90032
TROTH, PETER, PHILOSOPHY DEPT, UNIV OF CALGARY, CALGARY 44 ALB CAN
TROTTER, ROBERT S, PHIL DEPT, WILLIAM JEWELL COL, LIBERTY MO 64068
TROUTMAN, W, PHIL DEPT, W CONNECTICUT ST COL, DANBURY CT 06810
TROWBRIDGE, MARK, PHIL DEPT, UNIV OF CINCINNATI, CINCINNATI OH 45221

TROXELL, EUGENE A, PHIL DEPT, CALIFORNIA ST UNIV, SAN DIEGO CA 92115
TROYER, J D, PHIL DEPT, UNIV OF CONNECTICUT, STORRS CT 06268
TROYER, T L, SOC SCI DEPT, ST PETERSBURG JR COL, ST PETERSBURG FL 33733
TRUCINGER, PAUL, HUMANITIES DIV, N VIRGINIA COM COL, ALEXANDRIA VA 22311
TRUE, ISAAC D, PHILOSOPHY DEPT, CONCEPTIONS SEM COL, CONCEPTION MO 64433
TRUITT, WILLIS H, PHIL DEPT, UNIV OF S FLORIDA, TAMPA FL 33620
TRUNDLE, ROBERT C, PHIL DEPT, UNIVERSITY OF TOLEDO, TOLEDO OH 43606
TRUSIS, AIVARS, SOC SCI DEPT, BRONX COM COLLEGE, BRONX NY 10468
TSAI, L S C, PHIL FACULTY, UNIV OF OTTAWA, OTTAWA ONT CAN
TSAKARIS, A, PHILOSOPHY DEPT, UNIV OF RHODE ISLAND, KINGSTON RI 02881
TSANOFF, R A, PHILOSOPHY DEPT, RICE UNIVERSITY, HOUSTON TX 77001
TSE, CHUNG-MING, PHIL DEPT, S ILLINOIS UNIV, CARBONDALE IL 62901
TSUGAWA, ALBERT, PHILOSOPHY DEPT, PENN STATE UNIV, UNIV PARK PA 16802
TUCK, DONALD R, PHIL & RELIG, WEST KENTUCKY UNIV, BOWLING GREEN KY 42101
TUCK, WILLIAM P, VA INTERMONT COL, BRISTOL, VA 24201
TUCKER, JOHN W, PHILOSOPHY DEPT, UNIV OF WATERLOO, WATERLOO ONT CAN
TUFFT, JOHN R, SOCIAL SCIENCE DEPT, TAFT COLLEGE, TAFT CA 93268
TULLY, R, UNIV OF ST MICHAEL'S, TORONTO 181, ONT CAN
TUMLINSON, DON, HUMAN DEPT, SW TEXAS JR COL, UVALDE TX 78801
TUNYOGI, ANDREW C, PHILOSOPHY DEPT, OLD DOMINION UNIV, NORFOLK VA 23508
TUPPER, FRANK, CHRIST PHIL DEPT, S BAPTIST THEOL SEM, LOUISVILLE KY 40206
TURBAYNE, COLIN M, PHIL DEPT, UNIV OF ROCHESTER, ROCHESTER NY 14627
TURCOTTE, LUCIE, COL MARGUERITE-BOURG, MONTREAL, QUE CAN
TURCOTTE, PIERRE, PHILOSOPHY DEPT, COL DE MAISONNEUVE, MONTREAL QUE CAN
TURETZKY, PHILIP M, PHIL DEPT, COLORADO ST UNIV, FORT COLLINS CO 80521
TURNBULL, ROBERT G, PHILOSOPHY DEPT, OHIO STATE UNIV, COLUMBUS OH 43210
TURNER, CHARLES, SW MINNESOTA ST COL, MARSHALL, MN 56258
TURNER, DAN, PHILOSOPHY DEPT, OHIO STATE UNIV, COLUMBUS OH 43210
TURNER, JOHN S, PHIL DEPT, UNIV OF ILLINOIS, CHICAGO IL 60680
TURNER, WALTER H, PHIL DEPT, UNIV OF DETROIT, DETROIT MI 48221
TURGUETTE, A R, PHIL DEPT, UNIV OF ILLINOIS, URBANA IL 61801
TURSMAN, RICHARD A, GLENDON COLLEGE, TORONTO, ONT CAN
TUSSMAN, JOSEPH, PHIL DEPT, UNIV OF CALIFORNIA, BERKELEY CA 94720
TUTTLE, HOWARD N, PHIL DEPT, UNIV OF NEW MEXICO, ALBUQUERQUE NM 87106
TUTTLE, THOMAS, PHIL DEPT, BOWLING GREEN UNIV, BOWLING GREEN OH 43403
TWADDELL, GERALD E, PHIL DEPT, SEM OF ST PIUS X, ERLANGER KY 41018
TWEYMAN, STANLEY, GLENDON COLLEGE, TORONTO, ONT CAN
TWOHILL, M DOMINIC, PHIL DEPT, DOMINICAN COLLEGE, BLAUVELT NY 10913
TWOMEY, DONALD, PHILOSOPHY DEPT, VILLANOVA UNIV, VILLANOVA PA 19085
TWOMEY, JOHN E, PHIL DEPT, ST FRANCIS DE SALES, MILWAUKEE WI 53207
TYBOR, ARTHUR, PHILOSOPHY DEPT, CARLOW COLLEGE, PITTSBURGH PA 15213
TYE, MICHAEL, PHIL DEPT, ST UNIV OF NY, AMHERST NY 14226
TYMOCZKO, THOMAS, PHIL DEPT, SMITH COLLEGE, NORTHAMPTON MA 01060
TYREE, WILLIAM E, PHILOSOPHY DEPT, RIPON COLLEGE, RIPON WI 54971
TYRRELL, BERNARD, PHILOSOPHY DEPT, GONZAGA UNIV, SPOKANE WA 99202
UBERTI, J RICHARD, HUMAN DEPT, PEIRCE JR COLLEGE, PHILADELPHIA PA 19102
UCUZOGLU, NATHAN, PHIL DEPT, UNIV OF CALIFORNIA, LOS ANGELES CA 90024
UDELL, IRWIN L, PHILOSOPHY DEPT, OHIO STATE UNIV, COLUMBUS OH 43210
UDOFF, ALAN, PHIL & REL DEPT, TOWSON STATE COL, BALTIMORE MD 21204
UEBELHOER, JANE, PHIL DEPT, UNIV OF MISSOURI, COLUMBIA MO 65201
UEHLING, THEODORE, HUMAN DIV, UNIV OF MINNESOTA, MORRIS MN 56267
UEMURA, JOSEPH N, PHIL DEPT, HAMLINE UNIVERSITY, ST PAUL MN 55104
UFFELMANN, HANS, PHIL DEPT, UNIV OF MISSOURI, KANSAS CITY MO 64110
UHLINGER, PAUL J, PHILOSOPHY DEPT, UNIV OF AKRON, AKRON OH 44325
ULLIAN, JOSEPH S, PHIL DEPT, WASHINGTON UNIV, ST LOUIS MO 63130
ULM, MELVIN, PHILOSOPHY DEPT, OHIO STATE UNIV, COLUMBUS OH 43210
ULRICH, DOLPH E, PHIL DEPT, PURDUE UNIVERSITY, LAFAYETTE IN 47907
ULRICH, LAWRENCE P, PHIL DEPT, UNIVERSITY OF DAYTON, DAYTON OH 45469
ULRICH, REINHARD, PHIL & RELIG DEPT, LAKELAND COL, SHEBOYGAN WI 53081
ULRICH, WILLIAM, PHIL DEPT, UNIV OF CALIFORNIA, IRVINE CA 92664
UMBENHAUER, WILLIAM, PHIL DEPT, UNIV OF CINCINNATI, CINCINNATI OH 45221
UMEN, SAMUEL, PHILOSOPHY DEPT, NATH HAWTHORNE COL, ANTRIM NH 03440
UMPHREY, STEWART, PHIL DEPT, COL AT GENESEO, GENESEO NY 14454
UNDERHILL, PHIL DEPT, HASTINGS COLLEGE, HASTINGS, NE 68901

UNDERWOOD, RICHARD A, RELIG DEPT, HARTFORD SEM FOUND, HARTFORD CT 06105
UNGER, DANIEL, PHIL & RELIG DEPT, ALDERSON BROADDUS COL, PHILIPPI WV 26416
UNGER, PETER, PHIL DEPT, NEW YORK UNIVERSITY, NEW YORK NY 10003
UNGER, SUSAN, PHILOSOPHY DEPT, PENN STATE UNIV, UNIV PARK PA 16802
UNHJEM, ARNE, PHIL DEPT, WAGNER COLLEGE, STATEN ISLAND NY 10301
UNNI, CHITHARANJAN, PHIL DEPT, CHAMINADE COLLEGE, HONOLULU HI 96816
UPADHYAYA, K N, PHIL DEPT, UNIVERSITY OF HAWAII, HONOLULU HI 96822
UPHOLD, W B, PHILOSOPHY DEPT, CALIFORNIA ST UNIV, FRESNO CA 93740
UPIN, JANE, HUMAN DEPT, AMUNDSEN-MAYFAIR COL, CHICAGO IL 60630
URBAS, MICHAEL J, PHILOSOPHY DEPT, UNIV OF AKRON, AKRON OH 44325
URITUS, RONALD M, PHIL DEPT, BARRY COLLEGE, MIAMI SHORES FL 33153
URQUHART, A I F, PHILOSOPHY DEPT, UNIV OF TORONTO, TORONTO ONT CAN
UTSMAN, ROBERT S, PHILOSOPHY DEPT, UNIV OF UTAH, SALT LAKE CTY UT 84112
UTTER, ROBERT P, SOC SCI DEPT, CITY COLLEGE, SAN FRANCISCO CA 94112
UTZ, S, PHIL DEPT, LOUISIANA ST UNIV, BATON ROUGE LA 70803
UTZINGER, JOHN G, PHIL DEPT, CEN WASH STATE COL, ELLENSBURG WA 98926
VACCAREST, ANNE, HUMAN DIV, MOUNT ST MARY COL, HOOKSETT NH 03106
VACEK, EDWARD, PHIL DEPT, NORTHWESTERN UNIV, EVANSTON IL 60201
VACHER, MICHEL, COLLEGE D'AHUNTSIC, MONTREAL, QUE CAN
VAIL, ALICE, PHIL DEPT, UNIVERSITY OF DAYTON, DAYTON OH 45469
VAIL, LOY, PHILOSOPHY DEPT, RIDER COLLEGE, TRENTON NJ 08602
VAILLANCOURT, DANIEL, PHIL DEPT, MUNDELEIN COLLEGE, CHICAGO IL 60626
VAILLANT, D, PHIL FACULTY, UNIV OF OTTAWA, OTTAWA ONT CAN
VALAKIS, APOLLON, PHIL & RELIG DEPT, FRANKLIN PIERCE COL, RINDGE NH 03461
VALCKE, LOUIS, PHIL DEPT, UNIV DE SHERBROOKE, SHERBROOKE QUE CAN
VALDENAIRE, JEAN, PHIL DEPT, COL VIEUX-MONTREAL, MONTREAL QUE CAN
VALENTI, FREDERICK, PHIL DEPT, ADELPHI UNIVERSITY, GARDEN CITY NY 11530
VALENTINE, JOHN, PHILOSOPHY DEPT, VANDERBILT UNIV, NASHVILLE TN 37235
VALLICELLA, WILLIAM F, PHIL DEPT, BOSTON COLLEGE, CHESTNUT HILL MA 02167
VALLONE, GERARD, PHIL DEPT, COL OF WHITE PLAINS, WHITE PLAINS NY 10603
VALOIS, RAYNALD, PHIL FACULTE, UNIVERSITE LAVAL, CITE UNIV QUE CAN
VAN BUREN, JAMES G, HUMAN DEPT, MANHATTAN CHRIST COL, MANHATTAN KS 66502
VAN DE PITTE, F P, PHILOSOPHY DEPT, UNIV OF ALBERTA, EDMONTON ALB CAN
VAN DE VATE, DWIGHT, PHIL DEPT, UNIV OF TENNESSEE, KNOXVILLE TN 37916
VAN DER BOGERT, FRANS, APPALACHIAN ST UNIV, BOONE, NC 28607
VAN DERBECK, HOLMES, REL & PHIL DEPT, SPRINGFIELD COL, SPRINGFIELD MA 01109
VAN DORST, CORNELIUS, ST JOHN'S COLLEGE, CAMARILLO, CA 93010
VAN DYK, PHIL DEPT, DORDT COLLEGE, SIOUX CENTER, IA 51250
VAN DYKEN, SEYMOUR, GRAND RAPIDS JR COL, GRAND RAPIDS, MI 49502
VAN EVRA, JAMES W, PHILOSOPHY DEPT, UNIV OF WATERLOO, WATERLOO ONT CAN
VAN FLETEREN, F E, PHILOSOPHY DEPT, VILLANOVA UNIV, VILLANOVA PA 19085
VAN FRAASSEB, B C, PHILOSOPHY DEPT, UNIV OF TORONTO, TORONTO ONT CAN
VAN HEIJENOORT, JOHN, PHIL DEPT, BRANDEIS UNIVERSITY, WALTHAM MA 02154
VAN HOOK, JAY, REL & PHIL DEPT, HOOD COLLEGE, FREDERICK MD 21701
VAN HOOK, JOHN, PHIL DEPT, SIENA COLLEGE, LOUDONVILLE NY 12211
VAN INWAGEN, PETER, PHIL DEPT, SYRACUSE UNIVERSITY, SYRACUSE NY 13210
VAN ITEN, RICHARD J, PHIL DEPT, IOWA STATE UNIV, AMES IA 50010
VAN LEEUWEN, HENRY, PHIL DEPT, HANOVER COLLEGE, HANOVER IN 47243
VAN MARTER, LESLIE, PHILOSOPHY DEPT, CAL STATE COL, SN BERNARDINO CA 92407
VAN NUYS, KELVIN, RELIG & PHIL DEPT, WILMINGTON COL, WILMINGTON OH 45177
VAN PERNIS, JAMES, JACKSON COM COLLEGE, JACKSON, MI 49201
VAN RENSSELAER, W H, PHIL DEPT, BROOKLYN COLLEGE, BROOKLYN NY 11210
VAN SANT, GEORGE M, PHIL DEPT, MARY WASHINGTON COL, FREDERICKSBG VA 22401
VAN SCHENDEL, CELINE, COL EDOUARD-MONTPETIT, LONGUEUIL, QUE CAN
VAN STEENBURGH, E W, PHIL DEPT, N ILLINOIS UNIV, DEKALB IL 60115
VAN TIL, NICK, DORDT COLLEGE, SIOUX CENTER, IA 51250
VAN TUINEN, JACOB, PHILOSOPHY DEPT, CARROL COLLEGE, WAUKESHA WI 53186
VAN TUYLL, HENDRIK, SOC SCI, UNIV OF MONTEVALLO, MONTEVALLO AL 35115
VANAMAN, STEHEN, PHILOSOPHY DEPT, OHIO STATE UNIV, COLUMBUS OH 43210
VANCE, ROBERT D, PHIL DEPT, UNIV OF N CAROLINA, CHAPEL HILL NC 27514
VANDEN BURGT, R, HUM & FINE ARTS DEPT, ST NORBERT COL, DE PERE WI 54115
VANDER STELT, JOHN, DORDT COLLEGE, SIOUX CENTER, IA 51250
VANDER VEER, GARRETT, PHIL DEPT, VASSAR COLLEGE, POUGHKEEPSIE NY 12601
VANDERHOEVEN, JOHANN, PHIL DEPT, CALVIN COLLEGE, GRAND RAPIDS MI 49506

VANDERNAT, ARNOLD, PHIL DEPT, LOYOLA UNIVERSITY, CHICAGO IL 60626
VANDERPLOEG, W STEVENS, PHIL DEPT, UNIV OF ILLINOIS, URBANA IL 61801
VANDERWEEL, RICHARD L, PHIL DEPT, ST MICHAEL'S COLLEGE, WINOOSKI VT 05404
VANDEVEER, A DONALD, PHIL & REL DEPT, N CAROLINA ST UNIV, RALEIGH NC 27607
VANDEVELDE, R, PHILOSOPHY DEPT, UNIV OF TORONTO, TORONTO ONT CAN
VANLOO, INA KAY, PHIL DEPT, ST JOSEPH'S COLLEGE, EAST CHICAGO IN 46312
VANNOY, RUSSELL, PHIL DEPT, COL AT BUFFALO, BUFFALO NY 14222
VANTERPOOL, RUDOLPH, PHIL DEPT, S ILLINOIS UNIV, CARBONDALE IL 62901
VARCAMAN, E JERRY, MISSISSIPPI ST UNIV, ST COLLEGE, MS 39762
VARGA, ANDREW C, PHIL DEPT, FORDHAM UNIVERSITY, BRONX NY 10458
VARNEDOE, SAMUEL L, PHIL DEPT, UNIV OF MARYLAND, COLLEGE PARK MD 20742
VARNEY, MARY, PHIL DEPT, ST UNIV OF NY, AMHERST NY 14226
VASARADA, HEMLATA N, PHIL DEPT, SKAGIT VALLEY COL, MOUNT VERNON WA 98273
VASILOPOULOS, ANN E, PHIL DEPT, N ILLINOIS UNIV, DEKALB IL 60115
VASKA, VOOTELE, PHIL & REL DEPT, WAYNESBURG COLLEGE, WAYNESBURG PA 15370
VASKE, MARTIN O, PHIL DEPT, CREIGHTON UNIV, OMAHA NE 68178
VATER, MICHAEL, PHILOSOPHY DEPT, MARQUETTE UNIV, MILWAUKEE WI 53233
VAUGHAN, WILLIAM H, HUMAN DEPT, FLORIDA JUN COLLEGE, JACKSONVILLE FL 32205
VAUGHN, ADAMS, PHIL DEPT, UNIV OF DETROIT, DETROIT MI 48221
VAUGHT, CARL G, PHILOSOPHY DEPT, PENN STATE UNIV, UNIV PARK PA 16802
VAUSE, STEPHEN F, HUMAN DIV, UNIV OF ALABAMA, BIRMINGHAM AL 35233
VAY RY, MEREDITH, HUMANITIES DIV, GREEN RIVER COM COL, AUBURN WA 98002
VEATCH, HENRY B, PHIL DEPT, GEORGETOWN UNIV, WASHINGTON DC 20007
VEENKER, RONALD A, PHIL & RELIG, WEST KENTUCKY UNIV, BOWLING GREEN KY 42101
VELKLEY, RICHARD, PHILOSOPHY DEPT, PENN STATE UNIV, UNIV PARK PA 16802
VENA, JULIO, PHIL & REL DEPT, TOCCOA FALLS INST, TOCCOA FALLS GA 30577
VENABLE, VERNON, PHIL DEPT, VASSAR COLLEGE, POUGHKEEPSIE NY 12601
VENCETOULLI, JAMES, MATH & PHIL DEPT, OAKLAND COM COL, FARMINGTON MI 48024
VENCLER, ZENO, PHILOSOPHY DEPT, RICE UNIVERSITY, HOUSTON TX 77001
VENGRIN, MICHAEL, PHIL & RELIG DEPT, RADFORD COLLEGE, RADFORD VA 24141
VENN, DAVID, PHIL DEPT, UNIV OF S FLORIDA, TAMPA FL 33620
VENNE, LOUIS, COL MARGUERITE-BOURG, MONTREAL, QUE CAN
VENNES, A R, PHIL FACULTY, UNIV OF OTTAWA, OTTAWA ONT CAN
VER EECKE, WILFRIED, PHIL DEPT, GEORGETOWN UNIV, WASHINGTON DC 20007
VERCU, ALFONZO, PHIL DEPT, UNIVERSITY OF KANSAS, LAWRENCE KS 66044
VERENE, DONALD P, PHILOSOPHY DEPT, PENN STATE UNIV, UNIV PARK PA 16802
VERGES, FRANK G, PHIL DEPT, CALIFORNIA ST UNIV, FULLERTON CA 92634
VERHALEN, PHILIP, PHIL & REL STUD, COL OF GREAT FALLS, GREAT FALLS MT 59401
VERHAREN, CHARLES C, PHIL DEPT, HOWARD UNIVERSITY, WASHINGTON DC 20001
VERKAMP, BERNARD, HUMAN DIV, VINCENNES UNIV, VINCENNES IN 47591
VERKENNIS, ROLLANCE, PHIL DEPT, NORTHWESTERN UNIV, EVANSTON IL 60201
VERMAZEN, BRUCE, PHIL DEPT, UNIV OF CALIFORNIA, BERKELEY CA 94720
VERNON, THOMAS S, PHIL DEPT, UNIV OF ARKANSAS, FAYETTEVILLE AR 72701
VERSENYI, LASZLO, PHIL DEPT, WILLIAMS COLLEGE, WILLIAMSTOWN MA 01267
VESSEY, CLIFFORD, BEHAV SCI DEPT, PALOMAR COLLEGE, SAN MARCOS CA 92069
VETO, MIKLOS, PHIL DEPT, YALE UNIVERSITY, NEW HAVEN CT 06520
VETTERLING, MARY K, PHIL DEPT, UNION COLLEGE, SCHENECTADY NY 12308
VIAU, ROGER, PHIL DEPT, COL OUR LADY OF ELMS, CHICOPEE MA 01013
VICIAN, THOMAS, PHILOSOPHY DEPT, DE ANZA COLLEGE, CUPERTINO CA 95014
VICK, GEORGE, PHIL DEPT, CALIFORNIA ST UNIV, LOS ANGELES CA 90032
VICK, GEORGE, PHILOSOPHY DEPT, ART CTR COL OF DESIGN, LOS ANGELES CA 90020
VICK, O K, SOC SCI DEPT, PADUCAH COM COL, PADUCAH KY 42001
VICKERS, DENNIS WALTER, PHILOSOPHY DEPT, UNIV OF TEXAS, AUSTIN TX 78712
VICKERS, JOHN, PHIL DEPT, CLAREMONT GRAD SCH, CLAREMONT CA 91711
VIDRICAIRE, ANDRE, PHILOSOPHY DEPT, UNIV DU QUEBEC, MONTREAL QUE CAN
VIELKIND, JOHN, PHILOSOPHY DEPT, DUQUESNE UNIV, PITTSBURGH PA 15219
VIEYRA, S B, PHILOSOPHY DEPT, UNIV OF TORONTO, TORONTO ONT CAN
VIGORITO, JOHN V, PHIL DEPT, UNIV OF SW LOUISIANA, LAFAYETTE LA 70501
VILARO, NARCISO, PHIL DEPT, CATHOLIC UNIVERSITY, PONCE PR 00731
VILLAREAL, JAMES, ALVERNIA COLLEGE, READING, PA 19607
VINCENT, R H, PHIL DEPT, UNIV OF MANITOBA, WINNIPEG 19 MAN CAN
VINCENT, ROBERT, PHIL DEPT, COL TROIS-RIVIERES, 3 RIVIERES QUE CAN
VINGOE, ROBERT H, PHIL DEPT, DALHOUSIE UNIVERSITY, HALIFAX N S CAN
VIRAGH, ANDREW S, PHILOSOPHY DEPT, XAVIER UNIVERSITY, CINCINNATI OH 45207

VIRGINIA, MARY, COL OF NOTRE DAME, BALTIMORE, MD 21210
VISCARDI, L G, PHIL DEPT, UNIV OF FLORIDA, GAINESVILLE FL 32611
VISGILIO III, THOMAS, PHIL DEPT, KING'S COLLEGE, WILKES BARRE PA 18711
VISHNER, ANDREW B, PHILOSOPHY DEPT, ARIZONA STATE UNIV, TEMPE AZ 85281
VISION, GERALD, PHIL DEPT, TEMPLE UNIVERSITY, PHILADELPHIA PA 19122
VISKOVICK, FREDERICK, PHIL DEPT, UNIVERSITY OF DAYTON, DAYTON OH 45469
VISVADER, JOHN, PHIL DEPT, UNIV OF COLORADO, BOULDER CO 80302
VITRANO, STEVEN P, RELIG DEPT, ANDREWS UNIVERSITY, BERRIEN SPGS MI 49104
VITT, MARGARET M, PHIL & THEOL DEPT, MARILLAC COLLEGE, ST LOUIS MO 63121
VIVAS, ELISEO, PHIL DEPT, NORTHWESTERN UNIV, EVANSTON IL 60201
VLASTOS, GREGORY, PHIL DEPT, PRINCETON UNIVERSITY, PRINCETON NJ 08540
VODRASKA, STANLEY L, PHIL DEPT, CANISIUS COLLEGE, BUFFALO NY 14208
VOELKEL, THEODORE, PHIL DEPT, S CONNECTICUT ST COL, NEW HAVEN CT 06515
VOELLMECKE, FRANCIS, LIBR ARTS FAC, ATHENAEUM OF OHIO, CINCINNATI OH 45230
VOGEL, DWIGHT W, PHIL & RELIG, WESTMAR COLLEGE, LEMARS IA 51031
VOGEL, MUREL, PHIL DEPT, LOYOLA UNIVERSITY, CHICAGO IL 60626
VOIGHT, RICHARD C, PHIL DEPT, NORTHAMPTON COM COL, BETHLEHEM PA 18017
VOLKOMENER, HELEN, HUMAN DIV, SOUTHERN OREGON COL, ASHLAND OR 97520
VOLLRATH, ERNST, PHIL DEPT, NW SCH FOR SOC RES, NEW YORK NY 10003
VOLLRATH, JOHN, PHIL DEPT, UNIV OF WISCONSIN, STEVENS POINT WI 54481
VON BRETZEL, PHILIP, PHILOSOPHY DEPT, ARIZONA STATE UNIV, TEMPE AZ 85281
VON DER EMBSE, A, HUMANITIES DEPT, SINCLAIR COM COL, DAYTON OH 45402
VON DOHLEN, R, PHILOSOPHY DEPT, LENCIR-RHYNE COLLEGE, HICKORY NC 28601
VON FRANK, JAMES, SOC & PHIL DEPT, FRANCIS MARION COL, FLORENCE SC 29501
VON IMHOF, FLORIEN, PHIL DEPT, BOSTON UNIVERSITY, BOSTON MA 02215
VON MORSTEIN, PETRA, PHILOSOPHY DEPT, UNIV OF CALGARY, CALGARY 44 ALB   CAN
VON SCHOENBORN, A, PHILOSOPHY DEPT, UNIV OF TEXAS, AUSTIN TX 78712
VONK, PAUL K, HUMAN DIV, OGLETHORPE UNIV, ATLANTA GA 30319
VORSTEG, ROBERT H, PHIL DEPT, WAKE FOREST UNIV, WINSTON-SALEM NC 27109
VOS, ARVIN G, PHIL & RELIG, WEST KENTUCKY UNIV, BOWLING GREEN KY 42101
VOS, KENNETH D, LYNDON STATE COL, LYNDONVILLE, VT 05851
VOSBURGH, CLARENCE, SOC SCI & EDUC, CANAL ZONE COL, BALBOA CANAL ZONE
VOSKUIL, DUANE, PHIL DEPT, UNIV OF N DAKOTA, GRAND FORKS ND 58201
VOTICHENKO, T ALEX, PHILOSOPHY DEPT, ARIZONA STATE UNIV, TEMPE AZ 85281
VRARASIK, BOYDAN, PHIL DEPT, COL DE VALLEYFIELD, VALLEYFIELD QUE   CAN
VREELAND, ROBERT G, PHIL DEPT, UNIV OF N CAROLINA, CHAPEL HILL NC 27514
VUJICA, STANKO M, PHIL & REL STUD, WILKES COLLEGE, WILKES BARRE PA 18703
VUNDERINK, RALPH, PHIL DEPT, UNIV OF DETROIT, DETROIT MI 48221
WABER, WILLIAM, PHIL DEPT, OHIO WESLEYAN UNIV, DELAWARE OH 43105
WACHTEL, R, PHILOSOPHY DEPT, UNIV OF TORONTO, TORONTO ONT   CAN
WACKENZIE, JOHN S, HUMAN DEPT, GERMANNA COM COL, FREDERICKSBG VA 22401
WADDELL, JAMES E, REL & PHIL DEPT, STEPHENS COLLEGE, COLUMBIA MO 65201
WADE, FRANCIS C, PHILOSOPHY DEPT, MARQUETTE UNIV, MILWAUKEE WI 53233
WADIA, PHEROZE S, PHILOSOPHY DEPT, RUTGERS UNIV, NEW BRUNSWICK NJ 08903
WAGAND, PHILIP, HUMAN DIV, MACOMB CO COM COL, WARREN MI 48093
WAGER, JOHN, PHIL DEPT, NORTHWESTERN UNIV, EVANSTON IL 60201
WAGNER, DOUGLAS, PHIL DEPT, COLUMBIA UNIVERSITY, NEW YORK NY 10027
WAGNER, STEVE, PHIL DEPT, UNIV OF MICHIGAN, ANN ARBOR MI 48104
WAGCNER, ROBERT E, PHILOSOPHY DEPT, JUNIATA COLLEGE, HUNTINGDON PA 16652
WAINWRIGHT, WILLIAM, PHIL DEPT, UNIV OF WISCONSIN, MILWAUKEE WI 53201
WAITHE, LLOYD, PHIL DEPT, UNIV OF MINNESOTA, MINNEAPOLIS MN 55455
WAKEFIELD, DONAM H, PHIL & THEOL, DOMINICAN COLLEGE, HOUSTON TX 77021
WAKIN, MALHAM M, PHIL DEPT, U S AIR FORCE ACAD, COLORADO SPGS CO 80840
WALBERG, E H, PHIL DEPT, MANKATO STATE COL, MANKATO MN 56001
WALCOTT, LYLE O, PHILOSOPHY DEPT, GLENDALE COM COL, GLENDALE AZ 85301
WALC, JAN DAVID, PHIL DEPT, BRANDEIS UNIVERSITY, WALTHAM MA 02154
WALCEN, PHYLLIS, PHIL & RELIG DEPT, ANTIOCH COL, YELLOW SPGS OH 45387
WALCER, JOHN, PHILOSOPHY DEPT, NORTH ARIZONA UNIV, FLAGSTAFF AZ 86001
WALDMAN, ELLIOTT, PHIL & RELIG DEPT, COLGATE UNIVERSITY, HAMILTON NY 13346
WALDMAN, T, HUMAN & SOC SCI DEPT, HARVEY MUDD COL, CLAREMONT CA 91711
WALCNER, ILMAR, PHILOSOPHY DEPT, CASE WESTERN RESERVE, CLEVELAND OH 44106
WALCRON, JAMES, ST FRANCIS COL, LORETTO, PA 15940
WALCROP, CHARLES, PHIL DEPT, SKIDMORE COLLEGE, SARATOGA SPGS NY 12886
WALENDY, THOMAS, PHIL DEPT, MT ST MARY'S COL, LOS ANGELES CA 90049

WALHOUT, DONALD, REL & PHIL DEPT, ROCKFORD COLLEGE, ROCKFORD IL 61101
WALKER, DAN, HUMANITIES DIV, MCLENNAN COM COL, WACO TX 76703
WALKER, FOSTER, PHIL DEPT, UNIV OF WEST ONTARIO, LONDON ONT   CAN
WALKER, HAROLD, PHILOSOPHY DEPT, CALIFORNIA ST UNIV, FRESNO CA 93740
WALKER, JAMES S, PHIL DEPT, HASTINGS COLLEGE, HASTINGS NE 68901
WALKER, JAMES, PHIL DEPT, BOSTON UNIVERSITY, BOSTON MA 02215
WALKER, JEREMY, PHILOSOPHY DEPT, MCGILL UNIVERSITY, MONTREAL QUE   CAN
WALKER, JOHN MARK, NEBRASKA WES UNIV, LINCOLN, NE 68504
WALKER, NORMAN, HUMAN DEPT, SOUTHWEST COLLEGE, CHICAGO IL 60652
WALKER, PENELOPE, PHIL DEPT, UNIV OF CALIFORNIA, LOS ANGELES CA 90024
WALKER, ROBERT A, PHILOSOPHY DEPT, UNIV OF OREGON, EUGENE OR 97403
WALL, BARBARA E, PHILOSOPHY DEPT, VILLANOVA UNIV, VILLANOVA PA 19085
WALL, BRENDAN, HUM & SOC SCI, KAPIOLANI COM COL, HONOLULU HI 96814
WALL, GEORGE B, SOCIOLOGY DEPT, LAMAR UNIVERSITY, BEAUMONT TX 77710
WALL, JOSEPH, SYST & PHIL, GRADUATE THEOL UNION, BERKELEY CA 94709
WALL, KEVIN, ST ALBERT'S COLLEGE, OAKLAND, CA 94618
WALL, THEODORE E, SOC SCI DEPT, ORANGE COAST COLLEGE, COSTA MESA CA 92626
WALLACE, CAROL, BRYN MAWR COLLEGE, BRYN MAWR, PA 19010
WALLACE, DONALD, PHILOSOPHY DEPT, LOS ANGELES SW COL, LOS ANGELES CA 90047
WALLACE, JAMES D, PHIL DEPT, UNIV OF ILLINOIS, URBANA IL 61801
WALLACE, JEAN, PHILOSOPHY DEPT, UNIV OF WATERLOO, WATERLOO ONT   CAN
WALLACE, JOHN R, PHIL DEPT, UNIV OF MINNESOTA, MINNEAPOLIS MN 55455
WALLACE, PHILLIP A, PHIL DEPT, TULANE UNIVERSITY, NEW ORLEANS LA 70118
WALLACE, ROBERT, PHIL DEPT, MANKATO STATE COL, MANKATO MN 56001
WALLACE, WILLIAM A, PHIL SCH, CATH UNIV OF AMER, WASHINGTON DC 20017
WALLEN, RAEBURN, PHIL & RELIG DEPT, FINDLAY COLLEGE, FINDLAY OH 45840
WALLENMAIER, THOMAS, PHIL DEPT, UNIV OF DETROIT, DETROIT MI 48221
WALLER, BRUCE N, PHIL DEPT, UNIV OF N CAROLINA, CHAPEL HILL NC 27514
WALLHAUSSER, JOHN, PHIL & RELIG DEPT, UPSALA COL, EAST ORANGE NJ 07019
WALLICK, MERRITT, PHILOSOPHY DEPT, UNIV OF TEXAS, AUSTIN TX 78712
WALLNER, FRANK, PHIL DEPT, ST JOSEPH'S COL, PHILADELPHIA PA 19131
WALLS, VIVIEN A, PHIL DEPT, S ILLINOIS UNIV, CARBONDALE IL 62901
WALRAFF, CHARLES F, PHILOSOPHY DEPT, UNIV OF ARIZONA, TUCSON AZ 85721
WALSH, GEORGE V, HUMAN DIV, EISENHOWER COLLEGE, SENECA FALLS NY 13148
WALSH, HAROLD T, PHIL DEPT, MICHIGAN STATE UNIV, EAST LANSING MI 48823
WALSH, JAMES J, PHIL DEPT, COLUMBIA UNIVERSITY, NEW YORK NY 10027
WALSH, JOHN J, PHILOSOPHY DEPT, ALVERNO COLLEGE, MILWAUKEE WI 53215
WALSH, JOHN, PHIL DEPT, UNIV OF KENTUCKY, LEXINGTON KY 40506
WALSH, JOHN, PHIL PROGRAM, SANGAMON ST UNIV, SPRINGFIELD IL 62703
WALSH, JOSEPH M, ST PETER'S COLLEGE, JERSEY CITY, NJ 07306
WALSH, JOSEPH, PHIL DEPT, LOYOLA UNIVERSITY, CHICAGO IL 60626
WALSH, JOSEPH, PHIL DEPT, SPRING HILL COLLEGE, MOBILE AL 36608
WALSH, JOSEPH, PHIL OF RELIG, STOCTON STATE COL, POMONA NJ 08244
WALSH, P K J, PHILOSOPHY DEPT, UNIV OF TORONTO, TORONTO ONT   CAN
WALSH, PHILIP F, PHIL DEPT, TEXAS CHRISTIAN UNIV, FORT WORTH TX 76129
WALSH, THOMAS, PHILOSOPHY DEPT, MESA COMMUNITY COL, MESA AZ 85201
WALTER, DONALD, RELIG & PHIL DEPT, DAVIS & ELKINS COL, ELKINS WV 26241
WALTER, EDWARD, PHIL DEPT, UNIV OF MISSOURI, KANSAS CITY MO 64110
WALTERS, JAMES H, PHIL DEPT, UNIV OF MISSOURI, ST LOUIS MO 63121
WALTERS, K W, PHILOSOPHY DEPT, AUBURN UNIVERSITY, AUBURN AL 36830
WALTERS, WILLIAM, PHILOSOPHY DEPT, WRIGHT STATE UNIV, DAYTON OH 45431
WALTHER, ERIC, PHIL DEPT, LONG ISLAND UNIV, GREENVALE NY 11548
WALTHER, SANDRA, PHILOSOPHY DEPT, RIDER COLLEGE, TRENTON NJ 08602
WALTON, CRAIG, PHIL DEPT, UNIV OF NEVADA, LAS VEGAS NV 89154
WALTON, DOUGLAS N, PHILOSOPHY DEPT, UNIV OF WINNIPEG, WINNIPEG MAN   CAN
WALTON, HAL, SOC SCI DEPT, TARLETON ST UNIV, STEPHENVILLE TX 76401
WALTON, KENDALL L, PHIL DEPT, UNIV OF MICHIGAN, ANN ARBOR MI 48104
WALTON, RICHARD, PHIL DEPT, UNIV OF MONTANA, MISSOULA MT 59801
WALTON, WILLIAM M, PHIL DEPT, ST JOSEPH COLLEGE, WEST HARTFORD CT 06117
WANC, B, PHILOSOPHY DEPT, CARLETON UNIVERSITY, OTTAWA ONT   CAN
WANG, C S, PHIL DEPT, COLLEGE SAINT-LOUIS, EDMUNDSTON N B   CAN
WANTLAND, BURDETT, PHIL DEPT, WEST GEORGIA COLLEGE, CARROLLTON GA 30117
WARD, BENJAMIN, PHIL DEPT, YALE UNIVERSITY, NEW HAVEN CT 06520
WARD, DAVID, AURORA COLLEGE, AURORA, IL 60507

WARD, EUGENE, PHIL DEPT, COL OUR LADY OF ELMS, CHICOPEE MA   01013
WARD, JOEL F, PHIL DEPT, UNIV OF ILLINOIS, URBANA IL   61801
WARD, MICHAEL, PHIL DEPT, BOWLING GREEN UNIV, BOWLING GREEN OH   43403
WARD, THOMAS MORGAN, MIDWAY COLLEGE, MIDWAY, KY   40347
WARDEN, JOHN, PHIL DEPT, INDIANA ST UNIV, TERRE HAUTE IN   47809
WARE, JAMES, RELIG & PHIL DEPT, AUSTIN COLLEGE, SHERMAN TX   75090
WARE, ROBERT X, PHILOSOPHY DEPT, UNIV OF CALGARY, CALGARY 44 ALB   CAN
WARENDA, C J, PHILOSOPHY DEPT, LAURENTIAN UNIV, SUDBURY ONT   CAN
WARGANZ, JOSEPH F, PHILOSOPHY AREA, COUNTY COL OF MORRIS, RANDOLPH NJ   07801
WARGO, DONALD, PHIL DEPT, FORDHAM UNIVERSITY, BRONX NY   10458
WARMBROD, K, PHIL DEPT, UNIV OF MANITOBA, WINNIPEG 19 MAN   CAN
WARNER, C TERRY, PHILOSOPHY DEPT, BRIGHAM YOUNG UNIV, PROVO UT   84601
WARNER, PETER O, PHIL DIV, SACRED HEART SEM, DETROIT MI   48206
WARNER, SETH R, SOC STUD DEPT, SANTA MONICA COL, SANTA MONICA CA   90405
WARREN, EDWARD W, PHIL DEPT, CALIFORNIA ST UNIV, SAN DIEGO CA   92115
WARREN, JOHN, PHIL DEPT, MERRIMACK COLLEGE, NORTH ANDOVER MA   01845
WARREN, T B, PHIL OF REL & APOL, HARDING GRAD SCH REL, MEMPHIS AR   38117
WARREN, W PRESTON, PHIL DEPT, BUCKNELL UNIVERSITY, LEWISBURG PA   17837
WARTHLING, WILLIAM G, HUMAN DIV, NIAGARA CO COM COL, NIAGARA FALLS NY   14303
WARTOFSKY, MARX, PHIL DEPT, BOSTON UNIVERSITY, BOSTON MA   02215
WASHBURN, MICHAEL C, PHIL DEPT, INDIANA UNIVERSITY, SOUTH BEND IN   46615
WASHELL, RICHARD, PHILOSOPHY DEPT, KENT STATE UNIV, KENT OH   44242
WASOW, THOMAS, PHIL DEPT, STANFORD UNIVERSITY, STANFORD CA   94305
WASSERMAN, IRVING, PHIL DEPT, GRAND VALLEY ST COL, ALLENDALE MI   49401
WASSERSTROM, RICHARD, PHIL DEPT, UNIV OF CALIFORNIA, LOS ANGELES CA   90024
WASSMER, THOMAS A, PHIL DEPT, SE MASS UNIV, N DARTMOUTH MA   02747
WASSNER, GARY A, PHIL DEPT, ST UNIV OF NY, BINGHAMTON NY   13901
WATERHOUSE, JOSEPH B, PHIL DEPT, CALIFORNIA ST UNIV, SAN JOSE CA   95114
WATERS, ANTHONY, PHIL DEPT, XAVIER UNIVERSITY, NEW ORLEANS LA   70125
WATERS, F W, PHILOSOPHY DEPT, MCMASTER UNIVERSITY, HAMILTON ONT   CAN
WATERS, GARDNER, AMERICAN RIVER COL, SACRAMENTO, CA   95841
WATERS, RAPHAEL, PHIL FACULTY, UNIV OF OTTAWA, OTTAWA ONT   CAN
WATERS, THOMAS B, PHILOSOPHY DEPT, TEXAS TECH UNIV, LUBBOCK TX   79409
WATHEN, JAMES, HUMAN & FINE ARTS, S TEXAS JR COL, HOUSTON TX   77002
WATKINS, CHARLES, SOC SCI DEPT, KUTZTOWN STATE COL, KUTZTOWN PA   19530
WATSON-SCHIPPER, E, PHIL DEPT, UNIVERSITY OF MIAMI, CORAL GABLES FL   33124
WATSON, GARY, PHILOSOPHY DEPT, UNIV OF PENN, PHILADELPHIA PA   19174
WATSON, JAMES R, PHIL DEPT, LOYOLA UNIVERSITY, NEW ORLEANS LA   70118
WATSON, MARK, PHIL & REL DEPT, HILLSDALE COLLEGE, HILLSDALE MI   49242
WATSON, RICHARD A, PHIL DEPT, WASHINGTON UNIV, ST LOUIS MO   63130
WATSON, ROY M, PHILOSOPHY DEPT, UNIV OF UTAH, SALT LAKE CTY UT   84112
WATSON, S Y, PHIL DEPT, SPRING HILL COLLEGE, MOBILE AL   36608
WATSON, STEVE, PHIL & RELIG DEPT, BRIDGEWATER COL, BRIDGEWATER VA   22812
WATSON, WALTER, PHIL DEPT, ST UNIV OF NY, STONY BROOK NY   11790
WATTELLE, CHRISLAINE, PHIL DEPT, COL VIEUX-MONTREAL, MONTREAL QUE   CAN
WATTLES, JEFFREY, PHIL & RELIG, WEST KENTUCKY UNIV, BOWLING GREEN KY   42101
WATTS, ALAN, P O BOX 857, SAUSILITO, CA   94965
WATTS, DONALD F, PHILOSOPHY DEPT, BALDWIN-WALLACE COL, BEREA OH   44017
WATTS, HARVEY D, RELIG & PHIL, SOUTHWESTERN UNIV, GEORGETOWN TX   78626
WATTS, V ORVAL, SOC SCI DEPT, NORTHWOOD INSTITUTE, MIDLAND MI   48640
WAUGH, R O'BRIEN, PHIL DEPT, SAINT THOMAS UNIV, FREDERICTON N B   CAN
WAVELL, B B, REL & PHIL DEPT, ROLLINS COLLEGE, WINTER PARK FL   32789
WAWRYTKO, SANDRA A, PHIL DEPT, WASHINGTON UNIV, ST LOUIS MO   63130
WEAR, STEPHEN, PHILOSOPHY DEPT, UNIV OF TEXAS, AUSTIN TX   78712
WEARS, JAMES, PHIL DEPT, NORTHWESTERN UNIV, EVANSTON IL   60201
WEATHERFORD, ROY, PHIL DEPT, UNIV OF S FLORIDA, TAMPA FL   33620
WEATHERLY, OWEN M, REL & PHIL DEPT, HIGH POINT COLLEGE, HIGH POINT NC   27262
WEAVER, G B, CHRIST EDUC & PHIL, JOHN BROWN UNIV, SILOAM SPGS AR   72761
WEAVER, GEORGE, BRYN MAWR COLLEGE, BRYN MAWR, PA   19010
WEAVER, GWENDOLYN, PHIL DEPT, MICHIGAN STATE UNIV, EAST LANSING MI   48823
WEAVER, OLIVER C, PHIL DEPT, BIRMINGHAM S COLLEGE, BIRMINGHAM AL   35204
WEBB, C W, PHILOSOPHY DEPT, UNIV OF TORONTO, TORONTO ONT   CAN
WEBB, ILONA, PHIL DEPT, BOSTON UNIVERSITY, BOSTON MA   02215
WEBB, JUDSON, PHIL DEPT, BOSTON UNIVERSITY, BOSTON MA   02215

WEBB, STEVEN, PHIL DEPT, UNIV OF CALIFORNIA, SANTA BARBARA CA 93106
WEBB, WILSE B, PSYCH DEPT, UNIV OF FLORIDA, GAINESVILLE FL 32601
WEBER, CORNELIUS, HUMANITIES DEPT, COLLEGE OF MARIN, KENTFIELD CA 94904
WEBER, DOROTHY M, ANCILLA DOMINI COL, DONALDSON, IN 46513
WEBER, GARY, PHILOSOPHY DEPT, UNIV OF WATERLOO, WATERLOO ONT CAN
WEBER, RENEE, PHILOSOPHY DEPT, RUTGERS UNIV, NEW BRUNSWICK NJ 08903
WEBER, STEPHEN L, PHIL DEPT, UNIV OF MAINE, ORONO ME 04773
WEBSTER, GLENN A, PHIL DEPT, UNIV OF COLORADO, DENVER CO 80202
WEBSTER, WILLIAM E, LIBR ARTS, PHILADELPHIA COL ART, PHILADELPHIA PA 19102
WECKMAN, GEORGE, PHILOSOPHY DEPT, OHIO UNIVERSITY, ATHENS OH 45701
WEDDLE, PERRY, PHIL DEPT, CALIFORNIA ST UNIV, SACRAMENTO CA 95819
WEDEKING, GARY A, PHIL DEPT, UNIV BRIT COLUMBIA, VANCOUVER 8 B C CAN
WEDEMEYER, KARL H, PHIL DEPT, INDIANA ST UNIV, TERRE HAUTE IN 47809
WEDIN JR, VERNON E, PHIL DEPT, UNIV OF CALIFORNIA, DAVIS CA 95616
WEDIN, GALE J, PHIL DEPT, CALIFORNIA ST UNIV, SACRAMENTO CA 95819
WEDMORE, DELPHINE, THEOL & PHIL, MALLINCKRODT COL, WONDER LAKES IL 60097
WEEKS, LOUIS, HUMAN DIV, ST JOHN'S UNIV, STATEN ISLAND NY 10301
WEEMS JR, KELLY G, ENG DEPT, U S MILITARY ACAD, WEST POINT NY 10996
WEHRELL, R, PHILOSOPHY DEPT, UNIV OF ALBERTA, EDMONTON ALB CAN
WEHRLY JR, W F, PHIL DEPT, MONTGOMERY COLLEGE, TAKOMA PARK MD 20012
WEIERICH, ANDRE, HUMAN & PHIL DEPT, NW MISSOURI ST UNIV, MARYVILLE MC 64468
WEIGAN, BURT, PHIL DEPT, NIAGARA UNIVERSITY, NIAGARA UNIV NY 14109
WEIGHTMAN, DONALD, PHIL DEPT, BOSTON UNIVERSITY, BOSTON MA 02215
WEIHER, CHARLES, PHIL DEPT, UNIV OF NOTRE DAME, NOTRE DAME IN 46556
WEIL, H GIL, UNDERGRAD DEPT, ST JOHN VIANNEY SEM, E AURORA NY 14052
WEIL, VIVIAN M, HUMAN DEPT, ILLINOIS INST TECH, CHICAGO IL 60616
WEILER, WILLIAM J, PHIL DEPT, ST LOUIS UNIVERSITY, ST LOUIS MO 63103
WEINBERG, SUE, PHIL DEPT, HUNTER COLLEGE, NEW YORK NY 10021
WEINBERG, W, PHIL DEPT, BOSTON COLLEGE, CHESTNUT HILL MA 02167
WEINER, NEAL O, PHILOSOPHY DEPT, MARLBORO COLLEGE, MARLBORO VT 05344
WEINGARD, ROBERT, PHILOSOPHY DEPT, RUTGERS UNIV, NEW BRUNSWICK NJ 08903
WEINGARTNER, RUDOLPH H, PHIL DEPT, VASSAR COLLEGE, POUGHKEEPSIE NY 12601
WEINS, DELBERT, DIV OF HUMAN, PACIFIC COLLEGE, FRESNO CA 93702
WEINSTEIN, MARK, PHIL DEPT, HUNTER COLLEGE, NEW YORK NY 10021
WEINSTEIN, SCOTT, PHIL DEPT, UNIV OF MARYLAND, BALTIMORE MD 21228
WEINSTOCK, JEROME, PHIL DEPT, LEHMAN COLLEGE, BRONX NY 10468
WEINZWEIG, MARJORIE, PHIL DEPT, CALIFORNIA ST UNIV, NORTHRIDGE CA 91324
WEIR, WALTER, PHIL DEPT, UNIV OF COLORADO, BOULDER CO 80302
WEIRICH, PAUL, PHIL DEPT, UNIV OF CALIFORNIA, LOS ANGELES CA 90024
WEIS, RICHARD F, PHILOSOPHY DEPT, UNIV OF WISCONSIN, MADISON WI 53706
WEISBAKER, DONALD R, PHIL & RELIG, UNIV OF TENNESSEE, CHATTANOOGA TN 37401
WEISHEIPL, J A, UNIV OF ST MICHAEL'S, TORONTO 181, ONT CAN
WEISMAN, JEFFREY, PHIL DEPT, UNIV OF CALIFORNIA, LOS ANGELES CA 90024
WEISS, BRUCE S, PHIL DEPT, UNIV OF N CAROLINA, CHAPEL HILL NC 27514
WEISS, DONALD D, PHIL DEPT, ST UNIV OF NY, BINGHAMTON NY 13901
WEISS, DONALD H, HIST & PHIL DEPT, UNIV OF TEXAS, ARLINGTON TX 76010
WEISS, LARRY, AMER STUD SCHOOL, RAMAPO COLLEGE, MAHWAH NJ 07430
WEISS, PAUL, PHIL SCH, CATH UNIV OF AMER, WASHINGTON DC 20017
WEISS, RAYMOND L, PHIL DEPT, UNIV OF WISCONSIN, MILWAUKEE WI 53201
WEISSMAN, DAVID, PHIL DEPT, CITY COLLEGE, NEW YORK NY 10031
WEISSMAN, STANLEY N, PHIL DEPT, CALIFORNIA ST UNIV, SAN DIEGO CA 92115
WEITZ, MORRIS, PHIL DEPT, BRANDEIS UNIVERSITY, WALTHAM MA 02154
WEITZEL, RAY, PHIL DEPT, UNIV OF COLORADO, DENVER CO 80202
WEITZENFELD, JULIAN, PHIL DEPT, OAKLAND UNIVERSITY, ROCHESTER MI 48063
WELCH, C, PHILOSOPHY DEPT, MT ALLISON UNIV, SACKVILLE N B CAN
WELCH, JOHN J, ST PETER'S COLLEGE, JERSEY CITY, NJ 07306
WELCH, MARY F, ROSARY HILL COLLEGE, BUFFALO, NY 14226
WELCH, ROBERT, PHILOSOPHY DEPT, UNIV OF MASS, AMHERST MA 01002
WELCH, WILSON Q, RELIG & PHIL DEPT, FISK UNIVERSITY, NASHVILLE TN 37203
WELKER, DAVID, PHIL DEPT, TEMPLE UNIVERSITY, PHILADELPHIA PA 19122
WELLBANK, JOSEPH H, PHIL & REL DEPT, NORTHEASTERN UNIV, BOSTON MA 02115
WELLER, ERIC J, PHIL DEPT, SKIDMORE COLLEGE, SARATOGA SPGS NY 12886
WELLING, NORMAN, PHIL & REL DEPT, HILLSDALE COLLEGE, HILLSDALE MI 49242
WELLMAN, CARL P, PHIL DEPT, WASHINGTON UNIV, ST LOUIS MO 63130

WELLMER, ALBRECHT, PHIL DEPT, NW SCH FOR SOC RES, NEW YORK NY 10003
WELLMUTH, JOHN, PHILOSOPHY DEPT, JOHN F KENNEDY UNIV, MARTINEZ CA 94553
WELLS, DONALD A, HUMANITIES DIV, UNIVERSITY OF HAWAII, HILO HI 96720
WELLS, E FRANK, PHIL DEPT, SLIPPERY ROCK ST COL, SLIPPERY ROCK PA 16057
WELLS, JOHN D, PHIL DEPT, BROWARD CCM COL, FT LAUDERDALE FL 33314
WELLS, NORMAN J, PHIL DEPT, BOSTON COLLEGE, CHESTNUT HILL MA 02167
WELLS, RAYMOND, HUMAN SCHOOL, SEATTLE PACIFIC COL, SEATTLE WA 98119
WELLS, RONALD V, PHIL DEPT, SIOUX FALLS COLLEGE, SIOUX FALLS SD 57101
WELLS, RULON, PHIL DEPT, YALE UNIVERSITY, NEW HAVEN CT 06520
WELLS, STEPHEN, PHIL DEPT, OKLAHOMA CITY COL, OKLAHOMA CITY OK 73106
WELLS, WILLIAM, HUMANITIES DIV, UNIVERSITY OF HAWAII, HILO HI 96720
WELLWOOD, DAVID, PHIL DEPT, MIDDLE TENN ST UNIV, MURFREESBORO TN 37130
WELSH, PAUL, PHILOSOPHY DEPT, DUKE UNIVERSITY, DURHAM NC 27706
WELTON, DONN, PHIL DEPT, ST UNIV OF NY, STONY BROOK NY 11790
WENGER, LINDEN, BIB & PHIL DEPT, E MENNONITE COL, HARRISONBURG VA 22801
WENGERT, ROBERT G, PHIL DEPT, UNIV OF ILLINOIS, URBANA IL 61801
WENING, GERALD G, PHIL DEPT, UNIVERSITY OF DAYTON, DAYTON OH 45469
WENISCH, FRITZ, PHILOSOPHY DEPT, UNIV OF RHODE ISLAND, KINGSTON RI 02881
WENKER, KENNETH H, PHIL DEPT, U S AIR FORCE ACAD, COLORADO SPGS CO 80840
WENNBERG, R, REL STUD & PHIL, WESTMONT COLLEGE, SANTA BARBARA CA 93108
WENNINGER, WILLIAM A, HISTORY & PHIL, UNIV OF WISCONSIN, SUPERIOR WI 54880
WENTE, WALTER, HUMAN DIV, CONCORDIA SENIOR COL, FORT WAYNE IN 46825
WENTWORTH, ELIZABETH, SWEET BRIAR CCL, SWEET BRIAR, VA 24521
WENTZ, JAN T, PHIL DEPT, N ILLINOIS UNIV, DEKALB IL 60115
WENZ, PETER, PHIL DEPT, UNIV OF WISCONSIN, STEVENS POINT WI 54481
WERKING, ROBERT, REL & PHIL DIV, MARION COLLEGE, MARION IN 46952
WERKMEISTER, WILLIAM H, PHIL DEPT, FLORIDA STATE UNIV, TALLAHASSEE FL 32306
WERNEKE, LEO, PHIL DEPT, OKLAHOMA CITY COL, OKLAHOMA CITY OK 73106
WERNER, CHARLES G, PHIL DEPT, UNIVERSITY OF MIAMI, CORAL GABLES FL 33124
WERNER, LOUIS, PHIL DEPT, UNIV OF ILLINOIS, URBANA IL 61801
WERNER, RICHARD, PHIL DEPT, UNIV OF ROCHESTER, ROCHESTER NY 14627
WERNESS, GEORGE S, PHILOSOPHY DEPT, TEXAS TECH UNIV, LUBBOCK TX 79409
WERNHAM, J C S, PHILOSOPHY DEPT, CARLETON UNIVERSITY, OTTAWA ONT CAN
WERTH, LEE F, PHILOSOPHY DEPT, CLEVELAND ST UNIV, CLEVELAND OH 44115
WERTHEIMER, MICHAEL, PSYCH DEPT, SPRING HILL COLLEGE, MOBILE AL 36608
WERTHEIMER, ROGER, PHIL PROGRAM, GRADUATE SCH -CUNY, NEW YORK NY 10036
WERTZ, SPENCER K, PHIL DEPT, TEXAS CHRISTIAN UNIV, FORT WORTH TX 76129
WESSELL, DOUGLAS F, PHILOSOPHY DEPT, CERRITOS COLLEGE, NORWALK CA 90605
WESSLING, JOHN E, LIBR ARTS FAC, ATHENAEUM OF OHIO, CINCINNATI OH 45230
WEST, CHARLES C, THEOL DEPT, PRINCETON THEOL SEM, PRINCETON NJ 08540
WEST, CHARLES E, LINCOLN MEMORIAL, UNIVERSITY, HARROGATE TN 37752
WEST, CHARLES, RELIG & PHIL DEPT, ATHENS COLLEGE, ATHENS AL 35611
WEST, ELINOR J M, PHIL DEPT, LONG ISLAND UNIV, BROOKLYN NY 11201
WEST, HENRY R, PHILOSOPHY DEPT, MACALESTER COLLEGE, ST PAUL MN 55101
WEST, JAI, PHILOSOPHY DEPT, UNIV OF WISCONSIN, MADISON WI 53706
WEST, WILLIAM, HIST & PHIL & SOC SCI, SAN JOSE CITY COL, SAN JOSE CA 95114
WESTER, DONALD G, PHIL DEPT, OKLA BAPT UNIV, SHAWNEE OK 74801
WESTLEY, RICHARD, PHIL DEPT, LOYOLA UNIVERSITY, CHICAGO IL 60626
WESTON, THOMAS, PHIL SCH, UNIV OF S CALIFORNIA, LCS ANGELES CA 90007
WESTPHAL, DALE, PHIL DEPT, WEST MICHIGAN UNIV, KALAMAZOO MI 49001
WESTPHAL, FRED A, PHIL DEPT, UNIVERSITY OF MIAMI, CORAL GABLES FL 33124
WESTPHAL, MEROLD, PHIL DEPT, YALE UNIVERSITY, NEW HAVEN CT 06520
WESTWOOD, JOHN, PHILOSOPHY DEPT, UNIV OF WATERLOO, WATERLOO ONT CAN
WETTERSTEN, JOHN, PHILOSOPHY DEPT, UNIV OF S CAROLINA, COLUMBIA SC 29208
WETTSTEIN, A A, REL & PHIL DEPT, ROLLINS COLLEGE, WINTER PARK FL 32789
WETTSTEIN, HOWARD, PHIL DEPT, LEHMAN COLLEGE, BRONX NY 10468
WETZEL, C R, HUMANE LEARNING, MILLIGAN COLLEGE, MILLIGAN COL TN 37682
WETZEL, THOMAS, PHIL DEPT, UNIV OF CALIFORNIA, LOS ANGELES CA 90024
WHARTON, CHRISTINE, PHILOSOPHY DEPT, PENN STATE UNIV, UNIV PARK PA 16802
WHEARTY, LAURA, REL PHIL DEPT, ILIFF SCH OF THEOL, DENVER CO 80210
WHEATCROFT, N PAUL, HUMAN & PHIL DEPT, GROSSMONT COL, EL CAJON CA 92020
WHEATLEY, J M C, PHILOSOPHY DEPT, UNIV OF TORONTO, TORONTO ONT CAN
WHEATLEY, J, PHILOSOPHY DEPT, SIMON FRASER UNIV, BURNABY 2 B C CAN
WHEELER III, S C, PHIL DEPT, UNIV OF CONNECTICUT, STORRS CT 06268

WHEELER, ARTHUR M, PHILOSOPHY DEPT, KENT STATE UNIV, KENT OH 44242
WHEELER, LAWRENCE W, PHIL DEPT, LORAS COLLEGE, DUBUQUE IA 52001
WHEELER, MICHAEL O, PHIL DEPT, U S AIR FORCE ACAD, COLORADO SPGS CO 80840
WHEELER, WILLIAM, HUMANITIES DIV, AMERICAN CHRIST COL, TULSA OK 74129
WHELAN, JOHN M, PHIL DEPT, LYCOMING COLLEGE, WILLIAMSPORT PA 17701
WHIPPLE, KENNETH, PHIL DEPT, WAYNE STATE UNIV, DETROIT MI 48202
WHISNER, WILLIAM N, PHILOSOPHY DEPT, UNIV OF UTAH, SALT LAKE CTY UT 84112
WHITCRAFT, JOHN E, PHIL & RELIG DEPT, GLASSBORO ST COL, GLASSBORO NJ 08028
WHITE JR, DAVID F, HIST & PHIL DEPT, CLEMSON UNIVERSITY, CLEMSON SC 29631
WHITE, ALAN, PHIL DEPT, TEMPLE UNIVERSITY, PHILADELPHIA PA 19122
WHITE, CHARLES S J, PHIL DEPT, THE AMERICAN UNIV, WASHINGTON DC 20016
WHITE, DAVID B, PHILOSOPHY DEPT, MACALESTER COLLEGE, ST PAUL MN 55101
WHITE, DAVID C, CHRIST LIFE & THT, SCARRITT COLLEGE, NASHVILLE TN 37203
WHITE, FRANK, QUEENSBOROUGH COM COL, NEW YORK, NY 11364
WHITE, GEORGE, SETON HALL UNIV, SOUTH ORANGE, NJ 07079
WHITE, JAMES, PHIL DEPT, ST CLOUD ST COL, ST CLOUD MN 56301
WHITE, JEFFERSON, PHIL DEPT, UNIV OF MAINE, ORONO ME 04473
WHITE, JOAN, SOC SCI DEPT, AZUSA PACIFIC COL, AZUSA CA 91702
WHITE, L L, PHIL DEPT, SOUTH UNIV A & M COL, BATON ROUGE LA 70813
WHITE, MARGARET, PHILOSOPHY DEPT, UNIV OF WATERLOO, WATERLOO ONT   CAN
WHITE, NICHOLAS P, PHIL DEPT, UNIV OF MICHIGAN, ANN ARBOR MI 48104
WHITE, PATRICIA, PHIL DEPT, UNIV OF MICHIGAN, ANN ARBOR MI 48104
WHITE, PETER J, PHILOSOPHY DEPT, ARIZONA STATE UNIV, TEMPE AZ 85281
WHITE, R JERRY, HUMAN DEPT, MONTCALM COM COL, SIDNEY MI 48885
WHITE, ROBERT G, ENG & PHIL DEPT, MONTGOMERY COLLEGE, ROCKVILLE MD 20850
WHITE, RONALD, PHIL DEPT, UNIV OF KENTUCKY, LEXINGTON KY 40506
WHITE, STEPHEN, PHIL DEPT, E TENNESSEE ST UNIV, JOHNSON CITY TN 37601
WHITED, GARY, PHIL DEPT, UNIV OF MONTANA, MISSOULA MT 59801
WHITEHILL, JAMES D, REL & PHIL DEPT, STEPHENS COLLEGE, COLUMBIA MO 65201
WHITELY, ROBERT, PHIL DEPT, SUFFOLK CO COM COL, SELDEN NY 11784
WHITEWAY, LLOYD M, PHIL DEPT, SALISBURY STATE COL, SALISBURY MD 21801
WHITLING, D, PHILOSOPHY DEPT, UNIV OF ALBERTA, EDMONTON ALB   CAN
WHITNEY, RICHARD, PHIL DEPT, UNIV OF CALIFORNIA, LOS ANGELES CA 90024
WHITTAKER, GARETH, PHILOSOPHY DEPT, UNIV OF CALGARY, CALGARY 44 ALB   CAN
WHITTEMORE, ROBERT C, PHIL DEPT, TULANE UNIVERSITY, NEW ORLEANS LA 70118
WHITTIER, DUANE, PHILOSOPHY DEPT, UNIV OF NW HAMPSHIRE, DURHAM NH 03824
WHITWORTH, CHARLES W, REL & PHIL DEPT, SHORTER COLLEGE, ROME GA 30161
WICK, WARNER, PHIL DEPT, UNIV OF CHICAGO, CHICAGO IL 60637
WICKERSHAM, JOHN P, PHILOSOPHY DEPT, MARYVILLE COLLEGE, ST LOUIS MO 63141
WIDER, KATHLEEN, PHIL DEPT, WAYNE STATE UNIV, DETROIT MI 48202
WIEBOLDT, BARBARA, MARIA COLLEGE, ALBANY, NY 12208
WIECK, DAVID T, PHIL DEPT, RENSSELAER POLYTECH, TROY NY 12181
WIEDERHOLT, MARIE F, HUMAN DEPT, ST MARY'S COLLEGE, O'FALLON MO 63366
WIEGENSTEIN, FRANCIS J, PHIL DEPT, CARROLL COLLEGE, HELENA MT 59601
WIEHE, ROGER E, LANG & LIT DEPT, LOWELL TECH INST, LOWELL MA 01854
WIELER, JEROME A, PHIL DEPT, BOSTON COLLEGE, CHESTNUT HILL MA 02167
WIEMAN, HENRY N, PHIL DEPT, S ILLINOIS UNIV, CARBONDALE IL 62901
WIEMAN, ROBERT, PHILOSOPHY DEPT, OHIO UNIVERSITY, ATHENS OH 45701
WIENER, PHILIP, PHIL DEPT, TEMPLE UNIVERSITY, PHILADELPHIA PA 19122
WIENPAHL, PAUL, PHIL DEPT, UNIV OF CALIFORNIA, SANTA BARBARA CA 93106
WIERENGA, EDWARD, PHILOSOPHY DEPT, UNIV OF MASS, AMHERST MA 01002
WIESMANN, ROBERT J, PHIL DEPT, TUSKEGEE INSTITUTE, TUSKEGEE INST AL 36088
WIEST, WALTER E, CHURCH & MINISTRY, PITTS THEOL SEM, PITTSBURGH PA 15206
WIEZEL, JAMES, PHIL DEPT, UNIV OF MICHIGAN, ANN ARBOR MI 48104
WIGGINS JR, OSBORNE P, PHIL DEPT, S METHODIST UNIV, DALLAS TX 75222
WIGNEY, T J, PHIL OF EDUC & HIST, ONTARIO INSTITUTE, TORONTO ONT   CAN
WIKLER, DANIEL, PHIL DEPT, UNIV OF CALIFORNIA, LOS ANGELES CA 90024
WILBANKS, DANA W, REL PHIL DEPT, ILIFF SCH OF THEOL, DENVER CO 80210
WILBANKS, JAN J, PHILOSOPHY DEPT, MARIETTA COLLEGE, MARIETTA OH 45750
WILBUR, JAMES B, PHIL DEPT, COL AT GENESEO, GENESEO NY 14454
WILBURN, JAMES R, DIV II, BELHAVEN COLLEGE, JACKSON MS 39202
WILCOX, JOHN T, PHIL DEPT, ST UNIV OF NY, BINGHAMTON NY 13901
WILCOX, WILLIAM, PHIL DEPT, UNIV OF MISSOURI, COLUMBIA MO 65201
WILCOX, WILLIAM, PHIL & RELIG, UPPER IOWA UNIV, FAYETTE IA 52142

WILDER, ALFRED, PHILOSOPHY DEPT, AQUINAS INST THEOL, DUBUQUE IA 52001
WILDER, HUGH T, PHILOSOPHY DEPT, MIAMI UNIVERSITY, OXFORD OH 45056
WILDT, CAROL MARIE, PHILOSOPHY DEPT, NOTRE DAME COLLEGE, ST LOUIS MO 63125
WILES, ANN MCCOY, PHIL & RELIG DEPT, MADISON COL, HARRISONBURG VA 22801
WILEY, ELECTA C, ENG DEPT, SOUTH UNIV A & M COL, SHREVEPORT LA 71107
WILHELMSEN, FREDERICK, PHIL DEPT, UNIVERSITY OF DALLAS, IRVING TX 75062
WILHOIT, LAWRENCE R, PHILOSOPHY DEPT, UNIV OF TEXAS, AUSTIN TX 78712
WILK, GREGORY, PHIL DEPT, UNIVERSITY OF DAYTON, DAYTON OH 45469
WILKENS, THOMAS G, THEOL & PHIL DEPT, TEXAS LUTH COLLEGE, SEGUIN TX 78155
WILKERSON, J KENNETH, RELIG & PHIL CEPT, LAMBUTH COLLEGE, JACKSON TN 38301
WILKINS, BURLEIGH, PHIL DEPT, UNIV OF CALIFORNIA, SANTA BARBARA CA 93106
WILKINSON, PETER F, PHILOSOPHY DEPT, UNIV OF WINDSOR, WINDSOR ONT CAN
WILKINSON, WINSTON, PHIL DEPT, MICHIGAN STATE UNIV, EAST LANSING MI 48823
WILL, FREDERICK L, PHIL DEPT, UNIV OF ILLINOIS, URBANA IL 61801
WILL, JAMES E, PHIL DEPT, EVANGELICAL THEO SEM, NAPERVILLE IL 60540
WILL, R D, PHILOSOPHY DEPT, ST AUGUSTINE'S SEM, SCARBOROUGH ONT CAN
WILLARD, DALLAS, PHIL SCH, UNIV OF S CALIFORNIA, LOS ANGELES CA 90007
WILLARD, L DUANE, PHIL & REL DEPT, UNIV OF NEBRASKA, OMAHA NE 68132
WILLCOX, DAVID E, PHILOSOPHY DEPT, UNIV OF OKLAHOMA, NORMAN OK 73069
WILLENBECHER, THOMAS C, PHIL DEPT, BOSTON COLLEGE, CHESTNUT HILL MA 02167
WILLIAM, JOHN P, REL & PHIL DIV, MARION COLLEGE, MARION IN 46952
WILLIAMS, BERT C, PHILOSOPHY DEPT, CHAPMAN COLLEGE, ORANGE CA 92666
WILLIAMS, CLIFFORD, PHIL DEPT, ST JOHN FISHER COL, ROCHESTER NY 14618
WILLIAMS, DANIEL D, PHIL & RELIG DEPT, UNION THEOL SEM, NEW YORK NY 10027
WILLIAMS, DARYL E, PHIL & RELIG DEPT, DOANE COLLEGE, CRETE NE 68333
WILLIAMS, DONALD C, PHIL DEPT, HARVARD UNIVERSITY, CAMBRIDGE MA 02138
WILLIAMS, EDWIN L, PHIL DEPT, WEST CHESTER ST COL, WEST CHESTER PA 19380
WILLIAMS, ERNIE, HUMAN DEPT, HILLSBOROUGH JUN COL, TAMPA FL 33622
WILLIAMS, FORREST, PHIL DEPT, UNIV OF COLORADO, BOULDER CO 80302
WILLIAMS, FRANK, PHIL DEPT, EAST KENTUCKY UNIV, RICHMOND KY 40475
WILLIAMS, GEORGE, HUMAN DEPT, BURLINGTON CO COL, PEMBERTON NJ 08068
WILLIAMS, HARVEY, PHIL DEPT, WEST MICHIGAN UNIV, KALAMAZOO MI 49001
WILLIAMS, JAMES D, PHIL DEPT, BUTLER UNIVERSITY, INDIANAPOLIS IN 46205
WILLIAMS, MARTHA E, PHIL DEPT, UNIV OF WEST ONTARIO, LONDON ONT CAN
WILLIAMS, MARY B, HIST & PHIL SCI, INDIANA UNIV, BLOOMINGTON IN 47401
WILLIAMS, MICHAEL, PHIL DEPT, YALE UNIVERSITY, NEW HAVEN CT 06520
WILLIAMS, NEDRA T, PHIL DEPT, BOSTON COLLEGE, CHESTNUT HILL MA 02167
WILLIAMS, NEWTON, PHIL & RELIG DEPT, RUST COLLEGE, HOLLY SPRINGS MS 38635
WILLIAMS, PATRICIA, ENGLISH DEPT, DEL MAR COLLEGE, CORPUS CHRSTI TX 78404
WILLIAMS, RICHARD L, SOC SCI DIV, GLENDALE COM COL, GLENDALE CA 91208
WILLIAMS, ROBERT C, PHILOSOPHY DEPT, VANDERBILT UNIV, NASHVILLE TN 37235
WILLIAMS, ROBERT L, PHIL DEPT, PORTLAND ST UNIV, PORTLAND OR 97207
WILLIAMS, ROBERT, PHIL & RELIG DEPT, NORTHLAND COLLEGE, ASHLAND WI 54806
WILLIAMS, RONALD G, PHIL DEPT, COLORADO ST UNIV, FORT COLLINS CO 80521
WILLIAMS, ROY E, PHIL & REL STUD, WILKES COLLEGE, WILKES BARRE PA 18703
WILLIAMS, STERLING P, PHIL DEPT, LAKE FOREST COLLEGE, LAKE FOREST IL 60045
WILLIAMS, T C, PHILOSOPHY DEPT, UNIV OF GUELPH, GUELPH ONT CAN
WILLIAMS, THOMAS R, PHILOSOPHY DEPT, CARROL COLLEGE, WAUKESHA WI 53186
WILLIAMS, WARD, BIBL STUD & PHIL, EVANGEL COLLEGE, SPRINGFIELD MO 65802
WILLIAMS, WILLIAM H, PHIL & RELIG, VA POLYTECH INST, BLACKSBURG VA 24061
WILLIAMSON, WILLARD, PHIL DEPT, WM RAINEY HARPER COL, PALATINE IL 60067
WILLIAMSON, WILLIAM B, PHIL & RELIG, URSINUS COLLEGE, COLLEGEVILLE PA 19426
WILLMAN, JAMES, RELIG & PHIL DEPT, AUSTIN COLLEGE, SHERMAN TX 75090
WILLNER, DAVID, PHIL DEPT, COLUMBIA UNIVERSITY, NEW YORK NY 10027
WILLOUGHBY, W G, PHIL & RELIG DEPT, LA VERNE COLLEGE, LA VERNE CA 91750
WILSHIRE, BRUCE W, PHILOSOPHY DEPT, RUTGERS UNIV, NEW BRUNSWICK NJ 08903
WILSON JR, FRANCIS E, PHIL DEPT, BUCKNELL UNIVERSITY, LEWISBURG PA 17837
WILSON, ARNOLD, PHIL DEPT, UNIV OF CINCINNATI, CINCINNATI OH 45221
WILSON, BARRIE A, PHIL DEPT, ST LOUIS UNIVERSITY, ST LOUIS MO 63103
WILSON, CHARLES, PHILOSOPHY DEPT, TAYLOR UNIVERSITY, UPLAND IN 46989
WILSON, F F, PHILOSOPHY DEPT, UNIV OF TORONTO, TORONTO ONT CAN
WILSON, F, PHILOSOPHY DEPT, SHERIDAN COLLEGE, OAKVILLE ONT CAN
WILSON, GEORGE, PHIL DEPT, JOHNS HOPKINS UNIV, BALTIMORE MD 21218
WILSON, HELEN G, PHILOSOPHY DEPT, NM HIGHLANDS UNIV, LAS VEGAS NM 87701

WILSON, J B, PSYCH & PHIL DEPT, JACKSONVILLE ST COL, JACKSONVILLE AL   36265
WILSON, JACK, REL & PHIL DEPT, TENN WESLEYAN COL, ATHENS TN   37303
WILSON, JAMES, PHILOSOPHY DEPT, UNIV OF ARIZONA, TUCSON AZ   85721
WILSON, JAMES, PHIL DEPT, CALIFORNIA ST UNIV, LOS ANGELES CA   90032
WILSON, JOHN, PHIL DIV, C S MOTT COM COL, FLINT MI   48503
WILSON, KIRK D, PHIL DEPT, GEORGIA ST UNIV, ATLANTA GA   30303
WILSON, MARGARET, PHIL DEPT, PRINCETON UNIVERSITY, PRINCETON NJ   08540
WILSON, MAX, PHILOSOPHY DEPT, MORGAN STATE UNIV, BALTIMORE MD   21239
WILSON, NED M, PHIL & RELIG DEPT, ESSEX COUNTY COL, NEWARK NJ   07102
WILSON, NEIL, PHILOSOPHY DEPT, MCMASTER UNIVERSITY, HAMILTON ONT   CAN
WILSON, R A, HIST OF THEOL DIV, VANCOUVER SCH THEOL, VANCOUVER 8 B C   CAN
WILSON, R FRANCES, APPL & LIBR STUD, SHERIDAN COLLEGE, OAKVILLE ONT   CAN
WILSON, ROBERT K, PHIL & RELIG DEPT, VIRGINIA MIL INST, LEXINGTON VA   24450
WILSON, THOMAS A, PHIL DEPT, UNIVERSITY OF TOLEDO, TOLEDO OH   43606
WILSON, TOM B, PHIL DEPT, ARK POLYTECH COL, RUSSELLVILLE AR   72801
WILSON, WARREN K, PHIL DEPT, UNIV OF ILLINOIS, CHICAGO IL   60680
WILT, LAWRENCE, PHIL DEPT, INDIANA UNIVERSITY, BLOOMINGTON IN   47401
WIMSATT, WILLIAM W, PHIL DEPT, UNIV OF CHICAGO, CHICAGO IL   60637
WINANCE, ELEUTHERE, ST JOHN'S COLLEGE, CAMARILLO, CA   93010
WINCHESTER, I, PHIL OF EDUC & HIST, ONTARIO INSTITUTE, TORONTO ONT   CAN
WINCT, PETER Y, PHILOSOPHY DEPT, UNIV OF UTAH, SALT LAKE CTY UT   84112
WINEMAN, SHUL, HUMAN DIV, MACOMB CO COM COL, WARREN MI   48093
WINFREY, DAVID, HUMAN DEPT, HAGERSTOWN JR COL, HAGERSTOWN MD   21740
WINGARD II, GORDON G, HUMAN DEPT, WILKES COM COL, WILKESBORO NC   28697
WINGELL, A E, UNIV OF ST MICHAEL'S, TORONTO 181, ONT   CAN
WINKLER, EARL R, PHIL DEPT, UNIV BRIT COLUMBIA, VANCOUVER 8 B C   CAN
WINKLER, KENNETH, PHILOSOPHY DEPT, UNIV OF TEXAS, AUSTIN TX   78712
WINN, J, PHIL DEPT, UNIV OF FLORIDA, GAINESVILLE FL   32611
WINNES, GEORGE E, PHIL DEPT, MT SAINT MARY'S COL, EMMITSBURG MD   21727
WINNIE, JOHN A, HIST & PHIL SCI, INCIANA UNIV, BLOOMINGTON IN   47401
WINSCOTT, J G, PHIL & BIB DEPT, EAST MISS JUNIOR COL, SCOOBA MS   39358
WINSLADE, WILLIAM J, PHIL DEPT, UNIV OF CALIFORNIA, RIVERSIDE CA   92502
WINSTIN, REID, HUMAN DEPT, MT ANGEL COLLEGE, MT ANGEL OR   97362
WINSTON, KENNETH, PHIL DEPT, WHEATON COLLEGE, NORTON MA   02766
WINSTON, MORTON E, PHIL DEPT, UNIV OF ILLINOIS, URBANA IL   61801
WINTER, JOHN E, PHIL DEPT, MILLERSVILLE ST COL, MILLERSVILLE PA   17551
WINTER, KENNETH, SHIPPENSBURG ST COL, SHIPPENSBURG, PA   17257
WINTERSTEINER, GAIL, PHIL DEPT, BENTLEY COLLEGE, WALTHAM MA   02154
WIPPEL, JOHN F, PHIL SCH, CATH UNIV OF AMER, WASHINGTON DC   20017
WISAN, RICHARD N, PHIL & RELIG DEPT, HARTWICK COLLEGE, ONEONTA NY   13820
WISCOM, A JOHN, PHILOSOPHY DEPT, UNIV OF OREGON, EUGENE OR   97403
WISCOM, J O, PHILOSOPHY DEPT, YORK UNIVERSITY, DOWNSVIEW ONT   CAN
WISCOM, WILLIAM, PHIL DEPT, TEMPLE UNIVERSITY, PHILADELPHIA PA   19122
WISE, NEIL, ST EDWARD'S UNIV, AUSTIN, TX   78704
WISEMAN, MARY, PHIL DEPT, BROOKLYN COLLEGE, BROOKLYN NY   11210
WISNESKI, EDWARD J, PHIL DEPT, HOLY APOSTLES COL, CROMWELL CT   06416
WITKOWSKI, KENNETH S, PHIL DEPT, GEORGETOWN UNIV, WASHINGTON DC   20007
WITMAN, EDWARD P, PHILOSOPHY DEPT, GEORGIAN COURT COL, LAKEWOOD NJ   08701
WITMER, JOHN A, SYST THEOL DEPT, DALLAS THEOL SEM, DALLAS TX   75204
WITT, RICHARD, PHIL DEPT, BELLEVUE COLLEGE, BELLEVUE NE   68005
WITTE, WAYNE W, ASHLAND COLLEGE, ASHLAND, OH   44805
WITTE, WILLIAM D S, PHIL DEPT, BRADLEY UNIVERSITY, PEORIA IL   61606
WIXTED, WILLIAM, LIBR ARTS DIV, MARYMOUNT COLLEGE, BOCA RATON FL   33432
WOELFEL, JAMES, PHIL DEPT, UNIVERSITY OF KANSAS, LAWRENCE KS   66044
WOGAST, ELIZABETH, PHILOSOPHY DEPT, CALIFORNIA ST UNIV, HAYWARD CA   94542
WOJCIECHOWSKI, JERZY, PHIL FACULTY, UNIV OF OTTAWA, OTTAWA ONT   CAN
WOJICK, DAVID, PHIL DEPT, CARNEGIE-MELLON UNIV, PITTSBURGH PA   15213
WOLF, JOHN, PHIL DEPT, UNIVERSITY OF KANSAS, LAWRENCE KS   66044
WOLF, ROBERT G, PHIL STUD DEPT, S ILLINOIS UNIV, EDWARDSVILLE IL   62025
WOLF, THEODORE, PHILOSOPHY DEPT, GONZAGA UNIV, SPOKANE WA   99202
WOLFE, DAVID L, PHIL DEPT, WHEATON COLLEGE, WHEATON IL   60187
WOLFE, H KIRKE, PHIL DEPT, PORTLAND ST UNIV, PORTLAND OR   97207
WOLFE, J, PHILOSOPHY DEPT, CARLETON UNIVERSITY, OTTAWA ONT   CAN
WOLFE, MAURICE R, MERRITT COLLEGE, OAKLAND, CA   94619

WOLFE, ROBERT A, PHILOSOPHY DEPT, SOUTHWESTERN COL, CHULA VISTA CA 92010
WOLFF, DAVID R, PHILOSOPHY DEPT, BIG BEND COM COL, MOSES LAKE WA 98837
WOLFF, ROBERT, PHILOSOPHY DEPT, UNIV OF MASS, AMHERST MA 01002
WOLIN, SHELDON S, PHIL STUD BOARD, U OF CALIFORNIA, SANTA CRUZ CA 95060
WOLTER, ALLAN B, PHIL SCH, CATH UNIV OF AMER, WASHINGTON DC 20017
WOLTERS, RICHARD M, PHIL DEPT, AGNES SCOTT COLLEGE, DECATUR GA 30030
WOLTERSTORFF, NICHOLAS, PHIL DEPT, CALVIN COLLEGE, GRAND RAPIDS MI 49506
WOLZ, HENRY, PHILOSOPHY DEPT, QUEENS COLLEGE, FLUSHING NY 11367
WONDERS, ALICE W, PHIL & REL DIV, TEXAS WESLEYAN COL, FORT WORTH TX 76105
WOO, CHRISTINA, PHIL DEPT, UNIV OF CALIFORNIA, LOS ANGELES CA 90024
WOOD JR, FORREST, PHIL & RELIG DEPT, UNIV OF S MISS, HATTIESBURG MS 39401
WOOD, ALFRED J, PHILOSOPHY DEPT, UNIV OF DELAWARE, NEWARK DE 19711
WOOD, ALLEN, SAGE SCHOOL, CORNELL UNIVERSITY, ITHACA NY 14850
WOOD, BRADLEY, HUMAN & PHIL DEPT, GROSSMONT COL, EL CAJON CA 92020
WOOD, BRUCE KENNETH, PHILOSOPHY DEPT, REEDLEY COLLEGE, REEDLEY CA 93654
WOOD, CAROL, PHILOSOPHY DEPT, UNIV OF OKLAHOMA, NORMAN OK 73069
WOOD, CLARA, DIABLO VALLEY COL, PLEASANT HILL, CA 94523
WOOD, L C, RELIG & PHIL DEPT, PAUL QUINN COLLEGE, WACO TX 76703
WOOD, LAURENCE, RELIG & PHIL DEPT, HOUGHTON COLLEGE, HOUGHTON NY 14744
WOOD, MARIANNE, PHIL & THEOL, DOMINICAN COLLEGE, HOUSTON TX 77021
WOOD, PEARLE S, REL & PHIL DEPT, SOUTHWOOD COLLEGE, SALEMBURG NC 28385
WOOD, RICHARD A, PHILOSOPHY DEPT, NORTH ARIZONA UNIV, FLAGSTAFF AZ 86001
WOOD, RICHARD, PHIL DEPT, EARLHAM COLLEGE, RICHMOND IN 47374
WOOD, ROBERT, PHIL DEPT, ST JOSEPH'S COLLEGE, RENNSSELAER IN 47978
WOOD, SUSAN, PHIL DEPT, ST UNIV OF NY, AMHERST NY 14226
WOOLFIN, YANDALL, SW BAPT THEOL SEM, FORT WORTH, TX 76122
WOODHOUSE, MARK B, PHIL DEPT, GEORGIA ST UNIV, ATLANTA GA 30303
WOODHOUSE, ROBERT, ENG DEPT, ROCKLAND COM COL, SUFFERN NY 10901
WOODIE, NORRIS B, PHIL & REL DEPT, BEREA COLLEGE, BEREA KY 40403
WOODRING, KENNETH J, PHILOSOPHY DEPT, VILLANOVA UNIV, VILLANOVA PA 19085
WOODRUFF, PAUL, PHILOSOPHY DEPT, UNIV OF TEXAS, AUSTIN TX 78712
WOODRUFF, PETER, PHIL DEPT, UNIV OF CALIFORNIA, IRVINE CA 92664
WOODS, J H, PHILOSOPHY DEPT, UNIV OF VICTORIA, VICTORIA B C   CAN
WOODS, MARTIN, HUMAN & SOC SCI, NORTHROP INST OF TECH, INGLEWOOD CA 90306
WOODS, RICHARD, PHIL DEPT, LOYOLA UNIVERSITY, CHICAGO IL 60626
WOODSON, WILLIAM, BIB DEPT, FREED-HARDEMAN COL, HENDERSON TN 38348
WOODWARD, AL, RELIG DEPT, E NEW MEXICO UNIV, PORTALES NM 88130
WOODWARD, IRENE, PHILOSOPHY DEPT, COL OF HOLY NAMES, OAKLAND CA 94619
WOODWARD, JAMES, PHILOSOPHY DEPT, UNIV OF TEXAS, AUSTIN TX 78712
WOODY, J MELVIN, PHIL DEPT, CONNECTICUT COL, NEW LONDON CT 06320
WOODY, SUSAN M, PHIL DEPT, CONNECTICUT COL, NEW LONDON CT 06320
WOOLARD, H I, PHIL & RELIG DEPT, UNIV OF ARKANSAS, LITTLE ROCK AR 72204
WOOLF, EUGENE T, PHILOSOPHY DEPT, SOUTH UTAH ST COL, CEDAR CITY UT 84720
WOOLF, THOMAS H, PHILOSOPHY DEPT, UNIV OF UTAH, SALT LAKE CTY UT 84112
WOOLLAM, CLIFFORD R, PHIL DEPT, UNIVERSITY OF MIAMI, CORAL GABLES FL 33124
WOOZLEY, ANTHONY D, PHIL DEPT, UNIV OF VIRGINIA, CHARLOTTESVL VA 22903
WORKMAN, ALLEN J, PHIL DEPT, LOS ANGELES CY COL, LOS ANGELES CA 90029
WORKMAN, ROLLIN W, PHIL DEPT, UNIV OF CINCINNATI, CINCINNATI OH 45221
WORRAD JR, LEWIS H, PHILOSOPHY DEPT, KING'S COLLEGE, BRIARCLF MNR NY 10510
WOZNICKI, ANDREW, PHIL DEPT, UNIV OF SN FRANCISCO, SAN FRANCISCO CA 94117
WRATCHFORD, EUGENE, TUNXIS COM COLLEGE, FARMINGTON, CT 06032
WREN, DAVID, PHIL DEPT, COL OF ST CATHERINE, SAINT PAUL MN 55105
WREN, THOMAS, PHIL DEPT, LOYOLA UNIVERSITY, CHICAGO IL 60626
WRIGHT, ABBOTT, PHILOSOPHY DEPT, PENN STATE UNIV, UNIV PARK PA 16802
WRIGHT, C E LARRY, PHIL DEPT, UNIV OF CALIFORNIA, RIVERSIDE CA 92502
WRIGHT, JOHN, PHILOSOPHY DEPT, UNIV OF DELAWARE, NEWARK DE 19711
WRIGHT, JOHN, SYST & PHIL, GRADUATE THEOL UNION, BERKELEY CA 94709
WRIGHT, KATHLEEN R, PHIL DEPT, BOSTON COLLEGE, CHESTNUT HILL MA 02167
WRIGHT, MICHAEL, PHILOSOPHY DEPT, VANDERBILT UNIV, NASHVILLE TN 37235
WRIGHT, PHILIP B, PHILOSOPHY DEPT, UNIV OF WINNIPEG, WINNIPEG MAN   CAN
WRIGHT, RICHARD, HUMAN DIV, TALLADEGA COLLEGE, TALLADEGA AL 35160
WRIGHT, WALTER, PHIL DEPT, CLARK UNIVERSITY, WORCESTER MA 01610
WRIGHTSMAN, BRUCE, PHIL DEPT, LUTHER COLLEGE, DECORAH IA 52101
WROCKLAGE, BERNARD P, PHIL & THEOL, DIVINE WORD COLLEGE, EPWORTH IA 52045

WU, JOSEPH S, PHIL DEPT, CALIFORNIA ST UNIV, SACRAMENTO CA   95819
WU, KATHLEEN G J, PHIL DEPT, UNIV OF ALABAMA, UNIVERSITY AL   35486
WU, KUANG-MING, PHILOSOPHY DEPT, UNIV OF WISONSIN, OSH KOSH WI   54901
WU, LAURENCE, PHILOSOPHY DEPT, UNIV OF TEXAS, AUSTIN TX   78712
WUBNIG, JUDITH, PHILOSOPHY DEPT, UNIV OF WATERLOO, WATERLOO ONT   CAN
WUELLNER, BERNARD, PHILOSOPHY DEPT, XAVIER UNIVERSITY, CINCINNATI OH   45207
WUERCH, ROBERT, PHIL DEPT, WICHITA ST UNIV, WICHITA KS   67208
WULFF, JON V, BELLEVUE COM COL, BELLEVUE, WA   98007
WURZBURGER, WALTER, PHIL DEPT, YESHIVA UNIVERSITY, NEW YORK NY   10033
WYATT, STEPHEN, PHILOSOPHY DEPT, DUQUESNE UNIV, PITTSBURGH PA   15219
WYNKOOP, MILDRED, REL & PHIL DEPT, TREVECCA NAZ COL, NASHVILLE TN   37210
WYSCHOGROD, EDITH, PHILOSOPHY DEPT, QUEENS COLLEGE, FLUSHING NY   11367
WYSCHOGROD, MICHAEL, PHIL DEPT, BERNARD BARUCH COL, NEW YORK NY   10010
WYTWYCKY, BOHDAN, PHIL DEPT, COLUMBIA UNIVERSITY, NEW YORK NY   10027
YAFFE, MARTIN D, PHILOSOPHY DEPT, N TEXAS STATE UNIV, DENTON TX   76203
YAKE, J STANLEY, PHIL OPTION, UNIV OF WISCONSIN, GREEN BAY WI   54302
YALCEN-THOMSON, D C, PHIL DEPT, UNIV OF VIRGINIA, CHARLOTTESVL VA   22903
YAMAMOTO, CARL, PHIL DEPT, NORTHWESTERN UNIV, EVANSTON IL   60201
YAMAMOTO, LOUISE, HUM & SOC SCI, KAPIOLANI COM COL, HONOLULU HI   96814
YAMAMOTO, YUTAKA, PHIL DEPT, PURDUE UNIVERSITY, LAFAYETTE IN   47907
YAMASAKI, BEATRICE T, PHIL DEPT, UNIVERSITY OF HAWAII, HONOLULU HI   96822
YANCELL, KEITH E, PHILOSOPHY DEPT, UNIV OF WISCONSIN, MADISON WI   53706
YARBROUGH, M V, PHIL DEPT, UNIV OF FLORIDA, GAINESVILLE FL   32611
YARCAN, JOHN L, PHIL DEPT, COL AT PLATTSBURGH, PLATTSBURGH NY   12901
YARN, DAVID H, PHILOSOPHY DEPT, BRIGHAM YOUNG UNIV, PROVO UT   84601
YARNEVIC, DONALD, PHIL DEPT, MERCY COLLEGE, DETROIT MI   48219
YARTZ, FRANCIS, PHIL DEPT, LOYOLA UNIVERSITY, CHICAGO IL   60626
YARVIN, H, PHIL DEPT, UNIV OF MANITOBA, WINNIPEG 19 MAN   CAN
YATES, LAWRENCE E, PHILOSOPHY DEPT, WHITWORTH COLLEGE, SPOKANE WA   99251
YATES, LOUISE, SOC SCI DEPT, BLUEFIELD STATE COL, BLUEFIELD WV   24701
YEAGER, IVER F, PHIL & RELIG, ILLINOIS COLLEGE, JACKSONVILLE IL   62650
YEARGAIN, SCOTT, HUMAN DIV, JOHNSON CO COM COL, OVERLAND PARK KS   66210
YEE, RICHARD, PHILOSOPHY DEPT, COL OF HOLY NAMES, OAKLAND CA   94619
YEE, STEVAN, PHILOSOPHY DEPT, PENN STATE UNIV, READING PA   19608
YEH, SHIN-YUN, PHIL DEPT, INDIANA UNIVERSITY, BLOOMINGTON IN   47401
YEHLING, DONALD, PHIL DEPT, HUNTINGTON COLLEGE, HUNTINGTON IN   46750
YEZZI, RONALD, PHIL DEPT, MANKATO STATE COL, MANKATO MN   56001
YLVISAKER, RICHARD, PHIL DEPT, LUTHER COLLEGE, DECORAH IA   52101
YOCUM, D, PHIL DEPT, W CONNECTICUT ST COL, DANBURY CT   06810
YODER, JESSE, PHIL DEPT, ROCKEFELLER UNIV, NEW YORK NY   10021
YODER, JOHN H, THEOL & HIST, ASSOC MENN BIB SEM, ELKHART IN   46514
YOES JR, M G, PHILOSOPHY DEPT, UNIV OF HOUSTON, HOUSTON TX   77004
YOH, MAY, PHILOSOPHY DEPT, BRANDON UNIVERSITY, BRANDON MAN   CAN
YOHAN, WALTER, SOC DEPT, DEKALB COM COLLEGE, CLARKSTON GA   30021
YOLTON, JOHN W, PHILOSOPHY DEPT, YORK UNIVERSITY, DOWNSVIEW ONT   CAN
YOOS, GEORGE, PHIL DEPT, ST CLOUD ST COL, ST CLOUD MN   56301
YOSHIDA, R M, PHILOSOPHY DEPT, UNIV OF LETHBRIDGE, LETHBRIDGE ALB   CAN
YOST, ROBERT M, PHIL DEPT, UNIV OF CALIFORNIA, LOS ANGELES CA   90024
YOUNCE, RICHARD DALE, FRANK PHILLIPS COL, BORGER, TX   79007
YOUNG, CHARLES, PHIL DEPT, CLAREMONT GRAD SCH, CLAREMONT CA   91711
YOUNG, DWIGHT J, SOC SCI DEPT, SAN DIEGO COM CY COL, SAN DIEGO CA   92101
YOUNG, GARY, PHILOSOPHY DEPT, UNIV OF WISCONSIN, MADISON WI   53706
YOUNG, HENRY J, THEOL & PHIL, INTERDENOM THEOL CTR, ATLANTA GA   30314
YOUNG, JOHN, PHILOSOPHY DEPT, DAVIDSON COLLEGE, DAVIDSON NC   28036
YOUNG, MICHAEL, PHIL DEPT, UNIVERSITY OF KANSAS, LAWRENCE KS   66044
YOUNG, THEODORE A, PHIL DEPT, GRAND VALLEY ST COL, ALLENDALE MI   49401
YOUNG, THOMAS, GWYNEDD-MERCY COL, GWYNEDD VLY, PA   19437
YOUNG, WARREN C, THEOL & PHIL, N BAPTIST THEOL SEM, OAK BROOK IL   60521
YOUNG, WILLIAM, PHIL DEPT, BARRINGTON COLLEGE, BARRINGTON RI   22806
YOUNGBLOOD, SUSAN P, PHILOSOPHY DEPT, UNIV OF S ALABAMA, MOBILE AL   36688
YOUNGE, EDITH, PHILOSOPHY DEPT, SALESIAN COLLEGE, NORTH HALEDON NJ   07508
YU, DAVID, REL & PHIL DEPT, COLO WOMEN'S COL, DENVER CO   80220
YU, PAUL, PHIL DEPT, CEN MICHIGAN UNIV, MT PLEASANT MI   48858
ZABEEH, FARHANG, PHIL DEPT, ROOSEVELT UNIVERSITY, CHICAGO IL   60605

ZACIEK, A J, PHILOSOPHY DEPT, RICE UNIVERSITY, HOUSTON TX 77001
ZAFFRON, RICHARD H, PHIL DEPT, UNIV OF N CAROLINA, CHAPEL HILL NC 27514
ZAGAR, JANKO, ST ALBERT'S COLLEGE, CAKLAND, CA 94618
ZAKYDALSKY, TARAS D, PHIL & RELIG, URSINUS COLLEGE, COLLEGEVILLE PA 19426
ZALLYS, RICHARD, SOC SCI DEPT, CLARION STATE COL, CLARION PA 16214
ZAMBELLI, W VITO, PHIL DEPT, HOLY FAMILY COLLEGE, PHILADELPHIA PA 19114
ZAMBO, LOUIS, PHIL DEPT, COL VIEUX-MONTREAL, MONTREAL QUE   CAN
ZANER, RICHARD M, PHIL DEPT, S METHODIST UNIV, DALLAS TX 75222
ZASLOW, JON, PHIL DEPT, UNIV OF WEST ONTARIO, LONDON ONT   CAN
ZASLOW, ROBERT J, EMPIRE ST COL, SARATOGA SPGS, NY 12866
ZAWADSKY, JOHN P, PHIL DEPT, UNIV OF WISCONSIN, STEVENS POINT WI 54481
ZEDLER, BEATRICE H, PHILOSOPHY DEPT, MARQUETTE UNIV, MILWAUKEE WI 53233
ZEIGER, WILLIAM, RELIG & PHIL DEPT, SHELDON JACKSON COL, SITKA AK 99835
ZEIGLER, CARL W, RELIG & PHIL, ELIZABETHTOWN COL, ELIZABETHTOWN PA 17022
ZEIGLER, GREGORY, PHIL SCH, UNIV OF S CALIFORNIA, LOS ANGELES CA 90007
ZELCIN, MARY B, PHIL & RELIG DEPT, HOLLINS COLLEGE, HOLLINS COL VA 24020
ZELLNER, HAROLD, PHILOSOPHY DEPT, KENT STATE UNIV, KENT OH 44242
ZELTNER, PHILIP, PHIL DEPT, ST UNIV OF NY, AMHERST NY 14226
ZEMACH, EDDY, PHIL DEPT, ST UNIV OF NY, STONY BROOK NY 11790
ZEMAN, JOSEPH J, PHIL DEPT, UNIV OF FLORIDA, GAINESVILLE FL 32611
ZEMAN, VLADIMIR, PHIL DEPT, GEORGE WILLIAMS UNIV, MONTREAL 107 QUE   CAN
ZEMBATY, JANE S, PHIL DEPT, GEORGETCWN UNIV, WASHINGTON DC 20007
ZENO, CARL A, PHIL DEPT, ST MICHAEL'S COLLEGE, WINOOSKI VT 05404
ZENZEN, MICHAEL J, PHIL DEPT, RENSSELAER POLYTECH, TROY NY 12181
ZERBY, LEWIS K, PHIL DEPT, MICHIGAN STATE UNIV, EAST LANSING MI 48823
ZERWEKH, ROBERT, PHIL DEPT, UNIV OF ILLINOIS, URBANA IL 61801
ZEYL, DONALD J, PHILOSOPHY DEPT, UNIV OF RHODE ISLAND, KINGSTON RI 02881
ZHIRI, DEL, PSYCH & PHIL, GARDEN CY COM JR COL, GARDEN CITY KS 67846
ZIEGELMEYER, EDMUND, PHIL DEPT, ST LOUIS UNIVERSITY, ST LOUIS MO 63103
ZIEGLER, JOHN, PHIL DEPT, ST XAVIER COLLEGE, CHICAGO IL 60655
ZIFF, PAUL, PHIL DEPT, UNIV OF N CAROLINA, CHAPEL HILL NC 27514
ZILCNIS JR, WALTER A, PHIL DEPT, UNIV OF PITTSBURGH, PITTSBURGH PA 15260
ZIMMERMAN, DAVID P, PHIL DEPT, UNIV BRIT COLUMBIA, VANCOUVER 8 B C   CAN
ZIMMERMAN, MARVIN, PHIL DEPT, ST UNIV OF NY, AMHERST NY 14226
ZIMMERMAN, MICHAEL, PHIL DEPT, TULANE UNIVERSITY, NEW ORLEANS LA 70118
ZIMMERMAN, WALTER, RAYMOND COLLEGE, STOCKTON, CA 95204
ZINGER, DON, REL & PHIL DEPT, GRAND VIEW COLLEGE, DES MOINES IA 50140
ZINNER, JACQUELINE, PHIL DEPT, WEBSTER COLLEGE, ST LOUIS MO 63119
ZION, WILLIAM P, QUEEN'S THEOL COL, KINGSTON, ONT   CAN
ZIPSE, ERWIN, HIGHLAND COM COLLEGE, FREEPORT, IL 61032
ZOECKLEIN, WALTER, PHILOSOPHY DEPT, CAL STATE COL, SN BERNARDINO CA 92407
ZOGBY, JAMES, SHIPPENSBURG ST COL, SHIPPENSBURG, PA 17257
ZUCCO, JANE, PHIL DEPT, TEXAS CHRISTIAN UNIV, FORT WORTH TX 76129
ZUCH, TIM, PHILOSOPHY DEPT, UNIV OF WATERLOO, WATERLOO ONT   CAN
ZUCKER, ALFRED, PHILOSOPHY DEPT, LOS ANGELES SW COL, LOS ANGELES CA 90047
ZUCKER, ARTHUR, HUMANITIES DEPT, PENN STATE UNIV, HERSHEY PA 17033
ZUCKER, WOLFGANG MAX, PHIL & RELIG DEPT, UPSALA COL, EAST ORANGE NJ 07019
ZUCKERSTATTER, RUDOLF, PHIL DEPT, SUFFOLK UNIVERSITY, BOSTON MA 02114
ZULIANI, VINCENT A, PHILOSOPHY DEPT, DON BOSCO COLLEGE, NEWTON NJ 07860
ZUNIGA, JOAQUIN A, PHILOSOPHY DEPT, CALIFORNIA ST UNIV, HAYWARD CA 94542
ZUSIN, ELIZABETH, SOC SCI DEPT, KUTZTOWN STATE COL, KUTZTOWN PA 19530
ZUSY, DENNIS, PHILOSOPHY DEPT, AQUINAS INST THEOL, DUBUQUE IA 52001
ZVARA, ANDREW A, PHIL DEPT, UNIV OF MARYLAND, COLLEGE PARK MD 20742
ZWEIG, ARNULF, PHILOSOPHY DEPT, UNIV OF OREGON, EUGENE OR 97403
ZWEIG, MARILYN, PHIL DEPT, UNIV OF FLORIDA, GAINESVILLE FL 32611
ZYSKIND, HAROLD, PHIL DEPT, ST UNIV OF NY, STONY BROOK NY 11790

INDEX OF PUBLISHERS